Introductory Algebra

THIRD EDITION

Julie Miller
Daytona State College

Molly O'Neill
Daytona State College

Nancy Hyde
Broward College—
Professor Emeritus

MATH 029
Elementary Algebra
Special Edition for Camden County College

Mc
Graw
Hill
Education

8 9 0 BKM BKM 18 17 16 15

ISBN-13: 978-1-259-74466-2
ISBN-10: 1-259-74466-3

Solutions Program Manager: Nicole Schmitt
Project Manager: Lynn Nagel
Cover Photo Credits: Imagineering Media Services, Inc.

About the Authors

Julie Miller is from Daytona State College, where she has taught developmental and upper-level mathematics courses for 20 years. Prior to her work at Daytona State College, she worked as a software engineer for General Electric in the area of flight and radar simulation. Julie earned a bachelor of science in applied mathematics from Union College in Schenectady, New York, and a master of science in mathematics from the University of Florida. In addition to her textbooks in developmental mathematics, Julie has authored a college algebra textbook and several course supplements for college algebra, trigonometry, and precalculus.

"My father is a medical researcher, and I got hooked on math and science when I was young and would visit his laboratory. I can remember using graph paper to plot data points for his experiments and doing simple calculations. He would then tell me what the peaks and features in the graph meant in the context of his experiment. I think that applications and hands-on experience made math come alive for me and I'd like to see math come alive for my students."

— *Julie Miller*

Molly O'Neill is also from Daytona State College, where she has taught for 22 years in the School of Mathematics. She has taught a variety of courses from developmental mathematics to calculus. Before she came to Florida, Molly taught as an adjunct instructor at the University of Michigan–Dearborn, Eastern Michigan University, Wayne State University, and Oakland Community College. Molly earned a bachelor of science in mathematics and a master of arts and teaching from Western Michigan University in Kalamazoo, Michigan. Besides this textbook, she has authored several course supplements for college algebra, trigonometry, and precalculus and has reviewed texts for developmental mathematics.

"I differ from many of my colleagues in that math was not always easy for me. But in seventh grade I had a teacher who taught me that if I follow the rules of mathematics, even I could solve math problems. Once I understood this, I enjoyed math to the point of choosing it for my career. I now have the greatest job because I get to do math every day and I have the opportunity to influence my students just as I was influenced. Authoring these texts has given me another avenue to reach even more students."

— *Molly O'Neill*

Nancy Hyde served as a full-time faculty member of the Mathematics Department at Broward College for 24 years. During this time she taught the full spectrum of courses from developmental math through differential equations. She received a bachelor of science degree in math education from Florida State University and a master's degree in math education from Florida Atlantic University. She has conducted workshops and seminars for both students and teachers on the use of technology in the classroom. In addition to this textbook, she has authored a graphing calculator supplement for *College Algebra*.

"I grew up in Brevard County, Florida, where my father worked at Cape Canaveral. I was always excited by mathematics and physics in relation to the space program. As I studied higher levels of mathematics I became more intrigued by its abstract nature and infinite possibilities. It is enjoyable and rewarding to convey this perspective to students while helping them to understand mathematics."

— *Nancy Hyde*

Dedications

To my great-nephew, Max

— Nancy Hyde

To my granddaughter, Katie

— Molly O'Neill

To Erica and Robert

— Julie Miller

Contents

Chapter 6   Factoring Polynomials   425

Chapter 7   Rational Expressions and Equations   495

Chapter 8 | Radicals   577

Chapter 9 | More Quadratic Equations   643

How Will Miller/O'Neill/Hyde Help Your Students *Get Better Results?*

Better Clarity, Quality, and Accuracy!

Julie Miller, Molly O'Neill, and Nancy Hyde know what students need to be successful in mathematics. Better results come from clarity in their exposition, quality of step-by-step worked examples, and accuracy of their exercises sets; but it takes more than just great authors to build a textbook series to help students achieve success in mathematics. Our authors worked with a strong team of mathematics instructors from around the country to ensure that the clarity, quality, and accuracy you expect from the Miller/O'Neill/Hyde series was included in this edition.

> "The most complete text at this level in its thoroughness, accuracy, and pedagogical soundness. The best developmental mathematics text I have seen."
> —Frederick Bakenhus, *Saint Phillips College*

Better Exercise Sets!

Comprehensive sets of exercises are available for every student level. Julie Miller, Molly O'Neill, and Nancy Hyde worked with a board of advisors from across the country to offer the appropriate depth and breadth of exercises for your students. **Problem Recognition Exercises** were created to improve student performance while testing.

Practice exercise sets help students progress from skill development to conceptual understanding. Student tested and instructor approved, the Miller/O'Neill/Hyde exercise sets will help your students *get better results*.

- ▶ **Problem Recognition Exercises**
- ▶ **Skill Practice Exercises**
- ▶ **Study Skills Exercises**
- ▶ **Concept Connections Exercises**
- ▶ **Mixed Exercises**
- ▶ **Expanding Your Skills Exercises**
- ▶ **Vocabulary and Key Concepts Exercises**

> "This series was thoughtfully constructed with students' needs in mind. The Problem Recognition section was extremely well designed to focus on concepts that students often misinterpret."
> —Christine V. Wetzel-Ulrich, *Northampton Community College*

Better Step-By-Step Pedagogy!

Introductory Algebra provides enhanced step-by-step learning tools to help students *get better results*.

- ▶ **Worked Examples** provide an "easy-to-understand" approach, clearly guiding each student through a step-by-step approach to master each practice exercise for better comprehension.
- ▶ **TIPs** offer students extra cautious direction to help improve understanding through hints and further insight.
- ▶ **Avoiding Mistakes** boxes alert students to common errors and provide practical ways to avoid them. Both of these learning aids will help students get better results by showing how to work through a problem using a clearly defined step-by-step methodology that has been class tested and student approved.

> "The book is designed with both instructors and students in mind. I appreciate that great care was used in the placement of 'Tips' and 'Avoiding Mistakes' as it creates a lot of teachable moments in the classroom."
> —Shannon Vinson, *Wake Tech Community College*

Get Better Results

Formula for Student Success

Step-by-Step Worked Examples

- ▶ Do you get the feeling that there is a disconnection between your students' class work and homework?
- ▶ Do your students have trouble finding worked examples that match the practice exercises?
- ▶ Do you prefer that your students see examples in the textbook that match the ones you use in class?

Miller/O'Neill/Hyde's *Worked Examples* offer a clear, concise methodology that replicates the mathematical processes used in the authors' classroom lectures!

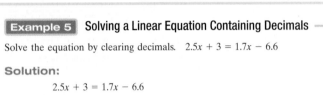

Example 5 Solving a Linear Equation Containing Decimals

Solve the equation by clearing decimals. $2.5x + 3 = 1.7x - 6.6$

Solution:

$$2.5x + 3 = 1.7x - 6.6$$
$$10(2.5x + 3) = 10(1.7x - 6.6) \quad \text{Multiply both sides of the equation by 10.}$$

Apply the distributive property.

$$25x + 30 = 17x - 66$$

Subtract $17x$ from both sides.

Subtract 30 from both sides.

Divide both sides by 8.

The solution is -12.

Skill Practice

Solve.

5. $1.2w + 3.5 = 2.1 + w$

"As always, MOH's Worked Examples are so clear and useful for the students. All steps have wonderfully detailed explanations written with wording that the students can understand. MOH is also excellent with arrows and labels making the Worked Examples extremely clear and understandable."
—Kelli Hammer, *Broward College–South*

"Easy to read step-by-step solutions to sample textbook problems. The 'why' is provided for students, which is invaluable when working exercises without available teacher/tutor assistance."
—Arcola Sullivan, *Copiah-Lincoln Community College*

Classroom Examples

To ensure that the classroom experience also matches the examples in the text and the practice exercises, we have included references to even-numbered exercises to be used as Classroom Examples. These exercises are highlighted in the Practice Exercises at the end of each section.

Skill Practice

Solve the system by graphing.

6. $y = 2x - 3$
   $6x + 2y = 4$

Example 3 Solving a System of Linear Equations by Graphing

Solve the system by the graphing method.

$$x - 2y = -2$$
$$-3x + 2y = 6$$

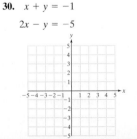

30. $x + y = -1$
   $2x - y = -5$

Better Learning Tools

Concept Connection Boxes

Concept Connections help students understand the conceptual meaning of the problems they are solving—a vital skill in mathematics.

When two lines are drawn in a rectangular coordinate system, three geometric relationships are possible:

1. Two lines may intersect at *exactly one point*.

2. Two lines may intersect at *no point*. This occurs if the lines are parallel.

Concept Connections

3. If the linear equations in a system represent a pair of parallel lines, how many solutions does the system have?

4. If the linear equations in a system represent a pair of perpendicular lines, how many solutions does the system have?

TIP and Avoiding Mistakes Boxes

TIP and **Avoiding Mistakes** boxes have been created based on the authors' classroom experiences—they have also been integrated into the **Worked Examples.** These pedagogical tools will help students get better results by learning how to work through a problem using a clearly defined step-by-step methodology.

Skill Practice

Simplify.

14. $\dfrac{x^2 - 1}{2x^2 - x - 3}$

Avoiding Mistakes

Given the expression

$$\dfrac{2c - 8}{10c^2 - 80c + 160}$$

do not be tempted to reduce before factoring. The terms $2c$ and $10c^2$ cannot be "canceled" because they are *terms* not factors.

The numerator and denominator must be in factored form before simplifying.

Example 6 Simplifying a Rational Expression

Simplify the rational expression. $\dfrac{2c - 8}{10c^2 - 80c + 160}$

Solution:

$$\dfrac{2c - 8}{10c^2 - 80c + 160}$$

$$= \dfrac{2(c - 4)}{10(c^2 - 8c + 16)} \qquad \text{Factor out the G}$$

$$= \dfrac{2(c - 4)}{10(c - 4)^2} \qquad \text{Factor th}$$

$$= \dfrac{\overset{1}{2}(c - 4)}{2 \cdot 5(c - 4)(c - 4)} \qquad \text{Simplify the rati}$$

$$= \dfrac{1}{5(c - 4)}$$

Avoiding Mistakes Boxes:

Avoiding Mistakes boxes are integrated throughout the textbook to alert students to common errors and how to avoid them.

TIP Boxes

Teaching tips are usually revealed only in the classroom. Not anymore! TIP boxes offer students helpful hints and extra direction to help improve understanding and provide further insight.

TIP: Notice that the product of two *binomials* equals the sum of the products of the **F**irst terms, the **O**uter terms, the **I**nner terms, and the **L**ast terms. The acronym **FOIL** (First Outer Inner Last) can be used as a memory device to multiply two binomials.

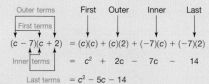

$$(c - 7)(c + 2) = (c)(c) + (c)(2) + (-7)(c) + (-7)(2)$$
$$= c^2 + 2c - 7c - 14$$
$$= c^2 - 5c - 14$$

Get Better Results

Better Exercise Sets! Better Practice! Better Results!

▶ Do your students have trouble with problem solving?

▶ Do you want to help students overcome math anxiety?

▶ Do you want to help your students improve performance on math assessments?

Problem Recognition Exercises

Problem Recognition Exercises present a collection of problems that look similar to a student upon first glance, but are actually quite different in the manner of their individual solutions. Students sharpen critical thinking skills and better develop their "solution recall" to help them distinguish the method needed to solve an exercise—an essential skill in developmental mathematics.

Problem Recognition Exercises were tested in the authors' developmental mathematics classes and were created to improve student performance on tests.

"The PREs are an excellent source of additional mixed problem sets. Frequently students have questions/comments like 'Where do I start?' or 'I know what to do once I get started, but I have trouble getting started.' Perhaps with these PREs, students will be able to overcome this obstacle."

—Erika Blanken, *Daytona State College*

Problem Recognition Exercises

Operations on Polynomials

For Exercises 1–40, perform the indicated operations and simplify.

1. **a.** $6x^2 + 2x^2$
   b. $(6x^2)(2x^2)$

2. **a.** $8y^3 + y^3$
   b. $(8y^3)(y^3)$

3. **a.** $(4x + y)^2$
   b. $(4xy)^2$

4. **a.** $(2a + b)^2$
   b. $(2ab)^2$

5. **a.** $(2x + 3) + (4x - 2)$
   b. $(2x + 3)(4x - 2)$

6. **a.** $(5m^2 + 1) + (m^2 + m)$
   b. $(5m^2 + 1)(m^2 + m)$

7. **a.** $(3z + 2)^2$
   b. $(3z + 2)(3z - 2)$

8. **a.** $(6y - 7)^2$
   b. $(6y - 7)(6y + 7)$

9. **a.** $(2x - 4)(x^2 - 2x + 3)$
   b. $(2x - 4) + (x^2 - 2x + 3)$

10. **a.** $(3y^2 + 8)(-y^2 - 4)$
    b. $(3y^2 + 8) - (-y^2 - 4)$

11. **a.** $x + x$
    b. $x \cdot x$

12. **a.** $2c + 2c$
    b. $2c \cdot 2c$

13. $(4xy)^2$

14. $(2ab)^2$

15. $(-2x^4 - 6x^3 + 8x^2) \div (2x^2)$

16. $(-15m^3 + 12m^2 - 3m) \div (-3m)$

17. $(m^3 - 4m^2 - 6) - (3m^2 + 7m) + (-m^3 - 9m + 6)$

18. $(n^4 + 2n^2 - 3n) + (4n^2 + 2n - 1) - (4n^5 + 6n - 3)$

19. $(8x^3 + 2x + 6) \div (x - 2)$

20. $(-4x^3 + 2x^2 - 5) \div (x - 3)$

21. $(2x - y)(3x^2 + 4xy - y^2)$

22. $(3a + b)(2a^2 - ab + 2b^2)$

23. $(x + y^2)(x^2 - xy^2 + y^4)$

24. $(m^2 + 1)(m^4 - m^2 + 1)$

25. $(a^2 + 2b) - (a^2 - 2b)$ **26.** $(y^3 - 6z) - (y^3 + 6z)$ **27.** $(a^3 + 2b)(a^3 - 2b)$ **28.** $(y^3 - 6z)(y^3 + 6z)$

29. $\dfrac{8p^2 + 4p - 6}{2p - 1}$ **30.** $\dfrac{4v^2 - 8v + 8}{2v + 3}$ **31.** $\dfrac{12x^3y^7}{3xy^5}$ **32.** $\dfrac{-18p^2q^4}{2pq^3}$

$\left(+ \dfrac{4}{3}\right)\left(\dfrac{2}{5}y - \dfrac{4}{3}\right)$ **35.** $\left(\dfrac{1}{9}x^3 + \dfrac{2}{3}x^2 + \dfrac{1}{6}x - 3\right) - \left(\dfrac{4}{3}x^3 + \dfrac{1}{9}x^2 + \dfrac{2}{3}x + 1\right)$

$y - \dfrac{1}{3}\right)$ **37.** $(0.05x^2 - 0.16x - 0.75) + (1.25x^2 - 0.14x + 0.25)$

$- 4.1w^2 - 7.3)$

40. $(10ab^4)(5a^3b^2)$

"These are so important to test whether a student can recognize different types of problems and the method of solving each. They seem very unique—I have not noticed this feature in many other texts or at least your presentation of the problems is very organized and unique."

—Linda Kuroski, *Erie Community College*

Student Centered Applications!

The Miller/O'Neill/Hyde Board of Advisors partnered with our authors to bring the *best applications* from every region in the country! These applications include real data and topics that are more relevant and interesting to today's student.

11. A bicyclist rides 24 mi against a wind and returns 24 mi with the same wind. His average speed for the return trip traveling with the wind is 8 mph faster than his speed going out against the wind. If x represents the bicyclist's speed going out against the wind, then the total time, t, required for the round trip is given by

$$t = \frac{24}{x} + \frac{24}{x+8}$$ where t is measured in hours.

a. Find the time required for the round trip if the cyclist rides 12 mph against the wind.

b. Find the time required for the round trip if the cyclist rides 24 mph against the wind.

Group Activities!

Each chapter concludes with a Group Activity to promote classroom discussion and collaboration—helping students not only to solve problems but to explain their solutions for better mathematical mastery. Group Activities are great for both full-time and adjunct instructors—bringing a more interactive approach to teaching mathematics! All required materials, activity time, and suggested group sizes are provided in the end-of-chapter material.

Group Activity

The Pythagorean Theorem and a Geometric "P

> "MOH's group activity involves true participation and interaction; fun with fractions!"
>
> —Monika Bender, *Central Texas College*

Estimated Time: 25–30 minutes

Group Size: 2

Right triangles occur in many applications of mathematics. By definition, a right triangle is a triangle that contains a 90° angle. The two shorter sides in a right triangle are referred to as the "legs," and the longest side is called the "hypotenuse." In the triangle, the legs are labeled as a and b, and the hypotenuse is labeled as c.

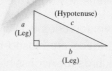

Right triangles have an important property that the sum of the squares of the two legs of a right triangle equals the square of the hypotenuse. This fact is referred to as the Pythagorean theorem. In symbols, the Pythagorean theorem is stated as:

$$a^2 + b^2 = c^2$$

1. The following triangles are right triangles. Verify that $a^2 + b^2 = c^2$. (The units may be left off when performing these calculations.)

$a = 3$
$b = 4$
$c = 5$

$a = \underline{\quad}$
$b = \underline{\quad}$
$c = \underline{\quad}$

$a^2 + b^2 = c^2$

$(3)^2 + (4)^2 \stackrel{?}{=} (5)^2$

$9 + 16 = 25$ ✔

$a^2 + b^2 = c^2$

$(\underline{\quad})^2 + (\underline{\quad})^2 \stackrel{?}{=} (\underline{\quad})^2$

$\underline{\quad} + \underline{\quad} = \underline{\quad}$ ✔

> "This is one part of the book that would have me adopt the MOH book. I am very big on group work and many times it is difficult to think of an activity. I would conclude the chapter doing the group activity in the class. Many books just have problems for this, but the MOH book provides an actual activity."
>
> —Sharon Giles, *Grossmont College*

geometric "proof" of the Pythagorean theorem uses addition, multiplication of polynomials. Consider the square figure. The side of the large outer square is $(a + b)$. Therefore, the area of the are is $(a + b)^2$.

f the large outer square can also be found by adding the area of the pictured in light gray) plus the area of the four right triangles rk gray).

square: c^2 Area of the four right triangles: $4 \cdot (\frac{1}{2} a \, b)$

½ Base · Height

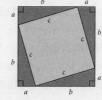

Get Better Results

Additional Supplements

Media Suite

NEW Lecture Videos Created by the Authors

Julie Miller began creating these lecture videos for her own students to use when they were absent from class. The student response was overwhelmingly positive, prompting the author team to create the lecture videos for their entire developmental math book series. In these new videos, the authors walk students through the learning objectives using the same language and procedures outlined in the book. Students learn and review right alongside the author! Students can also access the written notes that accompany the videos.

Dynamic Math Animations

The authors have constructed a series of Flash animations to illustrate difficult concepts where static images and text fall short. The animations leverage the use of on-screen movement and morphing shapes to give students an interactive approach to conceptual learning. Some provide a virtual laboratory for which an application is simulated and where students can collect data points for analysis and modeling. Others provide interactive question-and-answer sessions to test conceptual learning.

NEW Exercise Videos

The authors, along with a team of faculty who have used the Miller/O'Neill/Hyde textbooks for many years, have created new exercise videos for designated exercises in the textbook. These videos cover a representative sample of the main objectives in each section of the text. Each presenter works through selected problems, following the solution methodology employed in the text.

The video series is available online as part of Connect Math hosted by ALEKS as well as in ALEKS 360. The videos are closed-captioned for the hearing impaired, and meet the Americans with Disabilities Act Standards for Accessible Design.

Student Resource Manual

The *Student Resource Manual (SRM),* created by the authors, is a printable, electronic supplement available to students through Connect Math hosted by ALEKS. Instructors can also choose to customize this manual and package with their course materials. With increasing demands on faculty schedules, this resource offers a convenient means for both full-time and adjunct faculty to promote active learning and success strategies in the classroom.

This manual supports the series in a variety of different ways:

- NEW Additional Group Activities developed by the authors to supplement what is already available in the text.
- Discovery-based classroom activities written by the authors for each section
- Worksheets for extra practice written by the authors including Problem Recognition Exercise Worksheets
- NEW Lecture Notes designed to help students organize and take notes on key concepts
- Materials for a student portfolio

Annotated Instructor's Edition

In the *Annotated Instructor's Edition* (*AIE*), answers to all exercises appear adjacent to each exercise in a color used *only* for annotations. The *AIE* also contains Instructor Notes that appear in the margin. These notes offer instructors assistance with lecture preparation. In addition, there are Classroom Examples referenced in the text that are highlighted in the Practice Exercises. Also found in the *AIE* are icons within the Practice Exercises that serve to guide instructors in their preparation of homework assignments and lessons.

Powerpoints

The Powerpoints present key concepts and definitions with fully editable slides that follow the textbook. An instructor may project the slides in class or post to a website in an online course.

Instructor's Solutions Manual

The *Instructor's Solutions Manual* provides comprehensive, worked-out solutions to all exercises in the Chapter Openers, the Practice Exercises, the Problem Recognition Exercises, the end-of-chapter Review Exercises, the Chapter Tests, and the Cumulative Review Exercises.

Student's Solutions Manual

The *Student's Solutions Manual* provides comprehensive, worked-out solutions to the odd-numbered exercises in the Practice Exercise sets, the Problem Recognition Exercises, the end-of-chapter Review Exercises, the Chapter Tests, and the Cumulative Review Exercises. Answers to the Chapter Opener Puzzles are also provided.

Instructor's Test Bank

Among the supplements is a computerized test bank using the algorithm-based testing software TestGen® to create customized exams quickly. Hundreds of text-specific, open-ended, and multiple-choice questions are included in the question bank.

With **McGraw-Hill Create™**, you can easily rearrange chapters, combine material from other content sources, and quickly upload content you have written like your course syllabus or teaching notes. Find the content you need in Create by searching through thousands of leading McGraw-Hill textbooks. Arrange your book to fit your teaching style. Create even allows you to personalize your book's appearance by selecting the cover and adding your name, school, and course information. Assemble a Create book and you'll receive a complimentary print review copy in 3—5 business days or a complimentary electronic review copy (eComp) via email in minutes.

To learn more contact your sales rep or visit www.successinmath.com.

Get Better Results

iMATH

Hosted by ALEKS Corp.

- McGraw-Hill's Connect Math hosted by ALEKS® is a web-based assignment and assessment platform that helps students connect to their coursework and prepares them to succeed in and beyond the course.
- Connect Math hosted by ALEKS enables math and statistics instructors to create and share courses and assignments with colleagues and adjuncts with only a few clicks of the mouse. All exercises, learning objectives, and activities are developed by mathematics instructors to ensure consistency between the textbook and the online resources.
- Connect Math hosted by ALEKS also links students to an interactive eBook with a variety of media assets and a place to study, highlight, and keep track of class notes.

To learn more contact your sales rep or visit www.successinmath.com.

 **ALEKS® ALEKS® Prep Products**

- **ALEKS** is a Web-based program that uses artificial intelligence to assess a student's knowledge and provide personalized instruction on the exact topics the student is most ready to learn. By providing individualized assessment and learning, ALEKS helps students to master course content quickly and easily. ALEKS allows students to easily move between explanations and practice, and provides intuitive feedback to help students correct and analyze errors. ALEKS also includes a powerful instructor module that simplifies course management so instructors spend less time with administrative tasks and more time directing student learning.
- **ALEKS 360** includes a fully integrated, interactive eBook and textbook-specific lecture and exercise videos combined with ALEKS personalized assessment and learning.
- **ALEKS Prep** focuses on prerequisite and introductory material, and can be used during the first six weeks of the term to ensure student success in math courses ranging from Beginning Algebra through Calculus. ALEKS Prep quickly fill gaps in prerequisite knowledge by assessing precisely each student's preparedness and delivering individualized instruction on the exact topics students are most ready to learn.

To learn more contact your sales rep or visit www.successinmath.com.

LEARNSMART® SMARTBOOK™

- **LearnSmart®** is an adaptive study tool that strengthens student understanding and retention of your course's fundamental concepts. LearnSmart efficiently prepares your students for class so you can review *less* and teach *more*. The LearnSmart methodology is simple: determine the concepts students don't know or understand, and then teach those concepts using personalized plans designed for each student's success.
- **SmartBook®** is the first and only adaptive reading experience available for the higher education market. Powered by the intelligent and adaptive LearnSmart engine, SmartBook facilitates the reading process by identifying what content a student knows and doesn't know. As a student reads, the material continuously adapts to ensure the student is focused on the content he or she needs the most to close specific knowledge gaps.

To learn more contact your sales rep or visit www.successinmath.com.

Faculty Development and Digital Training

McGraw-Hill is excited to partner with our customers to ensure success in the classroom with our course solutions.

Looking for ways to be more effective in the classroom? Interested in the best practices for using available instructor resources?

Workshops are available on these topics for anyone using or considering the Miller, O'Neill, and Hyde Math Series. Led by the authors, contributors, and McGraw-Hill Learning consultants, each workshop is tailored to the needs of individual campuses or programs.

New to McGraw-Hill Digital Solutions? Need help setting up your course, using reports, and building assignments?

No need to wait for that big group training session during faculty development week. The McGraw-Hill Digital Implementation Team is a select group of advisors and experts in Connect Math. The Digital Implementation Team will work one-on-one with each instructor to make sure you are trained on the program and have everything you need to ensure a good experience for you and your students.

Are you redesigning a course or expanding your use of technology? Are you interested in getting ideas from other instructors who have used ALEKS™ or Connect Math in their courses?

Digital Faculty Consultants (DFCs) are instructors who have effectively incorporated technology such as ALEKS and Connect Math hosted by ALEKS in their courses. Discuss goals and best practices and improve outcomes in your course through peer-to-peer interaction and idea sharing.

Contact your local representative for more information about any of the faculty development, training, and support opportunities through McGraw-Hill. http://catalogs.mhhe.com/mhhe/findRep.do

Our Commitment to Market Development and Accuracy

McGraw-Hill's Development Process is an ongoing, never-ending, market-oriented approach to building accurate and innovative print and digital products. We begin developing a series by partnering with authors that desire to make an impact within their discipline to help students succeed. Next, we share these ideas and manuscript with instructors for review for feedback and to ensure that the authors' ideas represent the needs within that discipline. Throughout multiple drafts, we help our authors adapt to incorporate ideas and suggestions from reviewers to ensure that the series carries the same pulse as today's classrooms. With any new edition, we commit to accuracy across the series and its supplements. In addition to involving instructors as we develop our content, we also utilize accuracy checks through our various stages of development and production. The following is a summary of our commitment to market development and accuracy:

1. 2 drafts of author manuscript
2. 2 rounds of manuscript review
3. Multiple focus groups
4. 2 accuracy checks
5. 2 rounds of proofreading and copyediting
6. Toward the final stages of production, we are able to incorporate additional rounds of quality assurance from instructors as they help contribute toward our digital content and print supplements

This process then will start again immediately upon publication in anticipation of the next edition. With our commitment to this process, we are confident that our series has the most developed content the industry has to offer, thus pushing our desire for quality and accurate content that meets the needs of today's students and instructors.

Acknowledgments and Reviewers

Paramount to the development of this series was the invaluable feedback provided by the instructors from around the country who reviewed the manuscript or attended a market development event over the course of the several years the text was in development.

Albert Groccia, *Valencia College–Osceola*
Albert Guerra, *Saint Philips College*
Alexander Kasiukov, *Suffolk County Community College–Brentwood*
Alice Pollock-Cangemi, *Lone Star College*
Amber Smith, *Johnson County Community College*
Amtul Mujeeb Chaudry, *Rio Hondo College*
Anabel Darini, *Suffolk County Community College–Brentwood*
Andrea Blum, *Suffolk County Community College–Brentwood*
Angela Mccombs, *Illinois State University*
Ann Mccormick, *Lone Star College Kingwood*
Anne Prial, *Orange County Community College*
Antonnette Gibbs, *Broward College–North*
Anuradha Vadrevu, *Prince George's Community College*
Arlene Atchison, *South Seattle Community College*

Ashley Fuller, *John Tyler Community College–Chester*
Azzam Shihabi, *Long Beach City College*
Barbara Lott, *Seminole State College*
Barbara Purvis, *Centura College*
Barry Gibson, *Daytona State College–Daytona Beach*
Bashar Zogheib, *Nova Southeastern University*
Becky Schuering, *Blue River Community College–Independence*
Bernadette Turner, *Lincoln University*
Beverly Pepe, *Community College of Rhode Island–Warwick*
Bill Morrow, *Delaware Technical Community College*
Billie Shannon, *Southwestern Oregon Community College*
Brannen Smith, *Central Georgia Technical College*

Brenda Brown, *University of the District of Columbia*
Brent Pohlmann, *California Maritime Academy*
Bruce Legan, *Century Community & Technical College*
Carl Moxey, *Anna Maria College–Paxton*
Carol Curtis, *Fresno City College*
Carol Elias, *John Tyler Community College–Chester*
Carol Marinas, *Barry University*
Carol Mckillip, *Southwestern Oregon Community College*
Carol Rich, *Wallace Community College*
Carol Weideman, *Saint Petersburg College–Gibbs*
Carolyn Chapel, *Western Technical College*
Cassandra Johnson, *Robeson Community College*
Cassie Firth, *Northern Oklahoma College*

Cassondra Thompson, *York Technical College*

Chad Lower, *Pennsylvania College of Technology*

Christina Morian, *Lincoln University*

Cristi Whitfield, *Wallace Community College*

Cylinda Bray, *Yavapai College–Prescott*

Darla Aguilar, *Pima Community College*

Darlene Hatcher, *Metro Community College–South Campus–Omaha*

David Nusbaum, *Cypress College*

Dawn Chapman, *Columbus Technical College*

Deanna Hardy, *Bossier Parish Community College*

Deborah Logan, *Florida State College–South Campus*

Deborah Wolfson, *Suffolk County Community College–Brentwood*

Denise Nunley, *Glendale Community College*

Diana Dwan, *Yavapai College–Prescott*

D'marie Carver, *Portland Community College*

Don Anderson, *Northwest College*

Don Groninger, *Middlesex County College*

Don Solomon, *University of Wisconsin–Milwaukee*

Donald Robertson, *Olympic College*

Dot French, *Community College of Philadelphia*

Ed Thompson, *River Parishes Community College*

Edelma Simes, *Phillips Community College–Helena*

Eden Donahou, *Seminole State College*

Edith Lester, *Volunteer State Community College*

Edward Migliore, *University of California–Santa Cruz*

Eileen Diggle, *Bristol Community College*

Elaine Fitt, *Bucks Community College*

Eldon Baldwin, *Prince Georges Community College*

Elecia Ridley, *Durham Technical Community College*

Elena Litvinova, *Bloomsburg University of Pennsylvania*

Eleni Palmisano, *Centralia College*

Elisha Van Meenan, *Illinois State University*

Emily Simmons, *Centura College*

Eric Bennett, *Michigan State University–East Lansing*

Eric Kaljumagi, *Mt. San Antonio College*

Evon Lisle, *Seminole State College*

Gary Kersting, *North Central Michigan College*

Gene Ponthieux, *River Parishes Community College*

Gerald J. Lepage, *Bristol Community College*

Geri Philley, *Monterey Peninsula College*

Ghytana Goings, *Wallace Community College*

Ginger Eaves, *Bossier Parish Community College*

Gladys Bennett, *Centura College*

Gloria Hernandez, *Louisiana State University*

Greg Longanecker, *Leeward Community College*

Greg Rosik, *Century Community & Technical College*

Hadley Pridgen, *Gulf Coast Community College*

Heather Gallacher, *Cleveland State University*

Heidi Howard, *Florida State College–South Campus*

Heidi Kiley, *Suffolk County Community College–Brentwood*

Heidi Lyman, *South Seattle Community College*

Ignacio Alarcon, *Santa Barbara City College*

Irma Bakenhus, *San Antonio College*

J. Patrick Malone, *Victor Valley Community College*

James Dorn, *Barstow College*

James Miller, *Hillsborough Community College–Dale Mabry*

James Weeks, *Durham Technical Community College*

Jessica Lopez, *Saint Philips College*

Jean-Marie Magnier, *Springfield Technical Community College*

Jennifer Crowley, *Wallace Community College*

Jennifer Lempke, *North Central Michigan College*

Jian Zou, *South Seattle Community College*

Jill Wilsey, *Genesee Community College*

Joanne Strickland, *California Maritime Academy*

Jody Balzer, *Milwaukee Area Technical College*

Joe Jordan, *John Tyler Community College–Chester*

Joe Joyner, *Tidewater Community College–Norfolk*

Jonathan Cornick, *Queensborough Community College*

Joni Dugan, *Johnson County Community College*

Jordan Neus, *Suffolk County Community College–Brentwood*

Joshua Fontenot, *Louisiana State University*

Joyce Davis, *Heart of Georgia Technical College*

Judith Falk, *North Central Michigan College*

Judith Holbrook, *Yavapai College–Prescott*

Justin Dunham, *Johnson County Community College*

Karan Puri, *Queensborough Community College*

Karen Brown, *Wallace Community College*

Khaled Al-Agha, *Wiley College*

Karen Donnelly, *Saint Joseph's College*

Karen Estes, *Saint Petersburg College–Gibbs*

Karl Viehe, *University of the District of Columbia*

Kathleen Kane, *Community College Allegheny County–Pittsburgh*

Ketsia Chapman, *Centura College Online*

Ken Anderson, *Chemeketa Community College*

Kenneth Mead, *Genesee Community College*

Kenneth Williams, *Albany Technical College*

Kim Johnson, *Mesa Community College*

Kristin Good, *Washtenaw Community College*

Lakisha Holmes, *Daytona State College*

Laura Carroll, *Santa Rosa Junior College*

Laura Perez, *Washtenaw Community College*

Laura Stapleton, *Marshall University*

Lee Raubolt, *Yavapai College–Prescott*

Linda Schott, *Ozarks Technical Community College*

Linda Shackelford, *Tidewater Community College–Portsmouth*

Liz Delaney, *Grand Rapids Community College*

Lorena Goebel, *University of Arkansas–Fort Smith*

Loris Zucca, *Lone Star College Kingwood*

Lynette King, *Gadsden State Community College*

Lynn Irons, *College of Southern Idaho*

Mahshid Hassani, *Hillsborough Community College–Brandon*

Marc Campbell, *Daytona State College*

Marcial Echenique, *Broward College–North*

Maria Rodriguez, *Suffolk County Community College–Brentwood*

Marianna Mcclymonds, *Phoenix College*

Marilyn Peacock, *Tidewater Community College–Norfolk*

Marilyn S. Jacobi, *Gateway Community–Technical College*

Mark Anderson, *Durham Technical Community College*

Mark Batell, *Washtenaw Community College*

Mark Billiris, *St. Petersburg College*

Mark Littrell, *Rio Hondo College*

Marwan Abusawwa, *Florida State College–South Campus*

Mary Deas, *Johnson County Community College*

Mary Hito, *Los Angeles Valley College*

Mary Legner, *Riverside Community College*

Mary Wolyniak, *Broome Community College*

Matthew Pitassi, *Rio Hondo College*

Matthew Utz, *University of Arkansas–Fort Smith*

Maureen Loiacano, *Lone Star College*

Mauricio Marroquin, *Los Angeles Valley College*

Michael Cance, *Southeastern Community College*

Michelle Garey, *Delaware Technical & Community College–Dover*

Myrta Groeneveld, *Manchester Community College*

Nancy Eschen, *Florida State College–South Campus*

Natalie Weaver, *Daytona State College–Daytona Beach*

Nataliya Gavryshova, *College of San Mateo*

Nekeith Brown, *Richland College*

Nicole Francis, *Linn-Benton Community College*

Pam Ogaard, *Bismarck State College*

Pat Jones, *Methodist University*

Patricia Arteaga, *Bloomfield College*

Patricia Jones, *Methodist University*

Paula Looney, *Saint Philips College*
Paula Potter, *Yavapai College–Prescott*
Pavel Sikorskii, *Michigan State University–East Lansing*
Penny Marsh, *Johnson County Community College*
Philip Nelson, *Barstow College*
Phillip Taylor, *North Florida Community College*
Ramona Harris, *Gadsden State Community College*
Randey Burnette, *Tallahassee Community College*
Rhoda Oden, *Gadsden State Community College*
Richard Baum, *Santa Barbara City College*
Richard Hobbs, *Mission College*
Richard Pellerin, *Northern Virginia Community College*
Rick Downs, *South Seattle Community College*
Robbert Mckelvy, *Cossatot Community College*
Robert Cohen, *University of District of Columbia*
Robert Evans, *Monterey Peninsula College*
Robert Fusco, *Bergen Community College*
Rodney Oberdick, *Delaware Technical & Community College–Dover*
Roger Mccoach, *County College of Morris*
Roland Trevino, *San Antonio College*

Ron Powers, *Michigan State University–East Lansing*
Rosa Kontos, *Bergen Community College*
Rose Toering, *Kilian Community College*
Ruby Martinez, *San Antonio College*
Ruth Dellinger, *Florida State College Kent Campus*
Ryan Baxter, *Illinois State University*
Sally Jackman, *Richland College*
Sandra Cox, *Kaskaskia College*
Sandra Jovicic, *University of Akron*
Sandra Leabough, *Centura College*
Shanna Goff, *Grand Rapids Community College*
Shannon Miller-Mace, *Marshall University*
Sharon Hudson, *Gulf Coast Community College*
Shawn Krest, *Genesee Community College*
Sherri Kobis, *Erie Community College Northcamp–Williamsville*
Sima Dabir, *Western Iowa Technical Community College*
Spiros Karimbakas, *Fresno City College*
Stanley Hecht, *Santa Monica College*
Stephen Toner, *Victor Valley Community College*
Susan Metzger, *North Central Michigan College*
Susanna Gunther, *Solano Community College*
Suzette Goss, *Lone Star College Kingwood*

Sylvia Brown, *Mountain Empire Community College*
Tammy Potter, *Gadsden State Community College*
Tian Ren, *Queensborough Community College*
Timothy L. Warkentin, *Cloud County Community College*
Toni Houtteman, *Baker College of Clinton Township*
Tonya Michelle Davenport, *Rowan University*
Vernon Bridges, *Durham Technical Community College*
Wayne Barber, *Chemeketa Community College*
William Kirby, *Gadsden State Community College*
Yon Kim, *Passaic County Community College*

The author team most humbly would like to thank all the people who have contributed to this project.

Special thanks to our team of digital authors for their thousands of hours of work: Jody Harris, Linda Schott, Lizette Hernandez Foley, Michael Larkin, Alina Coronel, and to the masters of ceremonies in the digital world: Donna Gerken, Nicole Lloyd, and Steve Toner. We also offer our sincerest appreciation to the video talent: Jody Harris, Alina Coronel, Didi Quesada, Tony Alfonso, and Brianna Kurtz. You folks are the best! To Mitchel Levy our exercise consultant, thank you for your watchful eye fine-tuning the exercise sets and for your ongoing valuable feedback. To Gene Rumann, thank you so much for ensuring accuracy in our manuscripts.

Finally, we greatly appreciate the many people behind the scenes at McGraw-Hill without whom we would still be on page 1. To Emily Williams, the best developmental editor in the business and steady rock that has kept the train on the track. To Mary Ellen Rahn, our executive editor and overall team leader. We're forever grateful for your support and innovative ideas. To our copy editor Pat Steele who has watched over our manuscript for many years and has been a long-time mentor for our writing. You're amazing. To the marketing team Alex Gay, Peter Vanaria, Tim Cote, John Osgood, and Cherie Harshmann, thank you for your creative ideas in making our books come to life in the market. To the director of digital content, Nicole Lloyd, we are most grateful for your long hours of work and innovation in a world that changes day-to-day. And many thanks to the team at ALEKS that oversees quality control in the digital content. To the production team Peggy Selle, Laurie Janssen, and Carrie Burger for making the manuscript beautiful and bringing it all together. And finally to Ryan Blankenship, Marty Lange, and Kurt Strand, thank you for supporting our projects over the years and for the confidence you've always shown in us.

Most importantly, we give special thanks to the students and instructors who use our series in their classes.

Julie Miller   *Molly O'Neill*   *Nancy Hyde*

New and Updated Content for Miller, O'Neill, and Hyde's *Introductory Algebra*, Third Edition:

Updates throughout the Text:

- New Vocabulary and Key Concept Exercises
- New Tips, Avoiding Mistakes boxes, and Concept Connections
- New and Revised Study Skills Exercises
- Updated Applications and Data in all instances where appropriate
- Writing has been reworked throughout the text in order to improve clarity and understanding

Chapter by Chapter Changes:

Chapter R
- New Chapter Opener
- New Procedure Box on Rounding Decimals
- 16 New Exercises

Chapter 1
- New Chapter Opener
- New Narrative in Section 1.1 on Variables and Expressions
- New Narrative in Section 1.2 on Translations
- Removed Objectives in Section 1.2 on Variables and Expressions
- 6 New Examples
- 22 New PRE Exercises
- 56 New Exercises

Chapter 2
- New Chapter Opener
- New Definitions of a Linear Equation in One Variable, Literal Equation, and Linear Inequality in One Variable
- 11 New Examples
- 61 New Exercises

Chapter 3
- New Chapter Opener
- 85 New Exercises
- New Narrative on Horizontal and Vertical Lines
- 4 New Examples

Chapter 4
- New Chapter Opener
- New narrative on dependent and independent equations
- 33 New Exercises
- 4 New PRE Exercises
- 4 New Examples

Chapter 5
- New Chapter Opener
- 48 New Exercises
- 2 New Examples

Chapter 6
- New Chapter Opener
- New Narrative on Perfect Squares
- 39 New Exercises
- 4 New Examples

Chapter 7
- New Narrative on Restricted Values of a Rational Expression
- New Procedure Box on Writing Equivalent Fractions
- New Definition Box on Ratio and Proportion
- 4 New Examples
- 73 New Exercises

Chapter 8
- New Chapter Opener
- New Definition Box on Notation for Positive and Negative Square Roots
- New Definition Boxes on *n*th-Roots
- 6 New Exercises
- 1 New Example
- New Problem Recognition Exercise Set on Operations on Radicals
- New Group Activity on Calculating Standard Deviation

Chapter 9
- New Chapter Opener
- Introduction to Functions now appears in this Chapter
- New Definition Box on Quadratic Equations in Two Variables
- 22 New Exercises
- 2 New Examples

Additional Topics Appendix
- Entirely new section on Converting Units of Measurement

Strategies to Succeed in Math

Success

It is with great delight that we welcome you to this course and the materials we have provided you. You are embarking on perhaps the most rewarding experience of your life. College is a series of challenges that will prepare you for a lifetime of learning and accomplishments. At the end of your college education, you will be awarded a degree—a degree that establishes your ability to learn and to persevere. It is a statement that you can work to accomplish a goal, no matter what the obstacles.

At this point, you must evaluate the reason you are here. Are you here to fulfill your dreams or the dreams of someone else? To successfully complete this journey, you must be here to fulfill your own desires, not those of a friend or family member. It will be very difficult to withstand the trials of college if you do not have a personal desire to see it through.

A semester or quarter can be very overwhelming. Focus on one day at a time and not on everything that you must learn throughout the entire course. Before you know it, the course will be over. We know that it is very easy to get distracted from your goals. Stay committed and motivated by remembering your ultimate reason for attending school.

We wish you success in this course and in your future educational endeavors. It is our hope that you are successful, not only this semester or quarter, but every term until your ultimate goal is achieved. This course will pave the way for that success. It is the door to achieving your dreams.

Mrs. Andrea Hendricks   and   Mrs. Pauline Chow

Question for Thought: What do you dream about doing? How does attending college make that dream possible? How does this course help you meet your goals? What is your biggest obstacle in being successful in this course? What can you do to overcome that obstacle? What is your plan for succeeding in this course?

Chapter S will introduce some important strategies that can enhance your performance in this course.

Chapter Outline

> ❝Continuous effort—not strength or intelligence—is the key to unlocking our potential.❞
>
> Winston Churchill

SECTION S.1 Time Management and Goal Setting

▶ **OBJECTIVES**

As a result of completing this section, you will be able to

1. Set realistic grade and attendance goals.
2. Establish a schedule for studying math.
3. Establish an action plan.
4. Troubleshoot common errors.

A student might have great study skills but without good utilization of time, those skills are a wasted treasure. Time is like money; we should know how every moment is spent so that we do not waste it, and we should spend it wisely. The great news is that everyone has exactly the same amount of time. The bad news is that once the time has passed, it can never be recaptured. In this section, we will learn some helpful ways to manage our time and to set appropriate goals that make the best use of our time.

Setting Realistic Goals

Objective 1 ▶

Set realistic grade and attendance goals.

As we begin a new course, we have a "clean slate." No grades are in the grade book, no absences have been recorded, and no assignments are late or outstanding. We can control our behavior in such a way that we maximize our chance of success in this course. The beginning of a semester is an optimal time to set realistic goals that we can achieve by the end of the semester. Setting goals provides us with a sure focus and clarifies the direction in which we are headed. Activity 1 will provide us a chance to think about the goals we have for this course and for college in general.

INSTRUCTOR NOTE:
Tell students the importance of writing down their goals. Writing down goals makes them more tangible to us and it can also help motivate us.

ACTIVITY 1 Answer each question.

1. What was the last math course you took? When did you take it? Was it a successful experience? Why or why not? _____
   _____

2. What grade would you like to earn in this course? How many hours a week do you think you will need to devote outside of class to meet this goal?
   _____

3. How many absences do you think could put your goal at risk? What other activities could put your goal at risk?_____
   _____

4. What is your short-term goal? What do you hope to accomplish this semester?
   _____

5. What is your long-term goal? Why are you in college?_____
   _____

6. What are some things you can do that will enable you to reach your goals?
   _____

7. Are there any other activities that you need to avoid or limit that would prevent you from reaching your goals?_____
   _____

Note: *Keep in mind that being late or leaving class early can be just as harmful as missing class completely. Attending class regularly, punctually, and for the entire time is a goal that will lead us to success in math.*

Plan Study Time

Before we can establish study time, we need to know how we currently use and manage our time. One way to do this is by recording our activities in a calendar or planner. The key is to record all of our activities, including time for driving, sleeping, and eating, as shown in Figure S.1. When we do not take the time to record our activities, we are more apt to waste time and to spend time on things that are not aligned with our goals. Once we understand and realize how we use our time, we can be more deliberate in planning a schedule that is beneficial to our goals.

Figure S.1

Time	Monday, 9/22
7:00	Shower/get dressed
7:30	Breakfast
8:00	Leave for school
8:30	
9:00	Math 1001 (9–10:15)
9:30	
10:00	
10:30	Engl 1101 (10:30–11:30)
11:00	
11:30	
12:00	Lunch
12:30	
1:00	Drive to work
1:30	Work (1:30–6)
2:00	
2:30	
3:00	
3:30	
4:00	
4:30	
5:00	
5:30	
6:00	Drive home
6:30	Dinner
7:00	Watch TV
7:30	
8:00	Study
8:30	
9:00	Watch TV
9:30	
10:00	Exercise
10:30	
11:00	Go to bed

Following are some suggested guidelines for planning study time.

1. Make a daily appointment to study for this class.
   a. A general guideline is to spend 2 hr studying for each hour in class. For example, a 3-credit-hour class will require an average of 6 hr of study time each week.

   b. Devote some time each day to studying math. Do not cram the suggested
      hours into one day.

   c. The best time to study is the hour immediately following class time. If this is
      not doable, study time should be as soon after class as possible.

2. Multitask when feasible.

   a. When waiting in line or waiting for an appointment, review your class notes.

   b. When riding a bus, listen to a lecture or review note cards.

3. Prioritize tasks. Differentiate between the things that must be done and the things
   that you just want to do.

4. Maintain a balanced schedule by not overcommitting your time. Say no when
   you don't have the time to devote to a task.

5. Make a habit of writing things down in a calendar or a to-do list.

 Note: *Doing something right the first time takes less time in the long run than doing it poorly and having to redo it later.*

ACTIVITY 2   Answer each question.

1. Without using a calendar or planner, estimate how much time you spend sleeping, eating, watching TV, playing on the computer, working, socializing with friends, sitting in classes, studying, taking care of children, running errands, traveling from one place to another, exercising, and so on.

   a. What did you discover about yourself and how you spend your time? _____
   _____

   b. Is there anything that you want to spend more time doing? _____
   _____

   c. Is there anything you want to spend less time doing?_____
   _____

2. Create a planned time chart for next week using one similar to Figure S.1.

   a. First record large blocks of time commitments (class time, work time, driving time, church activities, and so on)._____
   _____

   b. Schedule necessary activities like sleeping and eating._____
   _____

   c. Schedule regular activities such as grocery shopping, going to the gym, cleaning house, putting kids to bed, and the like._____
   _____

   d. Based on suggested guidelines, you should study 2 hr for each hour you are in class. If you are enrolled in 12-credit hours, you should have 24 hr of study time. Distribute this time over the week in reasonable blocks of time. Do not set yourself up for cram sessions. _____
   _____

   e. Schedule yourself some fun time and time to decompress._____
   _____

   f. Allow flexibility in your schedule. Things will come up, so you shouldn't have every moment scheduled._____
   _____

3. Are there things in your life that need to be removed to improve your chances of success?_____
_____

Action Plan

1. Utilize the print and digital resources provided to you that accompany your textbook. Work with your instructor to access the available Success Strategies Manual. You will find things such as
   - a time tracker.
   - a tip sheet for getting to know your teacher.
   - a shopping list for math success that includes a list of supplies you might need.
   - positive affirmations that you can recite to help motivate you.
   - other resources to get organized and to help you have a productive semester.

2. Set some specific goals for this course.
   - I will get a grade of _____ in this course.
   - Three things I can do to ensure that I meet this goal are

     1. _____

     2. _____

     3. _____

   - I plan to spend _____ hours per week outside of class for this course.
   - Three things I can do to be sure that I have enough time to devote to math are

     1. _____

     2. _____

     3. _____

   - At most I will miss _____classes this semester.
   - Three things I can do to be sure I attend each class meeting are

     1. _____

     2. _____

     3. _____

   - What could interfere with my ability to meet these goals? _____
   - What can I do to overcome or prevent this challenge?_____

Troubleshooting Common Errors

Some of the common errors associated with time management are shown in the following table along with a more appropriate behavior.

Poor Time Management Behaviors	Better Time Management Behaviors
▶ Student waits until Sunday afternoon to do his homework for the week.	▶ Student sets aside 1 hr per night for math and gets a little bit done each day.
▶ Student arrives late to class each day.	▶ Student arrives on time and is ready for class to start.
▶ Student has no idea when the next test is scheduled.	▶ Student uses a planner to record due dates and exam dates.
▶ Student plans a vacation starting a week before the semester ends.	▶ Student checks the Academic Calendar for the college before making travel plans.

" You can't control how your instructor teaches, but you can control what you do to learn the material. Use strategies that emphasize your strengths and de-emphasize your weaknesses. "

Kelly Jackson, *Camden County College*

| SECTION S.2 | Learning Styles |

▶ OBJECTIVES

As a result of completing this section, you will be able to

1. Identify your dominant learning style(s).
2. Implement strategies to maximize success in math based on your learning style(s).
3. Establish an action plan.
4. Troubleshoot common errors.

People learn in many different ways. The way a person best gathers, processes, organizes, and remembers information refers to their **learning style.** There are three basic learning styles—auditory, visual, and kinesthetic. If you do not know how you best learn, it will be helpful for you to complete a learning styles inventory. One is included in this section, but there are many inventories available online.

| Objective 1 ▶ |

Identify your dominant learning style(s).

Learning Styles

The following survey has been created to identify a student's learning style as it pertains to mathematics. Following the survey is a tally sheet for your responses. The category with the highest percentage represents your dominant math learning style.

ACTIVITY 1 Complete the survey.

Math Learning Styles Survey

Answer each question with the number "3" if you agree most of the time, "2" if you agree sometimes, and "1" if you agree rarely or do not agree.

_____ 1. When there is talking or noise in class, I get easily distracted.

_____ 2. If a problem is written on the board, I have difficulty following the steps unless the teacher verbally explains the steps.

_____ 3. I find it easier to have someone explain something to me than to read it in my math book.

_____ 4. If I know how the math is used in real life, it is easier for me to learn.

_____ 5. To remember formulas and definitions, I need to write them down.

_____ 6. I prefer listening to the lecture rather than taking notes.

_____ 7. Using manipulatives, hands-on activities, or games helps me learn math concepts.

_____ 8. When solving a problem, I try to picture working it out in my mind first.

_____ 9. Quiet places are the best places to study math.

_____ 10. Talking myself through a math problem helps me solve it.

_____ 11. When I write things down I remember them better.

_____ 12. I have to do a math problem myself to learn it. I can't really know it by watching someone else do it.

_____ 13. If someone lectures about math without writing things down, I find it difficult to follow.

_____ 14. When I take a math test, I recall more of what was said to me than what I read in my notes or in my math book.

_____ 15. When I take a math test I can picture my notes or problems on the board in my head.

_____ 16. I can do math problems sometimes, but can't verbally explain what I did.

_____ 17. Reading math makes my eyes feel tired or strained.

_____ 18. When I study math I need to take a lot of breaks.

_____ 19. I am good at using my intuition to know how to solve a math problem.

_____ 20. I can learn math fast when someone explains it to me.

_____ 21. Puzzles and games are a good way to practice math.

_____ 22. When I work a math problem I say the numbers I am working with to myself.

_____ 23. I try to write down everything and take a lot of notes in math class.

_____ 24. I do best with math if I just roll up my sleeves and work on problems.

Developed by Kelly Jackson, Camden County College

Math Learning Styles Tally Sheet

Carefully copy your responses (1, 2, or 3) to each question on the survey into the spaces provided.

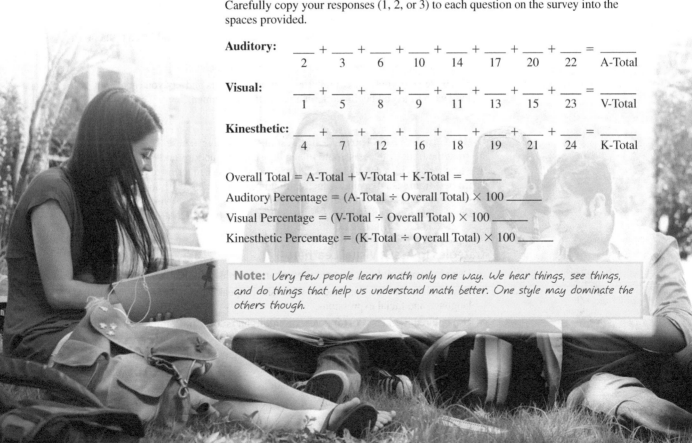

Auditory: ___ + ___ + ___ + ___ + ___ + ___ + ___ + ___ = _____
            2   3   6   10   14   17   20   22   A-Total

Visual: ___ + ___ + ___ + ___ + ___ + ___ + ___ + ___ = _____
           1   5   8   9   11   13   15   23   V-Total

Kinesthetic: ___ + ___ + ___ + ___ + ___ + ___ + ___ + ___ = _____
           4   7   12   16   18   19   21   24   K-Total

Overall Total = A-Total + V-Total + K-Total = _____

Auditory Percentage = (A-Total ÷ Overall Total) × 100 _____

Visual Percentage = (V-Total ÷ Overall Total) × 100 _____

Kinesthetic Percentage = (K-Total ÷ Overall Total) × 100 _____

Note: *Very few people learn math only one way. We hear things, see things, and do things that help us understand math better. One style may dominate the others though.*

Strategies to Enhance Your Learning

Objective 2

Objective 2 ▶

Implement strategies to maximize success in math that are specific to your learning style(s).

Now that you have identified your math learning style, some suggestions for things you can do to increase your success in math class based on which style(s) suits you best are provided. A summary of each type of learner and strategies to apply are shown next. General success strategies that apply to all students will be presented in a later section of this chapter.

> **Definition:** An **auditory learner** learns best through listening to lectures, having discussions, talking things through, and listening to what others have to say. These learners often benefit from reading the text aloud and using a recording device.

Strategies to Assist Auditory Learners

✔ Sit near the front of the class so you can hear your instructor.

✔ Sit away from auditory distractions (air conditioner, door, window, and so on).

✔ Participate in class discussions. Ask and answer questions.

✔ Listen carefully to what the teacher says, their tone of voice, inflection, and volume will give cues about what is important.

✔ Record lectures to aid in taking notes.

✔ Read the text out loud.

✔ Use computer tutorials, online sites, or videos with an audio track.

✔ Use songs, rhymes, and other auditory memory devices.

✔ Discuss your ideas verbally.

✔ Dictate to someone while they write down your thoughts.

✔ Study with a classmate, which allows you to talk about and hear the information.

✔ Recite out loud the information you want to remember several times.

✔ Make recordings of important points you want to remember and listen to them repeatedly.

✔ Ask your teacher to repeat or restate something, as needed.

✔ Verbalize your goals for completing your assignments and say your goals out loud each time you begin work on a particular assignment.

> **Definition:** A **visual learner** learns best through seeing. These learners prefer to sit at the front of the classroom to avoid visual obstructions and do best when the teacher provides detailed notes. They generally think in terms of pictures and learn best from visual displays, such as diagrams, illustrated textbooks, videos, PowerPoint slides, and handouts. During a lecture or classroom discussion, visual learners often prefer to take notes to help them grasp the material.

Strategies to Assist Visual Learners

✔ Use visual materials such as pictures, charts, graphs, and the like.

✔ Have a clear view of your teacher when she is speaking so you can see body language and facial expressions.

✔ Use colored markers, Post-it notes, or highlighters to identify important points in the text.

✔ Illustrate your ideas as a picture or brainstorming bubble before writing them down.

✔ Use multimedia (e.g., computers and videos) learning tools.

✔ Use different colors and pictures in your notes, exercise books, and the like.

✔ Study in a quiet place away from auditory disturbances.

✔ Visualize information as a picture to aid memorization.

✔ Write down things that you want to remember.

✔ Take many notes and write down lots of details.

✔ Learn new material by writing out notes, cover your notes then rewrite them.

✔ Write your goals down and read them as you complete your assignments.

✔ Take advantage of study guides, handouts, and workbooks that include worked out solutions.

✔ Choose a seat away from visual distractions and close to the front of the class.

✔ Prepare flashcards and review them often.

Definition: A **kinesthetic learner** learns best through moving, doing, and touching. These students learn best through a hands-on approach. It is difficult for these students to sit still for long periods.

Strategies to Assist Tactile/Kinesthetic Learners

✔ Practice, practice, practice. Because you prefer a hands-on approach, you need to work as many problems as possible.

✔ Take a 3- to 5-min study break every 15–25 min.

✔ Use manipulatives that can help you investigate the topic you are studying (algebra tiles, base 10 blocks, and the like).

✔ Work in a standing position.

✔ Chew gum while studying.

✔ Use bright colors to highlight what you are reading.

✔ If you wish, listen to music while you study (be sure it is not distracting though).

✔ Make or use a model.

✔ Pace or walk around while reciting to yourself or using flashcards or notes.

✔ If the opportunity arises, volunteer to go to the board to work problems.

✔ Study while sitting in a comfortable lounge chair or on cushions or a beanbag.

✔ Cover your desk with your favorite colored construction paper or even decorate your area to help you focus.

✔ Memorize information by closing your eyes and writing the information in the air, try to picture and hear the words in your head as you are doing this.

✔ Make flashcards, card games, floor games, and the like to help you process information.

✔ When working with someone, after they show you a problem, ask if you can try one.

✔ Make a graphic organizer showing the connections between topics.

✔ Get a study group together in a classroom where you can write on the board, walk around, talk about the math, but do problems.

✔ Use applets or computer tutorials with guided solutions in which you have to enter information throughout.

Note: *There is no right or wrong learning style. Determine what you have a tendency toward and use strategies to enhance your performance in class. You cannot control the way your instructor delivers information, but you can control what you do to best receive the information.*

Action Plan

Objective 3 ▶

Establish an action plan.

1. My dominant learning style(s) is(are) dominant _____

_____ .

2. Five strategies that I will implement immediately to improve my chances of success in math based on my learning style(s) are

    a. _____ .

    b. _____ .

    c. _____ .

    d. _____ .

    e. _____ .

3. Does it seem like my teacher's style of delivery matches my style or is it a mismatch? (Example: you prefer to learn visually but your teacher does not write on the board a lot)_____

_____ .

Troubleshooting Common Errors

Objective 4 ▶

Troubleshoot common errors.

One common error is how students deal with the situation in which their teacher's teaching style does not match their learning style. Students can control their own behavior but not those of others. Following are some suggestions on how to deal with this situation.

Learning Style/Teaching Style Mismatch	What Can You Do?
Visual learner with a teacher who talks a lot but doesn't write down a lot.	**1.** Record the lesson. Later go back and listen to the lesson and fill in your notes with anything you missed the first time. **2.** Read the section in the book prior to class so you know the topic that will be discussed and write down some of the vocabulary and steps. **3.** Visit your instructor or a tutor in a setting where you can ask questions and have time to write things down.
Kinesthetic learner with a teacher who does not use activities, does not have you work problems in class, and does not use manipulatives.	**1.** Rework the problems that the teacher did in class, check your work with your instructors, and then try some similar problems on your own. **2.** Use the Explain or Show me features in your online homework system that will ask you to enter each step. **3.** Meet with your instructor or a tutor. Each time they show you a problem ask, "Can I try one now?"
Auditory learner in a blended or online class, with limited access to "lectures."	**1.** Take advantage of lecture and exercise videos that accompany your textbook or from popular Internet sites that have great educational videos. **2.** Make audio notes for yourself, reading important rules, definitions, and processes into a recorder. Listen to your recordings as often as possible. **3.** Have a study group or tutoring session where you can discuss the math concepts with someone.

" Be committed in everything you do. The number of classes you attend, the number of hours you spend studying, the number of homework problems you work are all indications of how committed you are to the course and your ultimate reason for being in college. "

Andrea Hendricks, *Georgia Perimeter College*

SECTION S.3 / Study Skills

▶ **OBJECTIVES**

As a result of completing this section, you will be able to

1. Identify habits that good math students employ.
2. Read the textbook more effectively and efficiently.
3. Take quality notes.
4. Organize materials in a notebook or portfolio.
5. Complete homework in ways that maximize retention.
6. Establish an action plan.
7. Troubleshoot common errors.

Study skills are the skills students need to improve their learning capacity and to acquire new knowledge. No two students are going to employ the same set of study techniques, though there are some that every student should utilize when studying math. This section will address some of the skills that will enhance the success of all students.

Habits of Successful Math Students

Good math students study with purpose. When you underline something, it should be because it is important. If you write out a note card, it should be because it is something you want to remember long term. When you work a homework problem, it should lead to a better understanding of the process used to solve that problem. If you can't answer "Why am I doing this?" then what you are doing may not be a productive use of your time. You should always have goals to achieve when you sit down to study and everything you do during your study time should work toward those goals. The following suggestions will help you approach your math class with purpose.

Objective 1 ▶

Identify habits that good math students employ.

1. *Successful students are responsible.*
   - ▶ Attend every class meeting. Try to be a few minutes early so that your materials are out and you are ready for class to begin.
   - ▶ Find an accountability partner in class. Encourage one another and use each other as a resource if one of you is absent from class.
   - ▶ Adhere to all deadlines for assignments.

2. *Successful students make the most of their time in class.*
   - ▶ When you are in class, "be in class." Try not to worry about other things going on in your life. Focus your attention on the topics being discussed. (No texting, surfing, or doing other homework.)
   - ▶ Either take notes in class or record the lecture so that you can refer to it later. Some instructors even post their class notes on their website.
   - ▶ Actively participate in class. Follow along with the instructor. Ask questions when you don't understand and be prepared to answer questions that you know.

3. *Successful students dedicate an appropriate amount of time to math outside of class.*
   - ▶ Immediately after class, take a few minutes to write down a summary of the key concepts that you remember. (It has been shown that students who write down what they know retain 1½ times as much as those who don't, 6 weeks later.)
   - ▶ Review your class notes as soon after class as possible.
   - ▶ Begin your homework assignment as soon as you can.
   - ▶ Review notes from previous classes on a regular basis so that you do not forget material covered earlier in the course.
   - ▶ Devote some time every day to your math class.

4. *Successful students aren't afraid to ask for help.*

▶ Math does not need to be a solo activity. Ask your instructor, a tutor, or a classmate about problems you do not understand. Form a study group.

▶ Take advantage of your college's tutoring center and your instructor's office hours.

▶ Use self-help books, other texts, online websites, computer programs, DVDs, or any other outside sources you can find to supplement your course materials.

5. *Successful students are persistent.*

▶ If you get "stuck" on a problem, refer to your notes, the book, or other help resources. Rework the problem until you can do it without referring to these things.

▶ Be patient with yourself in learning the material. Don't get frustrated that other students may seem to learn more quickly than you. Every student comes to class with a different mathematical background. Some classmates just graduated from high school, while others may be returning after several years.

▶ Be willing to try new approaches to solving a problem. If your first attempt fails, continue trying other possible strategies. Often there is more than one way to get to the solution.

Study skills consist of the things you do in class as well as the things you do outside of class. We will take a closer look at four of these topics: reading a math textbook, taking notes, organizing your notebook/portfolio, and completing homework.

Reading a Math Textbook

Objective 2 ▶

Read the textbook more effectively and efficiently.

The textbook is a great resource to aid in the mastery of material presented in class. Many students pay a lot of money for a textbook but do not take the time to read it and often have never been shown how to read a math textbook. Before you attempt homework problems, it is important that you carefully read the relevant sections of your math textbook. The examples should be studied and definitions, properties, and formulas should be learned.

Reading a math textbook is very different than reading a psychology or history text and especially different from reading a novel or a newspaper. Math textbooks generally do not have a whole lot of prose. Textbooks are typically organized around new definitions, new procedures, and worked examples that illustrate these concepts. Graphs, tables, diagrams, equations, formulas, and notations are used to visualize some of the concepts, but these are no more and no less important that the worded passages themselves. Together, they explain the complete math concept you are reading about. When reading a page in your math textbook, you will be reading from left to right, right to left, up and down (think tables), diagonally (think graphs), and from the inside out (think equation solutions).

Some guidelines for reading a math textbook are

1. Skim a new section briefly to identify new vocabulary or processes. Identify the objectives to be presented in the section, which are located in the headings and subheadings.

2. Read the section a second time, using more time and concentration. Try to connect your prior knowledge with the new material you are reading. You will need to read slowly, reread sections, and constantly ask yourself if you understand.

3. When you get to the worked examples, use your own paper to work the problems in detail, making sure that you understand how each step follows from the previous one.

4. Make a list of concepts, formulas, and vocabulary you do *not* understand and seek help.

5. Make a list of formulas and vocabulary that you *do* know and understand.

6. Make sure you understand and use the mathematically correct definition for each vocabulary word. Often words are "borrowed" from everyday language and the meaning can be the same or different in mathematics.

7. You must be able to decode and understand the math notation along with the vocabulary.

8. Learn the formal definitions and properties. It is a good idea to be able to paraphrase into your own words but you don't want to create "new" math rules that may not always work.

9. Get help if you do not understand the reading material.
   - Go back and review the previous section to see if it might be related.
   - Review your instructor's notes on the material.
   - Use the resources that came with your book (videos, CDs, animations, etc.).
   - Ask a classmate, a tutor, or your instructor. Be specific with what you do not understand.

ACTIVITY 1   Get to know the features of this book.

1. Where are the answers located and which answers are available?_____
   _____

2. Where is the chapter review? What is included in the review?_____
   _____

3. What do the different icons used in the book mean?_____
   _____

4. What colors are used to set off definitions, formulas, tips, and other important information?_____
   _____

Taking Notes

Objective 3 ▶

Take quality notes.

Effective note taking begins when you enter the classroom. After you get to your seat, prepare to take notes by taking out your paper, pencil, and book. Taking notes enables you to record how your instructor explains processes, to record examples that are worked, and to identify important class information, such as homework assignments and test dates. Note taking also helps you listen more attentively and to be actively engaged in the learning process. Studies show that people may forget 50% of a lecture within 24 hr, 80% in 2 weeks, and 95% within 1 month if they do not take notes.

Some guidelines for taking notes are as follows.

1. To be an effective note taker, it is important that you attend class.
   Don't be late.
   Don't leave early.

2. To be an effective note taker, you must be a good listener.
   a. Be actively involved in the lecture so that you stay focused on what is being presented.
   b. Sit near the front of the class so that distractions are minimized.
   c. Try to relate the new topics to the material that you have already learned.
   d. Ask your instructor for clarification, if you do not understand. For example, "I don't understand how you got from step 2 to step 3…", "I don't know what the symbol ____ means.", and "What is the difference between ____ and ____?"
   e. Listen for words that signal important information.
   f. Notice how your teacher uses formal math vocabulary when speaking.

3. To be an effective note taker, you must actually take notes.
4. Bring pencils and paper to class and take math notes in pencil, not pen.
   a. Each day start a new set of notes on a new page. Date and label them with the chapter (and section) that is being discussed.
   b. Copy down *everything* that the instructor writes on the board. If the instructor takes the time to write something, it is important.
   c. Take notes, even though your understanding may not be complete.
   d. Leave a space where you may have missed steps or have questions so that you can get these filled in after class. Then actually get them filled in by reading your book, going to a tutor, visiting your instructor's office, or asking a study buddy.
   e. Develop a good note-taking system. Ideas for note-taking systems can be found on the Web or also available with the optional Success Strategies Manual.
5. To be an effective note taker, you should review your notes.
   a. Review and reorganize your notes as soon as possible after class. Fill in any steps you missed.
   b. Write clearly and legibly so you can understand what you have written later.
   c. Rewrite ideas in your own words.
   d. Highlight important ideas, examples and issues with colored pens, pencils, or highlighters.
   e. Review your class notes before the next class period.
   f. Ask questions during office hours or the next class period if there are items that are unclear.
   g. Review all of your notes at least once each week to get a perspective on the course.

The following is an example of a page of effective notes.

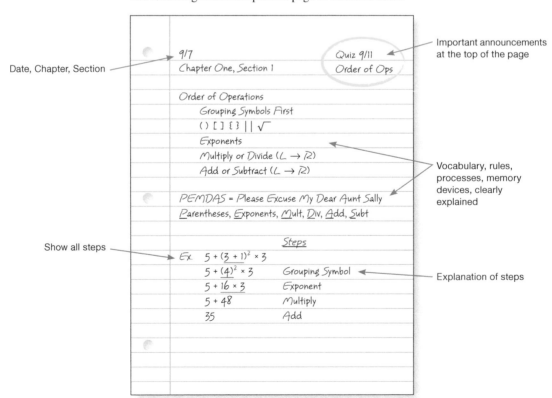

Organizing a Notebook

Objective 4 ▶

Organize materials in a notebook or portfolio.

You attend class, take notes, get handouts, complete homework assignments, and so on. All of this information can be overwhelming if it is not kept in an orderly fashion. The purpose of organizing your course materials is so that you can use them as tools to prepare for tests and other assignments. There are many different ways that you can organize your materials. The main thing is that you keep them all together and in a logical manner.

Some organization suggestions are presented next. Use what seems useful to your situation and adapt them as necessary. The key is to have a system that works for you.

1. Keep materials in a three-ring binder with pockets.
2. At the front of the binder, have a calendar and a copy of your syllabus, a list of homework assignments for the term, and other handouts your instructor gives you on the first day of class.
3. In the front pocket, keep a to-do list of what needs to be done in class.
4. Use dividers with tabs to divide the materials into different sections. Have a section for class notes and handouts, homework, study guides and test reviews, and tests and quizzes.
   - Class notes should be ordered by date. If your instructor provides a handout with additional notes or instructions for a section, keep this with your class notes for the day. (Use a three-hole punch on handouts so they fit in the binder.)
   - Homework should be written out neatly and brought to class each day.
   - If your instructor provides a study guide or test reviews, keep these together.
   - Finally, be sure to keep all of your tests and any other graded assignments to assist you in preparing for the final exam.

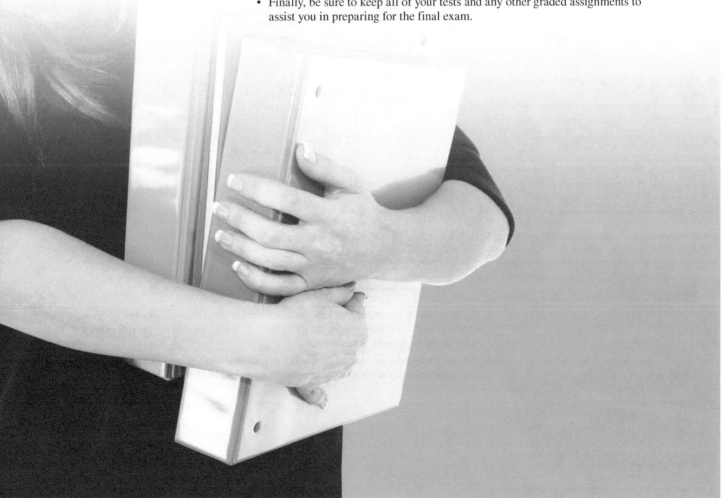

Completing Homework

Objective 5 ▶

Complete homework in ways that maximize retention.

Have you heard the saying, "Math is not a spectator sport?" What this means is that you cannot expect to watch someone else do it and master the material. A colleague used the following example with her class. One summer, she attended 37 Atlanta Braves baseball games. By the end of the summer, her ability to watch and enjoy baseball improved greatly. However, her ability to perform baseball did not improve at all, because she did not play baseball; she only observed it.

While math is not a baseball game, the same general rule applies. Attending class every day is definitely helpful (and fun!), but it is not the only thing needed to successfully master the subject. You must practice. This is where homework comes in. Homework is not just a necessary "evil." This is your opportunity to apply the new definitions, formulas, and procedures to gain deeper understanding.

Some guidelines for completing your homework are as follows.

1. Start your homework as soon after class as possible. The longer the time between class and homework, the more difficult it will be to remember everything you learned in class.

2. Complete your homework neatly and in order. It might look like this.

9/20

Chapter 1, Section 5
Order of Operations
Pg. 59   #2, 6, 10, 14, 18, 22

2. $10 + 5 \times 2$
      $10 + 10$ multiply first
 ✓ $\boxed{20}$ add

6. $20 \div 5 \times 2$
      $20 \div 10$ multiply first
      $\boxed{2}$ divide   *Ask why this is wrong*

10. $(3 + 2)^2$
      $(5)^2$ grouping symbols
      5×5 exponent
 ✓ $\boxed{25}$ multiply

14. $4 + 2 \times 3^2$
      $4 + 2 \times 9$ exponent first
      $4 + 18$ multiply
 ✓ $\boxed{22}$ add

---

3. If you cannot complete a problem after 10 minutes, skip the problem and continue with your assignment. If, after returning to the problem, you still cannot work it, get help from someone.

4. If you cannot even get started on the homework assignment, review your class notes and rework the problems the instructor worked in class.

5. At the top of the first page of your homework exercises, list the problems that you have questions on. At the next class meeting or during your instructor's office hours, ask for help with these exercises.

6. After completing your homework assignment, compare your answers with those in the back of the book. Most books contain answers to the odd-numbered problems. Rework any problems that you missed.

7. After completing your homework, answer the following questions.

    a. What do I understand clearly?

    b. What do I not understand?

    c. What new definitions, rules, or formulas did I apply?

    d. What types of mistakes did I make on problems I worked incorrectly?

        i. Secretarial: miscopied, misread handwriting, misaligned

        ii. Computational: arithmetic mistake (like $8 \times 7 = 54$)

        iii. Procedural: missed a step, steps out of order, stopped too soon

        iv. Conceptual: no idea how to start, wrong method or formula used

8. Review your homework each day until class meets again so you do not forget your newly acquired skills.

> **Note:** If your instructor requires you to complete online homework, print a copy of the homework and work it offline. Most systems will allow you to log back in and enter your answers. There really is no substitute for working problems by hand. As your brain directs the motor skills involved in writing the exercises out, a connection is made that impacts your ability to remember the academic concept.

Action Plan

Objective 6 ▶

Establish an action plan.

Check out additional homework strategies in the supplemental Success Strategies Manual. for examples of a "Homework Cover Sheet," a "Chapter Preview" note-taking tool for use when you read your textbook, a tip sheet for "Making Note Cards," "Creating Memory Devices and Mnemonics," "Getting the Most Out of Tutoring," and several other study aids.

List one new strategy under each heading that you will implement immediately to improve your chances of success in your math course:

1. I will make it a habit to _____

_____

2. From now on when I read my book I will _____

_____

3. My notes would be better if I _____

_____

4. I will make my notebook more organized by _____

_____

5. When I do my homework I will _____

_____

Troubleshooting Common Errors

Objective 7 ▶

Troubleshoot common errors.

Think about the behaviors on the left compared with those on the right. Which habits seem more likely to lead to success in your course?

Poor Habits	Better Habits
A student shows up 10 minutes late for class with a latte in hand but no pen or paper.	A student shows up 10 minutes early for class and has his supplies out and has some questions ready for the instructor.
A student texts friends during class and surfs the net.	A student records the lesson, noting in her notebook the counter number that goes with each problem she is working on.
A student emails her instructor with a message that looks like a text… "i missed ur class pls send HW"	Good Morning Dr. Jones, I missed the 10:00 Algebra class this morning. I got the homework and notes from a classmate. Would it be possible for you to email me a copy of the handout that you distributed in class?
A student comes to class and asks, "I wasn't here for the last class; what did I miss?"	A student misses class and contacts a classmate prior to the next class meeting to get the notes, HW assignment, and reads the book to try to learn what she missed.
A student starts his homework and feels stuck. He closes the book and decides to ask his teacher about it next class.	A student starts his homework and feels stuck. He looks to his notebook for a similar problem; he checks the textbook examples to see if he can find a similar problem. He checks the tutoring schedule to see when he can get in for some help.

" Study purposefully and frequently. Everything you do outside of class should prepare you for the "test." Tests determine our true level of commitment."

Andrea Hendricks, *Georgia Perimeter College*

SECTION S.4 / Test Taking

▶ **OBJECTIVES**

As a result of completing this section, you will be able to

1. Prepare for tests and quizzes.
2. Maximize success during the test-taking process.
3. Analyze mistakes on a test.
4. Establish an action plan.
5. Troubleshoot common errors.

Tests are used to demonstrate mastery or knowledge. Tests can show that we can apply what we have learned. With adequate preparation, tests should simply be an extension of homework. Test taking is only successful if you have employed successful study strategies prior to the test. As the saying goes, "practice makes perfect."

Objective 1 ▶

Prepare for tests and quizzes.

Before the Test

1. Complete your homework assignments regularly.
2. Review completed sections on a regular basis. Use the weekend to review the week's sections.
3. Create a practice test from the problems your teacher worked in class. Work the problems without referring to your notes or books so that you simulate a real test environment. Include problems at all levels of difficulty on the practice test. Check the answers by reviewing your notes or have a classmate check your work.
4. Know which formulas will be provided and which ones must be memorized.
5. Understand all formulas and definitions you need to know for the test. Flashcards are very helpful with this task. Use the front of an index card for the name of the formula or definition and write the formula or definition on the back of the card. Be sure you know what each symbol in a formula represents.
6. Begin preparing a week before an exam. Use your weekly planner to assist with study time. Record the date of the exam on your calendar and then schedule test preparation time beginning a week earlier.
7. Find out as much information about the test as you can:
   a. How many questions will be on the test?
   b. What types of questions (multiple choice, free response) will be included?
   c. How long will you be given to complete the test?
   d. What materials are you allowed to use?
   e. Will there be bonus or extra credit problems?
   f. What chapter/sections are covered?

During the Test

Objective 2 ▶

Maximize success during the test-taking process.

1. Arrive at class early with all the necessary supplies and any aids you are permitted to use, and be ready to begin.
2. When you get your exam, write down all of the formulas on the top or sides of the first page. If your test is computerized, use scratch paper to write down the formulas.
3. Read the instructions carefully.
4. Review the test and complete the problems you know how to do first. This will build your confidence and bring to mind other things you have learned.
5. Keep an eye on the time. Do not spend too much time on one problem (especially if it is a low-points question).

6. Check your answers to make sure they are reasonable. For example, if you are solving for a length, a negative answer would not make sense.

7. Show all of your work neatly and clearly.

8. If you have time, review your work. Don't change any answers unless you have good reason. Often times, first instincts are correct. Double check your signs and arithmetic.

9. Use all of the allotted time to take your test. There is no prize for finishing first nor is there a penalty for being the last one to turn in the exam.

10. Mark up the test paper, if you are allowed, with information that will help you save time.

   a. Circle what you are looking for.

   b. With multiple-choice questions, if you know an answer is impossible, cross it out.

   c. If you have checked an answer, put a check mark next to the problem.

   d. If you skipped a problem but want to come back to it, put a plus sign next to it.

   e. If you see a problem that you don't recognize at all, put a minus sign next to it and come back to it last.

   f. If you have eliminated some options in a multiple-choice question, put down how many options are left. When running out of time, go back to the ones with the fewest options first.

Here is what your test might look like after the first time through.

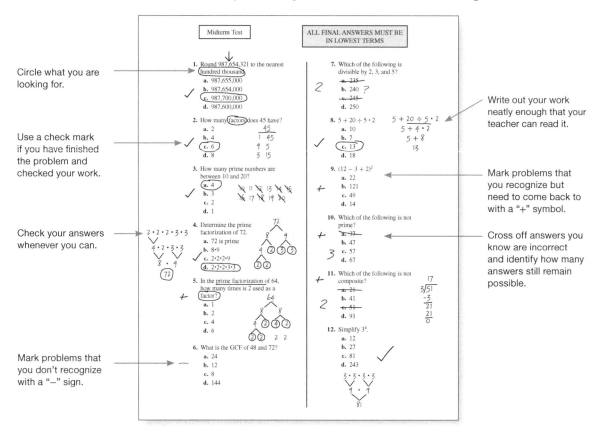

After the Test

1. Look through the test for the problems you missed. Rework these problems until you get them correct.
2. Keep your test corrections with the exam (if it is returned to you) for future studying.
3. Make an appointment to meet with your instructor to review any questions you cannot figure out.
4. Most likely, the material on your test will be covered on your final, so it is important that you keep the exam if your instructor allows you to do so. File it in your notebook so you can review it later in the course.
5. Here is a strategy for test corrections:
    a. Divide a piece of paper in thirds.
    b. On the left side, write out the original problem with your original work.
    c. In the middle, write out the correct answer to the problem.
    d. On the right side, work a similar problem to ensure that you can do this type of problem correctly.

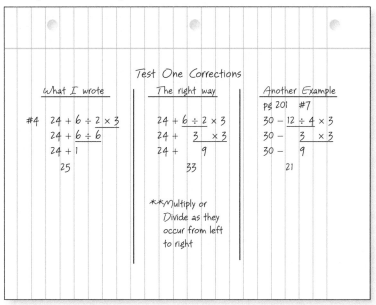

Action Plan

Check out additional homework strategies in the supplemental Success Strategies Manual for a "Test Preparation Worksheet," a "Post-Test Debriefing" form, suggestions for "How to Reduce Test Anxiety," and tips for "Problem-Solving Strategies."

1. Two things that I will commit to doing before a test to improve my chances of success:

    _____

    _____

2. Two strategies that I will employ during a test to keep my anxiety down:

    _____

    _____

3. After a test I will do the following to learn from my mistakes:

    _____

    _____

Troubleshooting Common Errors

After you check your homework or take a quiz or test, you should review it to determine the types of mistakes you made and think about how you can fix them. It is important to understand whether the errors you make are conceptual, procedural, computational, or secretarial.

A **conceptual error** shows little or no understanding of the underlying concept or procedure.

In a **procedural error**, the correct process is used but there is a mistake made with the steps.

In a **computational error,** an arithmetic mistake is made.

In a **secretarial error**, a miscopy of some kind is made.

Evaluate	
$24 + 6 \div 2 \times 3$	
$\underline{24 + 6} \div 2 \times 3$	Add
$\underline{30 \div 2} \times 3$	Divide
15×3	Multiply
45	

The student shows no understanding of the concept of "order of operations." He just works straight through from left to right. This is an example of a conceptual error.

Evaluate	
$24 + 6 \div 2 \times 3$ *PEMDAS*	
$24 + 6 \div \underline{2 \times 3}$	Multiply
$24 + \underline{6 \div 6}$	Divide
$24 + 1$	Add
25	

The student clearly identifies that the order of operations is being used as she uses the acronym PEMDAS. She knows the right process. However, she thinks that she must multiply then divide, rather than the correct rule: Multiplication and division are done as they occur, from left to right. This is an example of a procedural error.

Evaluate	
$24 + 6 \div 2 \times 3$ *PEMDAS*	
$24 + \underline{6 \div 2} \times 3$	Divide
$24 + \underline{3 \times 3}$	Multiply
$24 + 9$	Add
32	

The student clearly identifies that "order of operations" is being used as he uses the acronym PEMDAS. He does all of the right steps, but then adds incorrectly. This is an example of a computational error.

A fourth type of mistake is *simply secretarial*. This type of mistake includes miscopying any part of the problem, misreading your handwriting, misaligning the problem, or any other non-math-related issue with how you write out your work.

How do I correct these errors?

A conceptual error needs to be corrected before the test begins. This mistake is typically about lack of preparation for the test.

> **Note:** *Remember* P^5
>
> *Proper Preparation Prevents Poor Performance*

▶ If you have not been doing any homework, do some. If you have been doing some, do more. If you have been doing all of the homework and are still struggling with the concepts, you may need some tutoring.

▶ Sometimes the issue is problem recognition. Perhaps you can do all of the problems when they are organized into separate sections in the book, but not when they are jumbled together on a test.

  • A great way to mimic this situation is to mix up your notecards.

  • Don't study everything in the same order each time.

  • Mix problems from different sections and chapters together.

  • Work any cumulative reviews in the text.

  • Review old homework each time you complete a new homework assignment to compare how the new assignment is the same or different from the old topics.

A procedural mistake usually requires only a minor fix. You understand the concept; you know what the steps are, but have confused them in some way. This mistake is also about preparation; the steps should be natural by the time you get to a test. If you have repeated a process enough times, you will not even think about the steps any more, you will just know what to do. Whether it is playing music, throwing a baseball, making a pie, or doing a math problem, practice makes perfect!

Computational and secretarial mistakes both have similar fixes. Check your work and slow down. These mistakes are typically made on problems that you are very confident with and are working through quickly. You do not want quickly to mean *carelessly*!

▶ For many problem types, you can check your answers. When this is possible you should always do so. Check the solution of a problem with the original problem. In this way even a miscopy can be found.

▶ Estimate your answer before you begin your work. If your answer is not near the estimate, investigate why.

▶ Think about the reasonableness of your answer. If you made a secretarial error with a decimal point and have an answer where a car is driving 500 mph, it should be clear to you that this type of answer is not reasonable.

▶ If you are permitted to use a calculator, check hand calculations with the calculator. Also, check the calculator output with your reasonableness criteria. If you press the wrong buttons, a calculator can still give you a wrong answer.

▶ Use grid paper instead of lined paper to help with misalignment issues. You can also turn lined paper horizontally to create columns.

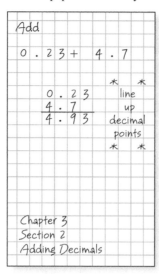
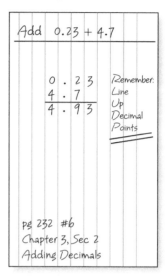

 Note: *If you can't read it, you can't review or study it. If your teacher can't read it, you may get it marked wrong.*
Be Neat!

Procedure: Determining the Type of Mistake on a Test or Quiz

Step 1: Conceptual: Left it blank, wrong process, mis-memorized rule
Step 2: Procedural: Performed steps out of order, missed a step, or couldn't finish all steps
Step 3: Computational: Added, subtracted, multiplied, or divided wrong
Step 4: Secretarial: Miscopy, omission, misalignment, misread handwriting

---

After a test, review each problem that you got wrong and evaluate what went wrong. What types of mistakes did you make? Is there a trend in which type of mistakes you make? What will you do to eliminate these mistakes in the future? Also, reflect about whether the test is helping you meet your grade goal or harming you in making your grade goal. After each test, you should evaluate your progress toward meeting your grade goal.

"Organization and Commitment go hand in hand. For each section, organize the study plan and make a commitment to follow the schedule."

Pauline Chow, *Harrisburg Area Community College*

SECTION S.5 — Blended and Online Classes

The desire for flexibility and convenience in scheduling classes has led to a continued increase in blended and online classes.

▶ OBJECTIVES

As a result of completing this section, you will be able to:

1. Differentiate between blended, hybrid, and online classes.
2. Use techniques to maximize your success in blended and online settings.
3. Establish an action plan.
4. Troubleshoot common errors.

Identifying Different Delivery Methods

Objective 1 ▶

Differentiate between blended, hybrid, and online classes.

Blended classes, or **hybrid** classes, incorporate traditional classroom experiences with online learning activities. Students in these types of classes are required to attend a specific number of on-campus class meetings. The remaining portion of the course is delivered online, thereby reducing the amount of time a student spends in class. In summary, blended classes strive to combine the best elements of traditional face-to-face instruction with the best aspects of learning at a distance.

Online classes, unlike blended classes, deliver entire courses at a distance. Some may have required meetings for exams, but typically all aspects of the course are provided online.

With a portion of a course or an entire course delivered at a distance, the roles of the teacher and student change. The teacher becomes more of a facilitator and the student becomes more like a teacher in these environments. While in a traditional classroom, the student's learning is his or her responsibility, this responsibility becomes even more important in blended and online courses. The information provided in the previous sections certainly applies to students in any type of class, but there are some additional tips for students in blended and online classes.

Tips for Blended and Online Classes

Objective 2 ▶

Use techniques to maximize your success in blended and online settings.

1. The first day of class is extremely important. If you are in a blended class, be sure to attend the first on-campus meeting. If you are in an online class, be sure to log into the course the first day the course is available.
2. Review the syllabus and course policies to determine what is expected of you.
   a. How many required on-campus meetings are there?
   b. Are there proctored exams?
   c. Upon what activities is your grade based (e.g., online homework, discussion board postings, online quizzes and/or tests, group projects, and so on)?
3. Familiarize yourself with the course resources.
   a. Does your instructor post notes or videos, solutions for quizzes/tests, or other material?
   b. Does your instructor hold online office hours through chat, email, or a live classroom? If so, when?
   c. What learning materials (videos, practice problems, ebook, and the like) are available with your textbook?

4. Make a calendar for the semester (one may be available by your instructor) and write down due dates for homework, quizzes, tests, discussion posts, and other assignments.

5. Determine a time each week to have class with yourself.

   a. If the face-to-face version of the class meets, for example, 2 days a week for 1 hr and 45 min, then you should set aside this same amount of time to "have class" on your own.

   b. Class time is time for you to watch videos, to read the textbook, to do what is necessary to learn the material, and to complete quizzes, tests, and discussions. As you watch videos or read the textbook, take notes as you would if you were attending a traditional class.

6. Determine a time each week to have study time. In addition to "class," you need study time.

   a. For each credit or contact hour for the course, you should have three hours of class plus study time (3 credit class = 9 hr, 3 hr for "class" and 6 hr of study time).

   b. Study time is time for you to complete homework. So that you do not get dependent on the help resources online, we suggest that you print the homework assignment, work it offline, and then log back in to enter your answers. For the problems that you answered incorrectly, use the help features to assist you.

7. Remember that you are not alone in the online classroom. Interact with your instructor and other classmates through discussion boards, email, and other features that are available in your class.

8. Ask your instructor for help when you do not understand the material or the technology.

9. Maintain your notes, homework, printed copies of assignments, and any other printables in your notebook.

10. Check in frequently, daily if possible, for announcements, changes to the calendar or assignments, and for any updates you need to know.

Action Plan

Objective 3 ▶
Establish an action plan.

Set some goals for how you will be successful in a class with a nontraditional delivery method.

1. I will "have class with myself" _____ times a week for _____ minutes each time.

2. If I find I can't do it alone, I will get help by _____

   _____.

3. Five things that I am committed to do to ensure that I maximize my success are

   _____.

   _____

   _____

   _____

   _____

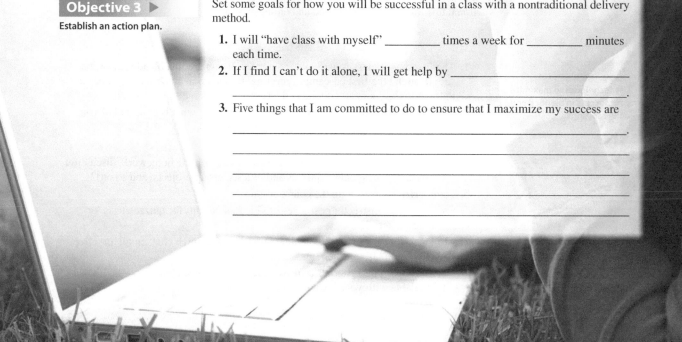

Troubleshooting Common Errors

Objective 4 ▶

Troubleshoot common errors.

Blended and online classes present some different challenges than face-to-face classes. Here are some suggestions to overcome those challenges from students who have taken blended and/or online classes.

Study Skills	Suggestions
Homework	"Plan ahead and don't procrastinate in completing your homework. And try to do the take home assignments without looking at notes . . . it will help a lot at test time!" "Follow the study guide, do all the online homework and take-home work. Try the practice tests to help with confidence if you get nervous taking tests."
Textbook	"Read the book first, then do book questions, then do all online homework until a score of 100 percent is reached. Review all materials again before an exam. You have to be disciplined in getting into a routine just like a classroom based course."
Communication	"I would recommend keeping in constant contact with the instructor. Monitor your progress and make sure you are constantly evaluating your study habits. Reviewing feedback is another great way to improve your understanding."
Time Management	"You will need a lot of time to succeed in this course. Just because it's an online class doesn't mean you can sign on for 5 minutes do some work and fly by. Time is essential to succeeding in this course." "This course requires a good bit of time, and dedication. Had I not spend much time on the course at the beginning, I would have not been able to perform well for the remainder of the course." "It is very flexible but students have to be prepared to discipline themselves enough to do the work on time and not wait until the last minute. Don't try to do all the problems at one time, it is very overwhelming. It's not always possible but try to treat it like a normal class and set aside an hour a day or every other day, to work on it. Sometimes you have a busy week and that's what's nice about having an online class, the flexibility to work on the material when you have time." "In order to succeed you have to put the time into this class as if it were on campus. I feel that if individuals apply themselves to this course they will succeed!!!!"

Reference

Chapter R

Chapter R is a reference chapter that reviews the basic operations on fractions, decimals, percents, and geometry. This chapter begins with a section of valuable study tips.

Getting Organized

Success as a college student requires a certain level of organization. This checklist will guide you in preparing for the upcoming term. Try to complete each item on the list either before your class begins or within the first few days of the term. Check off each item as you get yourself organized.

☐ Purchase a notebook and other materials for class.

☐ On the first page of your notebook, make note of your instructor's name, office location, office hours, phone number, and e-mail address.

☐ Obtain a calendar for keeping track of test dates, assignment due dates, college holidays, final exam schedule, and appointments.

☐ Arrange your work schedule and other obligations to allow adequate time for attending class and studying.

☐ Try to obtain the names, phone numbers, and e-mail addresses of 1 or 2 other students in your class to form a study group or to contact if you miss class.

☐ Locate the math lab or any tutoring services available on your campus.

Section R.1 | Study Tips

In taking a course in algebra, you are making a commitment to yourself, your instructor, and your classmates. Following some or all of the study tips presented here can help you succeed in this endeavor. The features of this text that will assist you are printed in blue.

1. Before the Course

1. Purchase the necessary materials for the course before the course begins or on the first day.
2. Obtain a three-ring binder to keep and organize your notes, homework, tests, and any other materials acquired in the class. We call this type of notebook a portfolio.
3. Arrange your schedule so that you have enough time to attend class and to do homework. A common rule is to set aside at least 2 hours for homework for every hour spent in class. That is, if you are taking a 4-credit-hour course, plan on at least 8 hours a week for homework. A 6-credit-hour course will then take *at least* 12 hours each week—about the same as a part-time job. If you experience difficulty in mathematics, plan for more time.
4. Communicate with your employer and family members the importance of your success in this course so that they can support you.
5. Be sure to find out the type of calculator (if any) that your instructor requires.

2. During the Course

1. Read the section in the text *before* the lecture to familiarize yourself with the material and terminology. It is recommended that you read your math book with paper and pencil in hand. Write a one-sentence preview of what the section is about.
2. Attend every class, and be on time. Be sure to bring any materials that are needed for class such as graph paper, a ruler, or a calculator.
3. Take notes in class. Write down all of the examples that the instructor presents. Read the notes after class, and add any comments to make your notes clearer to you. Use a tape recorder to record the lecture if the instructor permits the recording of lectures.
4. Ask questions in class.
5. Read the section in the text *after* the lecture, and pay special attention to the Tip boxes and Avoiding Mistakes boxes.
6. After you read an example, try the accompanying Skill Practice problem. The skill practice problem mirrors the example and tests your understanding of what you have read.
7. Do homework every day. Even if your class does not meet every day, you should still do some work every day to keep the material fresh in your mind.
8. Check your homework with the answers that are supplied in the back of this text. Correct the exercises that do not match, and circle or star those that you cannot correct yourself. This way you can easily find them and ask your instructor, tutor, online tutor, or math lab staff the next day.

9. Be sure to do the Vocabulary and Key Concepts exercises found at the beginning of the Practice Exercises.

10. The Problem Recognition Exercises are located in all chapters. These provide additional practice distinguishing among a variety of problem types. Sometimes the most difficult part of learning mathematics is retaining all that you learn. These exercises are excellent tools for retention of material.

11. Form a study group with fellow students in your class, and exchange phone numbers. You will be surprised by how much you can learn by talking about mathematics with other students.

12. If you use a calculator in your class, read the Calculator Connections boxes to learn how and when to use your calculator.

13. Ask your instructor where you might obtain extra help if necessary.

3. Preparation for Exams

1. Look over your homework. Pay special attention to the exercises you have circled or starred to be sure that you have learned that concept.

2. Begin preparations for exams on the first day of class. As you do each homework assignment, think about how you would recognize similar problems when they appear on a test.

3. Read through the Summary at the end of the chapter. Be sure that you understand each concept and example. If not, go to the section in the text and reread that section.

4. Give yourself enough time to take the Chapter Test uninterrupted. Then check the answers. For each problem you answered incorrectly, go to the Review Exercises and do all of the problems that are similar.

5. To prepare for the final exam, complete the Cumulative Review Exercises at the end of each chapter, starting with Chapter 2. If you complete the cumulative reviews after finishing each chapter, then you will be preparing for the final exam throughout the course. The Cumulative Review Exercises are another excellent tool for helping you retain material.

4. Where to Go for Help

1. At the first sign of trouble, see your instructor. Most instructors have specific office hours set aside to help students. Don't wait until after you have failed an exam to seek assistance.

2. Get a tutor. Most colleges and universities have free tutoring available. There may also be an online tutor available.

3. When your instructor and tutor are unavailable, use the Student Solutions Manual for step-by-step solutions to the odd-numbered problems in the exercise sets.

4. Work with another student from your class.

5. Work on the computer. Many mathematics tutorial programs and websites are available on the Internet, including the website that accompanies this text.

Group Activity

Becoming a Successful Student

Materials: Computer with Internet access (Optional)

Estimated Time: 15 minutes

Group Size: 4

Good time management, good study skills, and good organization will help you be successful in this course. Answer the following questions and compare your answers with your group members.

1. To motivate yourself to complete a course, it is helpful to have clear reasons for taking the course. List your goals for taking this course and discuss them with your group.

2. For the next week, write down the times each day that you plan to study math.

Monday	Tuesday	Wednesday	Thursday	Friday	Saturday	Sunday

3. Write down the date of your next math test. _____

4. Taking 12 credit-hours is the equivalent of a full-time job. Often students try to work too many hours while taking classes at school.

   a. Write down the number of hours you work per week and the number of credit-hours you are taking this term.

   Number of hours worked per week _____

   Number of credit-hours this term _____

   b. The table gives a recommended limit to the number of hours you should work for the number of credit-hours you are taking at school. (Keep in mind that other responsibilities in your life such as your family might also make it necessary to limit your hours at work even more.) How do your numbers from part (a) compare to those in the table? Are you working too many hours?

Number of Credit-Hours	Maximum Number of Hours of Work per Week
3	40
6	30
9	20
12	10
15	0

5. Discuss with your group members where you can go for extra help in math. Then write down three of the suggestions.

_____

_____

_____

6. Do you keep an organized notebook for this class? Can you think of any suggestions that you can share with your group members to help them keep their materials organized?

7. Look through Chapter 2 and find the page number corresponding to each feature in that chapter. Discuss with your group members how you might use each feature.

Problem Recognition Exercises: page _____

Chapter Summary: page _____

Chapter Review Exercises: page _____

Chapter Test: page _____

Cumulative Review Exercises: page _____

8. Look at the Skill Practice exercises. For example, find Skill Practice exercises 3 and 4 in Section R.2. Where are the answers to these exercises located? Discuss with your group members how you might use the Skill Practice exercises.

9. Do you think that you have math anxiety? Read the following list for some possible solutions. Check the activities that you can realistically try to help you overcome this problem.

_____ Read a book on math anxiety.

_____ Search the Web for tips on handling math anxiety.

_____ See a counselor to discuss your anxiety.

_____ Talk with your instructor to discuss strategies to manage math anxiety.

_____ Evaluate your time management to see if you are trying to do too much. Then adjust your schedule accordingly.

10. Some students favor different methods of learning over others. For example, you might prefer:

- Learning through listening and hearing.

- Learning through seeing images, watching demonstrations, and visualizing diagrams and charts.

- Learning by experience through a hands-on approach.

- Learning through reading and writing.

Most experts believe that the most effective learning comes when a student engages in *all* of these activities. However, each individual is different and may benefit from one activity more than another. You can visit a number of different websites to determine your "learning style." Try doing a search on the Internet with the key words *"learning styles assessment."* Once you have found a suitable website, answer the questionnaire and the site will give you feedback on what method of learning works best for you.

11. As you read through Chapter 1, try to become familiar with the features of this textbook. Then match the feature in column B with its description in column A.

Column A	Column B
1. Allows you to check your work as you do your homework	a. Tips
2. Shows you how to avoid common errors	b. ConnectMath
3. Provides an online tutorial and exercise supplement	c. Skill Practice exercises
4. Outlines key concepts for each section in the chapter	d. Problem Recognition Exercises
5. Provides exercises that allow you to distinguish between different types of problems	e. Answers to odd exercises
6. Offers helpful hints and insight	f. Chapter Summary
7. Offers practice exercises that go along with each example	g. Avoiding Mistakes

1. Basic Definitions

The study of algebra involves many of the operations and procedures used in arithmetic. Therefore, we begin this text by reviewing the basic operations of addition, subtraction, multiplication, and division on fractions and mixed numbers.

In day-to-day life, the numbers we use for counting are

the **natural numbers**: $1, 2, 3, 4, \ldots$

and

the **whole numbers**: $0, 1, 2, 3, \ldots$

Whole numbers are used to count the number of whole units in a quantity. A fraction is used to express part of a whole unit. If a child gains $2\frac{1}{2}$ lb, the child has gained two whole pounds plus a portion of a pound. To express the additional half pound mathematically, we may use the fraction, $\frac{1}{2}$.

Definition of a Fraction and Its Parts

Fractions are numbers of the form $\frac{a}{b}$, where $\frac{a}{b} = a \div b$ and b does not equal zero.

In the fraction $\frac{a}{b}$, the **numerator** is a, and the **denominator** is b.

The denominator of a fraction indicates how many equal parts divide the whole. The numerator indicates how many parts are being represented. For instance, suppose Jack wants to plant carrots in $\frac{2}{5}$ of a rectangular garden. He can divide the garden into five equal parts and use two of the parts for carrots (Figure R-1).

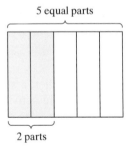

5 equal parts

2 parts   The shaded region represents $\frac{2}{5}$ of the garden.

Figure R-1

Definition of Proper Fractions, Improper Fractions, and Mixed Numbers

1. If the numerator of a fraction is less than the denominator, the fraction is a **proper fraction**. A proper fraction represents a quantity that is less than a whole unit.
2. If the numerator of a fraction is greater than or equal to the denominator, then the fraction is an **improper fraction**. An improper fraction represents a quantity greater than or equal to a whole unit.
3. A **mixed number** is a whole number added to a proper fraction.

Proper Fractions: $\frac{3}{5}$ $\frac{1}{8}$

Improper Fractions: $\frac{7}{5}$ $\frac{8}{8}$

Mixed Numbers: $1\frac{1}{5}$ $2\frac{3}{8}$

Concept Connections

1. Write a proper or improper fraction associated with the shaded region.

2. Which is greater, $\frac{3}{2}$ or $3\frac{1}{2}$?

2. Prime Factorization

To perform operations on fractions it is important to understand the concept of a factor. For example, when the numbers 2 and 6 are multiplied, the result (called the **product**) is 12.

$$2 \times 6 = 12$$

factors   product

The numbers 2 and 6 are said to be **factors** of 12. (In this context, we refer only to natural number factors.) The number 12 is said to be factored when it is written as the product of two or more natural numbers. For example, 12 can be factored in several ways:

$$12 = 1 \times 12 \qquad 12 = 2 \times 6 \qquad 12 = 3 \times 4 \qquad 12 = 2 \times 2 \times 3$$

A natural number greater than 1 that has only two factors, 1 and itself, is called a **prime number**. The first several prime numbers are 2, 3, 5, 7, 11, and 13. A natural number greater than 1 that is not prime is called a **composite number**. That is, a composite number has factors other than itself and 1. The first several composite numbers are 4, 6, 8, 9, 10, 12, 14, 15, and 16.

Avoiding Mistakes

The number 1 is neither prime nor composite.

| Example 1 | **Writing a Natural Number as a Product of Prime Factors** |

Write each number as a product of prime factors.

a. 12   **b.** 30

Skill Practice

Write the number as a product of prime factors.

3. 40   **4.** 72

Solution:

a. $12 = 2 \times 2 \times 3$ Divide 12 by prime numbers until the result is also prime.

$$\begin{array}{r} 2\overline{)12} \\ 2\overline{)6} \\ 3 \end{array}$$

Or use a factor tree

b. $30 = 2 \times 3 \times 5$

$$\begin{array}{r} 2\overline{)30} \\ 3\overline{)15} \\ 5 \end{array}$$

Answers

1. $\frac{7}{4}$ 2. $3\frac{1}{2}$

3. $2 \times 2 \times 2 \times 5$
4. $2 \times 2 \times 2 \times 3 \times 3$

3. Simplifying Fractions to Lowest Terms

The process of factoring numbers can be used to reduce or simplify fractions to lowest terms. A fractional portion of a whole can be represented by infinitely many fractions. For example, Figure R-2 shows that $\frac{1}{2}$ is equivalent to $\frac{2}{4}, \frac{3}{6}, \frac{4}{8}$, and so on.

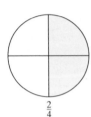

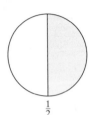

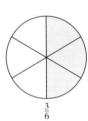

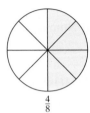

$$\frac{1}{2} \qquad \frac{2}{4} \qquad \frac{3}{6} \qquad \frac{4}{8}$$

Figure R-2

The fraction $\frac{1}{2}$ is said to be in **lowest terms** because the numerator and denominator share no common factor other than 1.

To simplify a fraction to lowest terms, we use the following important principle.

Fundamental Principle of Fractions

Suppose that a number, c, is a common factor in the numerator and denominator of a fraction. Then

$$\frac{a \times c}{b \times c} = \frac{a}{b} \times \frac{c}{c} = \frac{a}{b} \times 1 = \frac{a}{b}$$

To simplify a fraction, we begin by factoring the numerator and denominator into prime factors. This will help identify the common factors.

Example 2 Simplifying a Fraction to Lowest Terms

Simplify $\dfrac{45}{30}$ to lowest terms.

Solution:

$$\frac{45}{30} = \frac{3 \times 3 \times 5}{2 \times 3 \times 5} \qquad \text{Factor the numerator and denominator.}$$

$$= \frac{3}{2} \times \frac{3}{3} \times \frac{5}{5} \qquad \text{Apply the fundamental principle of fractions.}$$

$$= \frac{3}{2} \times 1 \times 1 \qquad \text{Any nonzero number divided by itself is 1.}$$

$$= \frac{3}{2} \qquad \text{Any number multiplied by 1 is itself.}$$

In Example 2, we showed numerous steps to reduce fractions to lowest terms. However, the process is often simplified. Notice that the same result can be obtained by dividing out the greatest common factor from the numerator and denominator. (The **greatest common factor** is the largest factor that is common to both numerator and denominator.)

$$\frac{45}{30} = \frac{3 \times 15}{2 \times 15} \qquad \text{The greatest common factor of 45 and 30 is 15.}$$

$$= \frac{3 \times \overset{1}{\cancel{15}}}{2 \times \underset{1}{\cancel{15}}} \qquad \text{The symbol } \diagup \text{ is often used to show that a common factor has been divided out.}$$

$$= \frac{3}{2} \qquad \text{Notice that "dividing out" the common factor of 15 has the same effect as dividing the numerator and denominator by 15. This is often done mentally.}$$

$$\frac{\overset{3}{\cancel{45}}}{\underset{2}{\cancel{30}}} = \frac{3}{2} \quad \longleftarrow \quad \text{45 divided by 15 equals 3.}$$
$$\qquad\qquad \longleftarrow \quad \text{30 divided by 15 equals 2.}$$

Example 3   **Simplifying a Fraction to Lowest Terms**

Simplify $\dfrac{14}{42}$ to lowest terms.

Solution:

$$\frac{14}{42} = \frac{1 \times 14}{3 \times 14} \qquad \text{The greatest common factor of 14 and 42 is 14.}$$

$$= \frac{1 \times \overset{1}{\cancel{14}}}{3 \times \underset{1}{\cancel{14}}}$$

$$= \frac{1}{3} \qquad\qquad \frac{\overset{1}{\cancel{14}}}{\underset{3}{\cancel{42}}} = \frac{1}{3} \quad \longleftarrow \quad \text{14 divided by 14 equals 1.}$$
$$\qquad\qquad\qquad\qquad\qquad \longleftarrow \quad \text{42 divided by 14 equals 3.}$$

Skill Practice

Simplify to lowest terms.

6. $\dfrac{32}{12}$

Avoiding Mistakes

In Example 3, the numerator and denominator can be divided by the common factor, 14. It is important to remember to write the result of 1 in the numerator. The simplified form of the fraction is $\frac{1}{3}$.

4. Multiplying Fractions

Multiplying Fractions

If b is not zero and d is not zero, then

$$\frac{a}{b} \times \frac{c}{d} = \frac{a \times c}{b \times d}$$

To multiply fractions, multiply the numerators and multiply the denominators.

Answer

6. $\dfrac{8}{3}$

Example 4 **Multiplying Fractions**

Multiply the fractions: $\dfrac{1}{4} \times \dfrac{1}{2}$

Solution:

$$\dfrac{1}{4} \times \dfrac{1}{2} = \dfrac{1 \times 1}{4 \times 2} = \dfrac{1}{8}$$ Multiply the numerators. Multiply the denominators.

Notice that the product $\dfrac{1}{4} \times \dfrac{1}{2}$ represents a quantity that is $\dfrac{1}{4}$ of $\dfrac{1}{2}$. Taking $\dfrac{1}{4}$ of a quantity is equivalent to dividing the quantity by 4. One-half of a pie divided into four pieces leaves pieces that each represent $\dfrac{1}{8}$ of the pie (Figure R-3).

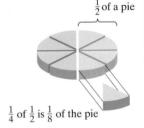

$\frac{1}{2}$ of a pie

$\frac{1}{4}$ of $\frac{1}{2}$ is $\frac{1}{8}$ of the pie

Figure R-3

Example 5 **Multiplying Fractions**

Multiply the fractions.

a. $\dfrac{7}{10} \times \dfrac{15}{14}$ **b.** $\dfrac{2}{13} \times \dfrac{13}{2}$ **c.** $5 \times \dfrac{1}{5}$

Solution:

a. $\dfrac{7}{10} \times \dfrac{15}{14} = \dfrac{7 \times 15}{10 \times 14}$ Multiply the numerators. Multiply the denominators.

$\qquad = \dfrac{\overset{3}{\cancel{105}}}{\underset{4}{\cancel{140}}}$ Divide out the common factor, 35.

$\qquad = \dfrac{3}{4}$

> **TIP:** The same result can be obtained by dividing out common factors *before* multiplying.
>
> $$\dfrac{\overset{1}{\cancel{7}}}{\underset{2}{\cancel{10}}} \times \dfrac{\overset{3}{\cancel{15}}}{\underset{2}{\cancel{14}}} = \dfrac{3}{4}$$

b. $\dfrac{2}{13} \times \dfrac{13}{2} = \dfrac{2 \times 13}{13 \times 2} = \dfrac{\overset{1}{\cancel{2}} \times \overset{1}{\cancel{13}}}{\underset{1}{\cancel{13}} \times \underset{1}{\cancel{2}}} = \dfrac{1}{1} = 1$ — Multiply $1 \times 1 = 1$.
— Multiply $1 \times 1 = 1$.

c. $5 \times \dfrac{1}{5} = \dfrac{5}{1} \times \dfrac{1}{5}$ The whole number 5 can be written as $\dfrac{5}{1}$.

$\qquad = \dfrac{\overset{1}{\cancel{5}} \times 1}{1 \times \underset{1}{\cancel{5}}} = \dfrac{1}{1} = 1$ Divide common factors and multiply.

5. Dividing Fractions

Before we divide fractions, we need to know how to find the reciprocal of a fraction. Notice from Example 5 that $\frac{2}{13} \times \frac{13}{2} = 1$ and $5 \times \frac{1}{5} = 1$. The numbers $\frac{2}{13}$ and $\frac{13}{2}$ are said to be reciprocals because their product is 1. Likewise the numbers 5 and $\frac{1}{5}$ are reciprocals.

The Reciprocal of a Number

Two nonzero numbers are **reciprocals** of each other if their product is 1. Therefore, the reciprocal of the fraction

$$\frac{a}{b} \text{ is } \frac{b}{a} \qquad \text{because} \qquad \frac{a}{b} \times \frac{b}{a} = 1$$

Number	Reciprocal	Product
$\dfrac{2}{15}$	$\dfrac{15}{2}$	$\dfrac{2}{15} \times \dfrac{15}{2} = 1$
$\dfrac{1}{8}$	$\dfrac{8}{1}$ (or equivalently 8)	$\dfrac{1}{8} \times 8 = 1$
$6 \left(\text{or equivalently } \dfrac{6}{1} \right)$	$\dfrac{1}{6}$	$6 \times \dfrac{1}{6} = 1$

Concept Connections

Write the reciprocal.

11. $\dfrac{9}{4}$ **12.** 7   **13.** $\dfrac{1}{15}$

To understand the concept of dividing fractions, consider a pie that is half-eaten. Suppose the remaining half must be divided among three people, that is, $\frac{1}{2} \div 3$. However, dividing by 3 is equivalent to taking $\frac{1}{3}$ of the remaining $\frac{1}{2}$ of the pie (Figure R-4).

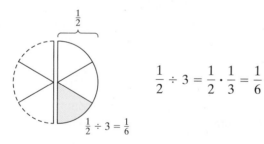

$$\frac{1}{2} \div 3 = \frac{1}{2} \cdot \frac{1}{3} = \frac{1}{6}$$

$$\frac{1}{2} \div 3 = \frac{1}{6}$$

Figure R-4

This example illustrates that dividing two numbers is equivalent to multiplying the first number by the reciprocal of the second number.

Dividing Fractions

Let a, b, c, and d be numbers such that b, c, and d are not zero. Then,

$$\frac{a}{b} \div \frac{c}{d} = \frac{a}{b} \times \frac{d}{c}$$

multiply

reciprocal

To divide fractions, multiply the first fraction by the reciprocal of the second fraction.

Answers

11. $\dfrac{4}{9}$ **12.** $\dfrac{1}{7}$ **13.** 15

Skill Practice

Divide.

14. $\dfrac{12}{25} \div \dfrac{8}{15}$ **15.** $\dfrac{1}{4} \div 2$

Example 6 Dividing Fractions

Divide the fractions.

a. $\dfrac{8}{5} \div \dfrac{3}{10}$ **b.** $\dfrac{12}{13} \div 6$

Solution:

a. $\dfrac{8}{5} \div \dfrac{3}{10} = \dfrac{8}{5} \times \dfrac{10}{3}$ Multiply by the reciprocal of $\frac{3}{10}$, which is $\frac{10}{3}$.

$$= \dfrac{8 \times \overset{2}{\cancel{10}}}{\underset{1}{\cancel{5}} \times 3} = \dfrac{16}{3}$$ Divide common factors and multiply.

b. $\dfrac{12}{13} \div 6 = \dfrac{12}{13} \div \dfrac{6}{1}$ Write the whole number 6 as $\frac{6}{1}$.

$$= \dfrac{12}{13} \times \dfrac{1}{6}$$ Multiply by the reciprocal of $\frac{6}{1}$, which is $\frac{1}{6}$.

$$= \dfrac{\overset{2}{\cancel{12}} \times 1}{13 \times \underset{1}{\cancel{6}}} = \dfrac{2}{13}$$ Divide common factors and multiply.

Avoiding Mistakes

Always check that the final answer is in lowest terms.

6. Adding and Subtracting Fractions

Adding and Subtracting Fractions

Two fractions can be added or subtracted if they have a common denominator. Let a, b, and c be numbers such that b does not equal zero. Then,

$$\dfrac{a}{b} + \dfrac{c}{b} = \dfrac{a + c}{b} \qquad \text{and} \qquad \dfrac{a}{b} - \dfrac{c}{b} = \dfrac{a - c}{b}$$

To add or subtract fractions with the same denominator, add or subtract the numerators and write the result over the common denominator.

Skill Practice

Add or subtract as indicated.

16. $\dfrac{2}{3} + \dfrac{5}{3}$ **17.** $\dfrac{5}{8} - \dfrac{1}{8}$

Example 7 Adding and Subtracting Fractions with the Same Denominator

Add or subtract as indicated.

a. $\dfrac{1}{12} + \dfrac{7}{12}$ **b.** $\dfrac{13}{5} - \dfrac{3}{5}$

Solution:

a. $\dfrac{1}{12} + \dfrac{7}{12} = \dfrac{1 + 7}{12}$ Add the numerators.

$$= \dfrac{8}{12}$$

$$= \dfrac{2}{3}$$ Simplify to lowest terms.

Answers

14. $\dfrac{9}{10}$ **15.** $\dfrac{1}{8}$ **16.** $\dfrac{7}{3}$ **17.** $\dfrac{1}{2}$

TIP: The sum $\frac{1}{12} + \frac{7}{12}$ can be visualized as the sum of the pink and blue sections of the figure.

b. $\dfrac{13}{5} - \dfrac{3}{5} = \dfrac{13 - 3}{5}$ Subtract the numerators.

$= \dfrac{10}{5}$ Simplify.

$= 2$ Simplify to lowest terms.

In Example 7, we added and subtracted fractions with the same denominators. To add or subtract fractions with different denominators, we must first become familiar with the idea of a least common multiple between two or more numbers. The **least common multiple (LCM)** of two numbers is the smallest whole number that is a multiple of each number. For example, the LCM of 6 and 9 is 18.

multiples of 6:   6, 12, 18, 24, 30, 36, . . .

multiples of 9:   9, 18, 27, 36, 45, 54, . . .

Listing the multiples of two or more given numbers can be a cumbersome way to find the LCM. Therefore, we offer the following method to find the LCM of two numbers.

Finding the LCM of Two Numbers

Step 1   Write each number as a product of prime factors.
Step 2   The LCM is the product of unique prime factors from *both* numbers. Use repeated factors the maximum number of times they appear in *either* factorization.

Example 8   **Finding the LCM of Two Numbers**

Find the LCM of 9 and 15.

Solution:

	3's	5's
9 =	③ × ③	
15 =	3 ×	⑤

LCM = 3 × 3 × 5 = 45

For the factors of 3 and 5, we circle the greatest number of times each occurs. The LCM is the product.

Skill Practice

Find the LCM.
18. 10 and 25

To add or subtract fractions with *different* denominators, we must first write each fraction as an equivalent fraction with a common denominator. A common denominator may be *any* common multiple of the denominators. However, we will use the least common denominator. The **least common denominator (LCD)** of two or more fractions is the LCM of the denominators of the fractions. Example 9 uses the Fundamental Principle of Fractions (p. 8) to rewrite fractions with the desired denominator. *Note:* Multiplying the numerator and denominator by the *same* nonzero quantity will not change the value of the fraction.

Answer
18. 50

Example 9   Writing Equivalent Fractions and Subtracting

a. Write each of the fractions $\frac{1}{9}$ and $\frac{1}{15}$ as an equivalent fraction with the LCD as its denominator.

b. Subtract $\dfrac{1}{9} - \dfrac{1}{15}$.

Solution:

From Example 8, we know that the LCM for 9 and 15 is 45. Therefore, the LCD of $\frac{1}{9}$ and $\frac{1}{15}$ is 45.

a. $\dfrac{1}{9} = \dfrac{}{45}$ $\dfrac{1 \times 5}{9 \times 5} = \dfrac{5}{45}$ So, $\dfrac{1}{9}$ is equivalent to $\dfrac{5}{45}$.

What number must we multiply 9 by to get 45?   Multiply numerator and denominator by 5.

$\dfrac{1}{15} = \dfrac{}{45}$ $\dfrac{1 \times 3}{15 \times 3} = \dfrac{3}{45}$ So, $\dfrac{1}{15}$ is equivalent to $\dfrac{3}{45}$.

What number must we multiply 15 by to get 45?   Multiply numerator and denominator by 3.

b. $\dfrac{1}{9} - \dfrac{1}{15}$

$= \dfrac{5}{45} - \dfrac{3}{45}$ Write $\frac{1}{9}$ and $\frac{1}{15}$ as equivalent fractions with the same denominator.

$= \dfrac{2}{45}$ Subtract.

Example 10   Adding and Subtracting Fractions

Simplify. $\dfrac{5}{12} + \dfrac{3}{4} - \dfrac{1}{2}$

Solution:

$\dfrac{5}{12} + \dfrac{3}{4} - \dfrac{1}{2}$

To find the LCD, we have:

LCD $= 2 \times 2 \times 3 = 12$

		2's	3's
12 =		②×②	③
4 =		2 × 2	
2 =		2	

$= \dfrac{5}{12} + \dfrac{3 \times 3}{4 \times 3} - \dfrac{1 \times 6}{2 \times 6}$ Write each fraction as an equivalent fraction with the LCD as its denominator.

$= \dfrac{5}{12} + \dfrac{9}{12} - \dfrac{6}{12}$

$= \dfrac{5 + 9 - 6}{12}$ Add and subtract the numerators.

$= \dfrac{\overset{2}{\cancel{8}}}{\underset{3}{\cancel{12}}}$ Simplify to lowest terms.

$= \dfrac{2}{3}$

7. Operations on Mixed Numbers

Recall that a mixed number is a whole number added to a fraction. The number $3\frac{1}{2}$ represents the sum of three wholes plus a half, that is, $3\frac{1}{2} = 3 + \frac{1}{2}$. For this reason, any mixed number can be converted to an improper fraction by using addition.

$$3\frac{1}{2} = 3 + \frac{1}{2} = \frac{6}{2} + \frac{1}{2} = \frac{7}{2}$$

TIP: A shortcut to writing a mixed number as an improper fraction is to multiply the whole number by the denominator of the fraction. Then add this value to the numerator of the fraction, and write the result over the denominator.

$3\frac{1}{2}$ ⟶ Multiply the whole number by the denominator: $3 \times 2 = 6$.
Add the numerator: $6 + 1 = 7$.
Write the result over the denominator: $\frac{7}{2}$.

To add, subtract, multiply, or divide mixed numbers, we will first write the mixed number as an improper fraction.

Example 11 **Operations on Mixed Numbers**

Subtract. $5\frac{1}{3} - 2\frac{1}{4}$

Solution:

$5\frac{1}{3} - 2\frac{1}{4}$

$= \frac{16}{3} - \frac{9}{4}$ Write the mixed numbers as improper fractions.

$= \frac{16 \times 4}{3 \times 4} - \frac{9 \times 3}{4 \times 3}$ The LCD is 12. Multiply numerators and denominators by the missing factors from the denominators.

$= \frac{64}{12} - \frac{27}{12}$

$= \frac{37}{12}$ or $3\frac{1}{12}$ Subtract the fractions.

TIP: An improper fraction can also be written as a mixed number. Both answers are acceptable. Note that

$$\frac{37}{12} = \frac{36}{12} + \frac{1}{12} = 3 + \frac{1}{12}, \text{ or } 3\frac{1}{12}$$

This can easily be found by dividing.

$\frac{37}{12}$ ⟶ $12\overline{)37}$ $\begin{array}{r} 3 \\ \underline{-36} \\ 1 \end{array}$ $3\frac{1}{12}$

quotient — remainder — divisor

Example 12 Operations on Mixed Numbers

Divide. $7\dfrac{1}{2} \div 3$

Solution:

$7\dfrac{1}{2} \div 3$

$= \dfrac{15}{2} \div \dfrac{3}{1}$ Write the mixed number and whole number as fractions.

$= \dfrac{\overset{5}{15}}{2} \times \dfrac{1}{\underset{1}{3}}$ Multiply by the reciprocal of $\frac{3}{1}$, which is $\frac{1}{3}$.

$= \dfrac{5}{2}$ or $2\dfrac{1}{2}$ The answer may be written as an improper fraction or as a mixed number.

Section R.2 Practice Exercises

Vocabulary and Key Concepts

1. a. A _____ is the result of multiplying two or more numbers.

   b. The numbers being multiplied in a product are called _____.

   c. Given a fraction $\frac{a}{b}$ with $b \neq 0$, the value a is the _____ and _____ is the denominator.

   d. A fraction is said to be in _____ terms if the numerator and denominator share no common factor other than 1.

   e. The fraction $\frac{4}{4}$ can also be written as the whole number _____, and the fraction $\frac{4}{1}$ can be written as the whole number _____.

   f. Two nonzero numbers $\frac{a}{b}$ and $\frac{b}{a}$ are _____ because their product is 1.

   g. The least common multiple (LCM) of two numbers is the smallest whole number that is a _____ of both numbers.

   h. The _____ common denominator of two or more fractions is the LCM of their denominators.

Concept 1: Basic Definitions

For Exercises 2–8, identify the numerator and denominator of the fraction. Then determine if the fraction is a proper fraction or an improper fraction.

2. $\dfrac{7}{8}$ **3.** $\dfrac{2}{3}$ **4.** $\dfrac{9}{5}$ **5.** $\dfrac{6}{6}$

6. $\dfrac{4}{4}$ **7.** $\dfrac{12}{1}$ **8.** $\dfrac{5}{1}$

For Exercises 9–16, write a proper or improper fraction associated with the shaded region of each figure.

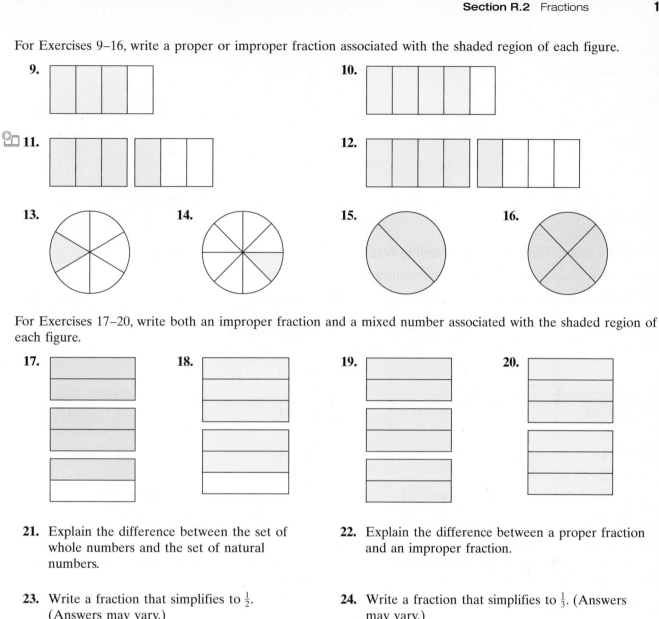

For Exercises 17–20, write both an improper fraction and a mixed number associated with the shaded region of each figure.

21. Explain the difference between the set of whole numbers and the set of natural numbers.

22. Explain the difference between a proper fraction and an improper fraction.

23. Write a fraction that simplifies to $\frac{1}{2}$. (Answers may vary.)

24. Write a fraction that simplifies to $\frac{1}{3}$. (Answers may vary.)

Concept 2: Prime Factorization

For Exercises 25–32, identify the number as either a prime number or a composite number.

25. 5   **26.** 9   **27.** 4   **28.** 2

29. 39   **30.** 23   **31.** 53   **32.** 51

For Exercises 33–40, write the number as a product of prime factors. **(See Example 1.)**

33. 36   **34.** 70   **35.** 42   **36.** 35

37. 110   **38.** 136   **39.** 135   **40.** 105

Concept 3: Simplifying Fractions to Lowest Terms

For Exercises 41–52, simplify each fraction to lowest terms. **(See Examples 2 and 3.)**

41. $\dfrac{3}{15}$ **42.** $\dfrac{8}{12}$ **43.** $\dfrac{16}{6}$ **44.** $\dfrac{20}{12}$

45. $\dfrac{42}{48}$ **46.** $\dfrac{35}{80}$ **47.** $\dfrac{48}{64}$ **48.** $\dfrac{32}{48}$

49. $\dfrac{110}{176}$ **50.** $\dfrac{70}{120}$ **51.** $\dfrac{200}{150}$ **52.** $\dfrac{210}{119}$

Concepts 4 and 5: Multiplying and Dividing Fractions

For Exercises 53 and 54, determine if the statement is true or false. If it is false, rewrite as a true statement.

53. When multiplying or dividing fractions, it is necessary to have a common denominator.

54. When dividing two fractions, it is necessary to multiply the first fraction by the reciprocal of the second fraction.

For Exercises 55–66, multiply or divide as indicated. **(See Examples 4–6.)**

55. $\dfrac{10}{13} \times \dfrac{26}{15}$ **56.** $\dfrac{15}{28} \times \dfrac{7}{9}$ **57.** $\dfrac{3}{7} \div \dfrac{9}{14}$ **58.** $\dfrac{7}{25} \div \dfrac{1}{5}$

59. $\dfrac{9}{10} \times 5$ **60.** $\dfrac{3}{7} \times 14$ **61.** $\dfrac{12}{5} \div 4$ **62.** $\dfrac{20}{6} \div 5$

63. $\dfrac{5}{2} \times \dfrac{10}{21} \times \dfrac{7}{5}$ **64.** $\dfrac{55}{9} \times \dfrac{18}{32} \times \dfrac{24}{11}$ **65.** $\dfrac{9}{100} \div \dfrac{13}{1000}$ **66.** $\dfrac{1000}{17} \div \dfrac{10}{3}$

67. Stephen's take-home pay is $4200 a month. If his rent is $\frac{1}{4}$ of his pay, how much is his rent?

68. Gus decides to save $\frac{1}{3}$ of his pay each month. If his monthly pay is $2112, how much will he save each month?

69. In Professor Foley's Beginning Algebra class, $\frac{5}{6}$ of the students passed the first test. If there are 42 students in the class, how many passed the test?

70. Shontell had only enough paper to print out $\frac{3}{5}$ of her book report before school. If the report is 10 pages long, how many pages did she print out?

71. Marty will reinforce a concrete walkway by cutting a steel rod (called rebar) that is 4 yd long. How many pieces can he cut if each piece must be $\frac{1}{2}$ yd in length?

72. There are 4 cups of oatmeal in a box. If each serving is $\frac{1}{3}$ of a cup, how many servings are contained in the box?

73. Anita buys 6 lb of mixed nuts to be divided into decorative jars that will each hold $\frac{3}{4}$ lb of nuts. How many jars will she be able to fill?

74. Beth has a $\frac{7}{8}$-in. nail that she must hammer into a board. Each strike of the hammer moves the nail $\frac{1}{16}$ in. into the board. How many strikes of the hammer must she make to drive the nail completely into the board?

Concept 6: Adding and Subtracting Fractions

For Exercises 75–78, add or subtract as indicated. **(See Example 7.)**

75. $\dfrac{5}{14} + \dfrac{1}{14}$ **76.** $\dfrac{9}{5} + \dfrac{1}{5}$ **77.** $\dfrac{17}{24} - \dfrac{5}{24}$ **78.** $\dfrac{11}{18} - \dfrac{5}{18}$

For Exercises 79–82, find the least common multiple for each list of numbers. **(See Example 8.)**

79. 6, 15 **80.** 12, 30 **81.** 20, 8, 4 **82.** 24, 40, 30

For Exercises 83–98, add or subtract as indicated. **(See Examples 9 and 10.)**

83. $\dfrac{1}{8} + \dfrac{3}{4}$ **84.** $\dfrac{3}{16} + \dfrac{1}{2}$ **85.** $\dfrac{11}{8} - \dfrac{3}{10}$ **86.** $\dfrac{12}{35} - \dfrac{1}{10}$

87. $\dfrac{7}{26} - \dfrac{2}{13}$ **88.** $\dfrac{25}{24} - \dfrac{5}{16}$ **89.** $\dfrac{7}{18} + \dfrac{5}{12}$ **90.** $\dfrac{3}{16} + \dfrac{9}{20}$

91. $\dfrac{5}{4} - \dfrac{1}{20}$ **92.** $\dfrac{7}{6} - \dfrac{1}{24}$ **93.** $\dfrac{5}{12} + \dfrac{5}{16}$ **94.** $\dfrac{3}{25} + \dfrac{8}{35}$

95. $\dfrac{1}{6} + \dfrac{3}{4} - \dfrac{5}{8}$ **96.** $\dfrac{1}{2} + \dfrac{2}{3} - \dfrac{5}{12}$ **97.** $\dfrac{4}{7} + \dfrac{1}{2} + \dfrac{3}{4}$ **98.** $\dfrac{9}{10} + \dfrac{4}{5} + \dfrac{3}{4}$

99. For his famous brownie recipe, Chef Alfonso combines $\frac{2}{3}$ cup granulated sugar with $\frac{1}{4}$ cup brown sugar. What is the total amount of sugar in his recipe?

100. Chef Alfonso eats too many of his brownies and his waistline increased by $\frac{3}{4}$ in. during one month and $\frac{3}{8}$ in. the next month. What was his total increase for the 2-month period?

101. Two of the most popular smart phones are $\frac{1}{2}$ in. thick and $\frac{9}{25}$ in. thick. What is the difference in thickness of the two phones?

102. The diameter of a penny is $\frac{3}{4}$ in., while the dime is $\frac{7}{10}$ in. How much larger is the penny than the dime?

Concept 7: Operations on Mixed Numbers

For Exercises 103–116, perform the indicated operations. **(See Examples 11 and 12.)**

103. $3\dfrac{1}{5} \times 2\dfrac{7}{8}$ **104.** $2\dfrac{1}{2} \times 1\dfrac{4}{5}$ **105.** $1\dfrac{2}{9} \div 7\dfrac{1}{3}$

106. $2\dfrac{2}{5} \div 1\dfrac{2}{7}$ **107.** $1\dfrac{2}{9} \div 6$ **108.** $2\dfrac{2}{5} \div 2$

109. $2\dfrac{1}{8} + 1\dfrac{3}{8}$ **110.** $1\dfrac{3}{14} + 1\dfrac{1}{14}$ **111.** $3\dfrac{1}{2} - 1\dfrac{7}{8}$

112. $5\dfrac{1}{3} - 2\dfrac{3}{4}$ **113.** $1\dfrac{1}{6} + 3\dfrac{3}{4}$ **114.** $4\dfrac{1}{2} + 2\dfrac{2}{3}$

115. $1 - \dfrac{7}{8}$ **116.** $2 - \dfrac{3}{7}$

117. A board $26\frac{3}{8}$ in. long must be cut into three pieces of equal length. Find the length of each piece.

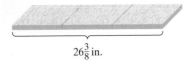

$26\frac{3}{8}$ in.

118. A futon, when set up as a sofa, measures $3\frac{5}{6}$ ft wide. When it is opened to be used as a bed, the width is increased by $1\frac{3}{4}$ ft. What is the total width of this bed?

$3\frac{5}{6}$ ft

119. A plane trip from Orlando to Detroit takes $2\frac{3}{4}$ hr. If the plane traveled for $1\frac{1}{6}$ hr, how much time remains for the flight?

120. Silvia manages a sub shop and needs to prepare smoked turkey sandwiches. She has $3\frac{3}{4}$ lb of turkey in the cooler, and each sandwich requires $\frac{3}{8}$ lb of turkey. How many sandwiches can she make?

121. José's catering company plans to prepare two different shrimp dishes for an upcoming event. One dish requires $1\frac{1}{2}$ lb of shrimp and the other requires $\frac{3}{4}$ lb of shrimp. How much shrimp should José order for the two dishes?

122. Ayako took a trip to the store $5\frac{1}{2}$ mi away. If she rode the bus for $4\frac{5}{6}$ mi and walked the rest of the way, how far did she have to walk?

123. If Tampa, Florida, averages $6\frac{1}{4}$ in. of rain during each summer month, how much total rain would be expected in June, July, August, and September?

124. Pete started working out and found that he lost approximately $\frac{3}{4}$ in. off his waistline every month. How much would he lose around his waist in 6 months?

Section R.3   Decimals and Percents

Concepts

1. Introduction to a Place Value System
2. Converting Fractions to Decimals
3. Converting Decimals to Fractions
4. Converting Percents to Decimals and Fractions
5. Converting Decimals and Fractions to Percents
6. Applications of Percents

1. Introduction to a Place Value System

In a **place value** number system, each digit in a numeral has a particular value determined by its location in the numeral (Figure R-5).

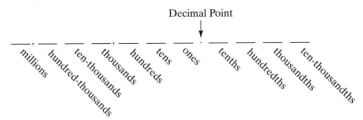

Decimal Point

millions, hundred-thousands, ten-thousands, thousands, hundreds, tens, ones . tenths, hundredths, thousandths, ten-thousandths

Figure R-5

For example, the number 197.215 represents

$$(1 \times 100) + (9 \times 10) + (7 \times 1) + \left(2 \times \frac{1}{10}\right) + \left(1 \times \frac{1}{100}\right) + \left(5 \times \frac{1}{1000}\right)$$

Each of the digits 1, 9, 7, 2, 1, and 5 is multiplied by 100, 10, 1, $\frac{1}{10}$, $\frac{1}{100}$, and $\frac{1}{1000}$, respectively, depending on its location in the numeral 197.215.

By obtaining a common denominator and adding fractions, we have

$$197.215 = 100 + 90 + 7 + \frac{200}{1000} + \frac{10}{1000} + \frac{5}{1000}$$

$$= 197 + \frac{215}{1000} \quad \text{or} \quad 197\frac{215}{1000}$$

Because 197.215 is equal to the mixed number $197\frac{215}{1000}$, we read 197.215 as one hundred ninety-seven *and* two hundred fifteen thousandths. The decimal point is read as the word *and*.

If there are no digits to the right of the decimal point, we usually omit the decimal point. For example, the number 7125. is written simply as 7125 without a decimal point.

2. Converting Fractions to Decimals

In Section R.2, we learned that a fraction represents part of a whole unit. Likewise, the digits to the right of the decimal point represent a fraction of a whole unit. In this section, we will learn how to convert a fraction to a decimal number and vice versa.

> **Converting a Fraction to a Decimal**
>
> To convert a fraction to a decimal, divide the numerator of the fraction by the denominator of the fraction.
>
> *Note:* Zeros may be inserted to the right of the decimal point in the dividend until the digits in the quotient either terminate or repeat.

Example 1   **Converting Fractions to Decimals**

Convert each fraction to a decimal.   **a.** $\frac{7}{40}$ **b.** $\frac{2}{3}$

Solution:

a. $\frac{7}{40} = 0.175$

$$\begin{array}{r} 0.175 \\ 40\overline{)7.000} \\ \underline{40} \\ 300 \\ \underline{280} \\ 200 \\ \underline{200} \\ 0 \end{array}$$

The number 0.175 is said to be a **terminating decimal** because there are no nonzero digits to the right of the last digit, 5.

b. $\frac{2}{3} = 0.666\ldots$

$$\begin{array}{r} 0.666\ldots \\ 3\overline{)2.00000} \\ \underline{18} \\ 20 \\ \underline{18} \\ 20 \\ \underline{18} \\ 2\ldots \end{array}$$

The pattern 0.666 . . . continues indefinitely. Therefore, we say that this is a **repeating decimal**.

For a repeating decimal, a horizontal bar is often used to denote the repeating pattern after the decimal point. Hence, $\frac{2}{3} = 0.\overline{6}$.

Sometimes it is useful to round a decimal number to a desired place value. This is demonstrated in Example 2.

> **Rounding Decimals to a Place Value to the Right of the Decimal Point**
> **Step 1** Identify the digit one position to the right of the given place value.
> **Step 2** If the digit in step 1 is 5 or greater, add 1 to the digit in the given place value. Then discard the digits to its right.
> **Step 3** If the digit in step 1 is less than 5, discard it and any digits to its right.

Example 2 Rounding Decimal Numbers

Round the numbers to the indicated place value.

a. 0.175 to the hundredths place   **b.** $0.\overline{54}$ to the thousandths place

Solution:

hundredths place

a. 0.17$\boxed{5}$ The digit to the right of the hundredths place is 5 or greater.

  ≈ 0.18 Add 1 to the hundredths place digit.

b. $0.\overline{54} = 0.545454\ldots$ This is a repeating decimal. We write out several digits.

thousandths place

  0.545$\boxed{4}$54 . . .   The digit to the right of the thousandths place is less than 5.

  ≈ 0.545

Skill Practice

Round to the indicated place value.
5. 0.624 hundredths place
6. $1.\overline{62}$ ten-thousandths place

3. Converting Decimals to Fractions

For a terminating decimal, use the word name to write the number as a fraction or mixed number.

Example 3 Converting Terminating Decimals to Fractions

Convert each decimal to a fraction.

a. 0.0023   **b.** 50.06

Solution:

a. 0.0023 is read as twenty-three ten-thousandths. Thus,

  $0.0023 = \dfrac{23}{10{,}000}$

b. 50.06 is read as fifty and six hundredths. Thus,

  $50.06 = 50\dfrac{6}{100}$

  $= 50\dfrac{3}{50}$ Simplify the fraction to lowest terms.

  $= \dfrac{2503}{50}$ Write the mixed number as a fraction.

Skill Practice

Convert to a fraction.
7. 0.107
8. 11.25

Answers
5. 0.62   **6.** 1.6263
7. $\dfrac{107}{1000}$ **8.** $\dfrac{45}{4}$

Repeating decimals also can be written as fractions. However, the procedure to convert a repeating decimal to a fraction requires some knowledge of algebra. Table R-1 shows some common repeating decimals and an equivalent fraction for each.

Table R-1

$0.\overline{1} = \dfrac{1}{9}$	$0.\overline{4} = \dfrac{4}{9}$	$0.\overline{7} = \dfrac{7}{9}$
$0.\overline{2} = \dfrac{2}{9}$	$0.\overline{5} = \dfrac{5}{9}$	$0.\overline{8} = \dfrac{8}{9}$
$0.\overline{3} = \dfrac{3}{9} = \dfrac{1}{3}$	$0.\overline{6} = \dfrac{6}{9} = \dfrac{2}{3}$	$0.\overline{9} = \dfrac{9}{9} = 1$

4. Converting Percents to Decimals and Fractions

The concept of percent (%) is widely used in a variety of mathematical applications. The word *percent* means "per 100." Therefore, we can write percents as fractions.

$6\% = \dfrac{6}{100}$ — A sales tax of 6% means that 6 cents in tax is charged for every 100 cents spent.

$91\% = \dfrac{91}{100}$ — The fact that 91% of the population is right-handed means that 91 people out of 100 are right-handed.

The quantity $91\% = \dfrac{91}{100}$ can be written as $91 \times \dfrac{1}{100}$ or as 91×0.01.

Notice that the % symbol implies "division by 100" or, equivalently, "multiplication by $\frac{1}{100}$." Thus, we have the following rule to convert a percent to a fraction (or to a decimal).

Converting a Percent to a Decimal or Fraction

Replace the % symbol by $\div 100$ (or equivalently $\times \dfrac{1}{100}$ or $\times 0.01$).

Example 4 Converting Percents to Decimals

Convert the percents to decimals.

a. 78% **b.** 412% **c.** 0.045%

Solution:

a. $78\% = 78 \times 0.01 = 0.78$

b. $412\% = 412 \times 0.01 = 4.12$

c. $0.045\% = 0.045 \times 0.01 = 0.00045$

TIP: Multiplying by 0.01 is equivalent to dividing by 100. This has the effect of moving the decimal point two places to the left.

Skill Practice

Convert the percent to a decimal.
9. 29%
10. 3.5%
11. 100%

Example 5 Converting Percents to Fractions

Convert the percents to fractions.

a. 52% **b.** $33\frac{1}{3}$% **c.** 6.5%

Solution:

a. $52\% = 52 \times \dfrac{1}{100}$ Replace the % symbol by $\frac{1}{100}$.

$= \dfrac{52}{100}$ Multiply.

$= \dfrac{13}{25}$ Simplify to lowest terms.

b. $33\dfrac{1}{3}\% = 33\dfrac{1}{3} \times \dfrac{1}{100}$ Replace the % symbol by $\frac{1}{100}$.

$= \dfrac{100}{3} \times \dfrac{1}{100}$ Write the mixed number as a fraction $33\frac{1}{3} = \frac{100}{3}$.

$= \dfrac{100}{300}$ Multiply the fractions.

$= \dfrac{1}{3}$ Simplify to lowest terms.

c. $6.5\% = 6.5 \times \dfrac{1}{100}$ Replace the % symbol by $\frac{1}{100}$.

$= \dfrac{65}{10} \times \dfrac{1}{100}$ Write 6.5 as an improper fraction.

$= \dfrac{65}{1000}$ Multiply the fractions.

$= \dfrac{13}{200}$ Simplify to lowest terms.

5. Converting Decimals and Fractions to Percents

To convert a percent to a decimal or fraction, we replace the % symbol by $\div 100$. To convert a decimal or fraction to a percent, we reverse this process.

Converting Decimals and Fractions to Percents

Multiply the fraction or decimal by 100%.

Answers

12. $\dfrac{3}{10}$ **13.** $\dfrac{241}{200}$ **14.** $\dfrac{1}{40}$

Example 6   Converting Decimals to Percents

Convert the decimals to percents.

a. 0.92   **b.** 10.80   **c.** 0.005

Solution:

a. $0.92 = 0.92 \times 100\% = 92\%$ Multiply by 100%.

b. $10.80 = 10.80 \times 100\% = 1080\%$ Multiply by 100%.

c. $0.005 = 0.005 \times 100\% = 0.5\%$ Multiply by 100%.

Example 7   Converting Fractions to Percents

Convert the fractions to percents.

a. $\dfrac{2}{5}$ **b.** $\dfrac{5}{3}$

Solution:

a. $\dfrac{2}{5} = \dfrac{2}{5} \times 100\%$ Multiply by 100%.

$= \dfrac{2}{5} \times \dfrac{100}{1}\%$ Write the whole number as a fraction.

$= \dfrac{2}{\cancel{5}_{1}} \times \dfrac{\overset{20}{\cancel{100}}}{1}\%$ Multiply fractions.

$= \dfrac{40}{1}\%$ or 40% Simplify.

b. $\dfrac{5}{3} = \dfrac{5}{3} \times 100\%$ Multiply by 100%.

$= \dfrac{5}{3} \times \dfrac{100}{1}\%$ Write the whole number as a fraction.

$= \dfrac{500}{3}\%$ Multiply fractions.

$= \dfrac{500}{3}\%$ or $166.\overline{6}\%$ The value $\frac{500}{3}$ can be written in decimal form by dividing 500 by 3.

6. Applications of Percents

Many applications involving percents involve finding a percent of some base number. For example, suppose a textbook is discounted 25%. If the book originally cost $60, find the amount of the discount.

In this example, we must find 25% of $60. In this context, the word *of* means multiply.

25% of $60

$0.25 \times 60 = 15$ The amount of the discount is $15.

Answers

Note that the *decimal form* of a percent is always used in calculations. Therefore, 25% was converted to 0.25 *before* multiplying by $60.

Example 8 Applying Percentages

Shauna received a raise, so now her new salary is 105% of her old salary. Find Shauna's new salary if her old salary was $36,000 per year.

Solution:

The new salary is 105% of $36,000.

$$1.05 \times 36,000 = 37,800$$ The new salary is $37,800 per year.

In some applications, it is necessary to convert a fractional part of a whole to a percent of the whole.

Example 9 Finding a Percentage

Union College in Schenectady, New York, accepts approximately 520 students each year from 3500 applicants. What percent does 520 represent? Round to the nearest tenth of a percent.

Solution:

$$\frac{520}{3500} \approx 0.149$$ Convert the fractional part of the total number of applicants to decimal form. (*Note:* Rounding the decimal form of the quotient to the thousandths place gives us the nearest tenth of a percent.)

$$= 0.149 \times 100\%$$ Convert the decimal to a percent.

$$= 14.9\%$$ Simplify.

Approximately 14.9% of the applicants to Union College are accepted.

Calculator Connections

Topic: Approximating Repeating Decimals on a Calculator

Calculators can display only a limited number of digits on the calculator screen. Therefore, repeating decimals and terminating decimals with a large number of digits will be truncated or rounded to fit the calculator display. For example, the fraction $\frac{2}{3} = 0.\overline{6}$ may be entered into the calculator as $\boxed{2}$ $\boxed{\div}$ $\boxed{3}$. The result may appear as 0.6666666667 or as 0.6666666666. The fraction $\frac{2}{11}$ equals the repeating decimal $0.\overline{18}$. However, the calculator converts $\frac{2}{11}$ to the terminating decimal 0.1818181818.

```
2/3
         .6666666667
2/11
         .1818181818
```

Calculator Exercises

Without using a calculator, find a repeating decimal to represent each of the fractions. Then use a calculator to confirm your answer.

1. $\dfrac{4}{9}$ **2.** $\dfrac{7}{11}$ **3.** $\dfrac{3}{22}$ **4.** $\dfrac{5}{13}$

Section R.3 Practice Exercises

Vocabulary and Key Concepts

1. **a.** The first three place values to the right of the decimal point are the _____ place, the _____ place, and the _____ place.

   b. The word _____ means per one hundred.

   c. To convert a percent to a decimal or fraction, remove the % symbol and multiply by _____ or _____.

   d. To convert a fraction or decimal to a percent, multiply by _____.

Concept 1: Introduction to a Place Value System

For Exercises 2–8, write the name of the place value for the underlined digit.

2. 1345.42   3. 2912.032   4. 4208.03   5. 2.381

6. 8.249   7. 21.413   8. 82.794

9. The first 10 Roman numerals are: I, II, III, IV, V, VI, VII, VIII, IX, X. Is this numbering system a place value system? Explain your answer.

10. Write the number in decimal form. $3(100) + 7(10) + 6 + \dfrac{1}{100} + \dfrac{5}{1000}$

Concept 2: Converting Fractions to Decimals

For Exercises 11–18, convert each fraction to a terminating decimal or a repeating decimal. **(See Example 1.)**

11. $\dfrac{7}{10}$ 12. $\dfrac{9}{10}$ 13. $\dfrac{9}{25}$ 14. $\dfrac{3}{25}$

15. $\dfrac{11}{9}$ 16. $\dfrac{16}{9}$ 17. $\dfrac{7}{33}$ 18. $\dfrac{2}{11}$

For Exercises 19–26, round the decimal to the given place value. **(See Example 2.)**

19. 214.059; tenths   20. 1004.165; hundredths

21. 39.26849; thousandths   22. 0.059499; thousandths

23. 39,918.2; thousands   24. 599,621.5; thousands

25. $0.\overline{72}$; hundredths   26. $0.\overline{34}$; thousandths

Concept 3: Converting Decimals to Fractions

For Exercises 27–38, convert each decimal to a fraction or a mixed number. **(See Example 3.)**

27. 0.45   28. 0.65   29. 0.181   30. 0.273

31. 2.04   32. 6.02   33. 13.007   34. 12.003

35. $0.\overline{5}$ (*Hint*: Refer to Table R-1)   36. $0.\overline{8}$ 37. $1.\overline{1}$ 38. $2.\overline{3}$

Concept 4: Converting Percents to Decimals and Fractions

For Exercises 39–48, convert each percent to a decimal and to a fraction. **(See Examples 4 and 5.)**

39. The sale price is 30% off of the original price.

40. An HMO (health maintenance organization) pays 80% of all doctors' bills.

41. The building will be 75% complete by spring.

42. Chan plants roses in 25% of his garden.

43. The bank pays $3\frac{3}{4}$% interest on a checking account.

44. A credit union pays $4\frac{1}{2}$% interest on a savings account.

45. Kansas received 15.7% of its annual rainfall in 1 week.

46. Social Security withholds 6.2% of an employee's gross pay.

47. The world population in 2008 was 270% of the world population in 1950.

48. The cost of a home is 140% of its cost 10 years ago.

Concept 5: Converting Decimals and Fractions to Percents

49. Explain how to convert a decimal to a percent.   **50.** Explain how to convert a percent to a decimal.

For Exercises 51–62, convert the decimal to a percent. **(See Example 6.)**

51. 0.05	**52.** 0.06	**53.** 0.90	**54.** 0.70
55. 1.2	**56.** 4.8	**57.** 7.5	**58.** 9.3
59. 0.135	**60.** 0.536	**61.** 0.003	**62.** 0.002

For Exercises 63–74, convert the fraction to a percent. **(See Example 7.)**

63. $\frac{3}{50}$	**64.** $\frac{23}{50}$	**65.** $\frac{9}{2}$	**66.** $\frac{7}{4}$
67. $\frac{5}{8}$	**68.** $\frac{1}{8}$	**69.** $\frac{5}{16}$	**70.** $\frac{7}{16}$
71. $\frac{5}{6}$	**72.** $\frac{4}{15}$	**73.** $\frac{14}{15}$	**74.** $\frac{5}{18}$

Concept 6: Applications of Percents

75. A suit that costs $140 is discounted by 30%. How much is the discount? **(See Example 8.)**

76. Louise completed 40% of her task that takes a total of 60 hr to finish. How many hours did she complete?

77. Tom's federal taxes amount to 27% of his income. If Tom earns $12,500 per quarter, how much will he pay in taxes for that quarter?

78. A tip of $7 is left for a meal that costs $56. What percent of the cost does the tip represent?

79. Jamie paid $5.95 in sales tax on a textbook that costs $85. Find the percent of the sales tax. **(See Example 9.)**

80. Sue saves $37.50 each week out of her paycheck of $625. What percent of her paycheck does her savings represent?

For Exercises 81–84, refer to the graph. The pie graph shows a family budget based on a net income of $2400 per month.

81. Determine the amount spent on rent.

82. Determine the amount spent on car payments.

83. Determine the amount spent on utilities.

84. How much more money is spent than saved?

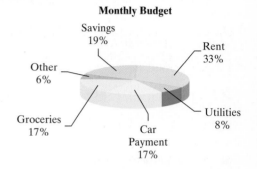

Monthly Budget

85. By the end of the year, Felipe will have 75% of his mortgage paid. If the mortgage was originally for $90,000, how much will have been paid at the end of the year?

86. A certificate of deposit (CD) earns 4% interest in 1 year. If Mr. Patel has $12,000 invested in the CD, how much interest will he receive at the end of the year?

Introduction to Geometry

Section R.4

1. Perimeter

In this section, we present several facts and formulas that may be used throughout the text in applications of geometry. One of the most important uses of geometry involves the measurement of objects of various shapes. We begin with an introduction to perimeter, area, and volume for several common shapes and objects.

Perimeter is defined as the distance around a figure. If we were to put up a fence around a field, the perimeter would determine the amount of fencing. For example, in Figure R-6 the distance around the field is 300 ft. For a polygon (a closed figure constructed from line segments), the perimeter is the sum of the lengths of the sides. For a circle, the distance around the outside is called the **circumference**.

Concepts

1. Perimeter
2. Area
3. Volume
4. Angles
5. Triangles

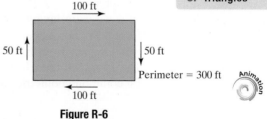

Figure R-6

Rectangle	Square	Triangle	Circle
$P = 2\ell + 2w$	$P = 4s$	$P = a + b + c$	Circumference: $C = 2\pi r$

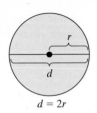

$d = 2r$

For a circle, r represents the length of a radius—the distance from the center to any point on the circle. The length of a diameter, d, of a circle is twice that of a radius. Thus, $d = 2r$. The number π is a constant equal to the circumference of a circle divided by the length of a diameter. That is, $\pi = \frac{C}{d}$. The value of π is often approximated by 3.14 or $\frac{22}{7}$.

Example 1   **Finding Perimeter and Circumference**

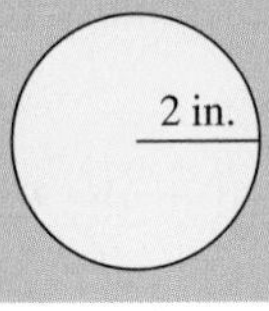

Find the perimeter or circumference as indicated. Use 3.14 for π.

a. Perimeter of the rectangle   **b.** Circumference of the circle

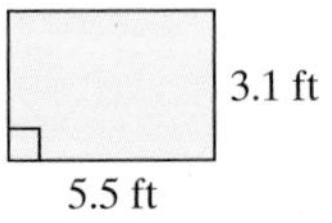

3.1 ft

5.5 ft

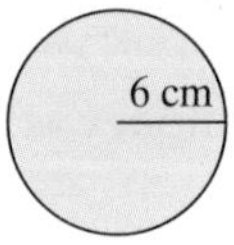

6 cm

Solution:

a. $P = 2\ell + 2w$

$= 2(5.5 \text{ ft}) + 2(3.1 \text{ ft})$ Substitute $\ell = 5.5$ ft and $w = 3.1$ ft.

$= 11 \text{ ft} + 6.2 \text{ ft}$

$= 17.2 \text{ ft}$ The perimeter is 17.2 ft.

b. $C = 2\pi r$

$= 2(3.14)(6 \text{ cm})$ Substitute 3.14 for π and $r = 6$ cm.

$= 6.28(6 \text{ cm})$

$= 37.68 \text{ cm}$ The circumference is 37.68 cm.

2. Area

The **area** of a geometric figure is the number of square units that can be enclosed within the figure. In applications, we would find the area of a region if we were laying carpet or putting down sod for a lawn. For example, the rectangle shown in Figure R-7 encloses 6 square inches (6 in.^{2}).

The formulas used to compute the area for several common geometric shapes are given here:

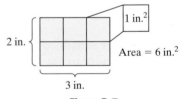

2 in.

3 in.

1 in.^{2}

Area = 6 in.^{2}

Figure R-7

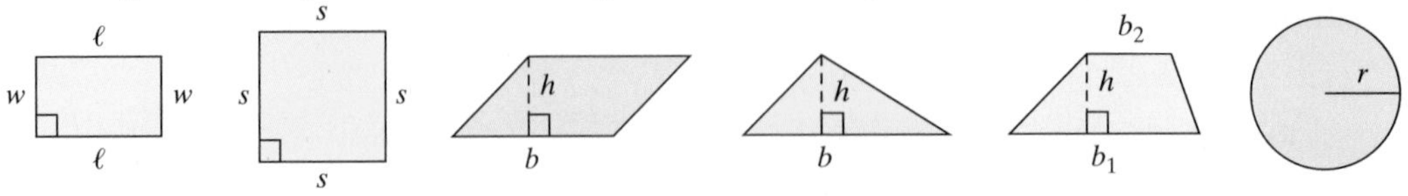

Rectangle	Square	Parallelogram	Triangle	Trapezoid	Circle
		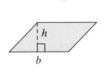			
$A = \ell w$	$A = s^2$	$A = bh$	$A = \frac{1}{2}bh$	$A = \frac{1}{2}(b_1 + b_2)h$	$A = \pi r^2$

Answers

1. 29 in.   **2.** 12.56 in.

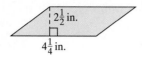 **Finding Area**

Find the area.

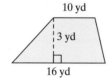

Solution:

$A = bh$ The figure is a parallelogram.

$\quad = (4\frac{1}{4} \text{ in.})(2\frac{1}{2} \text{ in.})$ Substitute $b = 4\frac{1}{4}$ in. and $h = 2\frac{1}{2}$ in.

$\quad = \left(\dfrac{17}{4} \text{ in.}\right)\left(\dfrac{5}{2} \text{ in.}\right)$

$\quad = \dfrac{85}{8} \text{ in.}^2 \text{ or } 10\frac{5}{8} \text{ in.}^2$

> **TIP:** Notice that the units of area are given in square units such as square inches (in.^{2}), square feet (ft^2), square yards (yd^2), square centimeters (cm^2), and so on.

Skill Practice

Find the area.

3.

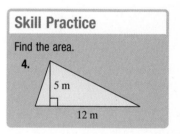

Example 3 **Finding Area**

Find the area.

10 yd
3 yd
16 yd

Solution:

$A = \dfrac{1}{2}(b_1 + b_2)h$ The figure is a trapezoid.

$\quad = \dfrac{1}{2}(16 \text{ yd} + 10 \text{ yd})(3 \text{ yd})$ Substitute $b_1 = 16$ yd, $b_2 = 10$ yd, and $h = 3$ yd.

$\quad = \dfrac{1}{2}(26 \text{ yd})(3 \text{ yd})$

$\quad = (13 \text{ yd})(3 \text{ yd})$

$\quad = 39 \text{ yd}^2$ The area is 39 yd^2.

Skill Practice

Find the area.

4.

5 m
12 m

> **TIP:** Notice that several of the formulas presented thus far involve multiple operations. The order in which we perform the arithmetic is called the **order of operations** and is covered in detail in Section 1.2. We will follow these guidelines in the order given below:
>
> **1.** Perform operations within parentheses first.
> **2.** Evaluate expressions with exponents.
> **3.** Perform multiplication or division in order from left to right.
> **4.** Perform addition or subtraction in order from left to right.

Answers

3. $\dfrac{9}{16}$ cm^2 **4.** 30 m^2

Example 4 **Finding the Area of a Circle**

Find the area of a circular fountain if the radius is 25 ft. Use 3.14 for π.

25 ft

Solution:

$A = \pi r^2$

$\approx (3.14)(25 \text{ ft})^2$

$= (3.14)(625 \text{ ft}^2)$ Substitute 3.14 for π and $r = 25$ ft.

$= 1962.5 \text{ ft}^2$ The area of the fountain is 1962.5 ft^2.

3. Volume

The **volume** of a solid is the number of cubic units that can be enclosed within a solid. The solid shown in Figure R-8 contains 18 cubic inches (18 in.^{3}). In applications, volume might refer to the amount of water in a swimming pool.

1 in.^{3}

Volume = 18 in.^{3}

2 in.

3 in.

3 in.

Figure R-8

The formulas used to compute the volume of several common solids are given here:

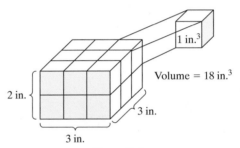

Rectangular Solid   **Cube**   **Right Circular Cylinder**

$V = \ell wh$ $V = s^3$ $V = \pi r^2 h$

TIP: Notice that the volume formulas for the three figures just shown are given by the product of the area of the base and the height of the figure:

$V = \ell wh$ $V = s \cdot s \cdot s$ $V = \pi r^2 h$

Area of Rectangular Base   Area of Square Base   Area of Circular Base

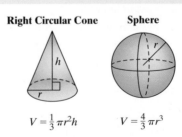

Right Circular Cone   **Sphere**

$V = \frac{1}{3}\pi r^2 h$ $V = \frac{4}{3}\pi r^3$

Example 5 **Finding Volume**

Find the volume.

$1\frac{1}{2}$ ft
$1\frac{1}{2}$ ft
$1\frac{1}{2}$ ft

Solution:

$V = s^3$ The object is a cube.

$= (1\frac{1}{2} \text{ ft})^3$ Substitute $s = 1\frac{1}{2}$ ft.

$= \left(\frac{3}{2} \text{ ft}\right)^3$

$= \left(\frac{3}{2} \text{ ft}\right)\left(\frac{3}{2} \text{ ft}\right)\left(\frac{3}{2} \text{ ft}\right)$

$= \frac{27}{8}$ ft^3, or $3\frac{3}{8}$ ft^3

TIP: Notice that the units of volume are cubic units such as cubic inches (in.^{3}), cubic feet (ft^3), cubic yards (yd^3), cubic centimeters (cm^3), and so on.

Skill Practice

6. Find the volume.

8 ft
4 ft
4 ft

Animation

Example 6 **Finding Volume**

Find the volume. Round to the nearest whole unit.

$h = 12$ cm
$r = 4$ cm

Skill Practice

7. Find the volume. Use 3.14 for π. Round to the nearest whole unit.

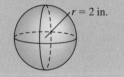

$r = 2$ in.

Solution:

$V = \frac{1}{3}\pi r^2 h$ The object is a right circular cone.

$\approx \frac{1}{3}(3.14)(4 \text{ cm})^2(12 \text{ cm})$ Substitute 3.14 for π, $r = 4$ cm, and $h = 12$ cm.

$= \frac{1}{3}(3.14)(16 \text{ cm}^2)(12 \text{ cm})$

$= 200.96$ cm^3

≈ 201 cm^3 Round to the nearest whole unit.

Example 7 **Finding Volume in an Application**

An underground gas tank is in the shape of a right circular cylinder.

a. Find the volume of the tank. Use 3.14 for π.

b. Find the cost to fill the tank with gasoline if gasoline costs $35/ft^3.

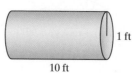

1 ft
10 ft

Answers
6. 128 ft^3 **7.** 33 in.^{3}

Skill Practice

8. Find the volume of soda in the can. Use 3.14 for π. Round to the nearest whole unit.

12 cm

⊢ 6 cm ⊣

9. How much soda is contained in a six-pack?

Solution:

a. $V = \pi r^2 h$

$\approx (3.14)(1 \text{ ft})^2(10 \text{ ft})$ Substitute 3.14 for π, $r = 1$ ft, and $h = 10$ ft.

$= (3.14)(1 \text{ ft}^2)(10 \text{ ft})$

$= 31.4 \text{ ft}^3$ The tank holds 31.4 ft^3 of gasoline.

b. $\text{Cost} = (\$35/\text{ft}^3)(31.4 \text{ ft}^3)$

$= \$1099$ It will cost \$1099 to fill the tank.

4. Angles

Applications involving angles and their measure come up often in the study of algebra, trigonometry, calculus, and applied sciences. The most common unit to measure an angle is the degree (°). Several angles and their corresponding degree measure are shown in Figure R-9.

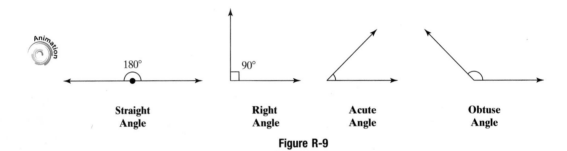

180°   90°

Straight Angle   **Right Angle**   **Acute Angle**   **Obtuse Angle**

Figure R-9

Concept Connections

10. Give the measures of two angles that are complementary. Answers may vary.

11. Give the measures of two angles that are supplementary. Answers may vary.

- An angle that measures 90° is a **right angle** (right angles are often marked with a square or corner symbol, □).
- An angle that measures 180° is called a **straight angle**.
- An angle that measures between 0° and 90° is called an **acute angle**.
- An angle that measures between 90° and 180° is called an **obtuse angle**.
- Two angles with the same measure are **equal angles** (or **congruent angles**).

The measure of an angle will be denoted by the symbol m written in front of the angle. Therefore, the measure of $\angle A$ is denoted $m(\angle A)$.

- Two angles are **complementary** if the sum of their measures is 90°.

- Two angles are **supplementary** if the sum of their measures is 180°.

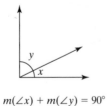

y x

$m(\angle x) + m(\angle y) = 90°$

y x

$m(\angle x) + m(\angle y) = 180°$

Answers

8. 339 cm^3 **9.** 2034 cm^3

10. For example, 70° and 20°.

11. For example, 80° and 100°.

When two lines intersect, four angles are formed (Figure R-10). In Figure R-10, $\angle a$ and $\angle b$ are a pair of **vertical angles**. Another set of vertical angles is the pair $\angle c$ and $\angle d$. An important property of vertical angles is that the measures of two vertical angles are *equal*. In the figure, $m(\angle a) = m(\angle b)$ and $m(\angle c) = m(\angle d)$.

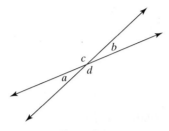

Figure R-10

Parallel lines are lines that lie in the same plane and do not intersect. In Figure R-11, the lines L_1 and L_2 are parallel lines. If a line intersects two parallel lines, the line forms eight angles with the parallel lines.

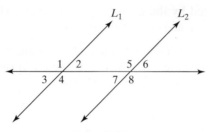

Figure R-11

The measures of angles 1–8 in Figure R-11 have the following special properties.

L_1 and L_2 are Parallel	Name of Angles	Property
	The following pairs of angles are called **alternate interior angles:**	Alternate interior angles are equal in measure.
	$\angle 2$ and $\angle 7$	$m(\angle 2) = m(\angle 7)$
	$\angle 4$ and $\angle 5$	$m(\angle 4) = m(\angle 5)$
	The following pairs of angles are called **alternate exterior angles:**	Alternate exterior angles are equal in measure.
	$\angle 1$ and $\angle 8$	$m(\angle 1) = m(\angle 8)$
	$\angle 3$ and $\angle 6$	$m(\angle 3) = m(\angle 6)$
	The following pairs of angles are called **corresponding angles:**	Corresponding angles are equal in measure.
	$\angle 1$ and $\angle 5$	$m(\angle 1) = m(\angle 5)$
	$\angle 2$ and $\angle 6$	$m(\angle 2) = m(\angle 6)$
	$\angle 3$ and $\angle 7$	$m(\angle 3) = m(\angle 7)$
	$\angle 4$ and $\angle 8$	$m(\angle 4) = m(\angle 8)$

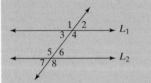
Example 8 **Finding Measures of Angles in a Diagram**

Find the measure of each angle and explain how the angle is related to the given angle of 70°.

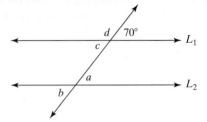

a. $\angle a$ **b.** $\angle b$

c. $\angle c$ **d.** $\angle d$

Solution:

a. $m(\angle a) = 70°$ $\angle a$ is a corresponding angle to the given angle of 70°.

b. $m(\angle b) = 70°$ $\angle b$ and the given angle of 70° are alternate exterior angles.

c. $m(\angle c) = 70°$ $\angle c$ and the given angle of 70° are vertical angles.

d. $m(\angle d) = 110°$ $\angle d$ is the supplement of the given angle of 70°.

5. Triangles

Triangles are categorized by the measures of the angles (Figure R-12) and by the number of equal sides or angles (Figure R-13).

- An **acute triangle** is a triangle in which all three angles are acute.
- A **right triangle** is a triangle in which one angle is a right angle.
- An **obtuse triangle** is a triangle in which one angle is obtuse.

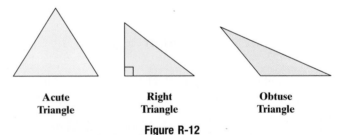

Figure R-12

- An **equilateral triangle** is a triangle in which all three sides (and all three angles) are equal in measure.
- An **isosceles triangle** is a triangle in which two sides are equal in measure (the angles opposite the equal sides are also equal in measure).
- A **scalene triangle** is a triangle in which no sides (or angles) are equal in measure.

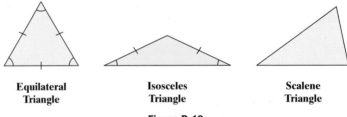

Figure R-13

The following important property is true for all triangles.

Sum of the Angles in a Triangle
The sum of the measures of the angles of a triangle is 180°.

Example 9 Finding Measures of Angles in a Diagram

Find the measure of each angle in the figure.

a. ∠a

b. ∠b

c. ∠c

d. ∠d

e. ∠e

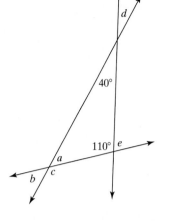

Solution:

a. $m(\angle a) = 30°$ The sum of the angles in a triangle is 180°.

b. $m(\angle b) = 30°$ ∠a and ∠b are vertical angles and are equal.

c. $m(\angle c) = 150°$ ∠c and ∠a are supplementary angles (∠c and ∠b are also supplementary).

d. $m(\angle d) = 40°$ ∠d and the given angle of 40° are vertical angles.

e. $m(\angle e) = 70°$ ∠e and the given angle of 110° are supplementary angles.

Skill Practice

For Exercises 13–17, refer to the figure. Find the measure of the indicated angle.

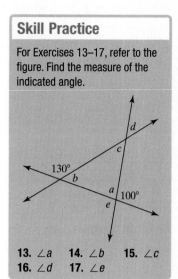

13. ∠a   14. ∠b   15. ∠c
16. ∠d   17. ∠e

Answers

13. 80°   14. 50°   15. 50°
16. 50°   17. 100°

Section R.4 Practice Exercises

Vocabulary and Key Concepts

1. a. The _____ of a polygon is the distance around the polygon. The _____ of a circle is the distance around the circle.

    b. The _____ of a region is the number of square units that can be enclosed within the region.

    c. The formula for the circumference of a circle of radius r is _____, while the formula for the area is _____.

    d. The volume of a rectangular solid with sides of lengths l, w, and h is given by $V = $ _____.

    e. An _____ angle measures less than 90° and an _____ angle measures between 90° and 180°.

    f. Two angles are called _____ angles if the sum of their measures is 90°. Two angles are called supplementary angles if the sum of their measures is _____.

    g. The sum of the measures of the angles of a triangle is _____°.

    h. A right triangle is a triangle in which one angle is a _____ angle.

Concept 1: Perimeter

2. Identify which units could be measures of perimeter or circumference.

    a. Square inches (in.²)   b. Meters (m)   c. Cubic feet (ft³)

    d. Cubic meters (m³)   e. Miles (mi)   f. Square centimeters (cm²)

    g. Square yards (yd²)   h. Cubic inches (in.³)   i. Kilometers (km)

For Exercises 3–10, find the perimeter or circumference of each figure. Use 3.14 for π. **(See Example 1.)**

3.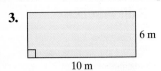
6 m
10 m

4.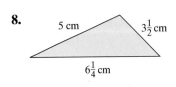
22 cm
32 cm

5.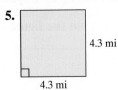
4.3 mi
4.3 mi

6.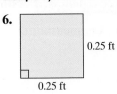
0.25 ft
0.25 ft

7.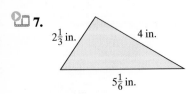
$2\frac{1}{3}$ in.   4 in.
$5\frac{1}{6}$ in.

8.
5 cm $3\frac{1}{2}$ cm
$6\frac{1}{4}$ cm

9.
10 ft

10.
4.2 yd

Concept 2: Area

11. Identify which units could be measures of area.

   a. Square inches (in.^{2})   **b.** Meters (m)   **c.** Cubic feet (ft^3)

   d. Cubic meters (m^3)   **e.** Miles (mi)   **f.** Square centimeters (cm^2)

   g. Square yards (yd^2)   **h.** Cubic inches (in.^{3})   **i.** Kilometers (km)

12. Would you measure area or perimeter to determine the amount of carpeting needed for a room?

For Exercises 13–26, find the area. Use 3.14 for π. **(See Examples 2–4.)**   Animation

13.
11 cm
3 cm

14.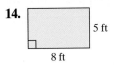
5 ft
8 ft

15.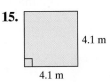
4.1 m
4.1 m

16.
6.1 in.
6.1 in.

17.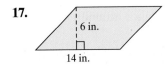
6 in.
14 in.

18.
0.01 m
0.04 m

19.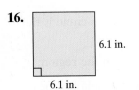
2.3 km
8.8 km

20.
5 mi
16 mi

21.
4.2 ft

22.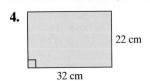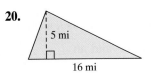
6.5 cm

23.
8 in.
6 in.
14 in.

24.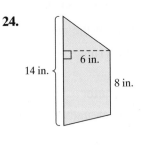
6 in.
14 in.
8 in.

25.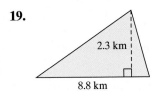
9 ft
7 ft

26.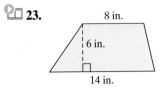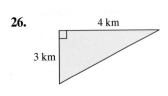
4 km
3 km

Concept 3: Volume

27. Identify which units could be measures of volume.

    a. Square inches (in.^{2})   **b.** Meters (m)   **c.** Cubic feet (ft^3)

    d. Cubic meters (m^3)   **e.** Miles (mi)   **f.** Square centimeters (cm^2)

    g. Square yards (yd^2)   **h.** Cubic inches (in.^{3})   **i.** Kilometers (km)

28. Would you measure perimeter, area, or volume to determine the amount of water needed to fill a swimming pool?

For Exercises 29–36, find the volume of each figure. Use 3.14 for π. **(See Examples 5–7.)**

29.
3.5 cm
8 cm

30.
2 ft
6 ft

31.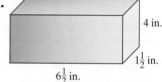
4 in.
$1\frac{1}{2}$ in.
$6\frac{1}{2}$ in.

32.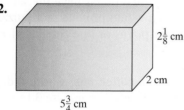
$2\frac{1}{8}$ cm
2 cm
$5\frac{3}{4}$ cm

33.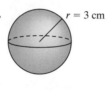
$r = 3$ cm

34.
$d = 12$ ft

35.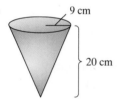
9 cm
20 cm

36.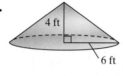
4 ft
6 ft

37. A florist sells balloons and needs to know how much helium to order. Each balloon is approximately spherical with a radius of 9 in. How much helium is needed to fill one balloon?

38. Find the volume of a spherical ball whose radius is 3 in. Use 3.14 for π.

39. Find the volume of a snow cone in the shape of a right circular cone whose radius is 3 cm and whose height is 12 cm. Use 3.14 for π.

40. A landscaping supply company has a pile of gravel in the shape of a right circular cone whose radius is 10 yd and whose height is 18 yd. Find the volume of the gravel. Use 3.14 for π.

Mixed Exercises: Perimeter, Area, and Volume

41. A wall measuring 20 ft by 8 ft can be painted for $40.

    a. What is the price per square foot?

    b. At this rate, how much would it cost to paint the remaining three walls that measure 20 ft by 8 ft, 16 ft by 8 ft, and 16 ft by 8 ft?

42. Suppose it costs $336 to carpet a 16 ft by 12 ft room.

    a. What is the price per square foot?

    b. At this rate, how much would it cost to carpet a room that is 20 ft by 32 ft?

43. If you were to purchase fencing for a garden, would you measure the perimeter or area of the garden?

44. If you were to purchase sod (grass) for your front yard, would you measure the perimeter or area of the yard?

45. How much fence is needed to enclose a triangularly shaped garden whose sides measure 12 ft, 22 ft, and 20 ft?

46. A regulation soccer field is 100 yd long by 60 yd wide. Find the perimeter of the field.

47. a. An American football field is 360 ft long by 160 ft wide. What is the area of the field?

    b. How many pieces of sod, each 1 ft wide and 3 ft long, are needed to sod an entire field? (*Hint:* First find the area of a piece of sod.)

48. The Transamerica Tower in San Francisco is a pyramid with triangular sides (excluding the "wings"). Each side measures 145 ft wide with a height of 853 ft. What is the area of each side?

49. a. Find the area of a circular pizza that is 8 in. in diameter (the radius is 4 in.). Use 3.14 for π.

    b. Find the area of a circular pizza that is 12 in. in diameter (the radius is 6 in.).

    c. Assume that the 8-in. diameter and 12-in. diameter pizzas are both the same thickness. Which would provide more pizza, two 8-in. pizzas or one 12-in. pizza?

50. a. Find the area of a rectangular pizza that is 12 in. by 8 in.

    b. Find the area of a circular pizza that has a 16-in. diameter. Use 3.14 for π.

    c. Assume that the two pizzas have the same thickness. Which would provide more pizza, two rectangular pizzas or one circular pizza?

51. Find the volume of a soup can in the shape of a right circular cylinder if its radius is 3.2 cm and its height is 9 cm. Use 3.14 for π.

52. Find the volume of a coffee mug whose radius is 2.5 in. and whose height is 6 in. Use 3.14 for π.

Concept 4: Angles

For Exercises 53–58, answer True or False. If an answer is false, explain why.

53. The sum of the measures of two right angles equals the measure of a straight angle.

54. Two right angles are complementary.

55. Two right angles are supplementary.

56. Two acute angles cannot be supplementary.

57. Two obtuse angles cannot be supplementary.

58. An obtuse angle and an acute angle can be supplementary.

59. If possible, find two acute angles that are supplementary.

60. If possible, find two acute angles that are complementary. Answers may vary.

61. If possible, find an obtuse angle and an acute angle that are supplementary. Answers may vary.

62. If possible, find two obtuse angles that are supplementary.

63. Refer to the figure.

    a. State all the pairs of vertical angles.

    b. State all the pairs of supplementary angles.

    c. If the measure of ∠4 is 80°, find the measures of ∠1, ∠2, and ∠3.

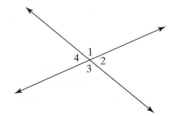

64. Refer to the figure.

  a. State all the pairs of vertical angles.

  b. State all the pairs of supplementary angles.

  c. If the measure of $\angle a$ is $25°$, find the measures of $\angle b$, $\angle c$, and $\angle d$.

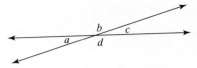

For Exercises 65–68, the measure of an angle is given. Find the measure of its complement.

65. $33°$ **66.** $87°$ **67.** $12°$ **68.** $45°$

For Exercises 69–72, the measure of an angle is given. Find the measure of its supplement.

69. $33°$ **70.** $87°$ **71.** $122°$ **72.** $90°$

For Exercises 73–80, refer to the figure. Assume that L_1 and L_2 are parallel lines. **(See Example 8.)**

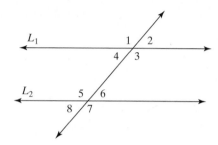

73. $m(\angle 5) = m(\angle \underline{\quad})$ Reason: Vertical angles have equal measures.

74. $m(\angle 5) = m(\angle \underline{\quad})$ Reason: Alternate interior angles have equal measures.

75. $m(\angle 5) = m(\angle \underline{\quad})$ Reason: Corresponding angles have equal measures.

76. $m(\angle 7) = m(\angle \underline{\quad})$ Reason: Corresponding angles have equal measures.

77. $m(\angle 7) = m(\angle \underline{\quad})$ Reason: Alternate exterior angles have equal measures.

78. $m(\angle 7) = m(\angle \underline{\quad})$ Reason: Vertical angles have equal measures.

79. $m(\angle 3) = m(\angle \underline{\quad})$ Reason: Alternate interior angles have equal measures.

80. $m(\angle 3) = m(\angle \underline{\quad})$ Reason: Vertical angles have equal measures.

81. Find the measure of angles a–g in the figure. Assume that L_1 and L_2 are parallel.

82. Find the measure of angles a–g in the figure. Assume that L_1 and L_2 are parallel.

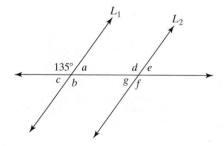

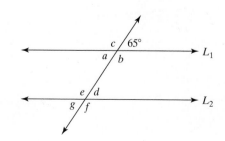

Concept 5: Triangles

For Exercises 83–86, identify the triangle as equilateral, isosceles, or scalene.

83.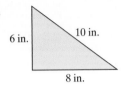

84.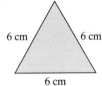

85.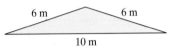

86.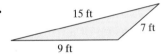

87. True or False? If a triangle is equilateral, then it is not scalene.

88. True or False? If a triangle is isosceles, then it is also scalene.

89. What angle is its own complement?

90. What angle is its own supplement?

91. Can a triangle be both a right triangle and an obtuse triangle? Explain.

92. Can a triangle be both a right triangle and an isosceles triangle? Explain.

For Exercises 93–96, find the measure of each missing angle.

93.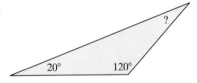

94.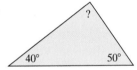

95.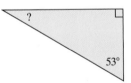

96.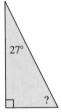

97. Refer to the figure. Find the measure of angles *a–j*. **(See Example 9.)**

98. Refer to the figure. Find the measure of angles *a–j*.

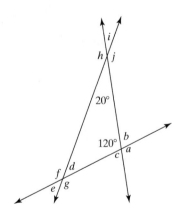

99. Refer to the figure. Find the measure of angles *a–k*. Assume that L_1 and L_2 are parallel.

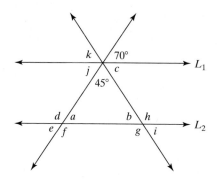

100. Refer to the figure. Find the measure of angles *a–k*. Assume that L_1 and L_2 are parallel.

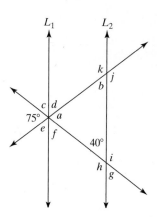

Expanding Your Skills

For Exercises 101 and 102, find the perimeter.

101.

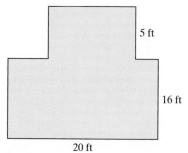

102.

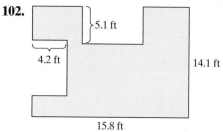

For Exercises 103–106, find the area of the shaded region. Use 3.14 for π.

103.

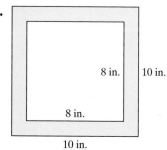

104.

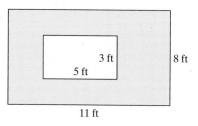

105.

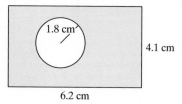

106.

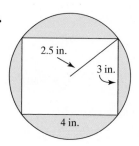

The Set of Real Numbers

1

CHAPTER OUTLINE

Chapter 1

In Chapter 1, we present operations on real numbers. The skills that you will learn in this chapter are particularly important as you continue in algebra.

Review Your Skills

Basic arithmetic skills are the foundation for learning operations on real numbers. This puzzle will help you refresh those skills.

Across

1. Area of a rectangle with length 35 ft and width 7 ft
3. $300 - 186$
5. Round 3549 to the tens place.

Down

1. LCD for $\dfrac{5}{6}, \dfrac{2}{3}, \dfrac{7}{8}$

2. $11.6 \div 0.2$

4. 1.25×116

5. The numerator of the sum $\dfrac{5}{2} + \dfrac{5}{8} + \dfrac{5}{4}$

6. The numerator when $7\dfrac{3}{8}$ is changed to an improper fraction.

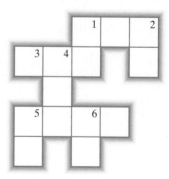

Section 1.1 Introduction to Algebra and the Set of Real Numbers

Concept Connections

1. Why is π not a variable?

1. Variables and Expressions

Doctors promote daily exercise as part of a healthy lifestyle. Aerobic exercise is exercise for the heart. During aerobic exercise the goal is to maintain a heart rate level between 65% and 85% of an individual's maximum recommended heart rate. The maximum recommended heart rate, in beats per minute, for an adult of age a is given by

$$\text{Maximum recommended heart rate} = 220 - a$$

In this example, the value a is called a **variable**. This is a symbol or letter, such as x, y, z, a, and the like, that is used to represent an unknown number that is subject to change. The number 220 is called a **constant**, because it does not vary. The quantity $220 - a$ is called an algebraic expression. An algebraic **expression** is a collection of variables and constants under algebraic operations. For example $\frac{3}{x}$, $y + z$, and $t - 1.4$ are algebraic expressions.

The symbols used in algebraic expressions to show the four basic operations are shown here:

Addition	$a + b$
Subtraction	$a - b$
Multiplication	$a \times b, a \cdot b, (a)b, a(b), (a)(b), ab$

(*Note:* We rarely use the notation $a \times b$ because the symbol, $\times$, may be confused with the variable x.)

Division	$a \div b, \dfrac{a}{b}, a/b, b\overline{)a}$

The value of an algebraic expression depends on the values of the variables within the expression.

Example 1 Evaluating an Algebraic Expression

The expression $220 - a$ represents the maximum recommended heart rate for an adult of age a. Determine the maximum heart rate for:

a. A 20-year-old   **b.** A 45-year-old

Skill Practice

2. After dining out at a restaurant, the minimum recommended tip for the server is 15% of the cost of the meal. This can be represented by 0.15c, where c is the cost of the meal. Compute the tip for a meal that costs
a. $18   **b.** $46

Solution:

a. In the expression $220 - a$, the variable, a, represents the age of the individual. To calculate the maximum recommended heart rate for a 20-year-old, substitute 20 for a in the expression.

$220 - a$

$220 - (\quad)$ When substituting a number for a variable, use parentheses.

$= 220 - (20)$ Substitute $a = 20$.

$= 200$ Subtract.

The maximum recommended heart rate for a 20-year-old is 200 beats per minute.

Answers

1. The symbol π is not a variable because its value does not vary. It is always equal to the irrational number 3.14159. . . .
2. **a.** $2.70   **b.** $6.90

b. To calculate the maximum recommended heart rate for a 45-year-old, substitute 45 for a in the expression.

$220 - a$

$220 - (\quad)$ When substituting a number for a variable, use parentheses.

$= 220 - (45)$ Substitute $a = 45$.

$= 175$ Subtract.

The maximum recommended heart rate for a 45-year-old is 175 beats per minute.

Example 2   Computing the Area of a Rectangle

The area of a rectangle is the product of the length, l, and the width, w. The area of a rectangle can be computed by evaluating the given algebraic expression for values of l and w.

$$\text{Area} = lw$$

Compute the area of a rectangle that is 12.5 ft long and 8 ft wide.

Solution:

lw

$(\quad)(\quad)$ When substituting numbers for variables, use parentheses for each variable.

$= (12.5 \text{ ft})(8 \text{ ft})$ Substitute $l = 12.5$ and $w = 8$.

$= 100 \text{ ft}^2$ Multiply.

The area of the rectangle is 100 ft^2.

Skill Practice

3. The perimeter of a triangle with sides a, b, and c can be represented by

Perimeter $= a + b + c$

Compute the perimeter of a triangle whose sides measure $2\frac{1}{2}$ cm, 6 cm, and $4\frac{1}{2}$ cm.

2. The Set of Real Numbers

Typically, the numbers represented by variables in an algebraic expression are all part of a set of **real numbers**. These are the numbers that we work with on a day-to-day basis. The real numbers encompass zero, all positive, and all negative numbers, including those represented by fractions and decimal numbers. The set of real numbers can be represented graphically on a horizontal number line with a point labeled as 0. Positive real numbers are graphed to the right of 0, and negative real numbers are graphed to the left of 0. Zero is neither positive nor negative. Each point on the number line corresponds to exactly one real number. For this reason, this number line is called the *real number line* (Figure 1-1).

Figure 1-1

Answer

3. 13 cm

Example 3   **Plotting Points on the Real Number Line**

Plot the points on the real number line that represent the following real numbers.

a. -3 b. $\dfrac{3}{2}$ c. -4.7 d. $\dfrac{16}{5}$

Solution:

a. Because -3 is negative, it lies three units to the left of 0.

b. The fraction $\frac{3}{2}$ can be expressed as the mixed number $1\frac{1}{2}$, which lies halfway between 1 and 2 on the number line.

c. The negative number -4.7 lies $\frac{7}{10}$ unit to the left of -4 on the number line.

d. The fraction $\frac{16}{5}$ can be expressed as the mixed number $3\frac{1}{5}$, which lies $\frac{1}{5}$ unit to the right of 3 on the number line.

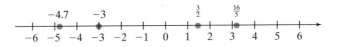

TIP: The natural numbers are used for counting. For this reason, they are sometimes called the "counting numbers."

In mathematics, a well-defined collection of elements is called a **set**. "Well-defined" means the set is described in such a way that it is clear whether an element is in the set. The symbols { } are used to enclose the elements of the set. For example, the set $\{A, B, C, D, E\}$ represents the set of the first five letters of the alphabet.

Several sets of numbers are used extensively in algebra and are *subsets* (or part) of the set of real numbers.

> **Natural Numbers, Whole Numbers, and Integers**
> The set of **natural numbers** is $\{1, 2, 3, \ldots\}$
> The set of **whole numbers** is $\{0, 1, 2, 3, \ldots\}$
> The set of **integers** is $\{\ldots -3, -2, -1, 0, 1, 2, 3, \ldots\}$

Notice that the set of whole numbers includes the natural numbers. Therefore, every natural number is also a whole number. The set of integers includes the set of whole numbers. Therefore, every whole number is also an integer.

Fractions are also among the numbers we use frequently. A number that can be written as a fraction whose numerator is an integer and whose denominator is a nonzero integer is called a *rational number*.

> **Rational Numbers**
> The set of **rational numbers** is the set of numbers that can be expressed in the form $\frac{p}{q}$, where both p and q are integers and q does not equal 0.

Answer

4.

We also say that a rational number $\frac{p}{q}$ is a *ratio* of two integers, p and q, where q is not equal to zero.

Example 4 Identifying Rational Numbers

Show that the numbers are rational numbers by finding an equivalent ratio of two integers.

a. $\dfrac{-2}{3}$ **b.** -12 **c.** 0.5 **d.** $0.\overline{6}$

Solution:

a. The fraction $\frac{-2}{3}$ is a rational number because it can be expressed as the ratio of -2 and 3.

b. The number -12 is a rational number because it can be expressed as the ratio of -12 and 1, that is, $-12 = \frac{-12}{1}$. In this example, we see that an integer is also a rational number.

c. The terminating decimal 0.5 is a rational number because it can be expressed as the ratio of 5 and 10. That is, $0.5 = \frac{5}{10}$. In this example, we see that a terminating decimal is also a rational number.

d. Table R-1 on page 23 shows that $0.\overline{6}$ is the decimal form of the fraction $\frac{2}{3}$. The repeating decimal $0.\overline{6}$ is a rational number because it can be expressed as the ratio of 2 and 3. In this example, we see that a repeating decimal is also a rational number.

Skill Practice

Show that each number is rational by finding an equivalent ratio of two integers.

5. $\dfrac{3}{7}$ **6.** -5

7. 0.3 **8.** $0.\overline{3}$

TIP: Any rational number can be represented by a terminating decimal or by a repeating decimal.

Some real numbers, such as the number π, cannot be represented by the ratio of two integers. These numbers are called irrational numbers and in decimal form are nonterminating, nonrepeating decimals. The value of π, for example, can be approximated as $\pi \approx 3.1415926535897932$. However, the decimal digits continue forever with no repeated pattern. Another example of an irrational number is $\sqrt{3}$ (read as "the positive square root of 3"). The expression $\sqrt{3}$ is a number that when multiplied by itself is 3. There is no rational number that satisfies this condition. Thus, $\sqrt{3}$ is an irrational number.

Irrational Numbers

The set of **irrational numbers** is a subset of the real numbers whose elements cannot be written as a ratio of two integers.

Note: An irrational number cannot be written as a terminating decimal or as a repeating decimal.

The set of real numbers consists of both the rational and the irrational numbers. The relationship among these important sets of numbers is illustrated in Figure 1-2.

Answers

5. ratio of 3 and 7
6. ratio of -5 and 1
7. ratio of 3 and 10
8. ratio of 1 and 3

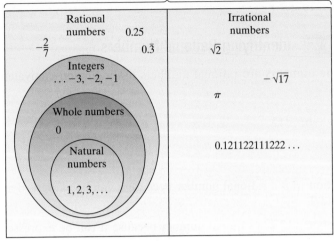

Figure 1-2

Example 5 **Classifying Numbers by Set**

Check the set(s) to which each number belongs. The numbers may belong to more than one set.

	Natural Numbers	Whole Numbers	Integers	Rational Numbers	Irrational Numbers	Real Numbers
5						
$\dfrac{-47}{3}$						
1.48						
$\sqrt{7}$						
0						

Solution:

	Natural Numbers	Whole Numbers	Integers	Rational Numbers	Irrational Numbers	Real Numbers
5	✔	✔	✔	✔ (ratio of 5 and 1)		✔
$\dfrac{-47}{3}$				✔ (ratio of -47 and 3)		✔
1.48				✔ (ratio of 148 and 100)		✔
$\sqrt{7}$					✔	✔
0		✔	✔	✔ (ratio of 0 and 1)		✔

3. Inequalities

The relative size of two real numbers can be compared using the real number line. Suppose a and b represent two real numbers. We say that a is less than b, denoted $a < b$, if a lies to the left of b on the number line.

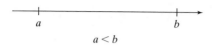

$$a < b$$

We say that a is greater than b, denoted $a > b$, if a lies to the right of b on the number line.

$$a > b$$

Table 1-1 summarizes the relational operators that compare two real numbers a and b.

Table 1-1

Mathematical Expression	Translation	Example
$a < b$	a is less than b.	$2 < 3$
$a > b$	a is greater than b.	$5 > 1$
$a \leq b$	a is less than or equal to b.	$4 \leq 4$
$a \geq b$	a is greater than or equal to b.	$10 \geq 9$
$a = b$	a is equal to b.	$6 = 6$
$a \neq b$	a is not equal to b.	$7 \neq 0$
$a \approx b$	a is approximately equal to b.	$2.3 \approx 2$

The symbols $<$, $>$, $\leq$, $\geq$, and $\neq$ are called *inequality signs*, and the statements $a < b$, $a > b$, $a \leq b$, $a \geq b$, and $a \neq b$ are called **inequalities**.

Example 6   **Ordering Real Numbers**

The average temperatures (in degrees Celsius) for selected cities in the United States and Canada in January are shown in Table 1-2.

Table 1-2

City	Temp (°C)
Prince George, British Columbia	-12.5
Corpus Christi, Texas	13.4
Parkersburg, West Virginia	-0.9
San Jose, California	9.7
Juneau, Alaska	-5.7
New Bedford, Massachusetts	-0.2
Durham, North Carolina	4.2

Plot a point on the real number line representing the temperature of each city. Compare the temperatures between the following cities, and fill in the blank with the appropriate inequality sign: $<$ or $>$.

Skill Practice

Fill in the blanks with the appropriate inequality sign: $<$ or $>$.

14. -11 _____ 20
15. -3 _____ -6
16. 0 _____ -9
17. -6.2 _____ -1.8

Answers
14. $<$ **15.** $>$ **16.** $>$ **17.** $<$

Based on the location of the numbers on the number line, fill in the blanks with the appropriate inequality sign: $<$ or $>$.

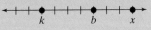

18. k _____ x

19. x _____ b

20. b _____ k

Solution:

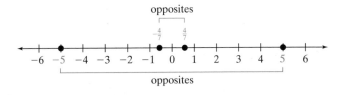

a. Temperature of San Jose $\boxed{<}$ temperature of Corpus Christi

b. Temperature of Juneau $\boxed{>}$ temperature of Prince George

c. Temperature of Parkersburg $\boxed{<}$ temperature of New Bedford

d. Temperature of Parkersburg $\boxed{>}$ temperature of Prince George

4. Opposite of a Real Number

To gain mastery of any algebraic skill, it is necessary to know the meaning of key definitions and key symbols. Two important definitions are the *opposite* of a real number and the *absolute value* of a real number.

> **The Opposite of a Real Number**
>
> Two numbers that are the same distance from 0 but on opposite sides of 0 on the number line are called **opposites** of each other. Symbolically, we denote the opposite of a real number a as $-a$.

Skill Practice

21. Find the opposite of 224.
22. Find the opposite of -3.4.

Example 7   Finding the Opposite of a Real Number

a. Find the opposite of 5.   **b.** Find the opposite of $-\dfrac{4}{7}$.

Solution:

a. The opposite of 5 is -5.   **b.** The opposite of $-\dfrac{4}{7}$ is $\dfrac{4}{7}$.

opposites

$-\frac{4}{7}$ $\frac{4}{7}$

$-6\ \ -5\ \ -4\ \ -3\ \ -2\ \ -1\ \ 0\ \ 1\ \ 2\ \ 3\ \ 4\ \ 5\ \ 6$

opposites

Skill Practice

Evaluate.

23. $-(2.8)$

24. $-\left(-\dfrac{1}{5}\right)$

Example 8   Finding the Opposite of a Real Number

Evaluate each expression.

a. $-(0.46)$ **b.** $-\left(-\dfrac{11}{3}\right)$

Solution:

a. $-(0.46) = -0.46$ The expression $-(0.46)$ represents the opposite of 0.46.

b. $-\left(-\dfrac{11}{3}\right) = \dfrac{11}{3}$ The expression $-\left(-\dfrac{11}{3}\right)$ represents the opposite of $-\dfrac{11}{3}$.

Answers

18. $<$ 19. $>$ 20. $>$
21. -224 22. 3.4 23. -2.8
24. $\dfrac{1}{5}$

5. Absolute Value of a Real Number

The concept of absolute value will be used to define the addition of real numbers in Section 1.3.

Informal Definition of the Absolute Value of a Real Number

The **absolute value** of a real number a, denoted $|a|$, is the distance between a and 0 on the number line.

Note: The absolute value of any real number is positive or zero.

For example, $|3| = 3$ and $|-3| = 3$.

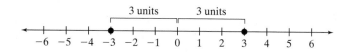

Example 9 Finding the Absolute Value of a Real Number

Evaluate the absolute value expressions.

a. $|-4|$ **b.** $\left|\frac{1}{2}\right|$ **c.** $|-6.2|$ **d.** $|0|$

Solution:

a. $|-4| = 4$ −4 is 4 units from 0 on the number line.

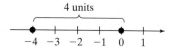

b. $\left|\frac{1}{2}\right| = \frac{1}{2}$ $\frac{1}{2}$ is $\frac{1}{2}$ unit from 0 on the number line.

c. $|-6.2| = 6.2$ −6.2 is 6.2 units from 0 on the number line.

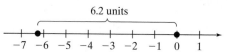

d. $|0| = 0$ 0 is 0 units from 0 on the number line.

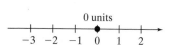

Skill Practice

Evaluate.

25. $|-99|$ **26.** $\left|\dfrac{7}{8}\right|$

27. $|-1.4|$ **28.** $|1|$

The absolute value of a number a is its distance from 0 on the number line. The definition of $|a|$ may also be given symbolically depending on whether a is negative or nonnegative.

Absolute Value of a Real Number

Let a be a real number. Then

1. If a is nonnegative (that is, $a \geq 0$), then $|a| = a$.

2. If a is negative (that is, $a < 0$), then $|a| = -a$.

Answers

25. 99   **26.** $\dfrac{7}{8}$

27. 1.4   **28.** 1

This definition states that if a is a nonnegative number, then $|a|$ equals a itself. If a is a negative number, then $|a|$ equals the opposite of a. For example:

$|9| = 9$ Because 9 is positive, then $|9|$ equals the number 9 itself.

$|-7| = 7$ Because -7 is negative, then $|-7|$ equals the opposite of -7, which is 7.

Skill Practice

Determine if the statements are true or false.

29. $-|4| > |-4|$
30. $|-17| = 17$

Answers

29. False   **30.** True

Example 10   **Comparing Absolute Value Expressions**

Determine if the statements are true or false.

a. $|3| \leq 3$ **b.** $-|5| = |-5|$

Solution:

a. $|3| \leq 3$ True. The symbol $\leq$ means "less than *or* equal to." Since $|3|$ is equal to 3, then $|3| \leq 3$ is a true statement.

b. $-|5| = |-5|$ False. On the left-hand side, $-|5|$ is the opposite of $|5|$. Hence $-|5| = -5$. On the right-hand side, $|-5| = 5$. Therefore, the original statement simplifies to $-5 = 5$, which is false.

Calculator Connections

Topic: Approximating Irrational Numbers on a Calculator

Scientific and graphing calculators approximate irrational numbers by using rational numbers in the form of terminating decimals. For example, consider approximating π and $\sqrt{3}$.

Scientific Calculator:

Enter: $\boxed{\pi}$ or $\boxed{2^{nd}}$ $\boxed{\pi}$ Result: $\boxed{3.141592654}$

Enter: 3 $\boxed{\sqrt{x}}$ Result: $\boxed{1.732050808}$

Graphing Calculator:

Enter: $\boxed{2^{nd}}$ $\boxed{\pi}$ $\boxed{ENTER}$

Enter: $\boxed{2^{nd}}$ $\boxed{\sqrt{}}$ 3 $\boxed{ENTER}$

```
π
            3.141592654
√(3)
            1.732050808
```

The symbol $\approx$ is read "is approximately equal to" and is used when writing approximations.

$$\pi \approx 3.141592654 \quad \text{and} \quad \sqrt{3} \approx 1.732050808$$

Calculator Exercises

Use a calculator to approximate the irrational numbers. Remember to use the appropriate symbol, $\approx$, when expressing answers.

1. $\sqrt{12}$ **2.** $\sqrt{99}$ **3.** $4 \cdot \pi$ **4.** $\sqrt{\pi}$

Section 1.1 Practice Exercises

Study Skills Exercise

In this text, we will provide skills for you to enhance your learning experience. In the first four chapters, each set of Practice Exercises begins with an activity that focuses on one of eight areas: learning about your course, using your text, taking notes, doing homework, taking an exam (test and math anxiety), managing your time, recognizing your learning style, and studying for the final exam.

Each activity requires only a few minutes and will help you to pass this course and become a better math student. Many of these skills can be carried over to other disciplines and help you to become a model college student. To begin, write down the following information on a clean sheet of paper and place it in the front of your notebook.

a. Instructor's name

b. Instructor's office number

c. Instructor's telephone number

d. Instructor's e-mail address

e. Instructor's office hours

f. Days of the week that the class meets

g. The room number in which the class meets

h. Is there a lab requirement for this course? How often must you attend lab and where is it located?

Vocabulary and Key Concepts

1. a. A _____ is a symbol or letter used to represent an unknown number.

b. Values that do not vary are called _____.

c. In mathematics, a well-defined collection of elements is called a _____.

d. The statements $a < b$, $a > b$, and $a \neq b$ are examples of _____.

e. The statement $a < b$ is read as "_____."

f. The statement $c \geq d$ is read as "_____."

g. The statement $5 \neq 6$ is read as "_____."

h. Two numbers that are the same distance from 0 but on opposite sides of 0 on the number line are called _____.

i. The absolute value of a real number, a, is denoted by _____ and is the distance between a and _____ on the number line.

Concept 1: Variables and Expressions

For Exercises 2–12, evaluate the expressions for the given substitutions. **(See Examples 1 and 2.)**

2. $y - 3$ when $y = 18$

3. $3q$ when $q = 5$

4. $\dfrac{15}{t}$ when $t = 5$

5. $8 + w$ when $w = 12$

6. $6d$ when $d = \dfrac{2}{3}$

7. $\dfrac{6}{5}h$ when $h = 10$

8. $x + 2y$ when $x = 4, y = 10$

9. $c - 2 - d$ when $c = 15.4, d = 8.1$

10. $1.1 + t + s$ when $t = 93.2$, $s = 11.5$

11. abc when $a = \frac{1}{10}$, $b = \frac{1}{4}$, $c = \frac{1}{2}$

12. $x - y - z$ when $x = \frac{7}{8}$, $y = \frac{1}{2}$, $z = \frac{1}{4}$

13. The cost of downloading songs from a music website can be represented by the expression $1.29s$, where s is the number of songs downloaded. Calculate the cost of downloading

    a. 3 songs   **b.** 8 songs   **c.** 10 songs

14. The number of calories burned by a 150-lb person by walking 2 mph can be represented by the expression $240\,h$, where h represents the number of hours spent walking. Calculate the number of calories burned by walking

    a. 4 hr   **b.** $2\frac{1}{2}$ hr   **c.** $1\frac{1}{4}$ hr

15. Aly is trying to limit her calorie intake for breakfast and lunch to 850 calories. The number of calories that she can consume for lunch is given by the expression $850 - b$, where b is the number of calories consumed for breakfast. Determine the number of calories allowed for lunch assuming that she had the following number of calories at breakfast.

    a. 475 calories   **b.** 220 calories   **c.** 580 calories

16. Lorenzo knows that the gas mileage on his small SUV is about 25 miles per gallon. The number of gallons needed to travel a certain distance is given by the expression $\frac{d}{25}$, where d is the distance traveled. Find the number of gallons of fuel needed if Lorenzo drives

    a. 200 mi   **b.** 450 mi   **c.** 180 mi

Concept 2: The Set of Real Numbers

17. Plot the numbers on a real number line: $\{1, -2, -\pi, 0, -\frac{5}{2}, 5.1\}$ **(See Example 3.)**

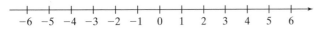

18. Plot the numbers on a real number line: $\{3, -4, \frac{1}{8}, -1.7, -\frac{4}{3}, 1.75\}$

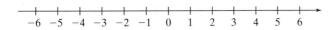

For Exercises 19–34, describe each number as (a) a terminating decimal, (b) a repeating decimal, or (c) a nonterminating, nonrepeating decimal. Then classify the number as a rational number or as an irrational number. **(See Example 4.)**

19. 0.29 **20.** 3.8 **21.** $\dfrac{1}{9}$ **22.** $\dfrac{1}{3}$

23. $\dfrac{1}{8}$ **24.** $\dfrac{1}{5}$ **25.** 2π **26.** 3π

27. -0.125 **28.** -3.24 **29.** -3 **30.** -6

31. $0.\overline{2}$ **32.** $0.\overline{6}$ **33.** $\sqrt{6}$ **34.** $\sqrt{10}$

35. List three numbers that are real numbers but not rational numbers.

36. List three numbers that are real numbers but not irrational numbers.

37. List three numbers that are integers but not natural numbers.

38. List three numbers that are integers but not whole numbers.

39. List three numbers that are rational numbers but not integers.

For Exercises 40–45, let $A = \{-\frac{3}{2}, \sqrt{11}, -4, 0.\overline{6}, 0, \sqrt{7}, 1\}$ **(See Example 5.)**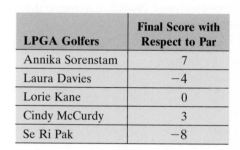

40. Are all of the numbers in set A real numbers?

41. List all of the rational numbers in set A.

42. List all of the whole numbers in set A.

43. List all of the natural numbers in set A.

44. List all of the irrational numbers in set A.

45. List all of the integers in set A.

46. Plot the real numbers from set A on a number line. (*Hint:* $\sqrt{11} \approx 3.3$ and $\sqrt{7} \approx 2.6$)

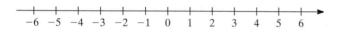

Concept 3: Inequalities

47. The LPGA Samsung World Championship of women's golf scores for selected players are given in the table. Compare the scores and fill in the blank with the appropriate inequality sign: $<$ or $>$. **(See Example 6.)**

    a. Kane's score _____ Pak's score.

    b. Sorenstam's score _____ Davies's score.

    c. Pak's score _____ McCurdy's score.

    d. Kane's score _____ Davies's score.

LPGA Golfers	Final Score with Respect to Par
Annika Sorenstam	7
Laura Davies	−4
Lorie Kane	0
Cindy McCurdy	3
Se Ri Pak	−8

48. The elevations of selected cities in the United States are shown in the figure. Compare the elevations and fill in the blank with the appropriate inequality sign: $<$ or $>$. (A negative number indicates that the city is below sea level.)

    a. Elevation of Tucson _____ elevation of Cincinnati.

    b. Elevation of New Orleans _____ elevation of Chicago.

    c. Elevation of New Orleans _____ elevation of Houston.

    d. Elevation of Chicago _____ elevation of Cincinnati.

Concept 4: Opposite of a Real Number

For Exercises 49–56, find the opposite of each number. **(See Example 7.)**

49. 18

50. 2

51. −6.1

52. −2.5

53. $-\frac{5}{8}$

54. $-\frac{1}{3}$

55. $\frac{7}{3}$

56. $\frac{1}{9}$

The opposite of a is denoted as $-a$. For Exercises 57–64, simplify. **(See Example 8.)**

57. $-(-3)$

58. $-(-5.1)$

59. $-\left(\dfrac{7}{3}\right)$

60. $-(-7)$

61. $-(-8)$

62. $-(36)$

63. $-(72.1)$

64. $-\left(\dfrac{9}{10}\right)$

Concept 5: Absolute Value of a Real Number

For Exercises 65–76, simplify. **(See Example 9.)**

65. $|-2|$

66. $|-7|$

67. $|-1.5|$

68. $|-3.7|$

69. $-|-1.5|$

70. $-|-3.7|$

71. $\left|\dfrac{3}{2}\right|$

72. $\left|\dfrac{7}{4}\right|$

73. $-|10|$

74. $-|20|$

75. $-\left|-\dfrac{1}{2}\right|$

76. $-\left|-\dfrac{11}{3}\right|$

For Exercises 77 and 78, answer true or false. If a statement is false, explain why.

77. If n is positive, then $|n|$ is negative.

78. If m is negative, then $|m|$ is negative.

For Exercises 79–102, determine if the statements are true or false. Use the real number line to justify the answer. **(See Example 10.)**

79. $5 > 2$

80. $8 < 10$

81. $6 < 6$

82. $19 > 19$

83. $-7 \geq -7$

84. $-1 \leq -1$

85. $\dfrac{3}{2} \leq \dfrac{1}{6}$

86. $-\dfrac{1}{4} \geq -\dfrac{7}{8}$

87. $-5 > -2$

88. $6 < -10$

89. $8 \neq 8$

90. $10 \neq 10$

91. $|-2| \geq |-1|$

92. $|3| \leq |-1|$

93. $\left|-\dfrac{1}{9}\right| = \left|\dfrac{1}{9}\right|$

94. $\left|-\dfrac{1}{3}\right| = \left|\dfrac{1}{3}\right|$

95. $|7| \neq |-7|$

96. $|-13| \neq |13|$

97. $-1 < |-1|$

98. $-6 < |-6|$

99. $|-8| \geq |8|$

100. $|-11| \geq |11|$

101. $|-2| \leq |2|$

102. $|-21| \leq |21|$

Expanding Your Skills

103. For what numbers, a, is $-a$ positive?

104. For what numbers, a, is $|a| = a$?

Exponents, Square Roots, and the Order of Operations

1. Exponential Expressions

In algebra, repeated multiplication can be expressed using exponents. The expression $4 \cdot 4 \cdot 4$ can be written as

exponent

4^3

base

In the expression 4^3, 4 is the base, and 3 is the exponent, or power. The exponent indicates how many factors of the base to multiply.

Concepts

1. Exponential Expressions
2. Square Roots
3. Order of Operations
4. Translations

Definition of b^n

Let b represent any real number and n represent a positive integer. Then,

$$b^n = \underbrace{b \cdot b \cdot b \cdot b \ldots \cdot b}_{n \text{ factors of } b}$$

b^n is read as "b to the nth power."

b is called the **base**, and n is called the **exponent**, or **power**.

b^2 is read as "b squared," and b^3 is read as "b cubed."

The exponent, n, is the number of times the base, b, is used as a factor.

> **TIP:** A number or variable with no exponent shown implies that there is an exponent of 1. That is, $b = b^1$.

Example 1   **Evaluating Exponential Expressions**

Translate the expression into words and then evaluate the expression.

a. 2^5 **b.** 5^2 **c.** $\left(\dfrac{3}{4}\right)^3$ **d.** 1^6

Solution:

a. The expression 2^5 is read as "two to the fifth power."
$2^5 = (2)(2)(2)(2)(2) = 32$

b. The expression 5^2 is read as "five to the second power" or "five, squared."
$5^2 = (5)(5) = 25$

c. The expression $\left(\frac{3}{4}\right)^3$ is read as "three-fourths to the third power" or "three-fourths, cubed."

$$\left(\frac{3}{4}\right)^3 = \left(\frac{3}{4}\right)\left(\frac{3}{4}\right)\left(\frac{3}{4}\right) = \frac{27}{64}$$

d. The expression 1^6 is read as "one to the sixth power."
$1^6 = (1)(1)(1)(1)(1)(1) = 1$

Skill Practice

Evaluate.

1. 4^3 2. 2^4

3. $\left(\dfrac{2}{3}\right)^2$ 4. $(1)^7$

Answers

1. 64   **2.** 16   **3.** $\dfrac{4}{9}$ **4.** 1

2. Square Roots

If we reverse the process of squaring a number, we can find the **square roots** of the number. For example, finding a square root of 9 is equivalent to asking "what number(s) when squared equals 9?" The symbol, $\sqrt{}$ (called a **radical sign**), is used to find the *principal* square root of a number. By definition, the principal square root of a number is nonnegative. Therefore, $\sqrt{9}$ is the nonnegative number that when squared equals 9. Hence $\sqrt{9} = 3$ because 3 is nonnegative and $(3)^2 = 9$.

Skill Practice

Evaluate.

5. $\sqrt{81}$　**6.** $\sqrt{100}$

7. $\sqrt{1}$　**8.** $\sqrt{\dfrac{9}{25}}$

Example 2 **Evaluating Square Roots**

Evaluate the square roots.

a. $\sqrt{64}$　　**b.** $\sqrt{121}$　　**c.** $\sqrt{0}$　　**d.** $\sqrt{\dfrac{4}{9}}$

Solution:

a. $\sqrt{64} = 8$　　Because $(8)^2 = 64$

b. $\sqrt{121} = 11$　　Because $(11)^2 = 121$

c. $\sqrt{0} = 0$　　Because $(0)^2 = 0$

d. $\sqrt{\dfrac{4}{9}} = \dfrac{2}{3}$　　Because $\dfrac{2}{3} \cdot \dfrac{2}{3} = \dfrac{4}{9}$

A perfect square is a number whose square root is a rational number. If a number is not a perfect square, its square root is an irrational number that can be approximated on a calculator.

TIP: To simplify square roots, it is advisable to become familiar with these perfect squares and square roots.

$0^2 = 0 \rightarrow \sqrt{0} = 0$	$7^2 = 49 \rightarrow \sqrt{49} = 7$
$1^2 = 1 \rightarrow \sqrt{1} = 1$	$8^2 = 64 \rightarrow \sqrt{64} = 8$
$2^2 = 4 \rightarrow \sqrt{4} = 2$	$9^2 = 81 \rightarrow \sqrt{81} = 9$
$3^2 = 9 \rightarrow \sqrt{9} = 3$	$10^2 = 100 \rightarrow \sqrt{100} = 10$
$4^2 = 16 \rightarrow \sqrt{16} = 4$	$11^2 = 121 \rightarrow \sqrt{121} = 11$
$5^2 = 25 \rightarrow \sqrt{25} = 5$	$12^2 = 144 \rightarrow \sqrt{144} = 12$
$6^2 = 36 \rightarrow \sqrt{36} = 6$	$13^2 = 169 \rightarrow \sqrt{169} = 13$

---

3. Order of Operations

When algebraic expressions contain numerous operations, it is important to evaluate the operations in the proper order. Parentheses ( ), brackets [ ], and braces { } are used for grouping numbers and algebraic expressions. It is important to recognize that operations must be done within parentheses and other grouping symbols first. Other grouping symbols include absolute value bars, radical signs, and fraction bars.

Answers

5. 9　**6.** 10

7. 1　**8.** $\dfrac{3}{5}$

Applying the Order of Operations

Step 1 Simplify expressions within parentheses and other grouping symbols first. These include absolute value bars, fraction bars, and radicals. If imbedded parentheses are present, start with the innermost parentheses.

Step 2 Evaluate expressions involving exponents, radicals, and absolute values.

Step 3 Perform multiplication or division in the order that they occur from left to right.

Step 4 Perform addition or subtraction in the order that they occur from left to right.

Example 3 Applying the Order of Operations

Simplify the expressions.

a. $17 - 3 \cdot 2 + 2^2$ **b.** $\dfrac{1}{2}\left(\dfrac{5}{6} - \dfrac{3}{4}\right)$

Solution:

a. $17 - 3 \cdot 2 + 2^2$

$= 17 - 3 \cdot 2 + 4$ Simplify exponents.

$= 17 - 6 + 4$ Multiply before adding or subtracting.

$= 11 + 4$ Add or subtract from left to right.

$= 15$

b. $\dfrac{1}{2}\left(\dfrac{5}{6} - \dfrac{3}{4}\right)$ Subtract fractions within the parentheses.

$= \dfrac{1}{2}\left(\dfrac{10}{12} - \dfrac{9}{12}\right)$ The least common denominator is 12.

$= \dfrac{1}{2}\left(\dfrac{1}{12}\right)$

$= \dfrac{1}{24}$ Multiply fractions.

Skill Practice

Simplify the expressions.

9. $14 - 3 \cdot 2 + 3^2$

10. $\dfrac{13}{4} - \dfrac{1}{4}(10 - 2)$

Answers

9. 17   **10.** $\dfrac{5}{4}$

Skill Practice

Simplify the expressions.

11. $1 + 2 \cdot 3^2 \div 6$

12. $|-20| - \sqrt{20 - 4}$

13. $60 - 5[(7 - 4) + 2^2]$

Example 4 **Applying the Order of Operations**

Simplify the expressions.

a. $25 - 12 \div 3 \cdot 4$

b. $6.2 - |-2.1| + \sqrt{16 + 9}$

c. $28 - 2[(6 - 3)^2 + 4]$

Solution:

Avoiding Mistakes

In Example 4(a), division is performed before multiplication because it occurs first as we read from left to right.

a. $25 - 12 \div 3 \cdot 4$ Multiply or divide in order from left to right.

$= 25 - 4 \cdot 4$ Notice that the operation $12 \div 3$ is performed first (not $3 \cdot 4$).

$= 25 - 16$ Multiply $4 \cdot 4$ before subtracting.

$= 9$ Subtract.

b. $6.2 - |-2.1| + \sqrt{16 + 9}$

$= 6.2 - |-2.1| + \sqrt{25}$ Simplify within the square root.

$= 6.2 - (2.1) + 5$ Simplify the absolute value and square root.

$= 4.1 + 5$ Add or subtract from left to right.

$= 9.1$ Add.

c. $28 - 2[(6 - 3)^2 + 4]$

$= 28 - 2[(3)^2 + 4]$ Simplify within the inner parentheses first.

$= 28 - 2[(9) + 4]$ Simplify exponents.

$= 28 - 2[13]$ Add within the square brackets.

$= 28 - 26$ Multiply before subtracting.

$= 2$ Subtract.

Skill Practice

Simplify the expression.

14. $\dfrac{60 - 3^2 \cdot 2}{3 + 8 \div 2}$

Example 5 **Applying the Order of Operations**

Simplify the expression. $\dfrac{32 + 8 \div 2}{2 \cdot 3^2}$

Solution:

$\dfrac{32 + 8 \div 2}{2 \cdot 3^2}$ In this expression, the fraction bar acts as a grouping symbol.

$= \dfrac{32 + 4}{2 \cdot 9}$ First, simplify the expressions above and below the fraction bar using order of operations.

$= \dfrac{36}{18}$ The last step is to simplify the fraction.

$= 2$

Answers

11. 4   **12.** 16

13. 25   **14.** 6

4. Translations

Algebra is a powerful tool used in science, business, economics, and many day-to-day applications. To apply algebra to a real-world application, we need the important skill of translating an English phrase to a mathematical expression. Table 1-3 summarizes commonly used phrases and expressions.

Table 1-3

Operation	Symbols	Translation
Addition	$a + b$	**sum** of a and b a plus b b added to a b more than a a increased by b the total of a and b
Subtraction	$a - b$	**difference** of a and b a minus b b subtracted from a a decreased by b b less than a a less b
Multiplication	$a \times b, a \cdot b, a(b), (a)b, (a)(b), ab$ (*Note:* We rarely use the notation $a \times b$ because the symbol, $\times$, might be confused with the variable, x.)	**product** of a and b a times b a multiplied by b
Division	$a \div b, \dfrac{a}{b}, a/b, b\overline{)a}$	**quotient** of a and b a divided by b b divided into a ratio of a and b a over b a per b

Example 6   **Writing an English Phrase as an Algebraic Expression**

Translate each English phrase to an algebraic expression.

a. The quotient of x and 5

b. The difference of p and the square root of q

c. Seven less than n

d. Seven less n

e. Eight more than the absolute value of w

f. x subtracted from 18

Skill Practice

Translate each English phrase to an algebraic expression.

15. The product of 6 and y

16. The difference of the square root of t and 7

17. Twelve less than x

18. Twelve less x

19. One more than two times x

20. Five subtracted from the absolute value of w

Answers

15. $6y$ **16.** $\sqrt{t} - 7$

17. $x - 12$ **18.** $12 - x$

19. $2x + 1$ **20.** $|w| - 5$

Solution:

a. $\dfrac{x}{5}$ or $x \div 5$ The quotient of x and 5

b. $p - \sqrt{q}$ The difference of p and the square root of q

c. $n - 7$ Seven less than n

d. $7 - n$ Seven less n

e. $|w| + 8$ Eight more than the absolute value of w

f. $18 - x$ x subtracted from 18

> **Avoiding Mistakes**
>
> Recall that "a less than b" is translated as $b - a$. Therefore, the statement "seven less than n" must be translated as $n - 7$, not $7 - n$.

Example 7   Writing an English Phrase as an Algebraic Expression

Translate each English phrase into an algebraic expression. Then evaluate the expression for $a = 6$, $b = 4$, and $c = 20$.

a. The product of a and the square root of b

b. Twice the sum of b and c

c. The difference of twice a and b

Solution:

a. The product of a and the square root of b

$a\sqrt{b}$

$= (\ )\sqrt{(\ )}$ Use parentheses to substitute a number for a variable.

$= (6)\sqrt{(4)}$ Substitute $a = 6$ and $b = 4$.

$= 6 \cdot 2$ Simplify the radical first.

$= 12$ Multiply.

b. Twice the sum of b and c

$2(b + c)$ To compute "twice the sum of b and c," it is necessary to take the sum first and then multiply by 2. To ensure the proper order, the sum of b and c must be enclosed in parentheses. The proper translation is $2(b + c)$.

$= 2((\ ) + (\ ))$ Use parentheses to substitute a number for a variable.

$= 2((4) + (20))$ Substitute $b = 4$ and $c = 20$.

$= 2(24)$ Simplify within the parentheses first.

$= 48$ Multiply.

c. The difference of twice a and b

$2a - b$

$= 2(\ ) - (\ )$ Use parentheses to substitute a number for a variable.

$= 2(6) - (4)$ Substitute $a = 6$ and $b = 4$.

$= 12 - 4$ Multiply first.

$= 8$ Subtract.

Calculator Connections

Topic: Evaluating Exponential Expressions on a Calculator

On a calculator, we enter exponents greater than the second power by using the key labeled $\boxed{y^x}$ or $\boxed{\wedge}$. For example, evaluate 2^4 and 10^6:

Scientific Calculator:

Enter: 2 $\boxed{y^x}$ 4 $\boxed{=}$ Result: $\boxed{16}$

Enter: 10 $\boxed{y^x}$ 6 $\boxed{=}$ Result: $\boxed{1000000}$

Graphing Calculator:

```
2^4
              16
10^6
         1000000
```

Topic: Applying the Order of Operations on a Calculator

Most calculators also have the capability to enter several operations at once. However, it is important to note that fraction bars and radicals require user-defined parentheses to ensure that the proper order of operations is followed. For example, evaluate the following expressions on a calculator:

a. $130 - 2(5 - 1)^3$ **b.** $\dfrac{18 - 2}{11 - 9}$ **c.** $\sqrt{25 - 9}$

Scientific Calculator:

Enter: 130 $\boxed{-}$ 2 $\boxed{\times}$ $\boxed{(}$ 5 $\boxed{-}$ 1 $\boxed{)}$ $\boxed{y^x}$ 3 $\boxed{=}$ Result: $\boxed{2}$

Enter: $\boxed{(}$ 18 $\boxed{-}$ 2 $\boxed{)}$ $\boxed{\div}$ $\boxed{(}$ 11 $\boxed{-}$ 9 $\boxed{)}$ $\boxed{=}$ Result: $\boxed{8}$

Enter: $\boxed{(}$ 25 $\boxed{-}$ 9 $\boxed{)}$ $\boxed{\sqrt{}}$ Result: $\boxed{4}$

Graphing Calculator:

```
130-2*(5-1)^3
               2
(18-2)/(11-9)
               8
√(25-9)
               4
```

Calculator Exercises

Simplify the expression without the use of a calculator. Then enter the expression into the calculator to verify your answer.

1. $\dfrac{4 + 6}{8 - 3}$ **2.** $110 - 5(2 + 1) - 4$ **3.** $100 - 2(5 - 3)^3$

4. $3 + (4 - 1)^2$ **5.** $(12 - 6 + 1)^2$ **6.** $3 \cdot 8 - \sqrt{32 + 2^2}$

7. $\sqrt{18 - 2}$ **8.** $(4 \cdot 3 - 3 \cdot 3)^3$ **9.** $\dfrac{20 - 3^2}{26 - 2^2}$

Section 1.2 Practice Exercises

Study Skills Exercise

Sometimes you may run into a problem with homework or you find that you are having trouble keeping up with the pace of the class. A tutor can be a good resource.

a. Does your college offer tutoring?

b. Is it free?

c. Where would you go to sign up for a tutor?

Vocabulary and Key Concepts

1. a. Fill in the blanks with the words *sum, difference, product,* or *quotient.*
The _____ of 10 and 2 is 5. The _____ of 10 and 2 is 20.
The _____ of 10 and 2 is 12. The _____ of 10 and 2 is 8.

b. In the expression b^n, the value b is called the _____ and n is called the _____ or _____.

c. The expression _____ is read as "eight, squared."

d. The expression _____ is read as "p to the fourth power."

e. The symbol $\sqrt{}$ is called a _____ sign and is used to find the principal _____ root of a nonnegative real number.

f. The set of rules that tell us the order in which to perform operations to simplify an algebraic expression is called the _____.

Review Exercises

2. Which of the following are rational numbers? $\left\{-4, 5.\overline{6}, \sqrt{29}, 0, \pi, 4.02, \dfrac{7}{9}\right\}$

3. Evaluate. $|-56|$

4. Evaluate. $|9.2|$

5. Evaluate. $-|-14|$

6. Evaluate. $|0|$

7. Find the opposite of 19.

8. Find the opposite of -34.2.

Concept 1: Exponential Expressions

For Exercises 9–14, write each of the products using exponents.

9. $\dfrac{1}{6} \cdot \dfrac{1}{6} \cdot \dfrac{1}{6} \cdot \dfrac{1}{6}$

10. $10 \cdot 10 \cdot 10 \cdot 10 \cdot 10 \cdot 10$

11. $a \cdot a \cdot a \cdot b \cdot b$

12. $7 \cdot x \cdot x \cdot y \cdot y$

13. $5c \cdot 5c \cdot 5c \cdot 5c \cdot 5c$

14. $3 \cdot w \cdot z \cdot z \cdot z \cdot z$

15. a. For the expression $5x^3$, what is the base for the exponent 3?

b. Does 5 have an exponent? If so, what is it?

16. a. For the expression $2y^4$, what is the base for the exponent 4?

b. Does 2 have an exponent? If so, what is it?

For Exercises 17–24, write each expression in expanded form using the definition of an exponent.

17. x^3 **18.** y^4 **19.** $(2b)^3$ **20.** $(8c)^2$

21. $10y^5$ **22.** x^2y^3 **23.** $2wz^2$ **24.** $3a^3b$

For Exercises 25–32, simplify the expressions. **(See Example 1.)**

25. 6^2 **26.** 5^3 **27.** $\left(\dfrac{1}{7}\right)^2$ **28.** $\left(\dfrac{1}{2}\right)^5$

29. $(0.2)^3$ **30.** $(0.8)^2$ **31.** 2^6 **32.** 13^2

Concept 2: Square Roots

For Exercises 33–44, simplify the square roots. **(See Example 2.)**

33. $\sqrt{81}$ **34.** $\sqrt{64}$ **35.** $\sqrt{4}$ **36.** $\sqrt{9}$

37. $\sqrt{144}$ **38.** $\sqrt{49}$ **39.** $\sqrt{16}$ **40.** $\sqrt{36}$

41. $\sqrt{\dfrac{1}{9}}$ **42.** $\sqrt{\dfrac{1}{64}}$ **43.** $\sqrt{\dfrac{25}{81}}$ **44.** $\sqrt{\dfrac{49}{100}}$

Concept 3: Order of Operations

For Exercises 45–76, use the order of operations to simplify the expressions. **(See Examples 3–5.)**

45. $8 + 2 \cdot 6$ **46.** $7 + 3 \cdot 4$ **47.** $(8 + 2) \cdot 6$ **48.** $(7 + 3) \cdot 4$

49. $4 + 2 \div 2 \cdot 3 + 1$ **50.** $5 + 12 \div 2 \cdot 6 - 1$ **51.** $81 - 4 \cdot 3 + 3^2$ **52.** $100 - 25 \cdot 2 - 5^2$

53. $\dfrac{1}{4} \cdot \dfrac{2}{3} - \dfrac{1}{6}$ **54.** $\dfrac{3}{4} \cdot \dfrac{2}{3} + \dfrac{2}{3}$ **55.** $\left(\dfrac{11}{6} - \dfrac{3}{8}\right) \cdot \dfrac{4}{5}$ **56.** $\left(\dfrac{9}{8} - \dfrac{1}{3}\right) \cdot \dfrac{3}{4}$

57. $3[5 + 2(8 - 3)]$ **58.** $2[4 + 3(6 - 4)]$ **59.** $10 + |-6|$ **60.** $18 + |-3|$

61. $21 - |8 - 2|$ **62.** $12 - |6 - 1|$ **63.** $2^2 + \sqrt{9} \cdot 5$ **64.** $3^2 + \sqrt{16} \cdot 2$

65. $3 \cdot 5^2$ **66.** $10 \cdot 2^3$ **67.** $\sqrt{9 + 16} - 2$ **68.** $\sqrt{36 + 13} - 5$

69. $[4^2 \cdot (6 - 4) \div 8] + [7 \cdot (8 - 3)]$ **70.** $(18 \div \sqrt{4}) \cdot \{[(9^2 - 1) \div 2] - 15\}$

71. $48 - 13 \cdot 3 + [(50 - 7 \cdot 5) + 2]$ **72.** $80 \div 16 \cdot 2 + (6^2 - |-2|)$

73. $\dfrac{7 + 3(8 - 2)}{(7 + 3)(8 - 2)}$ **74.** $\dfrac{16 - 8 \div 4}{4 + 8 \div 4 - 2}$ **75.** $\dfrac{15 - 5(3 \cdot 2 - 4)}{10 - 2(4 \cdot 5 - 16)}$ **76.** $\dfrac{5(7 - 3) + 8(6 - 4)}{4[7 + 3(2 \cdot 9 - 8)]}$

77. A person's debt-to-income ratio is the sum of all monthly installment payments (credit cards, loans, etc.) divided by monthly take-home pay. This number is often considered when one is applying for a loan. Each month, Monica makes credit card payments of $52 and $20, a student loan payment of $65, and a payment for furniture of $43. Her monthly take-home pay is $1500.

   a. Determine Monica's debt-to-income ratio.

   b. To obtain a car loan, Monica's debt-to-income ratio must be less than 0.20. Does she meet this criteria?

78. Each month, Jared makes credit card payments of $115, $63, and $95. He also makes a student loan payment of $77 and another loan payment of $100. His monthly take-home pay is $2000.

    a. Use the definition given in Exercise 77 to determine Jared's debt-to-income ratio.

    b. To obtain a loan for a new home theater system his debt-to-income ratio must be less than 0.15. Does he meet this criteria?

79. The area of a rectangle is given by $A = \ell w$, where ℓ is the length of the rectangle and w is the width. Find the area for the rectangle shown.

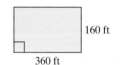

160 ft

80. The perimeter of a rectangle is given by $P = 2\ell + 2w$. Find the perimeter for the rectangle shown.

360 ft

81. The area of a trapezoid is given by $A = \frac{1}{2}(b_1 + b_2)h$, where b_1 and b_2 are the lengths of the two parallel sides and h is the height. A window is in the shape of a trapezoid. Find the area of the trapezoid with dimensions shown in the figure.

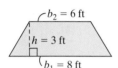

$b_2 = 6$ ft
$h = 3$ ft
$b_1 = 8$ ft

82. The volume of a rectangular solid is given by $V = \ell wh$, where ℓ is the length of the solid, w is the width, and h is the height. Find the volume of the box shown in the figure.

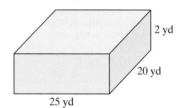

2 yd
20 yd
25 yd

Concept 4: Translations

For Exercises 83–94, translate each English phrase into an algebraic expression. **(See Example 6.)**

83. The product of 3 and x

84. The sum of b and 6

85. The quotient of x and 7

86. Four divided by k

87. The difference of 2 and a

88. Three subtracted from t

89. x more than twice y

90. Nine decreased by the product of 3 and p

91. Four times the sum of x and 12

92. Twice the difference of x and 3

93. Q less than 3

94. Fourteen less than t

For Exercises 95–102, translate the English phrase into an algebraic expression. Then evaluate the expression for $x = 4$, $y = 2$, and $z = 10$. **(See Example 7.)**

95. Two times y cubed

96. Three times z squared

97. The absolute value of the difference of z and 8

98. The absolute value of the difference of x and 3

99. The product of 5 and the square root of x

100. The square root of the difference of z and 1

101. The value x subtracted from the product of y and z

102. The difference of z and the product of x and y

Expanding Your Skills

For Exercises 103–106, use the order of operations to simplify the expressions.

103. $\dfrac{\sqrt{\frac{1}{9}} + \frac{2}{3}}{\sqrt{\frac{4}{25}} + \frac{3}{5}}$

104. $\dfrac{5 - \sqrt{9}}{\sqrt{\frac{4}{9}} + \frac{1}{3}}$

105. $\dfrac{|-2|}{|-10| - |2|}$

106. $\dfrac{|-4|^2}{2^2 + \sqrt{144}}$

107. Some students use the following common memorization device (mnemonic) to help them remember the order of operations: the acronym PEMDAS or **P**lease **E**xcuse **M**y **D**ear **A**unt **S**ally to remember **P**arentheses, **E**xponents, **M**ultiplication, **D**ivision, **A**ddition, and **S**ubtraction. The problem with this mnemonic is that it suggests that multiplication is done before division and similarly, it suggests that addition is performed before subtraction. Explain why following this acronym may give incorrect answers for the expressions

    a. $36 \div 4 \cdot 3$ **b.** $36 - 4 + 3$

108. If you use the acronym **P**lease **E**xcuse **M**y **D**ear **A**unt **S**ally to remember the order of operations, what must you keep in mind about the last four operations?

109. Explain why the acronym **P**lease **E**xcuse **D**r. **M**ichael **S**mith's **A**unt could also be used as a memory device for the order of operations.

Addition of Real Numbers   Section 1.3

1. Addition of Real Numbers and the Number Line

Adding real numbers can be visualized on the number line. To do so, we locate the first addend on the number line. Then to add a positive number, we move to the right on the number line. To add a negative number, we move to the left on the number line. The following example may help to illustrate the process.

On a winter day in Detroit, suppose the temperature starts out at 5 degrees Fahrenheit (5°F) at noon, and then drops 12° two hours later when a cold front passes through. The resulting temperature can be represented by the expression $5° + (-12°)$. On the number line, start at 5 and count 12 units to the left (Figure 1-3). The resulting temperature at 2:00 P.M. is −7°F.

Concepts

1. **Addition of Real Numbers and the Number Line**
2. **Addition of Real Numbers**
3. **Translations**
4. **Applications Involving Addition of Real Numbers**

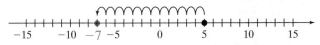

Figure 1-3

Example 1   **Using the Number Line to Add Real Numbers**

Use the number line to add the numbers.

    a. $-5 + 2$ **b.** $-1 + (-4)$ **c.** $7 + (-4)$

Solution:

a. $-5 + 2 = -3$

Start at −5, and count 2 units to the right.

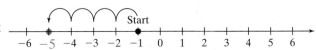

b. $-1 + (-4) = -5$

Start at −1, and count 4 units to the left.

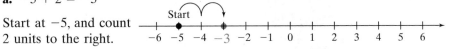

c. $7 + (-4) = 3$

Start at 7, and count 4 units to the left.

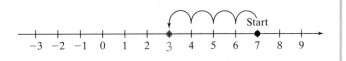

Skill Practice

Use the number line to add the numbers.

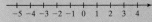

1. $-2 + 4$
2. $-2 + (-3)$
3. $5 + (-6)$

TIP: Note that we move to the left when we add a negative number, and we move to the right when we add a positive number.

Answers

1. 2   **2.** −5   **3.** −1

2. Addition of Real Numbers

When adding large numbers or numbers that involve fractions or decimals, counting units on the number line can be cumbersome. Study the following example to determine a pattern for adding two numbers with the *same* sign.

$1 + 4 = 5$

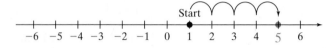

$-1 + (-4) = -5$

Adding Numbers with the *Same* Sign

To add two numbers with the *same* sign, add their absolute values and apply the common sign.

Skill Practice

Add the numbers.

4. $-5 + (-25)$

5. $-14.8 + (-9.7)$

6. $-\dfrac{1}{2} + \left(-\dfrac{5}{8}\right)$

 Example 2 **Adding Real Numbers with the Same Sign**

Add.

a. $-12 + (-14)$ **b.** $-8.8 + (-3.7)$ **c.** $-\dfrac{4}{3} + \left(-\dfrac{6}{7}\right)$

Solution:

a. $-12 + (-14)$

$= -(12 + 14)$

$\underset{\text{common sign is negative}}{\big\uparrow}$

$= -26$

First find the absolute value of the addends. $|-12| = 12$ and $|-14| = 14$.

Add their absolute values and apply the common sign (in this case, the common sign is negative).

The sum is -26.

b. $-8.8 + (-3.7)$

$= -(8.8 + 3.7)$

$\underset{\text{common sign is negative}}{\big\uparrow}$

$= -12.5$

First find the absolute value of the addends. $|-8.8| = 8.8$ and $|-3.7| = 3.7$.

Add their absolute values and apply the common sign (in this case, the common sign is negative).

The sum is -12.5.

Answers

4. -30 **5.** -24.5 **6.** $-\dfrac{9}{8}$

c. $-\dfrac{4}{3} + \left(-\dfrac{6}{7}\right)$ The least common denominator (LCD) is 21.

$= -\dfrac{4 \cdot 7}{3 \cdot 7} + \left(-\dfrac{6 \cdot 3}{7 \cdot 3}\right)$ Write each fraction with the LCD.

$= -\dfrac{28}{21} + \left(-\dfrac{18}{21}\right)$ Find the absolute value of the addends.

$$\left|-\dfrac{28}{21}\right| = \dfrac{28}{21} \text{ and } \left|-\dfrac{18}{21}\right| = \dfrac{18}{21}.$$

$= -\left(\dfrac{28}{21} + \dfrac{18}{21}\right)$ Add their absolute values and apply the common sign (in this case, the common sign is negative).

common sign is negative

$= -\dfrac{46}{21}$ The sum is $-\dfrac{46}{21}$.

Study the following example to determine a pattern for adding two numbers with *different* signs.

$1 + (-4) = -3$

$-1 + 4 = 3$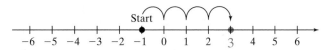

Adding Numbers with *Different* Signs

To add two numbers with *different* signs, subtract the smaller absolute value from the larger absolute value. Then apply the sign of the number having the larger absolute value.

Example 3 **Adding Real Numbers with Different Signs**

Add. **a.** $12 + (-17)$ **b.** $-8 + 8$

Solution:

a. $12 + (-17)$ First find the absolute value of the addends.
$|12| = 12$ and $|-17| = 17$.

The absolute value of -17 is greater than the absolute value of 12. Therefore, the sum is negative.

$= -(17 - 12)$ Next, subtract the smaller absolute value from the larger absolute value.

Apply the sign of the number with the larger absolute value.

$= -5$

b. $-8 + 8$ First find the absolute value of the addends.
$|-8| = 8$ and $|8| = 8$.

$= (8 - 8)$ The absolute values are equal. Therefore, their difference is 0. The number zero is neither positive nor negative.

$= 0$

Example 4   Adding Real Numbers with Different Signs

Add.   **a.** $-10.6 + 20.4$ **b.** $\dfrac{2}{15} + \left(-\dfrac{4}{5}\right)$

Solution:

a. $-10.6 + 20.4$ First find the absolute value of the addends. $|-10.6| = 10.6$ and $|20.4| = 20.4$.

The absolute value of 20.4 is greater than the absolute value of -10.6. Therefore, the sum is positive.

$= +(20.4 - 10.6)$ Next, subtract the smaller absolute value from the larger absolute value.

Apply the sign of the number with the larger absolute value.

$= 9.8$

b. $\dfrac{2}{15} + \left(-\dfrac{4}{5}\right)$ The least common denominator is 15.

$= \dfrac{2}{15} + \left(-\dfrac{4 \cdot 3}{5 \cdot 3}\right)$ Write each fraction with the LCD.

$= \dfrac{2}{15} + \left(-\dfrac{12}{15}\right)$ Find the absolute value of the addends.

$\left|\dfrac{2}{15}\right| = \dfrac{2}{15}$ and $\left|-\dfrac{12}{15}\right| = \dfrac{12}{15}$.

The absolute value of $-\dfrac{12}{15}$ is greater than the absolute value of $\dfrac{2}{15}$. Therefore, the sum is negative.

$= -\left(\dfrac{12}{15} - \dfrac{2}{15}\right)$ Next, subtract the smaller absolute value from the larger absolute value.

Apply the sign of the number with the larger absolute value.

$= -\dfrac{10}{15}$ Subtract.

$= -\dfrac{2}{3}$ Simplify to lowest terms.

3. Translations

Example 5   Translating Expressions Involving the Addition of Real Numbers

Translate each English phrase into an algebraic expression. Then simplify the result.

a. The sum of -12, -8, 9, and -1

b. Negative three-tenths added to $-\frac{7}{8}$

c. The sum of -12 and its opposite

Answers

9. 9.2   **10.** $-\dfrac{1}{2}$

Solution:

a. The sum of $-12, -8, 9,$ and -1

$$\underbrace{-12 + (-8)} + 9 + (-1)$$

$$= \underbrace{-20 + 9} + (-1) \qquad \text{Apply order of operations by adding from left to right.}$$

$$= \qquad \underbrace{-11 + (-1)}$$

$$= \qquad -12$$

b. Negative three-tenths added to $-\frac{7}{8}$

$$-\frac{7}{8} + \left(-\frac{3}{10}\right)$$

$$= -\frac{35}{40} + \left(-\frac{12}{40}\right) \qquad \text{The common denominator is 40.}$$

$$= -\frac{47}{40} \qquad \text{The numbers have the same signs. Add their absolute values and keep the common sign.}$$

$$-\left(\frac{35}{40} + \frac{12}{40}\right)$$

c. The sum of -12 and its opposite

$$-12 + (12)$$

$$= 0 \qquad \text{Add.}$$

TIP: The sum of any number and its opposite is 0.

4. Applications Involving Addition of Real Numbers

Example 6 Adding Real Numbers in Applications

a. It is common for newborn infants to fluctuate in weight. Elise and Benjamin's baby lost 7 oz the first week and gained 10 oz the second week. Write a mathematical expression to describe this situation and then simplify the result.

b. A student has $120 in her checking account. After depositing her paycheck of $215, she writes a check for $255 to cover her portion of the rent and another check for $294 to cover her car payment. Write a mathematical expression to describe this situation and then simplify the result.

Solution:

a. $-7 + 10$ A loss of 7 oz can be interpreted as -7 oz.

$\quad = 3$ The infant had a net gain of 3 oz.

b. $\underbrace{120 + 215} + (-255) + (-294)$ Writing a check is equivalent to adding a negative amount to the bank account.

$$= \underbrace{335 + (-255)} + (-294) \qquad \text{Use the order of operations. Add from left to right.}$$

$$= \qquad 80 + (-294)$$

$$= \qquad -214 \qquad \text{The student has overdrawn her account by \$214.}$$

Section 1.3   Practice Exercises

Study Skills Exercise

It is very important to attend class every day. Math is cumulative in nature, and you must master the material learned in the previous class to understand today's lesson. Because this is so important, many instructors have an attendance policy that may affect your final grade. Write down the attendance policy for your class.

Vocabulary and Key Concepts

1. a. If a and b are both negative, then $a + b$ will be (choose one: positive or negative).

    b. If a and b have different signs, and if $|b| > |a|$, then the sum will have the same sign as (choose one: a or b).

Review Exercises

Plot the points in set A on a number line. Then for Exercises 2–7 place the appropriate inequality ($<$, $>$) between the numbers.

$$A = \left\{ -2, \frac{3}{4}, -\frac{5}{2}, 3, \frac{9}{2}, 1.6, 0 \right\}$$

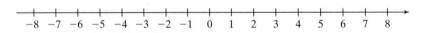

2. $-2 \,\square\, 0$

3. $\dfrac{9}{2} \,\square\, \dfrac{3}{4}$

4. $-2 \,\square\, -\dfrac{5}{2}$

5. $0 \,\square\, -\dfrac{5}{2}$

6. $\dfrac{3}{4} \,\square\, 1.6$

7. $\dfrac{3}{4} \,\square\, -\dfrac{5}{2}$

8. Evaluate the expressions.

    a. $-(-8)$ **b.** $-|-8|$

Concept 1: Addition of Real Numbers and the Number Line

For Exercises 9–16, add the numbers using the number line. **(See Example 1.)**

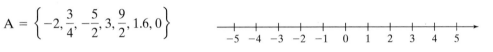

9. $-2 + (-4)$

10. $-3 + (-5)$

11. $-7 + 10$

12. $-2 + 9$

13. $6 + (-3)$

14. $8 + (-2)$

15. $2 + (-5)$

16. $7 + (-3)$

Concept 2: Addition of Real Numbers

For Exercises 17–70, add. **(See Examples 2–4.)**

 17. $-19 + 2$

18. $-25 + 18$

19. $-4 + 11$

20. $-3 + 9$

 21. $-16 + (-3)$

22. $-12 + (-23)$

23. $-2 + (-21)$

24. $-13 + (-1)$

25. $0 + (-5)$

26. $0 + (-4)$

27. $-3 + 0$

28. $-8 + 0$

29. $-16 + 16$

30. $11 + (-11)$

31. $41 + (-41)$

32. $-15 + 15$

33. $4 + (-9)$

34. $6 + (-9)$

35. $7 + (-2) + (-8)$

36. $2 + (-3) + (-6)$

37. $-17 + (-3) + 20$

38. $-9 + (-6) + 15$

39. $-3 + (-8) + (-12)$

40. $-8 + (-2) + (-13)$

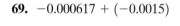 **41.** $-42 + (-3) + 45 + (-6)$

42. $36 + (-3) + (-8) + (-25)$

43. $-5 + (-3) + (-7) + 4 + 8$

44. $-13 + (-1) + 5 + 2 + (-20)$

45. $23.81 + (-2.51)$ **46.** $-9.23 + 10.53$

47. $-\dfrac{2}{7} + \dfrac{1}{14}$ **48.** $-\dfrac{1}{8} + \dfrac{5}{16}$

49. $\dfrac{2}{3} + \left(-\dfrac{5}{6}\right)$ **50.** $\dfrac{1}{2} + \left(-\dfrac{3}{4}\right)$ **51.** $-\dfrac{7}{8} + \left(-\dfrac{1}{16}\right)$ **52.** $-\dfrac{1}{9} + \left(-\dfrac{4}{3}\right)$

53. $-\dfrac{1}{4} + \dfrac{3}{10}$ **54.** $-\dfrac{7}{6} + \dfrac{7}{8}$ **55.** $-2.1 + \left(-\dfrac{3}{10}\right)$ **56.** $-8.3 + \left(-\dfrac{9}{10}\right)$

57. $\dfrac{3}{4} + (-0.5)$ **58.** $-\dfrac{3}{2} + 0.45$ **59.** $8.23 + (-8.23)$ **60.** $-7.5 + 7.5$

61. $-\dfrac{7}{8} + 0$ **62.** $0 + \left(-\dfrac{21}{22}\right)$ **63.** $-\dfrac{3}{2} + \left(-\dfrac{1}{3}\right) + \dfrac{5}{6}$ **64.** $-\dfrac{7}{8} + \dfrac{7}{6} + \dfrac{7}{12}$

65. $-\dfrac{2}{3} + \left(-\dfrac{1}{9}\right) + 2$ **66.** $-\dfrac{1}{4} + \left(-\dfrac{3}{2}\right) + 2$ **67.** $-47.36 + 24.28$ **68.** $-0.015 + (0.0026)$

69. $-0.000617 + (-0.0015)$

70. $-5315.26 + (-314.89)$

71. State the rule for adding two numbers with different signs.

72. State the rule for adding two numbers with the same signs.

For Exercises 73–80, evaluate the expression for $x = -3$, $y = -2$, and $z = 16$.

73. $x + y + \sqrt{z}$ **74.** $2z + x + y$ **75.** $y + 3\sqrt{z}$ **76.** $-\sqrt{z} + y$

77. $|x| + |y|$ **78.** $z + x + |y|$ **79.** $-x + y$ **80.** $x + (-y) + z$

Concept 3: Translations

For Exercises 81–90, translate the English phrase into an algebraic expression. Then simplify the result.
(See Example 5.)

81. The sum of -6 and -10

82. The sum of -3 and 5

83. Negative three increased by 8

84. Twenty-one increased by 4

85. Seventeen more than -21

86. Twenty-four more than -7

87. Three times the sum of -14 and 20

88. Two times the sum of 6 and -10

89. Five more than the sum of -7 and -2

90. Negative six more than the sum of 4 and -1

Concept 4: Applications Involving Addition of Real Numbers

91. The temperature in Minneapolis, Minnesota, began at $-5°F$ (5° below zero) at 6:00 A.M. By noon the temperature had risen 13°, and by the end of the day, the temperature had dropped 11° from its noontime high. Write an expression using addition that describes the change in temperatures during the day. Then evaluate the expression to give the temperature at the end of the day.

92. The temperature in Toronto, Ontario, Canada, began at $4°F$. A cold front went through at noon, and the temperature dropped 9°. By 4:00 P.M. the temperature had risen 2° from its noontime low. Write an expression using addition that describes the changes in temperature during the day. Then evaluate the expression to give the temperature at the end of the day.

93. For 4 months, Amara monitored her weight loss or gain. Her records showed that she lost 8 lb, gained 1 lb, gained 2 lb, and lost 5 lb. Write an expression using addition that describes Amara's total loss or gain and evaluate the expression. Interpret the result. (See Example 6.)

94. Alan just started an online business. His profit/loss records for the past 5 months show that he had a profit of $200, a profit of $750, a loss of $340, a loss of $290, and a profit of $900. Write an expression using addition that describes Alan's total profit or loss and evaluate the expression. Interpret the result.

95. Yoshima has $52.23 in her checking account. She writes a check for groceries for $52.95.

   a. Write an addition problem that expresses Yoshima's transaction.

   b. Is Yoshima's account overdrawn?

96. Mohammad has $40.02 in his checking account. He writes a check for a pair of shoes for $40.96.

   a. Write an addition problem that expresses Mohammad's transaction.

   b. Is Mohammad's account overdrawn?

97. In the game show *Jeopardy*, a contestant responds to six questions with the following outcomes:

$$\$100, \$200, -\$500, \$300, \$100, -\$200$$

   a. Write an expression using addition to describe the contestant's scoring activity.

   b. Evaluate the expression from part (a) to determine the contestant's final outcome.

98. A company that has been in business for 5 yr has the following profit and loss record.

   a. Write an expression using addition to describe the company's profit/loss activity.

   b. Evaluate the expression from part (a) to determine the company's net profit or loss.

Year	Profit/Loss ($)
1	−50,000
2	−32,000
3	−5,000
4	13,000
5	26,000

Subtraction of Real Numbers

1. Subtraction of Real Numbers

In Section 1.3, we learned the rules for adding real numbers. Subtraction of real numbers is defined in terms of the addition process. For example, consider the following subtraction problem and the corresponding addition problem:

$$6 - 4 = 2 \quad \Leftrightarrow \quad 6 + (-4) = 2$$

In each case, we start at 6 on the number line and move to the left 4 units. That is, adding the opposite of 4 produces the same result as subtracting 4. This is true in general. To subtract two real numbers, add the opposite of the second number to the first number.

Concepts

1. Subtraction of Real Numbers
2. Translations
3. Applications Involving Subtraction
4. Applying the Order of Operations

Subtracting Real Numbers
If a and b are real numbers, then $a - b = a + (-b)$.

$$\left. \begin{array}{l} 10 - 4 = 10 + (-4) = 6 \\ -10 - 4 = -10 + (-4) = -14 \end{array} \right\}$$ Subtracting 4 is the same as adding -4.

$$\left. \begin{array}{l} 10 - (-4) = 10 + (4) = 14 \\ -10 - (-4) = -10 + (4) = -6 \end{array} \right\}$$ Subtracting -4 is the same as adding 4.

Example 1   **Subtracting Integers**

Subtract the numbers.

  a. $4 - (-9)$ **b.** $-6 - 9$ **c.** $-11 - (-5)$ **d.** $7 - 10$

Solution:

a. $4 - (-9)$

    $= 4 + (9) = 13$

             Take the opposite of -9.
Change subtraction to addition.

b. $-6 - 9$

    $= -6 + (-9) = -15$

             Take the opposite of 9.
Change subtraction to addition.

c. $-11 - (-5)$

    $= -11 + (5) = -6$

             Take the opposite of -5.
Change subtraction to addition.

d. $7 - 10$

    $= 7 + (-10) = -3$

             Take the opposite of 10.
Change subtraction to addition.

Skill Practice

Subtract.
1. $1 - (-3)$
2. $-2 - 2$
3. $-6 - (-11)$
4. $8 - 15$

Answers
1. 4   **2.** -4 **3.** 5   **4.** -7

Example 2 Subtracting Real Numbers

Subtract.

a. $\dfrac{3}{20} - \left(-\dfrac{4}{15}\right)$ **b.** $-2.3 - 6.04$

Solution:

a. $\dfrac{3}{20} - \left(-\dfrac{4}{15}\right)$ The least common denominator is 60.

$= \dfrac{9}{60} - \left(-\dfrac{16}{60}\right)$ Write equivalent fractions with the LCD.

$= \dfrac{9}{60} + \left(\dfrac{16}{60}\right)$ Rewrite subtraction in terms of addition.

$= \dfrac{25}{60}$ Add.

$= \dfrac{5}{12}$ Simplify by dividing the numerator and denominator by the GCF of 5.

b. $-2.3 - 6.04$

$= -2.3 + (-6.04)$ Rewrite subtraction in terms of addition.

$= -8.34$ Add.

2. Translations

Example 3 Translating Expressions Involving Subtraction

Write an algebraic expression for each English phrase and then simplify the result.

a. The difference of -7 and -5

b. 12.4 subtracted from -4.7

c. -24 decreased by the sum of -10 and 13

d. Seven-fourths less than one-third

Solution:

a. The difference of -7 and -5

$-7 - (-5)$

$= -7 + (5)$ Rewrite subtraction in terms of addition.

$= -2$ Simplify.

Answers

5. $\dfrac{3}{4}$ **6.** -9 **7.** $-10 - 8; -18$

8. $-8.2 - (-7.2); -1$

9. $(-2 - 3) + 10; 5$

10. $\dfrac{2}{5} - \dfrac{4}{3}; -\dfrac{14}{15}$

b. 12.4 subtracted from -4.7

$-4.7 - 12.4$

$\quad = -4.7 + (-12.4)$ Rewrite subtraction in terms of addition.

$\quad = -17.1$ Simplify.

> **TIP:** Recall that "b subtracted from a" is translated as $a - b$. In Example 3(b), -4.7 is written first and then 12.4.

c. -24 decreased by the sum of -10 and 13

$-24 - (-10 + 13)$

$\quad = -24 - (3)$ Simplify inside parentheses.

$\quad = -24 + (-3)$ Rewrite subtraction in terms of addition.

$\quad = -27$ Simplify.

> **Avoiding Mistakes**
>
> Parentheses must be used around the sum of -10 and 13 so that -24 is decreased by the entire quantity $(-10 + 13)$.

d. Seven-fourths less than one-third

$\dfrac{1}{3} - \dfrac{7}{4}$

$\quad = \dfrac{1}{3} + \left(-\dfrac{7}{4}\right)$ Rewrite subtraction in terms of addition.

$\quad = \dfrac{4}{12} + \left(-\dfrac{21}{12}\right)$ The common denominator is 12.

$\quad = -\dfrac{17}{12} \quad \text{or} \quad -1\dfrac{5}{12}$

3. Applications Involving Subtraction

Example 4 **Using Subtraction of Real Numbers in an Application**

During one of his turns on *Jeopardy*, Harold selected the category "Show Tunes." He got the \$200, \$600, and \$1000 questions correct, but he got the \$400 and \$800 questions incorrect. Write an expression that determines Harold's score. Then simplify the expression to find his total winnings for that category.

Solution:

$200 + 600 + 1000 - 400 - 800$

$\quad = 200 + 600 + 1000 + (-400) + (-800)$ We can add the positive numbers together, and the negative numbers together.

$\quad = 1800 + (-1200)$ Then add the two results.

$\quad = 600$ Harold won \$600.

> **Skill Practice**
>
> **11.** During Harold's first round on *Jeopardy*, he got the \$100, \$200, and \$400 questions correct but he got the \$300 and \$500 questions incorrect. Determine Harold's score for this round.

Answer
11. -100, Harold lost \$100.

Skill Practice

12. The record high temperature for the state of Montana occurred in 1937 and was 117°F. The record low occurred in 1954 and was −70°F. Find the difference between the highest and lowest temperatures.

Example 5   Using Subtraction of Real Numbers in an Application

The highest recorded temperature in North America was 134°F, recorded on July 10, 1913, in Death Valley, California. The lowest temperature of −81°F was recorded on February 3, 1947, in Snag, Yukon, Canada.

    Find the difference between the highest and lowest recorded temperatures in North America.

Solution:

$$134 - (-81)$$

$$= 134 + (81) \qquad \text{Rewrite subtraction in terms of addition.}$$

$$= 215 \qquad\qquad \text{Add.}$$

The difference between the highest and lowest temperatures is 215°F.

4. Applying the Order of Operations

Example 6   Applying the Order of Operations

Simplify the expressions.

Skill Practice

Simplify the expressions.

13. $-11 - \{8 - [2 - (-3)]\}$

14. $(12 - 5)^2 + \sqrt{4 - (-21)}$

a. $-6 + \{10 - [7 - (-4)]\}$ **b.** $5 - \sqrt{35 - (-14)} - 2$

Solution:

a. $-6 + \{10 - [7 - (-4)]\}$ Simplify inside the inner brackets first.

$$= -6 + \{10 - [7 + (4)]\} \qquad \text{Rewrite subtraction in terms of addition.}$$

$$= -6 + \{10 - (11)\} \qquad \text{Simplify the expression inside brackets.}$$

$$= -6 + \{10 + (-11)\} \qquad \text{Rewrite subtraction in terms of addition.}$$

$$= -6 + (-1) \qquad \text{Simplify inside the braces.}$$

$$= -7 \qquad \text{Add.}$$

b. $5 - \sqrt{35 - (-14)} - 2$ Simplify inside the radical first.

$$= 5 - \sqrt{35 + (14)} - 2 \qquad \text{Rewrite subtraction in terms of addition.}$$

$$= 5 - \sqrt{49} - 2 \qquad \text{Add within the radical sign.}$$

$$= 5 - 7 - 2 \qquad \text{Simplify the radical.}$$

$$= 5 + (-7) + (-2) \qquad \text{Rewrite subtraction in terms of addition.}$$

$$= -2 + (-2) \qquad \text{Add from left to right.}$$

$$= -4$$

Answers

12. 187°F   **13.** −14   **14.** 54

Example 7 Applying the Order of Operations

Simplify the expressions.

a. $\left(-\dfrac{5}{8} - \dfrac{2}{3}\right) - \left(\dfrac{1}{8} + 2\right)$ **b.** $-6 - |7 - 11| + (-3 + 7)^2$

Solution:

a. $\left(-\dfrac{5}{8} - \dfrac{2}{3}\right) - \left(\dfrac{1}{8} + 2\right)$ Simplify inside the parentheses first.

$= \left[-\dfrac{5}{8} + \left(-\dfrac{2}{3}\right)\right] - \left(\dfrac{1}{8} + 2\right)$ Rewrite subtraction in terms of addition.

$= \left[-\dfrac{15}{24} + \left(-\dfrac{16}{24}\right)\right] - \left(\dfrac{1}{8} + \dfrac{16}{8}\right)$ Rewrite fractions with a common denominator in each parentheses.

$= \left(-\dfrac{31}{24}\right) - \left(\dfrac{17}{8}\right)$ Add fractions in each parentheses.

$= \left(-\dfrac{31}{24}\right) + \left(-\dfrac{17}{8}\right)$ Rewrite subtraction in terms of addition.

$= -\dfrac{31}{24} + \left(-\dfrac{51}{24}\right)$ The common denominator is 24.

$= -\dfrac{82}{24}$ Add.

$= -\dfrac{41}{12}$ Simplify to lowest terms.

b. $-6 - |7 - 11| + (-3 + 7)^2$ Simplify within absolute value bars and parentheses first.

$= -6 - |7 + (-11)| + (-3 + 7)^2$ Rewrite subtraction in terms of addition.

$= -6 - |-4| + (4)^2$

$= -6 - (4) + 16$ Simplify absolute value and exponent.

$= -6 + (-4) + 16$ Rewrite subtraction in terms of addition.

$= -10 + 16$ Add from left to right.

$= 6$

Calculator Connections

Topic: Operations with Signed Numbers on a Calculator

Most calculators can add, subtract, multiply, and divide signed numbers. It is important to note, however, that the key used for the negative sign is different from the key used for subtraction. On a scientific calculator, the $\boxed{+/-}$ key or $\boxed{+\circ-}$ key is used to enter a negative number or to change the sign of an existing number. On a graphing calculator, the $\boxed{(-)}$ key is used. These keys should not be confused with the $\boxed{-}$ key which is used for subtraction. For example, try simplifying the following expressions.

a. $-7 + (-4) - 6$ **b.** $-3.1 - (-0.5) + 1.1$

Scientific Calculator:

Enter: $7 \boxed{+\circ-} \boxed{+} \boxed{(} 4 \boxed{+\circ-} \boxed{)} \boxed{-} 6 \boxed{=}$ **Result:** | -17 |

Enter: $3.1 \boxed{+\circ-} \boxed{-} \boxed{(} 0.5 \boxed{+\circ-} \boxed{)} + 1.1 \boxed{=}$ **Result:** | -1.5 |

Graphing Calculator:

```
-7+(-4)-6
            -17
-3.1-(-0.5)+1.1
            -1.5
```

Calculator Exercises

Simplify the expression without the use of a calculator. Then use the calculator to verify your answer.

1. $-8 + (-5)$ **2.** $4 + (-5) + (-1)$ **3.** $627 - (-84)$ **4.** $-0.06 - 0.12$

5. $-3.2 + (-14.5)$ **6.** $-472 + (-518)$ **7.** $-12 - 9 + 4$ **8.** $209 - 108 + (-63)$

Section 1.4   Practice Exercises

Study Skills Exercise

Some instructors allow the use of calculators. What is your instructor's policy regarding calculators in class, on the homework, and on tests?

Helpful Hint: If you are not permitted to use a calculator on tests, it is a good idea to do your homework in the same way, without a calculator.

Vocabulary and Key Concepts

1. a. The expression $a - b$ is equal to $a +$ _____.

   b. If a is positive and b is negative, then the difference $a - b$ will be (choose one: positive or negative).

Review Exercises

For Exercises 2–5, translate each English phrase into an algebraic expression.

2. The square root of 6   **3.** The square of x

4. Negative seven increased by 10   **5.** Two more than $-b$

For Exercises 6–8, simplify the expression.

6. $4^2 - 6 \div 2$ **7.** $1 + 36 \div 9 \cdot 2$ **8.** $14 - |10 - 6|$

Concept 1: Subtraction of Real Numbers

For Exercises 9–14, fill in the blank to make each statement correct.

9. $5 - 3 = 5 +$ _____   **10.** $8 - 7 = 8 +$ _____   **11.** $-2 - 12 = -2 +$ _____

12. $-4 - 9 = -4 +$ _____   **13.** $7 - (-4) = 7 +$ _____   **14.** $13 - (-4) = 13 +$ _____

For Exercises 15–60, simplify. **(See Examples 1 and 2.)**

15. $3 - 5$ **16.** $9 - 12$ **17.** $3 - (-5)$ **18.** $9 - (-12)$

19. $-3 - 5$ **20.** $-9 - 12$ **21.** $-3 - (-5)$ **22.** $-9 - (-5)$

23. $23 - 17$ **24.** $14 - 2$ **25.** $23 - (-17)$ **26.** $14 - (-2)$

27. $-23 - 17$ **28.** $-14 - 2$ **29.** $-23 - (-23)$ **30.** $-14 - (-14)$

31. $-6 - 14$ **32.** $-9 - 12$ **33.** $-7 - 17$ **34.** $-8 - 21$

35. $13 - (-12)$ **36.** $20 - (-5)$ **37.** $-14 - (-9)$ **38.** $-21 - (-17)$

39. $-\dfrac{6}{5} - \dfrac{3}{10}$ **40.** $-\dfrac{2}{9} - \dfrac{5}{3}$ **41.** $\dfrac{3}{8} - \left(-\dfrac{4}{3}\right)$ **42.** $\dfrac{7}{10} - \left(-\dfrac{5}{6}\right)$

43. $\dfrac{1}{2} - \dfrac{1}{10}$ **44.** $\dfrac{2}{7} - \dfrac{3}{14}$ **45.** $-\dfrac{11}{12} - \left(-\dfrac{1}{4}\right)$ **46.** $-\dfrac{7}{8} - \left(-\dfrac{1}{6}\right)$

47. $6.8 - (-2.4)$ **48.** $7.2 - (-1.9)$ **49.** $3.1 - 8.82$ **50.** $1.8 - 9.59$

51. $-4 - 3 - 2 - 1$ **52.** $-10 - 9 - 8 - 7$ **53.** $6 - 8 - 2 - 10$ **54.** $20 - 50 - 10 - 5$

55. $10 + (-14) + 6 - 22$ **56.** $-3 - (-8) + (-11) - 6$

57. $-112.846 + (-13.03) - 47.312$ **58.** $-96.473 + (-36.02) - 16.617$

59. $0.085 - (-3.14) + 0.018$ **60.** $0.00061 - (-0.00057) + 0.0014$

Concept 2: Translations

For Exercises 61–70, translate each English phrase into an algebraic expression. Then evaluate the expression. **(See Example 3.)**

61. Six minus -7 **62.** Eighteen minus -1

63. Eighteen subtracted from 3   **64.** Twenty-one subtracted from 8

65. The difference of -5 and -11 **66.** The difference of -2 and -18

67. Negative thirteen subtracted from -1 **68.** Negative thirty-one subtracted from -19

69. Twenty less than -32 **70.** Seven less than -3

Concept 3: Applications Involving Subtraction

71. On the game, *Jeopardy*, Jasper selected the category "The Last." He got the first four questions correct (worth $200, $400, $600, and $800) but then missed the last question (worth $1000). Write an expression that determines Jasper's score. Then simplify the expression to find his total winnings for that category. **(See Example 4.)**

72. On Courtney's turn in *Jeopardy*, she chose the category "Birds of a Feather." She already had $1200 when she selected a Double Jeopardy question. She wagered $500 but guessed incorrectly (therefore she lost $500). On her next turn, she got the $800 question correct. Write an expression that determines Courtney's score. Then simplify the expression to find her total winnings for that category.

73. In Ohio, the highest temperature ever recorded was 113°F and the lowest was −39°F. Find the difference between the highest and lowest temperatures. (*Source: Information Please Almanac*) **(See Example 5.)**

74. In Mississippi, the highest temperature ever recorded was 115°F and the lowest was −19°F. Find the difference between the highest and lowest temperatures. (*Source: Information Please Almanac*)

75. The highest mountain in the world is Mt. Everest, located in the Himalayas. Its height is 8848 meters (m) (29,028 ft). The  lowest recorded depth in the ocean is located in the Marianas Trench in the Pacific Ocean. Its "height" relative to sea level is −11,033 m (−36,198 ft). Determine the difference in elevation, in meters, between the highest mountain in the world and the deepest ocean trench. (*Source: Information Please Almanac*)

76. The lowest point in North America is located in Death Valley, California, at an elevation of −282 ft (−86 m). The highest point in North America is Mt. McKinley, Alaska, at an elevation of 20,320 ft (6194 m). Find the difference in elevation, in feet, between the highest and lowest points in North America. (*Source: Information Please Almanac*)

Concept 4: Applying the Order of Operations

For Exercises 77–96, perform the indicated operations. **(See Examples 6 and 7.)**

77. $6 + 8 - (-2) - 4 + 1$

78. $-3 - (-4) + 1 - 2 - 5$

79. $-1 - 7 + (-3) - 8 + 10$

80. $13 - 7 + 4 - 3 - (-1)$

81. $2 - (-8) + 7 + 3 - 15$

82. $8 - (-13) + 1 - 9$

83. $-6 + (-1) + (-8) + (-10)$

84. $-8 + (-3) + (-5) + (-2)$

85. $-4 - \{11 - [4 - (-9)]\}$

86. $15 - \{25 + 2[3 - (-1)]\}$

87. $-\dfrac{13}{10} + \dfrac{8}{15} - \left(-\dfrac{2}{5}\right)$

88. $\dfrac{11}{14} - \left(-\dfrac{9}{7}\right) - \dfrac{3}{2}$

89. $\left(\dfrac{2}{3} - \dfrac{5}{9}\right) - \left(\dfrac{4}{3} - (-2)\right)$

90. $\left(-\dfrac{9}{8} - \dfrac{1}{4}\right) - \left(-\dfrac{5}{6} + \dfrac{1}{8}\right)$

91. $\sqrt{29 + (-4)} - 7$

92. $8 - \sqrt{98 + (-3) + 5}$

93. $|10 + (-3)| - |-12 + (-6)|$

94. $|6 - 8| + |12 - 5|$

95. $\dfrac{3 - 4 + 5}{4 + (-2)}$

96. $\dfrac{12 - 14 + 6}{6 + (-2)}$

For Exercises 97–104, evaluate the expressions for $a = -2$, $b = -6$, and $c = -1$.

97. $(a + b) - c$ **98.** $(a - b) + c$ **99.** $a - (b + c)$ **100.** $a + (b - c)$

101. $(a - b) - c$ **102.** $(a + b) + c$ **103.** $a - (b - c)$ **104.** $a + (b + c)$

Problem Recognition Exercises

Addition and Subtraction of Real Numbers

1. State the rule for adding two negative numbers.

2. State the rule for adding a negative number to a positive number.

For Exercises 3–10, perform the indicated operations.

3. a. $14 + (-8)$ **b.** $-14 + 8$ **c.** $-14 + (-8)$ **d.** $14 - (-8)$ **e.** $-14 - 8$

4. a. $-5 - (-3)$ **b.** $-5 + (-3)$ **c.** $-5 - 3$ **d.** $-5 + 3$ **e.** $5 - (-3)$

5. a. $-25 + 25$ **b.** $25 - 25$ **c.** $25 - (-25)$ **d.** $-25 - (-25)$ **e.** $-(25) + (-25)$

6. a. $\dfrac{1}{2} + \left(-\dfrac{2}{3}\right)$ **b.** $-\dfrac{1}{2} + \dfrac{2}{3}$ **c.** $-\dfrac{1}{2} + \left(-\dfrac{2}{3}\right)$ **d.** $\dfrac{1}{2} - \left(-\dfrac{2}{3}\right)$ **e.** $-\dfrac{1}{2} - \dfrac{2}{3}$

7. a. $3.5 - 7.1$ **b.** $3.5 - (-7.1)$ **c.** $-3.5 + 7.1$ **d.** $-3.5 - (-7.1)$ **e.** $-3.5 + (-7.1)$

8. a. $6 - 1 + 4 - 5$ **b.** $6 - (1 + 4) - 5$ **c.** $6 - (1 + 4 - 5)$ **d.** $(6 - 1) - (4 - 5)$

9. a. $-100 - 90 - 80$ **b.** $-100 - (90 - 80)$ **c.** $-100 + (90 - 80)$ **d.** $-100 - (90 + 80)$

10. a. $-8 - (-10) + 20^2$ **b.** $-8 - (-10 + 20)^2$ **c.** $[-8 - (-10) + 20]^2$ **d.** $[-8 - (-10)]^2 + 20$

Multiplication and Division of Real Numbers

1. Multiplication of Real Numbers

Multiplication of real numbers can be interpreted as repeated addition. For example:

$$3(4) = 4 + 4 + 4 = 12 \qquad \text{Add 3 groups of 4.}$$

$$3(-4) = -4 + (-4) + (-4) = -12 \qquad \text{Add 3 groups of } -4.$$

These results suggest that the product of a positive number and a negative number is *negative*. Consider the following pattern of products.

Concepts

1. Multiplication of Real Numbers
2. Exponential Expressions
3. Division of Real Numbers
4. Applying the Order of Operations

$$
\begin{array}{rcl}
4 \cdot 3 & = & 12 \\
4 \cdot 2 & = & 8 \\
4 \cdot 1 & = & 4 \\
4 \cdot 0 & = & 0 \\
4 \cdot (-1) & = & -4 \\
4 \cdot (-2) & = & -8 \\
4 \cdot (-3) & = & -12
\end{array}
$$

The pattern decreases by 4 with each row.

Thus, the product of a positive number and a negative number must be *negative* for the pattern to continue.

Now suppose we have a product of two negative numbers. To determine the sign, consider the following pattern of products.

$$
\begin{array}{rcr}
-4 \cdot & 3 & = -12 \\
-4 \cdot & 2 & = -8 \\
-4 \cdot & 1 & = -4 \\
-4 \cdot & 0 & = 0 \\
-4 \cdot (-1) & = & 4 \\
-4 \cdot (-2) & = & 8 \\
-4 \cdot (-3) & = & 12
\end{array}
$$

The pattern increases by 4 with each row.

Thus, the product of two negative numbers must be *positive* for the pattern to continue.

From the first four rows, we see that the product increases by 4 for each row. For the pattern to continue, it follows that the product of two negative numbers must be *positive*.

We now summarize the rules for multiplying real numbers.

Multiplying Real Numbers

- The product of two real numbers with the *same* sign is positive.

  <u>Examples:</u> $(5)(6) = 30$

  $(-4)(-10) = 40$

- The product of two real numbers with *different* signs is negative.

  <u>Examples:</u> $(-2)(5) = -10$

  $(4)(-9) = -36$

- The product of any real number and zero is zero.

  <u>Examples:</u> $(8)(0) = 0$

  $(0)(-6) = 0$

Skill Practice

Multiply.

1. $-9(-3)$ **2.** $-1.5(-1.5)$

3. $-6(4)$ **4.** $\dfrac{1}{3}(-15)$

5. $0(-4.1)$ **6.** $-\dfrac{5}{9}\left(-\dfrac{9}{5}\right)$

Example 1 **Multiplying Real Numbers**

Multiply the real numbers.

a. $-8(-4)$ **b.** $-2.5(-1.7)$ **c.** $-7(10)$

d. $\dfrac{1}{2}(-8)$ **e.** $0(-8.3)$ **f.** $-\dfrac{2}{7}\left(-\dfrac{7}{2}\right)$

Solution:

a. $-8(-4) = 32$ *Same* signs. Product is positive.

b. $-2.5(-1.7) = 4.25$ *Same* signs. Product is positive.

c. $-7(10) = -70$ *Different* signs. Product is negative.

d. $\dfrac{1}{2}(-8) = -4$ *Different* signs. Product is negative.

e. $0(-8.3) = 0$ The product of any real number and zero is zero.

f. $-\dfrac{2}{7}\left(-\dfrac{7}{2}\right) = \dfrac{14}{14}$ *Same* signs. Product is positive.

$= 1$ Simplify.

Answers

1. 27   **2.** 2.25   **3.** -24
4. -5 **5.** 0   **6.** 1

Observe the pattern for repeated multiplications.

$$(-1)(-1) \qquad \underline{(-1)(-1)}(-1) \qquad \underline{(-1)(-1)}(-1)(-1) \qquad \underline{(-1)(-1)}(-1)(-1)(-1)$$
$$= 1 \qquad\qquad = (1)(-1) \qquad\quad = \underline{(1)(-1)}(-1) \qquad\quad = \underline{(1)(-1)}(-1)(-1)$$
$$\qquad\qquad\quad = -1 \qquad\qquad = \underline{(-1)(-1)} \qquad\qquad = \underline{(-1)(-1)}(-1)$$
$$\qquad\qquad\qquad\qquad\qquad\quad = 1 \qquad\qquad\qquad = (1)(-1)$$
$$\qquad\qquad\qquad\qquad\qquad\qquad\qquad\qquad\qquad\qquad = -1$$

The pattern demonstrated in these examples indicates that

- The product of an even number of negative factors is positive.
- The product of an odd number of negative factors is negative.

Concept Connections

7. Without actually computing, determine if the product shown is positive or negative. Explain.

$$(-526)(420)(-105)$$

2. Exponential Expressions

Recall that for any real number b and any positive integer, n:

$$b^n = \underbrace{b \cdot b \cdot b \cdot b \ldots \cdot b}_{n \text{ factors of } b}$$

Be particularly careful when evaluating exponential expressions involving negative numbers. An exponential expression with a negative base is written with parentheses around the base, such as $(-2)^4$.

To evaluate $(-2)^4$, the base -2 is used as a factor four times:

$$(-2)^4 = (-2)(-2)(-2)(-2) = 16$$

If parentheses are *not* used, the expression -2^4 has a different meaning:

- The expression -2^4 has a base of 2 (not -2) and can be interpreted as $-1 \cdot 2^4$.

$$-2^4 = -1(2)(2)(2)(2) = -16$$

- The expression -2^4 can also be interpreted as the opposite of 2^4.

$$-2^4 = -(2 \cdot 2 \cdot 2 \cdot 2) = -16$$

TIP: The following expressions are translated as shown:

$-(-3)$ is read "the opposite of negative three."

-3^2 is read "the opposite of three squared."

$(-3)^2$ is read "negative three, squared."

Example 2 **Evaluating Exponential Expressions**

Simplify.

a. $(-5)^2$ **b.** -5^2 **c.** $(-0.4)^3$ **d.** -0.4^3 **e.** $\left(-\dfrac{1}{2}\right)^3$

Solution:

a. $(-5)^2 = (-5)(-5) = 25$ Multiply two factors of -5.

b. $-5^2 = -1(5)(5) = -25$ Multiply -1 by two factors of 5.

Avoiding Mistakes

The negative sign is not part of the base unless it is in parentheses with the base. Thus, in the expression -5^2, the exponent applies only to 5 and not to the negative sign.

Skill Practice

Simplify.

8. $(-7)^2$ **9.** -7^2

10. $\left(-\dfrac{2}{3}\right)^3$ **11.** -0.2^3

Answers

7. The product is positive because there is an even number of negative factors.

8. 49   **9.** -49

10. $-\dfrac{8}{27}$ **11.** -0.008

   c. $(-0.4)^3 = (-0.4)(-0.4)(-0.4) = -0.064$ Multiply three factors of -0.4.

   d. $-0.4^3 = -1(0.4)(0.4)(0.4) = -0.064$ Multiply -1 by three factors of 0.4.

   e. $\left(-\dfrac{1}{2}\right)^3 = \left(-\dfrac{1}{2}\right)\left(-\dfrac{1}{2}\right)\left(-\dfrac{1}{2}\right) = -\dfrac{1}{8}$ Multiply three factors of $-\dfrac{1}{2}$.

3. Division of Real Numbers

Two numbers are *reciprocals* if their product is 1. For example, $-\frac{2}{7}$ and $-\frac{7}{2}$ are reciprocals because $-\frac{2}{7}\left(-\frac{7}{2}\right) = 1$. Symbolically, if a is a nonzero real number, then the reciprocal of a is $\frac{1}{a}$ because $a \cdot \frac{1}{a} = 1$. This definition also implies that a number and its reciprocal have the same sign.

> ### The Reciprocal of a Real Number
> Let a be a nonzero real number. Then, the **reciprocal** of a is $\frac{1}{a}$.

Recall that to subtract two real numbers, we add the opposite of the second number to the first number. In a similar way, division of real numbers is defined in terms of multiplication. To divide two real numbers, we multiply the first number by the reciprocal of the second number.

> ### Division of Real Numbers
> Let a and b be real numbers such that $b \neq 0$. Then, $a \div b = a \cdot \frac{1}{b}$.

Consider the quotient $10 \div 5$. The reciprocal of 5 is $\frac{1}{5}$, so we have

$$10 \div 5 = 2 \qquad \text{or equivalently,} \qquad 10 \cdot \frac{1}{5} = 2$$

Because division of real numbers can be expressed in terms of multiplication, then the sign rules that apply to multiplication also apply to division.

> ### Dividing Real Numbers
> - The quotient of two real numbers with the *same* sign is positive.
>
>   <u>Examples:</u> $24 \div 4 = 6$
>
> $-36 \div -9 = 4$
>
> - The quotient of two real numbers with *different* signs is negative.
>
>   <u>Examples:</u> $100 \div (-5) = -20$
>
> $-12 \div 4 = -3$

Example 3 Dividing Real Numbers

Divide the real numbers.

a. $200 \div (-10)$ **b.** $\dfrac{-48}{16}$ **c.** $\dfrac{-6.25}{-1.25}$ **d.** $\dfrac{-9}{-5}$

Solution:

a. $200 \div (-10) = -20$ *Different* signs. Quotient is negative.

b. $\dfrac{-48}{16} = -3$ *Different* signs. Quotient is negative.

c. $\dfrac{-6.25}{-1.25} = 5$ *Same* signs. Quotient is positive.

d. $\dfrac{-9}{-5} = \dfrac{9}{5}$ *Same* signs. Quotient is positive.

Because 5 does not divide into 9 evenly the answer can be left as a fraction.

TIP: If the numerator and denominator of a fraction are both negative, then the quotient is positive. Therefore, $\frac{-9}{-5}$ can be simplified to $\frac{9}{5}$.

Example 4 Dividing Real Numbers

Divide the real numbers.

a. $15 \div -25$ **b.** $-\dfrac{3}{14} \div \dfrac{9}{7}$

Solution:

a. $15 \div -25$ *Different* signs. Quotient is negative.

$= \dfrac{15}{-25}$

$= -\dfrac{3}{5}$

TIP: If the numerator and denominator of a fraction have opposite signs, then the quotient will be negative. Therefore, a fraction has the same value whether the negative sign is written in the numerator, in the denominator, or in front of the fraction.

$$\dfrac{-3}{5} = \dfrac{3}{-5} = -\dfrac{3}{5}$$

b. $-\dfrac{3}{14} \div \dfrac{9}{7}$ *Different* signs. Quotient is negative.

$= -\dfrac{3}{14} \cdot \dfrac{7}{9}$ Multiply by the reciprocal of $\frac{9}{7}$ which is $\frac{7}{9}$.

$= -\dfrac{\overset{1}{\cancel{3}}}{\underset{2}{\cancel{14}}} \cdot \dfrac{\overset{1}{\cancel{7}}}{\underset{3}{\cancel{9}}}$ Divide out common factors.

$= -\dfrac{1}{6}$ Multiply the fractions.

Multiplication can be used to check any division problem. If $\frac{a}{b} = c$, then $bc = a$ (provided that $b \neq 0$). For example,

$$\frac{8}{-4} = -2 \;\blacktriangleright\; \underline{\text{Check:}} \quad (-4)(-2) = 8 \;\checkmark$$

This relationship between multiplication and division can be used to investigate division problems involving the number zero.

1. The quotient of 0 and any nonzero number is 0. For example:

$$\frac{0}{6} = 0 \qquad \text{because } 6 \cdot 0 = 0 \;\checkmark$$

Concept Connections

Simplify.

18. $\dfrac{0}{2}$ **19.** $\dfrac{4}{0}$

20. $-25 \div 0$ **21.** $0 \div (-8.2)$

2. The quotient of any nonzero number and 0 is undefined. For example,

$$\frac{6}{0} = ?$$

Finding the quotient $\frac{6}{0}$ is equivalent to asking, "What number times zero will equal 6?" That is, $(0)(?) = 6$. No real number satisfies this condition. Therefore, we say that division by zero is undefined.

3. The quotient of 0 and 0 cannot be determined. Evaluating an expression of the form $\frac{0}{0} = ?$ is equivalent to asking, "What number times zero will equal 0?" That is, $(0)(?) = 0$. Any real number will satisfy this requirement; however, expressions involving $\frac{0}{0}$ are usually discussed in advanced mathematics courses.

Division Involving Zero

Let a represent a nonzero real number. Then,

1. $\dfrac{0}{a} = 0$ **2.** $\dfrac{a}{0}$ is undefined

4. Applying the Order of Operations

Example 5 Applying the Order of Operations

Simplify. $-8 + 8 \div (-2) \div (-6)$

Solution:

$-8 + 8 \div (-2) \div (-6)$

$= -8 + (-4) \div (-6)$ Perform division before addition.

$= -8 + \dfrac{4}{6}$ The quotient of -4 and -6 is positive $\frac{4}{6}$ or $\frac{2}{3}$.

$= -\dfrac{8}{1} + \dfrac{2}{3}$ Write -8 as a fraction.

$= -\dfrac{24}{3} + \dfrac{2}{3}$ The common denominator is 3.

$= -\dfrac{22}{3}$ Add.

Skill Practice

Simplify.

22. $-36 + 36 \div (-4) \div (-3)$

Answers

18. 0   **19.** Undefined
20. Undefined   **21.** 0   **22.** -33

Example 6 **Applying the Order of Operations**

Simplify. $\dfrac{24 - 2[-3 + (5 - 8)]^2}{2|-12 + 3|}$

Solution:

$\dfrac{24 - 2[-3 + (5 - 8)]^2}{2|-12 + 3|}$ Simplify numerator and denominator separately.

$= \dfrac{24 - 2[-3 + (-3)]^2}{2|-9|}$ Simplify within the inner parentheses and absolute value.

$= \dfrac{24 - 2[-6]^2}{2(9)}$ Simplify within brackets, [ ]. Simplify the absolute value.

$= \dfrac{24 - 2(36)}{2(9)}$ Simplify exponents.

$= \dfrac{24 - 72}{18}$ Perform multiplication before subtraction.

$= \dfrac{-48}{18}$ or $-\dfrac{8}{3}$ Reduce to lowest terms.

Skill Practice

Simplify.

23. $\dfrac{100 - 3[-1 + (2 - 6)^2]}{|20 - 25|}$

Example 7 **Evaluating an Algebraic Expression**

Given $y = -6$, evaluate the expressions.

a. y^2 **b.** $-y^2$

Solution:

a. y^2

$= (\ )^2$ When substituting a number for a variable, use parentheses.

$= (-6)^2$ Substitute $y = -6$.

$= 36$ Square -6, that is, $(-6)(-6) = 36$.

b. $-y^2$

$= -(\ )^2$ When substituting a number for a variable, use parentheses.

$= -(-6)^2$ Substitute $y = -6$.

$= -(36)$ Square -6.

$= -36$ Multiply by -1.

Skill Practice

Given $a = -7$, evaluate the expressions.

24. a^2 **25.** $-a^2$

Answers

23. 11   **24.** 49   **25.** −49

Calculator Connections

Topic: Evaluating Exponential Expressions with Positive and Negative Bases

Be particularly careful when raising a negative number to an even power on a calculator. For example, the expressions $(-4)^2$ and -4^2 have different values. That is, $(-4)^2 = 16$ and $-4^2 = -16$. Verify these expressions on a calculator.

Scientific Calculator:

To evaluate $(-4)^2$

Enter: (4 +○-) x^2 **Result:**   16

To evaluate -4^2 on a scientific calculator, it is important to square 4 first and then take its opposite.

Enter: 4 x^2 +○-   **Result:** -16

Graphing Calculator:

```
(-4)2
            16
-42
           -16
```

The graphing calculator allows for several methods of denoting the multiplication of two real numbers. For example, consider the product of -8 and 4.

```
-8*4
           -32
-8(4)
           -32
(-8)(4)
           -32
```

Calculator Exercises

Simplify the expression without the use of a calculator. Then use the calculator to verify your answer.

1. $-6(5)$
2. $\dfrac{-5.2}{2.6}$
3. $(-5)(-5)(-5)(-5)$
4. $(-5)^4$
5. -5^4

6. -2.4^2
7. $(-2.4)^2$
8. $(-1)(-1)(-1)$
9. $\dfrac{-8.4}{-2.1}$
10. $90 \div (-5)(2)$

Section 1.5   Practice Exercises

Study Skills Exercise

Look through the text, and write down a page number that contains:

a. An Avoiding Mistakes box _____

b. A Tip box _____

c. A key term (shown in bold) _____

Vocabulary and Key Concepts

1. a. If a is a nonzero real number, then the reciprocal of a is _____.

b. If either a or b is zero then the product $ab =$ _____.

c. If $a = 0$, and $b \neq 0$, then $\frac{a}{b} =$ _____.

d. If $a \neq 0$, and $b = 0$, then $\frac{a}{b}$ is _____.

e. If a and b have the same sign, then the product ab is (choose one: positive or negative).

f. If a and b have different signs, then the quotient $\frac{a}{b}$ is (choose one: positive or negative).

g. The product of a number and its reciprocal is _____. For example $-\frac{2}{3} \cdot ($ $)$ $= 1$

h. Which of the expressions represents the product of 2 and x?

    a. $2x$ **b.** $2 \cdot x$ **c.** $2(x)$ **d.** $(2)x$ **e.** $(2)(x)$

Review Exercises

For Exercises 2–6, determine if the expression is true or false.

2. $6 + (-2) > -5 + 6$ **3.** $|-6| + |-14| \leq |-3| + |-17|$ **4.** $\sqrt{36} - |-6| > 0$

5. $\sqrt{9} + |-3| \leq 0$ **6.** $14 - |-3| \geq 12 + \sqrt{25}$

Concept 1: Multiplication of Real Numbers

For Exercises 7–14, multiply the real numbers. **(See Example 1.)**

7. $8(-7)$ **8.** $(-3) \cdot 4$ **9.** $(-11)(-13)$ **10.** $(-5)(-26)$

11. $(-2.2)(5.8)$ **12.** $(9.1)(-4.5)$ **13.** $\left(-\frac{2}{3}\right)\left(-\frac{9}{8}\right)$ **14.** $\left(-\frac{5}{4}\right)\left(-\frac{12}{25}\right)$

Concept 2: Exponential Expressions

For Exercises 15–22, simplify the exponential expression. **(See Example 2.)**

15. $(-6)^2$ **16.** $(-10)^2$ **17.** -6^2 **18.** -10^2

19. $\left(-\frac{3}{5}\right)^3$ **20.** $\left(-\frac{5}{2}\right)^3$ **21.** $(-0.2)^4$ **22.** $(-0.1)^4$

Concept 3: Division of Real Numbers

For Exercises 23–34, divide the real numbers. **(See Examples 3 and 4.)**

23. $\dfrac{54}{-9}$ **24.** $\dfrac{-27}{3}$ **25.** $\dfrac{-100}{-10}$ **26.** $\dfrac{-120}{-40}$

27. $\dfrac{-14}{-7}$ **28.** $\dfrac{-21}{-3}$ **29.** $\dfrac{7}{-7}$ **30.** $\dfrac{-12}{12}$

31. $\dfrac{-8}{-8}$ **32.** $\dfrac{-10}{-10}$ **33.** $\dfrac{13}{-65}$ **34.** $\dfrac{7}{-77}$

For Exercises 35–42, show how multiplication can be used to check the division problems.

35. $\dfrac{14}{-2} = -7$ **36.** $\dfrac{-18}{-6} = 3$ **37.** $\dfrac{0}{-5} = 0$ **38.** $\dfrac{0}{-4} = 0$

39. $\dfrac{6}{0}$ is undefined   **40.** $\dfrac{-4}{0}$ is undefined   **41.** $-24 \div (-6) = 4$ **42.** $-18 \div 2 = -9$

Mixed Exercises

For Exercises 43–86, multiply or divide as indicated.

43. $2 \cdot 3$

44. $8 \cdot 6$

45. $2(-3)$

46. $8(-6)$

47. $(-24) \div 3$

48. $(-52) \div 2$

49. $(-24) \div (-3)$

50. $(-52) \div (-2)$

51. $-6 \cdot 0$

52. $-8 \cdot 0$

53. $-18 \div 0$

54. $-42 \div 0$

55. $0\left(-\dfrac{2}{5}\right)$

56. $0\left(-\dfrac{1}{8}\right)$

57. $0 \div \left(-\dfrac{1}{10}\right)$

58. $0 \div \left(\dfrac{4}{9}\right)$

59. $\dfrac{-9}{6}$

60. $\dfrac{-15}{10}$

61. $\dfrac{-30}{-100}$

62. $\dfrac{-250}{-1000}$

63. $\dfrac{26}{-13}$

64. $\dfrac{52}{-4}$

65. $1.72(-4.6)$

66. $361.3(-14.9)$

67. $-0.02(-4.6)$

68. $-0.06(-2.15)$

69. $\dfrac{14.4}{-2.4}$

70. $\dfrac{50.4}{-6.3}$

71. $\dfrac{-5.25}{-2.5}$

72. $\dfrac{-8.5}{-27.2}$

73. $(-3)^2$

74. $(-7)^2$

75. -3^2

76. -7^2

77. $\left(-\dfrac{4}{3}\right)^3$

78. $\left(-\dfrac{1}{5}\right)^3$

79. $2.8(-5.1)$

80. $(7.21)(-0.3)$

81. $(-6.8) \div (-0.02)$

82. $(-12.3) \div (-0.03)$

83. $\left(-\dfrac{2}{15}\right)\left(\dfrac{25}{3}\right)$

84. $\left(-\dfrac{5}{16}\right)\left(\dfrac{4}{9}\right)$

85. $\left(-\dfrac{7}{8}\right) \div \left(-\dfrac{9}{16}\right)$

86. $\left(-\dfrac{22}{23}\right) \div \left(-\dfrac{11}{3}\right)$

Concept 4: Applying the Order of Operations

For Exercises 87–118, perform the indicated operations. **(See Examples 5 and 6.)**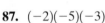

87. $(-2)(-5)(-3)$

88. $(-6)(-1)(-10)$

89. $(-8)(-4)(-1)(-3)$

90. $(-6)(-3)(-1)(-5)$

91. $100 \div (-10) \div (-5)$

92. $150 \div (-15) \div (-2)$

93. $-12 \div (-6) \div (-2)$

94. $-36 \div (-2) \div 6$

95. $\dfrac{2}{5} \cdot \dfrac{1}{3} \cdot \left(-\dfrac{10}{11}\right)$

96. $\left(-\dfrac{9}{8}\right) \cdot \left(-\dfrac{2}{3}\right) \cdot \left(1\dfrac{5}{12}\right)$

97. $\left(1\dfrac{1}{3}\right) \div 3 \div \left(-\dfrac{7}{9}\right)$

98. $-\dfrac{7}{8} \div \left(3\dfrac{1}{4}\right) \div (-2)$

99. $12 \div (-2)(4)$

100. $(-6) \cdot 7 \div (-2)$

101. $\left(-\dfrac{12}{5}\right) \div (-6) \cdot \left(-\dfrac{1}{8}\right)$

102. $10 \cdot \dfrac{1}{3} \div \dfrac{25}{6}$

103. $8 - 2^3 \cdot 5 + 3 - (-6)$

104. $-14 \div (-7) - 8 \cdot 2 + 3^3$

105. $-(2 - 8)^2 \div (-6) \cdot 2$

106. $-(3 - 5)^2 \cdot 6 \div (-4)$

107. $\dfrac{6(-4) - 2(5 - 8)}{-6 - 3 - 5}$

108. $\dfrac{3(-4) - 5(9 - 11)}{-9 - 2 - 3}$

109. $\dfrac{-4 + 5}{(-2) \cdot 5 + 10}$

110. $\dfrac{-3 + 10}{2(-4) + 8}$

111. $-4 - 3[2 - (-5 + 3)] - 8 \cdot 2^2$

112. $-6 - 5[-4 - (6 - 12)] + (-5)^2$

113. $-|-1| - |5|$

114. $-|-10| - |6|$

115. $\dfrac{|2 - 9| - |5 - 7|}{10 - 15}$

116. $\dfrac{|-2 + 6| - |3 - 5|}{13 - 11}$

117. $\dfrac{6 - 3[2 - (6 - 8)]^2}{-2|2 - 5|}$

118. $\dfrac{12 - 4[-6 - (5 - 8)]^2}{4|6 - 10|}$

For Exercises 119–124, evaluate the expression for $x = -2$, $y = -4$, and $z = 6$. **(See Example 7.)**

119. $-x^2$

120. x^2

121. $4(2x - z)$

122. $6(3x + y)$

123. $\dfrac{3x + 2y}{y}$

 **124.** $\dfrac{2z - y}{x}$

125. Is the expression $\dfrac{10}{5x}$ equal to 10/5x? Explain.

126. Is the expression $10/(5x)$ equal to $\dfrac{10}{5x}$? Explain.

For Exercises 127–134, translate the English phrase into an algebraic expression. Then evaluate the expression.

127. The product of -3.75 and 0.3

128. The product of -0.4 and -1.258

129. The quotient of $\frac{16}{5}$ and $\left(-\frac{8}{9}\right)$

130. The quotient of $\left(-\frac{3}{14}\right)$ and $\frac{1}{7}$

131. The number -0.4 plus the quantity 6 times -0.42

132. The number 0.5 plus the quantity -2 times 0.125

133. The number $-\frac{1}{4}$ minus the quantity 6 times $-\frac{1}{3}$

134. Negative five minus the quantity $\left(-\frac{5}{6}\right)$ times $\frac{3}{8}$

135. For 3 weeks, Jim pays $2 a week for lottery tickets. Jim has one winning ticket for $3. Write an expression that describes his net gain or loss. How much money has Jim won or lost?

136. Stephanie pays $2 a week for 6 weeks for lottery tickets. Stephanie has one winning ticket for $5. Write an expression that describes her net gain or loss. How much money has Stephanie won or lost?

137. Lorne sells ads for the local newspaper and has a quota for the number of ads he must sell each week. For the first two days of the week, Lorne was 5 above his daily quota. For the last three days of the week, Lorne was 3 below his daily quota. Write an expression that describes the net amount he was above or below his quota. Interpret the result.

138. Valerie trades stocks each day and analyzes her results at the end of the week. The first day of the week she had a profit of $650. The next two days she had a loss of $400 each day and the last two days she had a loss of $150 each day. Write an expression that describes Valerie's profit or loss for the week. Interpret the result.

139. A pediatrician analyzed the effect of a special baby food on five toddlers. He recorded the amount of weight lost or gained (in ounces) by each child for one month as shown in the table.

Baby	A	B	C	D	E
Gain/Loss (oz)	12	−15	4	−9	3

Write an expression to calculate the average gain or loss in weight of the children and then simplify. Interpret your answer.

140. At the end of a 2-month class, a personal trainer analyzed the effect of her new exercise routine by recording the gain or loss (in inches) in waist measurements of her clients. The results are shown in the table.

Client	A	B	C	D	E	F
Gain/Loss (in.)	−1.5	−2	1.5	2.5	−3	−0.5

Write an expression to calculate the average gain or loss in waist measurement and then simplify. Interpret your answer.

141. Evaluate the expressions in parts (a) and (b).

a. $-4 - 3 - 2 - 1$

b. $-4(-3)(-2)(-1)$

c. Explain the difference between the operations in parts (a) and (b).

142. Evaluate the expressions in parts (a) and (b).

a. $-10 - 9 - 8 - 7$

b. $-10(-9)(-8)(-7)$

c. Explain the difference between the operations in parts (a) and (b).

Problem Recognition Exercises

Adding, Subtracting, Multiplying, and Dividing Real Numbers

Perform the indicated operations.

1. a. $-8 - (-4)$ **b.** $-8(-4)$ **c.** $-8 + (-4)$ **d.** $-8 \div (-4)$

2. a. $12 + (-2)$ **b.** $12 - (-2)$ **c.** $12(-2)$ **d.** $12 \div (-2)$

3. a. $-36 + 9$ **b.** $-36(9)$ **c.** $-36 \div 9$ **d.** $-36 - 9$

4. a. $27 - (-3)$ **b.** $27 + (-3)$ **c.** $27(-3)$ **d.** $27 \div (-3)$

5. a. $-5(-10)$ **b.** $-5 + (-10)$ **c.** $-5 \div (-10)$ **d.** $-5 - (-10)$

6. a. $-20 \div 4$ **b.** $-20 - 4$ **c.** $-20 + 4$ **d.** $-20(4)$

7. a. $-4(-16)$ **b.** $-4 - (-16)$ **c.** $-4 \div (-16)$ **d.** $-4 + (-16)$

8. a. $-21 \div 3$ **b.** $-21 - 3$ **c.** $-21(3)$ **d.** $-21 + 3$

9. a. $80(-5)$ **b.** $80 - (-5)$ **c.** $80 \div (-5)$ **d.** $80 + (-5)$

10. a. $-14 - (-21)$ **b.** $-14(-21)$ **c.** $-14 \div (-21)$ **d.** $-14 + (-21)$

11. a. $|-6| + |2|$ **b.** $|-6 + 2|$ **c.** $|-6| - |-2|$ **d.** $|-6 - 2|$

12. a. $-|9| - |-7|$ **b.** $|-9| - |-7|$ **c.** $-|9 - 7|$ **d.** $|-9 - 7|$

Properties of Real Numbers and Simplifying Expressions

1. Commutative Properties of Real Numbers

When getting dressed in the morning, it makes no difference whether you put on your left shoe first and then your right shoe, or vice versa. This example illustrates a process in which the order does not affect the outcome. Such a process or operation is said to be *commutative*.

In algebra, the operations of addition and multiplication are commutative because the order in which we add or multiply two real numbers does not affect the result. For example:

$$10 + 5 = 5 + 10 \quad \text{and} \quad 10 \cdot 5 = 5 \cdot 10$$

Concepts

1. Commutative Properties of Real Numbers
2. Associative Properties of Real Numbers
3. Identity and Inverse Properties of Real Numbers
4. Distributive Property of Multiplication over Addition
5. Simplifying Algebraic Expressions

Commutative Properties of Real Numbers

If a and b are real numbers, then

1. $a + b = b + a$ **commutative property of addition**

2. $ab = ba$ **commutative property of multiplication**

It is important to note that although the operations of addition and multiplication are commutative, subtraction and division are *not* commutative. For example:

$$\underbrace{10 - 5}_{5} \neq \underbrace{5 - 10}_{-5} \quad \text{and} \quad \underbrace{10 \div 5}_{2} \neq \underbrace{5 \div 10}_{\frac{1}{2}}$$

Example 1	**Applying the Commutative Property of Addition**

Use the commutative property of addition to rewrite each expression.

a. $-3 + (-7)$ **b.** $3x^3 + 5x^4$

Solution:

a. $-3 + (-7) = -7 + (-3)$

b. $3x^3 + 5x^4 = 5x^4 + 3x^3$

Skill Practice

Use the commutative property of addition to rewrite each expression.

1. $-5 + 9$

2. $7y + x$

Recall that subtraction is not a commutative operation. However, if we rewrite $a - b$, as $a + (-b)$, we can apply the commutative property of addition. This is demonstrated in Example 2.

Answer

1. $9 + (-5)$ **2.** $x + 7y$

Example 2 **Applying the Commutative Property of Addition**

Rewrite the expression in terms of addition. Then apply the commutative property of addition.

   a. $5a - 3b$ **b.** $z^2 - \frac{1}{4}$

Solution:

   a. $5a - 3b$

$$= 5a + (-3b) \qquad \text{Rewrite subtraction as addition of } -3b.$$

$$= -3b + 5a \qquad \text{Apply the commutative property of addition.}$$

   b. $z^2 - \frac{1}{4}$

$$= z^2 + \left(-\frac{1}{4}\right) \qquad \text{Rewrite subtraction as addition of } -\tfrac{1}{4}.$$

$$= -\frac{1}{4} + z^2 \qquad \text{Apply the commutative property of addition.}$$

Example 3 **Applying the Commutative Property of Multiplication**

Use the commutative property of multiplication to rewrite each expression.

   a. $12(-6)$ **b.** $x \cdot 4$

Solution:

   a. $12(-6) = -6(12)$

   b. $x \cdot 4 = 4 \cdot x$ (or simply $4x$)

2. Associative Properties of Real Numbers

The associative property of real numbers states that the manner in which three or more real numbers are grouped under addition or multiplication will not affect the outcome. For example:

$$(5 + 10) + 2 = 5 + (10 + 2) \qquad \text{and} \qquad (5 \cdot 10)2 = 5(10 \cdot 2)$$

$$15 + 2 = 5 + 12 \qquad\qquad\qquad (50)2 = 5(20)$$

$$17 = 17 \qquad\qquad\qquad\qquad 100 = 100$$

Associative Properties of Real Numbers

If a, b, and c represent real numbers, then

   1. $(a + b) + c = a + (b + c)$ **associative property of addition**

   2. $(ab)c = a(bc)$ **associative property of multiplication**

Example 4 Applying the Associative Property

Use the associative property of addition or multiplication to rewrite each expression. Then simplify the expression if possible.

a. $(y + 5) + 6$ **b.** $4(5z)$ **c.** $-\frac{3}{2}\left(-\frac{2}{3}w\right)$

Solution:

a. $(y + 5) + 6$

$\qquad = y + (5 + 6)$ Apply the associative property of addition.

$\qquad = y + 11$ Simplify.

b. $4(5z)$

$\qquad = (4 \cdot 5)z$ Apply the associative property of multiplication.

$\qquad = 20z$ Simplify.

c. $-\frac{3}{2}\left(-\frac{2}{3}w\right)$

$\qquad = \left[-\frac{3}{2}\left(-\frac{2}{3}\right)\right]w$ Apply the associative property of multiplication.

$\qquad = 1w$ Simplify.

$\qquad = w$

Note: In most cases, a detailed application of the associative property will not be shown. Instead, the process will be written in one step, such as

$$(y + 5) + 6 = y + 11, \quad 4(5z) = 20z, \quad \text{and} \quad -\frac{3}{2}\left(-\frac{2}{3}w\right) = w$$

Skill Practice

Use the associative property of addition or multiplication to rewrite each expression. Simplify if possible.

7. $(x + 4) + 3$

8. $-2(4x)$

9. $\frac{5}{4}\left(\frac{4}{5}t\right)$

3. Identity and Inverse Properties of Real Numbers

The number 0 has a special role under the operation of addition. Zero added to any real number does not change the number. Therefore, the number 0 is said to be the *additive identity* (also called the *identity element of addition*). For example:

$$-4 + 0 = -4 \qquad 0 + 5.7 = 5.7 \qquad 0 + \frac{3}{4} = \frac{3}{4}$$

The number 1 has a special role under the operation of multiplication. Any real number multiplied by 1 does not change the number. Therefore, the number 1 is said to be the *multiplicative identity* (also called the *identity element of multiplication*). For example:

$$(-8)1 = -8 \qquad 1(-2.85) = -2.85 \qquad 1\left(\frac{1}{5}\right) = \frac{1}{5}$$

Identity Properties of Real Numbers

If a is a real number, then

1. $a + 0 = 0 + a = a$ **identity property of addition**

2. $a \cdot 1 = 1 \cdot a = a$ **identity property of multiplication**

Answers

7. $x + (4 + 3); x + 7$

8. $(-2 \cdot 4)x; -8x$

9. $\left(\frac{5}{4} \cdot \frac{4}{5}\right)t; t$

The sum of a number and its opposite equals 0. For example, $-12 + 12 = 0$. For any real number, a, the opposite of a (also called the *additive inverse* of a) is $-a$ and $a + (-a) = -a + a = 0$. The inverse property of addition states that the sum of any number and its additive inverse is the identity element of addition, 0. For example:

Number	Additive Inverse (Opposite)	Sum
9	-9	$9 + (-9) = 0$
-21.6	21.6	$-21.6 + 21.6 = 0$
$\dfrac{2}{7}$	$-\dfrac{2}{7}$	$\dfrac{2}{7} + \left(-\dfrac{2}{7}\right) = 0$

If b is a nonzero real number, then the reciprocal of b (also called the *multiplicative inverse* of b) is $\frac{1}{b}$. The inverse property of multiplication states that the product of b and its multiplicative inverse is the identity element of multiplication, 1. Symbolically, we have $b \cdot \frac{1}{b} = \frac{1}{b} \cdot b = 1$. For example:

Number	Multiplicative Inverse (Reciprocal)	Product
7	$\dfrac{1}{7}$	$7 \cdot \dfrac{1}{7} = 1$
3.14	$\dfrac{1}{3.14}$	$3.14\left(\dfrac{1}{3.14}\right) = 1$
$-\dfrac{3}{5}$	$-\dfrac{5}{3}$	$-\dfrac{3}{5}\left(-\dfrac{5}{3}\right) = 1$

Concept Connections

Fill in the blanks. State whether the property used is an inverse property or an identity property.

10. $5 + \square = 0$

11. $-8 \cdot \square = -8$

12. $\dfrac{1}{2} \cdot \square = 1$

13. $\dfrac{a}{b} + \square = \dfrac{a}{b}$

Inverse Properties of Real Numbers

If a is a real number and b is a nonzero real number, then

1. $a + (-a) = -a + a = 0$ **inverse property of addition**

2. $b \cdot \dfrac{1}{b} = \dfrac{1}{b} \cdot b = 1$ **inverse property of multiplication**

4. Distributive Property of Multiplication over Addition

The operations of addition and multiplication are related by an important property called the **distributive property of multiplication over addition**. Consider the expression $6(2 + 3)$. The order of operations indicates that the sum $2 + 3$ is evaluated first, and then the result is multiplied by 6:

$$6(2 + 3)$$
$$= 6(5)$$
$$= 30$$

Answers

10. -5; inverse   **11.** 1; identity
12. 2; inverse   **13.** 0; identity

Notice that the same result is obtained if the factor of 6 is multiplied by each of the numbers 2 and 3, and then their products are added:

$6(2 + 3)$ The factor of 6 is distributed to the numbers 2 and 3.

$= 6(2) + 6(3)$

$= \quad 12 + 18$

$= \qquad 30$

The distributive property of multiplication over addition states that this is true in general.

> **TIP:** The mathematical definition of the distributive property is consistent with the everyday meaning of the word *distribute*. To distribute means to "spread out from one to many." In the mathematical context, the factor *a* is distributed to both *b* and *c* in the parentheses.

Distributive Property of Multiplication over Addition

If a, b, and c are real numbers, then

$$a(b + c) = ab + ac \qquad \text{and} \qquad (b + c)a = ab + ac$$

Example 5   **Applying the Distributive Property**

Apply the distributive property: $2(a + 6b + 7)$

Solution:

$2(a + 6b + 7)$

$= 2(a + 6b + 7)$

$= 2(a) + 2(6b) + 2(7)$ Apply the distributive property.

$= 2a + 12b + 14$ Simplify.

> **Skill Practice**
>
> **14.** Apply the distributive property.
> $7(x + 4y + z)$

> **TIP:** Notice that the parentheses are removed after the distributive property is applied. Sometimes this is referred to as *clearing parentheses.*

Because the difference of two expressions $a - b$ can be written in terms of addition as $a + (-b)$, the distributive property can be applied when the operation of subtraction is present within the parentheses. For example:

$5(y - 7)$

$= 5[y + (-7)]$ Rewrite subtraction as addition of -7.

$= 5[y + (-7)]$ Apply the distributive property.

$= 5(y) + 5(-7)$

$= 5y + (-35)$, or $5y - 35$ Simplify.

Answer

14. $7x + 28y + 7z$

TIP: Notice that a negative factor preceding the parentheses changes the signs of all the terms to which it is multiplied.

$-1(-3a + 2b + 5c)$
$= +3a - 2b - 5c$

Example 6 **Applying the Distributive Property**

Use the distributive property to rewrite each expression.

a. $-(-3a + 2b + 5c)$ **b.** $-6(2 - 4x)$

Solution:

a. $-(-3a + 2b + 5c)$

$= -1(-3a + 2b + 5c)$ The negative sign preceding the parentheses can be interpreted as taking the opposite of the quantity that follows or as $-1(-3a + 2b + 5c)$

$= -1(-3a + 2b + 5c)$

$= -1(-3a) + (-1)(2b) + (-1)(5c)$ Apply the distributive property.

$= 3a + (-2b) + (-5c)$ Simplify.

$= 3a - 2b - 5c$

b. $-6(2 - 4x)$

$= -6[2 + (-4x)]$ Change subtraction to addition of $-4x$.

$= -6[2 + (-4x)]$ Apply the distributive property. Notice that multiplying by -6 changes the signs of all terms to which it is applied.

$= -6(2) + (-6)(-4x)$

$= -12 + 24x$ Simplify.

Note: In most cases, the distributive property will be applied without as much detail as shown in Examples 5 and 6. Instead, the distributive property will be applied in one step.

$2(a + 6b + 7)$ $-(3a + 2b + 5c)$ $-6(2 - 4x)$
1 step $= 2a + 12b + 14$ 1 step $= -3a - 2b - 5c$ 1 step $= -12 + 24x$

5. Simplifying Algebraic Expressions

An algebraic expression is the sum of one or more terms. A **term** is a constant or the product or quotient of constants and variables. For example, the expression

$$-7x^2 + xy - 100 \quad \text{or} \quad -7x^2 + xy + (-100)$$

consists of the terms $-7x^2, xy,$ and -100.

The terms $-7x^2$ and xy are **variable terms** and the term -100 is called a **constant term**. It is important to distinguish between a term and the factors within a term. For example, the quantity xy is one term, and the values x and y are factors within the term. The constant factor in a term is called the *numerical coefficient* (or simply **coefficient**) of the term. In the terms $-7x^2, xy,$ and -100, the coefficients are $-7, 1,$ and -100, respectively.

Answers
15. $-12x - 8y + 3z$
16. $18a - 42b$

Terms are *like* terms if they each have the same variables and the corresponding variables are raised to the same powers. For example:

Like Terms	Unlike Terms	
$-3b$ and $5b$	$-5c$ and $7d$	(different variables)
$9p^2q^3$ and p^2q^3	$4p^2q^3$ and $8p^3q^2$	(different powers)
$5w$ and $2w$	$5w$ and 2	(different variables)

Example 7 Identifying Terms, Factors, Coefficients, and *Like* Terms

a. List the terms of the expression $5x^2 - 3x + 2$.

b. Identify the coefficient of the term $6yz^3$.

c. Which of the pairs are *like* terms: $8b, 3b^2$ or $4c^2d, -6c^2d$?

Solution:

a. The terms of the expression $5x^2 - 3x + 2$ are $5x^2$, $-3x$, and 2.

b. The coefficient of $6yz^3$ is 6.

c. $4c^2d$ and $-6c^2d$ are *like* terms.

Two terms can be added or subtracted only if they are *like* terms. To add or subtract *like* terms, we use the distributive property as shown in Example 8.

Example 8 Using the Distributive Property to Add and Subtract *Like* Terms

Add or subtract as indicated.

a. $7x + 2x$ **b.** $-2p + 3p - p$

Solution:

a. $7x + 2x$

$= (7 + 2)x$ Apply the distributive property.

$= 9x$ Simplify.

b. $-2p + 3p - p$

$= -2p + 3p - 1p$ Note that $-p$ equals $-1p$.

$= (-2 + 3 - 1)p$ Apply the distributive property.

$= (0)p$ Simplify.

$= 0$

Although the distributive property is used to add and subtract *like* terms, it is tedious to write each step. Observe that adding or subtracting *like* terms is a matter of adding or subtracting the coefficients and leaving the variable factors unchanged. This can be shown in one step, a shortcut that we will use throughout the text. For example:

$$7x + 2x = 9x \qquad -2p + 3p - 1p = 0p = 0 \qquad -3a - 6a = -9a$$

Example 9   Combining *Like* Terms

Simplify by combining *like* terms.

a. $3yz + 5 - 2yz + 9$ **b.** $1.2w^3 + 5.7w^3$

Solution:

a. $3yz + 5 - 2yz + 9$

$= 3yz - 2yz + 5 + 9$ Arrange *like* terms together. Notice that constants such as 5 and 9 are *like* terms.

$= 1yz + 14$ Combine *like* terms.

$= yz + 14$

b. $1.2w^3 + 5.7w^3$

$= 6.9w^3$ Combine *like* terms.

Examples 10 and 11 illustrate how the distributive property is used to clear parentheses.

Example 10   Clearing Parentheses and Combining *Like* Terms

Simplify by clearing parentheses and combining *like* terms. $5 - 2(3x + 7)$

Solution:

$5 - 2(3x + 7)$ The order of operations indicates that we must perform multiplication before subtraction.

It is important to understand that a factor of -2 (not 2) will be multiplied to all terms within the parentheses. To see why this is so, we may rewrite the subtraction in terms of addition.

$= 5 + (-2)(3x + 7)$ Change subtraction to addition.

$= 5 + (-2)(3x + 7)$ A factor of -2 is to be distributed to terms in the parentheses.

$= 5 + (-2)(3x) + (-2)(7)$ Apply the distributive property.

$= 5 + (-6x) + (-14)$ Simplify.

$= 5 + (-14) + (-6x)$ Arrange *like* terms together.

$= -9 + (-6x)$ Combine *like* terms.

$= -9 - 6x$ Simplify by changing addition of the opposite to subtraction.

Example 11 Clearing Parentheses and Combining *Like* Terms

Simplify by clearing parentheses and combining *like* terms.

a. $10(5y + 2) - 6(y - 1)$

b. $\frac{1}{4}(4k + 2) - \frac{1}{2}(6k + 1)$

c. $-(4s - 6t) - (3t + 5s) - 2s$

Solution:

a. $10(5y + 2) - 6(y - 1)$

 $= 50y + 20 - 6y + 6$ Apply the distributive property. Notice that a factor of -6 is distributed through the second parentheses and changes the signs.

 $= 50y - 6y + 20 + 6$ Arrange *like* terms together.

 $= 44y + 26$ Combine *like* terms.

b. $\frac{1}{4}(4k + 2) - \frac{1}{2}(6k + 1)$

 $= \frac{4}{4}k + \frac{2}{4} - \frac{6}{2}k - \frac{1}{2}$ Apply the distributive property. Notice that a factor of $-\frac{1}{2}$ is distributed through the second parentheses and changes the signs.

 $= k + \frac{1}{2} - 3k - \frac{1}{2}$ Simplify fractions.

 $= k - 3k + \frac{1}{2} - \frac{1}{2}$ Arrange *like* terms together.

 $= -2k + 0$ Combine *like* terms.

 $= -2k$

c. $-(4s - 6t) - (3t + 5s) - 2s$

 $= -1(4s - 6t) - 1(3t + 5s) - 2s$ Notice that a factor of -1 is distributed through each parentheses.

 $= -4s + 6t - 3t - 5s - 2s$ Apply the distributive property.

 $= -4s - 5s - 2s + 6t - 3t$ Arrange *like* terms together.

 $= -11s + 3t$ Combine *like* terms.

Skill Practice

Clear the parentheses and combine *like* terms.

25. $5(2y + 3) - 3(3y + 1)$

26. $\frac{1}{2}(8x + 4) + \frac{1}{3}(3x - 9)$

27. $-4(x + 2y) - (2x - y) - 5x$

Answers

25. $4y + 13$ 26. $5x - 1$

27. $-11x - 7y$

Skill Practice

Clear the parentheses and combine *like* terms.

28. $6 - 5[-2y - 4(2y - 5)]$

Avoiding Mistakes

First clear the innermost parentheses and combine *like* terms within the brackets. Then use the distributive property to clear the brackets.

Answer

28. $50y - 94$

Example 12 Clearing Parentheses and Combining *Like* Terms

Simplify by clearing parentheses and combining *like* terms.

$$-7a - 4[3a - 2(a + 6)] - 4$$

Solution:

$-7a - 4[3a - 2(a + 6)] - 4$

$= -7a - 4[3a - 2a - 12] - 4$ Apply the distributive property to clear the innermost parentheses.

$= -7a - 4[a - 12] - 4$ Simplify within brackets by combining *like* terms.

$= -7a - 4a + 48 - 4$ Apply the distributive property to clear the brackets.

$= -11a + 44$ Combine *like* terms

Section 1.6   Practice Exercises

Study Skills Exercise

Write down the page number(s) for the Chapter Summary for this chapter. Describe one way in which you can use the Summary found at the end of each chapter.

Vocabulary and Key Concepts

1. a. Given the expression $12y + ab - 2x + 18$, the terms $12y$, ab, and $-2x$ are variable terms, whereas 18 is a _____ term.

  b. The constant factor in a term is called the _____.

  c. Given the expression x, the value of the coefficient is _____, and the exponent is _____.

  d. Terms that have the same variables, with corresponding variables raised to the same powers, are called _____ terms.

Review Exercises

For Exercises 2–14, perform the indicated operations.

2. $(-6) + 14$

3. $(-2) + 9$

4. $-13 - (-5)$

5. $-1 - (-19)$

6. $18 \div (-4)$

7. $-27 \div 5$

8. $-3 \cdot 0$

9. $0(-15)$

10. $\dfrac{1}{2} + \dfrac{3}{8}$

11. $\dfrac{25}{21} - \dfrac{6}{7}$

12. $\left(-\dfrac{3}{5}\right)\left(\dfrac{4}{27}\right)$

13. $\left(-\dfrac{11}{12}\right) \div \left(-\dfrac{5}{4}\right)$

14. $25 \cdot \left(-\dfrac{4}{5}\right)$

Concept 1: Commutative Properties of Real Numbers

For Exercises 15–22, rewrite each expression using the commutative property of addition or the commutative property of multiplication. **(See Examples 1 and 3.)**

15. $5 + (-8)$

16. $7 + (-2)$

17. $8 + x$

18. $p + 11$

19. $5(4)$

20. $10(8)$

21. $x(-12)$

22. $y(-23)$

For Exercises 23–26, rewrite each expression using addition. Then apply the commutative property of addition. **(See Example 2.)**

23. $x - 3$

24. $y - 7$

25. $4p - 9$

26. $3m - 12$

Concept 2: Associative Properties of Real Numbers

For Exercises 27–34, use the associative property of addition or multiplication to rewrite each expression. Then simplify the expression if possible. **(See Example 4.)**

27. $(x + 4) + 9$

28. $-3 + (5 + z)$

29. $-5(3x)$

30. $-12(4z)$

31. $\dfrac{6}{11}\left(\dfrac{11}{6}x\right)$

32. $\dfrac{3}{5}\left(\dfrac{5}{3}x\right)$

33. $-4\left(-\dfrac{1}{4}t\right)$

34. $-5\left(-\dfrac{1}{5}w\right)$

Concept 3: Identity and Inverse Properties of Real Numbers

35. What is another name for multiplicative inverse?

36. What is another name for additive inverse?

37. What is the additive identity?

38. What is the multiplicative identity?

Concept 4: Distributive Property of Multiplication over Addition

For Exercises 39–58, use the distributive property to clear parentheses. **(See Examples 5 and 6.)**

39. $6(5x + 1)$

40. $2(x + 7)$

41. $-2(a + 8)$

42. $-3(2z + 9)$

43. $3(5c - d)$

44. $4(w - 13z)$

45. $-7(y - 2)$

46. $-2(4x - 1)$

47. $-\dfrac{2}{3}(x - 6)$

48. $-\dfrac{1}{4}(2b - 8)$

49. $\dfrac{1}{3}(m - 3)$

50. $\dfrac{2}{5}(n - 5)$

51. $-(2p + 10)$

52. $-(7q + 1)$

53. $-2(-3w - 5z + 8)$

54. $-4(-7a - b - 3)$

55. $4(x + 2y - z)$

56. $-6(2a - b + c)$

57. $-(-6w + x - 3y)$

58. $-(-p - 5q - 10r)$

Mixed Exercises

For Exercises 59–70, use the associative property or distributive property to clear parentheses.

59. $-9 + (16 + y)$

60. $(b + 80) + 21$

61. $2(3 + x)$

62. $5(4 + y)$

63. $4(6z)$

64. $8(2p)$

65. $20 + (30 + r)$

66. $7 + (11 + a)$

67. $20(30 + r)$

68. $7(11 + a)$

69. $20(30r)$

70. $7(11a)$

For Exercises 71–79, match the statement with the property that describes it.

71. $6 \cdot \dfrac{1}{6} = 1$

72. $7(4 \cdot 9) = (7 \cdot 4)9$

73. $2(3 + k) = 6 + 2k$

74. $3 \cdot 7 = 7 \cdot 3$

75. $5 + (-5) = 0$

76. $18 \cdot 1 = 18$

77. $(3 + 7) + 19 = 3 + (7 + 19)$

78. $23 + 6 = 6 + 23$

79. $3 + 0 = 3$

a. Commutative property of addition

b. Inverse property of multiplication

c. Commutative property of multiplication

d. Associative property of addition

e. Identity property of multiplication

f. Associative property of multiplication

g. Inverse property of addition

h. Identity property of addition

i. Distributive property of multiplication over addition

Concept 5: Simplifying Algebraic Expressions

For Exercises 80–83, for each expression list the terms and their coefficients. **(See Example 7.)**

80. $3xy - 6x^2 + y - 17$

Term	Coefficient

81. $2x - y + 18xy + 5$

Term	Coefficient

82. $x^4 - 10xy + 12 - y$

Term	Coefficient

83. $-x + 8y - 9x^2y - 3$

Term	Coefficient

84. Explain why $12x$ and $12x^2$ are not *like* terms.

85. Explain why $3x$ and $3xy$ are not *like* terms.

86. Explain why $7z$ and $\sqrt{13}z$ are *like* terms.

87. Explain why πx and $8x$ are *like* terms.

88. Write three different *like* terms.

89. Write three terms that are not *like*.

For Exercises 90–98, simplify by combining *like* terms. **(See Examples 8 and 9.)**

90. $5k - 10k - 12k + 16 + 7$

91. $-4p - 2p + 8p - 15 + 3$

92. $9x - 7x^2 + 12x + 14x^2$

93. $2y^2 - 8y + y - 5y^2 - 3y^2$

94. $4ab^2 + 2a^2b - 6ab^2 + 5 + 3a^2b - 2$

95. $8x^3y - 5xy + 3 - 7 + 6xy - x^3y$

96. $\frac{1}{4}a + b - \frac{3}{4}a - 5b$

97. $\frac{2}{5} + 2t - \frac{3}{5} + t - \frac{6}{5}$

98. $2.8z - 8.1z + 6 - 15.2$

For Exercises 99–126, simplify by clearing parentheses and combining *like* terms. **(See Examples 10–12.)**

99. $-3(2x - 4) + 10$

100. $-2(4a + 3) - 14$

101. $4(w + 3) - 12$

102. $5(2r + 6) - 30$

103. $5 - 3(x - 4)$

104. $4 - 2(3x + 8)$

105. $-3(2t + 4w) + 8(2t - 4w)$

106. $-5(5y + 9z) + 3(3y + 6z)$

107. $2(q - 5u) - (2q + 8u)$

108. $6(x + 3y) - (6x - 5y)$

109. $-\frac{1}{3}(6t + 9) + 10$

110. $-\frac{3}{4}(8 + 4q) + 7$

111. $10(5.1a - 3.1) + 4$

112. $100(-3.14p - 1.05) + 212$

113. $-4m + 2(m - 3) + 2m$

114. $-3b + 4(b + 2) - 8b$

115. $\frac{1}{2}(10q - 2) + \frac{1}{3}(2 - 3q)$

116. $\frac{1}{5}(15 - 4p) - \frac{1}{10}(10p + 5)$

117. $7n - 2(n - 3) - 6 + n$

118. $8k - 4(k - 1) + 7 - k$

119. $6(x + 3) - 12 - 4(x - 3)$

120. $5(y - 4) + 3 - 6(y - 7)$

121. $0.2(6c - 1.6) + c$

122. $-1.1(5 + 8x) - 3.1$

123. $6 + 2[-8 - 3(2x + 4)] + 10x$

124. $-3 + 5[-3 - 4(y + 2)] - 8y$

125. $1 - 3[2(z + 1) - 5(z - 2)]$

126. $1 - 6[3(2t + 2) - 8(t + 2)]$

Expanding Your Skills

For Exercises 127–134, determine if the expressions are equivalent. If two expressions are not equivalent, state why.

127. $3a + b, b + 3a$

128. $4y + 1, 1 + 4y$

129. $2c + 7, 9c$

130. $5z + 4, 9z$

131. $5x - 3, 3 - 5x$

132. $6d - 7, 7 - 6d$

133. $5x - 3, -3 + 5x$

134. $8 - 2x, -2x + 8$

135. Which grouping of terms is easier to compute, $(14\frac{2}{7} + 2\frac{1}{3}) + \frac{2}{3}$ or $14\frac{2}{7} + (2\frac{1}{3} + \frac{2}{3})$?

136. Which grouping of terms is easier to compute, $(5\frac{1}{8} + 18\frac{2}{5}) + 1\frac{3}{5}$ or $5\frac{1}{8} + (18\frac{2}{5} + 1\frac{3}{5})$?

137. As a small child in school, the great mathematician Karl Friedrich Gauss (1777–1855) was said to have found the sum of the integers from 1 to 100 mentally:

$$1 + 2 + 3 + 4 + \cdots + 99 + 100$$

Rather than adding the numbers sequentially, he added the numbers in pairs:

$$(1 + 99) + (2 + 98) + (3 + 97) + \cdots + 100$$

a. Use this technique to add the integers from 1 to 10.

$$1 + 2 + 3 + 4 + 5 + 6 + 7 + 8 + 9 + 10$$

b. Use this technique to add the integers from 1 to 20.

Group Activity

Evaluating Formulas Using a Calculator

Materials: A calculator

Estimated Time: 15 minutes

Group Size: 2

In this chapter, we learned one of the most important concepts in mathematics—the order of operations. The proper order of operations is required whenever we evaluate any mathematical expression. The following formulas are taken from applications from science, math, statistics, and business. These are just some samples of what you may encounter as you work your way through college.

For Exercises 1–8, substitute the given values into the formula. Then use a calculator and the proper order of operations to simplify the result. Round to three decimal places if necessary.

1. $F = \dfrac{9}{5}C + 32$ (biology) $C = 35$

2. $V = \dfrac{nRT}{P}$ (chemistry) $n = 1.00, R = 0.0821, T = 273.15, P = 1.0$

3. $R = k\left(\dfrac{L}{r^2}\right)$ (electronics) $k = 0.05, L = 200, r = 0.5$

4. $m = \dfrac{y_2 - y_1}{x_2 - x_1}$ (mathematics) $x_1 = -8.3, x_2 = 3.3, y_1 = 4.6, y_2 = -9.2$

5. $z = \dfrac{\bar{x} - \mu}{\dfrac{\sigma}{\sqrt{n}}}$ (statistics) $\bar{x} = 69, \mu = 55, \sigma = 20, n = 25$

6. $S = R\left[\dfrac{(1 + i)^n - 1}{i}\right]$ (finance) $R = 200, i = 0.08, n = 30$

7. $x = \dfrac{-b + \sqrt{b^2 - 4ac}}{2a}$ (mathematics) $a = 2, b = -7, c = -15$

8. $h = \dfrac{1}{2}gt^2 + v_0t + h_0$ (physics) $g = -32, t = 2.4, v_0 = 192, h_0 = 288$

Chapter 1   Summary

Section 1.1   Introduction to Algebra and the Set of Real Numbers

Key Concepts

A **variable** is a symbol or letter used to represent an unknown number.

A **constant** is a value that is not variable.

An algebraic **expression** is a collection of variables and constants under algebraic operations.

Natural numbers: $\{1, 2, 3, \ldots\}$

Whole numbers: $\{0, 1, 2, 3, \ldots\}$

Integers: $\{\ldots -3, -2, -1, 0, 1, 2, 3, \ldots\}$

Rational numbers: The set of numbers that can be expressed in the form $\frac{p}{q}$, where p and q are integers and q does not equal 0. In decimal form, rational numbers are terminating or repeating decimals.

Irrational numbers: A subset of the real numbers whose elements cannot be written as a ratio of two integers. In decimal form, irrational numbers are nonterminating, nonrepeating decimals.

Real numbers: The set of both the rational numbers and the irrational numbers.

$a < b$ "a is less than b."

$a > b$ "a is greater than b."

$a \leq b$ "a is less than or equal to b."

$a \geq b$ "a is greater than or equal to b."

Two numbers that are the same distance from zero but on opposite sides of zero on the number line are called **opposites**. The opposite of a is denoted $-a$.

The **absolute value** of a real number, a, denoted $|a|$, is the distance between a and 0 on the number line.

If $a \geq 0$, $|a| = a$

If $a < 0$, $|a| = -a$

Examples

Example 1

Variables: x, y, z, a, b

Constants: $2, -3, \pi$

Expressions: $2x + 5, 3a + b^2$

Example 2

-5, 0, and 4 are integers.

$-\dfrac{5}{2}$, -0.5, and $0.\overline{3}$ are rational numbers.

$\sqrt{7}$, $-\sqrt{2}$, and π are irrational numbers.

Example 3

All real numbers can be located on the real number line.

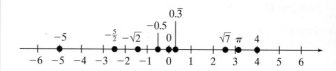

Example 4

$5 < 7$ "5 is less than 7."

$-2 > -10$ "-2 is greater than -10."

$y \leq 3.4$ "y is less than or equal to 3.4."

$x \geq \frac{1}{2}$ "x is greater than or equal to $\frac{1}{2}$."

Example 5

5 and -5 are opposites.

Example 6

$|7| = 7$

$|-7| = 7$

Section 1.2   Exponents, Square Roots, and the Order of Operations

Key Concepts

$$b^n = \underbrace{b \cdot b \cdot b \cdot b \ldots \cdot b}_{n \text{ factors of } b}$$ b is the **base**, n is the **exponent**

$\sqrt{x}$ is the positive **square root** of x.

The Order of Operations

1. Simplify expressions within parentheses and other grouping symbols first.
2. Evaluate expressions involving exponents, radicals, and absolute values.
3. Perform multiplication or division in the order that they occur from left to right.
4. Perform addition or subtraction in the order that they occur from left to right.

Examples

Example 1

$5^3 = 5 \cdot 5 \cdot 5 = 125$

Example 2

$\sqrt{49} = 7$

Example 3

$10 + 5(3 - 1)^2 - \sqrt{5 - 1}$

$= 10 + 5(2)^2 - \sqrt{4}$ Work within grouping symbols.

$= 10 + 5(4) - 2$ Simplify exponents and radicals.

$= 10 + 20 - 2$ Perform multiplication.

$= 30 - 2$ Add and subtract, left to right.

$= 28$

Section 1.3   Addition of Real Numbers

Key Concepts

Addition of Two Real Numbers

Same Signs   Add the absolute values of the numbers and apply the common sign to the sum.

Different Signs   Subtract the smaller absolute value from the larger absolute value. Then apply the sign of the number having the larger absolute value.

Examples

Example 1

$-3 + (-4) = -7$

$-1.3 + (-9.1) = -10.4$

Example 2

$-5 + 7 = 2$

$\dfrac{2}{3} + \left(-\dfrac{7}{3}\right) = -\dfrac{5}{3}$

| Section 1.4 | Subtraction of Real Numbers |

Key Concepts

Subtraction of Two Real Numbers

Add the opposite of the second number to the first number. That is,

$$a - b = a + (-b)$$

Examples

Example 1

$$7 - (-5) = 7 + (5) = 12$$

$$-3 - 5 = -3 + (-5) = -8$$

$$-11 - (-2) = -11 + (2) = -9$$

| Section 1.5 | Multiplication and Division of Real Numbers |

Key Concepts

Multiplication and Division of Two Real Numbers

Same Signs
Product is positive.
Quotient is positive.

Different Signs
Product is negative.
Quotient is negative.

Exponential Expressions
The negative sign is not part of the base unless it is included in parentheses.

The **reciprocal** of a nonzero number a is $\frac{1}{a}$.

Multiplication and Division Involving Zero

The product of any real number and 0 is 0.

The quotient of 0 and any nonzero real number is 0.

The quotient of any nonzero real number and 0 is undefined.

Examples

Example 1

$$(-5)(-2) = 10 \qquad \frac{-20}{-4} = 5$$

Example 2

$$(-3)(7) = -21 \qquad \frac{-4}{8} = -\frac{1}{2}$$

Example 3

$$-3^4 = -(3 \cdot 3 \cdot 3 \cdot 3) = -81$$
$$(-3)^4 = (-3) \cdot (-3) \cdot (-3) \cdot (-3) = 81$$

Example 4

The reciprocal of -6 is $-\frac{1}{6}$.

Example 5

$$4 \cdot 0 = 0$$

$$0 \div 4 = 0$$

$4 \div 0$ is undefined.

| **Section 1.6** | **Properties of Real Numbers and Simplifying Expressions** |

Key Concepts

Properties of Real Numbers

Commutative Properties

$a + b = b + a$

$ab = ba$

Associative Properties

$(a + b) + c = a + (b + c)$

$(ab)c = a(bc)$

Identity Properties

$0 + a = a$

$1 \cdot a = a$

Inverse Properties

$a + (-a) = 0$

$b \cdot \dfrac{1}{b} = 1$ for $b \neq 0$

Distributive Property of Multiplication over Addition

$a(b + c) = ab + ac$

A **term** is a constant or the product or quotient of constants and variables. The **coefficient** of a term is the numerical factor of the term.

Like **terms** have the same variables, and the corresponding variables have the same powers.

Terms can be added or subtracted if they are *like* terms. Sometimes it is necessary to clear parentheses before adding or subtracting *like* terms.

Examples

Example 1

$(-5) + (-7) = (-7) + (-5)$

$3 \cdot 8 = 8 \cdot 3$

Example 2

$(2 + 3) + 10 = 2 + (3 + 10)$

$(2 \cdot 4) \cdot 5 = 2 \cdot (4 \cdot 5)$

Example 3

$0 + (-5) = -5$

$1(-8) = -8$

Example 4

$1.5 + (-1.5) = 0$

$6 \cdot \dfrac{1}{6} = 1$

Example 5

$-2(x - 3y) = (-2)x + (-2)(-3y)$

$\qquad\qquad = -2x + 6y$

Example 6

$-2x$ is a term with coefficient -2.
yz^2 is a term with coefficient 1.

$3x$ and $-5x$ are *like* terms.
$4a^2b$ and $4ab$ are not *like* terms.

Example 7

$-2w - 4(w - 2) + 3$

$= -2w - 4w + 8 + 3 \qquad$ Clear parentheses.

$= -6w + 11 \qquad\qquad$ Combine *like* terms.

Chapter 1   Review Exercises

Section 1.1

1. Given the set $\{7, \frac{1}{3}, -4, 0, -\sqrt{3}, -0.\overline{2}, \pi, 1\}$,

   a. List the natural numbers.

   b. List the integers.

   c. List the whole numbers.

   d. List the rational numbers.

   e. List the irrational numbers.

   f. List the real numbers.

For Exercises 2–5, determine the absolute value.

2. $\left|\dfrac{1}{2}\right|$ 3. $|-6|$ 4. $|-\sqrt{7}|$ 5. $|0|$

For Exercises 6–13, identify whether the inequality is true or false.

6. $-6 > -1$ 7. $0 < -5$ 8. $-10 \le 0$

9. $5 \neq -5$ 10. $7 \ge 7$ 11. $7 \ge -7$

12. $0 \le -3$ 13. $-\dfrac{2}{3} \le -\dfrac{2}{3}$

For Exercises 14–17, evaluate the expressions for $x = 8$, $y = 4$, and $z = 1$.

14. $x - 2y$ 15. $x^2 - y$

16. $\sqrt{x + z}$ 17. $\sqrt{x + 2y}$

Section 1.2

For Exercises 18–23, write each English phrase as an algebraic expression.

18. The product of x and $\dfrac{2}{3}$

19. The quotient of 7 and y

20. The sum of 2 and $3b$

21. The difference of a and 5

22. Two more than $5k$

23. Seven less than $13z$

For Exercises 24–29, simplify the expressions.

24. 6^3 25. 15^2 26. $\sqrt{36}$

27. $\dfrac{1}{\sqrt{100}}$ 28. $\left(\dfrac{1}{4}\right)^2$ 29. $\left(\dfrac{3}{2}\right)^3$

For Exercises 30–33, perform the indicated operations.

30. $15 - 7 \cdot 2 + 12$ 31. $|-11| + |5| - (7 - 2)$

32. $4^2 - (5 - 2)^2$ 33. $22 - 3(8 \div 4)^2$

Section 1.3

For Exercises 34–46, add.

34. $-6 + 8$ 35. $14 + (-10)$

36. $21 + (-6)$ 37. $-12 + (-5)$

38. $\dfrac{2}{7} + \left(-\dfrac{1}{9}\right)$ 39. $\left(-\dfrac{8}{11}\right) + \left(\dfrac{1}{2}\right)$

40. $\left(-\dfrac{1}{10}\right) + \left(-\dfrac{5}{6}\right)$ 41. $\left(-\dfrac{5}{2}\right) + \left(-\dfrac{1}{5}\right)$

42. $-8.17 + 6.02$ 43. $2.9 + (-7.18)$

44. $13 + (-2) + (-8)$ 45. $-5 + (-7) + 20$

46. $2 + 5 + (-8) + (-7) + 0 + 13 + (-1)$

47. Under what conditions will the expression $a + b$ be negative?

48. The high temperatures (in degrees Celsius) for the province of Alberta, Canada, during a week in January were $-8, -1, -4, -3, -4, 0$, and 7. What was the average high temperature for that week? Round to the nearest tenth of a degree.

Section 1.4

For Exercises 49–61, subtract.

49. $13 - 25$ 50. $31 - (-2)$

51. $-8 - (-7)$ 52. $-2 - 15$

53. $\left(-\dfrac{7}{9}\right) - \dfrac{5}{6}$ 54. $\dfrac{1}{3} - \dfrac{9}{8}$

55. $7 - 8.2$

56. $-1.05 - 3.2$

57. $-16.1 - (-5.9)$

58. $7.09 - (-5)$

59. $\dfrac{11}{2} - \left(-\dfrac{1}{6}\right) - \dfrac{7}{3}$

60. $-\dfrac{4}{5} - \dfrac{7}{10} - \left(-\dfrac{13}{20}\right)$

61. $6 - 14 - (-1) - 10 - (-21) - 5$

62. Under what conditions will the expression $a - b$ be negative?

For Exercises 63–67, write an algebraic expression and simplify.

63. -18 subtracted from -7

64. The difference of -6 and 41

65. Seven decreased by 13

66. Five subtracted from the difference of 20 and -7

67. The sum of 6 and -12, decreased by 21

68. In Nevada, the highest temperature ever recorded was $125°F$ and the lowest was $-50°F$. Find the difference between the highest and lowest temperatures. (*Source: Information Please Almanac*)

Section 1.5

For Exercises 69–86, multiply or divide as indicated.

69. $10(-17)$

70. $(-7)13$

71. $(-52) \div 26$

72. $(-48) \div (-16)$

73. $\dfrac{7}{4} \div \left(-\dfrac{21}{2}\right)$

74. $\dfrac{2}{3}\left(-\dfrac{12}{11}\right)$

75. $-\dfrac{21}{5} \cdot 0$

76. $\dfrac{3}{4} \div 0$

77. $0 \div (-14)$

78. $(-0.45)(-5)$

79. $\dfrac{-21}{14}$

80. $\dfrac{-13}{-52}$

81. $(5)(-2)(3)$

82. $(-6)(-5)(15)$

83. $\left(-\dfrac{1}{2}\right)\left(\dfrac{7}{8}\right)\left(-\dfrac{4}{7}\right)$

84. $\left(\dfrac{12}{13}\right)\left(-\dfrac{1}{6}\right)\left(\dfrac{13}{14}\right)$

85. $40 \div 4 \div (-5)$

86. $\dfrac{10}{11} \div \dfrac{7}{11} \div \dfrac{5}{9}$

For Exercises 87–92, perform the indicated operations.

87. $9 - 4[-2(4 - 8) - 5(3 - 1)]$

88. $\dfrac{8(-3) - 6}{-7 - (-2)}$

89. $\dfrac{2}{3} - \left(\dfrac{3}{8} + \dfrac{5}{6}\right) \div \dfrac{5}{3}$

90. $5.4 - (0.3)^2 \div 0.09$

91. $\dfrac{5 - [3 - (-4)^2]}{36 \div (-2)(3)}$

92. $|-8 + 5| - \sqrt{5^2 - 3^2}$

For Exercises 93–96, evaluate each expression given the values $x = 4$ and $y = -9$.

93. $3(x + 2) \div y$

94. $\sqrt{x} - y$

95. $-xy$

96. $3x + 2y$

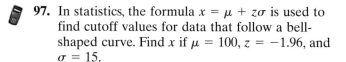 **97.** In statistics, the formula $x = \mu + z\sigma$ is used to find cutoff values for data that follow a bell-shaped curve. Find x if $\mu = 100$, $z = -1.96$, and $\sigma = 15$.

For Exercises 98–104, answer true or false. If a statement is false, explain why.

98. If n is positive, then $-n$ is negative.

99. If m is negative, then m^4 is negative.

100. If m is negative, then m^3 is negative.

101. If $m > 0$ and $n > 0$, then $mn > 0$.

102. If $p < 0$ and $q < 0$, then $pq < 0$.

103. A number and its reciprocal have the same signs.

104. A nonzero number and its opposite have different signs.

Section 1.6

For Exercises 105–112, answers may vary.

105. Give an example of the commutative property of addition.

106. Give an example of the associative property of addition.

107. Give an example of the inverse property of addition.

108. Give an example of the identity property of addition.

109. Give an example of the commutative property of multiplication.

110. Give an example of the associative property of multiplication.

111. Give an example of the inverse property of multiplication.

112. Give an example of the identity property of multiplication.

113. Explain why $5x - 2y$ is the same as $-2y + 5x$.

114. Explain why $3a - 9y$ is the same as $-9y + 3a$.

115. List the terms of the expression:
$3y + 10x - 12 + xy$

116. Identify the coefficients for the terms listed in Exercise 115.

For Exercises 117 and 118, simplify by combining *like* terms.

117. $3a + 3b - 4b + 5a - 10$

118. $-6p + 2q + 9 - 13q - p + 7$

For Exercises 119 and 120, use the distributive property to clear the parentheses.

119. $-2(4z + 9)$ **120.** $5(4w - 8y + 1)$

For Exercises 121–126, simplify the expression.

121. $2p - (p + 5w) + 3w$

122. $6(h + 3m) - 7h - 4m$

123. $\frac{1}{2}(-6q) + q - 4\left(3q + \frac{1}{4}\right)$

124. $0.3b + 12(0.2 - 0.5b)$

125. $-4[2(x + 1) - (3x + 8)]$

126. $5[(7y - 3) + 3(y + 8)]$

Chapter 1   Test

1. Is $0.\overline{315}$ a rational number or an irrational number? Explain your reasoning.

2. Plot the points on a number line: $|3|, 0, -2, 0.5,$ $\left|-\frac{3}{2}\right|, \sqrt{16}$.

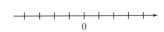

3. Use the number line in Exercise 2 to identify whether the statements are true or false.

  a. $|3| < -2$ **b.** $0 \le \left|-\frac{3}{2}\right|$

  c. $-2 < 0.5$ **d.** $|3| \ge \left|-\frac{3}{2}\right|$

4. Use the definition of exponents to expand the expressions:

  a. $(4x)^3$ **b.** $4x^3$

5. a. Translate the expression into an English phrase: $2(a - b)$. (Answers may vary.)

  b. Translate the expression into an English phrase: $2a - b$. (Answers may vary.)

6. Translate the phrase into an algebraic expression: "The quotient of the square root of c and the square of d."

For Exercises 7–23, perform the indicated operations.

7. $18 + (-12)$

8. $-10 + (-9)$

9. $-15 - (-3)$

10. $21 - (-7)$

11. $-\dfrac{1}{8} + \left(-\dfrac{3}{4}\right)$

12. $-10.06 - (-14.72)$

13. $-14 + (-2) - 16$

14. $-84 \div 7$

15. $38 \div 0$

16. $7(-4)$

17. $-22 \cdot 0$

18. $(-16)(-2)(-1)(-3)$

19. $\dfrac{2}{5} \div \left(-\dfrac{7}{10}\right) \cdot \left(-\dfrac{7}{6}\right)$

20. $(8 - 10) \cdot \dfrac{3}{2} + (-5)$

21. $8 - [(2 - 4) - (8 - 9)]$

22. $\dfrac{\sqrt{5^2 - 4^2}}{|-12 + 3|}$

23. $\dfrac{|4 - 10|}{2 - 3(5 - 1)}$

24. At the beginning of the month, Vienna owed $270 on her credit card. During the month she made two payments of $80 and $150. She spent $110 and was also charged $7 in interest. What was Vienna's credit card balance at the end of the month?

25. Hector's sales in his new auto parts business have been sporadic during the first year. During January his profit was –$1750. During February his profit was $4500. How much more was his profit in February than in January?

26. Identify the property that justifies each statement.

a. $6(-8) = (-8)6$

b. $5 + 0 = 5$

c. $(2 + 3) + 4 = 2 + (3 + 4)$

d. $\dfrac{1}{7} \cdot 7 = 1$

e. $8[7(-3)] = (8 \cdot 7)(-3)$

For Exercises 27–31, simplify the expression.

27. $-5x - 4y + 3 - 7x + 6y - 7$

28. $-3(4m + 8p - 7)$

29. $3k - 20 + (-9k) + 12$

30. $4(p - 5) - (8p + 3)$

31. $\dfrac{1}{2}(12p - 4) + \dfrac{1}{3}(2 - 6p)$

For Exercises 32–35, evaluate the expression given the values $x = 4$ and $y = -3$ and $z = -7$.

32. $y^2 - x$

33. $3x - 2y$

34. $y(x - 2)$

35. $-y^2 - 4x + z$

For Exercises 36–38, translate the English statement to an algebraic expression. Then simplify the expression.

36. Subtract -4 from 12

37. Find the difference of 6 and 8

38. The quotient of 10 and -12

Linear Equations and Inequalities

2

CHAPTER OUTLINE

Chapter 2

In this chapter, we learn how to solve linear equations and inequalities in one variable. This important category of equations and inequalities is used in a variety of applications.

Review Your Skills

Use what you have learned about operations on real numbers and order of operations to complete the table. Fill in each blank box with one of the four basic operations, $+$, $-$, $\cdot$, or $\div$ so that the statement is true both going across and going down. Pay careful attention to the order of operations. One row has been filled in to help you begin.

-10		2		-3	$=$	-11
12		-2		3	$=$	-18
$+$		$+$		$+$		$+$
6		4		10	$=$	-8
$=$		$=$		$=$		$=$
8		0		1	$=$	-1

Concepts

1. Definition of a Linear Equation in One Variable
2. Addition and Subtraction Properties of Equality
3. Multiplication and Division Properties of Equality
4. Translations

1. Definition of a Linear Equation in One Variable

An **equation** is a statement that indicates that two expressions are equal. The following are equations.

$$x = 5 \qquad y + 2 = 12 \qquad -4z = 28$$

All equations have an equal sign. Furthermore, notice that the equal sign separates the equation into two parts, the left-hand side and the right-hand side. A **solution to an equation** is a value of the variable that makes the equation a true statement. Substituting a solution into an equation for the variable makes the right-hand side equal to the left-hand side.

Equation	Solution	Check	
$x = 5$	5	$x = 5$ $\downarrow$ $5 = 5$ ✔	Substitute 5 for x. Right-hand side equals left-hand side.
$y + 2 = 12$	10	$y + 2 = 12$ $\downarrow$ $10 + 2 = 12$ ✔	Substitute 10 for y. Right-hand side equals left-hand side.
$-4z = 28$	-7	$-4z = 28$ $\downarrow$ $-4(-7) = 28$ ✔	Substitute -7 for z. Right-hand side equals left-hand side.

Avoiding Mistakes

Be sure to notice the difference between solving an equation versus simplifying an expression. For example, $2x + 1 = 7$ is an equation, whose solution is 3, while $2x + 1 + 7$ is an expression that simplifies to $2x + 8$.

Skill Practice

Determine if the number given is a solution to the equation.

1. $4x - 1 = 7;$ 3
2. $9 = -2y + 5;$ -2

Example 1 Determining Whether a Number Is a Solution to an Equation

Determine whether the given number is a solution to the equation.

a. $4x + 7 = 5;$ $-\frac{1}{2}$ **b.** $-4 = 6w - 14;$ 3

Solution:

a. $4x + 7 = 5$

$4(-\frac{1}{2}) + 7 \stackrel{?}{=} 5$ Substitute $-\frac{1}{2}$ for x.

$-2 + 7 \stackrel{?}{=} 5$ Simplify.

$5 \stackrel{?}{=} 5$ ✔   Right-hand side equals the left-hand side. Thus, $-\frac{1}{2}$ *is a solution* to the equation $4x + 7 = 5$.

b. $-4 = 6w - 14$

$-4 \stackrel{?}{=} 6(3) - 14$ Substitute 3 for w.

$-4 \stackrel{?}{=} 18 - 14$ Simplify.

$-4 \neq 4$ Right-hand side does not equal left-hand side. Thus, 3 is *not a solution* to the equation $-4 = 6w - 14$.

Answers

1. No   **2.** Yes

In the study of algebra, you will encounter a variety of equations. In this chapter, we will focus on a specific type of equation called a linear equation in one variable.

Definition of a Linear Equation in One Variable

Let a, b, and c be real numbers such that $a \neq 0$. A **linear equation in one variable** is an equation that can be written in the form

$$ax + b = c$$

Note: A linear equation in one variable is often called a first-degree equation because the variable x has an implied exponent of 1.

Examples	Notes
$2x + 4 = 20$	$a = 2, b = 4, c = 20$
$-3x - 5 = 16$ can be written as $-3x + (-5) = 16$	$a = -3, b = -5, c = 16$
$5x + 9 - 4x = 1$ can be written as $x + 9 = 1$	$a = 1, b = 9, c = 1$

---

2. Addition and Subtraction Properties of Equality

If two equations have the same solution then the equations are equivalent. For example, the following equations are equivalent because the solution for each equation is 6.

Equivalent Equations	**Check the Solution 6**
$2x - 5 = 7$ ⟶	$2(6) - 5 \overset{?}{=} 7 \Rightarrow 12 - 5 \overset{?}{=} 7$ ✔
$2x = 12$ ⟶	$2(6) \overset{?}{=} 12 \Rightarrow 12 \overset{?}{=} 12$ ✔
$x = 6$ ⟶	$6 \overset{?}{=} 6 \Rightarrow 6 \overset{?}{=} 6$ ✔

To solve a linear equation, $ax + b = c$, the goal is to find *all* values of x that make the equation true. One general strategy for solving an equation is to rewrite it as an equivalent but simpler equation. This process is repeated until the equation can be written in the form $x =$ number. The addition and subtraction properties of equality help us do this.

Addition and Subtraction Properties of Equality

Let a, b, and c represent algebraic expressions.

1. **Addition property of equality:**   If $a = b$,
   then $a + c = b + c$

2. ***Subtraction property of equality:***   If $a = b$,
   then $a - c = b - c$

*The subtraction property of equality follows directly from the addition property, because subtraction is defined in terms of addition.

If $a + (-c) = b + (-c)$

then, $a - c = b - c$

Concept Connections

State whether the equation is a linear equation in one variable.

3. $5y + 1 = 0$

4. $2a^2 + 4 = 0$

5. $6 - 3x = 0$

6. $6t + 8y = 0$

Answers

3. Yes **4.** No **5.** Yes **6.** No

The addition and subtraction properties of equality indicate that adding or subtracting the same quantity on each side of an equation results in an equivalent equation. This means that if two equal quantities are increased or decreased by the same amount, then the resulting quantities will also be equal (Figure 2-1).

$$50 = 50$$
$$50 + 20 = 50 + 20$$
$$70 = 70$$

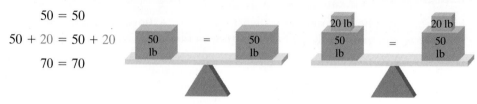

Figure 2-1

Skill Practice

Solve the equations.

7. $v - 7 = 2$

8. $x + 4 = 4$

Example 2 Applying the Addition and Subtraction Properties of Equality

Solve the equations.

a. $p - 4 = 11$ **b.** $w + 5 = -2$

Solution:

In each equation, the goal is to isolate the variable on one side of the equation. To accomplish this, we use the fact that the sum of a number and its opposite is zero and the difference of a number and itself is zero.

a. $p - 4 = 11$

$p - 4 + 4 = 11 + 4$ To isolate p, add 4 to both sides $(-4 + 4 = 0)$.

$p + 0 = 15$ Simplify.

$p = 15$ Check by substituting $p = 15$ into the original equation.

     Check: $p - 4 = 11$

           $15 - 4 \stackrel{?}{=} 11$

The solution is 15. $11 \stackrel{?}{=} 11$ ✔ True

b. $w + 5 = -2$

$w + 5 - 5 = -2 - 5$ To isolate w, subtract 5 from both sides $(5 - 5 = 0)$.

$w + 0 = -7$ Simplify.

$w = -7$ Check by substituting $w = -7$ into the original equation.

     Check: $w + 5 = -2$

           $-7 + 5 \stackrel{?}{=} -2$

The solution is -7. $-2 \stackrel{?}{=} -2$ ✔ True

Answers

7. 9   **8.** 0

In some situations, rather than writing the solution to an equation, we may write the solution *set* to an equation. The **solution set** is the set of all solutions to an equation. For instance, in Example 2(b), the solution is -7, but the *solution set* would be written as $\{-7\}$. Check to determine how your instructor prefers that you write the answer.

Example 3 Applying the Addition Property of Equality

Solve the equations.

a. $\dfrac{9}{4} = q - \dfrac{3}{4}$ **b.** $-1.2 + z = 4.6$

Solution:

a. $\dfrac{9}{4} = q - \dfrac{3}{4}$

$\dfrac{9}{4} + \dfrac{3}{4} = q - \dfrac{3}{4} + \dfrac{3}{4}$ To isolate q, add $\frac{3}{4}$ to both sides $\left(-\frac{3}{4} + \frac{3}{4} = 0\right)$.

$\dfrac{12}{4} = q + 0$ Simplify.

$3 = q$ or equivalently, $q = 3$

> **TIP:** The variable may be isolated on either side of the equation.

Check: $\dfrac{9}{4} = q - \dfrac{3}{4}$

$\dfrac{9}{4} \stackrel{?}{=} 3 - \dfrac{3}{4}$ Substitute $q = 3$.

$\dfrac{9}{4} \stackrel{?}{=} \dfrac{12}{4} - \dfrac{3}{4}$ Common denominator

$\dfrac{9}{4} \stackrel{?}{=} \dfrac{9}{4}$ ✔ True

The solution is 3.

b. $-1.2 + z = 4.6$

$-1.2 + 1.2 + z = 4.6 + 1.2$ To isolate z, add 1.2 to both sides.

$0 + z = 5.8$

$z = 5.8$ Check: $-1.2 + z = 4.6$

$-1.2 + 5.8 \stackrel{?}{=} 4.6$ Substitute $z = 5.8$.

The solution is 5.8. $4.6 \stackrel{?}{=} 4.6$ ✔ True

Skill Practice

Solve the equations.

9. $\dfrac{1}{4} = a - \dfrac{2}{3}$

10. $-8.1 + w = 11.5$

3. Multiplication and Division Properties of Equality

Adding or subtracting the same quantity to both sides of an equation results in an equivalent equation. In a similar way, multiplying or dividing both sides of an equation by the same nonzero quantity also results in an equivalent equation. This is stated formally as the multiplication and division properties of equality.

Answers

9. $\dfrac{11}{12}$ **10.** 19.6

Concept Connections

11. The division property of equality states that if

$$a = b, \text{ then } \frac{a}{c} = \frac{b}{c}$$

provided that $c \neq 0$. Why is the condition $c \neq 0$ necessary?

Multiplication and Division Properties of Equality

Let a, b, and c represent algebraic expressions, where $c \neq 0$.

1. Multiplication property of equality: If $a = b$,

then $ac = bc$

2. *Division property of equality: If $a = b$

then $\dfrac{a}{c} = \dfrac{b}{c}$

*The division property of equality follows directly from the multiplication property because division is defined as multiplication by the reciprocal.

If $a \cdot \dfrac{1}{c} = b \cdot \dfrac{1}{c}$

then, $\dfrac{a}{c} = \dfrac{b}{c}$

To understand the multiplication property of equality, suppose we start with a true equation such as $10 = 10$. If both sides of the equation are multiplied by a constant such as 3, the result is also a true statement (Figure 2-2).

$$10 = 10$$
$$3 \cdot 10 = 3 \cdot 10$$
$$30 = 30$$

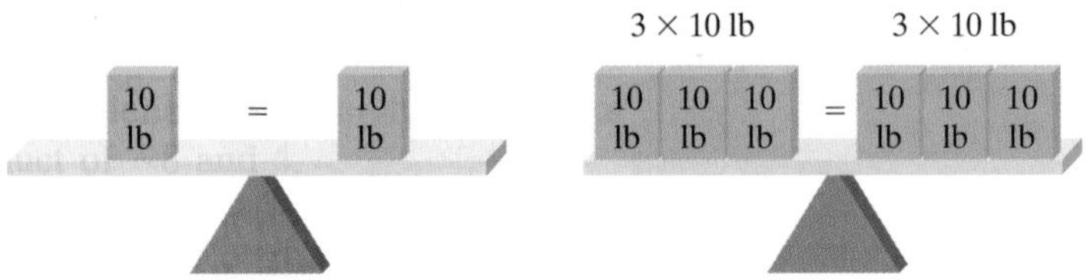

Figure 2-2

Similarly, if both sides of the equation are divided by a nonzero real number such as 2, the result is also a true statement (Figure 2-3).

$$10 = 10$$
$$\frac{10}{2} = \frac{10}{2}$$
$$5 = 5$$

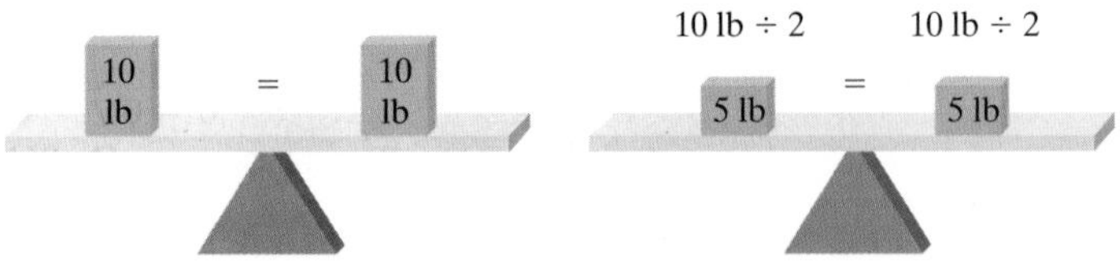

Figure 2-3

TIP: The product of a number and its reciprocal is always 1. For example:

$$\frac{1}{5}(5) = 1$$

$$-\frac{7}{2}\left(-\frac{2}{7}\right) = 1$$

To solve an equation in the variable x, the goal is to write the equation in the form $x = $ number. In particular, notice that we desire the coefficient of x to be 1. That is, we want to write the equation as $1x = $ number. Therefore, to solve an equation such as $5x = 15$, we can multiply both sides of the equation by the reciprocal of the x-term coefficient. In this case, multiply both sides by the reciprocal of 5, which is $\frac{1}{5}$.

$$5x = 15$$

$$\frac{1}{5}(5x) = \frac{1}{5}(15) \qquad \text{Multiply by } \frac{1}{5}.$$

$$1x = 3 \qquad \text{The coefficient of the } x\text{-term is now 1.}$$

$$x = 3$$

Answer

11. $c \neq 0$ because division by zero is undefined.

The division property of equality can also be used to solve the equation $5x = 15$ by dividing both sides by the coefficient of the x-term. In this case, divide both sides by 5 to make the coefficient of x equal to 1.

$$5x = 15$$

$$\frac{5x}{5} = \frac{15}{5} \qquad \text{Divide by } 5.$$

$$1x = 3 \qquad \text{The coefficient on the } x\text{-term is now 1.}$$

$$x = 3$$

> **TIP:** The quotient of a nonzero real number and itself is always 1. For example:
>
> $$\frac{5}{5} = 1$$
>
> $$\frac{-3.5}{-3.5} = 1$$

Example 4 **Applying the Division Property of Equality**

Solve the equations using the division property of equality.

a. $12x = 60$ **b.** $48 = -8w$ **c.** $-x = 8$

Solution:

a. $12x = 60$

$$\frac{12x}{12} = \frac{60}{12} \qquad \text{To obtain a coefficient of 1 for the } x\text{-term,}$$
$$\text{divide both sides by 12.}$$

$$1x = 5 \qquad \text{Simplify.}$$

$$x = 5 \qquad \underline{\text{Check:}} \quad 12x = 60$$

$$12(5) \stackrel{?}{=} 60$$

The solution is 5. $\qquad\qquad 60 \stackrel{?}{=} 60 \checkmark \quad \text{True}$

b. $48 = -8w$

$$\frac{48}{-8} = \frac{-8w}{-8} \qquad \text{To obtain a coefficient of 1 for the } w\text{-term, divide}$$
$$\text{both sides by } -8.$$

$$-6 = 1w \qquad \text{Simplify.}$$

$$-6 = w \qquad \underline{\text{Check:}} \ 48w = -8w$$

$$48 \stackrel{?}{=} -8(-6)$$

The solution is -6. $\qquad\qquad 48 \stackrel{?}{=} 48 \checkmark \quad \text{True}$

c. $-x = 8 \qquad\qquad$ Note that $-x$ is equivalent to $-1 \cdot x$.

$$-1x = 8$$

$$\frac{-1x}{-1} = \frac{8}{-1} \qquad \text{To obtain a coefficient of 1 for the } x\text{-term, divide}$$
$$\text{by } -1.$$

$$x = -8 \qquad \underline{\text{Check:}} \ -x = 8$$

$$-(-8) \stackrel{?}{=} 8$$

The solution is -8. $\qquad\qquad 8 \stackrel{?}{=} 8 \checkmark \quad \text{True}$

Skill Practice

Solve the equations.
12. $4x = -20$
13. $100 = -4p$
14. $-y = -11$

> **TIP:** In Example 4(c), we could also have *multiplied* both sides by -1 to create a coefficient of 1 on the x-term.
>
> $$-x = 8$$
>
> $$(-1)(-x) = (-1)8$$
>
> $$x = -8$$

Answers
12. -5 **13.** -25 **14.** 11

Example 5   Applying the Multiplication Property of Equality

Solve the equations by using the multiplication property of equality.

$$-\frac{2}{9}q = \frac{1}{3}$$

Solution:

$$-\frac{2}{9}q = \frac{1}{3}$$

$$\left(-\frac{9}{2}\right)\left(-\frac{2}{9}q\right) = \frac{1}{3}\left(-\frac{9}{2}\right)$$ To obtain a coefficient of 1 for the q-term, multiply by the reciprocal of $-\frac{2}{9}$, which is $-\frac{9}{2}$.

$$1q = -\frac{3}{2}$$ Simplify. The product of a number and its reciprocal is 1.

$$q = -\frac{3}{2}$$ Check: $-\dfrac{2}{9}q = \dfrac{1}{3}$

$$-\frac{2}{9}\left(-\frac{3}{2}\right) \stackrel{?}{=} \frac{1}{3}$$

The solution is $-\dfrac{3}{2}$. $\dfrac{1}{3} \stackrel{?}{=} \dfrac{1}{3}$ ✔   True

---

TIP: When applying the multiplication or division property of equality to obtain a coefficient of 1 for the variable term, we will generally use the following convention:

- If the coefficient of the variable term is expressed as a fraction, we will usually multiply both sides by its reciprocal, as in Example 5.
- If the coefficient of the variable term is an integer or decimal, we will divide both sides by the coefficient itself, as in Example 6.

Example 6   Applying the Division Property of Equality

Solve the equation by using the division property of equality.

$$-3.43 = -0.7z$$

Solution:

$$-3.43 = -0.7z$$

$$\frac{-3.43}{-0.7} = \frac{-0.7z}{-0.7}$$ To obtain a coefficient of 1 for the z-term, divide by -0.7.

$$4.9 = 1z$$ Simplify.

$$4.9 = z$$

$$z = 4.9$$ Check: $-3.43 = -0.7z$

$$-3.43 \stackrel{?}{=} -0.7(4.9)$$

The solution is 4.9. $-3.43 \stackrel{?}{=} -3.43$ ✔   True

Answers

15. $-\dfrac{3}{8}$ **16.** 3.1

Example 7   **Applying the Multiplication Property of Equality**

Solve the equation by using the multiplication property of equality.

$$\frac{d}{6} = -4$$

Solution:

$$\frac{d}{6} = -4$$

$$\frac{1}{6}d = -4 \qquad \frac{d}{6} \text{ is equivalent to } \frac{1}{6}d.$$

$$\frac{6}{1} \cdot \frac{1}{6}d = -4 \cdot \frac{6}{1} \qquad \begin{array}{l}\text{To obtain a coefficient of 1 for the } d\text{-term,} \\ \text{multiply by the reciprocal of } \frac{1}{6}, \text{ which is } \frac{6}{1}.\end{array}$$

$$1d = -24 \qquad \text{Simplify.}$$

$$d = -24 \qquad \underline{\text{Check:}} \ \frac{d}{6} = -4$$

$$\frac{-24}{6} \stackrel{?}{=} -4$$

The solution is -24. $-4 \stackrel{?}{=} -4$ ✔ True

Skill Practice

Solve the equation.

17. $\frac{x}{5} = -8$

It is important to distinguish between cases where the addition or subtraction properties of equality should be used to isolate a variable versus those in which the multiplication or division property of equality should be used. Remember the goal is to isolate the variable term and obtain a coefficient of 1. Compare the equations:

$$5 + x = 20 \qquad \text{and} \qquad 5x = 20$$

In the first equation, the relationship between 5 and x is addition. Therefore, we want to reverse the process by subtracting 5 from both sides. In the second equation, the relationship between 5 and x is multiplication. To isolate x, we reverse the process by dividing by 5 or equivalently, multiplying by the reciprocal, $\frac{1}{5}$.

$$5 + x = 20 \qquad \text{and} \qquad 5x = 20$$

$$5 - 5 + x = 20 - 5 \qquad\qquad \frac{5x}{5} = \frac{20}{5}$$

$$x = 15 \qquad\qquad\qquad x = 4$$

Answer

17. -40

4. Translations

Example 8　Translating to a Linear Equation

Write an algebraic equation to represent each English sentence. Then solve the equation.

a. The quotient of a number and 4 is 6.

b. The product of a number and 4 is 6.

c. Negative twelve is equal to the sum of -5 and a number.

d. The value 1.4 subtracted from a number is 5.7.

Solution:

For each case we will let x represent the unknown number.

a. The quotient of a number and 4 is 6.

$$\frac{x}{4} = 6$$

$$4 \cdot \frac{x}{4} = 4 \cdot 6 \qquad \text{Multiply both sides by } 4.$$

$$\frac{4}{1} \cdot \frac{x}{4} = 4 \cdot 6$$

$$x = 24 \qquad \underline{\text{Check:}} \quad \frac{24}{4} \overset{?}{=} 6 \ ✔ \quad \text{True}$$

The number is 24.

b. The product of a number and 4 is 6.

$$4x = 6$$

$$\frac{4x}{4} = \frac{6}{4} \qquad \text{Divide both sides by } 4.$$

$$x = \frac{3}{2} \qquad \underline{\text{Check:}} \quad 4\left(\frac{3}{2}\right) \overset{?}{=} 6 \ ✔ \quad \text{True}$$

The number is $\frac{3}{2}$.

c. Negative twelve is equal to the sum of -5 and a number.

$$-12 = -5 + x$$

$$-12 + 5 = -5 + 5 + x \qquad \text{Add } 5 \text{ to both sides.}$$

$$-7 = x \qquad \underline{\text{Check:}} \quad -12 \overset{?}{=} -5 + (-7) \ ✔ \quad \text{True}$$

The number is -7.

d. The value 1.4 subtracted from a number is 5.7.

$$x - 1.4 = 5.7$$

$$x - 1.4 + 1.4 = 5.7 + 1.4 \qquad \text{Add } 1.4 \text{ to both sides.}$$

$$x = 7.1 \qquad \underline{\text{Check:}} \quad 7.1 - 1.4 \overset{?}{=} 5.7 \ ✔ \quad \text{True}$$

The number is 7.1.

Skill Practice

Write an algebraic equation to represent each English sentence. Then solve the equation.

18. The quotient of a number and -2 is 8.

19. The product of a number and -3 is -24.

20. The sum of a number and 6 is -20.

21. 13 is equal to 5 subtracted from a number.

Answers

18. $\dfrac{x}{-2} = 8$; The number is -16.

19. $-3x = -24$; The number is 8.

20. $y + 6 = -20$; The number is -26.

21. $13 = x - 5$; The number is 18.

Section 2.1   Practice Exercises

Study Skills Exercise

After getting a test back, it is a good idea to correct the test so that you do not make the same errors again. One recommended approach is to use a clean sheet of paper, and divide the paper down the middle vertically as shown. For each problem that you missed on the test, rework the problem correctly on the left-hand side of the paper. Then give a written explanation on the right-hand side of the paper. To reinforce the correct procedure, do four more problems of that type.

Take the time this week to make corrections from your last test.

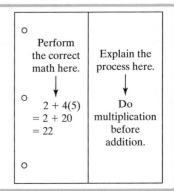

Perform the correct math here.	Explain the process here.
2 + 4(5) = 2 + 20 = 22	Do multiplication before addition.

Vocabulary and Key Concepts

1. a. An _____ is a statement that indicates that two expressions are equal.

  b. A _____ to an equation is a value of the variable that makes the equation a true statement.

  c. An equation that can be written in the form $ax + b = c\ (a \neq 0)$ is called a _____ equation in one variable.

Concept 1: Definition of a Linear Equation in One Variable

For Exercises 2–6, identify the following as either an expression or an equation.

2. $2 - 8x + 10$ **3.** $x - 4 + 5x$ **4.** $8x + 2 = 7$

5. $9 = 2x - 4$ **6.** $3x^2 + x = -3$

7. Explain how to determine if a number is a solution to an equation.

8. Explain why the equations $6x = 12$ and $x = 2$ are *equivalent equations*.

For Exercises 9–14, determine whether the given number is a solution to the equation. **(See Example 1.)**

9. $x - 1 = 5;\quad 4$ **10.** $x - 2 = 1;\quad -1$ **11.** $5x = -10;\quad -2$

12. $3x = 21;\quad 7$ **13.** $3x + 9 = 3;\quad -2$ **14.** $2x - 1 = -3;\quad -1$

Concept 2: Addition and Subtraction Properties of Equality

For Exercises 15–34, solve the equations using the addition or subtraction property of equality. Be sure to check your answers. **(See Examples 2 and 3.)**

15. $x + 6 = 5$ **16.** $x - 2 = 10$ **17.** $q - 14 = 6$ **18.** $w + 3 = -5$

19. $2 + m = -15$ **20.** $-6 + n = 10$ **21.** $-23 = y - 7$ **22.** $-9 = -21 + b$

23. $4 + c = 4$ **24.** $-13 + b = -13$ **25.** $4.1 = 2.8 + a$ **26.** $5.1 = -2.5 + y$

27. $5 = z - \dfrac{1}{2}$ **28.** $-7 = p + \dfrac{2}{3}$ **29.** $x + \dfrac{5}{2} = \dfrac{1}{2}$ **30.** $x - \dfrac{2}{3} = \dfrac{7}{3}$

31. $-6.02 + c = -8.15$ **32.** $p + 0.035 = -1.12$ **33.** $3.245 + t = -0.0225$ **34.** $-1.004 + k = 3.0589$

Concept 3: Multiplication and Division Properties of Equality

For Exercises 35–54, solve the equations using the multiplication or division property of equality. Be sure to check your answers. **(See Examples 4–7.)**

35. $6x = 54$

36. $2w = 8$

37. $12 = -3p$

38. $6 = -2q$

39. $-5y = 0$

40. $-3k = 0$

41. $-\dfrac{y}{5} = 3$

42. $-\dfrac{z}{7} = 1$

43. $\dfrac{4}{5} = -t$

44. $-\dfrac{3}{7} = -h$

45. $\dfrac{2}{5}a = -4$

46. $\dfrac{3}{8}b = -9$

47. $-\dfrac{1}{5}b = -\dfrac{4}{5}$

48. $-\dfrac{3}{10}w = \dfrac{2}{5}$

49. $-41 = -x$

50. $32 = -y$

51. $3.81 = -0.03p$

52. $2.75 = -0.5q$

53. $5.82y = -15.132$

54. $-32.3x = -0.4522$

Concept 4: Translations

For Exercises 55–64, write an algebraic equation to represent each English sentence. (Let x represent the unknown number.) Then solve the equation. **(See Example 8.)**

55. The sum of negative eight and a number is forty-two.

56. The sum of thirty-one and a number is thirteen.

57. The difference of a number and negative six is eighteen.

58. The sum of negative twelve and a number is negative fifteen.

59. The product of a number and seven is the same as negative sixty-three.

60. The product of negative three and a number is the same as twenty-four.

61. The quotient of a number and twelve is one-third.

62. Eighteen is equal to the quotient of a number and two.

63. The sum of a number and $\frac{5}{8}$ is $\frac{13}{8}$.

64. The difference of a number and $\frac{2}{3}$ is $\frac{1}{3}$.

Mixed Exercises

For Exercises 65–88, solve the equation using the appropriate property of equality.

65. a. $a - 9 = 1$
  b. $-9a = 1$

66. a. $k - 2 = -4$
  b. $-2k = -4$

67. a. $-\dfrac{2}{3}h = 8$
  b. $\dfrac{2}{3} + h = 8$

68. a. $\dfrac{3}{4}p = 15$
  b. $\dfrac{3}{4} + p = 15$

69. $\dfrac{r}{3} = -12$

70. $\dfrac{d}{-4} = 5$

71. $k + 16 = 32$

72. $-18 = -9 + t$

73. $16k = 32$

74. $-18 = -9t$

75. $7 = -4q$

76. $-3s = 10$

77. $-4 + q = 7$

78. $s - 3 = 10$

79. $-\dfrac{1}{3}d = 12$

80. $-\dfrac{2}{5}m = 10$

81. $4 = \dfrac{1}{2} + z$

82. $3 = \dfrac{1}{4} + p$

83. $1.2y = 4.8$

84. $4.3w = 8.6$

85. $4.8 = 1.2 + y$

86. $8.6 = w - 4.3$

87. $0.0034 = y - 0.405$

88. $-0.98 = m + 1.0034$

For Exercises 89–96, determine if the equation is a linear equation in one variable. Answer yes or no.

89. $4p + 5 = 0$ **90.** $3x - 5y = 0$ **91.** $4 + 2a^2 = 5$ **92.** $-8t = 7$

93. $x - 4 = 9$ **94.** $2x^3 + y = 0$ **95.** $19b = -3$ **96.** $13 + x = 19$

Expanding Your Skills

For Exercises 97–102, construct an equation with the given solution. Answers will vary.

97. $y = 6$ **98.** $x = 2$ **99.** $p = -4$

100. $t = -10$ **101.** $a = 0$ **102.** $k = 1$

For Exercises 103–106, simplify by collecting the *like* terms. Then solve the equation.

103. $5x - 4x + 7 = 8 - 2$ **104.** $2 + 3 = 2y + 1 - y$

105. $6p - 3p = 15 + 6$ **106.** $12 - 20 = 2t + 2t$

Solving Linear Equations

1. Solving Linear Equations Involving Multiple Steps

In Section 2.1, we studied a one-step process to solve linear equations by using the addition, subtraction, multiplication, and division properties of equality. In Example 1, we solve the equation $-2w - 7 = 11$. Solving this equation will require multiple steps. To understand the proper steps, always remember the ultimate goal is to isolate the variable. Therefore, we will first isolate the *term* containing the variable before dividing both sides by -2.

Concepts

1. Solving Linear Equations Involving Multiple Steps
2. Procedure for Solving a Linear Equation in One Variable
3. Conditional Equations, Identities, and Contradictions

Example 1 Solving a Linear Equation

Solve the equation. $-2w - 7 = 11$

Solution:

$$-2w - 7 = 11$$

$$-2w - 7 + 7 = 11 + 7 \qquad \text{Add } 7 \text{ to both sides of the equation. This isolates the } w\text{-term.}$$

$$-2w = 18$$

$$\frac{-2w}{-2} = \frac{18}{-2} \qquad \text{Next, apply the division property of equality to obtain a coefficient of 1 for } w. \text{ Divide by } -2 \text{ on both sides.}$$

$$w = -9$$

Check:

$$-2w - 7 = 11$$

$$-2(-9) - 7 \stackrel{?}{=} 11 \qquad \text{Substitute } w = -9 \text{ in the original equation.}$$

$$18 - 7 \stackrel{?}{=} 11$$

$$11 \stackrel{?}{=} 11 \checkmark \qquad \text{True. The solution is } -9.$$

Skill Practice

Solve the equation.
1. $-5y - 5 = 10$

Answer
1. -3

Example 2 Solving a Linear Equation

Solve the equation. $2 = \frac{1}{5}x + 3$

Solution:

$$2 = \frac{1}{5}x + 3$$

$2 - 3 = \frac{1}{5}x + 3 - 3$ Subtract 3 from both sides. This isolates the x-term.

$-1 = \frac{1}{5}x$ Simplify.

$5(-1) = 5 \cdot \left(\frac{1}{5}x\right)$ Next, apply the multiplication property of equality to obtain a coefficient of 1 for x. Multiply both sides by 5.

$-5 = 1x$

$-5 = x$ Simplify. The answer checks in the original equation.

The solution is -5.

In Example 3, the variable x appears on both sides of the equation. In this case, apply the addition or subtraction property of equality to collect the variable terms on one side of the equation and the constant terms on the other side. Then use the multiplication or division property of equality to get a coefficient equal to 1.

Example 3 Solving a Linear Equation

Solve the equation. $6x - 4 = 2x - 8$

Solution:

$$6x - 4 = 2x - 8$$

$6x - 2x - 4 = 2x - 2x - 8$ Subtract $2x$ from both sides leaving $0x$ on the right-hand side.

$4x - 4 = 0x - 8$ Simplify.

$4x - 4 = -8$ The x-terms have now been combined on one side of the equation.

$4x - 4 + 4 = -8 + 4$ Add 4 to both sides of the equation. This combines the constant terms on the *other* side of the equation.

$4x = -4$

$\frac{4x}{4} = \frac{-4}{4}$ To obtain a coefficient of 1 for x, divide both sides of the equation by 4.

$x = -1$ Simplify. The answer checks in the original equation.

The solution is -1.

Answers

2. 18   **3.** $\frac{1}{6}$

> **TIP:** It is important to note that the variable may be isolated on either side of the equation. We will solve the equation from Example 3 again, this time isolating the variable on the right-hand side.
>
> $$6x - 4 = 2x - 8$$
>
> $$6x - 6x - 4 = 2x - 6x - 8 \qquad \text{Subtract } 6x \text{ on both sides.}$$
>
> $$0x - 4 = -4x - 8$$
>
> $$-4 = -4x - 8$$
>
> $$-4 + 8 = -4x - 8 + 8 \qquad \text{Add } 8 \text{ to both sides.}$$
>
> $$4 = -4x$$
>
> $$\frac{4}{-4} = \frac{-4x}{-4} \qquad \text{Divide both sides by } -4.$$
>
> $$-1 = x \quad \text{or equivalently } x = -1$$

2. Procedure for Solving a Linear Equation in One Variable

In some cases, it is necessary to simplify both sides of a linear equation before applying the properties of equality. Therefore, we offer the following steps to solve a linear equation in one variable.

> ### Solving a Linear Equation in One Variable
>
> **Step 1** Simplify both sides of the equation.
> - Clear parentheses
> - Combine *like* terms
>
> **Step 2** Use the addition or subtraction property of equality to collect the variable terms on one side of the equation.
>
> **Step 3** Use the addition or subtraction property of equality to collect the constant terms on the other side of the equation.
>
> **Step 4** Use the multiplication or division property of equality to make the coefficient of the variable term equal to 1.
>
> **Step 5** Check your answer.

Example 4   **Solving a Linear Equation**

Solve the equation. $7 + 3 = 2(p - 3)$

Solution:

$$7 + 3 = 2(p - 3)$$

$$10 = 2p - 6 \qquad$$ **Step 1:** Simplify both sides of the equation by clearing parentheses and combining *like* terms.

                 Step 2: The variable terms are already on one side.

> **Skill Practice**
>
> Solve the equation.
> **4.** $12 + 2 = 7(3 - y)$

Answer

4. 1

$$10 + 6 = 2p - 6 + 6$$

Step 3: Add 6 to both sides to collect the constant terms on the other side.

$$16 = 2p$$

$$\frac{16}{2} = \frac{2p}{2}$$

Step 4: Divide both sides by 2 to obtain a coefficient of 1 for p.

$$8 = p$$

Step 5: Check:

$$7 + 3 = 2(p - 3)$$

$$10 \stackrel{?}{=} 2(8 - 3)$$

$$10 \stackrel{?}{=} 2(5)$$

The solution is 8.

$$10 \stackrel{?}{=} 10 \; \checkmark \quad \text{True}$$

Skill Practice	
Solve the equation.	
5. $1.5t + 2.3 = 3.5t - 1.9$	

Example 5   **Solving a Linear Equation**

Solve the equation. $2.2y - 8.3 = 6.2y + 12.1$

Solution:

$$2.2y - 8.3 = 6.2y + 12.1$$

Step 1: The right- and left-hand sides are already simplified.

$$2.2y - 2.2y - 8.3 = 6.2y - 2.2y + 12.1$$

$$-8.3 = 4.0y + 12.1$$

Step 2: Subtract $2.2y$ from both sides to collect the variable terms on one side of the equation.

$$-8.3 - 12.1 = 4.0y + 12.1 - 12.1$$

$$-20.4 = 4.0y$$

Step 3: Subtract 12.1 from both sides to collect the constant terms on the other side.

$$\frac{-20.4}{4.0} = \frac{4.0y}{4.0}$$

$$-5.1 = y$$

Step 4: To obtain a coefficient of 1 for the y-term, divide both sides of the equation by 4.0.

$$y = -5.1$$

Step 5: Check:

$$2.2y - 8.3 = 6.2y + 12.1$$

$$2.2(-5.1) - 8.3 \stackrel{?}{=} 6.2(-5.1) + 12.1$$

$$-11.22 - 8.3 \stackrel{?}{=} -31.62 + 12.1$$

The solution is -5.1.

$$-19.52 \stackrel{?}{=} -19.52 \; \checkmark \quad \text{True}$$

TIP: In Examples 5 and 6 we collect the variable terms on the right side to avoid negative coefficients on the variable term.

Answer

5. 2.1

Example 6 Solving a Linear Equation

Solve the equation. $2 + 7x - 5 = 6(x + 3) + 2x$

Solution:

$$2 + 7x - 5 = 6(x + 3) + 2x$$

$-3 + 7x = 6x + 18 + 2x$	**Step 1:** Add *like* terms on the left. Clear parentheses on the right.
$-3 + 7x = 8x + 18$	Combine *like* terms.
$-3 + 7x - 7x = 8x - 7x + 18$	**Step 2:** Subtract $7x$ from both sides.
$-3 = x + 18$	Simplify.
$-3 - 18 = x + 18 - 18$	**Step 3:** Subtract 18 from both sides.
$-21 = x$	**Step 4:** Because the coefficient of the
$x = -21$	x term is already 1, there is no need to apply the multiplication or division property of equality.

The solution is -21.   **Step 5:** The check is left to the reader.

Skill Practice

Solve the equation.
  6. $4(2y - 1) + y = 6y + 3 - y$

Example 7 Solving a Linear Equation

Solve the equation. $9 - (z - 3) + 4z = 4z - 5(z + 2) - 6$

Solution:

$$9 - (z - 3) + 4z = 4z - 5(z + 2) - 6$$

$9 - z + 3 + 4z = 4z - 5z - 10 - 6$	**Step 1:** Clear parentheses.
$12 + 3z = -z - 16$	Combine *like* terms.
$12 + 3z + z = -z + z - 16$	**Step 2:** Add z to both sides.
$12 + 4z = -16$	
$12 - 12 + 4z = -16 - 12$	**Step 3:** Subtract 12 from both sides.
$4z = -28$	
$\dfrac{4z}{4} = \dfrac{-28}{4}$	**Step 4:** Divide both sides by 4.
$z = -7$	**Step 5:** The check is left for the reader.

The solution is -7.

Skill Practice

Solve the equation.
  7. $10 - (x + 5) + 3x$
      $= 6x - 5(x - 1) - 3$

Avoiding Mistakes

When distributing a negative number through parentheses, be sure to change the signs of every term within parentheses.

---

3. Conditional Equations, Identities, and Contradictions

The solutions to a linear equation are the values of x that make the equation a true statement. A linear equation in one variable has one unique solution. Some types of equations, however, have no solution while others have infinitely many solutions.

Answers

  6. $\dfrac{7}{4}$ **7.** -3

I. Conditional Equations

An equation that is true for some values of the variable but false for other values is called a **conditional equation**. The equation $x + 4 = 6$, for example, is true on the condition that $x = 2$. For other values of x, the statement $x + 4 = 6$ is false.

$$x + 4 = 6$$
$$x + 4 - 4 = 6 - 4$$
$$x = 2 \quad \text{(Conditional equation)} \quad \text{The solution is 2.}$$

II. Contradictions

Some equations have no solution, such as $x + 1 = x + 2$. There is no value of x, that when increased by 1 will equal the same value increased by 2. If we tried to solve the equation by subtracting x from both sides, we get the contradiction $1 = 2$. This indicates that the equation has no solution. An equation that has no solution is called a **contradiction**.

$$x + 1 = x + 2$$
$$x - x + 1 = x - x + 2$$
$$1 = 2 \quad \text{(Contradiction)} \quad \text{No solution.}$$

III. Identities

An equation that has all real numbers as its solution set is called an **identity**. For example, consider the equation, $x + 4 = x + 4$. Because the left- and right-hand sides are *identical*, any real number substituted for x will result in equal quantities on both sides. If we subtract x from both sides of the equation, we get the identity $4 = 4$. In such a case, the solution is the set of all real numbers.

$$x + 4 = x + 4$$
$$x - x + 4 = x - x + 4$$
$$4 = 4 \quad \text{(Identity)} \quad \text{The solution is all real numbers.}$$

Concept Connections

8. Write a conditional equation. Answers may vary.
9. Write an equation that is a contradiction. Answers may vary.
10. Write an equation that is an identity. Answers may vary.

Skill Practice

Solve the equation. Identify the equation as a conditional equation, a contradiction, or an identity.

11. $4(2t + 1) - 1 = 8t + 3$
12. $3x - 5 = 4x + 1 - x$
13. $6(v - 2) = 2v - 4$

Answers

8. For example: $x = 5$
9. For example: $x + 3 = x + 8$
10. For example: $x - 9 = x - 9$
11. All real numbers; the equation is an identity.
12. No solution; the equation is a contradiction.
13. 2; the equation is a conditional equation.

Example 8 **Identifying Conditional Equations, Contradictions, and Identities**

Solve the equation. Identify each equation as a conditional equation, a contradiction, or an identity.

a. $4k - 5 = 2(2k - 3) + 1$ **b.** $2(b - 4) = 2b - 7$ **c.** $3x + 7 = 2x - 5$

Solution:

a.

$$4k - 5 = 2(2k - 3) + 1$$

$$4k - 5 = 4k - 6 + 1 \qquad \text{Clear parentheses.}$$

$$4k - 5 = 4k - 5 \qquad \text{Combine } like \text{ terms.}$$

$$4k - 4k - 5 = 4k - 4k - 5 \qquad \text{Subtract } 4k \text{ from both sides.}$$

$$-5 = -5 \quad \text{(Identity)}$$

This is an identity. The solution is all real numbers.

b.
$$2(b - 4) = 2b - 7$$

$$2b - 8 = 2b - 7 \qquad \text{Clear parentheses.}$$

$$2b - 2b - 8 = 2b - 2b - 7 \qquad \text{Subtract } 2b \text{ from both sides.}$$

$$-8 = -7 \quad \text{(Contradiction)}$$

This is a contradiction. There is no solution.

c.
$$3x + 7 = 2x - 5$$

$$3x - 2x + 7 = 2x - 2x - 5 \qquad \text{Subtract } 2x \text{ from both sides.}$$

$$x + 7 = -5 \qquad \text{Simplify.}$$

$$x + 7 - 7 = -5 - 7 \qquad \text{Subtract } 7 \text{ from both sides.}$$

$$x = -12 \quad \text{(Conditional equation)}$$

This is a conditional equation. The solution is -12. (The equation is true only on the condition that $x = -12$.)

Section 2.2 Practice Exercises

Study Skills Exercise

Several strategies are given here about taking notes. Check the activities that you routinely do and discuss how the other suggestions may improve your learning.

_____ Read your notes after class and complete any abbreviations or incomplete sentences.

_____ Highlight important terms and definitions.

_____ Review your notes from the previous class.

_____ Bring pencils (more than one) and paper to class.

_____ Sit in class where you can clearly read the board and hear your instructor.

_____ Turn off your cell phone and keep it off your desk to avoid distraction.

Vocabulary and Key Concepts

1. a. A _____ equation is true for some values of the variable, but false for other values.

b. An equation that has no solution is called a _____.

c. An equation that has all real numbers as its solution is called an _____.

Review Exercises

For Exercises 2–5, simplify the expressions by clearing parentheses and combining *like* terms.

2. $5z + 2 - 7z - 3z$

3. $10 - 4w + 7w - 2 + w$

4. $-(-7p + 9) + (3p - 1)$

5. $8y - (2y + 3) - 19$

6. Explain the difference between simplifying an expression and solving an equation.

For Exercises 7–12, solve the equations using the addition, subtraction, multiplication, or division property of equality.

7. $7 = p - 12$

8. $5w = -30$

9. $-7y = 21$

10. $x + 8 = -15$

11. $z - 23 = -28$

12. $-\dfrac{9}{8} = -\dfrac{3}{4}k$

Concept 1: Solving Linear Equations Involving Multiple Steps

For Exercises 13–36, solve the equations using the steps outlined in the text. **(See Examples 1–3.)**

13. $6z + 1 = 13$

14. $5x + 2 = -13$

15. $3y - 4 = 14$

16. $-7w - 5 = -19$

17. $-2p + 8 = 3$

18. $2b - \dfrac{1}{4} = 5$

19. $0.2x + 3.1 = -5.3$

20. $-1.8 + 2.4a = -6.6$

21. $\dfrac{5}{8} = \dfrac{1}{4} - \dfrac{1}{2}p$

22. $\dfrac{6}{7} = \dfrac{1}{7} + \dfrac{5}{3}r$

23. $7w - 6w + 1 = 10 - 4$

24. $5v - 3 - 4v = 13$

25. $11h - 8 - 9h = -16$

26. $6u - 5 - 8u = -7$

27. $3a + 7 = 2a - 19$

28. $6b - 20 = 14 + 5b$

29. $-4r - 28 = -58 - r$

30. $-6x - 7 = -3 - 8x$

31. $-2z - 8 = -z$

32. $-7t + 4 = -6t$

33. $\dfrac{5}{6}x + \dfrac{2}{3} = -\dfrac{1}{6}x - \dfrac{5}{3}$

34. $\dfrac{3}{7}x - \dfrac{1}{4} = -\dfrac{4}{7}x - \dfrac{5}{4}$

35. $3y - 2 = 5y - 2$

36. $4 + 10t = -8t + 4$

Concept 2: Procedure for Solving a Linear Equation in One Variable

For Exercises 37–58, solve the equations using the steps outlined in the text. **(See Examples 4–7.)**

37. $4q + 14 = 2$

38. $6 = 7m - 1$

39. $-9 = 4n - 1$

40. $-\dfrac{1}{2} - 4x = 8$

41. $3(2p - 4) = 15$

42. $4(t + 15) = 20$

43. $6(3x + 2) - 10 = -4$

44. $4(2k + 1) - 1 = 5$

45. $3.4x - 2.5 = 2.8x + 3.5$

46. $5.8w + 1.1 = 6.3w + 5.6$

47. $17(s + 3) = 4(s - 10) + 13$

48. $5(4 + p) = 3(3p - 1) - 9$

49. $6(3t - 4) + 10 = 5(t - 2) - (3t + 4)$

50. $-5y + 2(2y + 1) = 2(5y - 1) - 7$

51. $5 - 3(x + 2) = 5$

52. $1 - 6(2 - h) = 7$

53. $3(2z - 6) - 4(3z + 1) = 5 - 2(z + 1)$

54. $-2(4a + 3) - 5(2 - a) = 3(2a + 3) - 7$

55. $-2[(4p + 1) - (3p - 1)] = 5(3 - p) - 9$

56. $5 - (6k + 1) = 2[(5k - 3) - (k - 2)]$

57. $3(-0.9n + 0.5) = -3.5n + 1.3$

58. $7(0.4m - 0.1) = 5.2m + 0.86$

Concept 3: Conditional Equations, Identities, and Contradictions

For Exercises 59–64, identify the equation as a conditional equation, a contradiction, or an identity. Then describe the solution. **(See Example 8.)**

59. $2(k - 7) = 2k - 13$

60. $5h + 4 = 5(h + 1) - 1$

61. $7x + 3 = 6(x - 2)$

62. $3y - 1 = 1 + 3y$

63. $3 - 5.2p = -5.2p + 3$

64. $2(q + 3) = 4q + q - 9$

65. A conditional linear equation has (choose one): one solution, no solution, or infinitely many solutions.

66. An equation that is a contradiction has (choose one): one solution, no solution, or infinitely many solutions.

67. An equation that is an identity has (choose one): one solution, no solution, or infinitely many solutions.

68. If the only solution to a linear equation is 5, then is the equation a conditional equation, an identity, or a contradiction?

Mixed Exercises

For Exercises 69–92, find the solution, if possible.

69. $4p - 6 = 8 + 2p$

70. $\frac{1}{2}t - 2 = 3$

71. $2k - 9 = -8$

72. $3(y - 2) + 5 = 5$

73. $7(w - 2) = -14 - 3w$

74. $0.24 = 0.4m$

75. $2(x + 2) - 3 = 2x + 1$

76. $n + \frac{1}{4} = -\frac{1}{2}$

77. $0.5b = -23$

78. $3(2r + 1) = 6(r + 2) - 6$

79. $8 - 2q = 4$

80. $\frac{x}{7} - 3 = 1$

81. $2 - 4(y - 5) = -4$

82. $4 - 3(4p - 1) = -8$

83. $0.4(a + 20) = 6$

84. $2.2r - 12 = 3.4$

85. $10(2n + 1) - 6 = 20(n - 1) + 12$

86. $\frac{2}{5}y + 5 = -3$

87. $c + 0.123 = 2.328$

88. $4(2z + 3) = 8(z - 3) + 36$

89. $\frac{4}{5}t - 1 = \frac{1}{5}t + 5$

90. $6g - 8 = 4 - 3g$

91. $8 - (3q + 4) = 6 - q$

92. $6w - (8 + 2w) = 2(w - 4)$

Expanding Your Skills

93. Suppose -5 is a solution for x in the equation $x + a = 10$. Find the value of a.

94. Suppose 6 is a solution for x in the equation $x + a = -12$. Find the value of a.

95. Suppose 3 is a solution for x in the equation $ax = 12$. Find the value of a.

96. Suppose 11 is a solution for x in the equation $ax = 49.5$. Find the value of a.

97. Write an equation that is an identity. Answers may vary.

98. Write an equation that is a contradiction. Answers may vary.

Section 2.3 Linear Equations: Clearing Fractions and Decimals

Concepts

1. Solving Linear Equations Containing Fractions
2. Solving Linear Equations Containing Decimals

1. Solving Linear Equations Containing Fractions

Linear equations that contain fractions can be solved in different ways. The first procedure, illustrated here, uses the method outlined in Section 2.2.

$$\frac{5}{6}x - \frac{3}{4} = \frac{1}{3}$$

$$\frac{5}{6}x - \frac{3}{4} + \frac{3}{4} = \frac{1}{3} + \frac{3}{4}$$ To isolate the variable term, add $\frac{3}{4}$ to both sides.

$$\frac{5}{6}x = \frac{4}{12} + \frac{9}{12}$$ Find the common denominator on the right-hand side.

$$\frac{5}{6}x = \frac{13}{12}$$ Simplify.

$$\frac{6}{5}\left(\frac{5}{6}x\right) = \frac{\overset{1}{\cancel{6}}}{5}\left(\frac{13}{\underset{2}{\cancel{12}}}\right)$$ Multiply by the reciprocal of $\frac{5}{6}$, which is $\frac{6}{5}$.

$$x = \frac{13}{10}$$ The solution is $\frac{13}{10}$.

Sometimes it is simpler to solve an equation with fractions by eliminating the fractions first using a process called **clearing fractions**. To clear fractions in the equation $\frac{5}{6}x - \frac{3}{4} = \frac{1}{3}$, we can multiply both sides of the equation by the least common denominator (LCD) of all terms in the equation. In this case, the LCD of $\frac{5}{6}x$, $-\frac{3}{4}$, and $\frac{1}{3}$ is 12. Because each denominator in the equation is a factor of 12, we can simplify common factors to leave integer coefficients for each term.

Skill Practice

Solve the equation by clearing fractions.

1. $\frac{2}{5}y + \frac{1}{2} = -\frac{7}{10}$

TIP: Recall that the multiplication property of equality indicates that multiplying both sides of an equation by a nonzero constant results in an equivalent equation.

Example 1 Solving a Linear Equation by Clearing Fractions

Solve the equation by clearing fractions first. $\dfrac{5}{6}x - \dfrac{3}{4} = \dfrac{1}{3}$

Solution:

$$\frac{5}{6}x - \frac{3}{4} = \frac{1}{3}$$ The LCD of $\frac{5}{6}$, $-\frac{3}{4}$, and $\frac{1}{3}$ is 12.

$$12\left(\frac{5}{6}x - \frac{3}{4}\right) = 12\left(\frac{1}{3}\right)$$ Multiply both sides of the equation by the LCD, 12.

$$\frac{\overset{2}{\cancel{12}}}{1}\left(\frac{5}{\cancel{6}}x\right) - \frac{\overset{3}{\cancel{12}}}{1}\left(\frac{3}{\cancel{4}}\right) = \frac{\overset{4}{\cancel{12}}}{1}\left(\frac{1}{\cancel{3}}\right)$$ Apply the distributive property (recall that $12 = \frac{12}{1}$).

$$2(5x) - 3(3) = 4(1)$$ Simplify common factors to clear the fractions.

$$10x - 9 = 4$$

$$10x - 9 + 9 = 4 + 9$$ Add 9 to both sides.

$$10x = 13$$

$$\frac{10x}{10} = \frac{13}{10}$$ Divide both sides by 10.

$$x = \frac{13}{10}$$ The solution is $\frac{13}{10}$.

Answer

1. -3

In this section, we combine the process for clearing fractions and decimals with the general strategies for solving linear equations. To solve a linear equation, it is important to follow these steps.

Solving a Linear Equation in One Variable

Step 1 Simplify both sides of the equation.
  - Clear parentheses
  - Consider clearing fractions and decimals (if any are present) by multiplying both sides of the equation by a common denominator of all terms
  - Combine *like* terms

Step 2 Use the addition or subtraction property of equality to collect the variable terms on one side of the equation.

Step 3 Use the addition or subtraction property of equality to collect the constant terms on the other side of the equation.

Step 4 Use the multiplication or division property of equality to make the coefficient of the variable term equal to 1.

Step 5 Check your answer.

TIP: In Example 1, the fractions can be eliminated by multiplying both sides of the equation by *any* common multiple of the denominators. For example, try multiplying both sides of the equation by 24:

$$24\left(\frac{5}{6}x - \frac{3}{4}\right) = 24\left(\frac{1}{3}\right)$$

$$\overset{4}{\frac{24}{1}}\left(\frac{5}{6}x\right) - \overset{6}{\frac{24}{1}}\left(\frac{3}{4}\right) = \overset{8}{\frac{24}{1}}\left(\frac{1}{3}\right)$$

$$20x - 18 = 8$$
$$20x = 26$$
$$\frac{20x}{20} = \frac{26}{20}$$
$$x = \frac{13}{10}$$

Example 2 Solving a Linear Equation Containing Fractions

Solve the equation. $\dfrac{1}{6}x - \dfrac{2}{3} = \dfrac{1}{5}x - 1$

Solution:

$$\frac{1}{6}x - \frac{2}{3} = \frac{1}{5}x - 1 \qquad \text{The LCD of } \tfrac{1}{6}x, -\tfrac{2}{3}, \tfrac{1}{5}x, \text{ and } \tfrac{-1}{1} \text{ is 30.}$$

$$30\left(\frac{1}{6}x - \frac{2}{3}\right) = 30\left(\frac{1}{5}x - 1\right) \qquad \text{Multiply by the LCD, 30.}$$

$$\overset{5}{\frac{30}{1}} \cdot \frac{1}{6}x - \overset{10}{\frac{30}{1}} \cdot \frac{2}{3} = \overset{6}{\frac{30}{1}} \cdot \frac{1}{5}x - 30(1) \qquad \begin{array}{l}\text{Apply the distributive property} \\ \text{(recall } 30 = \tfrac{30}{1}\text{).}\end{array}$$

$$5x - 20 = 6x - 30 \qquad \text{Clear fractions.}$$

$$5x - 6x - 20 = 6x - 6x - 30 \qquad \text{Subtract } 6x \text{ from both sides.}$$

$$-x - 20 = -30$$

$$-x - 20 + 20 = -30 + 20 \qquad \text{Add 20 to both sides.}$$

$$-x = -10$$

$$\frac{-x}{-1} = \frac{-10}{-1} \qquad \text{Divide both sides by } -1.$$

$$x = 10 \qquad \text{The solution is 10.}$$

Skill Practice

Solve the equation.

2. $\dfrac{2}{5}x - \dfrac{1}{2} = \dfrac{7}{4} + \dfrac{3}{10}x$

Avoiding Mistakes

Remember to multiply all terms in the equation by the LCD, including those that are not fractions.

Answer

2. $\dfrac{45}{2}$

Example 3   **Solving a Linear Equation Containing Fractions**

Solve the equation. $\frac{1}{3}(x + 7) - \frac{1}{2}(x + 1) = 4$

Solution:

$$\frac{1}{3}(x + 7) - \frac{1}{2}(x + 1) = 4$$

$$\frac{1}{3}x + \frac{7}{3} - \frac{1}{2}x - \frac{1}{2} = 4 \qquad \text{Clear parentheses.}$$

$$6\left(\frac{1}{3}x + \frac{7}{3} - \frac{1}{2}x - \frac{1}{2}\right) = 6(4) \qquad \begin{array}{l}\text{The LCD of} \\ \frac{1}{3}x, \frac{7}{3}, -\frac{1}{2}x, \text{ and } \frac{4}{1} \text{ is } 6.\end{array}$$

$$\frac{\overset{2}{\cancel{6}}}{1}\cdot\frac{1}{\cancel{3}}x + \frac{\overset{2}{\cancel{6}}}{1}\cdot\frac{7}{\cancel{3}} + \frac{\overset{3}{\cancel{6}}}{1}\left(-\frac{1}{\cancel{2}}x\right) + \frac{\overset{3}{\cancel{6}}}{1}\left(-\frac{1}{\cancel{2}}\right) = 6(4) \qquad \begin{array}{l}\text{Apply the distributive} \\ \text{property.}\end{array}$$

$$2x + 14 - 3x - 3 = 24$$

$$-x + 11 = 24 \qquad \text{Combine } \textit{like} \text{ terms.}$$

$$-x + 11 - 11 = 24 - 11 \qquad \text{Subtract } 11.$$

$$-x = 13$$

$$\frac{-x}{-1} = \frac{13}{-1} \qquad \text{Divide by } -1.$$

$$x = -13 \qquad \text{The solution is } -13.$$

Example 4   **Solving a Linear Equation Containing Fractions**

Solve. $\frac{x - 2}{5} - \frac{x - 4}{2} = 2$

Solution:

$$\frac{x - 2}{5} - \frac{x - 4}{2} = \frac{2}{1} \qquad \text{The LCD of } \frac{x-2}{5}, \frac{x-4}{2}, \text{ and } \frac{2}{1} \text{ is } 10.$$

$$10\left(\frac{x - 2}{5} - \frac{x - 4}{2}\right) = 10\left(\frac{2}{1}\right) \qquad \text{Multiply both sides by } 10.$$

$$\frac{\overset{2}{\cancel{10}}}{1}\cdot\left(\frac{x - 2}{\cancel{5}}\right) - \frac{\overset{5}{\cancel{10}}}{1}\cdot\left(\frac{x - 4}{\cancel{2}}\right) = \frac{10}{1}\cdot\left(\frac{2}{1}\right) \qquad \text{Apply the distributive property.}$$

$$2(x - 2) - 5(x - 4) = 20 \qquad \text{Clear fractions.}$$

$$2x - 4 - 5x + 20 = 20 \qquad \text{Apply the distributive property.}$$

$$-3x + 16 = 20 \qquad \text{Simplify both sides of the equation.}$$

$$-3x + 16 - 16 = 20 - 16 \qquad \text{Subtract } 16 \text{ from both sides.}$$

$$-3x = 4$$

$$\frac{-3x}{-3} = \frac{4}{-3} \qquad \text{Divide both sides by } -3.$$

$$x = -\frac{4}{3} \qquad \text{The solution is } -\frac{4}{3}.$$

Skill Practice

Solve the equation.

3. $\frac{1}{5}(z + 1) + \frac{1}{4}(z + 3) = 2$

TIP: In Example 3 both parentheses and fractions are present within the equation. In such a case, we recommend that you clear parentheses first. Then clear the fractions.

Skill Practice

Solve the equation.

4. $\frac{x + 1}{4} + \frac{x + 2}{6} = 1$

Avoiding Mistakes

In Example 4, several of the fractions in the equation have two terms in the numerator. It is important to enclose these fractions in parentheses when clearing fractions. In this way, we will remember to use the distributive property to multiply the factors shown in blue with both terms from the numerator of the fractions.

Answers

3. $\frac{7}{3}$ **4.** 1

2. Solving Linear Equations Containing Decimals

The same procedure used to clear fractions in an equation can be used to **clear decimals**. For example, consider the equation

$$2.5x + 3 = 1.7x - 6.6$$

Recall that any terminating decimal can be written as a fraction. Therefore, the equation can be interpreted as

$$\frac{25}{10}x + 3 = \frac{17}{10}x - \frac{66}{10}$$

A convenient common denominator of all terms is 10. Therefore, we can multiply the original equation by 10 to clear decimals. The result is

$$25x + 30 = 17x - 66$$

Multiplying by the appropriate power of 10 moves the decimal points so that all coefficients become integers.

Example 5 **Solving a Linear Equation Containing Decimals**

Solve the equation by clearing decimals. $2.5x + 3 = 1.7x - 6.6$

Solution:

$$2.5x + 3 = 1.7x - 6.6$$

$10(2.5x + 3) = 10(1.7x - 6.6)$	Multiply both sides of the equation by 10.
$25x + 30 = 17x - 66$	Apply the distributive property.
$25x - 17x + 30 = 17x - 17x - 66$	Subtract $17x$ from both sides.
$8x + 30 = -66$	
$8x + 30 - 30 = -66 - 30$	Subtract 30 from both sides.
$8x = -96$	
$\dfrac{8x}{8} = \dfrac{-96}{8}$	Divide both sides by 8.
$x = -12$	The solution is -12.

Skill Practice

Solve.

5. $1.2w + 3.5 = 2.1 + w$

TIP: Notice that multiplying a decimal number by 10 has the effect of moving the decimal point one place to the right. Similarly, multiplying by 100 moves the decimal point two places to the right, and so on.

Answer

5. -7

Example 6   Solving a Linear Equation Containing Decimals

Solve the equation by clearing decimals. $0.2(x + 4) - 0.45(x + 9) = 12$

Solution:

$$0.2(x + 4) - 0.45(x + 9) = 12$$

$$0.2x + 0.8 - 0.45x - 4.05 = 12 \qquad \text{Clear parentheses first.}$$

$$100(0.2x + 0.8 - 0.45x - 4.05) = 100(12) \qquad \text{Multiply both sides by } 100.$$

$$20x + 80 - 45x - 405 = 1200 \qquad \text{Apply the distributive property.}$$

$$-25x - 325 = 1200 \qquad \text{Simplify both sides.}$$

$$-25x - 325 + 325 = 1200 + 325 \qquad \text{Add } 325 \text{ to both sides.}$$

$$-25x = 1525$$

$$\frac{-25x}{-25} = \frac{1525}{-25} \qquad \text{Divide both sides by } -25.$$

$$x = -61 \qquad \text{The solution is } -61.$$

TIP: The terms with the most digits following the decimal point are $-0.45x$ and -4.05. Each of these is written to the hundredths place. Therefore, we multiply both sides by 100.

Answer

6. 39.5

Section 2.3   Practice Exercises

Study Skills Exercise

Instructors vary in what they emphasize on tests. For example, test material may come from the textbook, notes, handouts, or homework. What does your instructor emphasize?

Vocabulary and Key Concepts

1. a. The process of eliminating fractions in an equation by multiplying both sides of the equation by the LCD is called _____ _____.

   b. The process of eliminating decimals in an equation by multiplying both sides of the equation by a power of 10 is called _____ _____.

Review Exercises

For Exercises 2–6, solve the equation.

2. $-5t - 17 = -2t + 49$

3. $5(x + 2) - 3 = 4x + 5$

4. $-2(2x - 4x) = 6 + 18$

5. $3(2y + 3) - 4(-y + 1) = 7y - 10$

6. $-(3w + 4) + 5(w - 2) - 3(6w - 8) = 10$

7. Solve the equation and describe the solution.
   $7x + 2 = 7(x - 12)$

8. Solve the equation and describe the solution.
   $2(3x - 6) = 3(2x - 4)$

Concept 1: Solving Linear Equations Containing Fractions

For Exercises 9–14, determine which of the values could be used to clear fractions or decimals in the given equation.

9. $\dfrac{2}{3}x - \dfrac{1}{6} = \dfrac{x}{9}$

   Values: 6, 9, 12, 18, 24, 36

10. $\dfrac{1}{4}x - \dfrac{2}{7} = \dfrac{1}{2}x + 2$

   Values: 4, 7, 14, 21, 28, 42

11. $0.02x + 0.5 = 0.35x + 1.2$

   Values: 10; 100; 1000; 10,000

12. $0.003 - 0.002x = 0.1x$
Values: 10; 100; 1000; 10,000

13. $\frac{1}{6}x + \frac{7}{10} = x$
Values: 3, 6, 10, 30, 60

14. $2x - \frac{5}{2} = \frac{x}{3} - \frac{1}{4}$
Values: 2, 3, 4, 6, 12, 24

For Exercises 15–36, solve the equation. **(See Examples 1–4.)**

15. $\frac{1}{2}x + 3 = 5$

16. $\frac{1}{3}y - 4 = 9$

17. $\frac{1}{6}y + 2 = \frac{5}{12}$

18. $\frac{2}{15}z + 3 = \frac{7}{5}$

19. $\frac{1}{3}q + \frac{3}{5} = \frac{1}{15}q - \frac{2}{5}$

20. $\frac{3}{7}x - 5 = \frac{24}{7}x + 7$

21. $\frac{12}{5}w + 7 = 31 - \frac{3}{5}w$

22. $-\frac{1}{9}p - \frac{5}{18} = -\frac{1}{6}p + \frac{1}{3}$

23. $\frac{1}{4}(3m - 4) - \frac{1}{5} = \frac{1}{4}m + \frac{3}{10}$

24. $\frac{1}{25}(20 - t) = \frac{4}{25}t - \frac{3}{5}$

25. $\frac{1}{6}(5s + 3) = \frac{1}{2}(s + 11)$

26. $\frac{1}{12}(4n - 3) = \frac{1}{4}(2n + 1)$

27. $\frac{2}{3}x + 4 = \frac{2}{3}x - 6$

28. $-\frac{1}{9}a + \frac{2}{9} = \frac{1}{3} - \frac{1}{9}a$

29. $\frac{1}{6}(2c - 1) = \frac{1}{3}c - \frac{1}{6}$

30. $\frac{3}{2}b - 1 = \frac{1}{8}(12b - 8)$

31. $\frac{2x + 1}{3} + \frac{x - 1}{3} = 5$

32. $\frac{4y - 2}{5} - \frac{y + 4}{5} = -3$

33. $\frac{3w - 2}{6} = 1 - \frac{w - 1}{3}$

34. $\frac{z - 7}{4} = \frac{6z - 1}{8} - 2$

35. $\frac{x + 3}{3} - \frac{x - 1}{2} = 4$

36. $\frac{5y - 1}{2} - \frac{y + 4}{5} = 1$

Concept 2: Solving Linear Equations Containing Decimals

For Exercises 37–54, solve the equation. **(See Examples 5 and 6.)**

37. $9.2y - 4.3 = 50.9$

38. $-6.3x + 1.5 = -4.8$

39. $0.05z + 0.2 = 0.15z - 10.5$

40. $21.1w + 4.6 = 10.9w + 35.2$

41. $0.2p - 1.4 = 0.2(p - 7)$

42. $0.5(3q + 87) = 1.5q + 43.5$

43. $0.20x + 53.60 = x$

44. $z + 0.06z = 3816$

45. $0.15(90) + 0.05p = 0.10(90 + p)$

46. $0.25(60) + 0.10x = 0.15(60 + x)$

47. $0.40(y + 10) - 0.60(y + 2) = 2$

48. $0.75(x - 2) + 0.25(x + 4) = 0.5$

49. $0.12x + 3 - 0.8x = 0.22x - 0.6$

50. $0.4x + 0.2 = -3.6 - 0.6x$

51. $0.06(x - 0.5) = 0.06x + 0.01$

52. $0.125x = 0.025(5x + 1)$

53. $-3.5x + 1.3 = -0.3(9x - 5)$

54. $x + 4 = 2(0.4x + 1.3)$

Mixed Exercises

For Exercises 55–64, solve the equation.

55. $0.2x - 1.8 = -3$

56. $9.8h + 2 = 3.8h + 20$

57. $\frac{1}{4}(x + 4) = \frac{1}{5}(2x + 3)$

58. $\frac{2}{3}(y - 1) = \frac{3}{4}(3y - 2)$

59. $0.05(2t - 1) - 0.03(4t - 1) = 0.2$

60. $0.3(x + 6) - 0.7(x + 2) = 4$

61. $\dfrac{2k+5}{4} = 2 - \dfrac{k+2}{3}$

62. $\dfrac{3d-4}{6} + 1 = \dfrac{d+1}{8}$

63. $\dfrac{1}{8}v + \dfrac{2}{3} = \dfrac{1}{6}v + \dfrac{3}{4}$

64. $\dfrac{2}{5}z - \dfrac{1}{4} = \dfrac{3}{10}z + \dfrac{1}{2}$

Expanding Your Skills

For Exercises 65–68, solve the equation.

65. $\dfrac{1}{2}a + 0.4 = -0.7 - \dfrac{3}{5}a$

66. $\dfrac{3}{4}c - 0.11 = 0.23(c-5)$

67. $0.8 + \dfrac{7}{10}b = \dfrac{3}{2}b - 0.8$

68. $0.78 - \dfrac{1}{25}h = \dfrac{3}{5}h - 0.5$

Problem Recognition Exercises

Equations and Expressions

For Exercises 1–32, identify each exercise as an expression or an equation. Then simplify the expression or solve the equation.

1. $2b + 23 - 6b - 5$

2. $10p - 9 + 2p - 3 + 8p - 18$

3. $\dfrac{y}{4} = -2$

4. $-\dfrac{x}{2} = 7$

5. $3(4h-2) - (5h-8) = 8 - (2h+3)$

6. $7y - 3(2y+5) = 7 - (10-10y)$

7. $3(8z-1) + 10 - 6(5+3z)$

8. $-5(1-x) - 3(2x+3) + 5$

9. $6c + 3(c+1) = 10$

10. $-9 + 5(2y+3) = -7$

11. $0.5(2a-3) - 0.1 = 0.4(6+2a)$

12. $0.07(2v-4) = 0.1(v-4)$

13. $-\dfrac{5}{9}w + \dfrac{11}{12} = \dfrac{23}{36}$

14. $\dfrac{3}{8}t - \dfrac{5}{8} = \dfrac{1}{2}t + \dfrac{1}{8}$

15. $\dfrac{3}{4}x + \dfrac{1}{2} - \dfrac{1}{8}x + \dfrac{5}{4}$

16. $\dfrac{7}{3}(6-12t) + \dfrac{1}{2}(4t+8)$

17. $2z - 7 = 2(z-13)$

18. $-6x + 2(x+1) = -2(2x+3)$

19. $\dfrac{2x-1}{4} + \dfrac{3x+2}{6} = 2$

20. $\dfrac{w-4}{6} - \dfrac{3w-1}{2} = -1$

21. $4b - 8 - b = -3b + 2(3b-4)$

22. $-k - 41 - 2 - k = -2(20+k) - 3$

23. $\dfrac{4}{3}(6y-3) = 0$

24. $\dfrac{1}{2}(2c-4) + 3 = \dfrac{1}{3}(6c+3)$

25. $3(x+6) - 7(x+2) - 4(1-x)$

26. $-10(2k+1) - 4(4-5k) + 25$

27. $3 - 2[4a - 5(a+1)]$

28. $-9 - 4[3 - 2(q+3)]$

29. $4 + 2[8 - (6+x)] = -2(x-1) - 4 + x$

30. $-1 - 5[2 + 3(w-2)] = 5(w+4)$

31. $\dfrac{1}{6}y + y - \dfrac{1}{3}(4y-1)$

32. $\dfrac{1}{2} - \dfrac{1}{5}\left(x + \dfrac{1}{2}\right) + \dfrac{9}{10}x$

Applications of Linear Equations: Introduction to Problem Solving

1. Problem-Solving Strategies

Linear equations can be used to solve many real-world applications. However, with "word problems," students often do not know where to start. To help organize the problem-solving process, we offer the following guidelines:

Concepts

1. Problem-Solving Strategies
2. Translating to Linear Equations
3. Consecutive Integer Problems
4. Applications of Linear Equations

Problem-Solving Flowchart for Word Problems

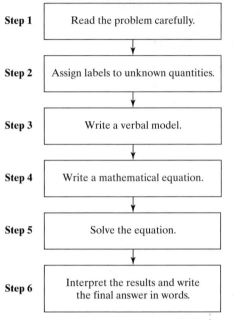

Step 1 Read the problem carefully.
• Familiarize yourself with the problem. Identify the unknown, and if possible, estimate the answer.

Step 2 Assign labels to unknown quantities.
• Identify the unknown quantity or quantities. Let x or another variable represent one of the unknowns. Draw a picture and write down relevant formulas when appropriate.

Step 3 Write a verbal model.
• Write an equation in *words*.

Step 4 Write a mathematical equation.
• Replace the verbal model with a mathematical equation using x or another variable.

Step 5 Solve the equation.
• Solve for the variable using the steps for solving linear equations.

Step 6 Interpret the results and write the final answer in words.
• Once you have obtained a numerical value for the variable, recall what it represents in the context of the problem. Can this value be used to determine other unknowns in the problem? Write an answer to the word problem in *words*.

Avoiding Mistakes

Once you have reached a solution to a word problem, verify that it is reasonable in the context of the problem.

2. Translating to Linear Equations

We have already practiced translating an English sentence to a mathematical equation. Recall from Section 1.2 that several key words translate to the algebraic operations of addition, subtraction, multiplication, and division.

Example 1   Translating to a Linear Equation

The sum of a number and negative eleven is negative fifteen. Find the number.

Solution:

	Step 1: Read the problem.
Let x represent the unknown number.	**Step 2:** Label the unknown.

$$\underset{\text{the sum of}}{\underbrace{(\text{a number}) + (-11)}} \underset{\text{is}}{=} (-15)$$

$$x + (-11) = -15 \qquad \textbf{Step 4: } \text{Write an equation.}$$

$$x + (-11) + 11 = -15 + 11 \qquad \textbf{Step 5: } \text{Solve the equation.}$$

$$x = -4$$

The number is -4.   **Step 6:** Write the final answer in words.

Step 3: Write a verbal model.

Skill Practice

1. The sum of a number and negative seven is 12. Find the number.

Answer

1. The number is 19.

Skill Practice

2. Thirteen more than twice a number is 5 more than the number. Find the number.

Example 2 **Translating to a Linear Equation**

Forty less than five times a number is fifty-two less than the number. Find the number.

Solution:

Let x represent the unknown number.

$$\left(\begin{array}{c}5\text{ times}\\\text{a number}\end{array}\right) \overset{\text{less}}{-} (40) \overset{\text{is}}{=} \left(\begin{array}{c}\text{the}\\\text{number}\end{array}\right) \overset{\text{less}}{-} (52)$$

$$5x \quad - 40 = \quad x \quad - 52$$

$$5x - 40 = x - 52$$

$$5x - x - 40 = x - x - 52$$

$$4x - 40 = -52$$

$$4x - 40 + 40 = -52 + 40$$

$$4x = -12$$

$$\frac{4x}{4} = \frac{-12}{4}$$

$$x = -3$$

The number is -3.

Step 1: Read the problem.

Step 2: Label the unknown.

Step 3: Write a verbal model.

Step 4: Write an equation.

Step 5: Solve the equation.

Step 6: Write the final answer in words.

Avoiding Mistakes

It is important to remember that subtraction is not a commutative operation. Therefore, the order in which two real numbers are subtracted affects the outcome. The expression "forty less than five times a number" must be translated as: $5x - 40$ (not $40 - 5x$). Similarly, "fifty-two less than the number" must be translated as: $x - 52$ (not $52 - x$).

Skill Practice

3. Three times the sum of a number and eight is 4 more than the number. Find the number.

Example 3 **Translating to a Linear Equation**

Twice the sum of a number and six is two more than three times the number. Find the number.

Solution:

Let x represent the unknown number.

$$\overset{\text{twice}}{2} \ \overset{\text{the sum}}{(x+6)} \ \overset{\text{is}}{=} \ \overset{\text{2 more than}}{3x+2}$$

$$\underset{\substack{\text{three times}\\\text{a number}}}{\uparrow}$$

Step 1: Read the problem.

Step 2: Label the unknown.

Step 3: Write a verbal model.

Step 4: Write an equation.

Answers

2. The number is -8.
3. The number is -10.

$$2(x + 6) = 3x + 2$$

$$2x + 12 = 3x + 2$$

$$2x - 2x + 12 = 3x - 2x + 2$$

$$12 = x + 2$$

$$12 - 2 = x + 2 - 2$$

$$10 = x$$

The number is 10.

Step 5: Solve the equation.

Step 6: Write the final answer in words.

> **Avoiding Mistakes**
>
> It is important to enclose "the sum of a number and six" within parentheses so that the entire quantity is multiplied by 2. Forgetting the parentheses would imply that only the *x*-term is multiplied by 2.
>
> Correct: $2(x + 6)$

3. Consecutive Integer Problems

The word *consecutive* means "following one after the other in order without gaps." The numbers 6, 7, and 8 are examples of three **consecutive integers**. The numbers $-4, -2, 0,$ and 2 are examples of **consecutive even integers**. The numbers 23, 25, and 27 are examples of **consecutive odd integers**.

Notice that any two consecutive integers differ by 1. Therefore, if x represents an integer, then $(x + 1)$ represents the next larger consecutive integer (Figure 2-4).

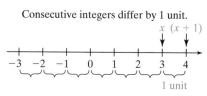

Figure 2-4

Any two consecutive even integers differ by 2. Therefore, if x represents an even integer, then $(x + 2)$ represents the next consecutive larger even integer (Figure 2-5).

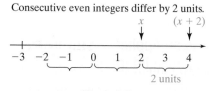

Figure 2-5

Likewise, any two consecutive odd integers differ by 2. If x represents an odd integer, then $(x + 2)$ is the next larger odd integer (Figure 2-6).

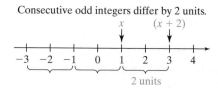

Figure 2-6

Skill Practice

4. The sum of two consecutive even integers is 66. Find the integers.

Example 4 Solving an Application Involving Consecutive Integers

The sum of two consecutive odd integers is -188. Find the integers.

Solution:

In this example we have two unknown integers. We can let x represent either of the unknowns.

Step 1: Read the problem.

Suppose x represents the first odd integer. **Step 2:** Label the unknowns.

Then $(x + 2)$ represents the second odd integer.

$$\left(\begin{array}{c}\text{First}\\\text{integer}\end{array}\right) + \left(\begin{array}{c}\text{second}\\\text{integer}\end{array}\right) = (\text{total})$$

Step 3: Write a verbal model.

$$x \quad + \quad (x + 2) \quad = -188$$

Step 4: Write a mathematical equation.

$$x + (x + 2) = -188$$

$$2x + 2 = -188$$

Step 5: Solve for x.

$$2x + 2 - 2 = -188 - 2$$

$$2x = -190$$

$$\frac{2x}{2} = \frac{-190}{2}$$

$$x = -95$$

The first integer is $x = -95$.

Step 6: Interpret the results and write the answer in words.

The second integer is $x + 2 = -95 + 2 = -93$.

The two integers are -95 and -93.

TIP: With word problems, it is advisable to check that the answer is reasonable.

The numbers -95 and -93 are consecutive odd integers. Furthermore, their sum is -188 as desired.

Skill Practice

5. Five times the smallest of three consecutive integers is 17 less than twice the sum of the integers. Find the integers.

Example 5 Solving an Application Involving Consecutive Integers

Ten times the smallest of three consecutive integers is twenty-two more than three times the sum of the integers. Find the integers.

Solution:

Step 1: Read the problem.

Let x represent the first integer.

Step 2: Label the unknowns.

$x + 1$ represents the second consecutive integer.

$x + 2$ represents the third consecutive integer.

Answers

4. The integers are 32 and 34.
5. The integers are 11, 12, and 13.

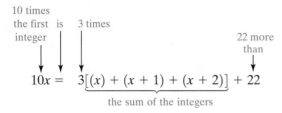

$\begin{pmatrix} 10 \text{ times} \\ \text{the first} \\ \text{integer} \end{pmatrix} = \begin{pmatrix} 3 \text{ times} \\ \text{the sum of} \\ \text{the integers} \end{pmatrix} + 22$

Step 3: Write a verbal model.

$10x = \underbrace{3[(x) + (x + 1) + (x + 2)]}_{\text{the sum of the integers}} + 22$

(10 times the first integer) (is) (3 times) (the sum of the integers) (22 more than)

Step 4: Write a mathematical equation.

$10x = 3(x + x + 1 + x + 2) + 22$

Step 5: Solve the equation.

$10x = 3(3x + 3) + 22$

Clear parentheses.

$10x = 9x + 9 + 22$

Combine *like* terms.

$10x = 9x + 31$

$10x - 9x = 9x - 9x + 31$

$x = 31$

Isolate the *x*-terms on one side.

The first integer is $x = 31$.

Step 6: Interpret the results and write the answer in words.

The second integer is $x + 1 = 31 + 1 = 32$.

The third integer is $x + 2 = 31 + 2 = 33$.

The three integers are 31, 32, and 33.

4. Applications of Linear Equations

Example 6 Using a Linear Equation in an Application

A carpenter cuts a 6-ft board in two pieces. One piece must be three times as long as the other. Find the length of each piece.

Solution:

In this problem, one piece must be three times as long as the other. Thus, if x represents the length of one piece, then $3x$ can represent the length of the other.

Step 1: Read the problem completely.

x represents the length of the smaller piece.
$3x$ represents the length of the longer piece.

Step 2: Label the unknowns. Draw a figure.

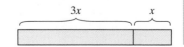

$3x$ x

Animation

Answer

6. One piece is 80 in. and the other is 16 in.

$$\begin{pmatrix} \text{Length of} \\ \text{one piece} \end{pmatrix} + \begin{pmatrix} \text{length of} \\ \text{other piece} \end{pmatrix} = \begin{pmatrix} \text{total length} \\ \text{of the board} \end{pmatrix}$$ **Step 3:**   Write a verbal model.

$$x \quad + \quad 3x \quad = \quad 6$$ **Step 4:**   Write an equation.

$$4x = 6$$ **Step 5:**   Solve the equation.

$$\frac{4x}{4} = \frac{6}{4}$$

$$x = 1.5$$

The smaller piece is $x = 1.5$ ft.   **Step 6:**   Interpret the results.

The longer piece is $3x$ or $3(1.5 \text{ ft}) = 4.5$ ft.

TIP: The variable can represent either unknown. In Example 6, if we let x represent the length of the longer piece of board, then $\frac{1}{3}x$ would represent the length of the smaller piece. The equation would become $x + \frac{1}{3}x = 6$. Try solving this equation and interpreting the result.

Skill Practice

7. There are 40 students in an algebra class. There are 4 more women than men. How many women and how many men are in the class?

Example 7   **Using a Linear Equation in an Application**

The hit movie *Harry Potter and the Deathly Hallows: Part 2* set a record for grossing the most money during its opening weekend. This amount surpassed the previous record set by the movie *The Dark Knight* by $10.8 million. The revenue from these two movies was $327.6 million. How much revenue did each movie bring in during its opening weekend?

Solution:

In this example, we have two unknowns. The variable x can represent *either* quantity. However, the revenue from *Harry Potter* is given in terms of the revenue for *The Dark Knight*.

Let x represent the revenue for *The Dark Knight*.

Step 1:   Read the problem.

Step 2:   Label the unknowns.

Then $x + 10.8$ represents the revenue for *Harry Potter*.

$$\begin{pmatrix} \text{Revenue from} \\ \text{\textit{The Dark Knight}} \end{pmatrix} + \begin{pmatrix} \text{revenue from} \\ \text{\textit{Harry Potter}} \end{pmatrix} = \begin{pmatrix} \text{total} \\ \text{revenue} \end{pmatrix}$$ **Step 3:**   Write a verbal model.

$$x \quad + \quad (x + 10.8) \quad = 327.6$$ **Step 4:**   Write an equation.

$$2x + 10.8 = 327.6$$ **Step 5:**   Solve the equation.

$$2x = 316.8$$

$$x = 158.4$$

- Revenue from *The Dark Knight*: $x = 158.4$
- Revenue from *Harry Potter*: $x + 10.8 = 158.4 + 10.8 = 169.2$

Answer

7. There are 22 women and 18 men.

The revenue from *Harry Potter and the Deathly Hallows: Part 2* was $169.2 million for its opening weekend. The revenue for *The Dark Knight* was $158.4 million.

Section 2.4 Practice Exercises

Study Skills Exercise

After doing a section of homework, check the odd-numbered answers in the back of the text. Choose a method to identify the exercises that gave you trouble (i.e., circle the number or put a star by the number). List some reasons why it is important to label these problems.

Vocabulary and Key Concepts

1. **a.** Integers that follow one after the other without "gaps" are called _____ integers.

   b. The integers –2, 0, 2, and 4 are examples of consecutive _____ integers.

   c. The integers –3, –1, 1, and 3 are examples of consecutive _____ integers.

   d. Two consecutive integers differ by _____.

   e. Two consecutive odd integers differ by _____.

   f. Two consecutive even integers differ by _____.

Concept 2: Translating to Linear Equations

For Exercises 2–8, write an expression representing the unknown quantity.

2. In a math class, the number of students who received an "A" in the class was 5 more than the number of students who received a "B." If x represents the number of "B" students, write an expression for the number of "A" students.

3. On a particular social network there are 5,682,080 fewer men than women. If x represents the number of women using the network, write an expression for the number of men using the network.

4. At a recent motorcycle rally, the number of men exceeded the number of women by 216. If x represents the number of women, write an expression for the number of men.

5. At one time there were 10 times as many Facebook users as Twitter users. If x represents the number of Twitter users, write an expression for the number of Facebook users.

6. Rebecca downloaded twice as many songs as Nigel. If x represents the number of songs downloaded by Nigel, write an expression for the number downloaded by Rebecca.

7. Sidney made $20 less than three times Casey's weekly salary. If x represents Casey's weekly salary, write an expression for Sidney's weekly salary.

8. David scored 26 points less than twice the number of points Rich scored in a video game. If x represents the number of points scored by Rich, write an expression representing the number of points scored by David.

For Exercises 9–18, use the problem-solving flowchart on page 147 (**See Examples 1–3.**)

9. Six less than a number is –10. Find the number.

10. Fifteen less than a number is 41. Find the number.

11. Twice the sum of a number and seven is eight. Find the number.

12. Twice the sum of a number and negative two is sixteen. Find the number.

13. A number added to five is the same as twice the number. Find the number.

14. Three times a number is the same as the difference of twice the number and seven. Find the number.

15. The sum of six times a number and ten is equal to the difference of the number and fifteen. Find the number.

16. The difference of fourteen and three times a number is the same as the sum of the number and negative ten. Find the number.

17. If the difference of a number and four is tripled, the result is six less than the number. Find the number.

18. Twice the sum of a number and eleven is twenty-two less than three times the number. Find the number.

Concept 3: Consecutive Integer Problems

19. a. If x represents the smallest of three consecutive integers, write an expression to represent each of the next two consecutive integers.

    b. If x represents the largest of three consecutive integers, write an expression to represent each of the previous two consecutive integers.

20. a. If x represents the smallest of three consecutive odd integers, write an expression to represent each of the next two consecutive odd integers.

    b. If x represents the largest of three consecutive odd integers, write an expression to represent each of the previous two consecutive odd integers.

For Exercises 21–30, use the problem-solving flowchart from page 147. (**See Examples 4 and 5.**)

21. The sum of two consecutive integers is -67. Find the integers.

22. The sum of two consecutive odd integers is 52. Find the integers.

23. The sum of two consecutive odd integers is 28. Find the integers.

24. The sum of three consecutive even integers is 66. Find the integers.

25. The perimeter of a pentagon (a five-sided polygon) is 80 in. The five sides are represented by consecutive integers. Find the measures of the sides.

26. The perimeter of a triangle is 96 in. The lengths of the sides are represented by consecutive integers. Find the measures of the sides.

27. The sum of three consecutive even integers is 48 less than twice the smallest of the three integers. Find the integers.

28. The sum of three consecutive odd integers is 89 less than twice the largest integer. Find the integers.

29. Eight times the sum of three consecutive odd integers is 210 more than 10 times the middle integer. Find the integers.

30. Five times the sum of three consecutive even integers is 140 more than ten times the smallest. Find the integers.

Concept 4: Applications of Linear Equations

For Exercises 31–42, use the problem-solving flowchart (page 147) to solve the problems.

31. A board is 86 cm in length and must be cut so that one piece is 20 cm longer than the other piece. Find the length of each piece. **(See Example 6.)**

32. A rope is 54 in. in length and must be cut into two pieces. If one piece must be twice as long as the other, find the length of each piece.

33. Karen's iPod contains 12 fewer playlists than Clarann's iPod. The total number of playlists on both iPods is 58. Find the number of playlists on each person's iPod.

34. Maria has 15 fewer apps on her phone than Orlando. If the total number of apps on both phones is 29, how many apps are on each phone?

35. For a recent year, 31 more Democrats than Republicans were in the U.S. House of Representatives. If the total number of representatives in the House from these two parties was 433, find the number of representatives from each party.

36. For a recent year, the number of men in the U.S. Senate totaled 4 more than 5 times the number of women. Find the number of men and the number of women in the Senate given that the Senate has 100 members.

37. During one week in a recent season, the show *CSI: Crime Scene Investigation* had 1.06 million fewer viewers than *Criminal Minds*. For both shows, the total number of viewers was 27.40 million. Find the number of viewers for each show during this week. **(See Example 7.)**

38. Two of the largest Internet retailers are e-Bay and Amazon.com. Recently, the estimated U.S. sales of e-Bay were $0.1 billion less than twice the sales of Amazon.com. Given the total sales of $5.6 billion, determine the sales of e-Bay and Amazon.com.

39. The longest river in Africa is the Nile. It is 2455 km longer than the Congo River, also in Africa. The sum of the lengths of these rivers is 11,195 km. What is the length of each river?

40. The average depth of the Gulf of Mexico is three times the depth of the Red Sea. The difference between the average depths is 1078 m. What is the average depth of the Gulf of Mexico and the average depth of the Red Sea?

41. Asia and Africa are the two largest continents in the world. The land area of Asia is approximately 14,514,000 km² larger than the land area of Africa. Together their total area is 74,644,000 km². Find the land area of Asia and the land area of Africa.

42. Mt. Everest, the highest mountain in the world, is 2654 m higher than Mt. McKinley, the highest mountain in the United States. If the sum of their heights is 15,042 m, find the height of each mountain.

Mixed Exercises

43. A group of hikers walked from Hawk Mt. Shelter to Blood Mt. Shelter along the Appalachian Trail, a total distance of 20.5 mi. It took 2 days for the walk. The second day the hikers walked 4.1 mi less than they did on the first day. How far did they walk each day?

44. $120 is to be divided among three restaurant servers. Angie made $10 more than Marie. Gwen, who went home sick, made $25 less than Marie. How much money should each server get?

45. A 4-ft piece of PVC pipe is cut into three pieces. The longest piece is 5 in. shorter than three times the shortest piece. The middle piece is 8 in. longer than the shortest piece. How long is each piece?

46. A 6-ft piece of copper wire must be cut into three pieces. The middle piece is 16 in. longer than the shortest piece. The longest piece is twice as long as the middle piece. How long is each piece?

47. Three consecutive integers are such that three times the largest exceeds the sum of the two smaller integers by 47. Find the integers.

48. Four times the smallest of three consecutive odd integers is 236 more than the sum of the other two integers. Find the integers.

49. In a recent year, the two top money earners of *American Idol* winners were Carrie Underwood and Jennifer Hudson. Jennifer's earnings were $2 million less than half of Carrie's earnings. If the total earnings were $19 million, find the individual earnings for Carrie Underwood and Jennifer Hudson?

50. Two of the longest-running TV series are *Gunsmoke* and *The Simpsons*. *Gunsmoke* ran 97 fewer episodes than twice the number of *The Simpsons*. If the total number of episodes is 998, how many of each show was produced?

51. Five times the difference of a number and three is four less than four times the number. Find the number.

52. Three times the difference of a number and seven is one less than twice the number. Find the number.

53. The sum of the page numbers on two facing pages in a book is 941. What are the page numbers?

54. Three raffle tickets are represented by three consecutive integers. If the sum of the three integers is 2,666,031, find the numbers.

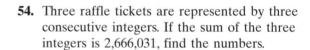

55. If three is added to five times a number, the result is forty-three more than the number. Find the number.

56. If seven is added to three times a number, the result is thirty-one more than the number.

57. The deepest point in the Pacific Ocean is 676 m more than twice the deepest point in the Arctic Ocean. If the deepest point in the Pacific is 10,920 m, how many meters is the deepest point in the Arctic Ocean?

58. The area of Greenland is 201,900 km^2 less than three times the area of New Guinea. What is the area of New Guinea if the area of Greenland is 2,175,600 km^2?

59. The sum of twice a number and $\frac{3}{4}$ is the same as the difference of four times the number and $\frac{1}{8}$. Find the number.

60. The difference of a number and $-\frac{11}{12}$ is the same as the difference of three times the number and $\frac{1}{6}$. Find the number.

61. The product of a number and 3.86 is equal to 7.15 more than the number. Find the number.

62. The product of a number and 4.6 is 33.12 less than the number. Find the number.

Applications Involving Percents

Section 2.5

1. Solving Basic Percent Equations

Recall from Section R.3 that the word *percent* means "per hundred." For example:

Percent	Interpretation
63% of homes have a computer	63 out of 100 homes have a computer.
5% sales tax	5¢ in tax is charged for every 100¢ in merchandise.
15% commission	$15 is earned in commission for every $100 sold.

Percents come up in a variety of applications in day-to-day life. Many such applications follow the basic percent equation:

$$\text{Amount} = (\text{percent})(\text{base}) \qquad \text{Basic percent equation}$$

In Example 1, we apply the basic percent equation to compute sales tax.

Concepts

1. Solving Basic Percent Equations
2. Applications Involving Simple Interest
3. Applications Involving Discount and Markup

Example 1 Computing Sales Tax

A new digital camera costs $429.95.

  a. Compute the sales tax if the tax rate is 4%.

  b. Determine the total cost, including tax.

Skill Practice

1. Find the amount of tax on a portable CD player that sells for $89. Assume the tax rate is 6%.
2. Find the total cost including tax.

Solution:

	Step 1:	Read the problem.
a. Let x represent the amount of tax.	Step 2:	Label the unknown.

Apply the percent equation to compute sales tax.

Amount = (percent) · (base)
  ↓ ↓ ↓

Step 3: Write a verbal model.

Sales tax = (tax rate)(price of merchandise)

Answers

1. The amount of tax is $5.34.
2. The total cost is $94.34.

$$x = (0.04)(\$429.95)$$

$$x = \$17.198$$

$$x = \$17.20$$

The tax on the merchandise is $17.20.

Step 4: Write a mathematical equation.

Step 5: Solve the equation. Round to the nearest cent.

Step 6: Interpret the results.

b. The total cost is found by:

total cost = cost of merchandise + amount of tax

Therefore the total cost is $429.95 + $17.20 = $447.15.

In Example 2, we solve a problem in which the percent is unknown.

Example 2   Finding an Unknown Percent

A group of 240 college men were asked what intramural sport they most enjoyed playing. The results are in the graph. What percent of the men surveyed preferred tennis?

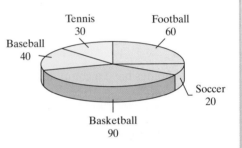

Tennis 30   Football 60   Baseball 40   Soccer 20   Basketball 90

Solution:

Step 1: Read the problem.

Let x represent the unknown percent (in decimal form).

Step 2: Label the unknown.

The problem can be rephrased as:

30 is what percent of 240?

↓ ↓ ↓   ↓ ↓

30 = x · 240

Step 3: Write a verbal model.

Step 4: Write a mathematical equation.

$$30 = 240x$$

Step 5: Solve the equation.

$$\frac{30}{240} = \frac{240x}{240}$$

Divide both sides by 240.

$$0.125 = x$$

$$0.125 \times 100\% = 12.5\%$$

In this survey, 12.5% of men prefer tennis.

Step 6: Interpret the results. Change the value of x to percent form by multiplying by 100%.

Answer

3. 37.5% of the men surveyed prefer basketball.

Example 3 Solving a Percent Equation with an Unknown Base

Andrea spends 20% of her monthly paycheck on rent each month. If her rent payment is $950, what is her monthly paycheck?

Solution:

	Step 1:	Read the problem.
Let x represent the amount of Andrea's monthly paycheck.	**Step 2:**	Label the unknown.

The problem can be rephrased as:

$950 is 20% of what number?	**Step 3:**	Write a verbal model.
$950 = 0.20 \cdot x$	**Step 4:**	Write a mathematical equation.
$950 = 0.20x$	**Step 5:**	Solve the equation.
$\dfrac{950}{0.20} = \dfrac{0.20x}{0.20}$		Divide both sides by 0.20.
$4750 = x$		

Andrea's monthly paycheck is $4750. **Step 6:** Interpret the results.

Skill Practice

4. In order to pass an exam, a student must answer 70% of the questions correctly. If answering 42 questions correctly results in a 70% score, how many questions are on the test?

2. Applications Involving Simple Interest

One important application of percents is in computing simple interest on a loan or on an investment.

Simple interest is interest that is earned on principal (the original amount of money). The following formula is used to compute simple interest:

$$\left(\begin{array}{c}\text{Simple}\\\text{interest}\end{array}\right) = \left(\text{principal}\right)\left(\begin{array}{c}\text{annual}\\\text{interest rate}\end{array}\right)\left(\begin{array}{c}\text{time}\\\text{in years}\end{array}\right)$$

This formula is often written symbolically as $I = Prt$.

For example, to find the simple interest earned on $2000 invested at 7.5% interest for 3 years, we have

$$I = Prt$$
$$\text{Interest} = (\$2000)(0.075)(3)$$
$$= \$450$$

Example 4 Applying Simple Interest

Jorge wants to save money to buy a car in 5 years. If Jorge needs to have $20,250 at the end of 5 years, how much money would he need to invest in a certificate of deposit (CD) at a 2.5% interest rate?

Solution:

	Step 1:	Read the problem.
Let P represent the original amount invested.	**Step 2:**	Label the unknown.

Skill Practice

5. Cassandra invested some money in her bank account, and after 10 years at 4% simple interest, it has grown to $7700. What was the initial amount invested?

Answers

4. There are 60 questions on the test.
5. The initial investment was $5500.

$$\left(\begin{array}{c}\text{Original}\\\text{principal}\end{array}\right) + (\text{interest}) = (\text{total})$$

$$P + Prt = \text{total}$$

$$P + P(0.025)(5) = 20{,}250$$

$$P + 0.125P = 20{,}250$$

$$1.125P = 20{,}250$$

$$\frac{1.125P}{1.125} = \frac{20{,}250}{1.125}$$

$$P = 18{,}000$$

The original investment should be \$18,000.

Step 3: Write a verbal model.

Step 4: Write a mathematical equation.

Step 5: Solve the equation.

Step 6: Interpret the results and write the answer in words.

3. Applications Involving Discount and Markup

Applications involving percent increase and percent decrease are abundant in many real-world settings. Sales tax for example is essentially a markup by a state or local government. It is important to understand that percent increase or decrease is always computed on the original amount given.

In Example 5, we illustrate an example of percent decrease in an application where merchandise is discounted.

Example 5 **Applying Percents to a Discount Problem**

After a 38% discount, a used treadmill costs \$868 on e-Bay. What was the original cost of the treadmill?

Solution:

Step 1: Read the problem.

Let x be the original cost of the treadmill.

Step 2: Label the unknown.

$$\left(\begin{array}{c}\text{Original}\\\text{cost}\end{array}\right) - (\text{discount}) = \left(\begin{array}{c}\text{sale}\\\text{price}\end{array}\right)$$

Step 3: Write a verbal model.

$$x - 0.38(x) = 868$$

Step 4: Write a mathematical equation. The discount is a percent of the *original* amount.

$$x - 0.38x = 868$$

Step 5: Solve the equation.

$$0.62x = 868$$

Combine *like* terms.

$$\frac{0.62x}{0.62} = \frac{868}{0.62}$$

Divide by 0.62.

$$x = 1400$$

The original cost of the treadmill was \$1400.

Step 6: Interpret the result.

Section 2.5 Practice Exercises

Study Skills Exercise

It is always helpful to read the material in a section and make notes before it is presented in class. Writing notes ahead of time will free you to listen more in class and to pay special attention to the concepts that need clarification. Refer to your class syllabus and identify the next two sections that will be covered in class. Then determine a time when you can read these sections before class.

Vocabulary and Key Concepts

1. a. Interest that is earned on principal is called _____ interest.

   b. 82% means 82 out of _____.

Review Exercises

2. List the six steps to solve an application.

For Exercises 3 and 4, use the steps for problem solving to solve these applications.

3. Find two consecutive integers such that three times the larger is the same as 45 more than the smaller.

4. The height of the Great Pyramid of Giza is 17 m more than twice the height of the pyramid found in Saqqara. If the difference in their heights is 77 m, find the height of each pyramid.

Concept 1: Solving Basic Percent Equations

For Exercises 5–16, find the missing values.

5. 45 is what percent of 360?

6. 338 is what percent of 520?

7. 544 is what percent of 640?

8. 576 is what percent of 800?

9. What is 0.5% of 150?

10. What is 9.5% of 616?

11. What is 142% of 740?

12. What is 156% of 280?

13. 177 is 20% of what number?

14. 126 is 15% of what number?

15. 275 is 12.5% of what number?

16. 594 is 45% of what number?

17. A Craftsman drill is on sale for $99.99. If the sales tax rate is 7%, how much will Molly have to pay for the drill?
(See Example 1.)

18. Patrick purchased four new tires that were regularly priced at $94.99 each, but are on sale for $20 off per tire. If the sales tax rate is 6%, how much will be charged to Patrick's VISA card?

For Exercises 19 and 20, use the graph showing the distribution for leading forms of cancer in men. (*Source:* Centers for Disease Control)

19. If there are 700,000 cases of cancer in men in the United States, approximately how many are prostate cancer?

20. Approximately how many cases of lung cancer would be expected in 700,000 cancer cases among men in the United States?

21. There were 14,000 cases of cancer of the pancreas diagnosed out of 700,000 cancer cases. What percent is this? (See Example 2.)

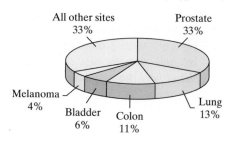

Percent of Cancer Cases by Type (Men)

All other sites 33%
Prostate 33%
Melanoma 4%
Bladder 6%
Colon 11%
Lung 13%

22. There were 21,000 cases of leukemia diagnosed out of 700,000 cancer cases. What percent is this?

23. Javon is in a 28% tax bracket for his federal income tax. If the amount of money that he paid for federal income tax was $23,520, what was his taxable income? **(See Example 3.)**

24. In a recent survey of college-educated adults, 155 indicated that they regularly work more than 50 hr a week. If this represents 31% of those surveyed, how many people were in the survey?

Concept 2: Applications Involving Simple Interest

For Exercises 25–32, solve these equations involving simple interest.

25. How much interest will Pam earn in 4 years if she invests $3000 in an account that pays 3.5% simple interest?

26. How much interest will Roxanne have to pay if she borrows $2000 for 2 years at a simple interest rate of 4%?

27. Bob borrowed some money for 1 year at 5% simple interest. If he had to pay back a total of $1260, how much did he originally borrow? **(See Example 4.)**

28. Andrea borrowed some money for 2 years at 6% simple interest. If she had to pay back a total of $3640, how much did she originally borrow?

29. If $1500 grows to $1950 after 5 years, find the simple interest rate.

30. If $9000 grows to $10,440 in 2 years, find the simple interest rate.

31. Perry is planning a vacation to Europe in 2 years. How much should he invest in a certificate of deposit that pays 3% simple interest to get the $3500 that he needs for the trip? Round to the nearest dollar.

32. Sherica invested in a mutual fund and at the end of 20 years she has $14,300 in her account. If the mutual fund returned an average yield of 8%, how much did she originally invest?

Concept 3: Applications Involving Discount and Markup

33. A CD/MP3 player for a car costs $170. It is on sale for 12% off with free installation.

  a. What is the discount on the CD/MP3 player?

  b. What is the sale price?

34. A laptop computer, originally selling for $899.00, is on sale for 10% off.

  a. What is the discount on the laptop?

  b. What is the sale price?

35. A digital camera is on sale for $400.00. This price is 15% off the original price. What was the original price? Round to the nearest cent. **(See Example 5.)**

36. The *Avatar* DVD is on sale for $18. If this represents an 18% discount rate, what was the original price of the DVD?

37. The original price of an Audio Jukebox was $250. It is on sale for $220. What percent discount does this represent?

38. During its first year, a popular game console sold for $425.00 in stores. This product was in such demand that it sold for $800 online. What percent markup does this represent? (Round to the nearest whole percent.)

39. A doctor ordered a dosage of medicine for a patient. After 2 days, she increased the dosage by 20% and the new dosage came to 18 cc. What was the original dosage?

40. In one area, the cable company marked up the monthly cost by 6%. The new cost is $63.60 per month. What was the cost before the increase?

Mixed Exercises

41. Sun Lei bought a laptop computer for $1800. The total cost, including tax, came to $1890. What is the tax rate?

42. Jamie purchased a compact disk and paid $18.26. If the disk price is $16.99, what is the sales tax rate (round to the nearest tenth of a percent)?

43. For a recent year, admission to Walt Disney World cost $74.37, including taxes of 11%. What was the original ticket price before taxes?

44. A hotel room rented for 5 nights costs $706.25 including 13% in taxes. Find the original price of the room (before tax) for the 5 nights. Then find the price per night.

45. Deon purchased a house and sold it for a 24% profit. If he sold the house for $260,400, what was the original purchase price?

46. To meet the rising cost of energy, the yearly membership at a YMCA had to be increased by 12.5% from the past year. The yearly membership fee is currently $450. What was the cost of membership last year?

47. Alina earns $1600 per month plus a 12% commission on pharmaceutical sales. If she sold $25,000 in pharmaceuticals one month, what was her salary that month?

48. Dan sold a beachfront home for $650,000. If his commission rate is 4%, what did he earn in commission?

49. Diane sells women's sportswear at a department store. She earns a regular salary and, as a bonus, she receives a commission of 4% on all sales over $200. If Diane earned an extra $25.80 last week in commission, how much merchandise did she sell over $200?

50. For selling software, Tom received a bonus commission based on sales over $500. If he received $180 in commission for selling a total of $2300 worth of software, what is his commission rate?

Concepts

1. **Formulas and Literal Equations**
2. **Geometry Applications**

1. Formulas and Literal Equations

A *literal equation* is an equation that has more than one variable. A formula is a literal equation with a specific application. For example, the perimeter of a triangle (distance around the triangle) can be found by the formula $P = a + b + c$, where a, b, and c are the lengths of the sides (Figure 2-7).

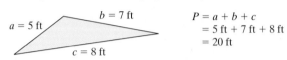

$$P = a + b + c$$
$$= 5 \text{ ft} + 7 \text{ ft} + 8 \text{ ft}$$
$$= 20 \text{ ft}$$

Figure 2-7

In this section, we will learn how to rewrite formulas to solve for a different variable within the formula. Suppose, for example, that the perimeter of a triangle is known and two of the sides are known (say, sides a and b). Then the third side, c, can be found by subtracting the lengths of the known sides from the perimeter (Figure 2-8).

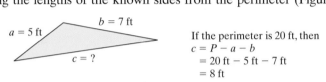

If the perimeter is 20 ft, then
$$c = P - a - b$$
$$= 20 \text{ ft} - 5 \text{ ft} - 7 \text{ ft}$$
$$= 8 \text{ ft}$$

Figure 2-8

To solve a formula for a different variable, we use the same properties of equality outlined in the earlier sections of this chapter. For example, consider the two equations $2x + 3 = 11$ and $wx + y = z$. Suppose we want to solve for x in each case:

$2x + 3 = 11$	$wx + y = z$
$2x + 3 - 3 = 11 - 3$ Subtract 3.	$wx + y - y = z - y$ Subtract y.
$2x = 8$	$wx = z - y$
$\dfrac{2x}{2} = \dfrac{8}{2}$ Divide by 2.	$\dfrac{wx}{w} = \dfrac{z - y}{w}$ Divide by w.
$x = 4$	$x = \dfrac{z - y}{w}$

The equation on the left has only one variable and we are able to simplify the equation to find a numerical value for x. The equation on the right has multiple variables. Because we do not know the values of w, y, and z, we are not able to simplify further. The value of x is left as a formula in terms of w, y, and z.

Skill Practice

Solve for the indicated variable.

1. $A = lw$ for l
2. $-2a + 4b = 7$ for a

Answers

1. $l = \dfrac{A}{w}$
2. $a = \dfrac{7 - 4b}{-2}$ or $a = \dfrac{4b - 7}{2}$

Example 1   Solving for an Indicated Variable

Solve for the indicated variables.

a. $d = rt$ for t **b.** $5x + 2y = 12$ for y

Solution:

a. $d = rt$ for t The goal is to isolate the variable t.

$\dfrac{d}{r} = \dfrac{rt}{r}$ Because the relationship between r and t is multiplication, we reverse the process by dividing both sides by r.

$\dfrac{d}{r} = t$, or equivalently $t = \dfrac{d}{r}$

b. $\qquad 5x + 2y = 12 \quad$ for $y \qquad$ The goal is to solve for y.

$5x - 5x + 2y = 12 - 5x \qquad$ Subtract $5x$ from both sides to isolate the y-term.

$\qquad 2y = -5x + 12 \qquad -5x + 12$ is the same as $12 - 5x$.

$$\frac{2y}{2} = \frac{-5x + 12}{2} \qquad \text{Divide both sides by 2 to isolate } y.$$

$$y = \frac{-5x + 12}{2}$$

Avoiding Mistakes

In the expression $\dfrac{-5x + 12}{2}$ do not try to divide the 2 into the 12. The divisor of 2 is dividing the entire quantity, $-5x + 12$ (not just the 12).

We may, however, apply the divisor to each term individually in the numerator. That is, $\dfrac{-5x + 12}{2}$ can be written in several different forms. Each is correct.

$$y = \frac{-5x + 12}{2} \qquad \text{or} \qquad y = \frac{-5x}{2} + \frac{12}{2} \quad \Rightarrow \quad y = -\frac{5x}{2} + 6$$

Example 2   Solving for an Indicated Variable

The formula $C = \frac{5}{9}(F - 32)$ is used to find the temperature, C, in degrees Celsius for a given temperature expressed in degrees Fahrenheit, F. Solve the formula $C = \frac{5}{9}(F - 32)$ for F.

Solution:

$$C = \frac{5}{9}(F - 32)$$

$$C = \frac{5}{9}F - \frac{5}{9} \cdot 32 \qquad \text{Clear parentheses.}$$

$$C = \frac{5}{9}F - \frac{160}{9} \qquad \text{Multiply: } \frac{5}{9} \cdot \frac{32}{1} = \frac{160}{9}.$$

$$9(C) = 9\left(\frac{5}{9}F - \frac{160}{9}\right) \qquad \text{Multiply by the LCD to clear fractions.}$$

$$9C = \frac{9}{1} \cdot \frac{5}{9}F - \frac{9}{1} \cdot \frac{160}{9} \qquad \text{Apply the distributive property.}$$

$$9C = 5F - 160 \qquad \text{Simplify.}$$

$$9C + 160 = 5F - 160 + 160 \qquad \text{Add 160 to both sides.}$$

$$9C + 160 = 5F$$

$$\frac{9C + 160}{5} = \frac{5F}{5} \qquad \text{Divide both sides by 5.}$$

$$\frac{9C + 160}{5} = F$$

The answer may be written in several forms:

$$F = \frac{9C + 160}{5} \quad \text{or} \quad F = \frac{9C}{5} + \frac{160}{5} \quad \Rightarrow \quad F = \frac{9}{5}C + 32$$

Skill Practice

3. Solve for the indicated variable.

$$y = \frac{1}{3}(x - 7) \text{ for } x.$$

Answer

3. $x = 3y + 7$

2. Geometry Applications

In Section R.4, we presented numerous facts and formulas related to geometry. Sometimes these are needed to solve applications in geometry.

Example 3 Solving a Geometry Application Involving Perimeter

The length of a rectangular lot is 1 m less than twice the width. If the perimeter is 190 m, find the length and width.

Solution:

Step 1: Read the problem.

Let x represent the width of the rectangle.   **Step 2:** Label the unknowns.

Then $2x - 1$ represents the length.

x

$2x - 1$

$$P = 2l + 2w$$ **Step 3:** Write the formula for perimeter.

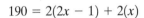

$$190 = 2(2x - 1) + 2(x)$$ **Step 4:** Write an equation in terms of x.

$$190 = 4x - 2 + 2x$$ **Step 5:** Solve for x.

$$190 = 6x - 2$$

$$192 = 6x$$

$$\frac{192}{6} = \frac{6x}{6}$$

$$32 = x$$

The width is $x = 32$.

The length is $2x - 1 = 2(32) - 1 = 63$.   **Step 6:** Interpret the results and write the answer in words.

The width of the rectangular lot is 32 m and the length is 63 m.

Recall some facts about angles.

- Two angles are complementary if the sum of their measures is 90°.
- Two angles are supplementary if the sum of their measures is 180°.
- The sum of the measures of the angles within a triangle is 180°.
- The measures of vertical angles are equal.

Answer

4. The length is 56′, and the width is 33′.

| Example 4 | Solving a Geometry Application Involving Complementary Angles |

Two complementary angles are drawn such that one angle is 4° more than seven times the other angle. Find the measure of each angle.

Solution:

Step 1: Read the problem.

Let x represent the measure of one angle.   Step 2: Label the unknowns.

Then $7x + 4$ represents the measure of the other angle.

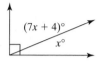

The angles are complementary, so the sum of their measures must be 90°.

$$\begin{pmatrix} \text{Measure of} \\ \text{first angle} \end{pmatrix} + \begin{pmatrix} \text{measure of} \\ \text{second angle} \end{pmatrix} = 90°$$ Step 3: Write a verbal model.

$$x \quad + \quad 7x + 4 \quad = 90$$ Step 4: Write a mathematical equation.

$$8x + 4 = 90$$ Step 5: Solve for x.

$$8x = 86$$

$$\frac{8x}{8} = \frac{86}{8}$$

$$x = 10.75$$

Step 6: Interpret the results and write the answer in words.

One measure is $x = 10.75$.

The other measure is $7x + 4 = 7(10.75) + 4 = 79.25$.

The measures of the angles are 10.75° and 79.25°.

| Example 5 | Solving a Geometry Application Involving Angles in a Triangle |

One angle in a triangle is twice as large as the smallest angle. The third angle is 10° more than seven times the smallest angle. Find the measure of each angle.

Solution:

Step 1: Read the problem.

Let x represent the measure of the smallest angle.   Step 2: Label the unknowns.

Then $2x$ and $7x + 10$ represent the measures of the other two angles.

The sum of the measures must be 180°.

$$\left(\begin{array}{c}\text{Measure of}\\\text{first angle}\end{array}\right) + \left(\begin{array}{c}\text{measure of}\\\text{second angle}\end{array}\right) + \left(\begin{array}{c}\text{measure of}\\\text{third angle}\end{array}\right) = 180°$$

Step 3: Write a verbal model.

$$x \qquad + \qquad 2x \qquad + \quad (7x + 10) = 180$$

Step 4: Write a mathematical equation.

$$x + 2x + 7x + 10 = 180$$ **Step 5:** Solve for x.

$$10x + 10 = 180$$

$$10x = 170$$

$$x = 17$$

Step 6: Interpret the results and write the answer in words.

The smallest measure is $x = 17$.

The other measures are $2x = 2(17) = 34$

$$7x + 10 = 7(17) + 10 = 129$$

The measures of the angles are 17°, 34°, and 129°.

Skill Practice

7. The circumference of a drain pipe is 12.5 cm. Find the radius. Round to the nearest tenth of a centimeter.

Example 6 Solving a Geometry Application Involving Circumference

The distance around a circular garden is 188.4 ft. Find the radius to the nearest tenth of a foot. Use 3.14 for π.

$C = 188.4$ ft

Solution:

$$C = 2\pi r \qquad \text{Use the formula for the circumference of a circle.}$$

$$188.4 = 2\pi r \qquad \text{Substitute 188.4 for } C.$$

$$\frac{188.4}{2\pi} = \frac{2\pi r}{2\pi} \qquad \text{Divide both sides by } 2\pi.$$

$$\frac{188.4}{2\pi} = r$$

$$r \approx \frac{188.4}{2(3.14)}$$

$$= 30.0$$

The radius is approximately 30.0 ft.

Answer

7. 2.0 cm

Calculator Connections

Topic: Using the π Key on a Calculator

In Example 6 we could have obtained a more accurate result if we had used the π key on the calculator.

Note that parentheses are required to divide 188.4 by the quantity 2π. This guarantees that the calculator follows the implied order of operations. Without parentheses, the calculator would divide 188.4 by 2 and then multiply the result by π.

Scientific Calculator

Enter: 188.4 [÷] [(] 2 [×] [π] [)] [=]   Result: [29.98479128] correct

Enter: 188.4 [÷] 2 [×] [π] [=]   Result: [295.938028] incorrect

Graphing Calculator

```
188.4/(2π)
          29.98479128   ←——— Correct
188.4/2π
          295.938028   ←——— Incorrect
```

Calculator Exercises

Approximate the expressions with a calculator. Round to three decimal places if necessary.

1. $\dfrac{880}{2\pi}$

2. $\dfrac{1600}{\pi(4)^2}$

3. $\dfrac{20}{5\pi}$

4. $\dfrac{10}{7\pi}$

Section 2.6 Practice Exercises

Study Skills Exercise

A good technique for studying for a test is to choose four problems from each section of the chapter and write the problems along with the directions on 3×5 cards. On the back of each card, put the page number where you found that problem. Then shuffle the cards and test yourself on the procedure to solve each problem. If you find one that you do not know how to solve, look at the page number and do several of that type. Write four problems you would choose for this section.

Review Exercises

For Exercises 1–8, solve the equation.

1. $3(2y + 3) - 4(-y + 1) = 7y - 10$

2. $-(3w + 4) + 5(w - 2) - 3(6w - 8) = 10$

3. $\dfrac{1}{2}(x - 3) + \dfrac{3}{4} = 3x - \dfrac{3}{4}$

4. $\dfrac{5}{6}x + \dfrac{1}{2} = \dfrac{1}{4}(x - 4)$

5. $0.5(y + 2) - 0.3 = 0.4y + 0.5$

6. $0.25(500 - x) + 0.15x = 75$

7. $8b + 6(7 - 2b) = -4(b + 1)$

8. $2 - 5(t - 3) + t = 7t - (6t + 8)$

Concept 1: Formulas and Literal Equations

For Exercises 9–40, solve for the indicated variable. **(See Examples 1 and 2.)**

9. $P = a + b + c$ for a

10. $P = a + b + c$ for b

11. $x = y - z$ for y

12. $c + d = e$ for d

13. $p = 250 + q$ for q

14. $y = 35 + x$ for x

15. $A = bh$ for b

16. $d = rt$ for r

17. $PV = nrt$ for t

18. $P_1V_1 = P_2V_2$ for V_1

19. $x - y = 5$ for x

20. $x + y = -2$ for y

21. $3x + y = -19$ for y

22. $x - 6y = -10$ for x

23. $2x + 3y = 6$ for y

24. $5x + 2y = 10$ for y

25. $-2x - y = 9$ for x

26. $3x - y = -13$ for x

27. $4x - 3y = 12$ for y

28. $6x - 3y = 4$ for y

29. $ax + by = c$ for y

30. $ax + by = c$ for x

31. $A = P(1 + rt)$ for t

32. $P = 2(L + w)$ for L

33. $a = 2(b + c)$ for c

34. $3(x + y) = z$ for x

35. $Q = \dfrac{x + y}{2}$ for y

36. $Q = \dfrac{a - b}{2}$ for a

37. $M = \dfrac{a}{S}$ for a

38. $A = \dfrac{1}{3}(a + b + c)$ for c

39. $P = I^2R$ for R

40. $F = \dfrac{GMm}{d^2}$ for m

Concept 2: Geometry Applications

For Exercises 41–62, use the problem-solving flowchart (page 147) from Section 2.4.

41. The perimeter of a rectangular garden is 24 ft. The length is 2 ft more than the width. Find the length and the width of the garden. **(See Example 3.)**

42. In a small rectangular wallet photo, the width is 7 cm less than the length. If the border (perimeter) of the photo is 34 cm, find the length and width.

43. The length of a rectangular parking area is four times the width. The perimeter is 300 yd. Find the length and width of the parking area.

44. The width of Jason's workbench is $\frac{1}{2}$ the length. The perimeter is 240 in. Find the length and the width of the workbench.

45. A builder buys a rectangular lot of land such that the length is 5 m less than two times the width. If the perimeter is 590 m, find the length and the width.

46. The perimeter of a rectangular pool is 140 yd. If the length is 20 yd less than twice the width, find the length and the width.

$2w - 5$

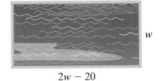

$2w - 20$

47. A triangular parking lot has two sides that are the same length and the third side is 5 m longer. If the perimeter is 71 m, find the lengths of the sides.

48. The perimeter of a triangle is 16 ft. One side is 3 ft longer than the shortest side. The third side is 1 ft longer than the shortest side. Find the lengths of all the sides.

49. Sometimes memory devices are helpful for remembering mathematical facts. Recall that the sum of the measures of two complementary angles is 90°. That is, two complementary angles when added together form a right angle or "corner." The words *Complementary* and *Corner* both start with the letter "*C*." Derive your own memory device for remembering that the sum of the measures of two supplementary angles is 180°.

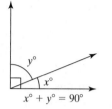
$x° + y° = 90°$

Complementary angles form a "Corner"

$x° + y° = 180°$

Supplementary angles . . .

50. What do you know about the measures of two vertical angles?

51. Two angles are complementary. One angle is 20° less than the other angle. Find the measures of the angles. **(See Example 4.)**

52. Two angles are complementary. One angle is 4° less than three times the other angle. Find the measures of the angles.

53. Two angles are supplementary. One angle is three times as large as the other angle. Find the measures of the angles.

54. Two angles are supplementary. One angle is 6° more than four times the other. Find the measures of the two angles.

55. Find the measures of the vertical angles labeled in the figure by first solving for x.

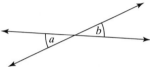

56. Find the measures of the vertical angles labeled in the figure by first solving for y.

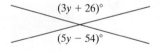

57. The largest angle in a triangle is three times the smallest angle. The middle angle is two times the smallest angle. Given that the sum of the angles in a triangle is 180°, find the measure of each angle. **(See Example 5.)**

58. The smallest angle in a triangle measures 90° less than the largest angle. The middle angle measures 60° less than the largest angle. Find the measure of each angle.

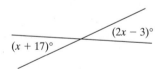

Animation

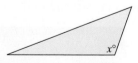

59. The smallest angle in a triangle is half the largest angle. The middle angle measures 30° less than the largest angle. Find the measure of each angle.

60. The largest angle of a triangle is three times the middle angle. The smallest angle measures 10° less than the middle angle. Find the measure of each angle.

61. Find the value of x and the measure of each angle labeled in the figure.

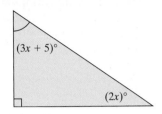

62. Find the value of y and the measure of each angle labeled in the figure.

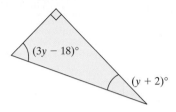

 63. a. A rectangle has length l and width w. Write a formula for the area.

b. Solve the formula for the width, w.

c. The area of a rectangular volleyball court is 1740.5 ft^2 and the length is 59 ft. Find the width.

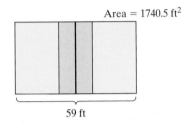

Area = 1740.5 ft^2

59 ft

64. a. A parallelogram has height h and base b. Write a formula for the area.

b. Solve the formula for the base, b.

c. Find the base of the parallelogram pictured if the area is 40 m^2.

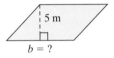

5 m

$b = ?$

65. a. A rectangle has length l and width w. Write a formula for the perimeter.

b. Solve the formula for the length, l.

c. The perimeter of the soccer field at Giants Stadium is 338 m. If the width is 66 m, find the length.

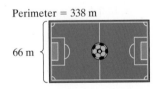

Perimeter = 338 m

66 m

66. a. A triangle has height h and base b. Write a formula for the area.

b. Solve the formula for the height, h.

c. Find the height of the triangle pictured if the area is 12 km^2.

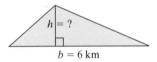

$h = ?$

$b = 6$ km

67. a. A circle has a radius of r. Write a formula for the circumference. **(See Example 6.)**

b. Solve the formula for the radius, r.

c. The circumference of the circular Buckingham Fountain in Chicago is approximately 880 ft. Find the radius. Round to the nearest foot.

68. a. The length of each side of a square is s. Write a formula for the perimeter of the square.

b. Solve the formula for the length of a side, s.

c. The Pyramid of Khufu (known as the Great Pyramid) at Giza has a square base. If the distance around the bottom is 921.6 m, find the length of the sides at the bottom of the pyramid.

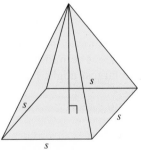

Expanding Your Skills

For Exercises 69 and 70, find the indicated area or volume. Be sure to include the proper units and round each answer to two decimal places if necessary.

69. a. Find the area of a circle with radius 11.5 m. Use the π key on the calculator.

  b. Find the volume of a right circular cylinder with radius 11.5 m and height 25 m.

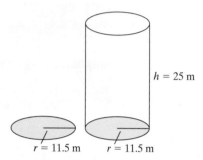

$h = 25$ m

$r = 11.5$ m $r = 11.5$ m

70. a. Find the area of a parallelogram with base 30 in. and height 12 in.

  b. Find the area of a triangle with base 30 in. and height 12 in.

  c. Compare the areas found in parts (a) and (b).

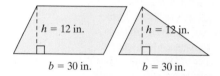

$h = 12$ in.

$b = 30$ in.

$h = 12$ in.

$b = 30$ in.

Mixture Applications and Uniform Motion

Section 2.7

1. Applications Involving Cost

In Examples 1 and 2, we will look at different kinds of mixture problems. The first example "mixes" two types of movie tickets, adult tickets that sell for $8 and children's tickets that sell for $6. Furthermore, there were 300 tickets sold for a total revenue of $2040. Before attempting the problem, we should try to gain some familiarity. Let's try a few combinations to see how many of each type of ticket might have been sold.

  Suppose 100 adult tickets were sold and 200 children's tickets were sold (a total of 300 tickets).

- 100 adult tickets at $8 each gives $\quad$ 100($8) = $800
- 200 children's tickets at $6 each gives $\quad$ 200($6) = $1200

$\qquad\qquad$ Total revenue: $\quad$ $2000 (not enough)

Suppose 150 adult tickets were sold and 150 children's tickets were sold (a total of 300 tickets).

- 150 adult tickets at $8 each gives $\quad$ 150($8) = $1200
- 150 children's tickets at $6 each gives $\quad$ 150($6) = $900

$\qquad\qquad$ Total revenue: $\quad$ $2100 (too much)

As you can see, the trial-and-error process can be tedious and time-consuming. Therefore we will use algebra to determine the correct combination of each type of ticket.

  Suppose we let x represent the number of adult tickets, then the number of children's tickets is the *total minus x*. That is

$$\left(\begin{array}{c}\text{Number of}\\ \text{children's tickets}\end{array}\right) = \left(\begin{array}{c}\text{total number}\\ \text{of tickets}\end{array}\right) - \left(\begin{array}{c}\text{number of}\\ \text{adult tickets, } x\end{array}\right)$$

Number of children's tickets = $300 - x$.

Concepts

1. Applications Involving Cost
2. Applications Involving Mixtures
3. Applications Involving Uniform Motion

Notice that the number of tickets sold times the price per ticket gives the revenue.

- x adult tickets at \$8 each gives a revenue of: $x(\$8)$ or simply $8x$.
- $300 - x$ children's tickets at \$6 each gives: $(300 - x)(\$6)$ or $6(300 - x)$

This will help us set up an equation in Example 1.

Example 1   Solving a Mixture Problem Involving Ticket Sales

At an IMAX theater, 300 tickets were sold. Adult tickets cost \$8 and tickets for children cost \$6. If the total revenue from ticket sales was \$2040, determine the number of each type of ticket sold.

Solution:

Let x represent the number of adult tickets sold.

$300 - x$ is the number of children's tickets.

Step 1: Read the problem.

Step 2: Label the unknowns.

	\$8 Tickets	**\$6 Tickets**	**Total**
Number of tickets	x	$300 - x$	300
Revenue	$8x$	$6(300 - x)$	2040

$$\left(\begin{array}{c}\text{Revenue from}\\\text{adult tickets}\end{array}\right) + \left(\begin{array}{c}\text{revenue from}\\\text{children's tickets}\end{array}\right) = \left(\begin{array}{c}\text{total}\\\text{revenue}\end{array}\right)$$

Step 3: Write a verbal model.

$$8x \qquad + \qquad 6(300 - x) \qquad = \qquad 2040$$

Step 4: Write a mathematical equation.

$$8x + 6(300 - x) = 2040$$

Step 5: Solve the equation.

$$8x + 1800 - 6x = 2040$$
$$2x + 1800 = 2040$$
$$2x = 240$$
$$x = 120$$

Step 6: Interpret the results.

There were 120 adult tickets sold. The number of children's tickets is $300 - x$ which is 180.

2. Applications Involving Mixtures

| Example 2 | Solving a Mixture Application

How many liters (L) of a 60% antifreeze solution must be added to 8 L of a 10% antifreeze solution to produce a 20% antifreeze solution?

Solution:

The information can be organized in a table. Notice that an algebraic equation is derived from the second row of the table. This relates the number of liters of pure antifreeze in each container.

Step 1: Read the problem.

	60% Antifreeze	10% Antifreeze	Final Mixture: 20% Antifreeze
Number of liters of solution	x	8	$(8 + x)$
Number of liters of pure antifreeze	$0.60x$	$0.10(8)$	$0.20(8 + x)$

Step 2: Label the unknowns.

The amount of pure antifreeze in the final solution equals the sum of the amounts of antifreeze in the first two solutions.

$$\begin{pmatrix}\text{Pure antifreeze}\\\text{from solution 1}\end{pmatrix} + \begin{pmatrix}\text{pure antifreeze}\\\text{from solution 2}\end{pmatrix} = \begin{pmatrix}\text{pure antifreeze}\\\text{in the final solution}\end{pmatrix}$$

Step 3: Write a verbal model.

$$0.60x \quad + \quad 0.10(8) \quad = \quad 0.20(8 + x)$$

$$0.60x + 0.10(8) = 0.20(8 + x)$$

Step 4: Write a mathematical equation.

$$0.6x + 0.8 = 1.6 + 0.2x$$

Step 5: Solve the equation.

$$0.6x - 0.2x + 0.8 = 1.6 + 0.2x - 0.2x$$

Subtract $0.2x$.

$$0.4x + 0.8 = 1.6$$

$$0.4x + 0.8 - 0.8 = 1.6 - 0.8$$

Subtract 0.8.

$$0.4x = 0.8$$

$$\frac{0.4x}{0.4} = \frac{0.8}{0.4}$$

Divide by 0.4.

$$x = 2$$

Step 6: Interpret the result.

Therefore, 2 L of 60% antifreeze solution is necessary to make a final solution that is 20% antifreeze.

3. Applications Involving Uniform Motion

The formula (distance) = (rate)(time) or simply, $d = rt$, relates the distance traveled to the rate of travel and the time of travel.

For example, if a car travels at 60 mph for 3 hr, then

$$d = (60 \text{ mph})(3 \text{ hours})$$

$$= 180 \text{ miles}$$

Answer

3. 5 gal is needed.

If a car travels at 60 mph for x hr, then

$$d = (60 \text{ mph})(x \text{ hours})$$
$$= 60x \text{ miles}$$

Example 3   Solving an Application Involving Distance, Rate, and Time

One bicyclist rides 4 mph faster than another bicyclist. The faster rider takes 3 hr to complete a race, while the slower rider takes 4 hr. Find the speed for each rider.

Solution:

Step 1: Read the problem.

The problem is asking us to find the speed of each rider.

Let x represent the speed of the slower rider. Then $(x + 4)$ is the speed of the faster rider.

Step 2: Label the unknowns and organize the information given in the problem. A distance-rate-time chart may be helpful.

	Distance	Rate	Time
Faster rider	$3(x + 4)$	$x + 4$	3
Slower rider	$4(x)$	x	4

To complete the first column, we can use the relationship, $d = rt$.

Because the riders are riding in the same race, their distances are equal.

$$\left(\begin{array}{c}\text{Distance} \\ \text{by faster rider}\end{array}\right) = \left(\begin{array}{c}\text{distance} \\ \text{by slower rider}\end{array}\right)$$

Step 3: Write a verbal model.

$$3(x + 4) = 4(x)$$

Step 4: Write a mathematical equation.

$$3x + 12 = 4x$$

Step 5: Solve the equation.

$$12 = x$$

Subtract $3x$ from both sides.

The variable x represents the slower rider's rate. The quantity $x + 4$ is the faster rider's rate. Thus, if $x = 12$, then $x + 4 = 16$.

The slower rider travels 12 mph and the faster rider travels 16 mph.

Example 4   Solving an Application Involving Distance, Rate, and Time

Two families that live 270 mi apart plan to meet for an afternoon picnic at a park that is located between their two homes. Both families leave at 9.00 A.M., but one family averages 12 mph faster than the other family. If the families meet at the designated spot $2\frac{1}{2}$ hr later, determine

a. The average rate of speed for each family.

b. The distance each family traveled to the picnic.

Solution:

For simplicity, we will call the two families, Family A and Family B. Let Family A be the family that travels at the slower rate (Figure 2-9).

Step 1: Read the problem and draw a sketch.

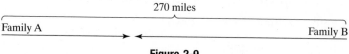

270 miles

Family A ————————————→ ←———————————— Family B

Figure 2-9

Let x represent the rate of Family A.

Then $(x + 12)$ is the rate of Family B.

Step 2: Label the unknowns.

	Distance	Rate	Time
Family A	$2.5x$	x	2.5
Family B	$2.5(x + 12)$	$x + 12$	2.5

To complete the first column, we can use the relationship $d = rt$.

To set up an equation, recall that the total distance between the two families is given as 270 mi.

$$\begin{pmatrix} \text{Distance} \\ \text{traveled by} \\ \text{Family A} \end{pmatrix} + \begin{pmatrix} \text{distance} \\ \text{traveled by} \\ \text{Family B} \end{pmatrix} = \begin{pmatrix} \text{total} \\ \text{distance} \end{pmatrix}$$

Step 3: Write a verbal model.

$$2.5x \quad + \quad 2.5(x + 12) \quad = \quad 270$$

Step 4: Write a mathematical equation.

$$2.5x + 2.5(x + 12) = 270$$
$$2.5x + 2.5x + 30 = 270$$
$$5.0x + 30 = 270$$
$$5x = 240$$
$$x = 48$$

Step 5: Solve for x.

a. Family A traveled 48 (mph).

Family B traveled $x + 12 = 48 + 12 = 60$ (mph).

Step 6: Interpret the results and write the answer in words.

b. To compute the distance each family traveled, use $d = rt$.

Family A traveled: $(48 \text{ mph})(2.5 \text{ hr}) = 120 \text{ mi}$

Family B traveled: $(60 \text{ mph})(2.5 \text{ hr}) = 150 \text{ mi}$

Section 2.7   Practice Exercises

Study Skills Exercise

The following is a list of steps to help you solve word problems. Check those that you follow on a regular basis when solving a word problem. Place an asterisk next to the steps that you need to improve.

_____   Read through the entire problem before writing anything down.

_____   Write down exactly what you are being asked to find.

_____   Write down what is known and assign variables to what is unknown.

_____   Draw a figure or diagram if it will help you understand the problem.

_____   Highlight key words like *total, sum, difference,* etc.

_____   Translate the word problem to a mathematical problem.

_____   After solving, check that your answer makes sense.

Review Exercises

For Exercises 1–3, solve for the indicated variable.

1. $ax - by = c$ for x

2. $cd = r$ for c

3. $7x + xy = 18$ for y

For Exercises 4–6, solve the equation.

4. $-2d + 11 = 4 - d$

5. $3(2y + 5) - 8(y - 1) = 3y + 3$

6. $0.02x + 0.04(10 - x) = 1.26$

Concept 1: Applications Involving Cost

For Exercises 7–12, write an algebraic expression as indicated.

7. Two numbers total 200. Let t represent one of the numbers. Write an algebraic expression for the other number.

8. The total of two numbers is 43. Let s represent one of the numbers. Write an algebraic expression for the other number.

9. Olivia needs to bring 100 cookies to her friend's party. She has already baked x cookies. Write an algebraic expression for the number of cookies Olivia still needs to bake.

10. Rachel needs a mixture of 55 pounds (lb) of nuts consisting of peanuts and cashews. Let p represent the number of pounds of peanuts in the mixture. Write an algebraic expression for the number of pounds of cashews that she needs to add.

11. Max has a total of $3000 in two bank accounts. Let y represent the amount in one account. Write an algebraic expression for the amount in the other account.

12. Roberto has a total of $7500 in two savings accounts. Let z represent the amount in one account. Write an algebraic expression for the amount in the other account.

13. A church had an ice cream social and sold tickets for $3 and $2. When the social was over, 81 tickets had been sold totaling $215. How many of each type of ticket did the church sell? **(See Example 1.)**

	$3 Tickets	$2 Tickets	Total
Number of tickets			
Cost of tickets			

14. Anna is a teacher at an elementary school. She purchased 72 tickets to take the first-grade children and some parents on a field trip to the zoo. She purchased children's tickets for $10 each and adult tickets for $18 each. She spent a total of $856. How many of each ticket did she buy?

	Adults	Children	Total
Number of tickets			
Cost of tickets			

15. Josh downloaded 25 tunes from an online site for his MP3 player. Some songs cost $0.90 each while others were $1.50 each. He spent a total of $27.30. How many of each type of song did he download?

16. During the past year, Mrs. Singh purchased 32 books at a wholesale club store. She purchased softcover books for $4.50 each and hardcover books for $13.50 each. The total cost of the books was $243. How many of each type of book did she purchase?

17. Angelina purchased 45 bottled drinks for her graduation party. She purchased soda for $1.60 each and bottles of flavored water for $2.00 each. The total cost of the drinks was $80. How many of each type did she buy?

18. Mr. Garvey purchased 58 food items at a fast food restaurant for his Little League team. He purchased hamburgers for $2.50 each and french fries for $1.50 each. He spent a total of $127. How many hamburgers and how many french fries did he purchase?

Concept 2: Applications Involving Mixtures

19. A container holds 7 ounces (oz) of liquid. Let x represent the number of ounces of liquid in another container. Write an expression for the total amount of liquid.

20. A bucket contains 2.5 L of a bleach solution. Let n represent the number of liters of bleach solution in a second bucket. Write an expression for the total amount of bleach solution.

21. If Charlene invests $2000 in a certificate of deposit and d dollars in a stock, write an expression for the total amount she invested.

22. James has $5000 in one savings account. Let y represent the amount he has in another savings account. Write an expression for the total amount of money in both accounts.

23. How much of a 5% ethanol fuel mixture should be mixed with 2000 gal of 10% ethanol fuel mixture to get a mixture that is 9% ethanol. **(See Example 2.)**

	5% Ethanol	10% Ethanol	Final Mixture: 9% Ethanol
Number of gallons of fuel mixture			
Number of gallons of pure ethanol			

24. How many ounces of a 50% antifreeze solution must be mixed with 10 oz of an 80% antifreeze solution to produce a 60% antifreeze solution?

	50% Antifreeze	80% Antifreeze	Final Mixture: 60% Antifreeze
Number of ounces of solution			
Number of ounces of pure antifreeze			

25. A pharmacist needs to mix a 1% saline (salt) solution with 24 milliliters (mL) of a 16% saline solution to obtain a 9% saline solution. How many milliliters of the 1% solution must she use?

26. A landscaper needs to mix a 75% pesticide solution with 30 gal of a 25% pesticide solution to obtain a 60% pesticide solution. How many gallons of the 75% solution must he use?

27. To clean a concrete driveway, a contractor needs a solution that is 30% acid. How many ounces of a 50% acid solution must be mixed with 15 oz of a 21% solution to obtain a 30% acid solution?

28. A veterinarian needs a mixture that contains 12% of a certain medication to treat an injured bird. How many milliliters of a 16% solution should be mixed with 6 mL of a 7% solution to obtain a solution that is 12% medication?

Concept 3: Applications Involving Uniform Motion

29. a. If a car travels 60 mph for 5 hr, find the distance traveled.

   b. If a car travels at x miles per hour for 5 hr, write an expression that represents the distance traveled.

   c. If a car travels at $x + 12$ mph for 5 hr, write an expression that represents the distance traveled.

30. a. If a plane travels 550 mph for 2.5 hr, find the distance traveled.

   b. If a plane travels at x miles per hour for 2.5 hr, write an expression that represents the distance traveled.

   c. If a plane travels at $x - 100$ mph for 2.5 hr, write an expression that represents the distance traveled.

31. A woman can walk 2 mph faster down a trail to Cochita Lake than she can on the return trip uphill. It takes her 2 hr to get to the lake and 4 hr to return. What is her speed walking down to the lake? **(See Example 3.)**

	Distance	Rate	Time
Downhill to the lake			
Uphill from the lake			

32. A car travels 20 mph slower in a bad rain storm than in sunny weather. The car travels the same distance in 2 hr in sunny weather as it does in 3 hr in rainy weather. Find the speed of the car in sunny weather.

	Distance	Rate	Time
Rain storm			
Sunny weather			

33. Bryan hiked up to the top of City Creek in 3 hr and then returned down the canyon to the trailhead in another 2 hr. His speed downhill was 1 mph faster than his speed uphill. How far up the canyon did he hike?

34. Laura hiked up Lamb's Canyon in 2 hr and then ran back down in 1 hr. Her speed running downhill was 2.5 mph greater than her speed hiking uphill. How far up the canyon did she hike?

35. Hazel and Emilie fly from Atlanta to San Diego. The flight from Atlanta to San Diego is against the wind and takes 4 hr. The return flight with the wind takes 3.5 hr. If the wind speed is 40 mph, find the speed of the plane in still air.

36. A boat on the Potomac River travels the same distance downstream in $\frac{2}{3}$ hr as it does going upstream in 1 hr. If the speed of the current is 3 mph, find the speed of the boat in still water.

37. Two cars are 200 mi apart and traveling toward each other on the same road. They meet in 2 hr. One car is traveling 4 mph faster than the other. What is the speed of each car? **(See Example 4.)**

38. Two cars are 238 mi apart and traveling toward each other along the same road. They meet in 2 hr. One car is traveling 5 mph slower than the other. What is the speed of each car?

39. After Hurricane Katrina, a rescue vehicle leaves a station at noon and heads for New Orleans. An hour later a second vehicle traveling 10 mph faster leaves the same station. By 4:00 P.M., the first vehicle reaches its destination, and the second is still 10 mi away. How fast is each vehicle?

40. A truck leaves a truck stop at 9:00 A.M. and travels toward Sturgis, Wyoming. At 10:00 A.M., a motorcycle leaves the same truck stop and travels the same route. The motorcycle travels 15 mph faster than the truck. By noon, the truck has traveled 20 mi farther than the motorcycle. How fast is each vehicle?

41. In the Disney Marathon, Jeanette's speed running was twice Sarah's speed walking. After 2 hr, Jeanette was 7 mi ahead of Sarah. Find Jeanette's speed and Sarah's speed.

42. Two canoes travel down a river, starting at 9:00 A.M. One canoe travels twice as fast as the other. After 3.5 hr, the canoes are 5.25 mi apart. Find the speed of each canoe.

Mixed Exercises

43. A certain granola mixture is 10% peanuts.

    a. If a container has 20 lb of granola, how many pounds of peanuts are there?

    b. If a container has x pounds of granola, write an expression that represents the number of pounds of peanuts in the granola.

    c. If a container has $x + 3$ lb of granola, write an expression that represents the number of pounds of peanuts.

44. A certain blend of coffee sells for $9.00 per pound.

    a. If a container has 20 lb of coffee, how much will it cost.

    b. If a container has x lb of coffee, write an expression that represents the cost.

    c. If a container has $40 - x$ lb of this coffee, write an expression that represents the cost.

45. The Coffee Company mixes coffee worth $12 per pound with coffee worth $8 per pound to produce 50 lb of coffee worth $8.80 per pound. How many pounds of the $12 coffee and how many pounds of the $8 coffee must be used?

46. The Nut House sells pecans worth $4 per pound and cashews worth $6 per pound. How many pounds of pecans and how many pounds of cashews must be mixed to form 16 lb of a nut mixture worth $4.50 per pound?

	$12 Coffee	$8 Coffee	Total
Number of pounds			
Value of coffee			

	$4 Pecans	$6 Cashews	Total
Number of pounds			
Value of nuts			

47. A boat in distress, 21 nautical miles from a marina, travels toward the marina at 3 knots (nautical miles per hour). A coast guard cruiser leaves the marina and travels toward the boat at 25 knots. How long will it take for the boats to reach each other?

48. An air traffic controller observes a plane heading from New York to San Francisco traveling at 450 mph. At the same time, another plane leaves San Francisco and travels 500 mph to New York. If the distance between the airports is 2850 mi, how long will it take for the planes to pass each other?

49. Surfer Sam purchased a total of 21 items at the surf shop. He bought wax for $3.00 per package and sunscreen for $8.00 per bottle. He spent a total amount of $88.00. How many of each item did he purchase?

50. Tonya Toast loves jam. She purchased 30 jars of gourmet jam for $178.50. She bought raspberry jam for $6.25 per jar and strawberry jam for $5.50 per jar. How many jars of each did she purchase?

51. How many quarts of 85% chlorine solution must be mixed with 5 quarts of 25% chlorine solution to obtain a 45% chlorine solution?

52. How many liters of a 58% sugar solution must be added to 14 L of a 40% sugar solution to obtain a 50% sugar solution?

Expanding Your Skills

53. How much pure water must be mixed with 12 L of a 40% alcohol solution to obtain a 15% alcohol solution? (*Hint:* Pure water is 0% alcohol.)

54. How much pure water must be mixed with 10 oz of a 60% alcohol solution to obtain a 25% alcohol solution?

55. Amtrak Acela Express is a high-speed train that runs in the United States between Washington, D.C., and Boston. In Japan, a bullet train along the Sanyo line operates at an average speed of 60 km/hr faster than the Amtrak Acela Express. It takes the Japanese bullet train 2.7 hr to travel the same distance as the Acela Express can travel in 3.375 hr. Find the speed of each train.

56. Amtrak Acela Express is a high-speed train along the northeast corridor between Washington, D.C., and Boston. Since its debut, it cuts the travel time from 4 hr 10 min to 3 hr 20 min. On average, if the Acela Express is 30 mph faster than the old train, find the speed of the Acela Express. (*Hint:* 4 hr 10 min = $4\frac{1}{6}$ hr.)

Section 2.8   Linear Inequalities

Concepts

1. Graphing Linear Inequalities
2. Set-Builder Notation and Interval Notation
3. Addition and Subtraction Properties of Inequality
4. Multiplication and Division Properties of Inequality
5. Inequalities of the Form $a < x < b$
6. Applications of Linear Inequalities

1. Graphing Linear Inequalities

Consider the following two statements.

$$2x + 7 = 11 \quad \text{and} \quad 2x + 7 < 11$$

The first statement is an equation (it has an = sign). The second statement is an inequality (it has an inequality symbol, <). In this section, we will learn how to solve linear *inequalities*, such as $2x + 7 < 11$.

> ### A Linear Inequality in One Variable
>
> A **linear inequality in one variable**, x, is any inequality that can be written in the form:
>
> $ax + b < c$, $ax + b \le c$, $ax + b > c$, or $ax + b \ge c$, where $a \ne 0$.

The following inequalities are linear equalities in one variable.

$$2x - 3 < 11 \qquad -4z - 3 > 0 \qquad a \le 4 \qquad 5.2y \ge 10.4$$

The number line is a useful tool to visualize the solution set of an equation or inequality. For example, the solution set to the equation $x = 2$ is $\{2\}$ and may be graphed as a single point on the number line.

$$x = 2 \qquad \underset{-6\ -5\ -4\ -3\ -2\ -1\ \ 0\ \ 1\ \ 2\ \ 3\ \ 4\ \ 5\ \ 6}{\longmapsto}$$

The solution set to an inequality is the set of real numbers that make the inequality a true statement. For example, the solution set to the inequality $x \geq 2$ is all real numbers 2 or greater. Because the solution set has an infinite number of values, we cannot list all of the individual solutions. However, we can graph the solution set on the number line.

$$x \geq 2 \qquad \begin{array}{c} \\ \hline -6\ -5\ -4\ -3\ -2\ -1\ \ 0\ \ 1\ \ 2\ \ 3\ \ 4\ \ 5\ \ 6 \end{array}$$

The square bracket symbol, [, is used on the graph to indicate that the point $x = 2$ is included in the solution set. By convention, square brackets, either [or], are used to *include* a point on a number line. Parentheses, (or), are used to *exclude* a point on a number line.

The solution set of the inequality $x > 2$ includes the real numbers greater than 2 but not including 2. Therefore, a (symbol is used on the graph to indicate that $x = 2$ is not included.

$$x > 2 \qquad \begin{array}{c} \\ \hline -6\ -5\ -4\ -3\ -2\ -1\ \ 0\ \ 1\ \ 2\ \ 3\ \ 4\ \ 5\ \ 6 \end{array}$$

In Example 1, we demonstrate how to graph linear inequalities. To graph an inequality means that we graph its *solution set*. That is, we graph all of the values on the number line that make the inequality true.

Example 1   Graphing Linear Inequalities

Graph the solution sets.

a. $x > -1$ **b.** $c \leq \dfrac{7}{3}$ **c.** $3 > y$

Solution:

a. $x > -1$ 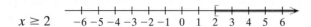

The solution set is the set of all real numbers strictly greater than -1. Therefore, we graph the region on the number line to the right of -1. Because $x = -1$ is not included in the solution set, we use the (symbol at $x = -1$.

b. $c \leq \frac{7}{3}$ is equivalent to $c \leq 2\frac{1}{3}$. $\begin{array}{c} 2\frac{1}{3} \\ \hline -6\ -5\ -4\ -3\ -2\ -1\ \ 0\ \ 1\ \ 2\ \ 3\ \ 4\ \ 5\ \ 6 \end{array}$

The solution set is the set of all real numbers less than or equal to $2\frac{1}{3}$. Therefore, graph the region on the number line to the left of and including $2\frac{1}{3}$. Use the symbol] to indicate that $c = 2\frac{1}{3}$ is included in the solution set.

c. $3 > y$ This inequality reads "3 is greater than y." This is equivalent to saying, "y is less than 3." The inequality $3 > y$ can also be written as $y < 3$.

$$y < 3 \qquad \begin{array}{c} \\ \hline -6\ -5\ -4\ -3\ -2\ -1\ \ 0\ \ 1\ \ 2\ \ 3\ \ 4\ \ 5\ \ 6 \end{array}$$

The solution set is the set of real numbers less than 3. Therefore, graph the region on the number line to the left of 3. Use the symbol) to denote that the endpoint, 3, is not included in the solution.

Answers

1.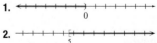
        0

2. $\begin{array}{c} \\ \hline \end{array}$
   $-\frac{5}{4}$

3. $\begin{array}{c} \\ \hline \end{array}$
       5

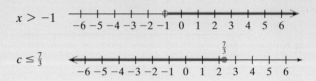

TIP: Some textbooks use a closed circle or an open circle (● or ○) rather than a bracket or parenthesis to denote inclusion or exclusion of a value on the real number line. For example, the solution sets for the inequalities $x > -1$ and $c \leq \frac{7}{3}$ are graphed here.

A statement that involves more than one inequality is called a **compound inequality**. One type of compound inequality is used to indicate that one number is between two others. For example, the inequality $-2 < x < 5$ means that $-2 < x$ and $x < 5$. In words, this is easiest to understand if we read the variable first: x is greater than -2 and x is less than 5. The numbers satisfied by these two conditions are those between -2 and 5.

Example 2 Graphing a Compound Inequality

Graph the solution set of the inequality: $-4.1 < y \leq -1.7$

Solution:

$-4.1 < y \leq -1.7$ means that

$-4.1 < y$ and $y \leq -1.7$

Shade the region of the number line greater than -4.1 and less than or equal to -1.7.

2. Set-Builder Notation and Interval Notation

Graphing the solution set to an inequality is one way to define the set. Two other methods are to use **set-builder notation** or **interval notation**.

Set-Builder Notation

The solution to the inequality $x \geq 2$ can be expressed in set-builder notation as follows:

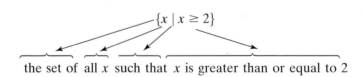

$$\{x \mid x \geq 2\}$$

the set of   all x such that x is greater than or equal to 2

Answer

4.

Interval Notation

To understand interval notation, first think of a number line extending infinitely far to the right and infinitely far to the left. Sometimes we use the infinity symbol, ∞, or negative infinity symbol, −∞, to label the far right and far left ends of the number line (Figure 2-10).

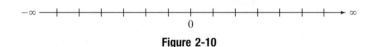

Figure 2-10

To express the solution set of an inequality in interval notation, sketch the graph first. Then use the endpoints to define the interval.

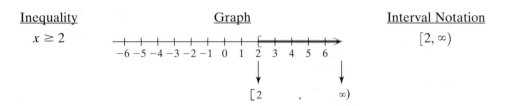

Inequality	Graph	Interval Notation
$x \geq 2$		$[2, \infty)$

The graph of the solution set $x \geq 2$ begins at 2 and extends infinitely far to the right. The corresponding interval notation begins at 2 and extends to ∞. Notice that a square bracket [is used at 2 for both the graph and the interval notation. A parenthesis is always used at ∞ and for −∞, because there is no endpoint.

Using Interval Notation

- The endpoints used in interval notation are always written from left to right. That is, the smaller number is written first, followed by a comma, followed by the larger number.
- A parenthesis, (or), indicates that an endpoint is excluded from the set.
- A square bracket, [or], indicates that an endpoint is included in the set.
- A parenthesis, (or), is always used with −∞ and ∞, respectively.

Animation

In Table 2-1, we present examples of eight different scenarios for interval notation and the corresponding graph.

Table 2-1

Interval Notation	Graph	Interval Notation	Graph
(a, ∞)	⟵———(———→ a	$[a, \infty)$	⟵———[———→ a
$(-\infty, a)$	⟵———)———→ a	$(-\infty, a]$	⟵———]———→ a
(a, b)	———(———)——— a b	$[a, b]$	———[———]——— a b
$(a, b]$	———(———]——— a b	$[a, b)$	———[———)——— a b

Answers
5. $\{b \mid b \geq -20\}$
6. $(-\infty, -30)$

Example 3   **Using Set-Builder Notation and Interval Notation**

Complete the chart.

Set-Builder Notation	Graph	Interval Notation
	←┼┼┼┼)┼┼┼┼┼┼┼→ −6 −5 −4 −3 −2 −1 0 1 2 3 4 5 6	
		$\left[-\frac{1}{2}, \infty\right)$
$\{y \mid -2 \le y < 4\}$		

Solution:

Set-Builder Notation	Graph	Interval Notation
$\{x \mid x < -3\}$	←┼┼┼┼)┼┼┼┼┼┼┼→ −6 −5 −4 −3 −2 −1 0 1 2 3 4 5 6	$(-\infty, -3)$
$\{x \mid x \ge -\frac{1}{2}\}$	┼┼┼┼┼┼[━━━━━━━→ −6 −5 −4 −3 −2 −1 0 1 2 3 4 5 6 $-\frac{1}{2}$	$\left[-\frac{1}{2}, \infty\right)$
$\{y \mid -2 \le y < 4\}$	┼┼┼┼[━━━━━)┼┼→ −6 −5 −4 −3 −2 −1 0 1 2 3 4 5 6	$[-2, 4)$

3. Addition and Subtraction Properties of Inequality

The process to solve a linear inequality is very similar to the method used to solve linear equations. Recall that adding or subtracting the same quantity to both sides of an equation results in an equivalent equation. The addition and subtraction properties of inequality state that the same is true for an inequality.

Addition and Subtraction Properties of Inequality

Let a, b, and c represent real numbers.

1. *Addition Property of Inequality: If $a < b$,
                                     then $a + c < b + c$

2. *Subtraction Property of Inequality: If $a < b$,
                                        then $a - c < b - c$

*These properties may also be stated for $a \le b$, $a > b$, and $a \ge b$.

To illustrate the addition and subtraction properties of inequality, consider the inequality $5 > 3$. If we add or subtract a real number such as 4 to both sides, the left-hand side will still be greater than the right-hand side. (See Figure 2-11.)

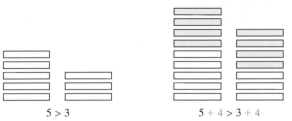

$5 > 3$ $5 + 4 > 3 + 4$

Figure 2-11

| **Example 4** | **Solving a Linear Inequality** |

Solve the inequality and graph the solution set. Express the solution set in set-builder notation and in interval notation.

$$-2p + 5 < -3p + 6$$

Solution:

$$-2p + 5 < -3p + 6$$

$$-2p + 3p + 5 < -3p + 3p + 6 \qquad \text{Addition property of inequality}$$
$$\text{(add } 3p \text{ to both sides).}$$

$$p + 5 < 6 \qquad \text{Simplify.}$$

$$p + 5 - 5 < 6 - 5 \qquad \text{Subtraction property of inequality.}$$

$$p < 1$$

Graph: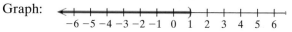

Set-builder notation: $\{p \mid p < 1\}$

Interval notation: $(-\infty, 1)$

Skill Practice

Solve the inequality. Graph the solution set and express in set-builder notation and interval notation.

10. $2y - 5 < y - 11$

TIP: The solution to an inequality gives a set of values that make the original inequality true. Therefore, you can test your final answer by using *test points.* That is, pick a value in the proposed solution set and verify that it makes the original inequality true. Furthermore, any test point picked outside the solution set should make the original inequality false. For example,

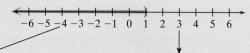

Pick $p = -4$ as an arbitrary test point within the proposed solution set.

$$-2p + 5 < -3p + 6$$
$$-2(-4) + 5 \overset{?}{<} -3(-4) + 6$$
$$8 + 5 \overset{?}{<} 12 + 6$$
$$13 < 18 \checkmark \qquad \text{True}$$

Pick $p = 3$ as an arbitrary test point outside the proposed solution set.

$$-2p + 5 < -3p + 6$$
$$-2(3) + 5 \overset{?}{<} -3(3) + 6$$
$$-6 + 5 \overset{?}{<} -9 + 6$$
$$-1 \overset{?}{<} -3 \qquad \text{False}$$

4. Multiplication and Division Properties of Inequality

Multiplying both sides of an equation by the same quantity results in an equivalent equation. However, the same is not always true for an inequality. If you multiply or divide an inequality by a negative quantity, the direction of the inequality symbol must be reversed.

Answer

10. ⟵————————⟩————————⟶
　　　　　　　-6
　　$\{y \mid y < -6\}; (-\infty, -6)$

For example, consider multiplying or dividing the inequality, $4 < 5$ by -1.

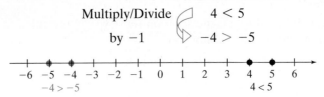

Figure 2-12

The number 4 lies to the left of 5 on the number line. However, -4 lies to the right of -5 (Figure 2-12). Changing the sign of two numbers changes their relative position on the number line. This is stated formally in the multiplication and division properties of inequality.

Multiplication and Division Properties of Inequality

Let a, b, and c represent real numbers, $c \neq 0$.

*If c is positive and $a < b$, then $ac < bc$ and $\dfrac{a}{c} < \dfrac{b}{c}$

*If c is negative and $a < b$, then $ac > bc$ and $\dfrac{a}{c} > \dfrac{b}{c}$

The second statement indicates that if both sides of an inequality are multiplied or divided by a negative quantity, the inequality sign must be reversed.

*These properties may also be stated for $a \leq b$, $a > b$, and $a \geq b$.

Skill Practice

Solve the inequality and graph the solution set. Express the solution set in set-builder notation and in interval notation.

11. $-5p + 2 > 22$

Example 5 Solving a Linear Inequality

Solve the inequality and graph the solution set. Express the solution set in set-builder notation and in interval notation.

$$-5x - 3 \leq 12$$

Solution:

$$-5x - 3 \leq 12$$

$$-5x - 3 + 3 \leq 12 + 3 \qquad \text{Add 3 to both sides.}$$

$$-5x \leq 15$$

$$\frac{-5x}{-5} \geq \frac{15}{-5} \qquad \text{Divide by } -5. \text{ Reverse the direction of the inequality sign.}$$

$$x \geq -3$$

Set-builder notation: $\{x \mid x \geq -3\}$

Interval notation: $[-3, \infty)$

Answer

11.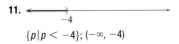

$\{p \mid p < -4\}; (-\infty, -4)$

TIP: The inequality $-5x - 3 \leq 12$, could have been solved by isolating x on the right-hand side of the inequality. This would create a positive coefficient on the variable term and eliminate the need to divide by a negative number.

$$-5x - 3 \leq 12$$

$$-3 \leq 5x + 12$$

$-15 \leq 5x$ Notice that the coefficient of x is positive.

$\dfrac{-15}{5} \leq \dfrac{5x}{5}$ Do not reverse the inequality sign because we are dividing by a positive number.

$-3 \leq x$, or equivalently, $x \geq -3$

Example 6   Solving a Linear Inequality

Solve the inequality and graph the solution set. Express the solution set in set-builder notation and in interval notation.

$$12 - 2(y + 3) < -3(2y - 1) + 2y$$

Solution:

$12 - 2(y + 3) < -3(2y - 1) + 2y$

$12 - 2y - 6 < -6y + 3 + 2y$ Clear parentheses.

$-2y + 6 < -4y + 3$ Combine *like* terms.

$-2y + 4y + 6 < -4y + 4y + 3$ Add $4y$ to both sides.

$2y + 6 < 3$ Simplify.

$2y + 6 - 6 < 3 - 6$ Subtract 6 from both sides.

$2y < -3$ Simplify.

$\dfrac{2y}{2} < \dfrac{-3}{2}$ Divide by 2. The direction of the inequality sign is *not* reversed because we divided by a positive number.

$y < -\dfrac{3}{2}$

Set-builder notation: $\left\{ x \mid x < -\dfrac{3}{2} \right\}$

Interval notation: $\left(-\infty, -\dfrac{3}{2} \right)$

Skill Practice

Solve the inequality and graph the solution set. Express the solution set in set-builder notation and in interval notation.

12. $-8 - 8(2x - 4) > -5(4x - 5) - 21$

Answer

12.

-5

$\{ x \mid x > -5 \}; (-5, \infty)$

Skill Practice

Solve the inequality and graph the solution set. Express the solution set in set-builder notation and in interval notation.

13. $\frac{1}{5}t + 7 \le \frac{1}{2}t - 2$

Example 7   Solving a Linear Inequality

Solve the inequality and graph the solution set. Express the solution set in set-builder notation and in interval notation.

$$-\frac{1}{4}k + \frac{1}{6} \le 2 + \frac{2}{3}k$$

Solution:

$$-\frac{1}{4}k + \frac{1}{6} \le 2 + \frac{2}{3}k$$

$$12\left(-\frac{1}{4}k + \frac{1}{6}\right) \le 12\left(2 + \frac{2}{3}k\right)$$ Multiply both sides by 12 to clear fractions. (Because we multiplied by a positive number, the inequality sign is not reversed.)

$$\frac{12}{1}\left(-\frac{1}{4}k\right) + \frac{12}{1}\left(\frac{1}{6}\right) \le 12(2) + \frac{12}{1}\left(\frac{2}{3}k\right)$$ Apply the distributive property.

$$-3k + 2 \le 24 + 8k$$ Simplify.

$$-3k - 8k + 2 \le 24 + 8k - 8k$$ Subtract $8k$ from both sides.

$$-11k + 2 \le 24$$

$$-11k + 2 - 2 \le 24 - 2$$ Subtract 2 from both sides.

$$-11k \le 22$$

$$\frac{-11k}{-11} \ge \frac{22}{-11}$$ Divide both sides by -11. Reverse the inequality sign.

$$k \ge -2$$

Set-builder notation: $\{k \mid k \ge -2\}$

Interval notation: $[-2, \infty)$

5. Inequalities of the Form $a < x < b$

To solve a compound inequality of the form $a < x < b$ we can work with the inequality as a three-part inequality and isolate the variable, x, as demonstrated in Example 8.

Skill Practice

Solve the inequality and graph the solution set. Express the solution set in set-builder notation and in interval notation.

14. $-3 \le -5 + 2y < 11$

Example 8   Solving a Compound Inequality of the Form $a < x < b$

Solve the inequality and graph the solution set. Express the solution set in set-builder notation and in interval notation.

$$-3 \le 2x + 1 < 7$$

Answers

13.

$\{t \mid t \ge 30\}$; $[30, \infty)$

14.

$\{y \mid 1 \le y < 8\}$; $[1, 8)$

Solution:

To solve the compound inequality $-3 \leq 2x + 1 < 7$ isolate the variable x in the middle. The operations performed on the middle portion of the inequality must also be performed on the left-hand side and right-hand side.

$$-3 \leq 2x + 1 < 7$$

$$-3 - 1 \leq 2x + 1 - 1 < 7 - 1 \qquad \text{Subtract } 1 \text{ from all three parts of the inequality.}$$

$$-4 \leq 2x < 6 \qquad \text{Simplify.}$$

$$\frac{-4}{2} \leq \frac{2x}{2} < \frac{6}{2} \qquad \text{Divide by } 2 \text{ in all three parts of the inequality.}$$

$$-2 \leq x < 3$$

Set-builder notation: $\{x \mid -2 \leq x < -3\}$

Interval notation: $[-2, 3)$

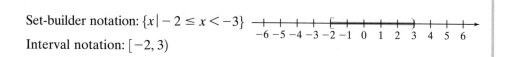

6. Applications of Linear Inequalities

Table 2-2 provides several commonly used translations to express inequalities.

Table 2-2

English Phrase	Mathematical Inequality
a is less than b	$a < b$
a is greater than b a exceeds b	$a > b$
a is less than or equal to b a is at most b a is no more than b	$a \leq b$
a is greater than or equal to b a is at least b a is no less than b	$a \geq b$

Example 9 **Translating Expressions Involving Inequalities**

Translate the English phrases into mathematical inequalities.

a. Claude's annual salary, s, is no more than $40,000.

b. A citizen must be at least 18 years old to vote. (Let a represent a citizen's age.)

c. An amusement park ride has a height requirement between 48 in. and 70 in. (Let h represent height in inches.)

Solution:

a. $s \leq 40{,}000$ Claude's annual salary, s, is no more than $40,000.

b. $a \geq 18$ A citizen must be at least 18 years old to vote.

c. $48 < h < 70$ An amusement park ride has a height requirement between 48 in. and 70 in.

Skill Practice

Translate the English phrase into a mathematical inequality.

15. Bill needs a score of at least 92 on the final exam. Let x represent Bill's score.

16. Fewer than 19 cars are in the parking lot. Let c represent the number of cars.

17. The heights, h, of women who wear petite size clothing are typically between 58 in. and 63 in., inclusive.

Linear inequalities are found in a variety of applications. Example 10 can help you determine the minimum grade you need on an exam to get an A in your math course.

Answers

15. $x \geq 92$ **16.** $c < 19$
17. $58 \leq h \leq 63$

18. To get at least a B in math, Simon must average at least 80 on all tests. Suppose Simon has scored 60, 72, 98, and 85 on the first four tests. Determine the minimum score he needs on the fifth test to receive a B.

Example 10 **Solving an Application with Linear Inequalities**

To earn an A in a math class, Alsha must average at least 90 on all of her tests. Suppose Alsha has scored 79, 86, 93, 90, and 95 on her first five math tests. Determine the minimum score she needs on her sixth test to get an A in the class.

Solution:

Let x represent the score on the sixth exam.   Label the unknown.

$$\left(\begin{array}{c}\text{Average of}\\\text{all tests}\end{array}\right) \geq 90$$ Create a verbal model.

$$\frac{79 + 86 + 93 + 90 + 95 + x}{6} \geq 90$$ The average score is found by taking the sum of the test scores and dividing by the number of scores.

$$\frac{443 + x}{6} \geq 90$$ Simplify.

$$6\left(\frac{443 + x}{6}\right) \geq (90)6$$ Multiply both sides by 6 to clear fractions.

$$443 + x \geq 540$$ Solve the inequality.

$$x \geq 540 - 443$$ Subtract 443 from both sides.

$$x \geq 97$$ Interpret the results.

Answer

18. Simon needs at least 85.

Alsha must score at least 97 on her sixth exam to receive an A in the course.

Section 2.8   Practice Exercises

Study Skills Exercise

Find the page numbers for the Chapter Review Exercises, the Chapter Test, and the Cumulative Review Exercises for this chapter.

Chapter Review Exercises _____   Chapter Test _____

Cumulative Review Exercises _____

Compare these features and state the advantages of each.

Vocabulary and Key Concepts

1. a. A relationship of the form $ax + b > c$ or $ax + b < c$ $(a \neq 0)$ is called a _____ in one variable.

b. A statement that involves more than one _____ is called a compound inequality.

c. The notation $\{x \mid x > -9\}$ is an example of _____ notation, whereas $(-9, \infty)$ is an example of _____ notation.

Review Problems

For Exercises 2–4, solve the equation.

2. $10y - 7(y + 8) + 13 = 13 - 6(2y + 1)$ **3.** $3(x + 2) - (2x - 7) = -(5x - 1) - 2(x + 6)$

4. $6 - 8(x + 3) + 5x = 5x - (2x - 5) + 13$

Concept 1: Graphing Linear Inequalities

For Exercises 5–16, graph the solution set of each inequality. **(See Examples 1 and 2.)**

5. $x > 5$

6. $x \geq -7.2$

7. $x \leq \dfrac{5}{2}$

8. $x < -1$

9. $13 > p$

10. $-12 \geq t$

11. $2 \leq y \leq 6.5$

12. $-3 \leq m \leq \dfrac{8}{9}$

13. $0 < x < 4$

14. $-4 < y < 1$

15. $1 < p \leq 8$

16. $-3 \leq t < 3$

Concept 2: Set-Builder Notation and Interval Notation

For Exercises 17–22, graph each inequality and write the solution set in interval notation. **(See Example 3.)**

Set-Builder Notation	Graph	Interval Notation
17. $\{x \mid x \geq 6\}$		
18. $\left\{x \mid \dfrac{1}{2} < x \leq 4\right\}$		
19. $\{x \mid x \leq 2.1\}$		
20. $\left\{x \mid x > \dfrac{7}{3}\right\}$		
21. $\{x \mid -2 < x \leq 7\}$		
22. $\{x \mid x < -5\}$		

For Exercises 23–28, write each set in set-builder notation and in interval notation. **(See Example 3.)**

Set-Builder Notation	Graph	Interval Notation
23.	$\dfrac{3}{4}$	
24.	-0.3	
25.	$-1 \qquad 8$	
26.	0	
27.	-14	
28.	$0 \qquad 9$	

For Exercises 29–34, graph each set and write the set in set-builder notation. **(See Example 3.)**

Set-Builder Notation	Graph	Interval Notation
29.	⟶	$[18, \infty)$
30.	⟶	$[-10, -2]$
31.	⟶	$(-\infty, -0.6)$
32.	⟶	$\left(-\infty, \dfrac{5}{3}\right)$
33.	⟶	$[-3.5, 7.1)$
34.	⟶	$[-10, \infty)$

Concepts 3 and 4: Properties of Inequality

For Exercises 35–42, solve the equation in part (a). For part (b), solve the inequality and graph the solution set. Write the answer in set-builder notation and interval notation. **(See Examples 4–7.)**

35. a. $x + 3 = 6$
   b. $x + 3 > 6$

36. a. $y - 6 = 12$
   b. $y - 6 \geq 12$

37. a. $p - 4 = 9$
   b. $p - 4 \leq 9$

38. a. $k + 8 = 10$
   b. $k + 8 < 10$

39. a. $4c = -12$
   b. $4c < -12$

40. a. $5d = -35$
   b. $5d > -35$

41. a. $-10z = 15$
   b. $-10z \leq 15$

42. a. $-2w = 14$
   b. $-2w < 14$

Concept 5: Inequalities of the Form $a < x < b$

For Exercises 43–48, graph the solution and write the set in interval notation. **(See Example 8.)**

43. $-1 < y \leq 4$

44. $2.5 \leq t < 5.7$

45. $0 < x + 3 < 8$

46. $-2 \leq x - 4 \leq 3$

47. $8 \leq 4x \leq 24$

48. $-9 < 3x < 12$

Mixed Exercises

For Exercises 49–96, solve the inequality and graph the solution set. Write the solution set in (a) set-builder notation and (b) interval notation. **(See Examples 4–8.)**

49. $x + 5 \leq 6$

50. $y - 7 < 6$

51. $3q - 7 > 2q + 3$

52. $5r + 4 \geq 4r - 1$

53. $4 < 1 + x$

54. $3 > z - 6$

55. $3c > 6$

56. $4d \leq 12$

57. $-3c > 6$

58. $-4d \leq 12$

59. $-h \leq -14$

60. $-q > -7$

61. $12 \geq -\dfrac{x}{2}$

62. $6 < -\dfrac{m}{3}$

63. $-2 \leq p + 1 < 4$

64. $0 < k + 7 < 6$

65. $-3 < 6h - 3 < 12$

66. $-6 \leq 4a - 2 \leq 12$

67. $-24 < -2x < -20$

68. $-12 \leq -3x \leq 6$

69. $-3 \leq \dfrac{1}{4}x - 1 < 5$

70. $-2 < \dfrac{1}{3}x - 2 \leq 2$

71. $-\dfrac{2}{3}y < 6$

72. $\dfrac{3}{4}x \leq -12$

73. $-2x - 4 \leq 11$

74. $-3x + 1 > 0$

75. $-12 > 7x + 9$

76. $8 < 2x - 10$

77. $-7b - 3 \leq 2b$

78. $3t \geq 7t - 35$

79. $4n + 2 < 6n + 8$

80. $2w - 1 \leq 5w + 8$

81. $8 - 6(x - 3) > -4x + 12$

82. $3 - 4(h - 2) > -5h + 6$

83. $3(x + 1) - 2 \leq \dfrac{1}{2}(4x - 8)$

84. $8 - (2x - 5) \geq \dfrac{1}{3}(9x - 6)$

85. $4(z - 1) - 6 \geq 6(2z + 3) - 12$

86. $3(2x + 5) + 2 < 5(2x + 2) + 3$

87. $2a + 3(a + 5) > -4a - (3a - 1) + 6$

88. $13 + 7(2y - 3) \leq 12 + 3(3y - 1)$

89. $\dfrac{7}{6}p + \dfrac{4}{3} \geq \dfrac{11}{6}p - \dfrac{7}{6}$

90. $\dfrac{1}{3}w - \dfrac{1}{2} \leq \dfrac{5}{6}w + \dfrac{1}{2}$

91. $\dfrac{y - 6}{3} > y + 4$

92. $\dfrac{5t + 7}{2} < t - 4$

93. $-1.2a - 0.4 < -0.4a + 2$

94. $-0.4c + 1.2 > -2c - 0.4$

95. $-2x + 5 \geq -x + 5$

96. $4x - 6 < 5x - 6$

For Exercises 97–100, determine whether the given number is a solution to the inequality.

97. $-2x + 5 < 4;\quad x = -2$

98. $-3y - 7 > 5;\quad y = 6$

99. $4(p + 7) - 1 > 2 + p;\quad p = 1$

100. $3 - k < 2(-1 + k);\quad k = 4$

Concept 6: Applications of Linear Inequalities

For Exercises 101–110, write each English phrase as a mathematical inequality. **(See Example 9.)**

101. The length of a fish, L, was at least 10 in.

102. Tasha's average test score, t, exceeded 90.

103. The wind speed, w, exceeded 75 mph.

104. The height of a cave, h, was no more than 2 ft.

105. The temperature of the water in Blue Spring, t, is no more than 72°F.

106. The temperature on the tennis court, t, was no less than 100°F.

107. The length of the hike, L, was no less than 8 km.

108. The depth, d, of a certain pool was at most 10 ft.

109. The snowfall, h, in Monroe County is between 2 in. and 5 in.

110. The cost, c, of carpeting a room is between $300 and $400.

111. The average summer rainfall for Miami, Florida, for June, July, and August is 7.4 in. per month. If Miami receives 5.9 in. of rain in June and 6.1 in. in July, how much rain is required in August to exceed the 3-month summer average? **(See Example 10.)**

112. The average winter snowfall for Burlington, Vermont, for December, January, and February is 18.7 in. per month. If Burlington receives 22 in. of snow in December and 24 in. in January, how much snow is required in February to exceed the 3-month winter average?

113. To earn a B in chemistry, Trevor's average on his five tests must be at least 80. Suppose that Trevor has scored 85, 75, 72, and 82 on his first four chemistry tests. Determine the minimum score needed on his fifth test to get a B in the class.

114. In speech class, Carolyn needs at least a B+ to keep her financial aid. To earn a B+, the average of her four speeches must be at least an 85. On the first three speeches she scored 87, 75, and 82. Determine the minimum score on her fourth speech to get a B+.

115. An artist paints wooden birdhouses. She buys the birdhouses for $9 each. However, for large orders, the price per birdhouse is discounted by a percentage off the original price. Let x represent the number of birdhouses ordered. The corresponding discount is given in the table.

Size of Order	Discount
$x \le 49$	0%
$50 \le x \le 99$	5%
$100 \le x \le 199$	10%
$x \ge 200$	20%

  a. If the artist places an order for 190 birdhouses, compute the total cost.

  b. Which costs more: 190 birdhouses or 200 birdhouses? Explain your answer.

116. A wholesaler sells T-shirts to a surf shop at $8 per shirt. However, for large orders, the price per shirt is discounted by a percentage off the original price. Let x represent the number of shirts ordered. The corresponding discount is given in the table.

Number of Shirts Ordered	Discount
$x \le 24$	0%
$25 \le x \le 49$	2%
$50 \le x \le 99$	4%
$100 \le x \le 149$	6%
$x \ge 150$	8%

  a. If the surf shop orders 50 shirts, compute the total cost.

  b. Which costs more: 148 shirts or 150 shirts? Explain your answer.

117. A cell phone provider offers one plan that charges $4.95 for the text messaging feature plus $0.09 for each individual incoming or outgoing text. Alternatively, the provider offers a second plan with a flat rate of $18.00 for unlimited text messaging. How many text messages would result in the unlimited option being the better deal?

118. Melissa runs a landscaping business. She has equipment and fuel expenses of $313 per month. If she charges $45 for each lawn, how many lawns must she service to make a profit of at least $600 a month?

119. Madison is planning a 5-night trip to Cancun, Mexico, with her friends. The airfare is $475, her share of the hotel room is $54 per night, and her budget for food and entertainment is $350. She has $700 in savings and has a job earning $10 per hour babysitting. What is the minimum number of hours of babysitting that Madison needs so that she will earn enough money to take the trip?

120. Luke and Landon are both tutors. Luke charges $50 for an initial assessment and $25 per hour for each hour he tutors. Landon charges $100 for an initial assessment and $20 per hour for tutoring. After how many hours of tutoring will Luke surpass Landon in earnings?

Group Activity

Computing Body Mass Index (BMI)

Materials: Calculator

Estimated Time: 10 minutes

Group Size: 2

Body mass index is a statistical measure of an individual's weight in relation to the person's height. It is computed by

$$\text{BMI} = \frac{703W}{h^2}$$
where W is a person's weight in *pounds*.
h is the person's height in *inches*.

The *National Institutes of Health* categorizes body mass indices as follows:

1. Compute the body mass index for a person 5′4″ tall weighing 160 lb. Is this person's weight considered ideal?

Body Mass Index (BMI)	Weight Status
$18.5 \leq \text{BMI} \leq 24.9$	considered ideal
$25.0 \leq \text{BMI} \leq 29.9$	considered overweight
$\text{BMI} \geq 30.0$	considered obese

2. At the time that basketball legend Michael Jordan played for the Chicago Bulls, he was 210 lb and stood 6′6″ tall. What was Michael Jordan's body mass index?

3. For a fixed height, body mass index is a function of a person's weight only. For example, for a person 72 in. tall (6 ft), solve the following inequality to determine the person's ideal weight range.

$$18.5 \leq \frac{703W}{(72)^2} \leq 24.9$$

4. At the time that professional bodybuilder, Jay Cutler, won the Mr. Olympia contest he was 260 lb and stood 5′10″ tall.

a. What was Jay Cutler's body mass index?

b. As a body builder, Jay Cutler has an extraordinarily small percentage of body fat. Yet, according to the chart, would he be considered overweight or obese? Why do you think that the formula is not an accurate measurement of Mr. Cutler's weight status?

Chapter 2   Summary

Section 2.1   Addition, Subtraction, Multiplication, and Division Properties of Equality

Key Concepts

An equation is an algebraic statement that indicates two expressions are equal. A **solution to an equation** is a value of the variable that makes the equation a true statement. The set of all solutions to an equation is the solution set of the equation.

A **linear equation in one variable** can be written in the form $ax + b = c$, where $a \neq 0$.

Addition Property of Equality:

If $a = b$, then $a + c = b + c$

Subtraction Property of Equality:

If $a = b$, then $a - c = b - c$

Multiplication Property of Equality:

If $a = b$, then $ac = bc$ $(c \neq 0)$

Division Property of Equality:

If $a = b$, then $\dfrac{a}{c} = \dfrac{b}{c}$ $(c \neq 0)$

Examples

Example 1

$2x + 1 = 9$ is an equation with solution 4.

Check: $2(4) + 1 \overset{?}{=} 9$

$8 + 1 \overset{?}{=} 9$

$9 \overset{?}{=} 9$ ✔ True

Example 2

$x - 5 = 12$

$x - 5 + 5 = 12 + 5$

$x = 17$ The solution is 17.

Example 3

$z + 1.44 = 2.33$

$z + 1.44 - 1.44 = 2.33 - 1.44$

$z = 0.89$ The solution is 0.89.

Example 4

$\dfrac{3}{4}x = 12$

$\dfrac{4}{3} \cdot \dfrac{3}{4}x = 12 \cdot \dfrac{4}{3}$

$x = 16$ The solution is 16.

Example 5

$16 = 8y$

$\dfrac{16}{8} = \dfrac{8y}{8}$

$2 = y$ The solution is 2.

Section 2.2   Solving Linear Equations

Key Concepts

Steps for Solving a Linear Equation in One Variable:

1. Simplify both sides of the equation.
   - Clear parentheses
   - Combine *like* terms
2. Use the addition or subtraction property of equality to collect the variable terms on one side of the equation.
3. Use the addition or subtraction property of equality to collect the constant terms on the other side of the equation.
4. Use the multiplication or division property of equality to make the coefficient of the variable term equal to 1.
5. Check your answer.

A **conditional equation** is true for some values of the variable but is false for other values.

An equation that has all real numbers as its solution set is an **identity**.

An equation that has no solution is a **contradiction**.

Examples

Example 1

$$5y + 7 = 3(y - 1) + 2$$

$5y + 7 = 3y - 3 + 2$	Clear parentheses.
$5y + 7 = 3y - 1$	Combine *like* terms.
$2y + 7 = -1$	Collect the variable terms.
$2y = -8$	Collect the constant terms.
$y = -4$	Divide both sides by 2.

The solution is -4.

Check:

$$5(-4) + 7 \stackrel{?}{=} 3[(-4) - 1] + 2$$
$$-20 + 7 \stackrel{?}{=} 3(-5) + 2$$
$$-13 \stackrel{?}{=} -15 + 2$$
$$-13 \stackrel{?}{=} -13 \quad \checkmark \quad \text{True}$$

Example 2

$x + 5 = 7$ is a conditional equation because it is true only on the condition that $x = 2$.

Example 3

$$x + 4 = 2(x + 2) - x$$
$$x + 4 = 2x + 4 - x$$
$$x + 4 = x + 4$$
$$4 = 4 \quad \text{is an identity}$$

The solution is all real numbers.

Example 4

$$y - 5 = 2(y + 3) - y$$
$$y - 5 = 2y + 6 - y$$
$$y - 5 = y + 6$$
$$-5 = 6 \quad \text{is a contradiction}$$

There is no solution.

Section 2.3	Linear Equations: Clearing Fractions and Decimals

Key Concepts

Steps for Solving a Linear Equation in One Variable:

1. Simplify both sides of the equation.
   - Clear parentheses
   - Consider clearing fractions or decimals (if any are present) by multiplying both sides of the equation by a common denominator of all terms
   - Combine *like* terms
2. Use the addition or subtraction property of equality to collect the variable terms on one side of the equation.
3. Use the addition or subtraction property of equality to collect the constant terms on the other side of the equation.
4. Use the multiplication or division property of equality to make the coefficient of the variable term equal to 1.
5. Check your answer.

Examples

Example 1

$$\frac{1}{2}x - 2 - \frac{3}{4}x = \frac{7}{4}$$

$$\frac{4}{1}\left(\frac{1}{2}x - 2 - \frac{3}{4}x\right) = \frac{4}{1}\left(\frac{7}{4}\right) \qquad \text{Multiply by the LCD.}$$

$$2x - 8 - 3x = 7 \qquad \text{Apply distributive property.}$$

$$-x - 8 = 7 \qquad \text{Combine } like \text{ terms.}$$

$$-x = 15 \qquad \text{Add 8 to both sides.}$$

$$x = -15 \qquad \text{Divide by } -1.$$

The solution -15 checks in the original equation.

Example 2

$$-1.2x - 5.1 = 16.5$$

$$10(-1.2x - 5.1) = 10(16.5) \qquad \text{Multiply both sides by 10.}$$

$$-12x - 51 = 165$$

$$-12x = 216$$

$$\frac{-12x}{-12} = \frac{216}{-12}$$

$$x = -18$$

The solution -18 checks in the original equation.

Section 2.4	Applications of Linear Equations: Introduction to Problem Solving

Key Concepts

Problem-Solving Steps for Word Problems:

1. Read the problem carefully.
2. Assign labels to unknown quantities.
3. Write a verbal model.
4. Write a mathematical equation.
5. Solve the equation.
6. Interpret the results and write the answer in words.

Examples

Example 1

The perimeter of a triangle is 54 m. The lengths of the sides are represented by three consecutive even integers. Find the lengths of the three sides.

1. Read the problem.

2. Let x represent one side, $x + 2$ represent the second side, and $x + 4$ represent the third side.

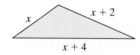

3. (First side) + (second side) + (third side) = perimeter

4. $x + (x + 2) + (x + 4) = 54$

5. $3x + 6 = 54$
   $3x = 48$
   $x = 16$

6. $x = 16$ represents the length of the shortest side. The lengths of the other sides are given by $x + 2 = 18$ and $x + 4 = 20$.

   The lengths of the three sides are 16 m, 18 m, and 20 m.

Section 2.5   Applications Involving Percents

Key Concepts

The following formula will help you solve basic percent problems.

$$\text{Amount} = (\text{percent})(\text{base})$$

One common use of percents is in computing sales tax.

Another use of percent is in computing **simple interest** using the formula:

$$\begin{pmatrix}\text{Simple} \\ \text{interest}\end{pmatrix} = (\text{principal})\begin{pmatrix}\text{annual} \\ \text{interest} \\ \text{rate}\end{pmatrix}\begin{pmatrix}\text{time in} \\ \text{years}\end{pmatrix}$$

or $I = Prt.$

Examples

Example 1

A flat screen television costs $1260.00 after a 5% sales tax is included. What was the price before tax?

$$\begin{pmatrix}\text{Price} \\ \text{before tax}\end{pmatrix} + (\text{tax}) = \begin{pmatrix}\text{total} \\ \text{price}\end{pmatrix}$$

$$x \qquad + 0.05x = 1260$$
$$1.05x = 1260$$
$$x = 1200$$

The television cost $1200 before tax.

Example 2

John Li invests $5400 at 2.5% simple interest. How much interest does he earn after 5 years?

$$I = Prt$$
$$I = (\$5400)(0.025)(5)$$
$$I = \$675$$

Section 2.6   Literal Equations and Applications of Geometry

Key Concepts

A **literal equation** is an equation that has more than one variable. Often such an equation can be manipulated to solve for different variables.

Formulas from Section R.4 can be used in applications involving geometry.

Examples

Example 1

$$P = 2a + b, \text{ solve for } a.$$
$$P - b = 2a + b - b$$
$$P - b = 2a$$
$$\frac{P - b}{2} = \frac{2a}{2}$$
$$\frac{P - b}{2} = a \quad \text{or} \quad a = \frac{P - b}{2}$$

Example 2

Find the length of a side of a square whose perimeter is 28 ft.

Use the formula $P = 4s$. Substitute 28 for P and solve:

$$P = 4s$$
$$28 = 4s$$
$$7 = s$$

The length of a side of the square is 7 ft.

Section 2.7 Mixture Applications and Uniform Motion

Examples

Example 1 illustrates a mixture problem.

Example 1

How much 80% disinfectant solution should be mixed with 8 L of a 30% disinfectant solution to make a 40% solution?

	80% Solution	30% Solution	40% Solution
Amount of Solution	x	8	$x + 8$
Amount of Pure Disinfectant	$0.80x$	$0.30(8)$	$0.40(x + 8)$

$0.80x + 0.30(8) = 0.40(x + 8)$

$0.80x + 2.4 = 0.40x + 3.2$

$0.40x + 2.4 = 3.2$ Subtract $0.40x$.

$0.40x = 0.80$ Subtract 2.4.

$x = 2$ Divide by 0.40.

2 L of 80% solution is needed.

Examples

Example 2 illustrates a uniform motion problem.

Example 2

Jack and Diane participate in a bicycle race. Jack rides the first half of the race in 1.5 hr. Diane rides the second half at a rate 5 mph slower than Jack and completes her portion in 2 hr. How fast does each person ride?

	Distance	Rate	Time
Jack	$1.5x$	x	1.5
Diane	$2(x - 5)$	$x - 5$	2

$\begin{pmatrix} \text{Distance} \\ \text{Jack rides} \end{pmatrix} = \begin{pmatrix} \text{distance} \\ \text{Diane rides} \end{pmatrix}$

$1.5x = 2(x - 5)$

$1.5x = 2x - 10$

$-0.5x = -10$ Subtract $2x$.

$x = 20$ Divide by -0.5.

Jack's speed is x. Jack rides 20 mph. Diane's speed is $x - 5$, which is 15 mph.

Section 2.8 Linear Inequalities

Key Concepts

A **linear inequality in one variable**, x, is any inequality that can be written in the form: $ax + b < c$, $ax + b > c$, $ax + b \leq c$, or $ax + b \geq c$, where $a \neq 0$.

    The solution set to an inequality can be expressed as a graph or in **set-builder notation** or in **interval notation**.

    When graphing an inequality or when writing interval notation, a parenthesis, (or), is used to denote that an endpoint is *not included* in a solution set. A square bracket, [or], is used to show that an endpoint *is included* in a solution set. A parenthesis (or) is always used with $-\infty$ and ∞, respectively.

    The inequality $a < x < b$ is used to show that x is greater than a and less than b. That is, x is *between a and b*.

    Multiplying or dividing an inequality by a negative quantity requires the direction of the inequality sign to be reversed.

Examples

Example 1

$-2x + 6 \geq 14$

$-2x + 6 - 6 \geq 14 - 6$ Subtract 6.

$-2x \geq 8$ Simplify.

$\dfrac{-2x}{-2} \leq \dfrac{8}{-2}$ Divide by -2. Reverse the inequality sign.

$x \leq -4$

Set-builder notation: $\{x \mid x \leq -4\}$

Graph:

-4

Interval notation: $(-\infty, -4]$

Chapter 2 Review Exercises

Section 2.1

1. Label the following as either an expression or an equation:

   a. $3x + y = 10$ **b.** $9x + 10y - 2xy$

   c. $4(x + 3) = 12$ **d.** $-5x = 7$

2. Explain how to determine whether an equation is linear in one variable.

3. Determine if the given equation is a linear equation in one variable or not. Answer yes or no.

   a. $4x^2 + 8 = -10$ **b.** $x + 18 = 72$

   c. $-3 + 2y^2 = 0$ **d.** $-4p - 5 = 6p$

4. For the equation, $4y + 9 = -3$, determine if the given numbers are solutions.

   a. $y = 3$ **b.** $y = 0$

   c. $y = -3$ **d.** $y = -2$

For Exercises 5–12, solve the equation using the addition property, subtraction property, multiplication property, or division property of equality.

5. $a + 6 = -2$

6. $6 = z - 9$

7. $-\dfrac{3}{4} + k = \dfrac{9}{2}$

8. $0.1r = 7$

9. $-5x = 21$

10. $\dfrac{t}{3} = -20$

11. $-\dfrac{2}{5}k = \dfrac{4}{7}$

12. $-m = -27$

13. The quotient of a number and negative six is equal to negative ten. Find the number.

14. The difference of a number and $-\frac{1}{8}$ is $\frac{5}{12}$. Find the number.

15. Four subtracted from a number is negative twelve. Find the number.

16. Six subtracted from a number is negative eight. Find the number.

Section 2.2

For Exercises 17–28, solve the equation.

17. $4d + 2 = 6$ 18. $5c - 6 = -9$

19. $-7c = -3c - 9$ 20. $-28 = 5w + 2$

21. $\dfrac{b}{3} + 1 = 0$ 22. $\dfrac{2}{3}h - 5 = 7$

23. $-3p + 7 = 5p + 1$ 24. $4t - 6 = 12t + 18$

25. $4a - 9 = 3(a - 3)$ 26. $3(2c + 5) = -2(c - 8)$

27. $7b + 3(b - 1) + 3 = 2(b + 8)$

28. $2 + (18 - x) + 2(x - 1) = 4(x + 2) - 8$

29. Explain the difference between an equation that is a contradiction and an equation that is an identity.

For Exercises 30–35, label each equation as a conditional equation, a contradiction, or an identity.

30. $x + 3 = 3 + x$ 31. $3x - 19 = 2x + 1$

32. $5x + 6 = 5x - 28$ 33. $2x - 8 = 2(x - 4)$

34. $-8x - 9 = -8(x - 9)$ 35. $4x - 4 = 3x - 2$

Section 2.3

For Exercises 36–53, solve the equation.

36. $\dfrac{x}{8} - \dfrac{1}{4} = \dfrac{1}{2}$ 37. $\dfrac{y}{15} - \dfrac{2}{3} = \dfrac{4}{5}$

38. $\dfrac{x + 5}{2} - \dfrac{2x + 10}{9} = 5$

39. $\dfrac{x - 6}{3} - \dfrac{2x + 8}{2} = 12$

40. $\dfrac{1}{10}p - 3 = \dfrac{2}{5}p$ 41. $\dfrac{1}{4}y - \dfrac{3}{4} = \dfrac{1}{2}y + 1$

42. $-\dfrac{1}{4}(2 - 3t) = \dfrac{3}{4}$ 43. $\dfrac{2}{7}(w + 4) = \dfrac{1}{2}$

44. $17.3 - 2.7q = 10.55$

45. $4.9z + 4.6 = 3.2z - 2.2$

46. $5.74a + 9.28 = 2.24a - 5.42$

47. $62.84t - 123.66 = 4(2.36 + 2.4t)$

48. $0.05x + 0.10(24 - x) = 0.75(24)$

49. $0.20(x + 4) + 0.65x = 0.20(854)$

50. $100 - (t - 6) = -(t - 1)$

51. $3 - (x + 4) + 5 = 3x + 10 - 4x$

52. $5t - (2t + 14) = 3t - 14$

53. $9 - 6(2z + 1) = -3(4z - 1)$

Section 2.4

54. Twelve added to the sum of a number and two is forty-four. Find the number.

55. Twenty added to the sum of a number and six is thirty-seven. Find the number.

56. Three times a number is the same as the difference of twice the number and seven. Find the number.

57. Eight less than five times a number is forty-eight less than the number. Find the number.

58. Three times the largest of three consecutive even integers is 76 more than the sum of the other two integers. Find the integers.

59. Ten times the smallest of three consecutive integers is 213 more than the sum of the other two integers. Find the integers.

60. The perimeter of a triangle is 78 in. The lengths of the sides are represented by three consecutive integers. Find the lengths of the sides of the triangle.

61. The perimeter of a pentagon (a five-sided polygon) is 190 cm. The five sides are represented by consecutive integers. Find the lengths of the sides.

62. Minimum salaries of major league baseball players soared after a new ruling in 1975. In 2010, the minimum salary for a major league player was $400,000. This is 25 times the minimum salary in 1975. Find the minimum salary in 1975.

63. The state of Indiana has approximately 2.1 million more people than Kentucky. Together their population totals 10.3 million. Approximately how many people are in each state?

Section 2.5

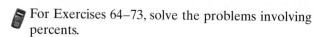 For Exercises 64–73, solve the problems involving percents.

64. What is 35% of 68?

65. What is 4% of 720?

66. 53.5 is what percent of 428?

67. 68.4 is what percent of 72?

68. 24 is 15% of what number?

69. 8.75 is 0.5% of what number?

70. A novel is discounted 30%. The sale price is $20.65. What was the original price?

71. A couple spent a total of $50.40 for dinner. This included a 20% tip and 6% sales tax on the price of the meal. What was the price of the dinner before tax and tip?

 72. Anna Tsao invested $3000 in an account paying 8% simple interest.

    a. How much interest will she earn in $3\frac{1}{2}$ years?

    b. What will her balance be at that time?

73. Eduardo invested money in an account earning 4% simple interest. At the end of 5 years, he had a total of $14,400. How much money did he originally invest?

Section 2.6

For Exercises 74–81, solve for the indicated variable.

74. $C = K - 273$ for K

75. $K = C + 273$ for C

76. $P = 4s$ for s

77. $P = 3s$ for s

78. $y = mx + b$ for x

79. $a + bx = c$ for x

80. $2x + 5y = -2$ for y

81. $4(a + b) = Q$ for b

For Exercises 82–88, use the appropriate geometry formula to solve the problem.

82. Find the height of a parallelogram whose area is 42 m² and whose base is 6 m.

83. The volume of a cone is given by the formula
$$V = \frac{1}{3}\pi r^2 h.$$

   a. Solve the formula for h.

   b. Find the height of a right circular cone whose volume is 47.8 in.³ and whose radius is 3 in. Round to the nearest tenth of an inch.

84. The smallest angle of a triangle is 2° more than $\frac{1}{4}$ of the largest angle. The middle angle is 2° less than the largest angle. Find the measure of each angle.

85. A carpenter uses a special saw to cut an angle on a piece of framing. If the angles are complementary and one angle is 10° more than the other, find the measure of each angle.

86. A rectangular window has width 1 ft less than its length. The perimeter is 18 ft. Find the length and the width of the window.

87. Find the measure of the vertical angles by first solving for x.

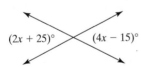

$(2x + 25)°$ $(4x − 15)°$

88. Find the measure of angle y.

37°

y

Section 2.7

89. In stormy conditions, a delivery truck can travel a route in 14 hr. In good weather, the same trip can be made in 10.5 hr because the truck travels 15 km/hr faster. Find the speed of the truck in stormy weather and the speed in good weather.

90. Winston and Gus ride their bicycles in a relay. Each person rides the same distance. Winston rides 3 mph faster than Gus and finishes the course in 2.5 hr. Gus finishes in 3 hr. How fast does each person ride?

91. Two cars leave a rest stop on Interstate I-10 at the same time. One heads east and the other heads west. One car travels 55 mph and the other 62 mph. How long will it take for them to be 327.6 mi apart?

92. Two hikers begin at the same time at opposite ends of a 9-mi trail and walk toward each other. One hiker walks 2.5 mph and the other walks 1.5 mph. How long will it be before they meet?

93. How much ground beef with 24% fat should be mixed with 8 lb of ground sirloin that is 6% fat to make a mixture that is 9.6% fat?

94. A soldering compound with 40% lead (the rest is tin) must be combined with 80 lb of solder that is 75% lead to make a compound that is 68% lead. How much solder with 40% lead should be used?

Section 2.8

For Exercises 95–97, graph the inequalities and write the set in interval notation.

95. $\{x \mid x > -2\}$ _____

96. $\left\{x \mid x \le \dfrac{1}{2}\right\}$

97. $\{x \mid -1 < x \le 4\}$

98. A landscaper buys potted geraniums from a nursery at a price of $5 per plant. However, for large orders, the price per plant is discounted by a percentage off the original price. Let x represent the number of potted plants ordered. The corresponding discount is given in the following table.

Number of Plants	Discount
$x \le 99$	0%
$100 \le x \le 199$	2%
$200 \le x \le 299$	4%
$x \ge 300$	6%

a. Find the cost to purchase 130 plants.

b. Which costs more, 300 plants or 295 plants? Explain your answer.

For Exercises 99–109, solve the inequality. Graph the solution set and express the answer in set-builder notation and interval notation.

99. $c + 6 < 23$ ──────────▶

100. $3w - 4 > -5$ ──────────▶

101. $-2x - 7 \geq 5$ ──────────▶

102. $5(y + 2) \leq -4$ ──────────▶

103. $-\dfrac{3}{7}a \leq -21$ ──────────▶

104. $1.3 > 0.4t - 12.5$ ──────────▶

105. $4k + 23 < 7k - 31$ ──────────▶

106. $\dfrac{6}{5}h - \dfrac{1}{5} \leq \dfrac{3}{10} + h$ ──────────▶

107. $-5x - 2(4x - 3) + 6 > 17 - 4(x - 1)$ ──────────▶

108. $-6 < 2b \leq 14$ ──────────▶

109. $-2 \leq z + 4 \leq 9$ ──────────▶

110. The summer average rainfall for Bermuda for June, July, and August is 5.3 in. per month. If Bermuda receives 6.3 in. of rain in June and 7.1 in. in July, how much rain is required in August to exceed the 3-month summer average?

111. Collette has $15.00 to spend on dinner. Of this, 25% will cover the tax and tip, resulting in $11.25 for her to spend on food. If Collette wants veggies and blue cheese, fries, and a drink, what is the maximum number of chicken wings she can get?

> **Wing Special**
>
> # 25¢ each
> 5:00–7:00 P.M.
>
> *Add veggies and blue cheese for $2.50
> *Add fries for $2.50
> *Add a drink for $1.75

Chapter 2 Test

1. Which of the equations have $x = -3$ as a solution?

   a. $4x + 1 = 10$ **b.** $6(x - 1) = x - 21$

   c. $5x - 2 = 2x + 1$ **d.** $\dfrac{1}{3}x + 1 = 0$

2. a. Simplify: $3x - 1 + 2x + 8$

   b. Solve: $3x - 1 = 2x + 8$

For Exercises 3–13, solve the equation.

3. $-3x + 5 = -2$ **4.** $3h + 1 = 3(h + 1)$

5. $t + 3 = -13$

6. $2 + d = 2 - 3(d - 5) - 2$

7. $8 = p - 4$

8. $\dfrac{3}{7} + \dfrac{2}{5}x = -\dfrac{1}{5}x + 1$ **9.** $\dfrac{t}{8} = -\dfrac{2}{9}$

10. $2(p - 4) = p + 7$

11. $-5(x + 2) + 8x = -2 + 3x - 8$

12. $\dfrac{3x + 1}{2} - \dfrac{4x - 3}{3} = 1$

13. $0.5c - 1.9 = 2.8 + 0.6c$

14. Solve the equation for y: $\quad 3x + y = -4$

15. Solve $C = 2\pi r$ for r.

16. 13% of what is 11.7?

17. Graph the inequalities and write the sets in interval notation.

   a. $\{x \mid x < 0\}$ _____→

   b. $\{x \mid -2 \le x < 5\}$ _____→

For Exercises 18–21, solve the inequality. Graph the solution and write the solution set in set-builder notation and interval notation.

18. $5x + 14 > -2x$ _____→

19. $2(3 - x) \ge 14$ _____→

20. $3(2y - 4) + 1 > 2(2y - 3) - 8$ _____→

21. $-13 \le 3p + 2 \le 5$ _____→

22. The total bill for a pair of basketball shoes (including sales tax) is $87.74. If the tax rate is 7%, find the cost of the shoes before tax.

23. Clarita borrowed money at a 6% simple interest rate. If she paid back a total of $8000 at the end of 10 yr, how much did she originally borrow?

24. One number is four plus one-half of another. The sum of the numbers is 31. Find the numbers.

25. Two families leave their homes at the same time to meet for lunch. The families live 210 mi apart, and one family drives 5 mph slower than the other. If it takes them 2 hr to meet at a point between their homes, how fast does each family travel?

26. The average winter snowfall for Syracuse, New York, for December, January, and February is 27.5 in. per month. If Syracuse receives 24 in. of snow in December and 32 in. in January, how much snow is required in February to exceed the 3-month average?

27. The perimeter of a pentagon (a five-sided polygon) is 315 in. The five sides are represented by consecutive integers. Find the measures of the sides.

28. Paula mixes macadamia nuts that cost $9.00 per pound with 50 lb of peanuts that cost $5.00 per pound. How many pounds of macadamia nuts should she mix to make a nut mixture that costs $6.50 per pound?

29. A couple purchased two hockey tickets and two basketball tickets for $153.92. A hockey ticket cost $4.32 more than a basketball ticket. What were the prices of the individual tickets?

30. Two angles are complementary. One angle is 26° more than the other angle. What are the measures of the angles?

31. The length of a soccer field for international matches is 40 m less than twice its width. If the perimeter is 370 m, what are the dimensions of the field?

32. Given the triangle, find the measures of each angle by first solving for y.

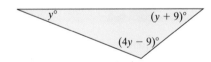

Chapters 1–2   Cumulative Review Exercises

For Exercises 1–5, perform the indicated operations.

1. $\left| -\dfrac{1}{5} + \dfrac{7}{10} \right|$

2. $5 - 2[3 - (4 - 7)]$

3. $-\dfrac{2}{3} + \left(\dfrac{1}{2} \right)^2$

4. $-3^2 + (-5)^2$

5. $\sqrt{5 - (-20) - 3^2}$

For Exercises 6 and 7, translate the mathematical expressions and simplify the results.

6. The square root of the difference of five squared and nine

7. The sum of -14 and 12

8. List the terms of the expression:
   $-7x^2y + 4xy - 6$

9. Simplify: $-4[2x - 3(x + 4)] + 5(x - 7)$

For Exercises 10–15, solve the equations.

10. $8t - 8 = 24$

11. $-2.5x - 5.2 = 12.8$

12. $-5(p - 3) + 2p = 3(5 - p)$

13. $\dfrac{x + 3}{5} - \dfrac{x + 2}{2} = 2$

14. $\dfrac{2}{9}x - \dfrac{1}{3} = x + \dfrac{1}{9}$

15. $-0.6w = 48$

16. The sum of two consecutive odd integers is 156. Find the integers.

17. The cost of an iPod speaker dock (including sales tax) is $374.50. If the tax rate is 7%, find the cost of the speaker dock before tax.

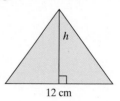 **18.** The area of a triangle is 41 cm². Find the height of the triangle if the base is 12 cm.

12 cm

For Exercises 19 and 20, solve the inequality. Graph the solution set on a number line and express the solution in set-builder notation and interval notation.

19. $-3x - 3(x + 1) < 9$ ───────→

20. $-6 \le 2x - 4 \le 14$ ───────→

Graphing Linear Equations in Two Variables

3

CHAPTER OUTLINE

Chapter 3

Review Your Skills

In this chapter, we study graphing and focus on the graphs of lines. Your skill at solving linear equations in one variable will be very important in this chapter.

Complete the puzzle to check your readiness.

Across

2. Solve. $\dfrac{z}{-6} = -81$

4. Simplify. $15x - 5(x - 49) - 10x + 2000$

5. Smallest positive integer that can be used to clear decimals.
$0.06x + 1.8 = 2 - 2.251$

Down

1. Solve. $2a - 3 = 45$

3. $-10^2 \cdot (-2)^3 \cdot 11$

4. Solve. $4(2x - 1) = 5x + 56$

5. Smallest positive integer that can be used to clear fractions.
$\dfrac{1}{2}y - \dfrac{3}{4} = \dfrac{5}{3}y + 1$

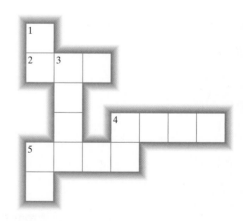

Section 3.1   Rectangular Coordinate System

1. Interpreting Graphs

Mathematics is a powerful tool used by scientists and has directly contributed to the highly technical world in which we live. Applications of mathematics have led to advances in the sciences, business, computer technology, and medicine.

One fundamental application of mathematics is the graphical representation of numerical information (or data). For example, Table 3-1 represents the number of clients admitted to a drug and alcohol rehabilitation program over a 12-month period.

Table 3-1

	Month	Number of Clients
Jan.	1	55
Feb.	2	62
March	3	64
April	4	60
May	5	70
June	6	73
July	7	77
Aug.	8	80
Sept.	9	80
Oct.	10	74
Nov.	11	85
Dec.	12	90

In table form, the information is difficult to picture and interpret. It appears that on a monthly basis, the number of clients fluctuates. However, when the data are represented in a graph, an upward trend is clear (Figure 3-1).

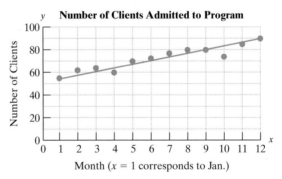

Figure 3-1

From the increase in clients shown in this graph, management for the rehabilitation center might make plans for the future. If the trend continues, management might consider expanding its facilities and increasing its staff to accommodate the expected increase in clients.

Example 1 Interpreting a Graph

Refer to Figure 3-1 and Table 3-1.

a. For which month was the number of clients the greatest?

b. How many clients were served in the first month (January)?

c. Which month corresponds to 60 clients served?

d. Between which two consecutive months did the number of clients decrease?

e. Between which two consecutive months did the number of clients remain the same?

Solution:

a. Month 12 (December) corresponds to the highest point on the graph. This represents the greatest number of clients, 90.

b. In month 1 (January), there were 55 clients served.

c. Month 4 (April).

d. The number of clients decreased between months 3 and 4 and between months 9 and 10.

e. The number of clients remained the same between months 8 and 9.

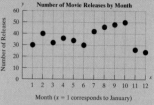
2. Plotting Points in a Rectangular Coordinate System

The data in Table 3-1 represent a relationship between two variables—the month number and the number of clients. The graph in Figure 3-1 enables us to visualize this relationship. In picturing the relationship between two quantities, we often use a graph with two number lines drawn at right angles to each other (Figure 3-2). This forms a **rectangular coordinate system**. The horizontal line is called the **x-axis**, and the vertical line is called the **y-axis**. The point where the lines intersect is called the **origin**. On the x-axis, the numbers to the right of the origin are positive and the numbers to the left are negative. On the y-axis, the numbers above the origin are positive and the numbers below are negative. The x- and y-axes divide the graphing area into four regions called **quadrants**.

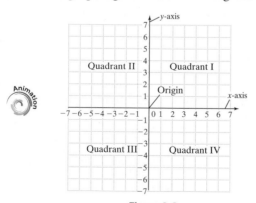

Figure 3-2

Points graphed in a rectangular coordinate system are defined by two numbers as an **ordered pair**, (x, y). The first number (called the **x-coordinate**, or the abscissa) is the horizontal position from the origin. The second number (called the **y-coordinate**, or the ordinate) is the vertical position from the origin. Example 2 shows how points are plotted in a rectangular coordinate system.

Answers

1. Month 10 (October)
2. 30 movies
3. Month 2 (February)
4. Months 1 and 6 (January and June)

Example 2 **Plotting Points in a Rectangular Coordinate System**

Plot the points.

a. $(4, 5)$ **b.** $(-4, -5)$ **c.** $(-1, 3)$ **d.** $(3, -1)$

e. $\left(\dfrac{1}{2}, -\dfrac{7}{3}\right)$ **f.** $(-2, 0)$ **g.** $(0, 0)$ **h.** $(\pi, 1.1)$

Solution:

See Figure 3-3.

a. The ordered pair $(4, 5)$ indicates that $x = 4$ and $y = 5$. Beginning at the origin, move 4 units in the positive x direction (4 units to the right), and from there move 5 units in the positive y direction (5 units up). Then plot the point. The point is in Quadrant I.

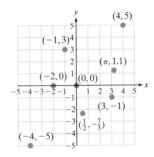

Figure 3-3

b. The ordered pair $(-4, -5)$ indicates that $x = -4$ and $y = -5$. Move 4 units in the negative x direction (4 units to the left), and from there move 5 units in the negative y direction (5 units down). Then plot the point. The point is in Quadrant III.

c. The ordered pair $(-1, 3)$ indicates that $x = -1$ and $y = 3$. Move 1 unit to the left and 3 units up. The point is in Quadrant II.

d. The ordered pair $(3, -1)$ indicates that $x = 3$ and $y = -1$. Move 3 units to the right and 1 unit down. The point is in Quadrant IV.

TIP: Notice that changing the order of the x- and y-coordinates changes the location of the point. For example, the point $(-1, 3)$ is in Quadrant II, whereas $(3, -1)$ is in Quadrant IV (Figure 3-3). This is why points are represented by *ordered* pairs. The order of the coordinates is important.

e. The improper fraction $-\dfrac{7}{3}$ can be written as the mixed number $-2\dfrac{1}{3}$. Therefore, to plot the point $\left(\dfrac{1}{2}, -\dfrac{7}{3}\right)$ move to the right $\dfrac{1}{2}$ unit, and down $2\dfrac{1}{3}$ units. The point is in Quadrant IV.

Avoiding Mistakes

Points that lie on either of the axes do not lie in any quadrant.

f. The point $(-2, 0)$ indicates $y = 0$. Therefore, the point is on the x-axis.

g. The point $(0, 0)$ is at the origin.

h. The irrational number, π, can be approximated as 3.14. Thus, the point $(\pi, 1.1)$ is located approximately 3.14 units to the right and 1.1 units up. The point is in Quadrant I.

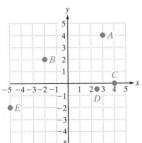

3. Applications of Plotting and Identifying Points

The effective use of graphs for mathematical models requires skill in identifying points and interpreting graphs.

Example 3 Determining Points from a Graph

A map of a national park is drawn so that the origin is placed at the ranger station (Figure 3-4). Four fire observation towers are located at points A, B, C, and D. Estimate the coordinates of the fire towers relative to the ranger station (all distances are in miles).

Solution:

Point A: $(-1, -3)$

Point B: $(-2, 3)$

Point C: $(3\frac{1}{2}, 1\frac{1}{2})$ or $(\frac{7}{2}, \frac{3}{2})$ or $(3.5, 1.5)$

Point D: $(1\frac{1}{2}, -2)$ or $(\frac{3}{2}, -2)$ or $(1.5, -2)$

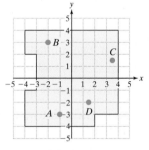

Figure 3-4

Skill Practice

6. Towers are located at points A, B, C, and D. Estimate the coordinates of the towers.

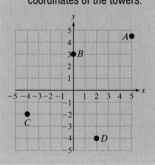

Example 4 Plotting Points in an Application

The daily low temperatures (in degrees Fahrenheit) for one week in January for Sudbury, Ontario, Canada, are given in Table 3-2.

a. Write an ordered pair for each row in the table using the day number as the x-coordinate and the temperature as the y-coordinate.

b. Plot the ordered pairs from part (a) on a rectangular coordinate system.

Solution:

a. Each ordered pair represents the day number and the corresponding low temperature for that day.

$(1, -3)$ $(2, -5)$ $(3, 1)$ $(4, 6)$ $(5, 5)$ $(6, 0)$ $(7, -4)$

Table 3-2

Day Number, x	Temperature (°F), y
1	-3
2	-5
3	1
4	6
5	5
6	0
7	-4

Skill Practice

7. The table shows the number of homes sold in one town for a 6-month period. Plot the ordered pairs.

Month, x	Number Sold, y
1	20
2	25
3	28
4	40
5	45
6	30

b.

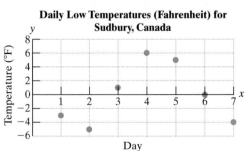

Daily Low Temperatures (Fahrenheit) for Sudbury, Canada

TIP: The graph in Example 4(b) shows only Quadrants I and IV because all x-coordinates are positive.

Answers

6. $A(5, 4\frac{1}{2})$
  $B(0, 3)$
  $C(-4, -2)$
  $D(2, -4)$

7.

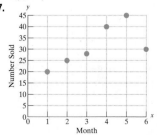

Section 3.1 Practice Exercises

Study Skills Exercise

Before you proceed further in Chapter 3, make your test corrections for the Chapter 2 test. See Study Skills Exercise in Section 2.1 for instructions.

Vocabulary and Key Concepts

1. a. In a rectangular coordinate system, two number lines are drawn at right angles to each other. The horizontal line is called the _____-axis, and the vertical line is called the _____.

   b. A point in a rectangular coordinate system is defined by an _____ pair, (x, y).

   c. In a rectangular coordinate system, the point where the x- and y-axes intersect is called the _____ and is represented by the ordered pair _____.

   d. The x- and y-axes divide the coordinate plane into four regions called _____.

   e. A point with a positive x-coordinate and a _____ y-coordinate is in Quadrant IV.

   f. In Quadrant _____, both the x- and y-coordinates are negative.

Concept 1: Interpreting Graphs

For Exercises 2–6, refer to the graphs to answer the questions.
(See Example 1.)

2. The number of Botox injection procedures (in millions) in the United States over a 5-yr period is shown in the graph.

   a. For which year was the number of procedures the greatest?

   b. Approximately how many procedures were performed in year 5?

   c. Which year corresponds to 2.3 million procedures?

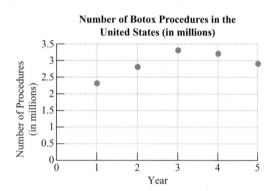

Number of Botox Procedures in the United States (in millions)

3. The number of patients served by a certain hospice care center for the first 12 months after it opened is shown in the graph.

   a. For which month was the number of patients greatest?

   b. How many patients did the center serve in the first month?

   c. Between which months did the number of patients decrease?

   d. Between which two months did the number of patients remain the same?

   e. Which month corresponds to 40 patients served?

   f. Approximately how many patients were served during the 10th month?

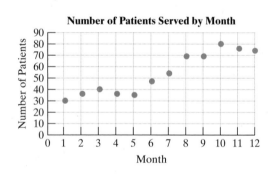

Number of Patients Served by Month

4. Recently the number of housing permits (in thousands) issued by a county in Texas between year 0 and year 6 is shown in the graph.

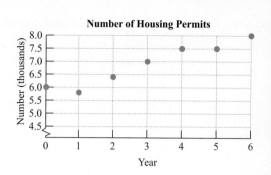

Number of Housing Permits

a. For which year was the number of permits greatest?

b. How many permits did the county issue in year 0?

c. Between which years did the number of permits decrease?

d. Between which two years did the number of permits remain the same?

e. Which year corresponds to 7000 permits issued?

5. The price per share of a stock (in dollars) over a period of 5 days is shown in the graph.

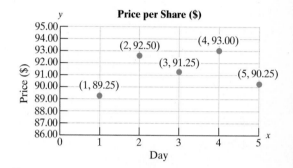

a. Interpret the meaning of the ordered pair $(1, 89.25)$.

b. What was the change in price between day 3 and day 4?

c. What was the change in price between day 4 and day 5?

6. The price per share of a stock (in dollars) over a period of 5 days is shown in the graph.

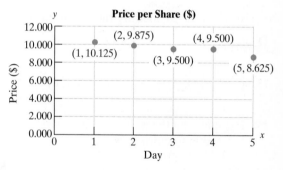

a. Interpret the meaning of the ordered pair $(1, 10.125)$.

b. What was the change in price between day 4 and day 5?

c. What was the change in price between day 1 and day 5?

Concept 2: Plotting Points in a Rectangular Coordinate System

7. Plot the points on a rectangular coordinate system. (See Example 2.)

a. $(2, 6)$ **b.** $(6, 2)$ **c.** $(-7, 3)$

d. $(-7, -3)$ **e.** $(0, -3)$ **f.** $(-3, 0)$

g. $(6, -4)$ **h.** $(0, 5)$

8. Plot the points on a rectangular coordinate system.

a. $(4, 5)$ **b.** $(-4, 5)$ **c.** $(-6, 0)$

d. $(6, 0)$ **e.** $(4, -5)$ **f.** $(-4, -5)$

g. $(0, -2)$ **h.** $(0, 0)$

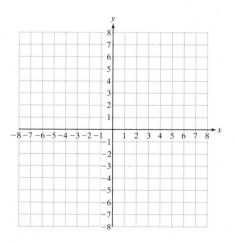

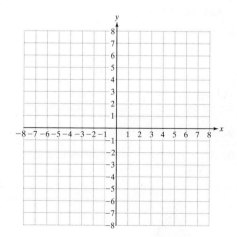

9. Plot the points on a rectangular coordinate system.

   a. $(-1, 5)$ **b.** $(0, 4)$ **c.** $\left(-2, -\dfrac{3}{2}\right)$

   d. $(2, -1.75)$ **e.** $(4, 2)$ **f.** $(-6, 0)$

10. Plot the points on a rectangular coordinate system.

   a. $(7, 0)$ **b.** $(-3, -2)$ **c.** $(6\tfrac{3}{5}, 1)$

   d. $(0, 1.5)$ **e.** $\left(\dfrac{7}{2}, -4\right)$ **f.** $\left(-\dfrac{7}{2}, 4\right)$

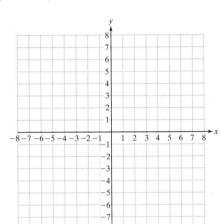

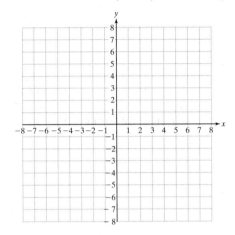

For Exercises 11–18, identify the quadrant in which the given point is found.

11. $(13, -2)$ **12.** $(25, 16)$ **13.** $(-8, 14)$ **14.** $(-82, -71)$

15. $(-5, -19)$ **16.** $(-31, 6)$ **17.** $\left(\dfrac{5}{2}, \dfrac{7}{4}\right)$ **18.** $(9, -40)$

19. Explain why the point $(0, -5)$ is *not* located in Quadrant IV.

20. Explain why the point $(-1, 0)$ is *not* located in Quadrant II.

21. Where is the point $(\tfrac{7}{8}, 0)$ located?

22. Where is the point $(0, \tfrac{6}{5})$ located?

Concept 3: Applications of Plotting and Identifying Points

For Exercises 23 and 24, refer to the graph. **(See Example 3.)**

23. Estimate the coordinates of the points A, B, C, D, E, and F.

24. Estimate the coordinates of the points G, H, I, J, K, and L.

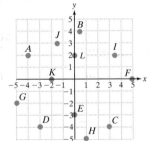

25. A map of a park is laid out with the visitor center located at the origin. Five visitors are in the park located at points A, B, C, D, and E. All distances are in meters.

   a. Estimate the coordinates of each visitor. **(See Example 3.)**

   b. How far apart are visitors C and D?

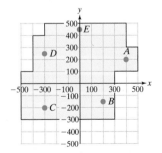

26. A townhouse has a sprinkler system in the backyard. With the water source at the origin, the sprinkler heads are located at points A, B, C, D, and E. All distances are in feet.

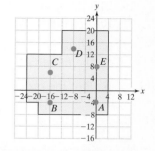

 a. Estimate the coordinates of each sprinkler head.

 b. How far is the distance from sprinkler head B to C?

27. A movie theater has kept records of popcorn sales versus movie attendance.

 a. Use the table shown to write the corresponding ordered pairs using the movie attendance as the x variable and sales of popcorn as the y variable. Interpret the meaning of the first ordered pair.
 (See Example 4.)

 b. Plot the data points on a rectangular coordinate system.

Movie Attendance (Number of People)	Sales of Popcorn ($)
250	225
175	193
315	330
220	209
450	570
400	480
190	185

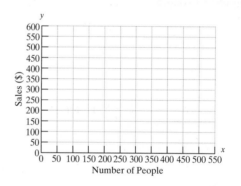

28. The age and systolic blood pressure (in millimeters of mercury, mm Hg) for eight different women are given in the table.

 a. Write the corresponding ordered pairs using the woman's age as the x variable and the systolic blood pressure as the y variable. Interpret the meaning of the first ordered pair.

 b. Plot the data points on a rectangular coordinate system.

Age (Years)	Systolic Blood Pressure (mm Hg)
57	149
41	120
71	158
36	115
64	151
25	110
40	118
77	165

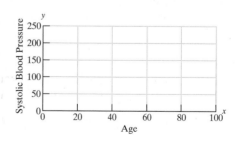

29. The following table shows the average temperature in degrees Celsius for Montreal, Quebec, Canada, by month.

a. Write the corresponding ordered pairs, letting $x = 1$ correspond to the month of January.

b. Plot the ordered pairs on a rectangular coordinate system.

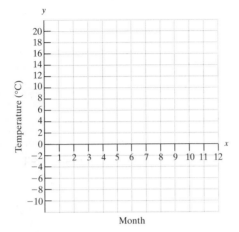

Month

Month, x		Temperature (°C), y
Jan.	1	−10.2
Feb.	2	−9.0
March	3	−2.5
April	4	5.7
May	5	13.0
June	6	18.3
July	7	20.9
Aug.	8	19.6
Sept.	9	14.8
Oct.	10	8.7
Nov.	11	2.0
Dec.	12	−6.9

30. The table shows the average temperature in degrees Fahrenheit for Fairbanks, Alaska, by month.

a. Write the corresponding ordered pairs, letting $x = 1$ correspond to the month of January.

b. Plot the ordered pairs on a rectangular coordinate system.

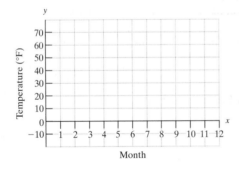

Month

Month, x		Temperature (°F), y
Jan.	1	−12.8
Feb.	2	−4.0
March	3	8.4
April	4	30.2
May	5	48.2
June	6	59.4
July	7	61.5
Aug.	8	56.7
Sept.	9	45.0
Oct.	10	25.0
Nov.	11	6.1
Dec.	12	−10.1

Expanding Your Skills

31. The data in the table give the percent of males and females who have completed 4 or more years of college education for selected years. Let x represent the number of years since 1960. Let y represent the percent of men and the percent of women that completed 4 or more years of college.

Year	x	Percent, y Men	Percent, y Women
1960	0	9.7	5.8
1970	10	13.5	8.1
1980	20	20.1	12.8
1990	30	24.4	18.4
2000	40	27.8	23.6
2005	45	28.9	26.5
2010	50	29.9	28.8

a. Plot the data points for men and for women on the same graph.

b. Is the percentage of men with 4 or more years of college increasing or decreasing?

c. Is the percentage of women with 4 or more years of college increasing or decreasing?

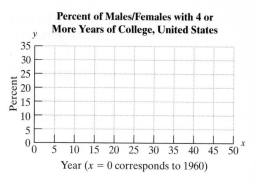

Percent of Males/Females with 4 or More Years of College, United States

32. Use the data and graph from Exercise 31 to answer the questions.

a. In which year was the difference in percentages between men and women with 4 or more years of college the greatest?

b. In which year was the difference in percentages between men and women the least?

c. If the trend continues beyond the data in the graph, does it seem possible that in the future, the percentage of women with 4 or more years of college will be greater than or equal to the percentage of men?

Linear Equations in Two Variables

Section 3.2

1. Definition of a Linear Equation in Two Variables

Recall that an equation in the form $ax + b = c$, where $a \neq 0$, is called a linear equation in one variable. A solution to such an equation is a value of x that makes the equation a true statement. For example, $3x + 5 = -1$ has a solution of -2.

In this section, we will look at linear equations in *two* variables.

Concepts

1. **Definition of a Linear Equation in Two Variables**
2. **Graphing Linear Equations in Two Variables by Plotting Points**
3. **x- and y-Intercepts**
4. **Horizontal and Vertical Lines**

Linear Equation in Two Variables

Let A, B, and C be real numbers such that A and B are not both zero. Then, an equation that can be written in the form:

$$Ax + By = C$$

is called a **linear equation in two variables**.

The equation $x + y = 4$ is a linear equation in two variables. A solution to such an equation is an ordered pair (x, y) that makes the equation a true statement. Several solutions to the equation $x + y = 4$ are listed here:

Solution:	Check:
(x, y)	$x + y = 4$
$(2, 2)$	$(2) + (2) = 4$ ✔
$(1, 3)$	$(1) + (3) = 4$ ✔
$(4, 0)$	$(4) + (0) = 4$ ✔
$(-1, 5)$	$(-1) + (5) = 4$ ✔

By graphing these ordered pairs, we see that the solution points line up (Figure 3-5).

Notice that there are infinitely many solutions to the equation $x + y = 4$ so they cannot all be listed. Therefore, to visualize all solutions to the equation $x + y = 4$, we draw the line through the points in the graph. Every point on the line represents an ordered pair solution to the equation $x + y = 4$, and the line represents the set of *all* solutions to the equation.

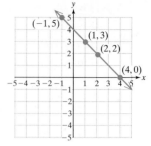

Figure 3-5

Skill Practice

Given the equation
$$3x - 2y = -12$$
determine whether the given ordered pair is a solution.

1. $(4, 0)$

2. $(-2, 3)$

3. $\left(1, \dfrac{15}{2}\right)$

Example 1   Determining Solutions to a Linear Equation

For the linear equation, $4x - 5y = 8$, determine whether the given ordered pair is a solution.

a. $(2, 0)$ **b.** $(3, 1)$ **c.** $\left(1, -\dfrac{4}{5}\right)$

Solution:

a. $4x - 5y = 8$

$4(2) - 5(0) \overset{?}{=} 8$ Substitute $x = 2$ and $y = 0$.

$8 - 0 \overset{?}{=} 8$ ✔ True   The ordered pair $(2, 0)$ is a solution.

b. $4x - 5y = 8$

$4(3) - 5(1) \overset{?}{=} 8$ Substitute $x = 3$ and $y = 1$.

$12 - 5 \neq 8$ The ordered pair $(3, 1)$ is *not* a solution.

c. $4x - 5y = 8$

$4(1) - 5\left(-\dfrac{4}{5}\right) \overset{?}{=} 8$ Substitute $x = 1$ and $y = -\dfrac{4}{5}$.

$4 + 4 \overset{?}{=} 8$ ✔ True   The ordered pair $\left(1, -\dfrac{4}{5}\right)$ is a solution.

2. Graphing Linear Equations in Two Variables by Plotting Points

In this section, we will graph linear equations in two variables.

The Graph of an Equation in Two Variables

The graph of an equation in two variables is the graph of all ordered pair solutions to the equation.

The word *linear* means "relating to or resembling a line." It is not surprising then that the solution set for any linear equation in two variables forms a line in a rectangular coordinate system. Because two points determine a line, to graph a linear equation it is sufficient to find two solution points and draw the line between them. We will find three solution points and use the third point as a check point. This process is demonstrated in Example 2.

Answers

1. No   **2.** Yes   **3.** Yes

Example 2 Graphing a Linear Equation

Graph the equation $x - 2y = 8$.

Solution:

We will find three ordered pairs that are solutions to $x - 2y = 8$. To find the ordered pairs choose arbitrary values of x or of y. Three choices are recorded in the table. To complete the table, individually substitute each choice into the equation and solve for the remaining variable. The substituted value and the solution to the equation form an ordered pair.

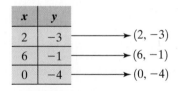

x	y
2	
	−1
0	

→ (2,   )
→ (, −1)
→ (0,   )

TIP: When choosing an arbitrary value for a variable, try to choose values that are convenient to graph. For example, we could let $x = 1000$ and solve for y. However, then we would need a very large graph or a large scale on the axes.

From the first row, substitute $x = 2$:

$$x - 2y = 8$$
$$(2) - 2y = 8$$
$$-2y = 8 - 2$$
$$-2y = 6$$
$$y = -3$$

From the second row, substitute $y = -1$:

$$x - 2y = 8$$
$$x - 2(-1) = 8$$
$$x + 2 = 8$$
$$x = 8 - 2$$
$$x = 6$$

From the third row, substitute $x = 0$:

$$x - 2y = 8$$
$$(0) - 2y = 8$$
$$-2y = 8$$
$$y = -4$$

The completed table is shown with the corresponding ordered pairs.

x	y
2	−3
6	−1
0	−4

→ (2, −3)
→ (6, −1)
→ (0, −4)

To graph the equation, plot the three solutions and draw the line through the points (Figure 3-6).

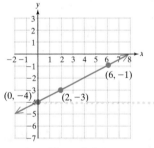

Figure 3-6

In Example 2, the original values for x and y given in the table were chosen arbitrarily by the authors. It is important to note, however, that once you choose an arbitrary value for x, the corresponding y value is determined by the equation. Similarly, once you choose an arbitrary value for y, the x value is determined by the equation.

Skill Practice

Graph the equation.
4. $2x + y = 6$

Avoiding Mistakes

Only two points are needed to graph a line. However, in Example 2, we found a third ordered pair, $(0, -4)$. Notice that this point "lines up" with the other two points. If the three points do not line up, then we know that a mistake was made in solving for at least one of the ordered pairs.

Answer

4.

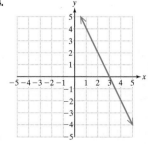

Skill Practice

Graph the equation.

5. $2x + 3y = 12$

Example 3 Graphing a Linear Equation

Graph the equation $4x + 3y = 15$.

Solution:

We will find three ordered pairs that are solutions to the equation $4x + 3y = 15$. In the table, we have selected arbitrary values for x and y and must complete the ordered pairs. Notice that in this case, we are choosing zero for x and zero for y to illustrate that the resulting equation is often easy to solve.

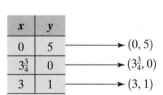

x	y
0	
	0
3	

→ $(0, \ )$
→ $(\ , 0)$
→ $(3, \ )$

From the first row, substitute $x = 0$:	From the second row, substitute $y = 0$:	From the third row, substitute $x = 3$:
$4x + 3y = 15$	$4x + 3y = 15$	$4x + 3y = 15$
$4(0) + 3y = 15$	$4x + 3(0) = 15$	$4(3) + 3y = 15$
$3y = 15$	$4x = 15$	$12 + 3y = 15$
$y = 5$	$x = \dfrac{15}{4} \text{ or } 3\dfrac{3}{4}$	$3y = 3$
		$y = 1$

Avoiding Mistakes

The substituted value is one coordinate of the ordered pair. The solution to the equation is the other coordinate.

The completed table is shown with the corresponding ordered pairs.

x	y
0	5
$3\frac{3}{4}$	0
3	1

→ $(0, 5)$
→ $(3\frac{3}{4}, 0)$
→ $(3, 1)$

To graph the equation, plot the three solutions and draw the line through the points (Figure 3-7).

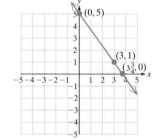

Figure 3-7

Example 4 Graphing a Linear Equation

Graph the equation $y = -\dfrac{1}{3}x + 1$.

Answer

5.

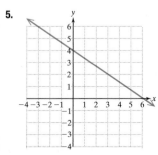

Solution:

Because the y variable is isolated in the equation, it is easy to substitute a value for x and simplify the right-hand side to find y. Since any number can be chosen for x, select numbers that are multiples of 3. These will simplify easily when multiplied by $-\frac{1}{3}$.

x	y	
3		⟶ (3,)
0		⟶ (0,)
−3		⟶ (−3,)

$$y = -\frac{1}{3}x + 1$$

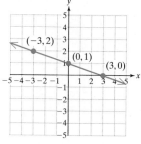

Let x = 3:	Let x = 0:	Let x = −3:
$y = -\frac{1}{3}(3) + 1$	$y = -\frac{1}{3}(0) + 1$	$y = -\frac{1}{3}(-3) + 1$
$y = -1 + 1$	$y = 0 + 1$	$y = 1 + 1$
$y = 0$	$y = 1$	$y = 2$

x	y	
3	0	⟶ (3, 0)
0	1	⟶ (0, 1)
−3	2	⟶ (−3, 2)

The line through the three ordered pairs $(3, 0)$, $(0, 1)$, and $(-3, 2)$ is shown in Figure 3-8. The line represents the set of all solutions to the equation $y = -\frac{1}{3}x + 1$.

Figure 3-8

3. *x*- and *y*-Intercepts

The *x*- and *y*-intercepts are the points where the graph intersects the *x*- and *y*-axes, respectively. From Example 4, we see that the *x*-intercept is at the point $(3, 0)$ and the *y*-intercept is at the point $(0, 1)$. See Figure 3-8. Notice that a *y*-intercept is a point on the *y*-axis and must have an *x*-coordinate of 0. Likewise, an *x*-intercept is a point on the *x*-axis and must have a *y*-coordinate of 0.

> **Definitions of *x*- and *y*-Intercepts**
>
> An ***x*-intercept** of a graph is a point $(a, 0)$ where the graph intersects the *x*-axis.
>
> A ***y*-intercept** of a graph is a point $(0, b)$ where the graph intersects the *y*-axis.

In some applications, an *x*-intercept is defined as the *x*-coordinate of a point of intersection that a graph makes with the *x*-axis. For example, if an *x*-intercept is at the point $(3, 0)$, it is sometimes stated simply as 3 (the *y*-coordinate is assumed to be 0). Similarly, a *y*-intercept is sometimes defined as the *y*-coordinate of a point of intersection that a graph makes with the *y*-axis. For example, if a *y*-intercept is at the point $(0, 7)$, it may be stated simply as 7 (the *x*-coordinate is assumed to be 0).

Although any two points may be used to graph a line, in some cases it is convenient to use the *x*- and *y*-intercepts of the line. To find the *x*- and *y*-intercepts of any two-variable equation in *x* and *y*, follow these steps:

> **Finding *x*- and *y*-Intercepts**
>
> **Step 1** Find the *x*-intercept(s) by substituting $y = 0$ into the equation and solving for *x*.
>
> **Step 2** Find the *y*-intercept(s) by substituting $x = 0$ into the equation and solving for *y*.

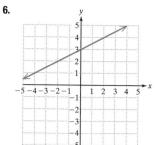

Example 5 Finding the x- and y-Intercepts of a Line

Given the equation $-3x + 2y = 8$,

a. Find the x-intercept.

b. Find the y-intercept.

c. Graph the equation.

Solution:

a. To find the x-intercept, substitute $y = 0$.

$$-3x + 2y = 8$$
$$-3x + 2(0) = 8$$
$$-3x = 8$$
$$\frac{-3x}{-3} = \frac{8}{-3}$$
$$x = -\frac{8}{3}$$

The x-intercept is $\left(-\frac{8}{3}, 0\right)$.

b. To find the y-intercept, substitute $x = 0$.

$$-3x + 2y = 8$$
$$-3(0) + 2y = 8$$
$$2y = 8$$
$$y = 4$$

The y-intercept is $(0, 4)$.

c. The line through the ordered pairs $\left(-\frac{8}{3}, 0\right)$ and $(0, 4)$ is shown in Figure 3-9. Note that the point $\left(-\frac{8}{3}, 0\right)$ can be written as $\left(-2\frac{2}{3}, 0\right)$.

The line represents the set of all solutions to the equation $-3x + 2y = 8$.

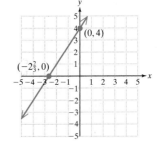

Figure 3-9

Example 6 Finding the x- and y-Intercepts of a Line

Given the equation $4x + 5y = 0$,

a. Find the x-intercept.

b. Find the y-intercept.

c. Graph the equation.

Solution:

a. To find the x-intercept, substitute $y = 0$.

$$4x + 5y = 0$$
$$4x + 5(0) = 0$$
$$4x = 0$$
$$x = 0$$

The x-intercept is $(0, 0)$.

b. To find the y-intercept, substitute $x = 0$.

$$4x + 5y = 0$$
$$4(0) + 5y = 0$$
$$5y = 0$$
$$y = 0$$

The y-intercept is $(0, 0)$.

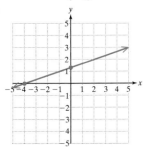

c. Because the *x*-intercept and the *y*-intercept are the same point (the origin), one or more additional points are needed to graph the line. In the table, we have arbitrarily selected additional values for *x* and *y* to find two more points on the line.

x	*y*
−5	
	2

Skill Practice

Given the equation
$2x - 3y = 0$,

10. Find the *x*-intercept.

11. Find the *y*-intercept.

12. Graph the equation. (*Hint:* You may need to find an additional point.)

Let $x = -5$: $4x + 5y = 0$

$4(-5) + 5y = 0$

$-20 + 5y = 0$

$5y = 20$

$y = 4$

$(-5, 4)$ is a solution.

Let $y = 2$: $4x + 5y = 0$

$4x + 5(2) = 0$

$4x + 10 = 0$

$4x = -10$

$x = -\dfrac{10}{4}$

$x = -\dfrac{5}{2}$

$\left(\dfrac{-5}{2}, 2\right)$ is a solution.

The line through the ordered pairs $(0, 0)$, $(-5, 4)$, and $(-\frac{5}{2}, 2)$ is shown in Figure 3-10. Note that the point $(-\frac{5}{2}, 2)$ can be written as $(-2\frac{1}{2}, 2)$.

The line represents the set of all solutions to the equation $4x + 5y = 0$.

x	*y*
−5	4
$-\frac{5}{2}$	2
0	0

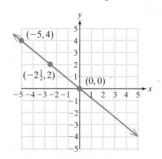

Figure 3-10

Avoiding Mistakes

Do not try to graph a line with only one point. At least two different points are needed.

4. Horizontal and Vertical Lines

Recall that a linear equation can be written in the form of $Ax + By = C$, where A and B are not both zero. However, if A or B is 0, then the line is either horizontal or vertical. A horizontal line either lies on the *x*-axis or is parallel to the *x*-axis. A vertical line either lies on the *y*-axis or is parallel to the *y*-axis.

Answers

10. (0, 0)   **11.** (0, 0)

12.

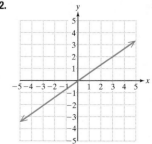

Equations of Vertical and Horizontal Lines

1. A **vertical line** can be represented by an equation of the form, $x = k$, where k is a constant.

2. A **horizontal line** can be represented by an equation of the form, $y = k$, where k is a constant.

Example 7 Graphing a Horizontal Line

Graph the equation $y = 3$.

Solution:

Because this equation is in the form $y = k$, the line is horizontal and must cross the y-axis at $y = 3$ (Figure 3-11).

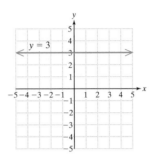

Figure 3-11

Alternative Solution:

Create a table of values for the equation $y = 3$. The choice for the y-coordinate must be 3, but x can be any real number.

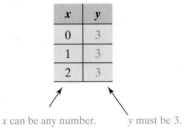

x	y
0	3
1	3
2	3

x can be any number. y must be 3.

TIP: Notice that a horizontal line has a y-intercept, but does not have an x-intercept (unless the horizontal line is the x-axis itself).

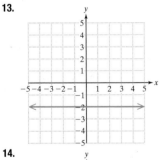
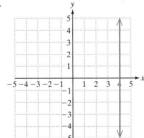
Example 8 Graphing a Vertical Line

Graph the equation $4x = -8$.

Solution:

Because the equation does not have a y variable, we can solve the equation for x.

$4x = -8$ is equivalent to $x = -2$

This equation is in the form $x = k$, indicating that the line is vertical and must cross the x-axis at $x = -2$ (Figure 3-12).

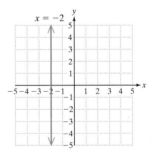

Figure 3-12

Alternative Solution:

Create a table of values for the equation $x = -2$. The choice for the x-coordinate must be -2, but y can be any real number.

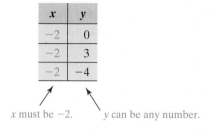

x	y
-2	0
-2	3
-2	-4

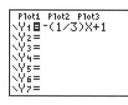

x must be -2. y can be any number.

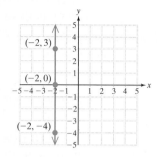

TIP: Notice that a vertical line has an x-intercept but does not have a y-intercept (unless the vertical line is the y-axis itself).

Calculator Connections

Topic: Graphing Linear Equations on an Appropriate Viewing Window

A viewing window of a graphing calculator shows a portion of a rectangular coordinate system. The standard viewing window for many calculators shows the x-axis between -10 and 10 and the y-axis between -10 and 10 (Figure 3-13). Furthermore, the scale defined by the "tick" marks on both the x- and y-axes is usually set to 1.

The "Standard Viewing Window"

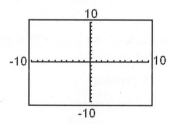

Figure 3-13

To graph an equation in x and y on a graphing calculator, the equation must be written with the y-variable isolated. For example, to graph the equation $x + 3y = 3$, we solve for y by applying the steps for solving a literal equation. The result, $y = -\frac{1}{3}x + 1$, can now be entered into a graphing calculator. To enter the equation $y = -\frac{1}{3}x + 1$ use parentheses around the fraction $\frac{1}{3}$. The *Graph* option displays the graph of the line.

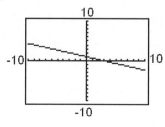

Sometimes the standard viewing window does not provide an adequate display for the graph of an equation. For example, the graph of $y = -x + 15$ is visible only in a small portion of the upper right corner of the standard viewing window.

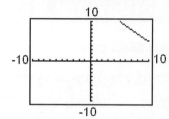

To see where this line crosses the x- and y-axes, we can change the viewing window to accommodate larger values of x and y. Most calculators have a *Range* feature or *Window* feature that allows the user to change the minimum and maximum x and y values.

To get a better picture of the equation $y = -x + 15$, change the minimum x value to -10 and the maximum x value to 20. Similarly, use a minimum y value of -10 and a maximum y value of 20.

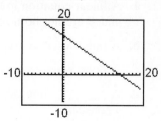

Calculator Exercises

For Exercises 1–8, graph the equations on the standard viewing window.

1. $y = -2x + 5$ **2.** $y = 3x - 1$

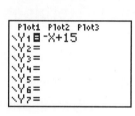

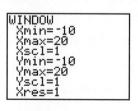

3. $y = \dfrac{1}{2}x - \dfrac{7}{2}$

4. $y = -\dfrac{3}{4}x + \dfrac{5}{3}$

5. $4x - 7y = 21$

6. $2x + 3y = 12$

7. $-3x - 4y = 6$

8. $-5x + 4y = 10$

For Exercises 9–12, graph the equations on the given viewing window.

9. $y = 3x + 15$

Window: $-10 \le x \le 10$
$-5 \le y \le 20$

10. $y = -2x - 25$

Window: $-30 \le x \le 30$
$-30 \le y \le 30$

Xscl = 3 (sets the x-axis tick marks to increments of 3)

Yscl = 3 (sets the y-axis tick marks to increments of 3)

11. $y = -0.2x + 0.04$

Window: $-0.1 \le x \le 0.3$
$-0.1 \le y \le 0.1$

Xscl = 0.01 (sets the x-axis tick marks to increments of 0.01)

Yscl = 0.01 (sets the y-axis tick marks to increments of 0.01)

12. $y = 0.3x - 0.5$

Window: $-1 \le x \le 3$
$-1 \le y \le 1$

Xscl = 0.1 (sets the x-axis tick marks to increments of 0.1)

Yscl = 0.1 (sets the y-axis tick marks to increments of 0.1)

Section 3.2 Practice Exercises

Study Skills Exercise

Check your progress by answering these questions.

Yes _____ No _____   Did you have sufficient time to study for the test on Chapter 2? If not, what could you have done to create more time for studying?

Yes _____ No _____   Did you work all of the assigned homework problems in Chapter 2?

Yes _____ No _____   If you encountered difficulty, did you see your instructor or tutor for help?

Yes _____ No _____   Have you taken advantage of the textbook supplements such as the *Student Solutions Manual*?

Vocabulary and Key Concepts

1. **a.** A linear equation in two variables is an equation that can be written in the form _____ , where A and B are not both zero.

    b. A point where a graph intersects the x-axis is called a(n) _____ .

    c. A point where a graph intersects the y-axis is called a(n) _____ .

    d. A _____ line can be represented by an equation of the form $x = k$, where k is a constant.

    e. A _____ line can be represented by an equation of the form $y = k$, where k is a constant.

Review Exercises

For Exercises 2–8, refer to the figure to give the coordinates of the labeled points, and state the quadrant or axis where the point is located.

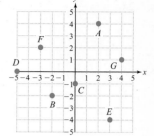

2. A

3. B

4. C

5. D

6. E

7. F

8. G

Concept 1: Definition of a Linear Equation in Two Variables

For Exercises 9–17, determine whether the given ordered pair is a solution to the equation. **(See Example 1.)**

9. $x - y = 6$; $(8, 2)$

10. $y = 3x - 2$; $(1, 1)$

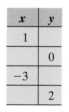 **11.** $y = -\dfrac{1}{3}x + 3$; $(-3, 4)$

12. $y = -\dfrac{5}{2}x + 5$; $\left(\dfrac{4}{5}, -3\right)$

13. $4x + 5y = 20$; $\left(\dfrac{1}{4}, -\dfrac{2}{5}\right)$

14. $y = 7$; $(0, 7)$

15. $y = -2$; $(-2, 6)$

16. $x = 1$; $(0, 1)$

17. $x = -5$; $(-5, 6)$

Concept 2: Graphing Linear Equations in Two Variables by Plotting Points

For Exercises 18–31, complete each table, and graph the corresponding ordered pairs. Draw the line defined by the points to represent all solutions to the equation. **(See Examples 2–4.)**

18. $x + y = 3$

x	y
2	
	3
−1	
	0

19. $x + y = -2$

x	y
1	
	0
−3	
	2

20. $y = 5x + 1$

x	y
1	
	1
−1	

21. $y = -3x - 3$

x	y
−2	
	0
−4	

22. $2x - 3y = 6$

x	y
0	
	0
2	

23. $4x + 2y = 8$

x	y
0	
	0
3	

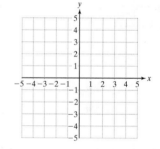
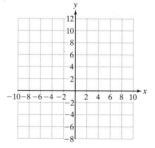
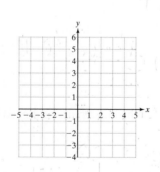
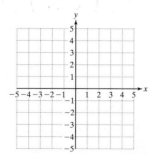
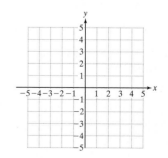

24. $y = \frac{2}{7}x - 5$

x	y
7	
-7	
0	

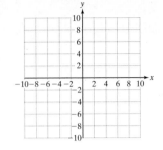

25. $y = -\frac{3}{5}x - 2$

x	y
0	
5	
10	

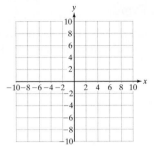

26. $y = 3$

x	y
2	
0	
-1	

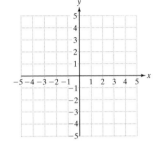

27. $y = -2$

x	y
0	
-3	
5	

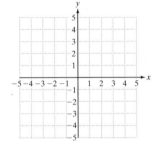

28. $x = -4$

x	y
	1
	-2
	4

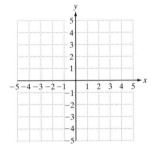

29. $x = \frac{3}{2}$

x	y
	-1
	2
	-3

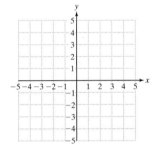

30. $y = -3.4x + 5.8$

x	y
0	
1	
2	

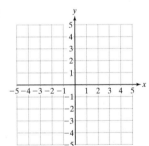

31. $y = -1.2x + 4.6$

x	y
0	
1	
2	

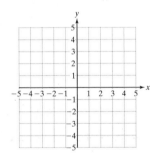

For Exercises 32–43, graph the lines by making a table of at least three ordered pairs and plotting the points.

32. $x - y = 2$

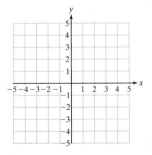

33. $x - y = 4$

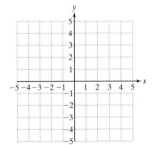

34. $-3x + y = -6$

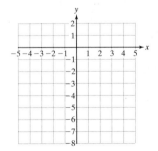

35. $2x - 5y = 10$

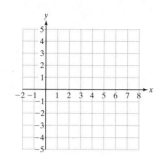

36. $y = 4x$

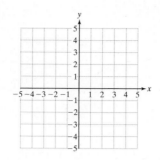

37. $y = -2x$

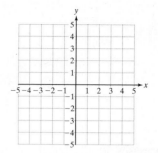

38. $y = -\dfrac{1}{2}x + 3$

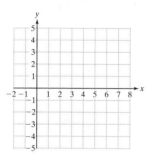

39. $y = \dfrac{1}{4}x - 2$

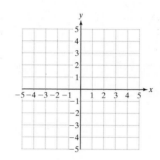

40. $x + y = 0$

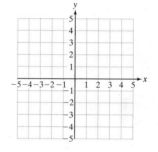

41. $-x + y = 0$

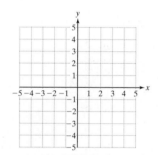

42. $50x - 40y = 200$

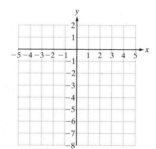

43. $-30x - 20y = 60$

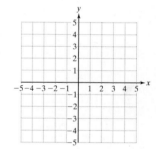

Concept 3: *x*- and *y*-Intercepts

44. The *x*-intercept is on which axis?

45. The *y*-intercept is on which axis?

For Exercises 46–49, estimate the coordinates of the *x*- and *y*-intercepts.

46.

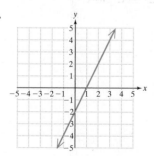

47.

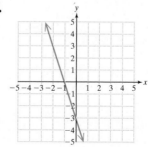

48.

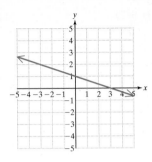

49.

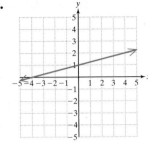

For Exercises 50–61, find the *x*- and *y*-intercepts (if they exist), and graph the line. **(See Examples 5 and 6.)**

50. $5x + 2y = 5$

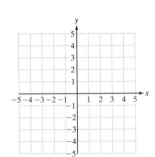

51. $4x - 3y = -9$

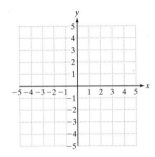

52. $y = \dfrac{2}{3}x - 1$

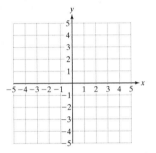

53. $y = -\dfrac{3}{4}x + 2$

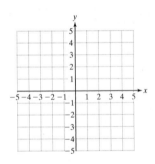

54. $x - 3 = y$

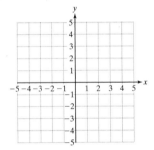

55. $2x + 8 = y$

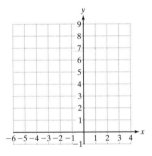

56. $-3x + y = 0$

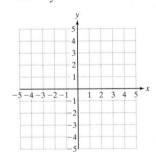

57. $2x - 2y = 0$

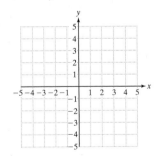

58. $25y = 10x + 100$

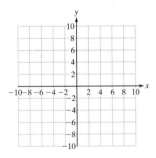

59. $20x = -40y + 200$

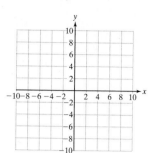

60. $x = 2y$

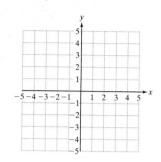

61. $x = -5y$

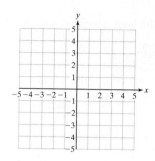

Concept 4: Horizontal and Vertical Lines

For Exercises 62–65, answer true or false. If the statement is false, rewrite it to be true.

62. The line defined by $x = 3$ is horizontal.

63. The line defined by $y = -4$ is horizontal.

64. A line parallel to the y-axis is vertical.

65. A line parallel to the x-axis is horizontal.

For Exercises 66–74,

a. Identify the equation as representing a horizontal or vertical line.

b. Graph the line.

c. Identify the x- and y-intercepts if they exist. **(See Examples 7 and 8.)**

66. $x = 3$

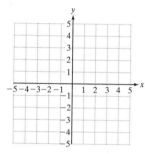

67. $y = -1$

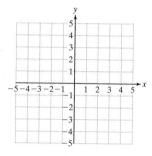

68. $-2y = 8$

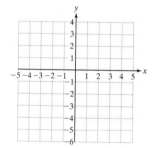

69. $5x = 20$

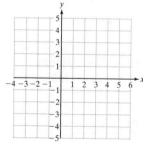

70. $x + 3 = 7$

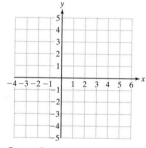

71. $y - 8 = -13$

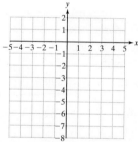

72. $3y = 0$

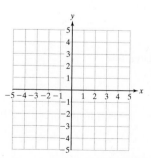

73. $5x = 0$

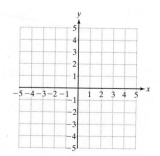

74. $2x + 7 = 10$

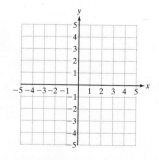

75. Explain why not every line has both an x- and a y-intercept.

76. Which of the lines has an x-intercept?

a. $2x - 3y = 6$ **b.** $x = 5$ **c.** $2y = 8$ **d.** $-x + y = 0$

77. Which of the lines has a y-intercept?

a. $y = 2$ **b.** $x + y = 0$ **c.** $2x - 10 = 2$ **d.** $x + 4y = 8$

Expanding Your Skills

78. The store "CDs R US" sells all compact disks for $13.99. The following equation represents the revenue, y, (in dollars) generated by selling x CDs.

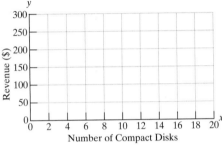

$$y = 13.99x \quad (x \geq 0)$$

a. Find y when $x = 13$.

b. Find x when $y = 279.80$.

c. Write the ordered pairs from parts (a) and (b), and interpret their meaning in the context of the problem.

d. Graph the ordered pairs and the line defined by the points.

79. The value of a car depreciates once it is driven off of the dealer's lot. For a Hyundai Accent, the value of the car is given by the equation $y = -1531x + 11{,}599 \ (x \geq 0)$ where y is the value of the car in dollars x years after its purchase. (*Source: Kelly Blue Book*)

a. Find y when $x = 1$.

b. Find x when $y = 7006$.

c. Write the ordered pairs from parts (a) and (b), and interpret their meaning in the context of the problem.

Section 3.3 Slope of a Line and Rate of Change

Concepts

1. Introduction to Slope
2. Slope Formula
3. Parallel and Perpendicular Lines
4. Applications of Slope: Rate of Change

1. Introduction to Slope

The x- and y-intercepts represent the points where a line crosses the x- and y-axes. Another important feature of a line is its slope. Geometrically, the slope of a line measures the "steepness" of the line. For example, two hiking trails are depicted by the lines in Figure 3-14.

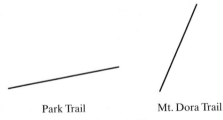

Park Trail   Mt. Dora Trail

Figure 3-14

By visual inspection, Mt. Dora Trail is "steeper" than Park Trail. To measure the slope of a line quantitatively, consider two points on the line. The **slope** of the line is the ratio of the vertical change (change in y) between the two points and the horizontal change (change in x). As a memory device, we might think of the slope of a line as "rise over run." See Figure 3-15.

$$\text{Slope} = \frac{\text{change in } y}{\text{change in } x} = \frac{\text{rise}}{\text{run}}$$

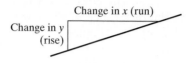

Figure 3-15

To move from point A to point B on Park Trail, rise 2 ft and move to the right 6 ft (Figure 3-16).

To move from point A to point B on Mt. Dora Trail, rise 12 ft and move to the right 6 ft (Figure 3-17).

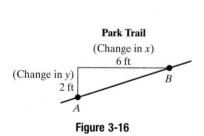

Figure 3-16

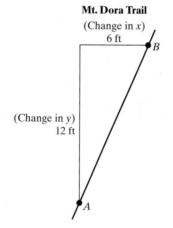

Figure 3-17

$$\text{Slope} = \frac{\text{change in } y}{\text{change in } x} = \frac{2 \text{ ft}}{6 \text{ ft}} = \frac{1}{3}$$

$$\text{Slope} = \frac{\text{change in } y}{\text{change in } x} = \frac{12 \text{ ft}}{6 \text{ ft}} = \frac{2}{1} = 2$$

The slope of Mt. Dora Trail is greater than the slope of Park Trail, confirming the observation that Mt. Dora Trail is steeper. On Mt. Dora Trail there is a 12-ft change in elevation for every 6 ft of horizontal distance (a 2:1 ratio). On Park Trail there is only a 2-ft change in elevation for every 6 ft of horizontal distance (a 1:3 ratio).

Example 1   **Finding Slope in an Application**

Determine the slope of the ramp up the stairs.

Solution:

$$\text{Slope} = \frac{\text{change in } y}{\text{change in } x} = \frac{8 \text{ ft}}{16 \text{ ft}}$$

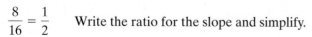

$$\frac{8}{16} = \frac{1}{2} \quad \text{Write the ratio for the slope and simplify.}$$

The slope is $\frac{1}{2}$.

Skill Practice

1. Determine the slope of the aircraft's takeoff path.

Answer

1. $\dfrac{500}{6000} = \dfrac{1}{12}$

2. Slope Formula

The slope of a line may be found using any two points on the line—call these points (x_1, y_1) and (x_2, y_2). The change in y between the points can be found by taking the difference of the y values: $y_2 - y_1$. The change in x can be found by taking the difference of the x values in the same order: $x_2 - x_1$ (Figure 3-18).

The slope of a line is often symbolized by the letter m and is given by the following formula.

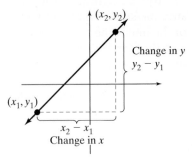

Figure 3-18

> ### Slope Formula
> The **slope** of a line passing through the distinct points (x_1, y_1) and (x_2, y_2) is
>
> $$m = \frac{y_2 - y_1}{x_2 - x_1} \quad \text{provided } x_2 - x_1 \neq 0.$$
>
> *Note:* If $x_2 - x_1 = 0$, the slope is undefined.

Skill Practice

Find the slope of the line through the given points.

2. $(-5, 2)$ and $(1, 3)$

Avoiding Mistakes

When calculating slope, always write the change in y in the numerator.

Example 2   Finding the Slope of a Line Given Two Points

Find the slope of the line through the points $(-1, 3)$ and $(-4, -2)$.

Solution:

To use the slope formula, first label the coordinates of each point and then substitute the coordinates into the slope formula.

$$\underset{(x_1, y_1)}{(-1, 3)} \quad \text{and} \quad \underset{(x_2, y_2)}{(-4, -2)} \qquad \text{Label the points.}$$

$$m = \frac{y_2 - y_1}{x_2 - x_1} = \frac{(-2) - (3)}{(-4) - (-1)} \qquad \text{Apply the slope formula.}$$

$$= \frac{-5}{-3}$$

$$= \frac{5}{3} \qquad \text{Simplify to lowest terms.}$$

The slope of the line can be verified from the graph (Figure 3-19).

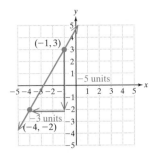

Figure 3-19

Answer

2. $\dfrac{1}{6}$

TIP: The slope formula is not dependent on which point is labeled (x_1, y_1) and which point is labeled (x_2, y_2). In Example 2, reversing the order in which the points are labeled results in the same slope.

$$\underset{(x_2,\,y_2)}{(-1, 3)} \quad \text{and} \quad \underset{(x_1,\,y_1)}{(-4, -2)} \qquad \text{Label the points.}$$

$$m = \frac{(3) - (-2)}{(-1) - (-4)} = \frac{5}{3} \qquad \text{Apply the slope formula.}$$

When you apply the slope formula, you will see that the slope of a line may be positive, negative, zero, or undefined.

- Lines that increase, or rise, from left to right have a positive slope.
- Lines that decrease, or fall, from left to right have a negative slope.
- Horizontal lines have a slope of zero.
- Vertical lines have an undefined slope.

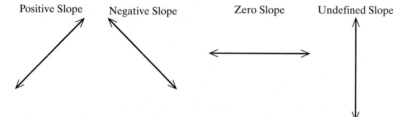

Positive Slope   Negative Slope   Zero Slope   Undefined Slope

---

Example 3   Finding the Slope of a Line Given Two Points

Find the slope of the line passing through the points $(-5, \frac{1}{2})$ and $(2, -\frac{3}{2})$.

Solution:

$$\underset{(x_1,\,y_1)}{\left(-5, \frac{1}{2}\right)} \quad \text{and} \quad \underset{(x_2,\,y_2)}{\left(2, -\frac{3}{2}\right)} \qquad \text{Label the points.}$$

$$m = \frac{y_2 - y_1}{x_2 - x_1} = \frac{\left(-\frac{3}{2}\right) - \left(\frac{1}{2}\right)}{(2) - (-5)} \qquad \text{Apply the slope formula.}$$

$$= \frac{-\frac{4}{2}}{2 + 5} \qquad \text{Simplify.}$$

$$= \frac{-2}{7} \quad \text{or} \quad -\frac{2}{7}$$

By graphing the points $(-5, \frac{1}{2})$ and $(2, -\frac{3}{2})$, we can verify that the slope is $-\frac{2}{7}$ (Figure 3-20). Notice that the line slopes downward from left to right.

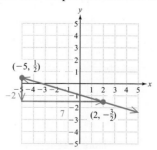

$\left(-5, \frac{1}{2}\right)$

$\left(2, -\frac{3}{2}\right)$

Figure 3-20

Skill Practice

Find the slope of the line through the given points.

3. $\left(\frac{2}{3}, 0\right)$ and $\left(-\frac{1}{6}, 5\right)$

Avoiding Mistakes

When applying the slope formula, y_2 and x_2 are taken from the same ordered pair. Likewise y_1 and x_1 are taken from the same ordered pair.

Answer

3. -6

Example 4 Determining the Slope of a Vertical Line

Find the slope of the line passing through the points $(2, -1)$ and $(2, 4)$.

Solution:

$$\underset{(x_1, y_1)}{(2, -1)} \quad \text{and} \quad \underset{(x_2, y_2)}{(2, 4)} \qquad \text{Label the points.}$$

$$m = \frac{y_2 - y_1}{x_2 - x_1} = \frac{(4) - (-1)}{(2) - (2)} \qquad \text{Apply the slope formula.}$$

$$m = \frac{5}{0} \quad \text{Undefined}$$

Because the slope, m, is undefined, we expect the points to form a vertical line as shown in Figure 3-21.

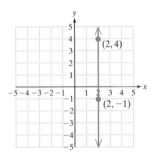

Figure 3-21

Example 5 Determine the Slope of a Horizontal Line

Find the slope of the line passing through the points $(3, -2)$ and $(-4, -2)$.

Solution:

$$\underset{(x_1, y_1)}{(3, -2)} \quad \text{and} \quad \underset{(x_2, y_2)}{(-4, -2)} \qquad \text{Label the points.}$$

$$m = \frac{y_2 - y_1}{x_2 - x_1} = \frac{(-2) - (-2)}{(-4) - (3)} \qquad \text{Apply the slope formula.}$$

$$m = \frac{-2 + 2}{-4 - 3} = \frac{0}{-7} = 0$$

Because the slope is 0, we expect the points to form a horizontal line, as shown in Figure 3-22.

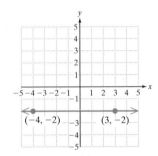

Figure 3-22

3. Parallel and Perpendicular Lines

Lines in the same plane that do not intersect are called **parallel lines**. Parallel lines have the same slope and different *y*-intercepts (Figure 3-23).

   Lines that intersect at a right angle are **perpendicular lines**. If two lines are perpendicular then the slope of one line is the opposite of the reciprocal of the slope of the other line (provided neither line is vertical) (Figure 3-24).

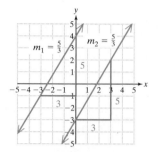

Figure 3-23

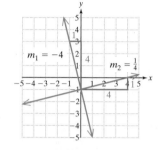

Figure 3-24

Slopes of Parallel Lines

If m_1 and m_2 represent the slopes of two parallel (nonvertical) lines, then

$$m_1 = m_2.$$

See Figure 3-23.

Slopes of Perpendicular Lines

If $m_1 \neq 0$ and $m_2 \neq 0$ represent the slopes of two perpendicular lines, then

$$m_1 = -\frac{1}{m_2} \text{ or equivalently, } m_1 m_2 = -1.$$

See Figure 3-24.

Example 6   **Determining the Slope of Parallel and Perpendicular Lines**

Suppose a given line has a slope of -6.

a. Find the slope of a line parallel to the given line.

b. Find the slope of a line perpendicular to the given line.

Solution:

a. Parallel lines must have the same slope. The slope of a line parallel to the given line is $m = -6$.

b. Perpendicular lines must have opposite and reciprocal slopes. The slope of a line perpendicular to the given line is $m = +\dfrac{1}{6}$.

If the slopes of two lines are known, then we can compare the slopes to determine if the lines are parallel, perpendicular, or neither.

Example 7   Determining If Lines Are Parallel, Perpendicular, or Neither

Lines l_1 and l_2 pass through the given points. Determine if l_1 and l_2 are parallel, perpendicular, or neither.

l_1: $(2, -7)$ and $(4, 1)$ l_2: $(-3, 1)$ and $(1, 0)$

Solution:

Find the slope of each line.

l_1: $(2, -7)$ and $(4, 1)$ l_2: $(-3, 1)$ and $(1, 0)$
      (x_1, y_1) (x_2, y_2) (x_1, y_1) (x_2, y_2)

$$m_1 = \frac{1 - (-7)}{4 - 2}$$ $$m_2 = \frac{0 - 1}{1 - (-3)}$$

$$m_1 = \frac{8}{2}$$ $$m_2 = \frac{-1}{4}$$

$$m_1 = 4$$ $$m_2 = -\frac{1}{4}$$

One slope is the opposite of the reciprocal of the other slope. Therefore, the lines are perpendicular.

4. Applications of Slope: Rate of Change

In many applications, the interpretation of slope refers to the *rate of change* of the y value compared to the x value.

Example 8   Interpreting Slope in an Application

The annual median income for males in the United States for selected years is shown in Figure 3-25. The trend is approximately linear. Find the slope of the line and interpret the meaning of the slope in the context of the problem.

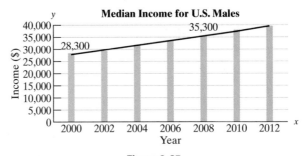

Figure 3-25

Source: U.S. Department of the Census

Solution:

To determine the slope we need to know two points on the line. From the graph, the median income for males in the year 2000 was approximately $28,300.

This gives us the ordered pair (2000, 28300). In the year 2008, the income was $35,300. This gives the ordered pair (2008, 35300).

$$(2000, 28300) \quad \text{and} \quad (2008, 35300)$$
$$\underset{(x_1,\, y_1)}{} \qquad\qquad \underset{(x_2,\, y_2)}{} \qquad \text{Label the points.}$$

$$m = \frac{y_2 - y_1}{x_2 - x_1} = \frac{35{,}300 - 28{,}300}{2008 - 2000} \qquad \text{Apply the slope formula.}$$

$$= \frac{7000}{8}$$

$$= 875 \qquad\qquad\qquad \text{Simplify.}$$

The slope is 875. This tells us the rate of change of the y value (income) compared to the x value (years). This means that men's median income in the United States increased at a rate of $875 per year during this time period.

Section 3.3 Practice Exercises

Study Skills Exercise

Each day after finishing your homework, choose two or three odd-numbered problems or examples from that section. Write the problem with the directions on one side of a 3 × 5 card. On the back write the section, page, and problem number along with the answer. Each week, shuffle your cards and pull out a few at random, to give yourself a review for $\frac{1}{2}$-hr or more.

Vocabulary and Key Concepts

1. **a.** The ratio of the vertical change and the horizontal change between two distinct points (x_1, y_1) and (x_2, y_2) on a line is called the _____ of the line. The slope can be computed from the formula $m =$ _____.

   b. Lines in the same plane that do not intersect are called _____ lines.

   c. Two lines are perpendicular if they intersect at a _____ angle.

   d. If m_1 and m_2 represent the slopes of two nonvertical perpendicular lines then $m_1 \cdot m_2 =$ _____.

   e. The slope of a vertical line is _____. The slope of a _____ line is 0.

Review Exercises

For Exercises 2–6, find the x- and y-intercepts (if they exist). Then graph the line.

2. $x - 5 = 2$

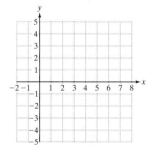

3. $x - 3y = 6$

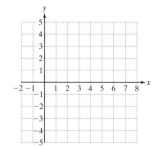

4. $y = \dfrac{2}{3}x$

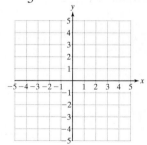

5. $2y - 3 = 0$

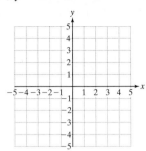

6. $2x = 4y$

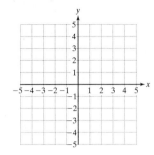

Concept 1: Introduction to Slope

7. Determine the pitch (slope) of the roof.
(See Example 1.)

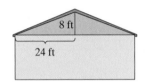

8. Determine the slope of the stairs.

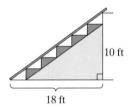

9. Calculate the slope of the handrail.

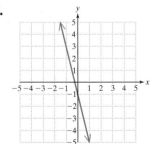

10. Determine the slope of the treadmill.

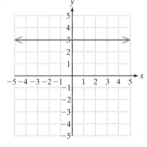

Concept 2: Slope Formula

For Exercises 11–14, fill in the blank with the appropriate term: *zero, negative, positive,* or *undefined.*

11. The slope of a line parallel to the *y*-axis is _____.

12. The slope of a horizontal line is ____.

13. The slope of a line that rises from left to right is _____.

14. The slope of a line that falls from left to right is _____.

For Exercises 15–23, determine if the slope is positive, negative, zero, or undefined.

15.

16.

17.

18.

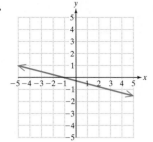

19.

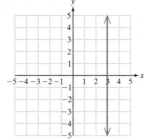

20.

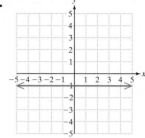

21.

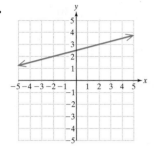

22.

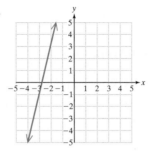

23.

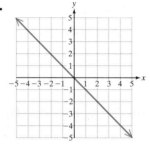

For Exercises 24–32, determine the slope by using the slope formula and any two points on the line. Check your answer by drawing a right triangle and labeling the "rise" and "run."

24.

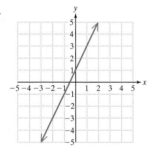

25.

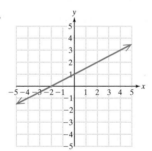

26.

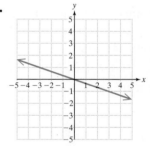

27.

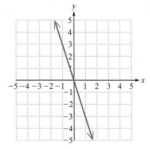

28.

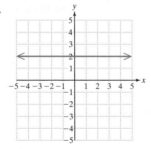

{width=0} **29.**

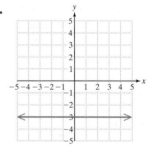

30.

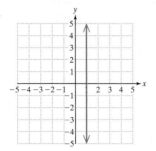

31.

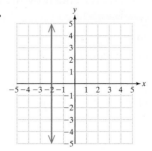

32.

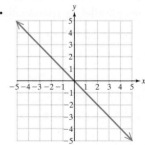

For Exercises 33–54, find the slope of the line that passes through the two points. **(See Examples 2–5.)**

33. $(2, 4)$ and $(-1, 3)$

34. $(0, 4)$ and $(3, 0)$

35. $(-2, 3)$ and $(-1, 0)$

36. $(-3, -4)$ and $(1, -5)$

37. $(1, 5)$ and $(-4, 2)$

38. $(-6, -1)$ and $(-2, -3)$

39. $(5, 3)$ and $(-2, 3)$

40. $(0, -1)$ and $(-4, -1)$

41. $(2, -7)$ and $(2, 5)$

42. $(-4, 3)$ and $(-4, -4)$

43. $\left(\frac{1}{2}, \frac{3}{5}\right)$ and $\left(\frac{1}{4}, -\frac{4}{5}\right)$

44. $\left(-\frac{2}{7}, \frac{1}{3}\right)$ and $\left(\frac{8}{7}, -\frac{5}{6}\right)$

45. $\left(-\frac{4}{3}, 3\right)$ and $\left(-\frac{1}{2}, -\frac{3}{4}\right)$

46. $\left(\frac{3}{2}, -\frac{1}{8}\right)$ and $\left(-2, \frac{2}{5}\right)$

47. $(3, -1)$ and $(-5, 6)$

48. $(-6, 5)$ and $(-10, 4)$

49. $(1.4, 0.5)$ and $(0.8, -1.3)$

50. $(0.25, -3.4)$ and $(0.23, -2.2)$

51. $(6.8, -3.4)$ and $(-3.2, 1.1)$

52. $(-3.15, 8.25)$ and $(6.85, -4.25)$

53. $(1994, 3.5)$ and $(2000, 2.6)$

54. $(1988, 4.65)$ and $(1998, 9.25)$

Concept 3: Parallel and Perpendicular Lines

For Exercises 55–60, the slope of a line is given. **(See Example 6.)**

a. Determine the slope of a line parallel to the given line.

b. Determine the slope of a line perpendicular to the given line.

55. $m = -2$

56. $m = \frac{2}{3}$

57. $m = 0$

58. The slope is undefined.

59. $m = \frac{4}{5}$

60. $m = -4$

For Exercises 61–66, let m_1 and m_2 represent the slopes of two lines. Determine if the lines are parallel, perpendicular, or neither. **(See Example 6.)**

61. $m_1 = -2$, $m_2 = \frac{1}{2}$

62. $m_1 = \frac{2}{3}$, $m_2 = \frac{3}{2}$

63. $m_1 = 1$, $m_2 = \frac{4}{4}$

64. $m_1 = \frac{3}{4}$, $m_2 = -\frac{8}{6}$

65. $m_1 = \frac{2}{7}$, $m_2 = -\frac{2}{7}$

66. $m_1 = 5$, $m_2 = 5$

For Exercises 67–72, find the slopes of the lines l_1 and l_2 defined by the two given points. Then determine whether l_1 and l_2 are parallel, perpendicular, or neither. **(See Example 7.)**

67. l_1: $(2, 4)$ and $(-1, -2)$
l_2: $(1, 7)$ and $(0, 5)$

68. l_1: $(0, 0)$ and $(-2, 4)$
l_2: $(1, -5)$ and $(-1, -1)$

69. l_1: $(1, 9)$ and $(0, 4)$
l_2: $(5, 2)$ and $(10, 1)$

70. l_1: $(3, -4)$ and $(-1, -8)$
l_2: $(5, -5)$ and $(-2, 2)$

71. l_1: $(4, 4)$ and $(0, 3)$
l_2: $(1, 7)$ and $(-1, -1)$

72. l_1: $(3, 5)$ and $(-2, -5)$
l_2: $(2, 0)$ and $(-4, -3)$

Concept 4: Applications of Slope: Rate of Change

73. For a recent year, the average earnings for male workers between the ages of 25 and 34 with a high school diploma was $32,000. Comparing this value in constant dollars to the average earnings 15 yr later showed that the average earnings have decreased to $29,600. Find the average rate of change in dollars per year. [*Hint:* Use the ordered pairs (0, 32000) and (15, 29600).]

74. In 1985, the U.S. Postal Service charged $0.22 for first class letters and cards up to 1 oz. By 2013, the price had increased to $0.46. Let *x* represent the year, and *y* represent the cost for 1 oz of first class postage. Find the average rate of change of the cost per year. Round to three decimal places.

75. In 1985, there were 539 thousand male inmates in federal and state prisons. By 2010, the number increased to 1714 thousand. Let *x* represent the year, and let *y* represent the number of prisoners (in thousands). **(See Example 8.)**

    a. Using the ordered pairs (1985, 539) and (2010, 1714), find the slope of the line.

    b. Interpret the slope in the context of this problem.

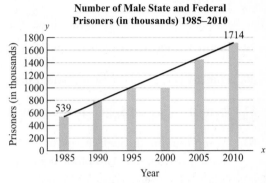

Number of Male State and Federal Prisoners (in thousands) 1985–2010

(*Source:* U.S. Bureau of Justice Statistics)

76. In the year 1985, there were 30 thousand female inmates in federal and state prisons. By 2010, the number increased to 120 thousand. Let *x* represent the year, and let *y* represent the number of prisoners (in thousands).

    a. Using the ordered pairs (1985, 30) and (2010, 120), find the slope of the line.

    b. Interpret the slope in the context of this problem.

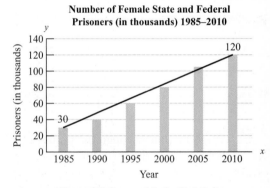

Number of Female State and Federal Prisoners (in thousands) 1985–2010

(*Source:* U.S. Bureau of Justice Statistics)

77. The distance, *d* (in miles), between a lightning strike and an observer is given by the equation $d = 0.2t$, where *t* is the time (in seconds) between seeing lightning and hearing thunder.

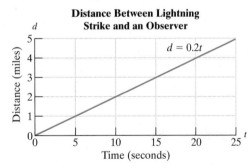

Distance Between Lightning Strike and an Observer

$d = 0.2t$

    a. If an observer counts 5 sec between seeing lightning and hearing thunder, how far away was the lightning strike?

    b. If an observer counts 10 sec between seeing lightning and hearing thunder, how far away was the lightning strike?

    c. If an observer counts 15 sec between seeing lightning and hearing thunder, how far away was the lightning strike?

    d. What is the slope of the line? Interpret the meaning of the slope in the context of this problem.

78. Michael wants to buy an efficient Smart car that according to the latest EPA standards gets 33 mpg in the city and 40 mpg on the highway. The car that Michael picked out costs \$12,600. His dad agreed to purchase the car if Michael would pay it off in equal monthly payments for the next 60 months. The equation $y = -210x + 12{,}600$ represents the amount, y (in dollars), that Michael owes his father after x months.

  a. How much does Michael owe his dad after 5 months?

  b. Determine the slope of the line and interpret its meaning in the context of this problem.

Mixed Exercises

For Exercises 79–82, determine the slope of the line passing through points A and B.

79. Point A is located 3 units up and 4 units to the right of point B.

80. Point A is located 2 units up and 5 units to the left of point B.

81. Point A is located 5 units to the right of point B.

82. Point A is located 3 units down from point B.

83. Graph the line through the point $(1, -2)$ having slope $-\frac{2}{3}$. Then give two other points on the line.

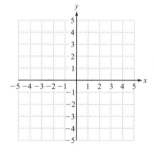

84. Graph the line through the point $(1, 2)$ having slope $-\frac{3}{4}$. Then give two other points on the line.

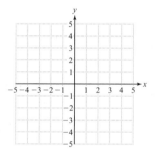

85. Graph the line through the point $(2, 2)$ having slope 3. Then give two other points on the line.

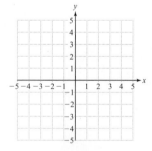

86. Graph the line through the point $(-1, 3)$ having slope 2. Then give two other points on the line.

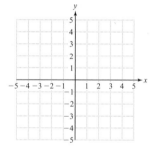

87. Graph the line through $(-3, -2)$ with an undefined slope. Then give two other points on the line.

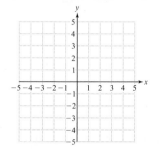

88. Graph the line through $(3, 3)$ with a slope of 0. Then give two other points on the line.

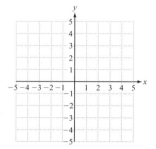

For Exercises 89–94, draw a line as indicated. Answers may vary.

89. Draw a line with a positive slope and a positive *y*-intercept.

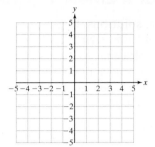

90. Draw a line with a positive slope and a negative *y*-intercept.

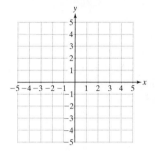

91. Draw a line with a negative slope and a negative *y*-intercept.

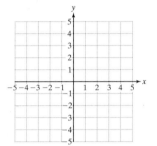

92. Draw a line with a negative slope and a positive *y*-intercept.

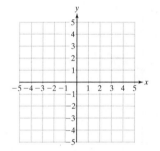

93. Draw a line with a zero slope and a positive *y*-intercept.

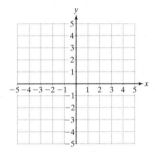

94. Draw a line with undefined slope and a negative *x*-intercept.

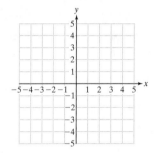

Expanding Your Skills

95. Determine the slope between the points $(a + b, 4m - n)$ and $(a - b, m + 2n)$.

96. Determine the slope between the points $(3c - d, s + t)$ and $(c - 2d, s - t)$.

97. Determine the *x*-intercept of the line $ax + by = c$.

98. Determine the *y*-intercept of the line $ax + by = c$.

99. Find another point on the line that contains the point $(2, -1)$ and has a slope of $\frac{2}{5}$.

100. Find another point on the line that contains the point $(-3, 4)$ and has a slope of $\frac{1}{4}$.

Section 3.4 Slope-Intercept Form of a Linear Equation

1. Slope-Intercept Form of a Linear Equation

In Section 3.2, we learned that the solutions to an equation of the form $Ax + By = C$ (where A and B are not both zero) represent a line in a rectangular coordinate system. An equation of a line written in this way is said to be in **standard form**. In this section, we will learn a new form, called **slope-intercept form**, that can be used to determine the slope and *y*-intercept of a line.

Let $(0, b)$ represent the *y*-intercept of a line. Let (x, y) represent any other point on the line (Figure 3-26). Then the slope of the line, m, can be found as follows:

Let $(0, b)$ represent (x_1, y_1), and let (x, y) represent (x_2, y_2). Apply the slope formula.

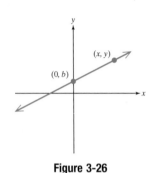

Figure 3-26

$$m = \frac{(y_2 - y_1)}{(x_2 - x_1)} \rightarrow m = \frac{y - b}{x - 0} \qquad \text{Apply the slope formula.}$$

$$m = \frac{y - b}{x} \qquad \text{Simplify.}$$

$$mx = \left(\frac{y - b}{x}\right)x \qquad \text{Multiply by } x \text{ to clear fractions.}$$

$$mx = y - b$$

$$mx + b = y - b + b \qquad \text{To isolate } y, \text{ add } b \text{ to both sides.}$$

$$mx + b = y \quad \text{or} \quad y = mx + b \qquad \text{The equation is in slope-intercept form.}$$

> **Slope-Intercept Form of a Linear Equation**
>
> $y = mx + b$ is the slope-intercept form of a linear equation.
>
> m is the slope and the point $(0, b)$ is the *y*-intercept.

Example 1 Identifying the Slope and *y*-Intercept from a Linear Equation

For each equation, identify the slope and *y*-intercept.

a. $y = 3x - 1$ **b.** $y = -2.7x + 5$ **c.** $y = 4x$

Solution:

Each equation is written in slope-intercept form, $y = mx + b$. The slope is the coefficient of x, and the *y*-intercept is determined by the constant term.

a. $y = 3x - 1$ The slope is 3.   The *y*-intercept is $(0, -1)$.

b. $y = -2.7x + 5$ The slope is -2.7.   The *y*-intercept is $(0, 5)$.

c. $y = 4x$ can be written as $y = 4x + 0$.   The slope is 4.
The *y*-intercept is $(0, 0)$.

Given the equation of a line, we can write the equation in slope-intercept form by solving the equation for the *y* variable. This is demonstrated in the next example.

Example 2 Identifying the Slope and *y*-Intercept from a Linear Equation

Given the equation of the line $-5x - 2y = 6$,

a. Write the equation in slope-intercept form.

b. Identify the slope and *y*-intercept.

Solution:

a. Write the equation in slope-intercept form, $y = mx + b$, by solving for *y*.

$$-5x - 2y = 6$$

$-2y = 5x + 6$	Add $5x$ to both sides.
$\dfrac{-2y}{-2} = \dfrac{5x + 6}{-2}$	Divide both sides by -2.
$y = \dfrac{5x}{-2} + \dfrac{6}{-2}$	Divide each term by -2 and simplify.
$y = -\dfrac{5}{2}x - 3$	Slope-intercept form.

b. The slope is $-\frac{5}{2}$, and the *y*-intercept is $(0, -3)$.

Skill Practice

Given the equation of the line $2x - 6y = -3$,

4. Write the equation in slope-intercept form.

5. Identify the slope and the *y*-intercept.

2. Graphing a Line from Its Slope and *y*-Intercept

Slope-intercept form is a useful tool to graph a line. The *y*-intercept is a known point on the line. The slope indicates the direction of the line and can be used to find a second point. Using slope-intercept form to graph a line is demonstrated in the next example.

Example 3 Graphing a Line Using the Slope and *y*-Intercept

Graph the equation of the line $y = -\frac{5}{2}x - 3$ by using the slope and *y*-intercept.

Solution:

First plot the *y*-intercept, $(0, -3)$.

The slope, $m = -\frac{5}{2}$, can be written as

$$m = \dfrac{-5}{2} \quad \begin{matrix} \longleftarrow \text{The change in } y \text{ is } -5. \\ \longleftarrow \text{The change in } x \text{ is } 2. \end{matrix}$$

To find a second point on the line, start at the *y*-intercept and move down 5 units and to the right 2 units. Then draw the line through the two points (Figure 3-27).

Similarly, the slope can be written as

$$m = \dfrac{5}{-2} \quad \begin{matrix} \longleftarrow \text{The change in } y \text{ is } 5. \\ \longleftarrow \text{The change in } x \text{ is } -2. \end{matrix}$$

To find a second point, start at the *y*-intercept and move up 5 units and to the left 2 units. Then draw the line through the two points (Figure 3-28).

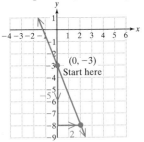

Figure 3-27

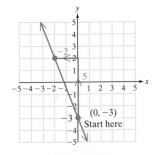

Figure 3-28

Skill Practice

6. Graph the equation by using the slope and the *y*-intercept.
$$y = 2x - 3$$

Answers

4. $y = \dfrac{1}{3}x + \dfrac{1}{2}$

5. slope is $\dfrac{1}{3}$; *y*-intercept is $\left(0, \dfrac{1}{2}\right)$

6.

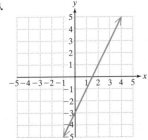

Example 4   **Graphing a Line from Its Slope and *y*-Intercept**

Graph the equation of the line $y = 4x$ by using the slope and *y*-intercept.

Solution:

The equation can be written as $y = 4x + 0$. Therefore, we can plot the *y*-intercept at $(0, 0)$. The slope $m = 4$ can be written as

The change in *y* is 4.

$$m = \frac{4}{1}$$

The change in *x* is 1.

To find a second point on the line, start at the *y*-intercept and move up 4 units and to the right 1 unit. Then draw the line through the two points (Figure 3-29).

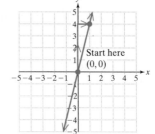

Figure 3-29

Skill Practice

7. Graph the equation by using the slope and the *y*-intercept.

$$y = -\frac{1}{4}x$$

Animation

3. Determining Whether Two Lines Are Parallel, Perpendicular, or Neither

The slope-intercept form provides a means to find the slope of a line by inspection. Recall that if the slopes of two lines are known, then we can compare the slopes to determine if the lines are parallel, perpendicular, or neither parallel nor perpendicular. (Two distinct nonvertical lines are parallel if their slopes are equal. Two lines are perpendicular if the slope of one line is the opposite of the reciprocal of the slope of the other line.)

Example 5   **Determining If Two Lines Are Parallel, Perpendicular, or Neither**

For each pair of lines, determine if they are parallel, perpendicular, or neither.

a. l_1: $y = 3x - 5$ **b.** l_1: $y = \frac{3}{2}x + 2$

  l_2: $y = 3x + 1$ l_2: $y = \frac{2}{3}x + 1$

Solution:

a. l_1: $y = 3x - 5$ The slope of l_1 is 3.

  l_2: $y = 3x + 1$ The slope of l_2 is 3.

Because the slopes are the same, the lines are parallel.

b. l_1: $y = \frac{3}{2}x + 2$ The slope of l_1 is $\frac{3}{2}$.

  l_2: $y = \frac{2}{3}x + 1$ The slope of l_2 is $\frac{2}{3}$.

The slopes are not the same. Therefore, the lines are not parallel. The values of the slopes are reciprocals, but they are not opposite in sign. Therefore, the lines are not perpendicular. The lines are neither parallel nor perpendicular.

Skill Practice

For each pair of lines determine if they are parallel, perpendicular, or neither.

8. $y = 3x - 5$
  $y = -3x - 15$

9. $y = \frac{5}{6}x - \frac{1}{2}$
  $y = \frac{5}{6}x + \frac{1}{2}$

Answers

7.

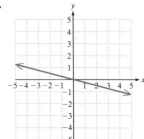

8. Neither   **9.** Parallel

Example 6 Determining If Two Lines Are Parallel, Perpendicular, or Neither

For each pair of lines, determine if they are parallel, perpendicular, or neither.

a. l_1: $x - 3y = -9$

l_2: $3x = -y + 4$

b. l_1: $x = 2$

l_2: $2y = 8$

Solution:

a. First write the equation of each line in slope-intercept form.

l_1: $x - 3y = -9$

$-3y = -x - 9$

$\dfrac{-3y}{-3} = \dfrac{-x}{-3} - \dfrac{9}{-3}$

$y = \dfrac{1}{3}x + 3$

l_2: $3x = -y + 4$

$3x + y = 4$

$y = -3x + 4$

l_1: $y = \frac{1}{3}x + 3$ The slope of l_1 is $\frac{1}{3}$.

l_2: $y = -3x + 4$ The slope of l_2 is -3.

The slope of $\frac{1}{3}$ is the opposite of the reciprocal of -3. Therefore, the lines are perpendicular.

b. The equation $x = 2$ represents a vertical line because the equation is in the form $x = k$.

The equation $2y = 8$ can be simplified to $y = 4$, which represents a horizontal line.

In this example, we do not need to analyze the slopes because vertical lines and horizontal lines are perpendicular.

Skill Practice

For each pair of lines, determine if they are parallel, perpendicular, or neither.

10. $x - 5y = 10$
$5x - 1 = -y$

11. $y = -5$
$x = 6$

4. Writing an Equation of a Line Using Slope-Intercept Form

The slope-intercept form of a linear equation can be used to write an equation of a line when the slope is known and the y-intercept is known.

Example 7 Writing an Equation of a Line Using Slope-Intercept Form

Write an equation of the line whose slope is $\frac{2}{3}$ and whose y-intercept is $(0, 8)$.

Solution:

The slope is given as $m = \frac{2}{3}$, and the y-intercept $(0, b)$ is given as $(0, 8)$. Substitute the values $m = \frac{2}{3}$ and $b = 8$ into slope-intercept form.

$$y = mx + b$$

$$y = \frac{2}{3}x + 8$$

Skill Practice

12. Write an equation of the line whose slope is -4 and y-intercept is $(0, -10)$.

Answers

10. Perpendicular
11. Perpendicular
12. $y = -4x - 10$

Example 8   Writing an Equation of a Line Using Slope-Intercept Form

Write an equation of the line having a slope of 2 and passing through the point $(-3, 1)$.

Solution:

To find an equation of a line using slope-intercept form, it is necessary to find the values of m and b. The slope is given in the problem as $m = 2$. Therefore, the slope-intercept form becomes

$$y = mx + b$$
$$\downarrow$$
$$y = 2x + b$$

Because the point $(-3, 1)$ is on the line, it is a solution to the equation. Therefore, to find b, substitute the values of x and y from the ordered pair $(-3, 1)$ and solve the resulting equation.

$y = 2x + b$

$1 = 2(-3) + b$ Substitute $y = 1$ and $x = -3$.

$1 = -6 + b$ Simplify and solve for b.

$7 = b$

Now with m and b known, the slope-intercept form is $y = 2x + 7$.

TIP: The equation from Example 8 can be checked by graphing the line $y = 2x + 7$. The slope $m = 2$ can be written as $m = \frac{2}{1}$. Therefore, to graph the line, start at the y-intercept $(0, 7)$ and move up 2 units and to the right 1 unit.
   The graph verifies that the line passes through the point $(-3, 1)$ as it should.

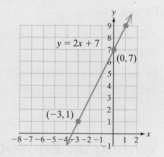

Answer

13. $y = -3x - 11$

Calculator Connections

Topic: Using the *ZSquare* Option in Zoom

In Example 6(a) we found that the equations $y = \frac{1}{3}x + 3$ and $y = -3x + 4$ represent perpendicular lines. We can verify our results by graphing the lines on a graphing calculator.
   Notice that the lines do not appear perpendicular

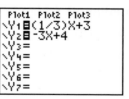

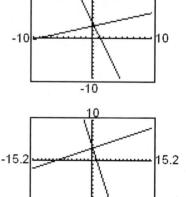

in the calculator display. That is, they do not appear to form a right angle at the point of intersection. Because many calculators have a rectangular screen, the standard viewing window is elongated in the horizontal direction. To eliminate this distortion, try using a *ZSquare* option, which is located under the Zoom menu. This feature will set the viewing window so that equal distances on the display denote an equal number of units on the graph.

Calculator Exercises

For each pair of lines, determine if the lines are parallel, perpendicular, or neither. Then use a square viewing window to graph the lines on a graphing calculator to verify your results.

1. $x + y = 1$

$x - y = -3$

2. $3x + y = -2$

$6x + 2y = 6$

3. $2x - y = 4$

$3x + 2y = 4$

4. Graph the lines defined by $y = x + 1$ and $y = 0.99x + 3$. Are these lines parallel? Explain.

5. Graph the lines defined by $y = -2x - 1$ and $y = -2x - 0.99$. Are these lines the same? Explain.

6. Graph the line defined by $y = 0.001x + 3$. Is this line horizontal? Explain.

Section 3.4 Practice Exercises

Study Skills Exercise

When taking a test, go through the test and do all the problems that you know first. Then go back and work on the problems that were more difficult. Give yourself a time limit for how much time you spend on each problem (maybe 3 to 5 min the first time through). Circle the importance of each statement.

	not important	somewhat important	very important
a. Read through the entire test first.	1	2	3
b. If time allows, go back and check each problem.	1	2	3
c. Write out all steps instead of doing the work in your head.	1	2	3

Vocabulary and Key Terms

1. a. Consider a line with slope m and y-intercept $(0, b)$. The slope-intercept form of an equation of the line is _____.

b. An equation of a line written in the form $Ax + By = C$ where A and B are not both zero is said to be in _____ form.

Review Exercises

2. For each equation given, determine if the line is horizontal, vertical, or slanted.

a. $3x = 6$ **b.** $y + 3 = 6$ **c.** $x + y = 6$

For Exercises 3–10, determine the x- and y-intercepts, if they exist.

3. $x - 5y = 10$ **4.** $3x + y = -12$ **5.** $3y = -9$ **6.** $2 + y = 5$

7. $-4x = 6y$ **8.** $-x + 3 = 8$ **9.** $5x = 20$ **10.** $y = \dfrac{1}{2}x$

Concept 1: Slope-Intercept Form of a Linear Equation

For Exercises 11–34, identify the slope and y-intercept, if they exist. **(See Examples 1 and 2.)**

11. $y = -2x + 3$

12. $y = \frac{2}{3}x + 5$

13. $y = x - 2$

14. $y = -x + 6$

15. $y = -x$

16. $y = -5x$

17. $y = \frac{3}{4}x - 1$

18. $y = x - \frac{5}{3}$

19. $2x - 5y = 4$

20. $3x + 2y = 9$

21. $3x - y = 5$

22. $7x - 3y = -6$

23. $x + y = 6$

24. $x - y = 1$

25. $x + 6 = 8$

26. $-4 + x = 1$

27. $-8y = 2$

28. $1 - y = 9$

29. $3y - 2x = 0$

30. $5x = 6y$

31. $15x + 5y = -20$

32. $6x - 2y = 4$

33. $4y - 11x = -3$

34. $10y - 2x = 5$

Concept 2: Graphing a Line from Its Slope and y-Intercept

For Exercises 35–38, graph the line using the slope and y-intercept. **(See Examples 3 and 4.)**

35. Graph the line through the point $(0, 2)$, having a slope of -4.

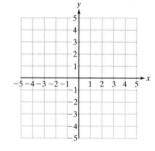

36. Graph the line through the point $(0, -1)$, having a slope of -3.

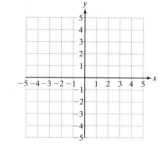

37. Graph the line through the point $(0, -5)$, having a slope of $\frac{3}{2}$.

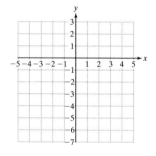

38. Graph the line through the point $(0, 3)$, having a slope of $-\frac{1}{4}$.

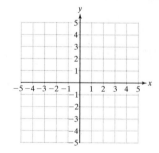

For Exercises 39–44, match the equation with the graph (a–f) by identifying if the slope is positive or negative and if the y-intercept is positive, negative, or zero.

39. $y = 2x + 3$

40. $y = -3x - 2$

41. $y = -\frac{1}{3}x + 3$

42. $y = \frac{1}{2}x - 2$

43. $y = x$

44. $y = -2x$

a.
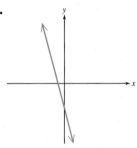

b.
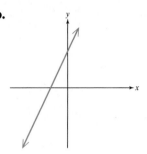

c.
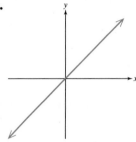

d.
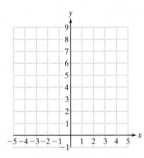

e.
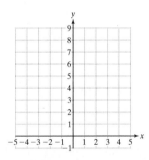

f.
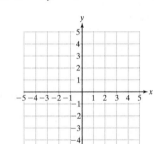

For Exercises 45–56, write each equation in slope-intercept form (if possible) and graph the line. **(See Examples 3 and 4.)**

45. $2x + y = 9$

46. $-6x + y = 8$

47. $x - 2y = 6$

48. $5x - 2y = 2$

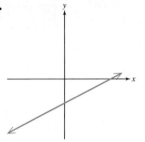

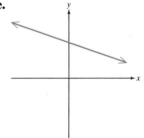

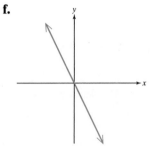

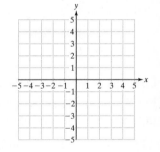

49. $2x = -4y + 6$

50. $6x = 2y - 14$

51. $x + y = 0$

52. $x - y = 0$

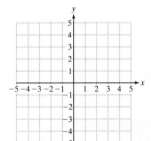

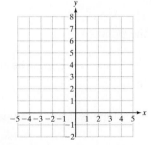

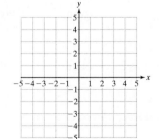

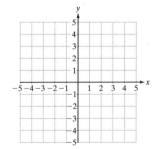

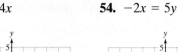 **53.** $5y = 4x$ **54.** $-2x = 5y$ **55.** $3y + 2 = 0$ **56.** $1 + 5y = 6$

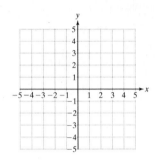
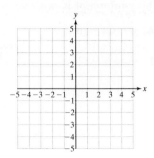

Concept 3: Determining Whether Two Lines Are Parallel, Perpendicular, or Neither

For Exercises 57–72, determine if the equations represent parallel lines, perpendicular lines, or neither.
(See Examples 5 and 6.)

57. l_1: $y = -2x - 3$ **58.** l_1: $y = \dfrac{4}{3}x - 2$ **59.** l_1: $y = \dfrac{4}{5}x - \dfrac{1}{2}$ **60.** l_1: $y = \dfrac{1}{5}x + 1$

  l_2: $y = \dfrac{1}{2}x + 4$ l_2: $y = -\dfrac{3}{4}x + 6$ l_2: $y = \dfrac{5}{4}x - \dfrac{2}{3}$ l_2: $y = 5x - 3$

61. l_1: $y = -9x + 6$ **62.** l_1: $y = 4x - 1$ **63.** l_1: $x = 3$ **64.** l_1: $y = \dfrac{2}{3}$

  l_2: $y = -9x - 1$ l_2: $y = 4x + \dfrac{1}{2}$ l_2: $y = \dfrac{7}{4}$ l_2: $x = 6$

65. l_1: $2x = 4$ **66.** l_1: $2y = 7$ **67.** l_1: $2x + 3y = 6$ **68.** l_1: $4x + 5y = 20$

  l_2: $6 = x$ l_2: $y = 4$ l_2: $3x - 2y = 12$ l_2: $5x - 4y = 60$

69. l_1: $4x + 2y = 6$ **70.** l_1: $3x + y = 5$ **71.** l_1: $y = \dfrac{1}{5}x - 3$ **72.** l_1: $y = \dfrac{1}{3}x + 2$

  l_2: $4x + 8y = 16$ l_2: $x + 3y = 18$ l_2: $2x - 10y = 20$ l_2: $-x + 3y = 12$

Concept 4: Writing an Equation of a Line Using Slope-Intercept Form

For Exercises 73–84, write an equation of the line given the following information. Write the answer in slope-intercept form if possible. **(See Examples 7 and 8.)**

73. The slope is $-\frac{1}{3}$, and the y-intercept is $(0, 2)$.   **74.** The slope is $\frac{2}{3}$, and the y-intercept is $(0, -1)$.

75. The slope is 10, and the y-intercept is $(0, -19)$. **76.** The slope is -14, and the y-intercept is $(0, 2)$.

77. The slope is 6, and the line passes through the point $(1, -2)$.   **78.** The slope is -4, and the line passes through the point $(4, -3)$.

79. The slope is $\frac{1}{2}$, and the line passes through the point $(-4, -5)$.   **80.** The slope is $-\frac{2}{3}$, and the line passes through the point $(3, -1)$.

81. The slope is 0, and the y-intercept is -11.   **82.** The slope is 0, and the y-intercept is $\dfrac{6}{7}$.

83. The slope is 5, and the line passes through the origin.   **84.** The slope is -3, and the line passes through the origin.

Expanding Your Skills

For Exercises 85–90, write an equation of the line that passes through two points by following these steps:

Step 1: Find the slope of the line using the slope formula, $m = \dfrac{y_2 - y_1}{x_2 - x_1}$.

Step 2: Using the slope from Step 1 and either given point, follow the procedure given in Example 8 to find an equation of the line in slope-intercept form.

85. $(2, -1)$ and $(0, 3)$ **86.** $(4, -8)$ and $(0, -4)$ **87.** $(3, 1)$ and $(-3, 3)$

88. $(2, -3)$ and $(4, -2)$ **89.** $(1, 3)$ and $(-2, -9)$ **90.** $(1, 7)$ and $(-2, 4)$

91. The number of reported cases of Lyme disease in the United States can be modeled by the equation $y = 1203x + 10{,}006$. In this equation, x represents the number of years since 1993, and y represents the number of cases of Lyme disease.

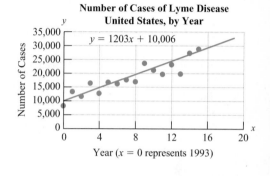

a. What is the slope of this line and what does it mean in the context of this problem?

b. What is the y-intercept, and what does it mean in the context of this problem?

c. Use the model to estimate the number of cases of Lyme disease in the year 2010.

d. During what year would the predicted number of cases be 36,472?

92. A phone bill is determined each month by a $16.95 flat fee plus $0.10/min of long distance. The equation, $C = 0.10x + 16.95$ represents the total monthly cost, C, for x minutes of long distance.

a. Identify the slope. Interpret the meaning of the slope in the context of this problem.

b. Identify the C-intercept. Interpret the meaning of the C-intercept in the context of this problem.

c. Use the equation to determine the total cost of 234 min of long distance.

93. A linear equation is written in standard form if it can be written as $Ax + By = C$, where A and B are not both zero. Write the equation $Ax + By = C$ in slope-intercept form to show that the slope is given by the ratio, $-\frac{A}{B}$. ($B \neq 0$.)

For Exercises 94–97, use the result of Exercise 93 to find the slope of the line.

94. $2x + 5y = 8$ **95.** $6x + 7y = -9$ **96.** $4x - 3y = -5$ **97.** $11x - 8y = 4$

Problem Recognition Exercises

Linear Equations in Two Variables

For Exercises 1–20, choose the equation(s) from the column on the right whose graph satisfies the condition described. Give all possible answers.

1. Line whose slope is positive.

2. Line whose slope is negative.

3. Line that passes through the origin.

4. Line that contains the point (3, –2).

5. Line whose y-intercept is (0, 4).

6. Line whose y-intercept is (0, –5).

7. Line whose slope is $\dfrac{1}{2}$.

8. Line whose slope is –2.

9. Line whose slope is 0.

10. Line whose slope is undefined.

11. Line that is parallel to the line with equation $y = -\dfrac{2}{3}x + 4$.

12. Line perpendicular to the line with equation $y = 2x + 9$.

13. Line that is vertical.

14. Line that is horizontal.

15. Line whose x-intercept is (10, 0).

16. Line whose x-intercept is (6, 0).

17. Line that is parallel to the x-axis.

18. Line that is perpendicular to the y-axis.

19. Line with a negative slope and positive y-intercept.

20. Line with a positive slope and negative y-intercept.

a. $y = 5x$

b. $2x + 3y = 12$

c. $y = \dfrac{1}{2}x - 5$

d. $3x - 6y = 10$

e. $2y = -8$

f. $y = -2x + 4$

g. $3x = 1$

h. $x + 2y = 6$

Point-Slope Formula

1. Writing an Equation of a Line Using the Point-Slope Formula

In Section 3.4, the slope-intercept form of a line was used as a tool to construct an equation of a line. Another useful tool to determine an equation of a line is the point-slope formula. The point-slope formula can be derived from the slope formula as follows:

Suppose a line passes through a given point (x_1, y_1) and has slope m. If (x, y) is any other point on the line, then:

$$m = \frac{y - y_1}{x - x_1} \qquad \text{Slope formula}$$

$$m(x - x_1) = \frac{y - y_1}{x - x_1}(x - x_1) \qquad \text{Clear fractions.}$$

$$m(x - x_1) = y - y_1$$

$$y - y_1 = m(x - x_1) \qquad \text{Point-slope formula}$$

> **Point-Slope Formula**
>
> The **point-slope formula** is given by
>
> $$y - y_1 = m(x - x_1)$$
>
> where m is the slope of the line and (x_1, y_1) is any known point on the line.

Example 1 demonstrates how to use the point-slope formula to find an equation of a line when a point on the line and slope are given.

Example 1 | **Writing an Equation of a Line Using the Point-Slope Formula**

Use the point-slope formula to write an equation of the line having a slope of 3 and passing through the point $(-2, -4)$. Write the answer in slope-intercept form.

Solution:

The slope of the line is given: $m = 3$.

A point on the line is given: $(x_1, y_1) = (-2, -4)$.

Concepts

1. Writing an Equation of a Line Using the Point-Slope Formula
2. Writing an Equation of a Line Given Two Points
3. Writing an Equation of a Line Parallel or Perpendicular to Another Line
4. Different Forms of Linear Equations: A Summary

Skill Practice

1. Use the point-slope formula to write an equation of the line having a slope of -4 and passing through $(-1, 5)$. Write the answer in slope-intercept form.

Answer

1. $y = -4x + 1$

The point-slope formula:

$$y - y_1 = m(x - x_1)$$

$$y - (-4) = 3[x - (-2)] \qquad \text{Substitute } m = 3, x_1 = -2, \text{ and } y_1 = -4.$$

$$y + 4 = 3(x + 2) \qquad \text{Simplify. Because the final answer is required in slope-intercept form, simplify the equation and solve for } y.$$

$$y + 4 = 3x + 6 \qquad \text{Apply the distributive property.}$$

$$y = 3x + 2 \qquad \text{Slope-intercept form}$$

The equation $y = 3x + 2$ from Example 1 is graphed in Figure 3-30. Notice that the line does indeed pass through the point $(-2, -4)$.

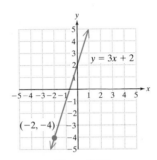

Figure 3-30

2. Writing an Equation of a Line Given Two Points

Example 2 is similar to Example 1; however, the slope must first be found from two given points.

Skill Practice

2. Use the point-slope formula to write an equation of the line passing through the points $(1, -1)$ and $(-1, -5)$.

Example 2 Writing an Equation of a Line Given Two Points

Use the point-slope formula to find an equation of the line passing through the points $(-2, 5)$ and $(4, -1)$. Write the final answer in slope-intercept form.

Solution:

Given two points on a line, the slope can be found with the slope formula.

$$\begin{array}{ccc} (-2, 5) & \text{and} & (4, -1) \\ (x_1, y_1) & & (x_2, y_2) \end{array} \qquad \text{Label the points.}$$

$$m = \frac{y_2 - y_1}{x_2 - x_1} = \frac{(-1) - (5)}{(4) - (-2)} = \frac{-6}{6} = -1$$

To apply the point-slope formula, use the slope, $m = -1$ and either given point. We will choose the point $(-2, 5)$ as (x_1, y_1).

$$y - y_1 = m(x - x_1)$$

$$y - 5 = -1[x - (-2)] \qquad \text{Substitute } m = -1, x_1 = -2, \text{ and } y_1 = 5.$$

$$y - 5 = -1(x + 2) \qquad \text{Simplify.}$$

$$y - 5 = -x - 2$$

$$y = -x + 3$$

TIP: The point-slope formula can be applied using either given point for (x_1, y_1). In Example 2, using the point $(4, -1)$ for (x_1, y_1) produces the same result.

$$y - y_1 = m(x - x_1)$$

$$y - (-1) = -1(x - 4)$$

$$y + 1 = -x + 4$$

$$y = -x + 3$$

Answer

2. $y = 2x - 3$

The solution to Example 2 can be checked by graphing the line $y = -x + 3$ using the slope and y-intercept. Notice that the line passes through the points $(-2, 5)$ and $(4, -1)$ as expected. See Figure 3-31.

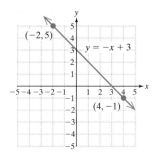

Figure 3-31

3. Writing an Equation of a Line Parallel or Perpendicular to Another Line

To write an equation of a line using the point-slope formula, the slope must be known. If the slope is not explicitly given, then other information must be used to determine the slope. In Example 2, the slope was found using the slope formula. Examples 3 and 4 show other situations in which we might find the slope.

Example 3 Writing an Equation of a Line Parallel to Another Line

Use the point-slope formula to find an equation of the line passing through the point $(-1, 0)$ and parallel to the line $y = -4x + 3$. Write the final answer in slope-intercept form.

Solution:

Figure 3-32 shows the line $y = -4x + 3$ (pictured in black) and a line parallel to it (pictured in blue) that passes through the point $(-1, 0)$. The equation of the given line, $y = -4x + 3$, is written in slope-intercept form, and its slope is easily identified as -4. The line parallel to the given line must also have a slope of -4.

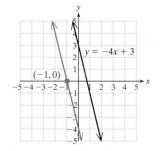

Figure 3-32

Apply the point-slope formula using $m = -4$ and the point $(x_1, y_1) = (-1, 0)$.

$$y - y_1 = m(x - x_1)$$
$$y - 0 = -4[x - (-1)]$$
$$y = -4(x + 1)$$
$$y = -4x - 4$$

Example 4 Writing an Equation of a Line Perpendicular to Another Line

Use the point-slope formula to find an equation of the line passing through the point $(-3, 1)$ and perpendicular to the line $3x + y = -2$. Write the final answer in slope-intercept form.

Solution:

The given line can be written in slope-intercept form as $y = -3x - 2$. The slope of this line is -3. Therefore, the slope of a line perpendicular to the given line is $\frac{1}{3}$.

Apply the point-slope formula with $m = \frac{1}{3}$, and $(x_1, y_1) = (-3, 1)$.

$y - y_1 = m(x - x_1)$ Point-slope formula

$y - (1) = \frac{1}{3}[x - (-3)]$ Substitute $m = \frac{1}{3}$, $x_1 = -3$, and $y_1 = 1$.

$y - 1 = \frac{1}{3}(x + 3)$ To write the final answer in slope-intercept form, simplify the equation and solve for y.

$y - 1 = \frac{1}{3}x + 1$ Apply the distributive property.

$y = \frac{1}{3}x + 2$ Add 1 to both sides.

A sketch of the perpendicular lines $y = \frac{1}{3}x + 2$ and $y = -3x - 2$ is shown in Figure 3-33. Notice that the line $y = \frac{1}{3}x + 2$ passes through the point $(-3, 1)$.

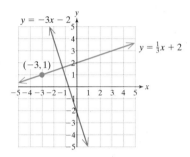

Figure 3-33

4. Different Forms of Linear Equations: A Summary

A linear equation can be written in several different forms, as summarized in Table 3-3.

Table 3-3

Form	Example	Comments
Standard Form $Ax + By = C$	$4x + 2y = 8$	A and B must not both be zero.
Horizontal Line $y = k$ (k is constant)	$y = 4$	The slope is zero, and the y-intercept is $(0, k)$.
Vertical Line $x = k$ (k is constant)	$x = -1$	The slope is undefined, and the x-intercept is $(k, 0)$.
Slope-Intercept Form $y = mx + b$ the slope is m y-intercept is $(0, b)$	$y = -3x + 7$ Slope $= -3$ y-intercept is $(0, 7)$	Solving a linear equation for y results in slope-intercept form. The coefficient of the x term is the slope, and the constant defines the location of the y-intercept.
Point-Slope Formula $y - y_1 = m(x - x_1)$	$m = -3$ $(x_1, y_1) = (4, 2)$ $y - 2 = -3(x - 4)$	This formula is typically used to build an equation of a line when a point on the line is known and the slope of the line is known.

Although standard form and slope-intercept form can be used to express an equation of a line, often the slope-intercept form is used to give a *unique* representation of the line. For example, the following linear equations are all written in standard form, yet they each define the same line.

$$2x + 5y = 10$$

$$-4x - 10y = -20$$

$$6x + 15y = 30$$

$$\frac{2}{5}x + y = 2$$

The line can be written uniquely in slope-intercept form as: $y = -\frac{2}{5}x + 2$.

Although it is important to understand and apply slope-intercept form and the point-slope formula, they are not necessarily applicable to all problems, particularly when dealing with a horizontal or vertical line.

Example 5   Writing an Equation of a Line

Find an equation of the line passing through the point $(2, -4)$ and parallel to the x-axis.

Solution:

Because the line is parallel to the x-axis, the line must be horizontal. Recall that all horizontal lines can be written in the form $y = k$, where k is a constant. A quick sketch can help find the value of the constant. See Figure 3-34.

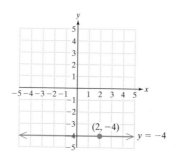

Figure 3-34

Because the line must pass through a point whose y-coordinate is -4, then the equation of the line must be $y = -4$.

Answer

7. $x = -7$

Section 3.5   Practice Exercises

Study Skills Exercise

Prepare a one-page summary sheet with the most important information that you need for the test. On the day of the test, look at this sheet several times to refresh your memory instead of trying to memorize new information.

Vocabulary and Key Concepts

1. **a.** The standard form of an equation of a line is _____, where A and B are not both zero and C is a constant.

   b. A line defined by an equation $y = k$, where k is a constant is a (horizontal/vertical) line.

   c. A line defined by an equation $x = k$, where k is a constant is a (horizontal/vertical) line.

   d. Given the slope-intercept form of an equation of a line, $y = mx + b$, the value of m is the _____ and b is the _____.

   e. Given a point (x_1, y_1) on a line with slope m, the point-slope formula is given by _____.

Review Exercises

For Exercises 2–6, graph each equation.

2. $-5x - 15 = 0$

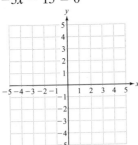

3. $2x - 3y = -3$

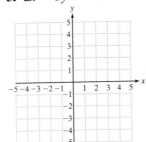

4. $y = -2x$

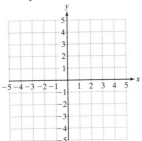

5. $3 - y = 9$

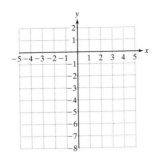

6. $y = \dfrac{4}{5}x$

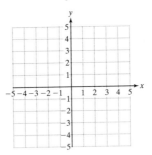

For Exercises 7–10, find the slope of the line that passes through the given points.

7. $(1, -3)$ and $(2, 6)$

8. $(2, -4)$ and $(-2, 4)$

9. $(-2, 5)$ and $(5, 5)$

10. $(6.1, 2.5)$ and $(6.1, -1.5)$

Concept 1: Writing an Equation of a Line Using the Point-Slope Formula

For Exercises 11–16, use the point-slope formula (if possible) to write an equation of the line given the following information. **(See Example 1.)**

11. The slope is 3, and the line passes through the point $(-2, 1)$.

12. The slope is -2, and the line passes through the point $(1, -5)$.

13. The slope is -4, and the line passes through the point $(-3, -2)$.

14. The slope is 5, and the line passes through the point $(-1, -3)$.

15. The slope is $-\frac{1}{2}$, and the line passes through $(-1, 0)$.

16. The slope is $-\frac{3}{4}$, and the line passes through $(2, 0)$.

Concept 2: Writing an Equation of a Line Given Two Points

For Exercises 17–22, use the point-slope formula to write an equation of the line given the following information. **(See Example 2.)**

17. The line passes through the points $(-2, -6)$ and $(1, 0)$.

18. The line passes through the points $(-2, 5)$ and $(0, 1)$.

19. The line passes through the points $(0, -4)$ and $(-1, -3)$.

20. The line passes through the points $(1, -3)$ and $(-7, 2)$.

21. The line passes through the points $(2.2, -3.3)$ and $(12.2, -5.3)$.

22. The line passes through the points $(4.7, -2.2)$ and $(-0.3, 6.8)$.

For Exercises 23–28, find an equation of the line through the given points. Write the final answer in slope-intercept form.

23.

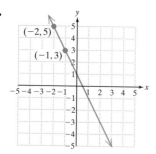

24.

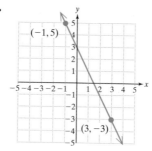

25.

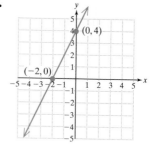

26.

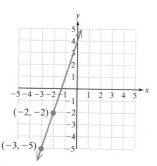

27.

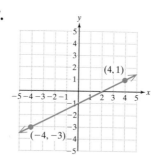

28.

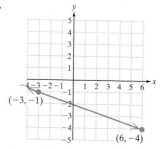

Concept 3: Writing an Equation of a Line Parallel or Perpendicular to Another Line

For Exercises 29–36, use the point-slope formula to write an equation of the line given the following information. **(See Examples 3 and 4.)**

29. The line passes through the point $(-3, 1)$ and is parallel to the line $y = 4x + 3$.

30. The line passes through the point $(4, -1)$ and is parallel to the line $y = 3x + 1$.

31. The line passes through the point $(4, 0)$ and is parallel to the line $3x + 2y = 8$.

32. The line passes through the point $(2, 0)$ and is parallel to the line $5x + 3y = 6$.

33. The line passes through the point $(-5, 2)$ and is perpendicular to the line $y = \frac{1}{2}x + 3$.

34. The line passes through the point $(-2, -2)$ and is perpendicular to the line $y = \frac{1}{3}x - 5$.

35. The line passes through the point $(0, -6)$ and is perpendicular to the line $-5x + y = 4$.

36. The line passes through the point $(0, -8)$ and is perpendicular to the line $2x - y = 5$.

Concept 4: Different Forms of Linear Equations: A Summary

For Exercises 37–42, match the form or formula on the left with its name on the right.

37. $x = k$

38. $y = mx + b$

39. $m = \dfrac{y_2 - y_1}{x_2 - x_1}$

40. $y - y_1 = m(x - x_1)$

41. $y = k$

42. $Ax + By = C$

i.   Standard form

ii. Point-slope formula

iii. Horizontal line

iv. Vertical line

v.   Slope-intercept form

vi. Slope formula

For Exercises 43–48, find an equation for the line given the following information. **(See Example 5.)**

43. The line passes through the point $(3, 1)$ and is parallel to the line $y = -4$. See the figure.

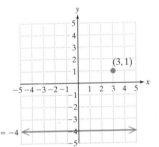

44. The line passes through the point $(-1, 1)$ and is parallel to the line $y = 2$. See the figure.

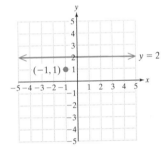

45. The line passes through the point $(2, 6)$ and is perpendicular to the line $y = 1$. (*Hint:* Sketch the line first.)

46. The line passes through the point $(0, 3)$ and is perpendicular to the line $y = -5$. (*Hint:* Sketch the line first.)

47. The line passes through the point $(2, 2)$ and is perpendicular to the line $x = 0$.

48. The line passes through the point $(5, -2)$ and is perpendicular to the line $x = 0$.

Mixed Exercises

For Exercises 49–60, write an equation of the line given the following information.

49. The slope is $\frac{1}{4}$, and the line passes through the point $(-8, 6)$.

50. The slope is $\frac{2}{5}$, and the line passes through the point $(-5, 4)$.

51. The line passes through the point $(4, 4)$ and is parallel to the line $3x - y = 6$.

52. The line passes through the point $(-1, -7)$ and is parallel to the line $5x + y = -5$.

53. The slope is 4.5, and the line passes through the point $(5.2, -2.2)$.

54. The slope is -3.6, and the line passes through the point $(10.0, 8.2)$.

55. The slope is undefined, and the line passes through the point $(-6, -3)$.

56. The slope is undefined, and the line passes through the point $(2, -1)$.

57. The slope is 0, and the line passes through the point $(3, -2)$.

58. The slope is 0, and the line passes through the point $(0, 5)$.

59. The line passes through the points $(-4, 0)$ and $(-4, 3)$.

60. The line passes through the points $(1, 3)$ and $(1, -4)$.

Expanding Your Skills

For Exercises 61–64, write an equation in slope-intercept form for the line shown.

61.

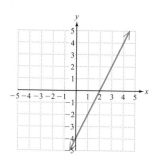

62.

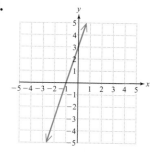

63.

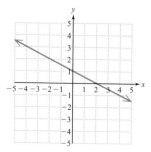

64.

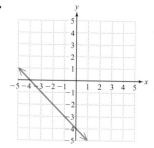

Applications of Linear Equations and Modeling

Section 3.6

1. Interpreting a Linear Equation in Two Variables

Linear equations can often be used to describe (or model) the relationship between two variables in a real-world event.

Concepts

1. Interpreting a Linear Equation in Two Variables
2. Writing a Linear Model Using Observed Data Points
3. Writing a Linear Model Given a Fixed Value and a Rate of Change

Example 1 Interpreting a Linear Equation

Since the year 1900, the tiger population in India has continually decreased. A recent study showed this decrease can be approximated by the equation $y = -350x + 42,000$. The variable y represents the number of tigers left in India, and x represents the number of years since 1900.

a. Use the equation to predict the number of tigers in 1960.

b. Use the equation to predict the number of tigers in 2015.

c. Determine the slope of the line. Interpret the meaning of the slope in terms of the number of tigers and the year.

d. Determine the x-intercept. Interpret the meaning of the x-intercept in terms of the number of tigers.

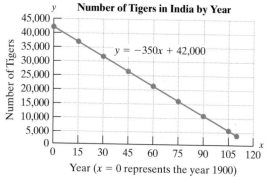

Number of Tigers in India by Year

$y = -350x + 42,000$

Year ($x = 0$ represents the year 1900)

Solution:

a. The year 1960 is 60 yr since 1900. Substitute $x = 60$ into the equation.

$$y = -350x + 42{,}000$$

$$y = -350(60) + 42{,}000$$

$$= 21{,}000$$ There were approximately 21,000 tigers in India in 1960.

b. The year 2015 is 115 yr since 1900. Substitute $x = 115$.

$$y = -350(115) + 42{,}000$$

$$= 1750$$ There will be approximately 1750 tigers in India in 2015.

c. The slope is -350.   The slope means that the tiger population is decreasing by 350 tigers per year.

d. To find the x-intercept, substitute $y = 0$.

$$y = -350x + 42{,}000$$

$$0 = -350x + 42{,}000 \qquad \text{Substitute } 0 \text{ for } y.$$

$$-42{,}000 = -350x$$

$$120 = x$$

The x-intercept is $(120, 0)$. This means that 120 yr after the year 1900, the tiger population would be expected to reach zero. That is, in the year 2020, there will be no tigers left in India if this linear trend continues.

2. Writing a Linear Model Using Observed Data Points

Example 2   Writing a Linear Model from Observed Data Points

The monthly sales of hybrid cars sold in the United States are given for a recent year. The sales for the first 8 months of the year are shown in Figure 3-35. The value $x = 0$ represents January, $x = 1$ represents February, and so on.

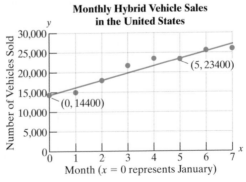

Figure 3-35

a. Use the data points from Figure 3-35 to find a linear equation that represents the monthly sales of hybrid cars in the United States. Let x represent the month number and let y represent the number of vehicles sold.

b. Use the linear equation in part (a) to estimate the number of hybrid vehicles sold in month 7 (August).

Solution:

a. The ordered pairs $(0, 14400)$ and $(5, 23400)$ are given in the graph. Use these points to find the slope.

$$\underset{(x_1, y_1)}{(0,\, 14400)} \quad \text{and} \quad \underset{(x_2, y_2)}{(5,\, 23400)} \qquad \text{Label the points.}$$

$$m = \frac{y_2 - y_1}{x_2 - x_1} = \frac{23{,}400 - 14{,}400}{5 - 0}$$

$$= \frac{9000}{5}$$

$$= 1800 \qquad \text{The slope is 1800. This indicates that sales increased by approximately 1800 per month during this time period.}$$

With $m = 1800$, and the y-intercept given as $(0, 14400)$, we have the following linear equation in slope-intercept form.

$$y = 1800x + 14{,}400$$

b. To approximate the sales in month 7, substitute $x = 7$ into the equation from part (a).

$$y = 1800(7) + 14{,}400 \qquad \text{Substitute } x = 7.$$

$$= 27{,}000$$

The monthly sales for August (month 7) would be 27,000 vehicles.

3. Writing a Linear Model Given a Fixed Value and a Rate of Change

Another way to look at the equation $y = mx + b$ is to identify the term mx as the variable term and the term b as the constant term. The value of the term mx will change with the value of x (this is why the slope, m, is called a *rate of change*). However, the term b will remain constant regardless of the value of x. With these ideas in mind, we can write a linear equation if the rate of change and the constant are known.

Example 3 **Writing a Linear Model**

A stack of posters to advertise a production by the theater department costs $19.95 plus $1.50 per poster at the printer.

a. Write a linear equation to compute the cost, c, of buying x posters.

b. Use the equation to compute the cost of 125 posters.

Skill Practice

The monthly cost for a "minimum use" cellular phone is $19.95 plus $0.10 per minute for all calls.

7. Write a linear equation to compute the cost, c, of using t minutes.

8. Use the equation to determine the cost of using 150 minutes.

Answers

7. $c = 0.10t + 19.95$ **8.** $34.95

Solution:

a. The constant cost is $19.95. The variable cost is $1.50 per poster. If m is replaced with 1.50 and b is replaced with 19.95, the equation is

$c = 1.50x + 19.95$ where c is the cost (in dollars) of buying x posters.

b. Because x represents the number of posters, substitute $x = 125$.

$$c = 1.50(125) + 19.95$$

$$= 187.5 + 19.95$$

$$= 207.45$$

The total cost of buying 125 posters is $207.45.

Calculator Connections

Topic: Using the Evaluate Feature on a Graphing Calculator

In Example 3, the equation $c = 1.50x + 19.95$ was used to represent the cost, c, to buy x posters. To graph this equation on a graphing calculator, first replace the variable c by y.

$$y = 1.50x + 19.95$$

We enter the equation into the calculator and set the viewing window.

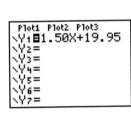
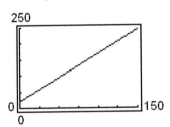

To evaluate the equation for a user-defined value of x, use the *Value* feature in the CALC menu. In this case, we entered $x = 125$, and the calculator returned $y = 207.45$.

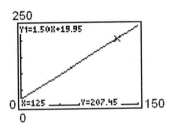

Calculator Exercises

Use a graphing calculator to graph the lines on an appropriate viewing window. Evaluate the equation at the given values of x.

1. $y = -4.6x + 27.1$ at $x = 3$

2. $y = -3.6x - 42.3$ at $x = 0$

3. $y = 40x + 105$ at $x = 6$

4. $y = 20x - 65$ at $x = 8$

Section 3.6 Practice Exercises

Study Skills Exercise

On test day, take a look at any formulas or important points that you had to memorize before you enter the classroom. Then when you sit down to take your test, write these formulas on the test or on scrap paper. This is called a memory dump. Write down the formulas from Chapter 3.

Review Exercises

1. Determine the slope of the line defined by $5x + 2y = -6$.

2. Determine the slope of the line defined by $2x - 8y = 15$.

For Exercises 3–8, find the x- and y-intercepts of the lines, if possible.

3. $5x + 6y = 30$

4. $3x + 4y = 1$

5. $y = -2x - 4$

6. $y = 5x$

7. $y = -9$

8. $x = 2$

Concept 1: Interpreting a Linear Equation in Two Variables

9. The minimum hourly wage, y (in dollars per hour), in the United States can be approximated by the equation $y = 0.14x + 1.60$. In this equation, x represents the number of years since 1970 ($x = 0$ represents 1970, $x = 5$ represents 1975, and so on). **(See Example 1.)**

   a. Use the equation to approximate the minimum wage in the year 1980.

   b. Use the equation to predict the minimum wage in 2015.

   c. Determine the y-intercept. Interpret the meaning of the y-intercept in the context of this problem.

   d. Determine the slope. Interpret the meaning of the slope in the context of this problem.

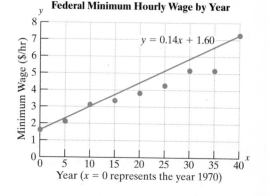

10. The average daily temperature in January for cities along the eastern seaboard of the United States and Canada generally decreases for cities farther north. A city's latitude in the northern hemisphere is a measure of how far north it is on the globe.

   The average temperature, y (measured in degrees Fahrenheit), can be described by the equation

   $y = -2.333x + 124.0$ where x is the latitude of the city.

   a. Use the equation to predict the average daily temperature in January for Philadelphia, Pennsylvania, whose latitude is 40.0°N. Round to one decimal place.

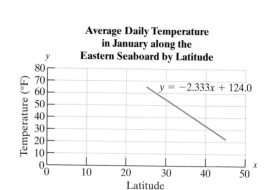

(Source: U.S. National Oceanic and Atmospheric Administration)

   b. Use the equation to predict the average daily temperature in January for Edmundston, New Brunswick, Canada, whose latitude is 47.4°N. Round to one decimal place.

   c. What is the slope of the line? Interpret the meaning of the slope in terms of latitude and temperature.

   d. From the equation, determine the value of the x-intercept. Round to one decimal place. Interpret the meaning of the x-intercept in terms of latitude and temperature.

11. Veterinarians keep records of the weights of animals that are brought in for examination. Grindel, the cat, weighed 42 oz when she was 70 days old. She weighed 46 oz when she was 84 days old. Her sister, Frisco, weighed 40 oz when she was 70 days old and 48 oz at 84 days old.

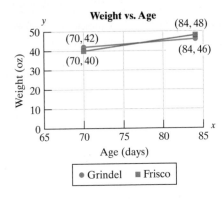

a. Compute the slope of the line representing Grindel's weight.

b. Compute the slope of the line representing Frisco's weight.

c. Interpret the meaning of each slope in the context of this problem.

d. Which cat gained weight more rapidly during this time period?

12. The graph depicts the rise in the number of jail inmates in the United States since 2000. Two linear equations are given: one to describe the number of female inmates and one to describe the number of male inmates by year.

Let y represent the number of inmates (in thousands). Let x represent the number of years since 2000.

a. What is the slope of the line representing the number of female inmates? Interpret the meaning of the slope in the context of this problem.

b. What is the slope of the line representing the number of male inmates? Interpret the meaning of the slope in the context of this problem.

c. Which group, males or females, has the larger slope? What does this imply about the rise in the number of male and female prisoners?

d. Assuming this trend continues, use the equation to predict the number of female inmates in 2015.

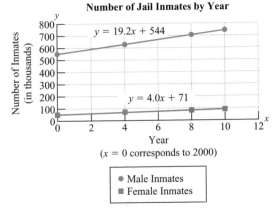

Number of Jail Inmates by Year

$y = 19.2x + 544$

$y = 4.0x + 71$

($x = 0$ corresponds to 2000)

● Male Inmates
■ Female Inmates

(*Source:* U.S. Bureau of Justice Statistics)

13. The electric bill charge for a certain utility company is $0.095 per kilowatt-hour plus a fixed monthly tax of $11.95. The total cost, y, depends on the number of kilowatt-hours, x, according to the equation $y = 0.095x + 11.95$, $x \geq 0$.

a. Determine the cost of using 1000 kilowatt-hours.

b. Determine the cost of using 2000 kilowatt-hours.

c. Determine the y-intercept. Interpret the meaning of the y-intercept in the context of this problem.

d. Determine the slope. Interpret the meaning of the slope in the context of this problem.

14. For a recent year, children's admission to the Minnesota State Fair was $8. Ride tickets were $0.75 each. The equation $y = 0.75x + 8$ represented the cost, y, in dollars to be admitted to the fair and to purchase x ride tickets.

    a. Determine the slope of the line represented by $y = 0.75x + 8$. Interpret the meaning of the slope in the context of this problem.

    b. Determine the y-intercept. Interpret its meaning in the context of this problem.

    c. Use the equation to determine how much money a child needed for admission and to ride 10 rides.

Concept 2: Writing a Linear Model Using Observed Data Points

15. Meteorologists often measure the intensity of a tropical storm or hurricane by the maximum sustained wind speed and the minimum pressure. The relationship between these two quantities is approximately linear. Hurricane Katrina had a maximum sustained wind speed of 150 knots and a minimum pressure of 902 mb (millibars). Hurricane Ophelia had maximum sustained winds of 75 knots and a pressure of 976 mb. **(See Example 2.)**

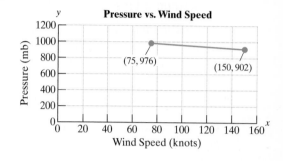

    a. Find the slope of the line between these two points. Round to one decimal place.

    b. Using the slope found in part (a) and the point (75, 976), find a linear model that represents the minimum pressure of a hurricane, y, versus its maximum sustained wind speed, x.

    c. Hurricane Dennis had a maximum wind speed of 130 knots. Using the equation you found in part (b), predict the minimum pressure.

16. The figure depicts a relationship between a person's height, y (in inches), and the length of the person's arm, x (measured in inches from shoulder to wrist).

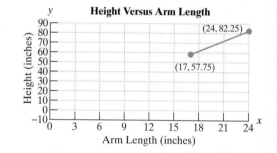

    a. Use the points (17, 57.75) and (24, 82.25) to find a linear equation relating height to arm length.

    b. What is the slope of the line? Interpret the slope in the context of this problem.

    c. Use the equation from part (a) to estimate the height of a person whose arm length is 21.5 in.

17. Wind energy is one type of renewable energy that does not produce dangerous greenhouse gases as a by-product. The graph shows the consumption of wind energy in the United States for selected years. The variable y represents the amount of wind energy in trillions of Btu, and the variable x represents the number of years since 2000.

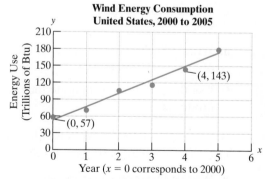

    a. Use the points (0, 57) and (4, 143) to determine the slope of the line.

    b. Interpret the slope in the context of this problem?

    c. Use the points (0, 57) and (4, 143) to find a linear equation relating the consumption of wind energy, y, to the number of years, x, since 2000.

    d. If this linear trend continues beyond the observed data values, use the equation in part (c) to predict the consumption of wind energy in the year 2010.

18. The graph shows the average height for boys based on age. Let x represent a boy's age, and let y represent his height (in inches).

   a. Find a linear equation that represents the height of a boy versus his age.

   b. Use the linear equation found in part (a) to predict the average height of a 5-year-old boy.

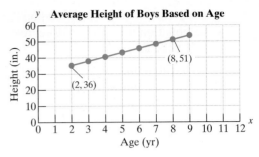

(*Source*: National Parenting Council)

Concept 3: Writing a Linear Model Given a Fixed Value and a Rate of Change

19. Andrés has a cell phone plan with a local telephone company. His bill is determined each month by a \$39.99 flat fee plus \$0.20 for each text message sent or received. **(See Example 3.)**

   a. Write a linear model to compute the monthly cost, y, of Andrés's cell phone bill if x text messages are sent or received.

   b. Use the equation to compute Andrés's cell phone bill for a month in which he sent or received a total of 40 text messages.

20. Anabel lives in New York and likes to keep in touch with her family in Texas. She uses 10-10-987 to call them. The cost of a long distance call is \$0.53 plus \$0.06 per minute.

   a. Write an equation that represents the cost, C, of a long distance call that is x minutes long.

   b. Use the equation to compute the cost of a long distance phone call that lasted 32 minutes.

21. The cost to rent a 10-ft by 10-ft storage space is \$90 per month plus a nonrefundable deposit of \$105.

   a. Write a linear equation to compute the cost, y, of renting a 10-ft by 10-ft space for x months.

   b. What is the cost of renting such a storage space for 1 year (12 months)?

22. An air-conditioning and heating company has a fixed monthly cost of \$5000. Furthermore, each service call costs the company \$25.

   a. Write a linear equation to compute the total cost, y, for 1 month if x service calls are made.

   b. Use the equation to compute the cost for 1 month if 150 service calls are made.

23. A bakery that specializes in bread rents a booth at a flea market. The daily cost to rent the booth is \$100. Each loaf of bread costs the bakery \$0.80 to produce.

   a. Write a linear equation to compute the total cost, y, for 1 day if x loaves of bread are produced.

   b. Use the equation to compute the cost for 1 day if 200 loaves of bread are produced.

24. A beverage company rents a booth at an art show to sell lemonade. The daily cost to rent a booth is \$35. Each lemonade costs \$0.50 to produce.

   a. Write a linear equation to compute the total cost, y, for 1 day if x lemonades are produced.

   b. Use the equation to compute the cost for 1 day if 350 lemonades are produced.

Group Activity

Modeling a Linear Equation

Materials: Yardstick or other device for making linear measurements

Estimated Time: 15–20 minutes

Group Size: 3

1. The members of each group should measure the length of their arms (in inches) from elbow to wrist. Record this measurement as x and the person's height (in inches) as y. Write these values as ordered pairs for each member of the group. Then write the ordered pairs on the board.

2. Next, copy the ordered pairs collected from all groups in the class and plot the ordered pairs. (This is called a "scatter diagram.")

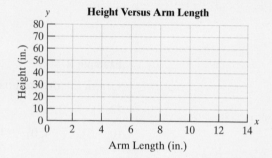

3. Select two ordered pairs that seem to follow the upward trend of the data. Using these data points, determine the slope of the line.

   Slope: _____

4. Using the data points and slope from question 3, find an equation of the line through the two points. Write the equation in slope-intercept form, $y = mx + b$.

   Equation: _____

5. Using the equation from question 4, estimate the height of a person whose arm length from elbow to wrist is 8.5 in.

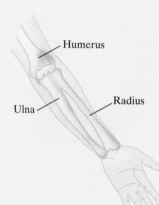

6. Suppose a crime scene investigator uncovers a partial skeleton and identifies a bone as a human ulna (the ulna is one of two bones in the forearm and extends from elbow to wrist). If the length of the bone is 12 in., estimate the height of the person before death. Would you expect this person to be male or female?

Chapter 3   Summary

Section 3.1   Rectangular Coordinate System

Key Concepts

Graphical representation of numerical data is often helpful to study problems in real-world applications.

A **rectangular coordinate system** is made up of a horizontal line called the **x-axis** and a vertical line called the **y-axis**. The point where the lines meet is the **origin**. The four regions of the plane are called **quadrants**.

The point (x, y) is an **ordered pair**. The first element in the ordered pair is the point's horizontal position from the origin. The second element in the ordered pair is the point's vertical position from the origin.

Examples

Example 1

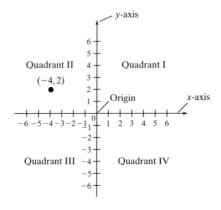

Example 2

Graph the ordered pairs.

$(2, 5)$ $(-3, -4)$ $(-2, 3)$,

$(0, -3)$, $(-4, 0)$, $(4, -5)$

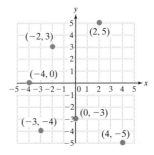

Section 3.2   Linear Equations in Two Variables

Key Concepts

An equation written in the form $Ax + By = C$ (where A and B are not both zero) is a **linear equation in two variables**.

A solution to a linear equation in x and y is an ordered pair (x, y) that makes the equation a true statement. The graph of the set of all solutions of a linear equation in two variables is a line in a rectangular coordinate system.

A linear equation can be graphed by finding at least two solutions and graphing the line through the points.

Examples

Example 1

Graph the equation $2x + y = 2$.

Select arbitrary values of x or y such as those shown in the table. Then complete the table to find the corresponding ordered pairs.

x	y	
0	2	$\longrightarrow (0, 2)$
−1	4	$\longrightarrow (−1, 4)$
1	0	$\longrightarrow (1, 0)$

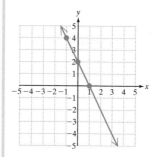

An **x-intercept** of a graph is a point $(a, 0)$ where the graph intersects the x-axis.

A **y-intercept** of a graph is a point $(0, b)$ where the graph intersects the y-axis.

Example 2

For the line $2x + y = 2$, the x-intercept is $(1, 0)$ and the y-intercept is $(0, 2)$.

A **vertical line** can be represented by an equation of the form $x = k$.

A **horizontal line** can be represented by an equation of the form $y = k$.

Example 3

$x = 3$ represents a vertical line

$y = 3$ represents a horizontal line

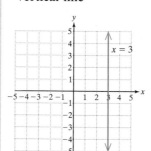

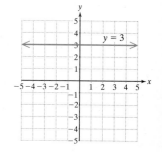

Section 3.3 Slope of a Line and Rate of Change

Key Concepts

The **slope**, m, of a line between two points (x_1, y_1) and (x_2, y_2) is given by

$$m = \frac{y_2 - y_1}{x_2 - x_1} \quad \text{or} \quad \frac{\text{change in } y}{\text{change in } x}$$

The slope of a line may be positive, negative, zero, or undefined.

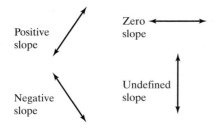

Positive slope

Zero slope

Negative slope

Undefined slope

If m_1 and m_2 represent the slopes of two **parallel lines** (nonvertical), then $m_1 = m_2$.

If $m_1 \neq 0$ and $m_2 \neq 0$ represent the slopes of two nonvertical **perpendicular lines**, then

$$m_1 = -\frac{1}{m_2} \quad \text{or equivalently, } m_1 m_2 = -1.$$

Examples

Example 1

Find the slope of the line between $(1, -5)$ and $(-3, 7)$.

$$m = \frac{7 - (-5)}{-3 - 1} = \frac{12}{-4} = -3$$

Example 2

The slope of the line $y = -2$ is 0 because the line is horizontal.

Example 3

The slope of the line $x = 4$ is undefined because the line is vertical.

Example 4

The slopes of two distinct lines are given. Determine whether the lines are parallel, perpendicular, or neither.

a. $m_1 = -7$ and $m_2 = -7$ Parallel

b. $m_1 = -\dfrac{1}{5}$ and $m_2 = 5$ Perpendicular

c. $m_1 = -\dfrac{3}{2}$ and $m_2 = -\dfrac{2}{3}$ Neither

23. Determine whether the equations represent parallel lines, perpendicular lines, or neither.

l_1: $2y = 3x - 3$ l_2: $4x = -6y + 1$

24. Write an equation of the line that passes through the point $(3, 0)$ and is parallel to the line $2x + 6y = -5$.

25. Write an equation of the line that passes through the points $(2, 8)$ and $(4, 1)$.

26. Write an equation of the line that has y-intercept $(0, \frac{1}{2})$ and slope $\frac{1}{4}$.

27. Write an equation of the line that passes through the point $(-3, -1)$ and is perpendicular to the line $x + 3y = 9$.

28. Write an equation of the line that passes through the point $(2, -6)$ and is parallel to the x-axis.

29. Write an equation of the line that has slope -1 and passes through the point $(-5, 2)$.

30. To attend a state fair, the cost is \$10 per person to cover exhibits and musical entertainment. There is an additional cost of \$1.50 per ride.

   a. Write an equation that gives the total cost, y, of visiting the state fair and going on x rides.

   b. Use the equation from part (a) to determine the cost of going to the state fair and going on 10 rides.

31. The number of medical doctors for selected years is shown in the graph. Let x represent the number of years since 1980, and let y represent the number of medical doctors (in thousands) in the United States.

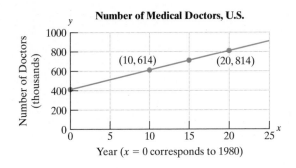

Number of Medical Doctors, U.S.

a. Find the slope of the line shown in the graph. Interpret the meaning of the slope in the context of this problem.

b. Find an equation of the line.

c. Use the equation from part (b) to predict the number of medical doctors in the United States for the year 2015.

Chapters 1–3   Cumulative Review Exercises

1. Identify the numbers as rational or irrational.

   a. -3 **b.** $\dfrac{5}{4}$ **c.** $\sqrt{10}$ **d.** 0

2. Write the opposite and the absolute value for each number.

   a. $-\dfrac{2}{3}$ **b.** 5.3

3. Simplify the expression using the order of operations: $32 \div 2 \cdot 4 + 5$

4. Add: $3 + (-8) + 2 + (-10)$

5. Subtract: $16 - 5 - (-7)$

For Exercises 6 and 7, translate the English phrase into an algebraic expression. Then evaluate the expression.

6. The quotient of $\dfrac{3}{4}$ and $-\dfrac{7}{8}$.

7. The product of -2.1 and -6.

8. Name the property that is illustrated by the following statement. $6 + (8 + 2) = (6 + 8) + 2$

For Exercises 9–12, solve the equation.

9. $6x - 10 = 14$ **10.** $3(m + 2) - 3 = 2m + 8$

11. $\dfrac{2}{3}y - \dfrac{1}{6} = y + \dfrac{4}{3}$ **12.** $1.7z + 2 = -2(0.3z + 1.3)$

13. The area of Texas is 267,277 mi². If this is 712 mi² less than 29 times the area of Maine, find the area of Maine.

14. For the formula $3a + b = c$, solve for a.

15. Graph the equation $-6x + 2y = 0$.

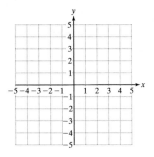

16. Find the x- and y-intercepts of $-2x + 4y = 4$.

17. Write the equation in slope-intercept form. Then identify the slope and the y-intercept.
$3x + 2y = -12$

18. Explain why the line $2x + 3 = 5$ has only one intercept.

19. Find an equation of a line passing through $(2, -5)$ with slope -3.

20. Find an equation of the line passing through $(0, 6)$ and $(-3, 4)$.

Systems of Linear Equations in Two Variables

4

Chapter 4

This chapter is devoted to solving systems of linear equations and inequalities. Finding ordered pair solutions to linear equations in two variables and graphing lines are two skills that you will need in this chapter.

Review Your Skills

For each equation, complete the ordered pairs and graph the line defined by the two given points. Then determine where all four lines intersect.

$y = x$ (1,) and (, 7)

$x = 4$ (, 9) and (, 0)

$x + y = 8$ (, 7) and (7,)

$y = 4$ (0,) and (9,)

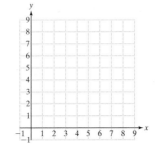

Section 4.1

Solving Systems of Equations by the Graphing Method

Concepts

1. Solutions to a System of Linear Equations
2. Solving Systems of Linear Equations by Graphing

1. Solutions to a System of Linear Equations

Recall from Section 3.2 that a linear equation in two variables has an infinite number of solutions. The set of all solutions to a linear equation forms a line in a rectangular coordinate system. Two or more linear equations form a **system of linear equations**. For example, here are three systems of equations:

$$x - 3y = -5 \qquad\qquad y = \tfrac{1}{4}x - \tfrac{3}{4} \qquad\qquad 5a + b = 4$$
$$2x + 4y = 10 \qquad\qquad -2x + 8y = -6 \qquad\qquad -10a - 2b = 8$$

A **solution to a system of linear equations** is an ordered pair that is a solution to *both* individual equations.

Skill Practice

Determine whether the ordered pair is a solution to the system.

$5x - 2y = 24$
$2x + y = 6$

1. $(6, 3)$
2. $(4, -2)$

Example 1 Determining Solutions to a System of Linear Equations

Determine whether the ordered pairs are solutions to the system.

$$x + y = 4$$
$$-2x + y = -5$$

a. $(3, 1)$ **b.** $(0, 4)$

Solution:

a. Substitute the ordered pair $(3, 1)$ into both equations:

$$x + y = 4 \longrightarrow (3) + (1) \stackrel{?}{=} 4 \;✔ \qquad \text{True}$$
$$-2x + y = -5 \longrightarrow -2(3) + (1) \stackrel{?}{=} -5 \;✔ \qquad \text{True}$$

Avoiding Mistakes

It is important to test an ordered pair in *both* equations to determine if the ordered pair is a solution.

Because the ordered pair $(3, 1)$ is a solution to both equations, it is a solution to the *system* of equations.

b. Substitute the ordered pair $(0, 4)$ into both equations.

$$x + y = 4 \longrightarrow (0) + (4) \stackrel{?}{=} 4 \;✔ \qquad \text{True}$$
$$-2x + y = -5 \longrightarrow -2(0) + (4) \stackrel{?}{=} -5 \qquad \text{False}$$

Because the ordered pair $(0, 4)$ is not a solution to the second equation, it is *not* a solution to the system of equations.

A solution to a system of two linear equations may be interpreted graphically as a point of intersection of the two lines. Using slope-intercept form to graph the lines from Example 1, we have

$$l_1: \quad x + y = 4 \longrightarrow y = -x + 4$$
$$l_2: -2x + y = -5 \longrightarrow y = 2x - 5$$

All points on l_1 are solutions to the equation $y = -x + 4$.

All points on l_2 are solutions to the equation $y = 2x - 5$.

The point of intersection $(3, 1)$ is the only point that is a solution to both equations. (See Figure 4-1.)

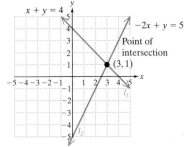

Figure 4-1

Answers

1. No
2. Yes

When two lines are drawn in a rectangular coordinate system, three geometric relationships are possible:

1. Two lines may intersect at *exactly one point*.

2. Two lines may intersect at *no point*. This occurs if the lines are parallel.

3. Two lines may intersect at *infinitely many points* along the line. This occurs if the equations represent the same line (the lines coincide).

Concept Connections

3. If the linear equations in a system represent a pair of parallel lines, how many solutions does the system have?
4. If the linear equations in a system represent a pair of perpendicular lines, how many solutions does the system have?

If a system of linear equations has one or more solutions, the system is said to be **consistent**. If a system of linear equations has no solution, it is said to be **inconsistent**.

If two equations represent the same line, the equations are said to be **dependent equations**. In this case, all points on the line are solutions to the system. If two equations represent two different lines the equations are said to be **independent equations**. In this case, the lines either intersect at one point or are parallel.

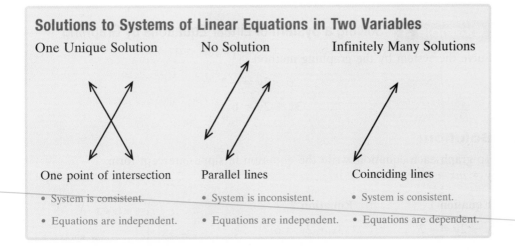

Solutions to Systems of Linear Equations in Two Variables

One Unique Solution   No Solution   Infinitely Many Solutions

One point of intersection   Parallel lines   Coinciding lines

• System is consistent.   • System is inconsistent.   • System is consistent.

• Equations are independent. • Equations are independent. • Equations are dependent.

2. Solving Systems of Linear Equations by Graphing

One way to find a solution to a system of equations is to graph the equations and find the point (or points) of intersection. This is called the *graphing method* to solve a system of equations.

Answers

3. Zero   **4.** One

Example 2 **Solving a System of Linear Equations by Graphing**

Solve the system by the graphing method. $y = 2x$

$$y = 2$$

Solution:

The equation $y = 2x$ is written in slope-intercept form as $y = 2x + 0$. The line passes through the origin, with a slope of 2.

The line $y = 2$ is a horizontal line and has a slope of 0.

Because the lines have different slopes, the lines must be different and nonparallel. From this, we know that the lines must intersect at exactly one point. Graph the lines to find the point of intersection (Figure 4-2).

The point $(1, 2)$ appears to be the point of intersection. This can be confirmed by substituting $x = 1$ and $y = 2$ into both original equations.

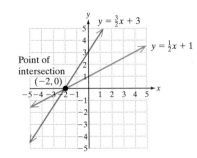

Figure 4-2

$$y = 2x \qquad (2) \overset{?}{=} 2(1) \checkmark \quad \text{True}$$

$$y = 2 \qquad (2) \overset{?}{=} 2 \checkmark \quad \text{True}$$

The solution is $(1, 2)$.

Example 3 **Solving a System of Linear Equations by Graphing**

Solve the system by the graphing method.

$$x - 2y = -2$$

$$-3x + 2y = 6$$

Solution:

To graph each equation, write the equation in slope-intercept form: $y = mx + b$.

Equation 1

$$x - 2y = -2$$

$$-2y = -x - 2$$

$$\frac{-2y}{-2} = \frac{-x}{-2} - \frac{2}{-2}$$

$$y = \frac{1}{2}x + 1$$

Equation 2

$$-3x + 2y = 6$$

$$2y = 3x + 6$$

$$\frac{2y}{2} = \frac{3x}{2} + \frac{6}{2}$$

$$y = \frac{3}{2}x + 3$$

Figure 4-3

From their slope-intercept forms, we see that the lines have different slopes, indicating that the lines are different and nonparallel. Therefore, the lines must intersect at exactly one point. Graph the lines to find that point (Figure 4-3).

Answers

5. $(-1, 3)$

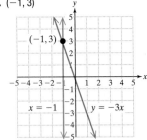

6. $(1, -1)$

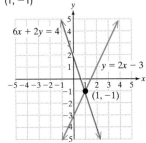

The point $(-2, 0)$ appears to be the point of intersection. This can be confirmed by substituting $x = -2$ and $y = 0$ into both equations.

$$x - 2y = -2 \longrightarrow (-2) - 2(0) \overset{?}{=} -2 \; ✔ \quad \text{True}$$

$$-3x + 2y = 6 \longrightarrow -3(-2) + 2(0) \overset{?}{=} 6 \; ✔ \quad \text{True}$$

The solution is $(-2, 0)$.

TIP: In Examples 2 and 3, the lines could also have been graphed by using the *x*- and *y*-intercepts or by using a table of points. However, the advantage of writing the equations in slope-intercept form is that we can compare the slopes and *y*-intercepts of the two lines.

1. If the slopes differ, the lines are different and nonparallel and must intersect in exactly one point.

2. If the slopes are the same and the *y*-intercepts are different, the lines are parallel and will not intersect.

3. If the slopes are the same and the *y*-intercepts are the same, the two equations represent the same line.

Example 4 **Graphing an Inconsistent System**

Solve the system by graphing.

$$-x + 3y = -6$$

$$6y = 2x + 6$$

Solution:

To graph the lines, write each equation in slope-intercept form.

Equation 1	**Equation 2**
$-x + 3y = -6$	$6y = 2x + 6$
$3y = x - 6$	
$\dfrac{3y}{3} = \dfrac{x}{3} - \dfrac{6}{3}$	$\dfrac{6y}{6} = \dfrac{2x}{6} + \dfrac{6}{6}$
$y = \dfrac{1}{3}x - 2$	$y = \dfrac{1}{3}x + 1$

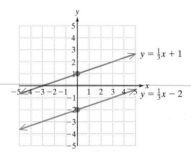

Figure 4-4

Because the lines have the same slope but different *y*-intercepts, they are parallel (Figure 4-4). Two parallel lines do not intersect, which implies that the system has no solution. The system is inconsistent.

Skill Practice

Solve the system by graphing.

7. $4x + y = 8$
   $y = -4x + 3$

Answer

7.

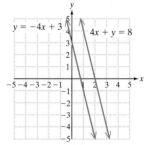

No solution, the lines are parallel. The system is inconsistent.

Example 5 Graphing a System of Dependent Equations

Solve the system by graphing.

$$x + 4y = 8$$

$$y = -\frac{1}{4}x + 2$$

Solution:

Write the first equation in slope-intercept form. The second equation is already in slope-intercept form.

Equation 1	**Equation 2**
$x + 4y = 8$	$y = -\dfrac{1}{4}x + 2$
$4y = -x + 8$	
$\dfrac{4y}{4} = \dfrac{-x}{4} + \dfrac{8}{4}$	
$y = -\dfrac{1}{4}x + 2$	

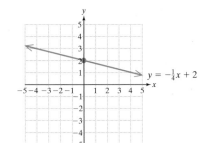

Figure 4-5

Answer

8.

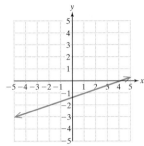

$$\left\{(x, y)\,\middle|\, y = \frac{1}{3}x - \frac{4}{3}\right\}$$

The equations are dependent.

Notice that the slope-intercept forms of the two lines are identical. Therefore, the equations represent the same line (Figure 4-5). The equations are dependent, and the solution to the system of equations is the set of all points on the line.

Because the ordered pairs in the solution set cannot all be listed, we can write the solution in set-builder notation: $\{(x, y)\,|\, y = -\frac{1}{4}x + 2\}$. This can be read as "the set of all ordered pairs (x, y) such that the ordered pairs satisfy the equation $y = -\frac{1}{4}x + 2$."

In summary:

- There are infinitely many solutions to the system of equations.
- The solution set is $\{(x, y)\,|\, y = -\frac{1}{4}x + 2\}$.
- The equations are dependent.

Calculator Connections

Topic: Graphing Systems of Linear Equations in Two Variables

The solution to a system of equations can be found by using either a *Trace* feature or an *Intersect* feature on a graphing calculator to find the point of intersection of two graphs.

For example, consider the system:

$$-2x + y = 6$$

$$5x + y = -1$$

First graph the equations together on the same viewing window. Recall that to enter the equations into the calculator, the equations must be written with the y variable isolated.

Isolate y.

$$-2x + y = 6 \longrightarrow y = 2x + 6$$

$$5x + y = -1 \longrightarrow y = -5x - 1$$

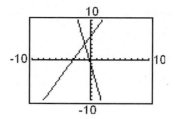

By inspection of the graph, it appears that the solution is $(-1, 4)$. The *Trace* option on the calculator may come close to $(-1, 4)$ but may not show the exact solution (Figure 4-6). However, an *Intersect* feature on a graphing calculator may provide the exact solution (Figure 4-7).

Using *Trace*

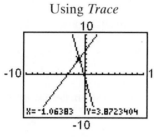

Using *Intersect*

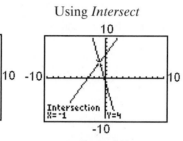

Figure 4-6

Figure 4-7

Calculator Exercises

Use a graphing calculator to graph each pair of linear equations on the same viewing window. Use a *Trace* or *Intersect* feature to find the point(s) of intersection.

1. $y = 2x - 3$
$y = -4x + 9$

2. $y = -\dfrac{1}{2}x + 2$
$y = \dfrac{1}{3}x - 3$

3. $x + y = 4$ (Example 1)
$-2x + y = -5$

4. $x - 2y = -2$ (Example 3)
$-3x + 2y = 6$

5. $-x + 3y = -6$ (Example 4)
$6y = 2x + 6$

6. $x + 4y = 8$ (Example 5)
$y = -\dfrac{1}{4}x + 2$

Section 4.1 Practice Exercises

Study Skills Exercise

Figure out your grade at this point. Are you earning the grade that you want? If not, maybe organizing a study group would help.

In a study group, check the activities that you might try to help you learn and understand the material.

_____ Quiz each other by asking each other questions.

_____ Practice teaching each other.

_____ Share and compare class notes.

_____ Support and encourage each other.

_____ Work together on exercises and sample problems.

Vocabulary and Key Concepts

1. **a.** A _____ of linear equations consists of two or more linear equations.

   b. A _____ to a system of linear equations must be a solution to both individual equations in the system.

   c. Graphically, a solution to a system of linear equations in two variables is a point where the lines _____.

   d. A system of equations that has one or more solutions is said to be _____.

   e. A system of equations with no solution is said to be _____.

   f. Two equations in a system of linear equations in two variables are said to be _____ if they represent the same line.

   g. Two equations in a system of linear equations in two variables are said to be _____ if they represent different lines.

Concept 1: Solutions to a System of Linear Equations

For Exercises 2–10, determine if the given point is a solution to the system. **(See Example 1.)**

2. $6x - y = -9$ $(-1, 3)$
   $x + 2y = 5$

3. $3x - y = 7$ $(2, -1)$
   $x - 2y = 4$

4. $x - y = 3$ $(4, 1)$
   $x + y = 5$

5. $4y = -3x + 12$ $(0, 4)$
   $y = \dfrac{2}{3}x - 4$

6. $y = -\dfrac{1}{3}x + 2$ $(9, -1)$
   $x = 2y + 6$

7. $3x - 6y = 9$ $\left(4, \dfrac{1}{2}\right)$
   $x - 2y = 3$

8. $x - y = 4$ $(6, 2)$
   $3x - 3y = 12$

9. $\dfrac{1}{3}x = \dfrac{2}{5}y - \dfrac{4}{5}$ $(0, 2)$
   $\dfrac{3}{4}x + \dfrac{1}{2}y = 2$

10. $\dfrac{1}{4}x + \dfrac{1}{2}y = \dfrac{3}{2}$ $(4, 1)$
    $y = \dfrac{3}{2}x - 6$

For Exercises 11–14, match the graph of the system of equations with the appropriate description of the solution.

11.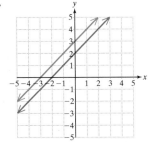

a. The solution is $(1, 3)$.

b. No solution.

c. There are infinitely many solutions.

d. The solution is $(0, 0)$.

12.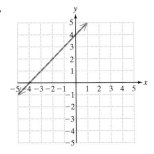

13.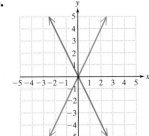

14.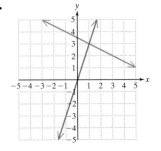

15. Graph each system of equations.

a. $y = 2x - 3$

$y = 2x + 5$

b. $y = 2x + 1$

$y = 4x - 5$

c. $y = 3x - 5$

$y = 3x - 5$

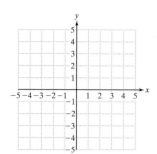 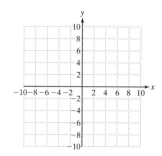 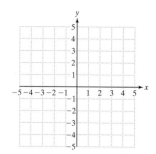

For Exercises 16–26, determine which system of equations (a, b, or c) makes the statement true. (*Hint:* Refer to the graphs from Exercise 15.)

a. $y = 2x - 3$

$y = 2x + 5$

b. $y = 2x + 1$

$y = 4x - 5$

c. $y = 3x - 5$

$y = 3x - 5$

16. The lines are parallel.

17. The lines coincide.

18. The lines intersect at exactly one point.

19. The system is inconsistent.

20. The equations are dependent.

21. The lines have the same slope but different y-intercepts.

22. The lines have the same slope and same y-intercept.

23. The lines have different slopes.

24. The system has exactly one solution.

25. The system has infinitely many solutions.

26. The system has no solution.

Concept 2: Solving Systems of Linear Equations by Graphing

For Exercises 27–50, solve the system by graphing. For systems that do not have one unique solution, also state the number of solutions and whether the system is inconsistent or the equations are dependent. **(See Examples 2–5.)**

27. $y = -x + 4$

$y = x - 2$

28. $y = 3x + 2$

$y = 2x$

29. $2x + y = 0$

$3x + y = 1$

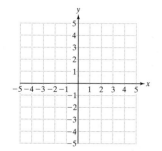 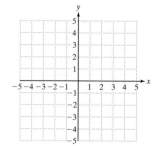 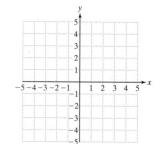

30. $x + y = -1$

  $2x - y = -5$

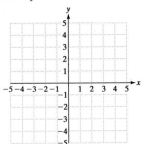

31. $2x + y = 6$

  $x = 1$

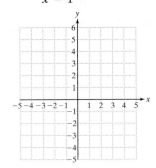

32. $4x + 3y = 9$

  $x = 3$

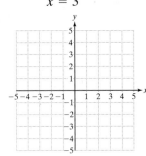

33. $-6x - 3y = 0$

  $4x + 2y = 4$

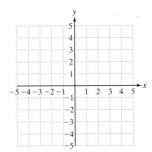

34. $2x - 6y = 12$

  $-3x + 9y = 12$

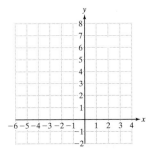

35. $-2x + y = 3$

  $6x - 3y = -9$

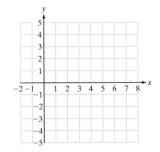

36. $x + 3y = 0$

  $-2x - 6y = 0$

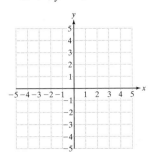

37. $y = 6$

  $2x + 3y = 12$

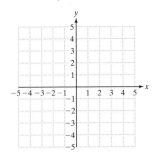

38. $y = -2$

  $x - 2y = 10$

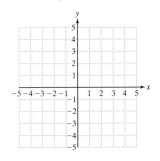

39. $x = 4 + y$

  $3y = -3x$

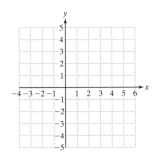

40. $3y = 4x$

  $x - y = -1$

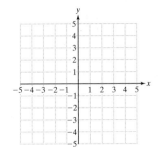

41. $-x + y = 3$

  $4y = 4x + 6$

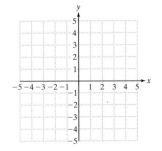

42. $x - y = 4$

$3y = 3x + 6$

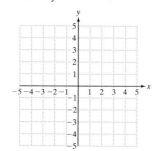

43. $x = 4$

$2y = 4$

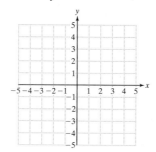

44. $-3x = 6$

$y = 2$

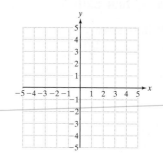

45. $2x + y = 4$

$4x - 2y = 0$

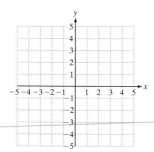

46. $3x + 3y = 3$

$2x - y = 5$

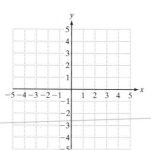

47. $y = 0.5x + 2$

$-x + 2y = 4$

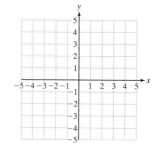

48. $3x - 4y = 6$

$-6x + 8y = -12$

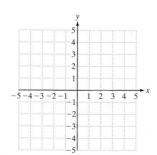

49. $x - 3y = 0$

$y = -x - 4$

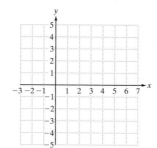

50. $-6x + 3y = -6$

$4x + y = -2$

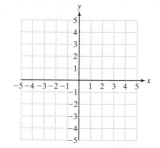

51. A wholesale club offers two types of memberships. The Executive Membership is $100 a year, including an annual 2% reward. The Business Membership is $50 a year without a reward. The total cost for membership, y, depends on the amount of money spent on merchandise, x, and can be represented by the following equations:

Executive Membership: $y = 100 - 0.02x$

Business Membership: $y = 50$

According to the graph, how much money spent on merchandise would result in the same cost for each membership?

52. The cost to rent a 10-ft by 10-ft storage space is different for two different storage companies. The Storage Bin charges \$90 per month plus a nonrefundable deposit of \$120. AAA Storage charges \$110 per month with no deposit. The total cost, y, to rent a 10-ft by 10-ft space depends on the number of months, x, according to the equations

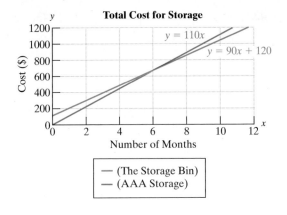

Total Cost for Storage

The Storage Bin: $y = 90x + 120$

AAA Storage: $y = 110x$

From the graph, determine the number of months required for which the cost to rent space is equal for both companies.

For the systems graphed in Exercises 53 and 54, explain why the ordered pair cannot be a solution to the system of equations.

53. $(-3, 1)$

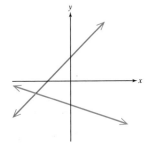

54. $(-1, -4)$

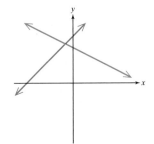

Expanding Your Skills

55. Write a system of linear equations whose solution is $(2, 1)$.

56. Write a system of linear equations whose solution is $(1, 4)$.

57. One equation in a system of linear equations is $x + y = 4$. Write a second equation such that the system will have no solution. (Answers may vary.)

58. One equation in a system of linear equations is $x - y = 3$. Write a second equation such that the system will have infinitely many solutions. (Answers may vary.)

Section 4.2 Solving Systems of Equations by the Substitution Method

Concepts

1. Solving Systems of Linear Equations by Using the Substitution Method
2. Applications of the Substitution Method

1. Solving Systems of Linear Equations by Using the Substitution Method

In Section 4.1, we used the graphing method to find the solution(s) to a system of equations. However, sometimes it is difficult to determine the solution using this method because of limitations in the accuracy of the graph. This is particularly true when the coordinates of a solution are not integer values or when the solution is a point not sufficiently close to the origin. Identifying the coordinates of the point $\left(\frac{3}{17}, -\frac{23}{9}\right)$ or $(-251, 8349)$, for example, might be difficult from a graph.

In this section and the next, we will cover two algebraic methods to solve a system of equations that do not require graphing. The first method, called the *substitution method*, is demonstrated in Examples 1–5.

| **Example 1** | Solving a System of Linear Equations by Using the Substitution Method |

Solve by using the substitution method.

$$x = 2y - 3$$
$$-4x + 3y = 2$$

Solution:

The variable x has been isolated in the first equation. The quantity $2y - 3$ is equal to x and therefore can be substituted for x in the second equation. This leaves the second equation in terms of y only.

First equation: $x = \underbrace{2y - 3}$

Second equation: $-4x + 3y = 2$

$-4(2y - 3) + 3y = 2$ This equation now contains only one variable.

$-8y + 12 + 3y = 2$ Solve the resulting equation.

$-5y + 12 = 2$

$-5y = -10$

$y = 2$

To find x, substitute $y = 2$ back into the first equation.

$$x = 2y - 3$$
$$x = 2(2) - 3$$
$$x = 1$$

Check the ordered pair $(1, 2)$ in both original equations.

$x = 2y - 3 \longrightarrow 1 \stackrel{?}{=} 2(2) - 3$ ✔   True

$-4x + 3y = 2 \longrightarrow -4(1) + 3(2) \stackrel{?}{=} 2$ ✔   True

The solution is $(1, 2)$ because it checks in both original equations.

Skill Practice

Solve the system by the substitution method.
1. $2x + 3y = -2$
     $y = x + 1$

In Example 1, we eliminated the x variable from the second equation by substituting an equivalent expression for x. The resulting equation was relatively simple to solve because it had only one variable. This is the premise of the substitution method.

Answer

1. $(-1, 0)$

The substitution method can be summarized as follows.

Solving a System of Equations by Using the Substitution Method

Step 1 Isolate one of the variables from one equation.

Step 2 Substitute the expression found in step 1 into the other equation.

Step 3 Solve the resulting equation.

Step 4 Substitute the value found in step 3 back into the equation in step 1 to find the value of the remaining variable.

Step 5 Check the solution in both original equations and write the answer as an ordered pair.

Skill Practice

Solve the system by the substitution method.

2. $x + y = 3$
$-2x + 3y = 9$

Example 2 Solving a System of Linear Equations by Using the Substitution Method

Solve the system using the substitution method.

$$x + y = 4$$
$$-5x + 3y = -12$$

Solution:

The x or y variable in the first equation is easy to isolate because the coefficients are both 1. While either variable can be isolated, we arbitrarily choose to solve for the x variable.

$x + y = 4 \longrightarrow x = \underbrace{4 - y}$ **Step 1:** Isolate x in the first equation.

$-5(4 - y) + 3y = -12$ **Step 2:** Substitute $4 - y$ for x in the other equation.

$-20 + 5y + 3y = -12$ **Step 3:** Solve for y.

$-20 + 8y = -12$

$8y = 8$

$y = 1$

$x = 4 - y$ **Step 4:** Substitute $y = 1$ into the equation $x = 4 - y$.

$x = 4 - 1$

$x = 3$

Step 5: Check the ordered pair $(3, 1)$ in both original equations.

$$x + y = 4 \qquad (3) + (1) \stackrel{?}{=} 4 ✔ \qquad \text{True}$$
$$-5x + 3y = -12 \qquad -5(3) + 3(1) \stackrel{?}{=} -12 ✔ \qquad \text{True}$$

The solution is $(3, 1)$ because it checks in both original equations.

Answer

2. $(0, 3)$

TIP: The solution to a system of linear equations can be confirmed by graphing. The system from Example 2 is graphed here.

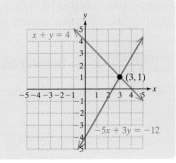

Example 3 Solving a System of Linear Equations by Using the Substitution Method

Solve the system by using the substitution method.

$$3x + 5y = 17$$
$$2x - y = -6$$

Solution:

The y variable in the second equation is the easiest variable to isolate because its coefficient is -1.

$3x + 5y = 17$

$2x - y = -6 \longrightarrow -y = -2x - 6$

$\qquad\qquad\qquad y = \underline{2x + 6}$ **Step 1:** Isolate y in the second equation.

$3x + 5(2x + 6) = 17$ **Step 2:** Substitute the quantity $2x + 6$ for y in the other equation.

$3x + 10x + 30 = 17$ **Step 3:** Solve for x.

$13x + 30 = 17$

$\qquad 13x = 17 - 30$

$\qquad 13x = -13$

$\qquad\quad x = -1$

$y = 2x + 6$ **Step 4:** Substitute $x = -1$ into the equation $y = 2x + 6$.

$y = 2(-1) + 6$

$y = -2 + 6$

$y = 4$

Step 5: The ordered pair $(-1, 4)$ can be checked in the original equations to verify the answer.

$3x + 5y = 17 \longrightarrow 3(-1) + 5(4) \stackrel{?}{=} 17 \longrightarrow -3 + 20 \stackrel{?}{=} 17$ ✔ True

$2x - y = -6 \longrightarrow 2(-1) - (4) \stackrel{?}{=} -6 \longrightarrow -2 - 4 \stackrel{?}{=} -6$ ✔ True

The solution is $(-1, 4)$.

Skill Practice

Solve the system by the substitution method.

3. $x + 4y = 11$
     $2x - 5y = -4$

Avoiding Mistakes

Do not substitute $y = 2x + 6$ into the same equation from which it came. This mistake will result in an identity:

$$2x - y = -6$$
$$2x - (2x + 6) = -6$$
$$2x - 2x - 6 = -6$$
$$-6 = -6$$

Answer

3. $(3, 2)$

Recall from Section 4.1 that a system of linear equations may represent two parallel lines. In such a case, there is no solution to the system.

Skill Practice

Solve the system by the substitution method.

4. $y = -\dfrac{1}{2}x + 3$

$2x + 4y = 5$

Example 4 Solving an Inconsistent System Using Substitution

Solve the system by using the substitution method.

$$2x + 3y = 6$$
$$y = -\tfrac{2}{3}x + 4$$

Solution:

$$2x + 3y = 6$$

$$y = -\tfrac{2}{3}x + 4 \qquad \textbf{Step 1:} \quad \text{The variable } y \text{ is already isolated in the second equation.}$$

$$2x + 3\left(-\tfrac{2}{3}x + 4\right) = 6 \qquad \textbf{Step 2:} \quad \text{Substitute } y = -\tfrac{2}{3}x + 4 \text{ from the second equation into the first equation.}$$

$$2x - 2x + 12 = 6 \qquad \textbf{Step 3:} \quad \text{Solve the resulting equation.}$$

$$12 = 6 \quad \text{(contradiction)}$$

The equation results in a contradiction. There are no values of x and y that will make 12 equal to 6. Therefore, there is no solution, and the system is inconsistent.

TIP: The answer to Example 4 can be verified by writing each equation in slope-intercept form and graphing the lines.

Equation 1	Equation 2
$2x + 3y = 6$	$y = -\dfrac{2}{3}x + 4$

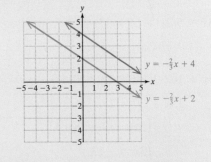

$$3y = -2x + 6$$

$$\frac{3y}{3} = \frac{-2x}{3} + \frac{6}{3}$$

$$y = -\frac{2}{3}x + 2$$

The equations indicate that the lines have the same slope but different y-intercepts. Therefore, the lines must be parallel. There is no point of intersection, indicating that the system has no solution.

Recall that a system of two linear equations may represent the same line. In such a case, the solution is the set of all points on the line.

Answer

4. No solution.

| Example 5 | Solving a System of Dependent Equations Using Substitution |

Solve the system by using the substitution method.

$$\frac{1}{2}x - \frac{1}{4}y = 1$$

$$6x - 3y = 12$$

Solution:

$\frac{1}{2}x - \frac{1}{4}y = 1$ To make the first equation easier to work with, we have

$6x - 3y = 12$ the option of clearing fractions.

$$\frac{1}{2}x - \frac{1}{4}y = 1 \xrightarrow{\text{Multiply by 4.}} 4\left(\frac{1}{2}x\right) - 4\left(\frac{1}{4}y\right) = 4(1) \longrightarrow 2x - y = 4$$

Now the system becomes:

$2x - y = 4$ The y variable in the first equation is the easiest to

$6x - 3y = 12$ isolate because its coefficient is -1.

$\begin{matrix} 2x - y = 4 \\ 6x - 3y = 12 \end{matrix} \xrightarrow{\text{Solve for } y.} -y = -2x + 4 \rightarrow y = 2x - 4$ **Step 1:** Isolate one of the variables.

$6x - 3(2x - 4) = 12$ **Step 2:** Substitute $y = 2x - 4$ from the first equation into the second equation.

$6x - 6x + 12 = 12$ **Step 3:** Solve the resulting equation.
$\quad\quad 12 = 12$ (identity)

     Because the equation produces an identity, all values of x make this equation true. Thus, x can be any real number. Substituting any real number, x, into the equation $y = 2x - 4$ produces an ordered pair on the line $y = 2x - 4$. Hence, the solution set to the system of equations is the set of all ordered pairs on the line $y = 2x - 4$. This can be written as $\{(x, y) | y = 2x - 4\}$. The equations are dependent.

Skill Practice

Solve the system by using the substitution method.

5. $2x + \frac{1}{3}y = -\frac{1}{3}$

     $12x + 2y = -2$

TIP: The solution to Example 5 can be verified by writing each equation in slope-intercept form and graphing the lines.

Equation 1	**Equation 2**

Clear fractions $\begin{cases} \frac{1}{2}x - \frac{1}{4}y = 1 \\ 2x - y = 4 \end{cases}$ $6x - 3y = 12$

$\qquad\qquad -3y = -6x + 12$

$-y = -2x + 4 \qquad\qquad \dfrac{-3y}{-3} = \dfrac{-6x}{-3} + \dfrac{12}{-3}$

$y = 2x - 4 \qquad\qquad\qquad y = 2x - 4$

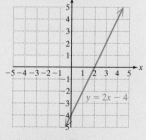

Notice that the slope-intercept forms for both equations are identical. The equations represent the same line, indicating that the equations are dependent. Each point on the line is a solution to the system of equations.

Answer

5. Infinitely many solutions;
    $\{(x, y) | 12x + 2y = -2\}$;
    dependent equations

The following summary reviews the three different geometric relationships between two lines and the solutions to the corresponding systems of equations.

> **Interpreting Solutions to a System of Two Linear Equations**
> - The lines may intersect at one point (yielding one unique solution).
> - The lines may be parallel and have no point of intersection (yielding no solution). This is detected algebraically when a contradiction (false statement) is obtained (for example, $0 = -3$ and $12 = 6$).
> - The lines may be the same and intersect at all points on the line (yielding an infinite number of solutions). This is detected algebraically when an identity is obtained (for example, $0 = 0$ and $12 = 12$).

2. Applications of the Substitution Method

In Chapter 2, we solved word problems using one linear equation and one variable. In this chapter, we investigate application problems with two unknowns. In such a case, we can use two variables to represent the unknown quantities. However, if two variables are used, we must write a system of *two* distinct equations.

Skill Practice

6. One number is 16 more than another. Their sum is 92. Use a system of equations to find the numbers.

Example 6 Applying the Substitution Method

One number is 3 more than 4 times another. Their sum is 133. Find the numbers.

Solution:

We can use two variables to represent the two unknown numbers.

Let x represent one number.
Let y represent the other number.   Label the unknowns.

We must now write two equations. Each of the first two sentences gives a relationship between x and y:

One number is 3 more than 4 times another. $\longrightarrow x = 4y + 3$ (first equation)

Their sum is 133. $\longrightarrow x + y = 133$ (second equation)

	Step 1: Notice that x is already isolated in the first equation.
$(4y + 3) + y = 133$	**Step 2:** Substitute $x = 4y + 3$ into the second equation, $x + y = 133$.
$5y + 3 = 133$	**Step 3:** Solve the resulting equation.
$5y = 130$	
$y = 26$	

Answer

6. One number is 38, and the other number is 54.

$$x = 4y + 3$$

$$x = 4(26) + 3$$ **Step 4:** To solve for x, substitute $y = 26$ into the equation
$$x = 104 + 3$$ $x = 4y + 3$.

$$x = 107$$

One number is 26, and the other is 107.

Avoiding Mistakes

Notice that the answer for an application is not represented by an ordered pair.

TIP: Check that the numbers 26 and 107 meet the conditions of Example 6.
- 4 times 26 is 104. Three more than 104 is 107. ✔
- The sum of the numbers should be 133: $26 + 107 = 133$. ✔

Example 7 **Using the Substitution Method in a Geometry Application**

Two angles are supplementary. The measure of one angle is 15° more than twice the measure of the other angle. Find the measures of the two angles.

Solution:

Let x represent the measure of one angle.
Let y represent the measure of the other angle.

The sum of the measures of supplementary angles is 180°. ⟶ $x + y = 180$

The measure of one angle is 15° more than
twice the other angle. ⟶ $x = 2y + 15$

$$x + y = 180$$
$$x = 2y + 15$$ **Step 1:** The x variable in the second equation is already isolated.

$$(2y + 15) + y = 180$$ **Step 2:** Substitute $2y + 15$ into the first equation for x.

$$2y + 15 + y = 180$$ **Step 3:** Solve the resulting equation.
$$3y + 15 = 180$$
$$3y = 165$$
$$y = 55$$

$$x = 2y + 15$$ **Step 4:** Substitute $y = 55$ into the equation
$$x = 2(55) + 15$$ $x = 2y + 15$.
$$x = 110 + 15$$
$$x = 125$$

The measure of one angle is 55°, and the other is 125°.

Skill Practice

7. The measure of one angle is 2° less than 3 times the measure of another angle. The angles are complementary. Use a system of equations to find the measures of the two angles.

TIP: Check that the angles 55° and 125° meet the conditions of Example 7.
- Because $55° + 125° = 180°$, the angles are supplementary. ✔
- The measure 125° is 15° more than twice 55°: $125° = 2(55°) + 15°$. ✔

Answer

7. The measures of the angles are 23° and 67°.

Section 4.2 Practice Exercises

Review Exercises

For Exercises 1–6, write each pair of lines in slope-intercept form. Then identify whether the lines intersect in exactly one point or if the lines are parallel or coinciding.

1. $2x - y = 4$
$-2y = -4x + 8$

2. $x - 2y = 5$
$3x = 6y + 15$

3. $2x + 3y = 6$
$x - y = 5$

4. $x - y = -1$
$x + 2y = 4$

5. $2x = \frac{1}{2}y + 2$
$4x - y = 13$

6. $4y = 3x$
$3x - 4y = 15$

Concept 1: Solving Systems of Linear Equations by Using the Substitution Method

For Exercises 7–10, solve each system using the substitution method. **(See Example 1.)**

7. $3x + 2y = -3$
$y = 2x - 12$

8. $4x - 3y = -19$
$y = -2x + 13$

9. $x = -4y + 16$
$3x + 5y = 20$

10. $x = -y + 3$
$-2x + y = 6$

11. Given the system: $4x - 2y = -6$
$3x + y = 8$

  a. Which variable from which equation is easiest to isolate and why?

  b. Solve the system using the substitution method.

12. Given the system: $x - 5y = 2$
$11x + 13y = 22$

  a. Which variable from which equation is easiest to isolate and why?

  b. Solve the system using the substitution method.

For Exercises 13–48, solve the system by using the substitution method. For systems that do not have one unique solution, also state the number of solutions and whether the system is inconsistent or the equations are dependent. **(See Examples 1–5.)**

13. $x = 3y - 1$
$2x - 4y = 2$

14. $2y = x + 9$
$y = -3x + 1$

15. $-2x + 5y = 5$
$x = 4y - 10$

16. $y = -2x + 27$
$3x - 7y = -2$

17. $4x - y = -1$
$2x + 4y = 13$

18. $5x - 3y = -2$
$10x - y = 1$

19. $4x - 3y = 11$
$x = 5$

20. $y = -3x - 9$
$y = 12$

21. $2y = x - 1$
$5x - 3y = 5$

22. $3y = 6x - 6$
$-3x + y = -4$

23. $x - 3y = -11$
$6x - y = 2$

24. $-2x - y = 9$
$x + 7y = 15$

25. $3x + 2y = -1$
$\frac{3}{2}x + y = 4$

26. $5x - 2y = 6$
$-\frac{5}{2}x + y = 5$

27. $10x - 30y = -10$
$2x - 6y = -2$

28. $3x + 6y = 6$
$-6x - 12y = -12$

29. $2x + y = 3$
$y = -7$

30. $-3x = 2y + 23$
$x = -1$

31. $x + 2y = -2$
$4x = -2y - 17$

32. $x + y = 1$
$2x - y = -2$

33. $y = -\frac{1}{2}x - 4$
$y = 4x - 13$

34. $y = \frac{2}{3}x - 3$
$y = 6x - 19$

35. $y = 6$
$y - 4 = -2x - 6$

36. $x = 9$
$x - 3 = 6y + 12$

37. $y = \dfrac{3}{2}x + 2$

    $3x + 4y = -1$

38. $x = \dfrac{3}{4}y - 1$

    $8x - 5y = -7$

39. $y = 0.25x + 1$

    $-x + 4y = 4$

40. $y = 0.75x - 3$

    $-3x + 4y = -12$

41. $0.2x + 0.1y = 1.1$

    $1.5x - 0.2y = 5.4$

42. $0.1x = 0.3y + 0.7$

    $0.1y = -0.5x + 0.3$

43. $x + 2y = 4$

    $4y = -2x - 8$

44. $-y = x - 6$

    $2x + 2y = 4$

45. $2x = 3 - y$

    $x + y = 4$

46. $2x = 4 + 2y$

    $3x + y = 10$

47. $\dfrac{x}{3} + \dfrac{y}{2} = -4$

    $x - 3y = 6$

48. $x - 2y = -5$

    $\dfrac{2x}{3} + \dfrac{y}{3} = 0$

Concept 2: Applications of the Substitution Method

For Exercises 49–58, set up a system of linear equations and solve for the indicated quantities. **(See Examples 6 and 7.)**

49. Two numbers have a sum of 106. One number is 10 less than the other. Find the numbers.

50. Two positive numbers have a difference of 8. The larger number is 2 less than 3 times the smaller number. Find the numbers.

51. The difference between two positive numbers is 26. The larger number is three times the smaller. Find the numbers.

52. The sum of two numbers is 956. One number is 94 less than 6 times the other. Find the numbers.

53. Two angles are supplementary. One angle is 15° more than 10 times the other angle. Find the measure of each angle.

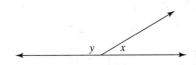

54. Two angles are complementary. One angle is 1° less than 6 times the other angle. Find the measure of each angle.

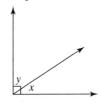

55. Two angles are complementary. One angle is 10° more than 3 times the other angle. Find the measure of each angle.

56. Two angles are supplementary. One angle is 5° less than twice the other angle. Find the measure of each angle.

57. In a right triangle, one of the acute angles is 6° less than the other acute angle. Find the measure of each acute angle.

58. In a right triangle, one of the acute angles is 9° less than twice the other acute angle. Find the measure of each acute angle.

Expanding Your Skills

59. The following system consists of dependent equations and therefore has infinitely many solutions. Find three ordered pairs that are solutions to the system of equations.

$$y = 2x + 3$$
$$-4x + 2y = 6$$

60. The following system consists of dependent equations and therefore has infinitely many solutions. Find three ordered pairs that are solutions to the system of equations.

$$y = -x + 1$$
$$2x + 2y = 2$$

Section 4.3 Solving Systems of Equations by the Addition Method

1. Solving Systems of Linear Equations by Using the Addition Method

Thus far in Chapter 4 we have used the graphing method and the substitution method to solve a system of linear equations in two variables. In this section, we present another algebraic method to solve a system of linear equations, called the *addition method* (sometimes called the *elimination method*). The purpose of the addition method is to eliminate one variable.

Skill Practice

Solve the system using the addition method.

1. $x + y = 13$
    $2x - y = 2$

Example 1   Solving a System of Equations by Using the Addition Method

Solve the system using the addition method.

$$x + y = -2$$
$$x - y = -6$$

Solution:

Notice that the coefficients of the y variables are opposites:

Coefficient is 1.

$$x + 1y = -2$$
$$x - 1y = -6$$

Coefficient is -1.

Because the coefficients of the y variables are opposites, we can add the two equations to eliminate the y variable.

$$x + y = -2$$
$$\underline{x - y = -6}$$
$$2x \qquad = -8 \quad \leftarrow \text{After adding the equations, we have one equation and one variable.}$$

$$2x = -8 \qquad \text{Solve the resulting equation.}$$
$$x = -4$$

To find the value of y, substitute $x = -4$ into *either* of the original equations.

$$x + y = -2 \qquad \text{First equation}$$
$$(-4) + y = -2$$
$$y = -2 + 4$$
$$y = 2$$

The solution is $(-4, 2)$.

TIP: Notice that the value $x = -4$ could have been substituted into the second equation to obtain the same value for y.

$$x - y = -6$$
$$(-4) - y = -6$$
$$-y = -6 + 4$$
$$-y = -2$$
$$y = 2$$

Check:

$$x + y = -2 \longrightarrow (-4) + (2) \stackrel{?}{=} -2 \longrightarrow -2 \stackrel{?}{=} -2 \ \checkmark \ \text{True}$$
$$x - y = -6 \longrightarrow (-4) - (2) \stackrel{?}{=} -6 \longrightarrow -6 \stackrel{?}{=} -6 \ \checkmark \ \text{True}$$

Answer

1. $(5, 8)$

It is important to note that the addition method works on the premise that the two equations have *opposite* values for the coefficients of one of the variables. Sometimes it is necessary to manipulate the original equations to create two coefficients that are opposites. This is accomplished by multiplying one or both equations by an appropriate constant. The process is outlined as follows.

Solving a System of Equations by Using the Addition Method

Step 1 Write both equations in standard form: $Ax + By = C$.

Step 2 Clear fractions or decimals (optional).

Step 3 Multiply one or both equations by nonzero constants to create opposite coefficients for one of the variables.

Step 4 Add the equations from step 3 to eliminate one variable.

Step 5 Solve for the remaining variable.

Step 6 Substitute the known value from step 5 into one of the original equations to solve for the other variable.

Step 7 Check the solution in both original equations.

Example 2 Solving a System of Linear Equations Using the Addition Method

Solve the system using the addition method.

$$3x + 5y = 17$$
$$2x - y = -6$$

Solution:

$3x + 5y = 17$ **Step 1:** Both equations are already written in standard form.

$2x - y = -6$ **Step 2:** There are no fractions or decimals.

Notice that neither the coefficients of x nor the coefficients of y are opposites. However, multiplying the second equation by 5 creates the term $-5y$ in the second equation. This is the opposite of the term $+5y$ in the first equation.

$3x + 5y = 17$ $\qquad$ $3x + 5y = 17$ **Step 3:** Multiply the second equation by 5.

$2x - y = -6$ $\xrightarrow{\text{Multiply by 5.}}$ $\dfrac{10x - 5y = -30}{13x = -13}$ **Step 4:** Add the equations.

$13x = -13$ **Step 5:** Solve the equation.

$x = -1$

$3x + 5y = 17$ $\quad$ First equation **Step 6:** Substitute $x = -1$ into one of the original equations.

$3(-1) + 5y = 17$

$-3 + 5y = 17$

$5y = 20$

$y = 4$

The solution is $(-1, 4)$. **Step 7:** Check the solution in both original equations.

Check:

$3x + 5y = 17 \longrightarrow 3(-1) + 5(4) \overset{?}{=} 17 \longrightarrow -3 + 20 \overset{?}{=} 17 \checkmark$ True

$2x - y = -6 \longrightarrow 2(-1) - (4) \overset{?}{=} -6 \longrightarrow -2 - 4 \overset{?}{=} -6 \checkmark$ True

---

Skill Practice

Solve the system using the addition method.

2. $4x + 3y = 3$
$x - 2y = 9$

Avoiding Mistakes

Remember to multiply both sides of the equation by the chosen constant.

Answer

2. $(3, -3)$

In Example 3, the system of equations uses the variables a and b instead of x and y. In such a case, we will write the solution as an ordered pair with the variables written in alphabetical order, such as (a, b).

Skill Practice

Solve the system using the addition method.

3. $8n = 4 - 5m$
  $7m + 6n = -10$

Example 3 **Solve a System of Linear Equations Using the Addition Method**

Solve the system using the addition method.

$$5b = 7a + 8$$
$$-4a - 2b = -10$$

Solution:

Step 1: Write the equations in standard form.

The first equation becomes: $5b = 7a + 8 \longrightarrow -7a + 5b = 8$

The system becomes: $-7a + 5b = 8$
                          $-4a - 2b = -10$

Step 2: There are no fractions or decimals.

Step 3: We need to obtain opposite coefficients on either the a or b term.

Notice that neither the coefficients of a nor the coefficients of b are opposites. However, it is possible to change the coefficients of b to 10 and -10 (this is because the LCM of 5 and 2 is 10). This is accomplished by multiplying the first equation by 2 and the second equation by 5.

$$
\begin{array}{ll}
 & \text{Multiply by 2.} \\
-7a + 5b = 8 & \longrightarrow \quad -14a + 10b = 16 \\
-4a - 2b = -10 & \longrightarrow \quad \underline{-20a - 10b = -50} \\
 & \text{Multiply by 5.} \quad -34a = -34 \quad \textbf{Step 4:} \ \text{Add the equations.}
\end{array}
$$

$$-34a = -34 \qquad \textbf{Step 5:} \ \text{Solve the resulting equation.}$$

$$\frac{-34a}{-34} = \frac{-34}{-34}$$

$$a = 1$$

$5b = 7a + 8$ First equation   **Step 6:** Substitute $a = 1$ into one of the original equations.

$5b = 7(1) + 8$

$5b = 15$

$b = 3$

The solution is $(1, 3)$.   **Step 7:** Check the solution in the original equations.

Check:

$5b = 7a + 8 \longrightarrow 5(3) \overset{?}{=} 7(1) + 8 \longrightarrow 15 \overset{?}{=} 7 + 8 \ ✔ \ \text{True}$

$-4a - 2b = -10 \longrightarrow -4(1) - 2(3) \overset{?}{=} -10 \longrightarrow -4 - 6 \overset{?}{=} -10 \ ✔ \ \text{True}$

Answer

3. $(-4, 3)$

Example 4   Solving a System of Linear Equations Using the Addition Method

Solve the system using the addition method.

$$34x - 22y = 4$$
$$17x - 88y = -19$$

Solution:

The equations are already in standard form. There are no fractions or decimals to clear.

$$34x - 22y = 4 \longrightarrow 34x - \ 22y = 4$$
$$17x - 88y = -19 \xrightarrow{\text{Multiply by } -2.} \underline{-34x + 176y = 38}$$
$$154y = 42$$

Solve for y. $154y = 42$

$$\frac{154y}{154} = \frac{42}{154}$$

Simplify. $y = \dfrac{3}{11}$

To find the value of x, we normally substitute y into one of the original equations and solve for x. In this example, we will show an alternative method for finding x. By repeating the addition method, this time eliminating y, we can solve for x. This approach allows us to avoid substitution of the fractional value for y.

$$34x - 22y = 4 \xrightarrow{\text{Multiply by } -4.} -136x + 88y = -16$$
$$17x - 88y = -19 \longrightarrow \underline{17x - 88y = -19}$$
$$-119x = -35$$

Solve for x. $-119x = -35$

$$\frac{-119x}{-119} = \frac{-35}{-119}$$

Simplify. $x = \dfrac{5}{17}$

The solution is $\left(\frac{5}{17}, \frac{3}{11}\right)$. These values can be checked in the original equations:

$$34x - 22y = 4 \qquad\qquad\qquad 17x - 88y = -19$$

$$34\left(\frac{5}{17}\right) - 22\left(\frac{3}{11}\right) \stackrel{?}{=} 4 \qquad 17\left(\frac{5}{17}\right) - 88\left(\frac{3}{11}\right) \stackrel{?}{=} -19$$

$$10 - 6 \stackrel{?}{=} 4 \ \checkmark \text{ True} \qquad\qquad 5 - 24 \stackrel{?}{=} -19 \ \checkmark \text{ True}$$

Example 5 Solving an Inconsistent System Using the Addition Method

Solve the system using the addition method.

$$2x - 5y = 10$$

$$\frac{1}{2}x - \frac{5}{4}y = 1$$

Solution:

$$2x - 5y = 10$$

$$\frac{1}{2}x - \frac{5}{4}y = 1$$ **Step 1:**   The equations are in standard form.

Step 2:   Multiply both sides of the second equation by 4 to clear fractions.

$$\frac{1}{2}x - \frac{5}{4}y = 1 \longrightarrow 4\left(\frac{1}{2}x - \frac{5}{4}y\right) = 4(1) \longrightarrow 2x - 5y = 4$$

Now the system becomes

$$2x - 5y = 10$$
$$2x - 5y = 4$$

To make either the x coefficients or y coefficients opposites, multiply either equation by -1.

$$2x - 5y = 10 \xrightarrow{\text{Multiply by }-1.} -2x + 5y = -10$$ **Step 3:**   Create opposite coefficients.

$$2x - 5y = 4 \longrightarrow \underline{2x - 5y = 4}$$

$$0 = -6$$ **Step 4:**   Add the equations.

Because the result is a contradiction, there is no solution, and the system of equations is inconsistent. Writing each equation in slope-intercept form verifies that the lines are parallel (Figure 4-8).

$$2x - 5y = 10 \xrightarrow{\text{slope-intercept form}} y = \frac{2}{5}x - 2$$

$$\frac{1}{2}x - \frac{5}{4}y = 1 \xrightarrow{\text{slope-intercept form}} y = \frac{2}{5}x - \frac{4}{5}$$

There is no solution.

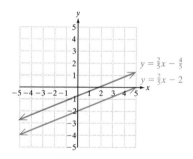

Figure 4-8

Example 6 Solving a System of Dependent Equations Using the Addition Method

Solve the system by the addition method.

$$3x - y = 4$$
$$2y = 6x - 8$$

Solution:

$3x - y = 4 \longrightarrow 3x - y = 4$ **Step 1:** Write the equations in standard form.

$2y = 6x - 8 \longrightarrow -6x + 2y = -8$ **Step 2:** There are no fractions or decimals.

Notice that the equations differ exactly by a factor of -2, which indicates that these two equations represent the same line. Multiply the first equation by 2 to create opposite coefficients for the variables.

$$
\begin{array}{ll}
3x - y = 4 \xrightarrow{\text{Multiply by 2.}} & 6x - 2y = 8 \\
-6x + 2y = -8 & \underline{-6x + 2y = -8} \\
& 0 = 0
\end{array}
$$

Step 3: Create opposite coefficients.

Step 4: Add the equations.

Because the resulting equation is an identity, the original equations represent the same line. This can be confirmed by writing each equation in slope-intercept form.

$$
\begin{array}{lll}
3x - y = 4 & \longrightarrow -y = -3x + 4 & \longrightarrow y = 3x - 4 \\
-6x + 2y = -8 & \longrightarrow 2y = 6x - 8 & \longrightarrow y = 3x - 4
\end{array}
$$

The solution is the set of all points on the line, or equivalently, $\{(x, y) | y = 3x - 4\}$.

2. Summary of Methods for Solving Systems of Linear Equations in Two Variables

If no method of solving a system of linear equations is specified, you may use the method of your choice. However, we recommend the following guidelines:

1. If one of the equations is written with a variable isolated, the substitution method is a good choice. For example:

$$2x + 5y = 2 \qquad \text{or} \qquad y = \frac{1}{3}x - 2$$
$$x = y - 6 \qquad\qquad\qquad x - 6y = 9$$

2. If both equations are written in standard form, $Ax + By = C$, where none of the variables has coefficients of 1 or -1, then the addition method is a good choice.

$$4x + 5y = 12$$
$$5x + 3y = 15$$

3. If both equations are written in standard form, $Ax + By = C$, and at least one variable has a coefficient of 1 or -1, then either the substitution method or the addition method is a good choice.

Section 4.3 Practice Exercises

Study Skills Exercise

Now that you have learned three methods of solving a system of linear equations with two variables, choose a system and solve it all three ways. There are two advantages to this. One is to check your answer (you should get the same answer using all three methods). The second advantage is to show you which method is the easiest for you to use.

Solve the system by using the graphing method, the substitution method, and the addition method.

$$2x + y = -7$$
$$x - 10 = 4y$$

Review Exercises

For Exercises 1–5, check whether the given ordered pair is a solution to the system.

1. $-\dfrac{3}{4}x + 2y = -10$ $(8, -2)$

     $x - \dfrac{1}{2}y = 7$

2. $x + y = 8$ $(5, 3)$

     $y = x - 2$

3. $x = y + 1$ $(3, 2)$

     $-x + 2y = 0$

4. $3x + 2y = 14$ $(5, -2)$

     $5x - 2y = 29$

5. $x = 2y - 11$ $(-3, 4)$

     $-x + 5y = 23$

Concept 1: Solving Systems of Linear Equations by Using the Addition Method

For Exercises 6 and 7, answer as true or false.

6. Given the system $5x - 4y = 1$

                    $7x - 2y = 5$

   a. To eliminate the y variable using the addition method, multiply the second equation by 2.

   b. To eliminate the x variable using the addition method, multiply the first equation by 7 and the second equation by -5.

7. Given the system $3x + 5y = -1$

                    $9x - 8y = -26$

   a. To eliminate the x variable using the addition method, multiply the first equation by -3.

   b. To eliminate the y variable using the addition method, multiply the first equation by 8 and the second equation by -5.

8. Given the system $3x - 4y = 2$

                    $17x + y = 35$

   a. Which variable, x or y, is easier to eliminate using the addition method?

   b. Solve the system using the addition method.

9. Given the system $-2x + 5y = -15$

                    $6x - 7y = 21$

   a. Which variable, x or y, is easier to eliminate using the addition method?

   b. Solve the system using the addition method.

For Exercises 10–24, solve the systems using the addition method. **(See Examples 1–4.)**

10. $x + 2y = 8$
     $5x - 2y = 4$

11. $2x - 3y = 11$
     $-4x + 3y = -19$

12. $a + b = 3$
     $3a + b = 13$

13. $-2u + 6v = 10$
     $-2u + v = -5$

14. $-3x + y = 1$
     $-6x - 2y = -2$

15. $5m - 2n = 4$
     $3m + n = 9$

16. $3x - 5y = 13$

$x - 2y = 5$

17. $7a + 2b = -1$

$3a - 4b = 19$

18. $6c - 2d = -2$

$5c = -3d + 17$

19. $2s + 3t = -1$

$5s = 2t + 7$

20. $6y - 4z = -2$

$4y + 6z = 42$

21. $4k - 2r = -4$

$3k - 5r = 18$

22. $2x + 3y = 6$

$x - y = 5$

23. $6x + 6y = 8$

$9x - 18y = -3$

24. $2x - 5y = 4$

$3x - 3y = 4$

25. In solving a system of equations, suppose you get the statement $0 = 5$. How many solutions will the system have? What can you say about the graphs of these equations?

26. In solving a system of equations, suppose you get the statement $0 = 0$. How many solutions will the system have? What can you say about the graphs of these equations?

27. In solving a system of equations, suppose you get the statement $3 = 3$. How many solutions will the system have? What can you say about the graphs of these equations?

28. In solving a system of equations, suppose you get the statement $2 = -5$. How many solutions will the system have? What can you say about the graphs of these equations?

29. Suppose in solving a system of linear equations, you get the statement $x = 0$. How many solutions will the system have? What can you say about the graphs of these equations?

30. Suppose in solving a system of linear equations, you get the statement $y = 0$. How many solutions will the system have? What can you say about the graphs of these equations?

For Exercises 31–42, solve the system by using the addition method. For systems that do not have one unique solution, also state the number of solutions and whether the system is inconsistent or the equations are dependent. **(See Examples 5 and 6.)**

31. $-2x + y = -5$

$8x - 4y = 12$

32. $x - 3y = 2$

$-5x + 15y = 10$

33. $x + 2y = 2$

$-3x - 6y = -6$

34. $4x - 3y = 6$

$-12x + 9y = -18$

35. $3a + 2b = 11$

$7a - 3b = -5$

36. $4y + 5z = -2$

$5y - 3z = 16$

37. $3x - 5y = 7$

$5x - 2y = -1$

38. $4s + 3t = 9$

$3s + 4t = 12$

39. $2x + 2 = -3y + 9$

$3x - 10 = -4y$

40. $-3x + 6 + 7y = 5$

$5y = 2x$

41. $4x - 5y = 0$

$8(x - 1) = 10y$

42. $y = 2x + 1$

$-3(2x - y) = 0$

Concept 2: Summary of Methods for Solving Systems of Linear Equations in Two Variables

For Exercises 43–63, solve the system of equations by either the addition method or the substitution method.

43. $5x - 2y = 4$

$y = -3x + 9$

44. $-x = 8y + 5$

$4x - 3y = -20$

45. $0.1x + 0.1y = 0.6$

$0.1x - 0.1y = 0.1$

46. $0.1x + 0.1y = 0.2$

$0.1x - 0.1y = 0.3$

47. $3x = 5y - 9$

$2y = 3x + 3$

48. $10x - 5 = 3y$

$4x + 5y = 2$

49. $\dfrac{1}{10}y = -\dfrac{1}{2}x - \dfrac{1}{2}$

$\dfrac{3}{2}x - \dfrac{3}{4} = -\dfrac{3}{4}y$

50. $x + \dfrac{5}{4}y = -\dfrac{1}{2}$

$\dfrac{3}{4}x = -\dfrac{1}{2}y - \dfrac{5}{4}$

51. $x = -\dfrac{1}{2}$

$6x - 5y = -8$

52. $4x - 2y = 1$

$y = 3$

53. $0.02x + 0.04y = 0.12$

$0.03x - 0.05y = -0.15$

54. $-0.04x + 0.03y = 0.03$

$-0.06x - 0.02y = -0.02$

55. $8x - 16y = 24$

$2x - 4y = 0$

56. $y = -\dfrac{1}{2}x - 5$

$2x + 4y = -8$

57. $\dfrac{m}{2} + \dfrac{n}{5} = \dfrac{13}{10}$

$3m - 3n = m - 10$

58. $\dfrac{a}{4} - \dfrac{3b}{2} = \dfrac{15}{2}$

$a + 2b = -10$

59. $2m - 6n = m + 4$

$3m + 8 = 5m - n$

60. $m - 3n = 10$

$3m + 12n = -12$

61. $9a - 2b = 8$

$18a + 6 = 4b + 22$

62. $a = 5 + 2b$

$3a - 6b = 15$

63. $6x - 5y = 7$

$4x - 6y = 7$

For Exercises 64–69, set up a system of linear equations, and solve for the indicated quantities.

64. The sum of two positive numbers is 26. Their difference is 14. Find the numbers.

65. The difference of two positive numbers is 2. The sum of the numbers is 36. Find the numbers.

66. Eight times the smaller of two numbers plus 2 times the larger number is 44. Three times the smaller number minus 2 times the larger number is zero. Find the numbers.

67. Six times the smaller of two numbers minus the larger number is −9. Ten times the smaller number plus five times the larger number is 5. Find the numbers.

68. Twice the difference of the measures of two angles is 64°. If the angles are complementary, find the measures of the angles.

69. The difference of the measure of an angle and twice the measure of another angle is 42°. If the angles are supplementary, find the measures of the angles.

For Exercises 70–72, solve the system by using each of the three methods: (a) the graphing method, (b) the substitution method, and (c) the addition method.

70. $2x + y = 1$

$-4x - 2y = -2$

71. $3x + y = 6$

$-2x + 2y = 4$

72. $2x - 2y = 6$

$5y = 5x + 5$

Expanding Your Skills

73. Explain why a system of linear equations cannot have exactly two solutions.

74. The solution to the system of linear equations is $(1, 2)$. Find A and B.

$Ax + 3y = 8$

$x + By = -7$

75. The solution to the system of linear equations is $(-3, 4)$. Find A and B.

$4x + Ay = -32$

$Bx + 6y = 18$

Problem Recognition Exercises

Systems of Equations

For Exercises 1–6, determine the number of solutions to the system without solving the system. Explain your answers.

1. $y = -4x + 2$
   $y = -4x + 2$

2. $y = -4x + 6$
   $y = -4x + 1$

3. $y = 4x - 3$
   $y = -4x + 5$

4. $y = 7$
   $2x + 3y = 1$

5. $2x + 3y = 1$
   $2x + 3y = 8$

6. $8x - 2y = 6$
   $12x - 3y = 9$

For Exercises 7–10, a method of solving has been suggested for each system of equations. Explain why that method was suggested for the system and then solve the system using the method given.

7. $2x - 5y = -11$ Addition Method
   $7x + 5y = -16$

8. $4x + 11y = 56$ Addition Method
   $-2x - 5y = -26$

9. $x = -3y + 4$ Substitution Method
   $5x + 4y = -2$

10. $2x + 3y = 16$ Substitution Method
   $y = x - 8$

For Exercises 11–30, solve the system using the method of your choice. For systems that do not have one unique solution, also state the number of solutions and whether the system is inconsistent or the equations are dependent.

11. $x = -2y + 5$
   $2x - 4y = 10$

12. $y = -3x - 4$
   $2x - y = 9$

13. $3x - 2y = 22$
   $5x + 2y = 10$

14. $-4x + 2y = -2$
   $4x - 5y = -7$

15. $\frac{1}{3}x + \frac{1}{2}y = \frac{2}{3}$
   $-\frac{2}{3}x + y = -\frac{4}{3}$

16. $\frac{1}{4}x + \frac{2}{5}y = 6$
   $\frac{1}{2}x - \frac{1}{10}y = 3$

17. $2c + 7d = -1$
   $c = 2$

18. $-3w + 5z = -6$
   $z = -4$

19. $y = 0.4x - 0.3$
   $-4x + 10y = 20$

20. $x = -0.5y + 0.1$
   $-10x - 5y = 2$

21. $3a + 7b = -3$
   $-11a + 3b = 11$

22. $2v - 5w = 10$
   $9v + 7w = 45$

23. $y = 2x - 14$
   $4x - 2y = 28$

24. $x = 5y - 9$
   $-2x + 10y = 18$

25. $x + y = 3200$
   $0.06x + 0.04y = 172$

26. $x + y = 4500$
   $0.07x + 0.05y = 291$

27. $3x + y - 7 = x - 4$
   $3x - 4y + 4 = -6y + 5$

28. $7y - 8y - 3 = -3x + 4$
   $10x - 5y - 12 = 13$

29. $3x - 6y = -1$
   $9x + 4y = 8$

30. $8x - 2y = 5$
   $12x + 4y = -3$

Section 4.4   Applications of Systems of Equations

Skill Practice

1. Lynn went to a fast-food restaurant and spent $9.00. She purchased 4 hamburgers and 5 orders of fries. The next day, Ricardo went to the same restaurant and purchased 10 hamburgers and 7 orders of fries. He spent $18.10. Use a system of equations to determine the cost of a burger and the cost of an order of fries.

1. Applications Involving Cost

In Sections 2.4–2.7, we solved several applied problems by setting up a linear equation in one variable. When solving an application that involves two unknowns, sometimes it is convenient to use a system of linear equations in two variables.

Example 1 **Using a System of Linear Equations Involving Cost**

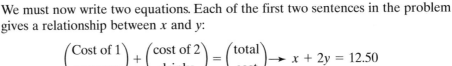

At a movie theater a couple buys one large popcorn and two small drinks for $12.50. A group of teenagers buys two large popcorns and five small drinks for $28.50. Find the cost of one large popcorn and the cost of one small drink.

Solution:

In this application we have two unknowns, which we can represent by x and y.

Let x represent the cost of one large popcorn.
Let y represent the cost of one small drink.

We must now write two equations. Each of the first two sentences in the problem gives a relationship between x and y:

$$\left(\begin{array}{c}\text{Cost of 1}\\\text{popcorn}\end{array}\right) + \left(\begin{array}{c}\text{cost of 2}\\\text{drinks}\end{array}\right) = \left(\begin{array}{c}\text{total}\\\text{cost}\end{array}\right) \longrightarrow x + 2y = 12.50$$

$$\left(\begin{array}{c}\text{Cost of 2}\\\text{popcorns}\end{array}\right) + \left(\begin{array}{c}\text{cost of 5}\\\text{drinks}\end{array}\right) = \left(\begin{array}{c}\text{total}\\\text{cost}\end{array}\right) \longrightarrow 2x + 5y = 28.50$$

To solve this system, we may either use the substitution method or the addition method. We will use the substitution method by solving for x in the first equation.

$x + 2y = 12.50 \longrightarrow x = -2y + 12.50$ Isolate x in the first equation.

$2x + 5y = 28.50$

$2(-2y + 12.50) + 5y = 28.50$ Substitute $x = -2y + 12.50$ into the other equation.

$-4y + 25.00 + 5y = 28.50$ Solve for y.

$y + 25.00 = 28.50$

$y = 3.50$

$x = -2y + 12.50$

$x = -2(3.50) + 12.50$ Substitute $y = 3.50$ into the equation $x = -2y + 12.50$.

$x = -7.00 + 12.50$

$x = 5.50$

The cost of one large popcorn is $5.50 and the cost of one small drink is $3.50.

Check by verifying that the solutions meet the specified conditions.

1 popcorn + 2 drinks = 1($5.50) + 2($3.50) = $12.50 ✔   True

2 popcorns + 5 drinks = 2($5.50) + 5($3.50) = $28.50 ✔   True

Answer

1. The cost of a burger is $1.25 and the cost of an order of fries is $0.80.

2. Applications Involving Principal and Interest

In Section 2.5, we learned that simple interest is interest computed on the principal amount of money invested (or borrowed). Simple interest, I, is found by using the formula

$$I = Prt \quad \text{where } P \text{ is the principal,}$$
$$r \text{ is the annual interest rate, and}$$
$$t \text{ is the time in years.}$$

In Example 2, we apply the concept of simple interest to two accounts to produce a desired amount of interest after 1 yr.

Example 2 **Using a System of Linear Equations Involving Investments**

Joanne has a total of $6000 to deposit in two accounts. One account earns 3.5% simple interest and the other earns 2.5% simple interest. If the total amount of interest at the end of 1 yr is $195, find the amount she deposited in each account.

Solution:

Let x represent the principal deposited in the 2.5% account.
Let y represent the principal deposited in the 3.5% account.

	2.5% Account	3.5% Account	Total
Principal	x	y	6000
Interest $(I = Prt)$	$0.025x(1)$	$0.035y(1)$	195

Each row of the table yields an equation in x and y:

$$\begin{pmatrix} \text{Principal} \\ \text{invested} \\ \text{at } 2.5\% \end{pmatrix} + \begin{pmatrix} \text{principal} \\ \text{invested} \\ \text{at } 3.4\% \end{pmatrix} = \begin{pmatrix} \text{total} \\ \text{principal} \end{pmatrix} \longrightarrow x + y = 6000$$

$$\begin{pmatrix} \text{Interest} \\ \text{earned} \\ \text{at } 2.5\% \end{pmatrix} + \begin{pmatrix} \text{interest} \\ \text{earned} \\ \text{at } 3.5\% \end{pmatrix} = \begin{pmatrix} \text{total} \\ \text{interest} \end{pmatrix} \longrightarrow 0.025x + 0.035y = 195$$

We will choose the addition method to solve the system of equations. First multiply the second equation by 1000 to clear decimals.

Multiply by -25.
$$x + y = 6000 \longrightarrow \quad x + y = 6000 \quad \longrightarrow -25x - 25y = -150{,}000$$
$$0.025x + 0.035y = 195 \longrightarrow 25x + 35y = 195{,}000 \longrightarrow \underline{\quad 25x + 35y = \quad 195{,}000}$$
Multiply by 1000.
$$10y = \quad 45{,}000$$

$10y = 45{,}000$ \quad After eliminating the x variable, solve for y.

$\dfrac{10y}{10} = \dfrac{45{,}000}{10}$

$y = 4500$ \quad The amount invested in the 3.5% account is $4500.

$$x + y = 6000 \qquad \text{Substitute } y = 4500 \text{ into the equation } x + y = 6000.$$

$$x + 4500 = 6000$$

$$x = 1500 \qquad \text{The amount invested in the 2.5\% account is \$1500.}$$

Joanne deposited \$1500 in the 2.5% account and \$4500 in the 3.5% account.

To check, verify that the conditions of the problem have been met.

1. The sum of \$1500 and \$4500 is \$6000 as desired. ✔ True

2. The interest earned on \$1500 at 2.5% is: 0.025(\$1500) = \$37.50
   The interest earned on \$4500 at 3.5% is: 0.035(\$4500) = \$157.50

   Total interest: \$195.00 ✔ True

3. Applications Involving Mixtures

Example 3 **Using a System of Linear Equations in a Mixture Application**

According to new hospital standards, a certain disinfectant solution needs to be 20% alcohol instead of 10% alcohol. There is a 40% alcohol disinfectant available to adjust the mixture. Determine the amount of 10% solution and the amount of 40% solution needed to produce 30 L of a 20% solution.

Solution:

Each solution contains a percentage of alcohol plus some other mixing agent such as water. Before we set up a system of equations to model this situation, it is helpful to have background understanding of the problem. In Figure 4-9, the liquid depicted in blue is pure alcohol and the liquid shown in gray is the mixing agent (such as water). Together these liquids form a solution. (Realistically the mixture may not separate as shown, but this image may be helpful for your understanding.)

Let x represent the number of liters of 10% solution.
Let y represent the number of liters of 40% solution.

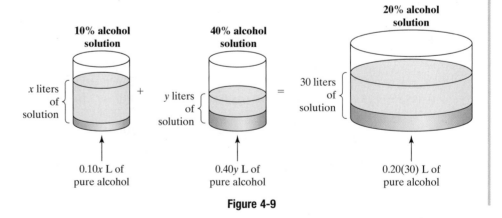

Figure 4-9

The information given in the statement of the problem can be organized in a chart.

	10% Alcohol	40% Alcohol	20% Alcohol
Number of liters of solution	x	y	30
Number of liters of pure alcohol	$0.10x$	$0.40y$	$0.20(30) = 6$

From the first row, we have

$$\begin{pmatrix} \text{Amount of} \\ 10\% \text{ solution} \end{pmatrix} + \begin{pmatrix} \text{amount of} \\ 40\% \text{ solution} \end{pmatrix} = \begin{pmatrix} \text{total amount} \\ \text{of } 20\% \text{ solution} \end{pmatrix} \longrightarrow x + y = 30$$

From the second row, we have

$$\begin{pmatrix} \text{Amount of} \\ \text{alcohol in} \\ 10\% \text{ solution} \end{pmatrix} + \begin{pmatrix} \text{amount of} \\ \text{alcohol in} \\ 40\% \text{ solution} \end{pmatrix} = \begin{pmatrix} \text{total amount of} \\ \text{alcohol in} \\ 20\% \text{ solution} \end{pmatrix} \longrightarrow 0.10x + 0.40y = 6$$

We will solve the system with the addition method by first clearing decimals.

$$
\begin{array}{llll}
 & & \text{Multiply by } -1. \\
x + y = 30 & \longrightarrow & x + y = 30 & \longrightarrow & -x - y = -30 \\
0.10x + 0.40y = 6 & \longrightarrow & x + 4y = 60 & \longrightarrow & \underline{x + 4y = 60} \\
 & \text{Multiply by } 10. & & & 3y = 30
\end{array}
$$

$3y = 30$ After eliminating the x variable, solve for y.

$y = 10$ 10 L of 40% solution is needed.

$x + y = 30$ Substitute $y = 10$ into either of the original equations.

$x + (10) = 30$

$x = 20$ 20 L of 10% solution is needed.

10 L of 40% solution must be mixed with 20 L of 10% solution.

4. Applications Involving Distance, Rate, and Time

The following formula relates the distance traveled to the rate and time of travel.

$$d = rt \qquad \text{distance} = \text{rate} \cdot \text{time}$$

For example, if a car travels at 60 mph for 3 hr, then

$$d = (60 \text{ mph})(3 \text{ hr})$$

$$= 180 \text{ mi}$$

If a car travels at 60 mph for x hr, then

$$d = (60 \text{ mph})(x \text{ hr})$$

$$= 60x \text{ mi}$$

The relationship $d = rt$ is used in Example 4.

Skill Practice

4. Dan and Cheryl paddled their canoe 40 mi in 5 hr with the current and 16 mi in 8 hr against the current. Find the speed of the current and the speed of the canoe in still water.

Example 4 **Using a System of Linear Equations in a Distance, Rate, and Time Application**

A plane travels with the wind from Kansas City, Missouri, to Denver, Colorado, a distance of 600 mi in 2 hr. The return trip against the same wind takes 3 hr. Find the speed of the plane in still air, and find the speed of the wind.

Solution:

Let p represent the speed of the plane in still air.
Let w represent the speed of the wind.

Notice that when the plane travels with the wind, the net speed is $p + w$. When the plane travels against the wind, the net speed is $p - w$.

The information given in the problem can be organized in a chart.

	Distance	Rate	Time
With the wind	600	$p + w$	2
Against the wind	600	$p - w$	3

To set up two equations in p and w, recall that $d = rt$.

From the first row, we have

$$\left(\begin{array}{c}\text{Distance} \\ \text{with the wind}\end{array}\right) = \left(\begin{array}{c}\text{rate with} \\ \text{the wind}\end{array}\right)\left(\begin{array}{c}\text{time traveled} \\ \text{with the wind}\end{array}\right) \longrightarrow 600 = (p + w) \cdot 2$$

From the second row, we have

$$\left(\begin{array}{c}\text{Distance} \\ \text{against the wind}\end{array}\right) = \left(\begin{array}{c}\text{rate against} \\ \text{the wind}\end{array}\right)\left(\begin{array}{c}\text{time traveled} \\ \text{against the wind}\end{array}\right) \longrightarrow 600 = (p - w) \cdot 3$$

Using the distributive property to clear parentheses produces the following system:

$$2p + 2w = 600$$
$$3p - 3w = 600$$

The coefficients of the w variable can be changed to 6 and -6 by multiplying the first equation by 3 and the second equation by 2.

$$2p + 2w = 600 \xrightarrow{\text{Multiply by 3.}} 6p + 6w = 1800$$
$$3p - 3w = 600 \xrightarrow[\text{Multiply by 2.}]{} \underline{6p - 6w = 1200}$$
$$12p \quad\quad = 3000$$

$$12p = 3000$$

$$\frac{12p}{12} = \frac{3000}{12}$$

$$p = 250 \qquad \begin{array}{l}\text{The speed of the plane} \\ \text{in still air is 250 mph.}\end{array}$$

Answer

4. The speed of the canoe in still water is 5 mph. The speed of the current is 3 mph.

TIP: To create opposite coefficients on the w variables, we could have divided the first equation by 2 and divided the second equation by 3:

Divide by 2.

$2p + 2w = 600 \longrightarrow p + w = 300$

$3p - 3w = 600 \longrightarrow p - w = 200$

Divide by 3.

$2p = 500$

$p = 250$

$2p + 2w = 600$ Substitute $p = 250$ into the first equation.

$2(250) + 2w = 600$

$500 + 2w = 600$

$2w = 100$

$w = 50$ The speed of the wind is 50 mph.

The speed of the plane in still air is 250 mph. The speed of the wind is 50 mph.

Section 4.4   Practice Exercises

Review Exercises

For Exercises 1–4, solve each system of equations by three different methods:

   a. Graphing method   **b.** Substitution method   **c.** Addition method

1. $-2x + y = 6$ **2.** $x - y = 2$

     $2x + y = 2$ $x + y = 6$

3. $y = -2x + 6$ **4.** $2x = y + 4$

     $4x - 2y = 8$ $4x = 2y + 8$

For Exercises 5–8, set up a system of linear equations in two variables to solve for the unknown quantities.

5. One number is eight more than twice another. Their sum is 20. Find the numbers.

6. The difference of two positive numbers is 264. The larger number is three times the smaller number. Find the numbers.

7. Two angles are complementary. The measure of one angle is 10° less than nine times the measure of the other. Find the measure of each angle.

8. Two angles are supplementary. The measure of one angle is 9° more than twice the measure of the other angle. Find the measure of each angle.

Concept 1: Applications Involving Cost

9. Two video games and three DVDs can be rented for $34.10. One video game and two DVDs can be rented for $19.80. Find the cost to rent one video game and the cost to rent one DVD. **(See Example 1.)**

10. Tanya bought three adult tickets and one child's ticket to a movie for $23.00. Li bought two adult tickets and five children's tickets for $30.50. Find the cost of one adult ticket and the cost of one children's ticket.

11. Amber bought 100 shares of a technology stock and 200 shares of a mutual fund for $3800. Her sister, Sandy, bought 300 shares of technology stock and 50 shares of a mutual fund for $5350. Find the cost per share of the technology stock, and the cost per share of the mutual fund.

12. Two video games and three DVDs can be rented for $19.15. Four video games and one DVD can be rented for $17.35. Find the cost to rent one video game and the cost to rent one DVD.

13. Mylee buys a combination of 46-cent stamps and 65-cent stamps at the Post Office. If she spends exactly $24.90 on 50 stamps, how many of each type did she buy?

14. Zoey purchased some beef and some chicken for a family barbeque. The beef cost $6.00 per pound and the chicken cost $4.50 per pound. She bought a total of 18 lb of meat and spent $96. How much of each type of meat did she purchase?

Concept 2: Applications Involving Principal and Interest

15. Shanelle invested $10,000, and at the end of 1 yr, she received $805 in interest. She invested part of the money in an account earning 10% simple interest and the remaining money in an account earning 7% simple interest. How much did she invest in each account? **(See Example 2.)**

16. $12,000 was invested in two accounts, one earning 12% simple interest and the other earning 8% simple interest. If the total interest at the end of 1 yr was $1240, how much was invested in each account?

	10% Account	7% Account	Total
Principal invested			
Interest earned			

	12% Account	8% Account	Total
Principal invested			
Interest earned			

17. Troy borrowed a total of $12,000 in two different loans to help pay for his new Chevy Silverado. One loan charges 9% simple interest, and the other charges 6% simple interest. If he is charged $810 in interest after 1 yr, find the amount borrowed at each rate.

18. Blake has a total of $4000 to invest in two accounts. One account earns 2% simple interest, and the other earns 5% simple interest. How much should be invested in each account to earn exactly $155 at the end of 1 yr?

19. Suppose a rich uncle dies and leaves you an inheritance of $30,000. You decide to invest part of the money in a relatively safe bond fund that returns 8%. You invest the rest of the money in a riskier stock fund that you hope will return 12% at the end of 1 yr. If you need $3120 at the end of 1 yr to make a down payment on a car, how much should you invest at each rate?

20. As part of his retirement strategy, John plans to invest $200,000 in two different funds. He projects that the moderately high risk investments should return, over time, about 9% per year, while the low risk investments should return about 4% per year. If he wants a supplemental income of $12,000 a year, how should he divide his investments?

Concept 3: Applications Involving Mixtures

21. How much 50% disinfectant solution must be mixed with a 40% disinfectant solution to produce 25 gal of a 46% disinfectant solution? (See Example 3.)

	50% Mixture	40% Mixture	46% Mixture
Amount of solution			
Amount of disinfectant			

22. How many gallons of 20% antifreeze solution and a 10% antifreeze solution must be mixed to obtain 40 gal of a 16% antifreeze solution?

	20% Mixture	10% Mixture	16% Mixture
Amount of solution			
Amount of antifreeze			

23. How much 45% disinfectant solution must be mixed with a 30% disinfectant solution to produce 20 gal of a 39% disinfectant solution?

24. How many gallons of a 25% antifreeze solution and a 15% antifreeze solution must be mixed to obtain 15 gal of a 23% antifreeze solution?

25. A nurse needs 50 mL of a 16% salt solution for a patient. She can only find a 13% salt solution and an 18% salt solution in the supply room. How many milliliters of the 13% solution should be mixed with the 18% solution to produce the desired amount of the 16% solution?

26. Meadowsilver Dairy keeps two kinds of milk on hand, skim milk that has 0.3% butterfat and whole milk that contains 3.3% butterfat. How many gallons of each type of milk does the company need to produce 300 gal of 1% milk for the P&A grocery store?

27. The cooling system in most cars requires a mixture that is 50% antifreeze. How many liters of pure antifreeze and how many liters of 40% antifreeze solution should Chad mix to obtain 6 L of 50% antifreeze solution? (*Hint:* Pure antifreeze is 100% antifreeze.)

28. Silvia wants to mix a 40% apple juice drink with pure apple juice to make 2 L of a juice drink that is 80% apple juice. How much pure apple juice should she use?

Concept 4: Applications Involving Distance, Rate, and Time

29. It takes a boat 2 hr to go 16 mi downstream with the current and 4 hr to return against the current. Find the speed of the boat in still water and the speed of the current. (See Example 4.)

	Distance	Rate	Time
Downstream			
Upstream			

30. A boat takes 1.5 hr to go 12 mi upstream against the current. It can go 24 mi downstream with the current in the same amount of time. Find the speed of the current and the speed of the boat in still water.

	Distance	Rate	Time
Upstream			
Downstream			

31. A plane can fly 960 mi with the wind in 3 hr. It takes the same amount of time to fly 840 mi against the wind. What is the speed of the plane in still air and the speed of the wind?

32. A plane flies 720 mi with the wind in 3 hr. The return trip takes 4 hr. What is the speed of the wind and the speed of the plane in still air?

33. Tony Markins flew from JFK Airport to London. It took him 6 hr to fly with the wind, and 8 hr on the return flight against the wind. If the distance is approximately 3600 mi, determine the speed of the plane in still air and the speed of the wind.

34. A riverboat cruise upstream on the Mississippi River from New Orleans, Louisiana, to Natchez, Mississippi, takes 10 hr and covers 140 mi. The return trip downstream with the current takes only 7 hr. Find the speed of the riverboat in still water and the speed of the current.

Mixed Exercises

35. Debi has $2.80 in a collection of dimes and nickels. The number of nickels is five more than the number of dimes. Find the number of each type of coin.

36. A child is collecting state quarters and new $1 coins. If she has a total of 25 coins, and the number of quarters is nine more than the number of dollar coins, how many of each type of coin does she have?

37. How many quarts of water should be mixed with a 30% vinegar solution to obtain 12 qt of a 25% vinegar solution? (*Hint:* Water is 0% vinegar.)

38. How much water should be mixed with an 8% plant fertilizer solution to make a half gallon of a 6% plant fertilizer solution?

39. In the 1961–1962 NBA basketball season, Wilt Chamberlain of the Philadelphia Warriors made 2432 baskets. Some of the baskets were free throws (worth 1 point each) and some were field goals (worth 2 points each). The number of field goals was 762 more than the number of free throws.

   a. How many field goals did he make and how many free throws did he make?

   b. What was the total number of points scored?

   c. If Wilt Chamberlain played 80 games during this season, what was the average number of points per game?

40. In the 1971–1972 NBA basketball season, Kareem Abdul-Jabbar of the Milwaukee Bucks made 1663 baskets. Some of the baskets were free throws (worth 1 point each) and some were field goals (worth 2 points each). The number of field goals he scored was 151 more than twice the number of free throws.

   a. How many field goals did he make and how many free throws did he make?

   b. What was the total number of points scored?

   c. If Kareem Abdul-Jabbar played 81 games during this season, what was the average number of points per game?

41. A small plane can fly 350 mi with the wind in $1\frac{3}{4}$ hr. In the same amount of time, the same plane can travel only 210 mi against the wind. What is the speed of the plane in still air and the speed of the wind?

42. A plane takes 2 hr to travel 1000 mi with the wind. It can travel only 880 mi against the wind in the same amount of time. Find the speed of the wind and the speed of the plane in still air.

43. A total of $60,000 is invested in two accounts, one that earns 5.5% simple interest, and one that earns 6.5% simple interest. If the total interest at the end of 1 yr is $3750, find the amount invested in each account.

44. Jacques borrows a total of $15,000. Part of the money is borrowed from a bank that charges 12% simple interest per year. Jacques borrows the remaining part of the money from his sister and promises to pay her 7% simple interest per year. If Jacques's total interest for the year is $1475, find the amount he borrowed from each source.

45. At the holidays, Erica likes to sell a candy/nut mixture to her neighbors. She wants to combine candy that costs $1.80 per pound with nuts that cost $1.20 per pound. If Erica needs 20 lb of mixture that will sell for $1.56 per pound, how many pounds of candy and how many pounds of nuts should she use?

46. Mary Lee's natural food store sells a combination of teas. The most popular is a mixture of a tea that sells for $3.00 per pound with one that sells for $4.00 per pound. If she needs 40 lb of tea that will sell for $3.65 per pound, how many pounds of each tea should she use?

47. In the 1994 Super Bowl, the Dallas Cowboys scored four more points than twice the number of points scored by the Buffalo Bills. If the total number of points scored by both teams was 43, find the number of points scored by each team.

48. In the 1973 Super Bowl, the Miami Dolphins scored twice as many points as the Washington Redskins. If the total number of points scored by both teams was 21, find the number of points scored by each team.

Expanding Your Skills

49. In a survey conducted among 500 college students, 340 said that the campus lacked adequate lighting. If $\frac{4}{5}$ of the women and $\frac{1}{2}$ of the men said that they thought the campus lacked adequate lighting, how many men and how many women were in the survey?

50. During a 1-hr television program, there were 22 commercials. Some commercials were 15 sec and some were 30 sec long. Find the number of 15-sec commercials and the number of 30-sec commercials if the total playing time for commercials was 9.5 min.

Linear Inequalities and Systems of Inequalities in Two Variables

Section 4.5

1. Graphing Linear Inequalities in Two Variables

A **linear inequality in two variables** x and y is an inequality that can be written in one of the following forms: $Ax + By < C$, $Ax + By > C$, $Ax + By \leq C$, or $Ax + By \geq C$.

A solution to a linear inequality in two variables is an ordered pair that makes the inequality true. For example, solutions to the inequality $x + y < 3$ are ordered pairs (x, y) such that the sum of the x- and y-coordinates is less than 3. Several such examples are $(0,0), (-2, -2)$, $(3, -2)$, and $(-4, 1)$. There are actually infinitely many solutions to this inequality, and therefore it is convenient to express the solution set as a graph. The shaded area in Figure 4-10 represents all solutions (x, y), whose coordinates total less than 3.

Concepts

1. Graphing Linear Inequalities in Two Variables
2. Graphing Systems of Linear Inequalities in Two Variables

Concept Connections

Determine which of the ordered pairs are solutions to the inequality $y < 4x - 2$.

1. $(3, -1)$ **2.** $(0, 0)$

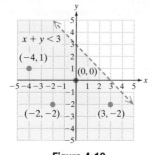

Figure 4-10

Answers

1. Solution
2. Not a solution

To graph a linear inequality in two variables we will use a process called the test point method. To use the test point method, first graph the related equation. In this case, the related equation represents a line in the xy-plane. Then choose a test point *not* on the line to determine which side of the line to shade. This process is demonstrated in Example 1.

Skill Practice

Graph the solution set.

3. $3x + 2y \geq -6$

Example 1   Graphing a Linear Inequality in Two Variables

Graph the solution set. $2x + y \leq 3$

Solution:

$2x + y \leq 3 \longrightarrow 2x + y = 3$ **Step 1:** Set up the related equation.

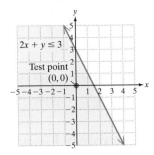

Figure 4-11

Step 2: Graph the related equation.

Graph the line by either setting up a table of points, or by using the slope-intercept form (Figure 4-11).

Table:

x	y
1	1
0	3
$\frac{3}{2}$	0

Slope-intercept form:

$$2x + y = 3$$
$$y = -2x + 3$$

Step 3: The solution to $2x + y \leq 3$ includes points for which $2x + y$ is less than *or equal to* 3. Because equality is included, points on the line $2x + y = 3$ are included. A solid line shows that the points on the line are included.

Now we must determine which side of the line to shade. To do so, we choose an arbitrary test point *not* on the line. The point $(0, 0)$ is a convenient choice.

Test point: $(0, 0)$

$$2x + y \leq 3$$
$$2(0) + (0) \overset{?}{\leq} 3$$
$$0 \overset{?}{\leq} 3 \; ✔ \quad \text{True}$$

The test point $(0, 0)$ is true in the original inequality. This means that the region from which the test point was taken is part of the solution set. Therefore, shade below the line (Figure 4-12).

Figure 4-12

TIP: If a point above the line is selected as a test point, notice that it will *not* make the original inequality true. For example, test the point $(2, 2)$.

$$2x + y \leq 3$$
$$2(2) + (2) \overset{?}{\leq} 3$$
$$6 \overset{?}{\leq} 3 \quad \text{False}$$

A false result tells us to shade the *other* side of the line.

Answer

3.

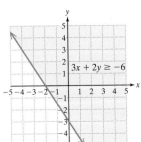

Now suppose the inequality from Example 1 had the strict inequality symbol, $<$. That is, consider the inequality $2x + y < 3$. The boundary line $2x + y = 3$ is *not* included in the solution set, because the expression $2x + y$ must be *strictly less than* 3 (not equal to 3). To show that the boundary line is not included in the solution set, we draw a dashed line (Figure 4-13).

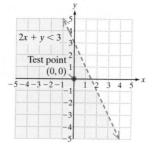

Figure 4-13

The test point method to graph linear inequalities in two variables is summarized as follows:

Test Point Method

Step 1 Set up the related equation.

Step 2 Graph the related equation from step 1. The equation will be a boundary line in the xy-plane.
- If the original inequality is a strict inequality, $<$ or $>$, then the line is *not* part of the solution set. Graph the line as a *dashed line*.
- If the original inequality is not strict, $\leq$ or $\geq$, then the line *is* part of the solution set. Graph the line as a *solid line*.

Step 3 Choose a point not on the line and substitute its coordinates into the original inequality.
- If the test point makes the inequality true, then the region it represents is part of the solution set. Shade that region.
- If the test point makes the inequality false, then the other region is part of the solution set and should be shaded.

Example 2 **Graphing a Linear Inequality in Two Variables**

Graph the solution set. $4x - 2y > 6$

Solution:

$4x - 2y > 6 \longrightarrow 4x - 2y = 6$ **Step 1:** Set up the related equation.

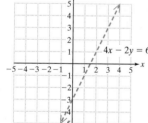

Figure 4-14

Step 2: Graph the equation. Draw a dashed line because the inequality is strict, $>$ (Figure 4-14).

Table:

x	y
0	-3
$\frac{3}{2}$	0
2	1

Slope-intercept form:

$$4x - 2y = 6$$
$$-2y = -4x + 6$$
$$y = 2x - 3$$

Step 3: Choose a test point. Again $(0, 0)$ is a good choice because, when substituted into the original inequality, the arithmetic will be minimal.

$$4x - 2y > 6$$
$$4(0) - 2(0) \stackrel{?}{>} 6$$
$$0 \stackrel{?}{>} 6 \quad \text{False}$$

The test point from above the line does not check in the original inequality. Therefore, shade below the line (Figure 4-15).

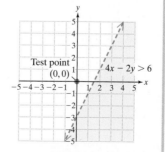

Figure 4-15

Answer

4.

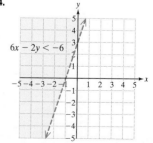

TIP: An inequality can also be graphed by first solving the inequality for *y*. Then,

- Shade *below* the line if the inequality is of the form $y < mx + b$ or $y \leq mx + b$.
- Shade *above* the line if the inequality is of the form $y > mx + b$ or $y \geq mx + b$.

From Example 2, we have

$$4x - 2y > 6$$

$$-2y > -4x + 6$$

$$\frac{-2y}{-2} < \frac{-4x}{-2} + \frac{6}{-2} \qquad \text{Reverse the inequality sign.}$$

$$y < 2x - 3 \qquad \text{Shade below the line.}$$

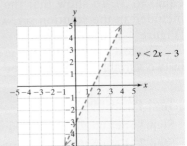

$y < 2x - 3$

Skill Practice

Graph the solution set.

5. $-2y < x$

Example 3 **Graphing a Linear Inequality in Two Variables**

Graph the solution set. $2y \geq 5x$

Solution:

$$2y \geq 5x \longrightarrow 2y = 5x \qquad \textbf{Step 1: } \text{Set up the related equation.}$$

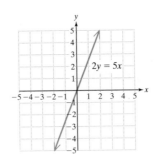

Figure 4-16

Step 2: Graph the equation. Draw a solid line because the symbol $\geq$ is used (Figure 4-16).

Table:

x	y
0	0
1	$\frac{5}{2}$
−1	$-\frac{5}{2}$

Slope-intercept form:

$$2y = 5x$$

$$y = \frac{5}{2}x$$

Step 3: The point $(0, 0)$ cannot be used as a test point because it is on the boundary line. Choose a different point such as $(1, 1)$.

$$2y \geq 5x$$

$$2(1) \overset{?}{\geq} 5(1)$$

$$2 \overset{?}{\geq} 5 \quad \text{False}$$

The test point from below the line does not check in the original inequality. Therefore, shade above the line (Figure 4-17).

Answer

5.

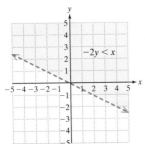

$-2y < x$

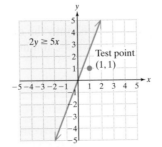

$2y \geq 5x$

Test point $(1, 1)$

Figure 4-17

| Example 4 | Graphing a Linear Inequality in Two Variables

Graph the solution set. $2x > -4$

Solution:

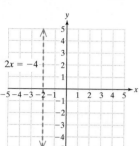

$2x > -4 \longrightarrow 2x = -4$

Step 1: Set up the related equation.

Step 2: Graph the equation. The equation represents a vertical line.

$$2x = -4$$

$$x = -2$$

Draw a dashed vertical line (Figure 4-18).

Figure 4-18

Step 3: Choose a test point such as $(0, 0)$.

$$2x > -4$$
$$2(0) \overset{?}{>} -4$$
$$0 \overset{?}{>} -4 \ ✔ \ \text{True}$$

The test point from the right of the line checks in the original inequality. Therefore, shade to the right of the line (Figure 4-19).

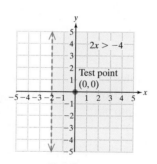

Figure 4-19

2. Graphing Systems of Linear Inequalities in Two Variables

In Sections 4.1–4.4, we studied systems of linear equations in two variables. Graphically, a solution to such a system is a point of intersection of two lines. In this section, we will study systems of linear *inequalities* in two variables. Graphically, the solution set to such a system is the intersection (or "overlap") of the shaded regions of the two inequalities.

Answer

6.

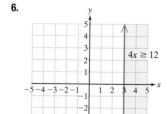

Example 5 **Graphing a System of Linear Inequalities**

Graph the solution set. $y > \dfrac{1}{2}x - 2$

$$x + y \leq 1$$

Solution:

Sketch each inequality.

$$y > \frac{1}{2}x - 2 \xrightarrow{\text{Related equation}} y = \frac{1}{2}x - 2 \qquad x + y \leq 1 \xrightarrow{\text{Related equation}} x + y = 1$$

The line $y = \dfrac{1}{2}x - 2$ is drawn in red in Figure 4-20. Substituting the test point $(0, 0)$ into the inequality results in a true statement. Therefore, we shade above the line.

The line $x + y = 1$ is drawn in blue in Figure 4-21. Substituting the test point $(0, 0)$ into the inequality results in a true statement. Therefore, we shade below the line.

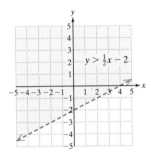

Figure 4-20

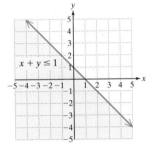

Figure 4-21

Next, we draw these regions on the same graph. The intersection ("overlap") is shown in purple (Figure 4-22).

In Figure 4-23, we show the solution to the system of inequalities. Notice that the portions of the lines not bounding the solution are dashed.

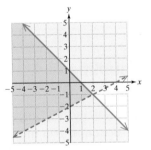

Figure 4-22

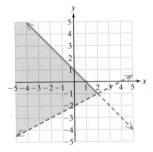

Figure 4-23

Answer

7.

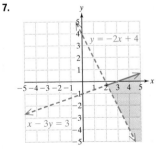

Example 6 **Graphing a System of Linear Inequalities**

Graph the solution set.

$$y \le 3$$

$$2x - y < 2$$

Solution:

Sketch each inequality.

$$y \le 3 \xrightarrow{\text{Related equation}} y = 3 \qquad \qquad 2x - y < 2 \xrightarrow{\text{Related equation}} 2x - y = 2$$

The line $y = 3$ is drawn in red in Figure 4-24. Substituting $(0, 0)$ into the inequality results in a true statement. Therefore, shade below the red line.

The line $2x - y = 2$ is drawn in blue in Figure 4-24. Substituting $(0, 0)$ into the inequality results in a true statement. Therefore, shade above the blue line.

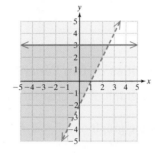

Figure 4-24

In Figure 4-25, we show the solution to the system of inequalities. Notice that the portions of the lines not bounding the solution set are dashed.

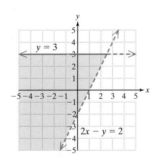

Figure 4-25

Answer

8.

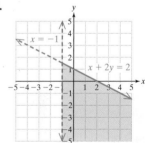

Section 4.5 Practice Exercises

Vocabulary and Key Concepts

1. a. An inequality that can be written in the form $Ax + By > C$ is called a _____ inequality in two variables.

b. The solution to a system of linear inequalities is the region where the graphs _____.

Review Exercises

For Exercises 2–4, graph the equations.

2. $x = -3$

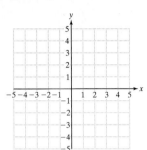

3. $y = \dfrac{3}{5}x + 2$

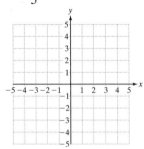

4. $y = -\dfrac{4}{3}x$

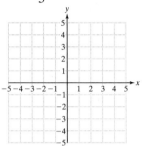

Concept 1: Graphing Linear Inequalities in Two Variables

5. When is a solid line used in the graph of a linear inequality in two variables?

6. When is a dashed line used in the graph of a linear inequality in two variables?

7. What does the shaded region represent in the graph of a linear inequality in two variables?

8. When graphing a linear inequality in two variables, how do you determine which side of the boundary line to shade?

9. Which is the graph of $-2x - y \leq 2$?

a.

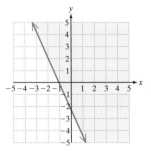

b.

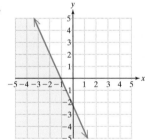

c.

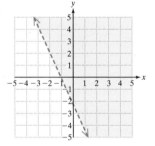

10. Which is the graph of $-3x + y > -1$?

a.

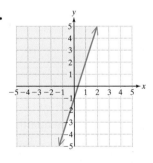

b.

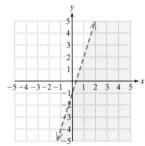

c.

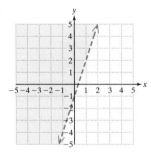

For Exercises 11–16, answer true or false.

11. The point $(3, -1)$ is a solution to $3x + 2y > 1$.

12. The point $(-2, -2)$ is a solution to $-2x + y > 9$.

13. The point $(2, 0)$ is a solution $y < -2x + 4$.

14. The point $(0, 4)$ is a solution to $3x + y \leq 4$.

15. The point $(-3, 0)$ is a solution to $x + 10y < 1$.

16. The point $(1, 1)$ is a solution to $y \geq x - 4$.

For Exercises 17–22, graph the solution set. Then write three ordered pairs that are solutions to the inequality. (See Examples 1–4.)

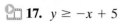 **17.** $y \geq -x + 5$

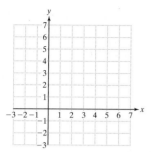

18. $y \leq 2x - 1$

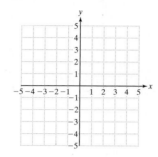

19. $y < 4x$

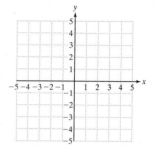

20. $y > -5x$

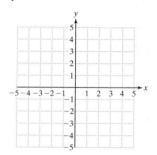

21. $3x + 7y \leq 14$

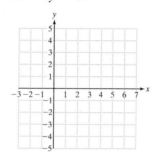

22. $5x - 6y \geq 18$

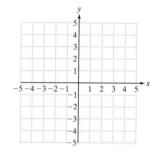

For Exercises 23–40, graph the solution set. (See Examples 1–4.)

23. $x - y > 6$

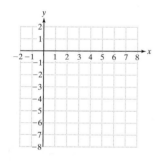

24. $x + y < 5$

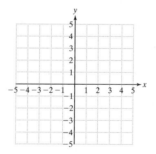

25. $x \geq -1$

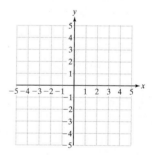

26. $x \leq 6$

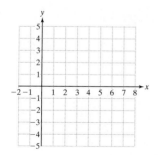

27. $y < 3$

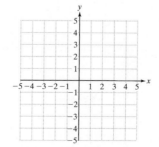

28. $y > -3$

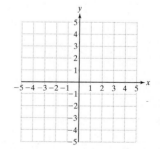

29. $y \leq -\dfrac{3}{4}x + 2$

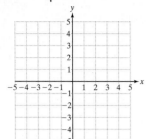

30. $y \geq \dfrac{2}{3}x + 1$

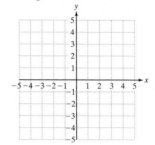

31. $y - 2x > 0$

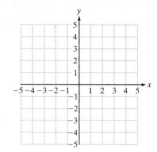

32. $y + 3x < 0$

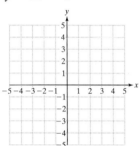

33. $x \leq 0$

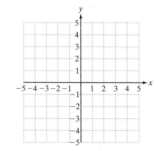

34. $y \leq 0$

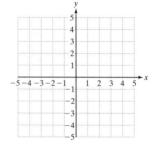

35. $y \geq 0$

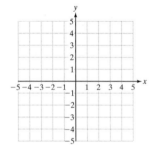

36. $x \geq 0$

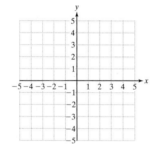

37. $-x \leq \dfrac{1}{2}y - 2$

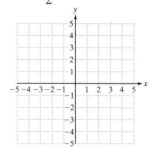

38. $-3 + 2x \leq -y$

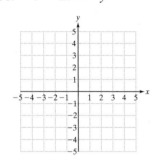

39. $2x > 3y$

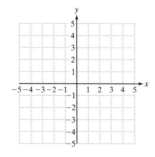

40. $-4x > 5y$

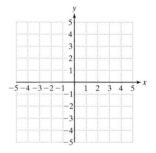

41. a. Describe the graph of the inequality $x + y > 4$. Find three solutions to the inequality (answers will vary).

b. Describe the graph of the equation $x + y = 4$. Find three solutions to the equation (answers will vary).

c. Describe the graph of the inequality $x + y < 4$. Find three solutions to the inequality (answers will vary).

42. a. Describe the graph of the inequality $x + y < 3$. Find three solutions to the inequality (answers will vary).

b. Describe the graph of the equation $x + y = 3$. Find three solutions to the equation (answers will vary).

c. Describe the graph of the inequality $x + y > 3$. Find three solutions to the inequality (answers will vary).

Concept 2: Graphing Systems of Linear Inequalities in Two Variables

For Exercises 43–60, graph the solution set. **(See Examples 5 and 6.)**

43. $2x + y < 3$

$y \geq x + 3$

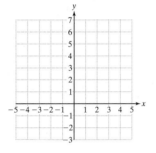

44. $x + y < 3$

$y - x \geq 0$

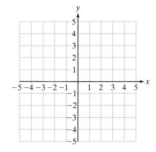

45. $x + y \geq -3$

$x - 2y \geq 6$

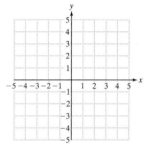

46. $y \geq -3x + 4$

$x + y \leq 4$

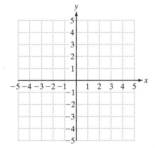

47. $2x + 3y < 6$

$3x + y > -5$

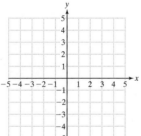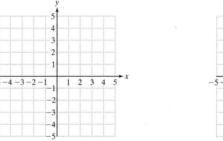

48. $-2x - y < 5$

$x + 2y \geq 2$

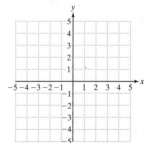

49. $y > 2x$

$y > -4x$

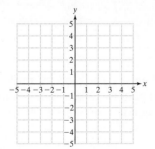

50. $2y \geq 6x$

$y \leq x$

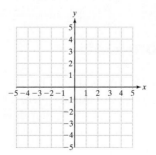

51. $y < \dfrac{1}{2}x - 1$

$x + y \leq -4$

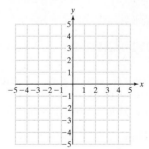

52. $y \geq \dfrac{1}{3}x + 2$

$4x + y < -2$

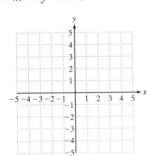

53. $y < 4$

$4x + 3y \geq 12$

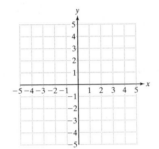

54. $x \geq -3$

$2x + 4y < 4$

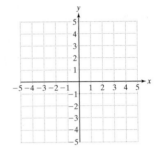

55. $x > -4$

$y \leq 3$

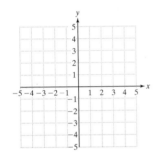

56. $x \leq 3$

$y > 1$

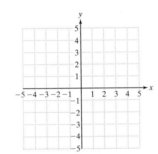

57. $2x \geq 5$

$6 > 3y$

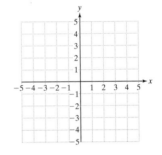

58. $4y \geq 6$

$8 > 2x$

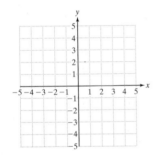

59. $x \geq -4$

$x \leq 1$

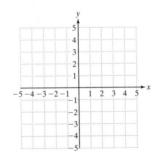

60. $y \geq -2$

$y \leq 3$

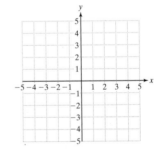

Group Activity

Creating Linear Models from Data

Materials: Two pieces of rope for each group. The ropes should be of different thicknesses. The piece of thicker rope should be between 4 and 5 ft long. The thinner piece of rope should be 8 to 12 in. shorter than the thicker rope. You will also need a yardstick or other device for making linear measurements.

Estimated Time: 30–35 minutes

Group Size: 4 (2 pairs)

1. Each group of 4 should divide into two pairs, and each pair will be given a piece of rope. Each pair will measure the initial length of rope. Then students will tie a series of knots in the rope and measure the new length after each knot is tied. (*Hint:* Try to tie the knots with an equal amount of force each time. Also, as the ropes are straightened for measurement, try to use the same amount of tension in the rope.) The results should be recorded in the table.

Thick Rope	
Number of Knots, x	Length (in.), y
0	
1	
2	
3	
4	

Thin Rope	
Number of Knots, x	Length (in.), y
0	
1	
2	
3	
4	

2. Graph each set of data points. Use a different color pen or pencil for each set of points. Does it appear that each set of data follows a linear trend? Draw a line through each set of points.

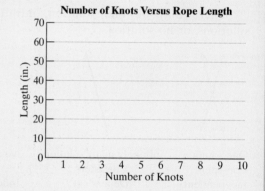

3. Each time a knot is tied, the rope decreases in length. Using the results from question 1, compute the average amount of length lost per knot tied.

   For the thick rope, the length decreases by _____ inches per knot tied.

   For the thin rope, the length decreases by _____ inches per knot tied.

4. For each set of data points, find an equation of the line through the points. Write the equation in slope-intercept form, $y = mx + b$.

   [*Hint:* The slope of the line will be negative and will be represented by the amount of length lost per knot (see question 3). The value of b will be the original length of the rope.]

   Equation for the thick rope: _____

   Equation for the thin rope: _____

5. Next, you will try to predict the number of knots that you need to tie in each rope so that the ropes will be equal in length. To do this, solve the system of equations in question 4.

   Solution to the system of equations: (_____, _____)

   number of knots, x   length, y

   Interpret the meaning of the ordered pair in terms of the number of knots tied and the length of the ropes.

6. Check your answer from question 5 by actually tying the required number of knots in each rope. After doing this, are the ropes the same length? What is the length of each rope? Does this match the length predicted from question 5?

Chapter 4   Summary

Section 4.1 ## Solving Systems of Equations by the Graphing Method

Key Concepts

A **system of two linear equations** can be solved by graphing.

A **solution to a system of linear equations** is an ordered pair that satisfies both equations in the system. Graphically, this represents a point of intersection of the lines.

There may be one solution, infinitely many solutions, or no solution.

One solution
Consistent
Independent

Infinitely many solutions
Consistent
Dependent

No solution
Inconsistent
Independent

A system of equations is **consistent** if there is at least one solution. A system is **inconsistent** if there is no solution.

If two equations represent the same line, the equations are said to be **dependent equations**. In this case, all points on the line are solutions to the system. If two equations represent different lines, the equations are said to be **independent equations**. In this case, the lines either intersect at one point or are parallel.

Examples

Example 1

Solve by graphing.

$$x + y = 3$$
$$2x - y = 0$$

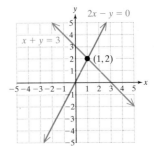

The solution is $(1, 2)$.

Example 2

Solve by graphing.

$$3x - 2y = 2$$
$$-6x + 4y = 4$$

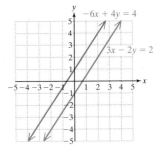

There is no solution. The system is inconsistent.

Example 3

Solve by graphing.

$$x + 2y = 2$$
$$-3x - 6y = -6$$

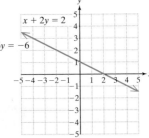

The equations are dependent, and the solution set consists of all points on the line, given by $\{(x, y) | x + 2y = 2\}$.

Section 4.2 Solving Systems of Equations by the Substitution Method

Key Concepts

Steps to Solve a System of Equations by the

Substitution Method:

1. Isolate one of the variables from one equation.
2. Substitute the expression found in step 1 into the other equation.
3. Solve the resulting equation.
4. Substitute the value found in step 3 back into the equation in step 1 to find the remaining variable.
5. Check the solution in both original equations and write the answer as an ordered pair.

An inconsistent system has no solution and is detected algebraically by a contradiction (such as $0 = 3$).

If two linear equations represent the same line, the equations are dependent. This is detected algebraically by an identity (such as $0 = 0$).

Examples

Example 1

Solve by the substitution method.

$$x + 4y = -11$$

$$3x - 2y = -5$$

Isolate x in the first equation: $x = -4y - 11$.
Substitute into the second equation.

$$3(-4y - 11) - 2y = -5 \qquad \text{Solve the}$$
$$-12y - 33 - 2y = -5 \qquad \text{equation.}$$
$$-14y = 28$$
$$y = -2$$

$$\qquad\qquad\qquad\qquad\qquad \text{Substitute}$$
$$x = -4y - 11 \qquad y = -2.$$
$$x = -4(-2) - 11 \qquad \text{Solve for } x.$$
$$x = -3$$

The solution is $(-3, -2)$ and checks in both original equations.

Example 2

Solve by the substitution method.

$$3x + y = 4$$

$$-6x - 2y = 2$$

Isolate y in the first equation: $y = -3x + 4$.
Substitute into the second equation.

$$-6x - 2(-3x + 4) = 2$$
$$-6x + 6x - 8 = 2$$
$$-8 = 2 \qquad \text{Contradiction}$$

The system is inconsistent and has no solution.

Example 3

Solve by the substitution method.

$$y = x + 2 \qquad y \text{ is already isolated.}$$
$$x - y = -2$$

$$x - (x + 2) = -2 \qquad \text{Substitute } y = x + 2 \text{ into the}$$
$$x - x - 2 = -2 \qquad \text{second equation.}$$
$$-2 = -2 \qquad \text{Identity}$$

The equations are dependent. The solution set is all points on the line $y = x + 2$ or $\{(x, y) | y = x + 2\}$.

Section 4.3   Solving Systems of Equations by the Addition Method

Key Concepts

Solving a System of Linear Equations

by the Addition Method:

1. Write both equations in standard form: $Ax + By = C$.
2. Clear fractions or decimals (optional).
3. Multiply one or both equations by a nonzero constant to create opposite coefficients for one of the variables.
4. Add the equations to eliminate one variable.
5. Solve for the remaining variable.
6. Substitute the known value into one of the original equations to solve for the other variable.
7. Check the solution in both original equations.

Examples

Example 1

Solve by using the addition method.

$$5x = -4y - 7 \qquad \text{Write the first equation in}$$
$$6x - 3y = 15 \qquad \text{standard form.}$$

Multiply by 3.
$$5x + 4y = -7 \longrightarrow 15x + 12y = -21$$
$$6x - 3y = 15 \longrightarrow \underline{24x - 12y = 60}$$
$$\text{Multiply by 4.} \qquad 39x = 39$$
$$x = 1$$

$$5x = -4y - 7$$
$$5(1) = -4y - 7$$
$$5 = -4y - 7$$
$$12 = -4y$$
$$-3 = y \qquad \text{The solution is } (1, -3) \text{ and checks in both original equations.}$$

Section 4.4 Applications of Systems of Equations

Examples

Example 1

A riverboat travels 36 mi with the current in 2 hr. The return trip takes 3 hr against the current. Find the speed of the current and the speed of the boat in still water.

Let x represent the speed of the boat in still water. Let y represent the speed of the current.

	Distance	Rate	Time
Against current	36	$x - y$	3
With current	36	$x + y$	2

Distance $=$ (rate)(time)

$$36 = (x - y) \cdot 3 \longrightarrow 36 = 3x - 3y$$
$$36 = (x + y) \cdot 2 \longrightarrow 36 = 2x + 2y$$
$$36 = 3x - 3y \xrightarrow{\text{Multiply by 2.}} 72 = 6x - 6y$$
$$36 = 2x + 2y \xrightarrow{\text{Multiply by 3.}} 108 = 6x + 6y$$
$$180 = 12x$$
$$15 = x$$

$$36 = 2(15) + 2y$$
$$36 = 30 + 2y$$
$$6 = 2y$$
$$3 = y$$

The speed of the boat in still water is 15 mph, and the speed of the current is 3 mph.

Example 2

Diane borrows a total of \$15,000. Part of the money is borrowed from a lender that charges 8% simple interest. She borrows the rest of the money from her mother and will pay back the money at 5% interest. If the total interest after one year is \$900, how much did she borrow from each source?

	8%	5%	Total
Principal	x	y	15,000
Interest	0.08x	0.05y	900

$$x + y = 15{,}000$$
$$0.08x + 0.05y = 900$$

Substitute $x = 15{,}000 - y$ into the second equation.

$$0.08(15{,}000 - y) + 0.05y = 900$$
$$1200 - 0.08y + 0.05y = 900$$
$$1200 - 0.03y = 900$$
$$-0.03y = -300$$
$$y = 10{,}000$$

$$x = 15{,}000 - 10{,}000$$
$$= 5000$$

The amount borrowed at 8% is \$5000.
The amount borrowed from her mother is \$10,000.

Section 4.5   Linear Inequalities and Systems of Inequalities in Two Variables

Key Concepts

A **linear inequality in two variables** can be written in one of the forms: $Ax + By < C$, $Ax + By > C$, $Ax + By \leq C$, or $Ax + By \geq C$.

Steps for Using the Test Point Method to Solve a Linear Inequality in Two Variables:

1. Set up the related *equation*.
2. Graph the related equation. This will be a line in the *xy*-plane.
   - If the original inequality is a strict inequality, $<$ or $>$, then the line is *not* part of the solution set. Therefore, graph the boundary as a dashed line.

   - If the original inequality is not strict, $\leq$ or $\geq$, then the line *is* part of the solution set. Therefore, graph the boundary as a solid line.

3. Choose a point not on the line and substitute its coordinates into the original inequality.
   - If the test point makes the inequality true, then the region it represents is part of the solution set. Shade that region.
   - If the test point makes the inequality false, then the other region is part of the solution set and should be shaded.

Examples

Example 1

Graph the inequality. $2x - y < 4$

1. The related equation is $2x - y = 4$.
2. Graph the equation $2x - y = 4$ (dashed line).

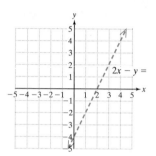

3. Choose an arbitrary test point not on the line such as $(0, 0)$.

$$2x - y < 4$$
$$2(0) - (0) \overset{?}{<} 4$$
$$0 \overset{?}{<} 4 \; \checkmark \quad \text{True}$$

Shade the region represented by the test point (in this case, above the line).

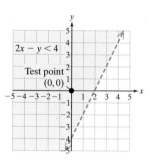

Chapter 4   Review Exercises

Section 4.1

For Exercises 1–4, determine if the ordered pair is a solution to the system.

1. $x - 4y = -4$ $(4, 2)$

    $x + 2y = 8$

2. $x - 6y = 6$ $(12, 1)$

    $-x + y = 4$

3. $3x + y = 9$ $(1, 3)$

    $y = 3$

4. $2x - y = 8$ $(2, -4)$

    $x = 2$

For Exercises 5–10, identify whether the system represents intersecting lines, parallel lines, or coinciding lines by comparing their slopes and y-intercepts.

5. $y = -\dfrac{1}{2}x + 4$

    $y = x - 1$

6. $y = -3x + 4$

    $y = 3x + 4$

7. $y = -\dfrac{4}{7}x + 3$

    $y = -\dfrac{4}{7}x - 5$

8. $y = 5x - 3$

    $y = \dfrac{1}{5}x - 3$

9. $y = 9x - 2$

    $9x - y = 2$

10. $x = -5$

    $y = 2$

For Exercises 11–18, solve the system by graphing. For systems that do not have one unique solution, also state the number of solutions and whether the system is inconsistent or the equations are dependent.

11. $y = -\dfrac{2}{3}x - 2$

    $-x + 3y = -6$

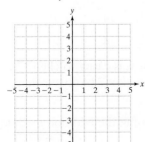

12. $y = -2x - 1$

    $x + 2y = 4$

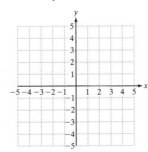

13. $4x = -2y + 10$

    $2x + y = 5$

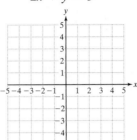

14. $10y = 2x - 10$

    $-x + 5y = -5$

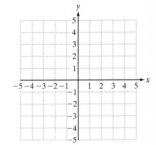

15. $6x - 3y = 9$

    $y = -1$

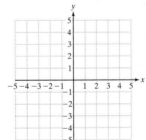

16. $5x + y = -3$

    $x = -1$

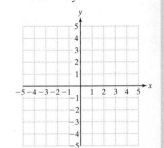

17. $x - 7y = 14$

    $-2x + 14y = 14$

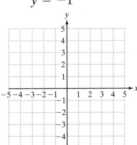

18. $y = -5x + 4$

    $10x + 2y = -4$

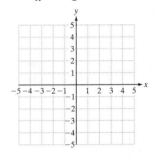

19. A rental car company rents a compact car for $20 a day plus $0.25 per mile. A midsize car rents for $30 a day plus $0.20 per mile.

The cost, y_c, to rent a compact car for one day is given by the equation:

$y_c = 20 + 0.25x$ where x is the number of miles driven

The cost, y_m, to rent a midsize car for one day is given by the equation:

$y_m = 30 + 0.20x$ where x is the number of miles driven

From the graph, determine the number of miles at which the cost to rent either car for a day would be the same. Confirm your answer by substituting into each equation.

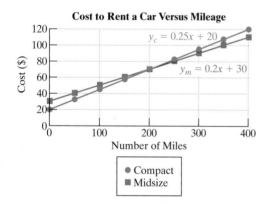

Cost to Rent a Car Versus Mileage

● Compact
■ Midsize

Section 4.2

For Exercises 20–23, solve the systems using the substitution method.

20. $6x + y = 2$
$y = 3x - 4$

21. $2x + 3y = -5$
$x = y - 5$

22. $2x + 6y = 10$
$x = -3y + 6$

23. $4x + 2y = 4$
$y = -2x + 2$

24. Given the system:

$$x + 2y = 11$$
$$5x + 4y = 40$$

a. Which variable from which equation is easiest to isolate and why?

b. Solve the system using the substitution method.

25. Given the system:

$$4x - 3y = 9$$
$$2x + y = 12$$

a. Which variable from which equation is easiest to isolate and why?

b. Solve the system using the substitution method.

For Exercises 26–29, solve the systems using the substitution method.

26. $3x - 2y = 23$
$x + 5y = -15$

27. $x + 5y = 20$
$3x + 2y = 8$

28. $x - 3y = 9$
$5x - 15y = 45$

29. $-3x + y = 15$
$6x - 2y = 12$

30. The difference of two positive numbers is 42. The larger number is 2 more than 6 times the smaller number. Find the numbers.

31. In a right triangle, one of the acute angles measures 6° less than the other acute angle. Find the measure of each acute angle.

32. Two angles are supplementary. One angle measures 14° less than two times the other angle. Find the measure of each angle.

Section 4.3

33. Explain the process for solving a system of two equations using the addition method.

34. Given the system:

$$3x - 5y = 1$$
$$2x - y = -4$$

a. Which variable, x or y, is easier to eliminate using the addition method? (Answers may vary.)

b. Solve the system using the addition method.

35. Given the system:

$$9x - 2y = 14$$
$$4x + 3y = 14$$

a. Which variable, x or y, is easier to eliminate using the addition method? (Answers may vary.)

b. Solve the system using the addition method.

For Exercises 36–43, solve the systems using the addition method.

36. $2x + 3y = 1$

   $x - 2y = 4$

37. $x + 3y = 0$

   $-3x - 10y = -2$

38. $8x + 8 = -6y + 6$

   $10x = 9y - 8$

39. $12x = 5y + 5$

   $5y = -1 - 4x$

40. $-4x - 6y = -2$

   $6x + 9y = 3$

41. $-8x - 4y = 16$

   $10x + 5y = 5$

42. $\dfrac{1}{2}x - \dfrac{3}{4}y = -\dfrac{1}{2}$

   $\dfrac{1}{3}x + y = -\dfrac{10}{3}$

43. $0.5x - 0.2y = 0.5$

   $0.4x + 0.7y = 0.4$

44. Given the system:

$$4x + 9y = -7$$
$$y = 2x - 13$$

a. Which method would you choose to solve the system, the substitution method or the addition method? Explain your choice. (Answers may vary.)

b. Solve the system.

45. Given the system:

$$5x - 8y = -2$$
$$3x - y = -5$$

a. Which method would you choose to solve the system, the substitution method or the addition method? Explain your choice. (Answers may vary.)

b. Solve the system.

Section 4.4

46. Miami Metrozoo charges $11.50 for adult admission and $6.75 for children under 12. The total bill before tax for a school group of 60 people is $443. How many adults and how many children were admitted?

47. As part of his retirement strategy Winston plans to invest $600,000 in two different funds. He projects that the high-risk investments should return, over time, about 12% per year, while the low-risk investments should return about 4% per year. If he wants a supplemental income of $30,000 a year, how should he divide his investments?

48. Suppose that whole milk with 4% fat is mixed with 1% low fat milk to make a 2% reduced fat milk. How much of the whole milk should be mixed with the low fat milk to make 60 gal of 2% reduced fat milk?

49. A boat travels 80 mi downstream with the current in 4 hr and 80 mi upstream against the current in 5 hr. Find the speed of the current and the speed of the boat in still water.

50. A plane travels 870 miles against the wind in 3 hr. Traveling with the wind, the plane travels 700 mi in 2 hr. Find the speed of the plane in still air and the speed of the wind.

51. At Conseco Fieldhouse, home of the Indiana Pacers, the total cost of a soft drink and a hot dog is $8.00. The price of the hot dog is $1.00 more than the cost of the soft drink. Find the cost of a soft drink and the cost of a hot dog.

52. Ray played two rounds of golf at Pebble Beach for a total score of 154. If his score in the second round is 10 more than his score in the first round, find the scores for each round.

Section 4.5

For Exercises 53–56, graph the inequalities. Then write three ordered pairs that are in the solution set (answers may vary).

53. $y < 3x - 1$

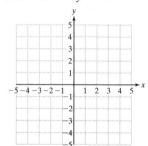

54. $y > -2x + 6$

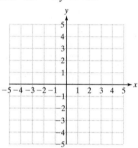

55. $-2x - 3y \geq 8$

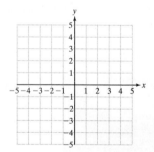

56. $4x - 2y \leq 10$

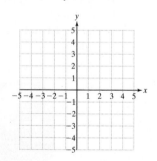

For Exercises 57–62, graph the solution set.

57. $x - 5y \geq 0$

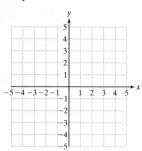

58. $7x - y \leq 0$

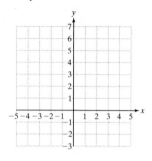

59. $x > 5$

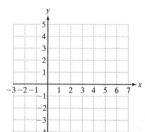

60. $y < -4$

61. $y \geq 0$

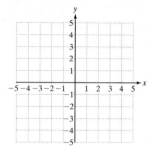

62. $x \geq 0$

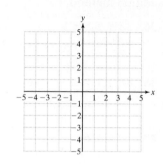

For Exercises 63–66, graph the solution set.

63. $2x - y \geq 8$

$x + y \leq 3$

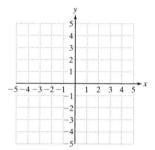

64. $y \leq x - 1$

$x + 2y \geq 4$

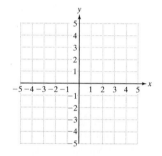

65. $y \leq 2x$

$-2x - y > -3$

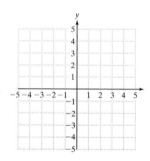

66. $y \leq 4$

$2x - y < 1$

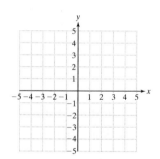

Chapter 4 Test

1. Write each line in slope-intercept form. Then determine if the lines represent intersecting lines, parallel lines, or coinciding lines.

$$5x + 2y = -6$$

$$-\frac{5}{2}x - y = -3$$

2. a. How many solutions does a system of two linear equations have if the equations represent parallel lines?

   b. How many solutions does a system of two linear equations have if the equations represent coinciding lines?

   c. How many solutions does a system of two linear equations have if the equations represent intersecting lines?

For Exercises 3 and 4 solve the system by graphing.

3. $y = 2x - 4$

   $-2x + 3y = 0$

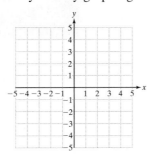

4. $2x + 4y = 6$

   $2y - 3 = -x$

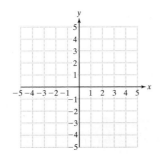

5. Solve the system using the substitution method.

$$x = 5y - 2$$

$$2x + y = -4$$

6. Solve the system using the addition method.

$$3x - 6y = 8$$

$$2x + 3y = 3$$

For Exercises 7–12, solve the systems using any method.

7. $\frac{1}{3}x + y = \frac{7}{3}$

   $x = \frac{3}{2}y - 11$

8. $2x - 12 = y$

   $2x - \frac{1}{2}y = x + 5$

9. $3x - 4y = 29$

   $2x + 5y = -19$

10. $2x = 6y - 14$

    $2y = 3 - x$

11. $-0.25x - 0.05y = 0.2$

    $10x + \quad 2y = -8$

12. $3x + 3y = -2y - 7$

    $-3y = 10 - 4x$

13. Graph the solution set. $5x - y \geq -6$

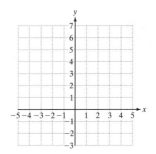

14. Graph the solution set.

    $2x + y > 1$

    $x + y < 2$

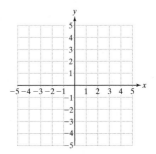

15. In the 2005 WNBA (basketball) season, the league's leading scorer was Sheryl Swoopes from the Houston Comets. Swoopes scored 17 points more than the second leading scorer, Lauren Jackson from the Seattle Storm. Together they scored a total of 1211 points. How many points did each player score?

16. At Best Buy, Latrell buys four CDs and two DVDs for $54 from the sale rack. Kendra buys two CDs and three DVDs from the same rack for $49. What is the price per CD and the price per DVD?

17. How many milliliters of a 50% acid solution and how many milliliters of a 20% acid solution must be mixed to produce 36 mL of a 30% acid solution?

18. The cost to ride the trolley one-way in San Diego is $2.25. Kelly and Hazel had to buy eight tickets for their group.

    a. What was the total amount of money required?

    b. Kelly and Hazel had only quarters and $1 bills. They also determined that they used twice as many quarters as $1 bills. How many quarters and how many $1 bills did they use?

19. Suppose a total of $5000 is borrowed from two different loans. One loan charges 10% simple interest, and the other charges 8% simple interest. How much was borrowed at each rate if $424 in interest is charged at the end of 1 yr?

20. Mark needs to move to a new apartment and is trying to find the most affordable moving truck. He will only need the truck for one day. After checking the U-Haul website, he finds that he can rent a 10-ft truck for $20.95 a day plus $1.89 per mile. He then checks the Public Storage website and finds the charge to be $37.95 a day plus $1.19 per mile for the same size truck. Determine the number of miles for which the cost to rent from either company would be the same. Round the answer to the nearest mile.

21. A plane travels 910 mi in 2 hr against the wind and 1090 mi in 2 hr with the same wind. Find the speed of the plane in still air and the speed of the wind.

22. The number of calories in a piece of cake is 20 less than 3 times the number of calories in a scoop of ice cream. Together, the cake and ice cream have 460 calories. How many calories are in each?

23. How much 10% acid solution should be mixed with a 25% acid solution to create 100 mL of a 16% acid solution?

Chapters 1–4   Cumulative Review Exercises

1. Simplify.

   $$\frac{|2 - 5| + 10 \div 2 + 3}{\sqrt{10^2 - 8^2}}$$

2. Solve for x. $\dfrac{1}{3}x - \dfrac{3}{4} = \dfrac{1}{2}(x + 2)$

3. Solve for a. $-4(a + 3) + 2 = -5(a + 1) + a$

4. Solve for y. $3x - 2y = 6$

5. Solve for x. $z = \dfrac{x - m}{5}$

6. Solve for z. Graph the solution set on a number line and write the solution in interval notation:

   $$-2(3z + 1) \le 5(z - 3) + 10$$

   ⟶

7. The largest angle in a triangle measures 110°. Of the remaining two angles, one measures 4° less than the other angle. Find the measures of the three angles.

8. Two hikers start at opposite ends of an 18-mi trail and walk toward each other. One hiker walks predominately down hill and averages 2 mph faster than the other hiker. Find the average rate of each hiker if they meet in 3 hr.

9. Jesse Ventura became the 38th governor of Minnesota by receiving 37% of the votes. If approximately 2,060,000 votes were cast, how many did Mr. Ventura get?

10. The YMCA wants to raise $2500 for its summer program for disadvantaged children. If the YMCA has already raised $900, what percent of its goal has been achieved?

11. Two angles are complementary. One angle measures 17° more than the other angle. Find the measure of each angle.

12. Find the slope and y-intercept of the line $5x + 3y = -6$.

13. The slope of a given line is $-\frac{2}{3}$.

    a. What is the slope of a line parallel to the given line?

    b. What is the slope of a line perpendicular to the given line?

14. Find an equation of the line passing through the point $(2, -3)$ and having a slope of -3. Write the final answer in slope-intercept form.

15. Sketch the following equations on the same graph.

    a. $2x + 5y = 10$

    b. $2y = 4$

    c. Find the point of intersection and check the solution in each equation.

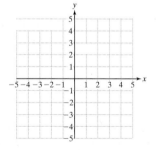

16. Solve the system of equations by using the substitution method.

$$2x + 5y = 10$$
$$2y = 4$$

17. a. Graph the line $2x + y = 3$.

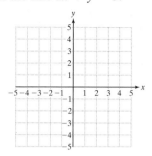

    b. Graph the inequality $2x + y < 3$.

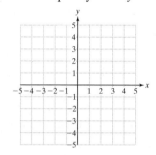

    c. Explain the difference between the graphs in parts (a) and (b).

18. How many gallons of a 15% antifreeze solution should be mixed with a 60% antifreeze solution to produce 60 gal of a 45% antifreeze solution?

19. Use a system of linear equations to solve for x and y.

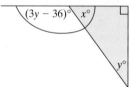

20. In 1920, the average speed for the winner of the Indianapolis 500 car race was 88.6 mph. By 1990, the average speed of the winner was 186.0 mph.

    a. Find the slope of the line shown in the figure. Round to one decimal place.

    b. Interpret the meaning of the slope in the context of this problem.

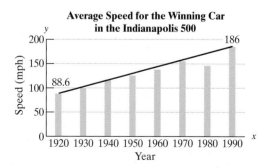

Average Speed for the Winning Car in the Indianapolis 500

Polynomials and Properties of Exponents

5

Chapter 5

In this chapter, we will learn how to add, subtract, multiply, and divide polynomials. In addition, we will simplify expressions with exponents and expressions involving scientific notation.

Review Your Skills

The skills we need to practice include clearing parentheses and combining like terms.

   Simplify each expression. Find the answer in the table and cross out the letter above it. When you have finished, the answer to the statement will remain.

1. $6x - (4x + 2) - 7$ **4.** $5(x - 6) - 3(2x + 1)$

2. $2x + 3(x - 5) + x$ **5.** $3(8 - x) + 5x$

3. $5 + 2(4x - 1) + 2x$ **6.** $7(2 + 3x) - 8$

A polynomial that has two terms is called a _____.

P	B	E	I	N	D	O	K	M	Y	T	I	A	L
$-x - 33$	$8x + 24$	$2x + 24$	$5x - 14$	$2x - 5$	$6x - 15$	$-x - 27$	$10x + 3$	$8x + 5$	$2x - 9$	$21x + 6$	$35x - 8$	$-8x - 30$	$x - 21$

Section 5.1   Multiplying and Dividing Expressions with Common Bases

1. Review of Exponential Notation

Recall that an **exponent** is used to show repeated multiplication of the **base**.

> **Definition of b^n**
>
> Let b represent any real number and n represent a positive integer. Then,
>
> $$b^n = \underbrace{b \cdot b \cdot b \cdot b \cdot \ldots b}_{n \text{ factors of } b}$$

Example 1   **Evaluating Expressions with Exponents**

For each expression, identify the exponent and base. Then evaluate the expression.

a. 6^2 **b.** $\left(-\dfrac{1}{2}\right)^3$ **c.** 0.8^4

Solution:

Expression	Base	Exponent	Result
a. 6^2	6	2	$(6)(6) = 36$
b. $\left(-\dfrac{1}{2}\right)^3$	$-\dfrac{1}{2}$	3	$\left(-\dfrac{1}{2}\right)\left(-\dfrac{1}{2}\right)\left(-\dfrac{1}{2}\right) = -\dfrac{1}{8}$
c. 0.8^4	0.8	4	$(0.8)(0.8)(0.8)(0.8) = 0.4096$

Note that if no exponent is explicitly written for an expression, then the expression has an implied exponent of 1. For example, $x = x^1$.

Consider an expression such as $3y^6$. The factor 3 has an exponent of 1, and the factor y has an exponent of 6. That is, the expression $3y^6$ is interpreted as $3^1 y^6$.

2. Evaluating Expressions with Exponents

Recall from Section 1.5 that particular care must be taken when evaluating exponential expressions involving negative numbers. An exponential expression with a negative base is written with parentheses around the base, such as $(-3)^2$.

To evaluate $(-3)^2$, we have: $(-3)^2 = (-3)(-3) = 9$

If no parentheses are present, the expression -3^2 is the *opposite* of 3^2, or equivalently, $-1 \cdot 3^2$.

$$-3^2 = -1(3^2) = -1(3)(3) = -9$$

Example 2 Evaluating Expressions with Exponents

Evaluate each expression.

a. -5^4 **b.** $(-5)^4$ **c.** $(-0.2)^3$ **d.** -0.2^3

Solution:

a. -5^4

$= -1 \cdot 5^4$ 5 is the base with exponent 4.

$= -1 \cdot 5 \cdot 5 \cdot 5 \cdot 5$ Multiply -1 by four factors of 5.

$= -625$

b. $(-5)^4$

$= (-5)(-5)(-5)(-5)$ Parentheses indicate that -5 is the base with exponent 4.

$= 625$ Multiply four factors of -5.

c. $(-0.2)^3$ Parentheses indicate that -0.2 is the base with exponent 3.

$= (-0.2)(-0.2)(-0.2)$ Multiply three factors of -0.2.

$= -0.008$

d. -0.2^3

$= -1 \cdot 0.2^3$ 0.2 is the base with exponent 3.

$= -1 \cdot 0.2 \cdot 0.2 \cdot 0.2$ Multiply -1 by three factors of 0.2.

$= -0.008$

Skill Practice

Evaluate.

4. -2^4 **5.** $(-2)^4$
6. $(-0.1)^3$ **7.** -0.1^3

Concept Connections

8. Will the value of a negative base with an odd exponent be negative or positive?
9. Will the value of a negative base with an even exponent be negative or positive?

Example 3 Evaluating Expressions with Exponents

Evaluate each expression for $a = 2$ and $b = -3$.

a. $5a^2$ **b.** $(5a)^2$ **c.** $5ab^2$ **d.** $(b + a)^2$

Solution:

a. $5a^2$

$= 5(\ )^2$ Use parentheses to substitute a number for a variable.

$= 5(2)^2$ Substitute $a = 2$.

$= 5(4)$ Simplify.

$= 20$

b. $(5a)^2$

$= [5(\ )]^2$ Use parentheses to substitute a number for a variable. The original parentheses are replaced with brackets.

$= [5(2)]^2$ Substitute $a = 2$.

$= (10)^2$ Simplify inside the parentheses first.

$= 100$

Skill Practice

Evaluate each expression for $x = 2$ and $y = -5$.

10. $6x^2$ **11.** $(6x)^2$
12. $2xy^2$ **13.** $(y - x)^2$

Answers

4. -16 **5.** 16   **6.** -0.001
7. -0.001 **8.** Negative
9. Positive   **10.** 24   **11.** 144
12. 100   **13.** 49

c. $5ab^2$

$= 5(2)(-3)^2$ Substitute $a = 2$, $b = -3$.

$= 5(2)(9)$ Simplify.

$= 90$ Multiply.

d. $(b + a)^2$

$= [(-3) + (2)]^2$ Substitute $b = -3$ and $a = 2$.

$= (-1)^2$ Simplify within the parentheses first.

$= 1$

3. Multiplying and Dividing Expressions with Common Bases

In this section, we investigate the effect of multiplying or dividing two quantities with the same base. For example, consider the expressions: x^5x^2 and $\frac{x^5}{x^2}$. Simplifying each expression, we have:

$$x^5x^2 = (x \cdot x \cdot x \cdot x \cdot x)(x \cdot x) = \overbrace{x \cdot x \cdot x \cdot x \cdot x \cdot x \cdot x}^{\text{7 factors of } x} = x^7$$

$$\frac{x^5}{x^2} = \frac{x \cdot x \cdot x \cdot \cancel{x} \cdot \cancel{x}}{\cancel{x} \cdot \cancel{x}} = \frac{x \cdot x \cdot x}{1} = x^3$$

These examples suggest that to multiply two quantities with the same base, we add the exponents and leave the base unchanged. To divide two quantities with the same base, we subtract the exponent in the denominator from the exponent in the numerator and leave the base unchanged. These rules are stated formally in the following two properties.

Multiplication of Expressions with Like Bases

Assume that b is a real number and that m and n represent positive integers. Then,

$$b^mb^n = b^{m+n}$$

Division of Expressions with Like Bases

Assume that $b \neq 0$ is a real number and that m and n represent positive integers such that $m > n$. Then,

$$\frac{b^m}{b^n} = b^{m-n}$$

Example 4 Simplifying Expressions with Exponents

Simplify the expressions. **a.** w^3w^4 **b.** $2^3 \cdot 2^4$

Solution:

a. w^3w^4 $\quad (w \cdot w \cdot w)(w \cdot w \cdot w \cdot w)$

$= w^{3+4}$ $\quad$ To multiply expressions with like bases, add the exponents.

$= w^7$

b. $2^3 \cdot 2^4$ $\quad (2 \cdot 2 \cdot 2)(2 \cdot 2 \cdot 2 \cdot 2)$

$= 2^{3+4}$ $\quad$ To multiply expressions with like bases, add the exponents (the base is unchanged).

$= 2^7$ or 128

Skill Practice

Simplify the expressions.
14. q^4q^8 **15.** $8^4 \cdot 8^8$

Avoiding Mistakes

When we multiply expressions with like bases, we add the exponents. The base does not change. In Example 4(b), we have $2^3 \cdot 2^4 = 2^7$.

Example 5 Simplifying Expressions with Exponents

Simplify the expressions. **a.** $\dfrac{t^6}{t^4}$ **b.** $\dfrac{5^6}{5^4}$

Skill Practice

Simplify the expressions.
16. $\dfrac{y^{15}}{y^8}$ **17.** $\dfrac{3^{15}}{3^8}$

Solution:

a. $\dfrac{t^6}{t^4}$ $\quad \dfrac{t \cdot t \cdot t \cdot t \cdot t \cdot t}{t \cdot t \cdot t \cdot t}$

$= t^{6-4}$ $\quad$ To divide expressions with like bases subtract the exponents.

$= t^2$

b. $\dfrac{5^6}{5^4}$ $\quad \dfrac{5 \cdot 5 \cdot 5 \cdot 5 \cdot 5 \cdot 5}{5 \cdot 5 \cdot 5 \cdot 5}$

$= 5^{6-4}$ $\quad$ To divide expressions with like bases subtract the exponents (the base is unchanged).

$= 5^2$ or 25

Answers

14. q^{12} **15.** 8^{12}
16. y^7 **17.** 3^7

| **Example 6** | **Simplifying Expressions with Exponents** |

Simplify the expressions.   **a.** $\dfrac{z^4 z^5}{z^3}$ **b.** $\dfrac{10^7}{10^2 \cdot 10}$

Solution:

a. $\dfrac{z^4 z^5}{z^3}$

$= \dfrac{z^{4+5}}{z^3}$ Simplify the numerator by adding the exponents (the base is unchanged).

$= \dfrac{z^9}{z^3}$

$= z^{9-3}$ Subtract the exponents.

$= z^6$

b. $\dfrac{10^7}{10^2 \cdot 10}$

$= \dfrac{10^7}{10^2 \cdot 10^1}$ Note that 10 is equivalent to 10^1.

$= \dfrac{10^7}{10^{2+1}}$ Simplify the denominator by adding the exponents (the base is unchanged).

$= \dfrac{10^7}{10^3}$

$= 10^{7-3}$ Subtract the exponents.

$= 10^4$ or $10,000$ Simplify.

4. Simplifying Expressions with Exponents

| **Example 7** | **Simplifying Expressions with Exponents** |

Use the commutative and associative properties of real numbers and the properties of exponents to simplify the expressions.

a. $(-3p^2 q^4)(2pq^5)$ **b.** $\dfrac{16w^9 z^3}{4w^8 z}$

Solution:

a. $(-3p^2 q^4)(2pq^5)$

$= (-3 \cdot 2)(p^2 p)(q^4 q^5)$ Apply the associative and commutative properties of multiplication to group coefficients and like bases.

$= (-3 \cdot 2)p^{2+1} q^{4+5}$ Add the exponents when multiplying expressions with like bases.

$= -6p^3 q^9$ Simplify.

b. $\dfrac{16w^9z^3}{4w^8z}$

$= \left(\dfrac{16}{4}\right)\left(\dfrac{w^9}{w^8}\right)\left(\dfrac{z^3}{z}\right)$ Group coefficients and like bases.

$= 4w^{9-8}z^{3-1}$ Subtract the exponents when dividing expressions with like bases.

$= 4wz^2$ Simplify.

> **Avoiding Mistakes**
>
> In Example 7(b) we divide the coefficients. However, to divide the expressions with like bases, we subtract the exponents.

5. Applications of Exponents

Simple interest on an investment or loan is computed by the formula $I = Prt$, where P is the amount of principal, r is the annual interest rate, and t is the time in years. Simple interest is based only on the original principal. However, in most day-to-day applications, the interest computed on money invested or borrowed is compound interest. **Compound interest** is computed on the original principal and on the interest already accrued.

Suppose $1000 is invested at 8% interest for 3 years. Compare the total amount in the account if the money earns simple interest versus if the interest is compounded annually.

Simple Interest

The simple interest earned is given by $I = Prt$

$$= (1000)(0.08)(3)$$

$$= \$240$$

The total amount, A, at the end of 3 years is $A = P + I$

$$= \$1000 + \$240$$

$$= \$1240$$

Compound Annual Interest

The total amount, A, in an account earning compound annual interest may be computed using the formula:

$A = P(1 + r)^t$ where P is the amount of principal, r is the annual interest rate (expressed in decimal form), and t is the number of years.

For example, for $1000 invested at 8% interest compounded annually for 3 years, we have $P = 1000$, $r = 0.08$, and $t = 3$.

$$A = P(1 + r)^t$$

$$A = 1000(1 + 0.08)^3$$

$$= 1000(1.08)^3$$

$$= 1000(1.259712)$$

$$= 1259.712$$

Rounding to the nearest cent, we have $A = \$1259.71$.

> **Concept Connections**
>
> **22.** Identify the values for the variables P, r, and t if $19,000 is invested for 10 years at 7% interest compounded annually.

> **Answer**
>
> **22.** $P = 19,000$; $r = 0.07$; $t = 10$

Example 8   Using Exponents in an Application

Find the amount in an account after 8 years if the initial investment is $7000, invested at 2.25% interest compounded annually.

Solution:

Identify the values for each variable.

$$P = 7000$$

$$r = 0.0225$$ Note that the decimal form of a percent is used for calculations.

$$t = 8$$

$$A = P(1 + r)^t$$

$$= 7000(1 + 0.0225)^8 \qquad \text{Substitute.}$$

$$= 7000(1.0225)^8 \qquad \text{Simplify inside the parentheses.}$$

$$\approx 7000(1.194831142) \qquad \text{Approximate } (1.0225)^8.$$

$$\approx 8363.82 \qquad \text{Multiply (round to the nearest cent).}$$

The amount in the account after 8 years is $8363.82.

Answer

23. $4630.50

Calculator Connections

Topic: Review of Evaluating Exponential Expressions on a Calculator

In Example 8, it was necessary to evaluate the expression $(1.0225)^8$. Recall that the [^] or [y^x] key may be used to enter expressions with exponents.

Scientific Calculator

Enter: 1.0225 [y^x] 8 [=]   **Result:** | 1.194831142 |

Graphing Calculator

```
1.0225^8
        1.194831142
```

Calculator Exercises

Use a calculator to evaluate the expressions.

1. $(1.06)^5$

2. $(1.02)^{40}$

3. $5000(1.06)^5$

4. $2000(1.02)^{40}$

5. $3000(1 + 0.06)^2$

6. $1000(1 + 0.05)^3$

Section 5.1   Practice Exercises

For this exercise set, assume all variables represent nonzero real numbers.

Vocabulary and Key Concepts

1. a. A(n) _____ is used to show repeated multiplication of the base.

   b. Given the expression b^n, the value b is the _____ and n is the _____.

   c. Given the expression x, the value of the exponent on x is understood to be _____.

   d. The formula to compute simple interest is _____.

   e. Interest that is computed on the original principal and on the accrued interest is called _____ _____.

Concept 1: Review of Exponential Notation

For Exercises 2–13, identify the base and the exponent. **(See Example 1.)**

2. c^3 **3.** x^4 **4.** 5^2 **5.** 3^5

6. $(-4)^8$ **7.** $(-1)^4$ **8.** x **9.** 13

10. -4^2 **11.** -10^3 **12.** $-y^5$ **13.** $-t^6$

14. What base corresponds to the exponent 5 in the expression $x^3y^5z^2$?

15. What base corresponds to the exponent 2 in the expression w^3v^2?

16. What is the exponent for the factor of 2 in the expression $2x^3$?

17. What is the exponent for the factor of p in the expression pq^7?

For Exercises 18–26, write the expression using exponents.

18. $(4n)(4n)(4n)$ **19.** $(-6b)(-6b)$ **20.** $4 \cdot n \cdot n \cdot n$

21. $-6 \cdot b \cdot b$ **22.** $(x-5)(x-5)(x-5)$ **23.** $(y+2)(y+2)(y+2)(y+2)$

24. $\dfrac{4}{x \cdot x \cdot x \cdot x \cdot x}$ **25.** $\dfrac{-2}{t \cdot t \cdot t}$ **26.** $\dfrac{5 \cdot x \cdot x \cdot x}{(y-7)(y-7)}$

Concept 2: Evaluating Expressions with Exponents

For Exercises 27–34, evaluate the two expressions and compare the answers. Do the expressions have the same value? **(See Example 2.)**

27. -5^2 and $(-5)^2$ **28.** -3^4 and $(-3)^4$ **29.** -2^5 and $(-2)^5$ **30.** -5^3 and $(-5)^3$

31. $\left(\dfrac{1}{2}\right)^3$ and $\dfrac{1}{2^3}$ **32.** $\left(\dfrac{1}{5}\right)^2$ and $\dfrac{1}{5^2}$ **33.** $-(-2)^4$ and $-(2)^4$ **34.** $-(-3)^3$ and $-(3)^3$

For Exercises 35–42, evaluate each expression. **(See Example 2.)**

35. 16^1 **36.** 20^1 **37.** $(-1)^{21}$ **38.** $(-1)^{30}$

39. $\left(-\dfrac{1}{3}\right)^2$ **40.** $\left(-\dfrac{1}{4}\right)^3$ **41.** $-\left(\dfrac{2}{5}\right)^2$ **42.** $-\left(\dfrac{3}{5}\right)^2$

For Exercises 43–50, simplify using the order of operations.

43. $3 \cdot 2^4$ **44.** $2 \cdot 0^5$ **45.** $-4(-1)^7$ **46.** $-3(-1)^4$

47. $6^2 - 3^3$ **48.** $4^3 + 2^3$ **49.** $2 \cdot 3^2 + 4 \cdot 2^3$ **50.** $6^2 - 3 \cdot 1^3$

For Exercises 51–62, evaluate each expression for $a = -4$ and $b = 5$. (See Example 3.)

51. $-4b^2$ **52.** $3a^2$ **53.** $(-4b)^2$ **54.** $(3a)^2$

55. $(a + b)^2$ **56.** $(a - b)^2$ **57.** $a^2 + 2ab + b^2$ **58.** $a^2 - 2ab + b^2$

59. $-10ab^2$ **60.** $-6a^3b$ **61.** $-10a^2b$ **62.** $-a^2b$

Concept 3: Multiplying and Dividing Expressions with Common Bases

63. Expand the expressions first. Then simplify using exponents.

     a. $x^4 \cdot x^3$ **b.** $5^4 \cdot 5^3$

64. Expand the expressions first. Then simplify using exponents.

     a. $y^2 \cdot y^4$ **b.** $3^2 \cdot 3^4$

For Exercises 65–76, simplify the expressions. Write the answers in exponent form. (See Example 4.)

65. $z^5 z^3$ **66.** $w^4 w^7$ **67.** $a \cdot a^8$ **68.** $p^4 p$

69. $4^5 \cdot 4^9$ **70.** $6^7 \cdot 6^5$ **71.** $\left(\dfrac{2}{3}\right)^3\left(\dfrac{2}{3}\right)$ **72.** $\left(\dfrac{1}{x}\right)\left(\dfrac{1}{x}\right)^2$

73. $c^5 c^2 c^7$ **74.** $b^7 b^2 b^8$ **75.** $x \cdot x^4 \cdot x^{10} \cdot x^3$ **76.** $z^7 \cdot z^{11} \cdot z^{60} \cdot z$

77. Expand the expressions. Then simplify.

     a. $\dfrac{p^8}{p^3}$ **b.** $\dfrac{8^8}{8^3}$

78. Expand the expressions. Then simplify.

     a. $\dfrac{w^5}{w^2}$ **b.** $\dfrac{4^5}{4^2}$

For Exercises 79–94, simplify the expressions. Write the answers in exponent form. (See Examples 5 and 6.)

79. $\dfrac{x^8}{x^6}$ **80.** $\dfrac{z^5}{z^4}$ **81.** $\dfrac{a^{10}}{a}$ **82.** $\dfrac{b^{12}}{b}$

83. $\dfrac{7^{13}}{7^6}$ **84.** $\dfrac{2^6}{2^4}$ **85.** $\dfrac{5^8}{5}$ **86.** $\dfrac{3^5}{3}$

87. $\dfrac{y^{13}}{y^{12}}$ **88.** $\dfrac{w^7}{w^6}$ **89.** $\dfrac{h^3 h^8}{h^7}$ **90.** $\dfrac{n^5 n^4}{n^2}$

91. $\dfrac{7^2 \cdot 7^6}{7}$ **92.** $\dfrac{5^3 \cdot 5^8}{5}$ **93.** $\dfrac{10^{20}}{10^3 \cdot 10^8}$ **94.** $\dfrac{3^{15}}{3^2 \cdot 3^{10}}$

Concept 4: Simplifying Expressions with Exponents (Mixed Exercises)

For Exercises 95–114, use the commutative and associative properties of real numbers and the properties of exponents to simplify the expressions. (See Example 7.)

95. $(2x^3)(3x^4)$ **96.** $(10y)(2y^3)$ **97.** $(5a^2b)(8a^3b^4)$ **98.** $(10xy^3)(3x^4y)$

99. $s^3 \cdot t^5 \cdot t \cdot t^{10} \cdot s^6$ **100.** $c \cdot c^4 \cdot d^2 \cdot c^3 \cdot d^3$ **101.** $(-2v^2)(3v)(5v^5)$ **102.** $(10q^5)(-3q^8)(q)$

103. $\left(\frac{2}{3}m^{13}n^8\right)(24m^7n^2)$ **104.** $\left(\frac{1}{4}c^6d^6\right)(28c^2d^7)$ **105.** $\dfrac{14c^4d^5}{7c^3d}$ **106.** $\dfrac{36h^5k^2}{9h^3k}$

107. $\dfrac{z^3z^{11}}{z^4z^6}$ **108.** $\dfrac{w^{12}w^2}{w^4w^5}$ **109.** $\dfrac{25h^3jk^5}{12h^2k}$ **110.** $\dfrac{15m^5np^{12}}{4mp^9}$

111. $(-4p^6q^8r^4)(2pqr^2)$ **112.** $(-5a^4bc)(-10a^2b)$ **113.** $\dfrac{-12s^2tu^3}{4su^2}$ **114.** $\dfrac{15w^5x^{10}y^3}{-15w^4x}$

Concept 5: Applications of Exponents

 Use the formula $A = P(1 + r)^t$ for Exercises 115–118. **(See Example 8.)**

115. Find the amount in an account after 2 years if the initial investment is \$5000, invested at 7% interest compounded annually.

116. Find the amount in an account after 5 years if the initial investment is \$2000, invested at 4% interest compounded annually.

117. Find the amount in an account after 3 years if the initial investment is \$4000, invested at 6% interest compounded annually.

118. Find the amount in an account after 4 years if the initial investment is \$10,000, invested at 5% interest compounded annually.

For Exercises 119–122, use the geometry formulas found in Section R.4.

119. Find the area of the pizza shown in the figure. Round to the nearest square inch.

120. Find the volume of the sphere shown in the figure. Round to the nearest cubic centimeter.

16 in.

$r = 3$ cm

121. Find the volume of a spherical balloon that is 8 in. in diameter. Round to the nearest cubic inch.

122. Find the area of a circular pool 50 ft in diameter. Round to the nearest square foot.

Expanding Your Skills

For Exercises 123–130, simplify the expressions using the addition or subtraction rules of exponents. Assume that a, b, m, and n represent positive integers.

123. $x^n x^{n+1}$ **124.** $y^a y^{2a}$ **125.** $p^{3m+5}p^{-m-2}$ **126.** $q^{4b-3}q^{-4b+4}$

127. $\dfrac{z^{b+1}}{z^b}$ **128.** $\dfrac{w^{5n+3}}{w^{2n}}$ **129.** $\dfrac{r^{3a+3}}{r^{3a}}$ **130.** $\dfrac{t^{3+2m}}{t^{2m}}$

| Section 5.2 | More Properties of Exponents |

Concepts

1. Power Rule for Exponents
2. The Properties
   $(ab)^m = a^m b^m$ and
   $\left(\dfrac{a}{b}\right)^m = \dfrac{a^m}{b^m}$

1. Power Rule for Exponents

The expression $(x^2)^3$ indicates that the quantity x^2 is cubed.

$$(x^2)^3 = (x^2)(x^2)(x^2) = (x \cdot x)(x \cdot x)(x \cdot x) = x^6$$

From this example, it appears that to raise a base to successive powers, we multiply the exponents and leave the base unchanged. This is stated formally as the power rule for exponents.

> **Power Rule for Exponents**
> Assume that b is a real number and that m and n represent positive integers. Then,
> $$(b^m)^n = b^{m \cdot n}$$

Skill Practice

Simplify the expressions.
1. $(y^3)^5$
2. $(2^8)^{10}$
3. $(q^5 q^4)^3$

| Example 1 | Simplifying Expressions with Exponents |

Simplify the expressions.

a. $(s^4)^2$　　　**b.** $(3^4)^2$　　　**c.** $(x^2 x^5)^4$

Solution:

a. $(s^4)^2$

$\quad = s^{4 \cdot 2}$　　　　Multiply exponents (the base is unchanged).

$\quad = s^8$

b. $(3^4)^2$

$\quad = 3^{4 \cdot 2}$　　　　Multiply exponents (the base is unchanged).

$\quad = 3^8$ or 6561

c. $(x^2 x^5)^4$

$\quad = (x^7)^4$　　　　Simplify inside the parentheses by adding exponents.

$\quad = x^{7 \cdot 4}$　　　　Multiply exponents (the base is unchanged).

$\quad = x^{28}$

2. The Properties $(ab)^m = a^m b^m$ and $\left(\dfrac{a}{b}\right)^m = \dfrac{a^m}{b^m}$

Consider the following expressions and their simplified forms:

$$(xy)^3 = (xy)(xy)(xy) = (x \cdot x \cdot x)(y \cdot y \cdot y) = x^3 y^3$$

$$\left(\frac{x}{y}\right)^3 = \left(\frac{x}{y}\right)\left(\frac{x}{y}\right)\left(\frac{x}{y}\right) = \left(\frac{x \cdot x \cdot x}{y \cdot y \cdot y}\right) = \frac{x^3}{y^3}$$

The expressions were simplified using the commutative and associative properties of multiplication. The simplified forms for each expression could have been reached in one step by applying the exponent to each factor inside the parentheses.

Answers

1. y^{15}　　2. 2^{80}　　3. q^{27}

Power of a Product and Power of a Quotient

Assume that a and b are real numbers. Let m represent a positive integer. Then,

$$(ab)^m = a^m b^m$$

$$\left(\frac{a}{b}\right)^m = \frac{a^m}{b^m}, \quad b \neq 0$$

Avoiding Mistakes

The power rule of exponents can be applied to a product of bases but in general cannot be applied to a sum or difference of bases.

$$(ab)^n = a^n b^n$$

but $\quad (a + b)^n \neq a^n + b^n$

Applying these properties of exponents, we have

$$(xy)^3 = x^3 y^3 \quad \text{and} \quad \left(\frac{x}{y}\right)^3 = \frac{x^3}{y^3}$$

Example 2 Simplifying Expressions with Exponents

Simplify the expressions.

a. $(-2xyz)^4$ 　　**b.** $(5x^2y^7)^3$ 　　**c.** $\left(\frac{2}{5}\right)^3$ 　　**d.** $\left(\frac{1}{3xy^4}\right)^2$

Solution:

a. $(-2xyz)^4$

$= (-2)^4 x^4 y^4 z^4$ 　　Raise each factor within parentheses to the fourth power.

$= 16x^4 y^4 z^4$

b. $(5x^2y^7)^3$

$= 5^3 (x^2)^3 (y^7)^3$ 　　Raise each factor within parentheses to the third power.

$= 125 x^6 y^{21}$ 　　Multiply exponents and simplify.

c. $\left(\frac{2}{5}\right)^3$

$= \dfrac{(2)^3}{(5)^3}$ 　　Apply the exponent to each factor in parentheses.

$= \dfrac{8}{125}$ 　　Simplify.

d. $\left(\dfrac{1}{3xy^4}\right)^2$

$= \dfrac{1^2}{3^2 x^2 (y^4)^2}$ 　　Square each factor within parentheses.

$= \dfrac{1}{9x^2 y^8}$ 　　Multiply exponents and simplify.

Skill Practice

Simplify the expressions.

4. $(3abc)^5$ 　　**5.** $(-2t^2w^4)^3$

6. $\left(\frac{3}{4}\right)^3$ 　　**7.** $\left(\frac{2x^3}{y^5}\right)^2$

Answers

4. $3^5 a^5 b^5 c^5$ or $243 a^5 b^5 c^5$

5. $-8t^6 w^{12}$ 　　**6.** $\dfrac{27}{64}$ 　　**7.** $\dfrac{4x^6}{y^{10}}$

The properties of exponents can be used along with the properties of real numbers to simplify complicated expressions.

Example 3 Simplifying Expressions with Exponents

Simplify the expression. $\dfrac{(x^2)^6(x^3)}{(x^7)^2}$

Solution:

$\dfrac{(x^2)^6(x^3)}{(x^7)^2}$ Clear parentheses by applying the power rule.

$= \dfrac{x^{2 \cdot 6} x^3}{x^{7 \cdot 2}}$ Multiply exponents.

$= \dfrac{x^{12} x^3}{x^{14}}$

$= \dfrac{x^{12+3}}{x^{14}}$ Add exponents in the numerator.

$= \dfrac{x^{15}}{x^{14}}$

$= x^{15-14}$ Subtract exponents.

$= x$ Simplify.

Example 4 Simplifying Expressions with Exponents

Simplify the expression. $(3cd^2)(2cd^3)^3$

Solution:

$(3cd^2)(2cd^3)^3$ Clear parentheses by applying the power rule.

$= 3cd^2 \cdot 2^3 c^3 d^9$ Raise each factor in the second parentheses to the third power.

$= 3 \cdot 2^3 cc^3 d^2 d^9$ Group like factors.

$= 3 \cdot 8c^{1+3} d^{2+9}$ Add exponents on like bases.

$= 24c^4 d^{11}$ Simplify.

Example 5 Simplifying Expressions with Exponents

Simplify the expression. $\left(\dfrac{x^7yz^4}{8xz^3}\right)^2$

Solution:

$$\left(\dfrac{x^7yz^4}{8xz^3}\right)^2$$

$$=\left(\dfrac{x^{7-1}yz^{4-3}}{8}\right)^2 \qquad \text{First simplify inside the parentheses by subtracting exponents on like bases.}$$

$$=\left(\dfrac{x^6yz}{8}\right)^2$$

$$=\dfrac{(x^6)^2y^2z^2}{8^2} \qquad \text{Apply the power rule of exponents.}$$

$$=\dfrac{x^{12}y^2z^2}{64}$$

Skill Practice

Simplify the expression.

10. $\left(\dfrac{w^2xy^4}{6xy^3}\right)^2$

Answer

10. $\dfrac{w^4y^2}{36}$

Section 5.2 Practice Exercises

For this exercise set assume all variables represent nonzero real numbers.

Review Exercises

For Exercises 1–8, simplify.

1. $4^2 \cdot 4^7$

2. $5^8 \cdot 5^3 \cdot 5$

3. $a^{13} \cdot a \cdot a^6$

4. $y^{14}y^3$

5. $\dfrac{d^{13}d}{d^5}$

6. $\dfrac{3^8 \cdot 3}{3^2}$

7. $\dfrac{7^{11}}{7^5}$

8. $\dfrac{z^4}{z^3}$

9. Explain when to add exponents versus when to subtract exponents.

10. Explain when to add exponents versus when to multiply exponents.

Concept 1: Power Rule for Exponents

For Exercises 11–22, simplify and write answers in exponent form. **(See Example 1.)**

11. $(5^3)^4$

12. $(2^8)^7$

13. $(12^3)^2$

14. $(6^4)^4$

15. $(y^7)^2$

16. $(z^6)^4$

17. $(w^5)^5$

18. $(t^3)^6$

19. $(a^2a^4)^6$

20. $(z \cdot z^3)^2$

21. $(y^3y^4)^2$

22. $(w^5w)^4$

23. Evaluate the two expressions and compare the answers: $(2^2)^3$ and $(2^3)^2$.

24. Evaluate the two expressions and compare the answers: $(4^4)^2$ and $(4^2)^4$.

25. Evaluate the two expressions and compare the answers. Which expression is greater? Why?

$$2^{(2^4)} \quad \text{and} \quad (2^2)^4$$

26. Evaluate the two expressions and compare the answers. Which expression is greater? Why?

$$3^{(2^4)} \quad \text{and} \quad (3^2)^4$$

Concept 2: The Properties $(ab)^m = a^m b^m$ and $\left(\frac{a}{b}\right)^m = \frac{a^m}{b^m}$

For Exercises 27–42, use the appropriate property to clear the parentheses. **(See Example 2.)**

27. $(5w)^2$

28. $(4y)^3$

29. $(srt)^4$

30. $(wxy)^6$

31. $\left(\frac{2}{r}\right)^4$

32. $\left(\frac{1}{t}\right)^8$

33. $\left(\frac{x}{y}\right)^5$

34. $\left(\frac{w}{z}\right)^7$

35. $(-3a)^4$

36. $(2x)^5$

37. $(-3abc)^3$

38. $(-5xyz)^2$

39. $\left(-\frac{4}{x}\right)^3$

40. $\left(-\frac{1}{w}\right)^4$

41. $\left(-\frac{a}{b}\right)^2$

42. $\left(-\frac{r}{s}\right)^3$

Mixed Exercises

For Exercises 43–74, simplify the expressions. **(See Examples 3–5.)**

43. $(6u^2v^4)^3$

44. $(3a^5b^2)^6$

45. $5(x^2y)^4$

46. $18(u^3v^4)^2$

47. $(-h^4)^7$

48. $(-k^6)^3$

49. $(-m^2)^6$

50. $(-n^3)^8$

51. $\left(\frac{4}{rs^4}\right)^5$

52. $\left(\frac{2}{h^7k}\right)^3$

53. $\left(\frac{3p}{q^3}\right)^5$

54. $\left(\frac{5x^2}{y^3}\right)^4$

55. $\dfrac{y^8(y^3)^4}{(y^2)^3}$

56. $\dfrac{(w^3)^2(w^4)^5}{(w^4)^2}$

57. $(x^2)^5(x^3)^7$

58. $(y^3)^4(y^2)^5$

59. $(2a^2b)^3(5a^4b^3)^2$

60. $(4c^3d^5)^2(3cd^3)^2$

61. $(-2p^2q^4)^4$

62. $(-7x^4y^5)^2$

63. $(-m^7n^3)^5$

64. $(-a^3b^6)^7$

65. $\dfrac{(5a^3b)^4(a^2b)^4}{(5ab)^2}$

66. $\dfrac{(6s^3)^2(s^4t^5)^2}{(3s^4t^2)^2}$

67. $\left(\dfrac{2c^3d^4}{3c^2d}\right)^2$

68. $\left(\dfrac{x^3y^5z}{5xy^2}\right)^2$

69. $(2c^3d^2)^5\left(\dfrac{c^6d^8}{4c^2d}\right)^3$

70. $\left(\dfrac{s^5t^6}{2s^2t}\right)^2(10s^3t^3)^2$

71. $\left(\dfrac{-3a^3b}{c^2}\right)^3$

72. $\left(\dfrac{-4x^2}{y^4z}\right)^3$

73. $\dfrac{(-8b^6)^2(b^3)^5}{4b}$

74. $\dfrac{(-6a^2)^2(a^3)^4}{9a}$

Expanding Your Skills

For Exercises 75–82, simplify the expressions using the addition or subtraction properties of exponents. Assume that a, b, m, n, and x represent positive integers.

75. $(x^m)^2$

76. $(y^3)^n$

77. $(5a^{2n})^3$

78. $(3b^4)^m$

79. $\left(\dfrac{m^2}{n^3}\right)^b$

80. $\left(\dfrac{x^5}{y^3}\right)^m$

81. $\left(\dfrac{3a^3}{5b^4}\right)^n$

82. $\left(\dfrac{4m^6}{3n^2}\right)^x$

Definitions of b^0 and b^{-n}

In Sections 5.1 and 5.2, we learned several rules that enable us to manipulate expressions containing *positive* integer exponents. In this section, we present definitions that can be used to simplify expressions with negative exponents or with an exponent of zero.

Concepts

1. Definition of b^0
2. Definition of b^{-n}
3. Properties of Integer Exponents: A Summary

1. Definition of b^0

To begin, consider the following pattern.

$3^3 = 27$ — Divide by 3.
$3^2 = 9$ — Divide by 3.
$3^1 = 3$ — Divide by 3.
$3^0 = 1$

As the exponents decrease by 1, the resulting expressions are divided by 3.

For the pattern to continue, we define $3^0 = 1$.

This pattern suggests that we should define an expression with a zero exponent as follows.

> **Definition of b^0**
>
> Let b be a nonzero real number. Then, $b^0 = 1$.
>
> *Note:* The value of 0^0 is not defined by this definition because the base b must not equal zero.

Example 1 **Simplifying Expressions with a Zero Exponent**

Simplify (assume $z \neq 0$).

a. 4^0 **b.** $(-4)^0$ **c.** -4^0

d. z^0 **e.** $-4z^0$ **f.** $(4z)^0$

Solution:

a. $4^0 = 1$ By definition

b. $(-4)^0 = 1$ By definition

c. $-4^0 = -1 \cdot 4^0 = -1 \cdot 1 = -1$ The exponent 0 applies only to 4.

d. $z^0 = 1$ By definition

e. $-4z^0 = -4 \cdot z^0 = -4 \cdot 1 = -4$ The exponent 0 applies only to z.

f. $(4z)^0 = 1$ The parentheses indicate that the exponent, 0, applies to both factors 4 and z.

Skill Practice

Evaluate the expressions. Assume all variables represent nonzero real numbers.

1. 7^0 2. $(-7)^0$
3. -5^0 4. y^0
5. $-2x^0$ 6. $(2x)^0$

The definition of b^0 is consistent with the other properties of exponents learned thus far. For example, we know that $1 = \frac{5^3}{5^3}$. If we subtract exponents, the result is 5^0.

Subtract exponents.

$1 = \dfrac{5^3}{5^3} = 5^{3-3} = 5^0$.   Therefore, 5^0 must be defined as 1.

Answers

1. 1   2. 1   3. −1
4. 1   5. −2   6. 1

2. Definition of b^{-n}

To understand the concept of a *negative* exponent, consider the following pattern.

$3^3 = 27$
 Divide by 3.
$3^2 = 9$
 Divide by 3.   As the exponents decrease by
$3^1 = 3$ 1, the resulting expressions are
 Divide by 3.   divided by 3.
$3^0 = 1$
 Divide by 3.

$3^{-1} = \dfrac{1}{3}$ ⟵ For the pattern to continue, we define $3^{-1} = \dfrac{1}{3^1} = \dfrac{1}{3}$.

$3^{-2} = \dfrac{1}{9}$ ⟵ For the pattern to continue, we define $3^{-2} = \dfrac{1}{3^2} = \dfrac{1}{9}$.

$3^{-3} = \dfrac{1}{27}$ ⟵ For the pattern to continue, we define $3^{-3} = \dfrac{1}{3^3} = \dfrac{1}{27}$.

This pattern suggests that $3^{-n} = \frac{1}{3^n}$ for all integers, n. In general, we have the following definition involving negative exponents.

> ### Definition of b^{-n}
>
> Let n be an integer and b be a nonzero real number. Then,
>
> $$b^{-n} = \left(\dfrac{1}{b}\right)^n \quad \text{or} \quad \dfrac{1}{b^n}$$

The definition of b^{-n} implies that to evaluate b^{-n}, take the reciprocal of the base and change the sign of the exponent.

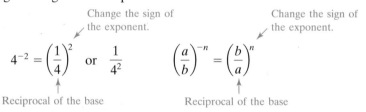

Change the sign of the exponent.

$$4^{-2} = \left(\dfrac{1}{4}\right)^2 \quad \text{or} \quad \dfrac{1}{4^2}$$

Reciprocal of the base

Change the sign of the exponent.

$$\left(\dfrac{a}{b}\right)^{-n} = \left(\dfrac{b}{a}\right)^n$$

Reciprocal of the base

Skill Practice

Simplify.

7. p^{-4} **8.** 3^{-3}

9. $(-5)^{-2}$

Avoiding Mistakes

A negative exponent does *not* affect the sign of the base.

Answers

7. $\dfrac{1}{p^4}$ **8.** $\dfrac{1}{3^3}$ or $\dfrac{1}{27}$

9. $\dfrac{1}{(-5)^2}$ or $\dfrac{1}{25}$

Example 2   **Simplifying Expressions with Negative Exponents**

Simplify. Assume that $c \neq 0$.

a. c^{-3} **b.** 5^{-1} **c.** $(-3)^{-4}$

Solution:

a. $c^{-3} = \dfrac{1}{c^3}$ By definition

b. $5^{-1} = \dfrac{1}{5^1}$ By definition

$\phantom{5^{-1}} = \dfrac{1}{5}$ Simplify.

c. $(-3)^{-4} = \dfrac{1}{(-3)^4}$ The base is -3 and must be enclosed in parentheses.

$\phantom{(-3)^{-4}} = \dfrac{1}{81}$ Simplify. Note that $(-3)^4 = (-3)(-3)(-3)(-3) = 81$.

Example 3 Simplifying Expressions with Negative Exponents

Simplify. Assume that $y \neq 0$.

a. $\left(\dfrac{1}{6}\right)^{-2}$ **b.** $\left(-\dfrac{3}{5}\right)^{-3}$ **c.** $\dfrac{1}{y^{-5}}$

Solution:

a. $\left(\dfrac{1}{6}\right)^{-2} = 6^2$ Take the reciprocal of the base, and change the sign of the exponent.

$\qquad = 36$ Simplify.

b. $\left(-\dfrac{3}{5}\right)^{-3} = \left(-\dfrac{5}{3}\right)^{3}$ Take the reciprocal of the base, and change the sign of the exponent.

$\qquad = -\dfrac{125}{27}$ Simplify.

c. $\dfrac{1}{y^{-5}} = \left(\dfrac{1}{y}\right)^{-5}$ Apply the power of a quotient rule from Section 5.2.

$\qquad = (y)^5$ Take the reciprocal of the base, and change the sign of the exponent.

$\qquad = y^5$

TIP: Example 3(c) implies $\dfrac{1}{b^{-n}} = b^n$, for $b \neq 0$.

Example 4 Simplifying Expressions with Negative Exponents

Simplify. Assume that $x \neq 0$.

a. $(5x)^{-3}$ **b.** $5x^{-3}$ **c.** $-5x^{-3}$

Solution:

a. $(5x)^{-3} = \left(\dfrac{1}{5x}\right)^{3}$ Take the reciprocal of the base, and change the sign of the exponent.

$\qquad = \dfrac{(1)^3}{(5x)^3}$ Apply the exponent of 3 to each factor within parentheses.

$\qquad = \dfrac{1}{125x^3}$ Simplify.

b. $5x^{-3} = 5 \cdot x^{-3}$ Note that the exponent, -3, applies only to x.

$\qquad = 5 \cdot \dfrac{1}{x^3}$ Rewrite x^{-3} as $\dfrac{1}{x^3}$.

$\qquad = \dfrac{5}{x^3}$ Multiply.

c. $-5x^{-3} = -5 \cdot x^{-3}$ Note that the exponent, -3, applies only to x, and that -5 is a coefficient.

$\qquad = -5 \cdot \dfrac{1}{x^3}$ Rewrite x^{-3} as $\dfrac{1}{x^3}$.

$\qquad = -\dfrac{5}{x^3}$ Multiply.

It is important to note that the definition of b^{-n} is consistent with the other properties of exponents learned thus far. For example, consider the expression

$$\frac{x^4}{x^7} = \frac{\cancel{x} \cdot \cancel{x} \cdot \cancel{x} \cdot \cancel{x}}{\cancel{x} \cdot \cancel{x} \cdot \cancel{x} \cdot \cancel{x} \cdot x \cdot x \cdot x} = \frac{1}{x^3}$$

Subtract exponents.

$$\frac{x^4}{x^7} = x^{4-7} = x^{-3}$$

By subtracting exponents, we have

Hence, $x^{-3} = \dfrac{1}{x^3}$

3. Properties of Integer Exponents: A Summary

The definitions of b^0 and b^{-n} allow us to extend the properties of exponents learned in Sections 5.1 and 5.2 to include integer exponents. These are summarized in Table 5-1.

Table 5-1

Properties of Integer Exponents		
Assume that a and b are real numbers $(b \neq 0)$ and that m and n represent integers.		
Property	**Example**	**Details/Notes**
Multiplication of Expressions with Like Bases $b^m b^n = b^{m+n}$	$b^2 b^4 = b^{2+4} = b^6$	$b^2 b^4 = (b \cdot b)(b \cdot b \cdot b \cdot b) = b^6$
Division of Expressions with Like Bases $\dfrac{b^m}{b^n} = b^{m-n}$	$\dfrac{b^5}{b^2} = b^{5-2} = b^3$	$\dfrac{b^5}{b^2} = \dfrac{\cancel{b} \cdot \cancel{b} \cdot b \cdot b \cdot b}{\cancel{b} \cdot \cancel{b}} = b^3$
The Power Rule $(b^m)^n = b^{m \cdot n}$	$(b^4)^2 = b^{4 \cdot 2} = b^8$	$(b^4)^2 = (b \cdot b \cdot b \cdot b)(b \cdot b \cdot b \cdot b) = b^8$
Power of a Product $(ab)^m = a^m b^m$	$(ab)^3 = a^3 b^3$	$(ab)^3 = (ab)(ab)(ab)$ $= (a \cdot a \cdot a)(b \cdot b \cdot b) = a^3 b^3$
Power of a Quotient $\left(\dfrac{a}{b}\right)^m = \dfrac{a^m}{b^m}$	$\left(\dfrac{a}{b}\right)^3 = \dfrac{a^3}{b^3}$	$\left(\dfrac{a}{b}\right)^3 = \left(\dfrac{a}{b}\right)\left(\dfrac{a}{b}\right)\left(\dfrac{a}{b}\right) = \dfrac{a \cdot a \cdot a}{b \cdot b \cdot b} = \dfrac{a^3}{b^3}$
Definitions		
Assume that b is a real number $(b \neq 0)$ and that n represents an integer.		
Definition	**Example**	**Details/Notes**
$b^0 = 1$	$(4)^0 = 1$	Any nonzero quantity raised to the zero power equals 1.
$b^{-n} = \left(\dfrac{1}{b}\right)^n = \dfrac{1}{b^n}$	$b^{-5} = \left(\dfrac{1}{b}\right)^5 = \dfrac{1}{b^5}$	To simplify a negative exponent, take the reciprocal of the base and make the exponent positive.

Example 5   Simplifying Expressions with Exponents

Simplify the expressions. Write the answers with positive exponents only. Assume all variables are nonzero.

a. $\dfrac{a^3 b^{-2}}{c^{-5}}$ **b.** $\dfrac{x^2 x^{-7}}{x^3}$ **c.** $\dfrac{z^2}{w^{-4} w^4 z^{-8}}$

Solution:

a. $\dfrac{a^3 b^{-2}}{c^{-5}}$

$= \dfrac{a^3}{1} \cdot \dfrac{b^{-2}}{1} \cdot \dfrac{1}{c^{-5}}$

$= \dfrac{a^3}{1} \cdot \dfrac{1}{b^2} \cdot \dfrac{c^5}{1}$ Simplify negative exponents.

$= \dfrac{a^3 c^5}{b^2}$ Multiply.

b. $\dfrac{x^2 x^{-7}}{x^3}$

$= \dfrac{x^{2+(-7)}}{x^3}$ Add the exponents in the numerator.

$= \dfrac{x^{-5}}{x^3}$ Simplify.

$= x^{-5-3}$ Subtract the exponents.

$= x^{-8}$

$= \dfrac{1}{x^8}$ Simplify the negative exponent.

c. $\dfrac{z^2}{w^{-4} w^4 z^{-8}}$

$= \dfrac{z^2}{w^{-4+4} z^{-8}}$ Add the exponents in the denominator.

$= \dfrac{z^2}{w^0 z^{-8}}$

$= \dfrac{z^2}{(1) z^{-8}}$ Recall that $w^0 = 1$.

$= z^{2-(-8)}$ Subtract the exponents.

$= z^{10}$ Simplify.

Skill Practice

Simplify the expressions. Assume all variables are nonzero.

16. $\dfrac{x^{-6}}{y^4 z^{-8}}$

17. $\dfrac{x^3 x^{-8}}{x^4}$

18. $\dfrac{p^3}{w^7 w^{-7} z^{-2}}$

Answers

16. $\dfrac{z^8}{y^4 x^6}$ 17. $\dfrac{1}{x^9}$ 18. $p^3 z^2$

Example 6 **Simplifying Expressions with Exponents**

Simplify the expressions. Write the answers with positive exponents only. Assume that all variables are nonzero.

a. $(-4ab^{-2})^{-3}$ **b.** $\left(\dfrac{2p^{-4}q^3}{5p^2q}\right)^{-2}$

Solution:

a. $(-4ab^{-2})^{-3}$

$\quad = (-4)^{-3}a^{-3}(b^{-2})^{-3}$ Apply the power rule of exponents.

$\quad = (-4)^{-3}a^{-3}b^6$

$\quad = \dfrac{1}{(-4)^3} \cdot \dfrac{1}{a^3} \cdot b^6$ Simplify the negative exponents.

$\quad = \dfrac{1}{-64} \cdot \dfrac{1}{a^3} \cdot b^6$ Simplify.

$\quad = -\dfrac{b^6}{64a^3}$ Multiply fractions.

b. $\left(\dfrac{2p^{-4}q^3}{5p^2q}\right)^{-2}$ First simplify within the parentheses.

$\quad = \left(\dfrac{2p^{-4-2}q^{3-1}}{5}\right)^{-2}$ Divide expressions with like bases by subtracting exponents.

$\quad = \left(\dfrac{2p^{-6}q^2}{5}\right)^{-2}$ Simplify.

$\quad = \dfrac{(2p^{-6}q^2)^{-2}}{(5)^{-2}}$ Apply the power rule of a quotient.

$\quad = \dfrac{2^{-2}(p^{-6})^{-2}(q^2)^{-2}}{5^{-2}}$ Apply the power rule of a product.

$\quad = \dfrac{2^{-2}p^{12}q^{-4}}{5^{-2}}$ Simplify.

$\quad = \dfrac{5^2p^{12}}{2^2q^4}$ Simplify the negative exponents.

$\quad = \dfrac{25p^{12}}{4q^4}$ Simplify.

TIP: For Example 6(b), the power rule of exponents can be performed first. In that case, the second step would be

$$\dfrac{2^{-2}p^8q^{-6}}{5^{-2}p^{-4}q^{-2}}$$

Example 7 **Simplifying an Expression with Exponents**

Simplify the expression $2^{-1} + 3^{-1} + 5^0$. Write the answer with positive exponents only.

Solution:

$2^{-1} + 3^{-1} + 5^0$

$= \dfrac{1}{2} + \dfrac{1}{3} + 1$ Simplify negative exponents. Simplify $5^0 = 1$.

$= \dfrac{3}{6} + \dfrac{2}{6} + \dfrac{6}{6}$ The least common denominator is 6.

$= \dfrac{11}{6}$ Simplify.

Section 5.3 **Practice Exercises**

For this exercise set, assume all variables represent nonzero real numbers.

Study Skills Exercise

To help you remember the properties of exponents, write them on 3×5 cards. On each card, write a property on one side and an example using that property on the other side. Keep these cards with you, and when you have a spare moment (such as waiting at the doctor's office), pull out these cards and go over the properties.

Vocabulary and Key Concepts

1. a. The expression b^0 is defined to be _____ provided that $b \neq 0$.

  b. The expression b^{-n} is defined as _____ provided that $b \neq 0$.

Review Exercises

For Exercises 2–9, simplify the expressions.

2. $b^3 b^8$ **3.** $c^7 c^2$ **4.** $\dfrac{x^6}{x^2}$ **5.** $\dfrac{y^9}{y^8}$

6. $\dfrac{9^4 \cdot 9^8}{9}$ **7.** $\dfrac{3^{14}}{3^3 \cdot 3^5}$ **8.** $(6ab^3c^2)^5$ **9.** $(7w^7z^2)^4$

Concept 1: Definition of b^0

10. Simplify.   **11.** Simplify.   **12.** Simplify.

  a. 8^0 **b.** $\dfrac{8^4}{8^4}$ **a.** d^0 **b.** $\dfrac{d^3}{d^3}$ **a.** m^0 **b.** $\dfrac{m^5}{m^5}$

For Exercises 13–24, simplify the expression. **(See Example 1.)**

13. p^0 **14.** k^0 **15.** 5^0 **16.** 2^0

17. -4^0 **18.** -1^0 **19.** $(-6)^0$ **20.** $(-2)^0$

21. $(8x)^0$ **22.** $(-3y^3)^0$ **23.** $-7x^0$ **24.** $6y^0$

Concept 2: Definition of b^{-n}

25. Simplify and write the answers with positive exponents.

    a. t^{-5} **b.** $\dfrac{t^3}{t^8}$

26. Simplify and write the answers with positive exponents.

    a. 4^{-3} **b.** $\dfrac{4^2}{4^5}$

For Exercises 27–46, simplify. **(See Examples 2–4.)**

27. $\left(\dfrac{2}{7}\right)^{-3}$ **28.** $\left(\dfrac{5}{4}\right)^{-1}$ **29.** $\left(-\dfrac{1}{5}\right)^{-2}$ **30.** $\left(-\dfrac{1}{3}\right)^{-3}$

31. a^{-3} **32.** c^{-5} **33.** 12^{-1} **34.** 4^{-2}

35. $(4b)^{-2}$ **36.** $(3z)^{-1}$ **37.** $6x^{-2}$ **38.** $7y^{-1}$

39. $(-8)^{-2}$ **40.** -8^{-2} **41.** $-3y^{-4}$ **42.** $-6a^{-2}$

43. $(-t)^{-3}$ **44.** $(-r)^{-5}$ **45.** $\dfrac{1}{a^{-5}}$ **46.** $\dfrac{1}{b^{-6}}$

Concept 3: Properties of Integer Exponents: A Summary

For Exercises 47–50, correct the statement.

47. $\dfrac{x^4}{x^{-6}} = x^{4-6} = x^{-2}$

48. $\dfrac{y^5}{y^{-3}} = y^{5-3} = y^2$

49. $2a^{-3} = \dfrac{1}{2a^3}$

50. $5b^{-2} = \dfrac{1}{5b^2}$

Mixed Exercises

For Exercises 51–94, simplify the expression. Write the answer with positive exponents only. **(See Examples 5 and 6.)**

51. $x^{-8}x^4$ **52.** s^5s^{-6} **53.** $a^{-8}a^8$ **54.** q^3q^{-3}

55. $y^{17}y^{-13}$ **56.** $b^{20}b^{-14}$ **57.** $(m^{-6}n^9)^3$ **58.** $(c^4d^{-5})^{-2}$

59. $(-3j^{-5}k^6)^4$ **60.** $(6xy^{-11})^{-3}$ **61.** $\dfrac{p^3}{p^9}$ **62.** $\dfrac{q^2}{q^{10}}$

63. $\dfrac{r^{-5}}{r^{-2}}$ **64.** $\dfrac{u^{-2}}{u^{-6}}$ **65.** $\dfrac{a^2}{a^{-6}}$ **66.** $\dfrac{p^3}{p^{-5}}$

67. $\dfrac{y^{-2}}{y^6}$ **68.** $\dfrac{s^{-4}}{s^3}$ **69.** $\dfrac{7^3}{7^2 \cdot 7^8}$ **70.** $\dfrac{3^4 \cdot 3}{3^7}$

71. $\dfrac{a^2a}{a^3}$

72. $\dfrac{t^5}{t^2t^3}$

73. $\dfrac{a^{-1}b^2}{a^3b^8}$

74. $\dfrac{k^{-4}h^{-1}}{k^6h}$

75. $\dfrac{w^{-8}(w^2)^{-5}}{w^3}$

76. $\dfrac{p^2p^{-7}}{(p^2)^3}$

77. $\dfrac{3^{-2}}{3}$

78. $\dfrac{5^{-1}}{5}$

79. $\left(\dfrac{p^{-1}q^5}{p^{-6}}\right)^0$

80. $\left(\dfrac{ab^{-4}}{a^{-5}}\right)^0$

81. $(8x^3y^0)^{-2}$

82. $(3u^2v^0)^{-3}$

83. $(-8y^{-12})(2y^{16}z^{-2})$

84. $(5p^{-2}q^5)(-2p^{-4}q^{-1})$

85. $\dfrac{-18a^{10}b^6}{108a^{-2}b^6}$

86. $\dfrac{-35x^{-4}y^{-3}}{-21x^2y^{-3}}$

87. $\dfrac{(-4c^{12}d^7)^2}{(5c^{-3}d^{10})^{-1}}$

88. $\dfrac{(s^3t^{-2})^4}{(3s^{-4}t^6)^{-2}}$

89. $\dfrac{(2x^3y^2)^{-3}}{(3x^2y^4)^{-2}}$

90. $\dfrac{(5p^4q)^{-3}}{(p^3q^5)^{-4}}$

91. $\left(\dfrac{5cd^{-3}}{10d^5}\right)^{-2}$

92. $\left(\dfrac{4m^{10}n^4}{2m^{12}n^{-2}}\right)^{-1}$

93. $(2xy^3)\left(\dfrac{9xy}{4x^3y^2}\right)$

94. $(-3a^3)\left(\dfrac{ab}{27a^4b^2}\right)$

For Exercises 95–102, simplify the expression. **(See Example 7.)**

95. $5^{-1} + 2^{-2}$

96. $4^{-2} + 8^{-1}$

97. $10^0 - 10^{-1}$

98. $3^0 - 3^{-2}$

99. $2^{-2} + 1^{-2}$

100. $4^{-1} + 8^{-1}$

101. $4 \cdot 5^0 - 2 \cdot 3^{-1}$

102. $2 \cdot 4^0 - 3 \cdot 4^{-1}$

Expanding Your Skills

For Exercises 103–106, determine the missing exponent.

103. $\dfrac{y^4y^{\square}}{y^{-2}} = y^8$

104. $\dfrac{x^4x^{\square}}{x^{-1}} = x^9$

105. $\dfrac{w^{-9}}{w^{\square}} = w^2$

106. $\dfrac{a^{-2}}{a^{\square}} = a^6$

Problem Recognition Exercises

Properties of Exponents

Simplify completely. Assume all variables represent nonzero real numbers.

1. a. t^3t^5 **b.** $\dfrac{t^3}{t^5}$ **c.** $(t^3)^5$ **2. a.** 2^32^5 **b.** $\dfrac{2^3}{2^5}$ **c.** $(2^3)^5$

3. a. $\dfrac{y^7}{y^2}$ **b.** $(y^7)^2$ **c.** y^7y^2 **4. a.** $\dfrac{p^9}{p^3}$ **b.** $(p^9)^3$ **c.** p^9p^3

5. a. $(w^4)^{-2}$ **b.** w^4w^{-2} **c.** $\dfrac{w^4}{w^{-2}}$ **6. a.** $m^{-14}m^2$ **b.** $(m^{-14})^2$ **c.** $\dfrac{m^{-14}}{m^2}$

7. a. $(r^2s^4)^2$ **b.** $\left(\dfrac{r^2}{s^4}\right)^2$ **c.** $\dfrac{(r^2)^2}{s^4}$ **8. a.** $(ab^3c^2)^3$ **b.** $\dfrac{a}{(b^3c^2)^3}$ **c.** $ab^3(c^2)^3$

9. a. $\dfrac{x^{-7}x^4}{x^{-3}}$ **b.** $\dfrac{x^{-7}y^4}{y^{-3}}$ **c.** $\dfrac{x^4y^{-7}}{z^{-3}}$ **10. a.** $\dfrac{a^3b^{-6}}{c^{-8}}$ **b.** $\dfrac{a^3b^{-6}}{a^{-8}}$ **c.** $\dfrac{a^3a^{-6}}{a^{-8}}$

11. a. $(2^5 b^{-3})^{-3}$ **b.** $\left(\dfrac{2^5}{b^{-3}}\right)^{-3}$ **c.** $\left(\dfrac{2b^2}{2^5 b^{-3}}\right)^{-3}$ **12. a.** $(3^{-2} y^3)^{-2}$ **b.** $\left(\dfrac{3^{-2}}{y^3}\right)^{-2}$ **c.** $\left(\dfrac{3y^{-1}}{3^{-2} y^3}\right)^{-2}$

13. a. $\dfrac{(t^{-2})^3}{t^{-4}}$ **b.** $\dfrac{t^{-2} t^3}{t^{-4}}$ **c.** $\left(\dfrac{t^{-2} t}{t^{-4}}\right)^3$ **14. a.** $\dfrac{p^3 p^{-4}}{p^{-5}}$ **b.** $\dfrac{(p^3)^{-4}}{p^{-5}}$ **c.** $\left(\dfrac{p^3 p^{-4}}{p}\right)^{-5}$

15. a. $(5h^{-2} k^0)^3 (5k^{-2})^{-4}$ **b.** $\left(\dfrac{5h^{-2} k^0}{5hk^2}\right)^3$ **c.** $\dfrac{(5h^{-2} k^0)^3}{(5k^{-2})^{-4}}$

16. a. $\dfrac{(6m^3 n^{-5})^{-2}}{(6m^0 n^{-2})^5}$ **b.** $(6m^3 n^{-5})^{-2}(6m^0 n^{-2})^5$ **c.** $\left(\dfrac{6m^0 n^{-2}}{6m^3 n^{-5}}\right)^{-4}$

Section 5.4   Scientific Notation

Concepts

1. Writing Numbers in Scientific Notation
2. Writing Numbers in Standard Form
3. Multiplying and Dividing Numbers in Scientific Notation

1. Writing Numbers in Scientific Notation

In many applications in mathematics, it is necessary to work with very large or very small numbers. For example, the number of movie tickets sold in the United States recently was estimated to be 1,500,000,000. The weight of a flea is approximately 0.00066 lb. To avoid writing numerous zeros in very large or small numbers, scientific notation was devised as a shortcut.

The principle behind scientific notation is to use a power of 10 to express the magnitude of the number. For example, the numbers 4000 and 0.07 can be written as:

$$4000 = 4 \times 1000 = 4 \times 10^3$$

$$0.07 = 7.0 \times 0.01 = 7.0 \times 10^{-2} \qquad \text{Note that } 10^{-2} = \frac{1}{100} = 0.01$$

> **Definition of Scientific Notation**
>
> A positive number expressed in the form: $a \times 10^n$, where $1 \le a < 10$ and n is an integer, is said to be written in **scientific notation**.

To write a positive number in scientific notation, we apply the following guidelines:

1. Move the decimal point so that its new location is to the right of the first nonzero digit. The number should now be greater than or equal to 1 but less than 10. Count the number of places that the decimal point is moved.

2. If the original number is *large* (greater than or equal to 10), use the number of places the decimal point was moved as a *positive* power of 10.

$$\underset{\substack{\uparrow\;\;\;\;\;|\\ \text{5 places}}}{450{,}000} \qquad = 4.5 \times 100{,}000 = 4.5 \times 10^5$$

3. If the original number is *small* (between 0 and 1), use the number of places the decimal point was moved as a *negative* power of 10.

$$\underset{\substack{\uparrow\;\;\;\;\\ \text{4 places}}}{0.0002} \qquad = 2.0 \times 0.0001 = 2.0 \times 10^{-4}$$

4. If the original number is greater than or equal to 1 but less than 10, use 0 as the power of 10.

$$7.592 = 7.592 \times 10^0$$ *Note:* A number between 1 and 10 is seldom written in scientific notation.

5. If the original number is negative, then $-10 < a \leq -1$.

$$-450,000 = -4.5 \times 100,000 = -4.5 \times 10^5$$

5 places

Example 1   **Writing Numbers in Scientific Notation**

Write the numbers in scientific notation.

a. 53,000   **b.** 0.00053

Solution:

a. $53,000. = 5.3 \times 10^4$ To write 53,000 in scientific notation, the decimal point must be moved four places to the left. Because 53,000 is larger than 10, a *positive* power of 10 is used.

b. $0.00053 = 5.3 \times 10^{-4}$ To write 0.00053 in scientific notation, the decimal point must be moved four places to the right. Because 0.00053 is less than 1, a *negative* power of 10 is used.

Example 2   **Writing Numbers in Scientific Notation**

Write the numerical values in scientific notation.

a. The number of movie tickets sold in the United States for a recent year was estimated to be 1,500,000,000.

b. The weight of a flea is approximately 0.00066 lb.

c. The temperature on a January day in Fargo dropped to $-43°$F.

d. A bench is 8.2 ft long.

Solution:

a. $1,500,000,000 = 1.5 \times 10^9$ **b.** $0.00066 \text{ lb} = 6.6 \times 10^{-4} \text{ lb}$

c. $-43°F = -4.3 \times 10^1 \text{ °F}$ **d.** $8.2 \text{ ft} = 8.2 \times 10^0 \text{ ft}$

---

2. Writing Numbers in Standard Form

Example 3   **Writing Numbers in Standard Form**

Write the numerical values in standard form.

a. The mass of a proton is approximately 1.67×10^{-24} g.

b. The "nearby" star Vega is approximately 1.552×10^{14} miles from Earth.

Skill Practice

Write the numerical values in standard form.

5. The probability of winning the California Super Lotto Jackpot is 5.5×10^{-8}.

6. The Sun's mass is 2×10^{30} kilograms.

Solution:

a. 1.67×10^{-24} g = 0.000 000 000 000 000 000 000 001 67 g

Because the power of 10 is negative, the value of 1.67×10^{-24} is a decimal number between 0 and 1. Move the decimal point 24 places to the *left*.

b. 1.552×10^{14} miles = 155,200,000,000,000 miles

Because the power of 10 is a positive integer, the value of 1.552×10^{14} is a large number greater than 10. Move the decimal point 14 places to the *right*.

3. Multiplying and Dividing Numbers in Scientific Notation

To multiply or divide two numbers in scientific notation, use the commutative and associative properties of multiplication to group the powers of 10. For example:

$$400 \times 2000 = (4 \times 10^2)(2 \times 10^3) = (4 \cdot 2) \times (10^2 \cdot 10^3) = 8 \times 10^5$$

$$\frac{0.00054}{150} = \frac{5.4 \times 10^{-4}}{1.5 \times 10^2} = \left(\frac{5.4}{1.5}\right) \times \left(\frac{10^{-4}}{10^2}\right) = 3.6 \times 10^{-6}$$

Skill Practice

Multiply or divide as indicated.

7. $(7 \times 10^5)(5 \times 10^3)$

8. $\dfrac{1 \times 10^{-2}}{4 \times 10^{-7}}$

Example 4 **Multiplying and Dividing Numbers in Scientific Notation**

Multiply or divide as indicated.

a. $(8.7 \times 10^4)(2.5 \times 10^{-12})$

b. $\dfrac{4.25 \times 10^{13}}{8.5 \times 10^{-2}}$

Solution:

a. $(8.7 \times 10^4)(2.5 \times 10^{-12})$

$= (8.7 \cdot 2.5) \times (10^4 \cdot 10^{-12})$ Regroup factors using the commutative and associative properties of multiplication.

$= 21.75 \times 10^{-8}$ The number 21.75×10^{-8} is not in proper scientific notation because 21.75 is not between 1 and 10.

$= (2.175 \times 10^1) \times 10^{-8}$ Rewrite 21.75 as 2.175×10^1.

$= 2.175 \times (10^1 \times 10^{-8})$ Associative property of multiplication

$= 2.175 \times 10^{-7}$ Simplify.

b. $\dfrac{4.25 \times 10^{13}}{8.5 \times 10^{-2}}$

$= \left(\dfrac{4.25}{8.5}\right) \times \left(\dfrac{10^{13}}{10^{-2}}\right)$ Regroup factors using the commutative and associative properties.

$= 0.5 \times 10^{15}$ The number 0.5×10^{15} is not in proper scientific notation because 0.5 is not between 1 and 10.

$= (5.0 \times 10^{-1}) \times 10^{15}$ Rewrite 0.5 as 5.0×10^{-1}.

$= 5.0 \times (10^{-1} \times 10^{15})$ Associative property of multiplication

$= 5.0 \times 10^{14}$ Simplify.

Answers

5. 0.000 000 055
6. 2,000,000,000,000,000,000,000,000,000,000
7. 3.5×10^9
8. 2.5×10^4

Calculator Connections

Topic: Using Scientific Notation

Both scientific and graphing calculators can perform calculations involving numbers written in scientific notation. Most calculators use an [EE] key or an [EXP] key to enter the power of 10.

Scientific Calculator

Enter: 2.7 [EE] 5 [=]   or   2.7 [EXP] 5 [=]   **Result:** | 270000 |

Enter: 7.1 [EE] 3 [+○-] [=]   or   7.1 [EXP] 3 [+○-] [=]   **Result:** | 0.0071 |

Graphing Calculator

```
2.7E5
          270000
7.1E-3
           .0071
```

We recommend that you use parentheses to enclose each number written in scientific notation when performing calculations. Try using your calculator to perform the calculations from Example 4.

a. $(8.7 \times 10^4)(2.5 \times 10^{-12})$ **b.** $\dfrac{4.25 \times 10^{13}}{8.5 \times 10^{-2}}$

Scientific Calculator

Enter: [( ] 8.7 [EE] 4 [ )] [×] [( ] 2.5 [EE] 12 [+○-] [ )] [=]   **Result:** | 0.000000218 |

Enter: [( ] 4.25 [EE] 13 [ )] [÷] [( ] 8.5 [EE] 2 [+○-] [ )] [=]   **Result:** | 5E14 |

Notice that the answer to part (b) is shown on the calculator in scientific notation. The calculator does not have enough room to display 14 zeros. Also notice that the calculator rounds the answer to part (a). The exact answer is 2.175×10^{-7} or 0.0000002175.

Graphing Calculator

```
(8.7E4)*(2.5E-12
)
         2.175E-7
(4.25E13)/(8.5E-
2)
            5E14
```

Avoiding Mistakes

A display of 5E14 on a calculator does not mean 5^{14}. It is scientific notation and means 5×10^{14}.

Calculator Exercises

Use a calculator to perform the indicated operations:

1. $(5.2 \times 10^6)(4.6 \times 10^{-3})$

2. $(2.19 \times 10^{-8})(7.84 \times 10^{-4})$

3. $\dfrac{4.76 \times 10^{-5}}{2.38 \times 10^9}$

4. $\dfrac{8.5 \times 10^4}{4.0 \times 10^{-1}}$

5. $\dfrac{(9.6 \times 10^7)(4.0 \times 10^{-3})}{2.0 \times 10^{-2}}$

6. $\dfrac{(5.0 \times 10^{-12})(6.4 \times 10^{-5})}{(1.6 \times 10^{-8})(4.0 \times 10^2)}$

Section 5.4 Practice Exercises

Vocabulary and Key Concepts

1. A positive number expressed in the form $a \times 10^n$, where $1 \le a < 10$ and n is an integer, is said to be written in _____ _____.

Review Exercises

For Exercises 2–13, simplify the expression. Assume all variables represent nonzero real numbers.

2. $a^3 a^{-4}$

3. $b^5 b^8$

4. $10^3 \cdot 10^{-4}$

5. $10^5 \cdot 10^8$

6. $\dfrac{x^3}{x^6}$

7. $\dfrac{y^2}{y^7}$

8. $(c^4 d^2)^3$

9. $(x^5 y^{-3})^4$

10. $\dfrac{z^9 z^4}{z^3}$

11. $\dfrac{w^{-2} w^5}{w^{-1}}$

12. $\dfrac{10^9 \cdot 10^4}{10^3}$

13. $\dfrac{10^{-2} \cdot 10^5}{10^{-1}}$

Concept 1: Writing Numbers in Scientific Notation

14. Explain how scientific notation might be valuable in studying astronomy. Answers may vary.

15. Explain how you would write the number 0.000 000 000 23 in scientific notation.

16. Explain how you would write the number 23,000,000,000,000 in scientific notation.

For Exercises 17–28, write the number in scientific notation. **(See Example 1.)**

17. 50,000

18. 900,000

19. 208,000

20. 420,000,000

21. 6,010,000

22. 75,000

23. 0.000008

24. 0.003

 25. 0.000125

26. 0.00000025

27. 0.006708

28. 0.02004

For Exercises 29–34, write the numbers in scientific notation. **(See Example 2.)**

29. The mass of a proton is approximately 0.000 000 000 000 000 000 000 0017 g.

30. The total combined salaries of the president, vice president, senators, and representatives of the United States federal government is approximately $85,000,000.

31. The Bill Gates Foundation has over $27,000,000,000 from which it makes contributions to global charities.

32. One gram is equivalent to 0.0035 oz.

 33. In one of the world's largest tanker disasters, *Amoco Cadiz* spilled 68,000,000 gal of oil off Portsall, France, causing widespread environmental damage over 100 miles of Brittany coast.

34. The human heart pumps about 2100 gal of blood per day. That means that it pumps approximately 767,000 gal per year.

Concept 2: Writing Numbers in Standard Form

35. Explain how you would write the number 3.1×10^{-9} in standard form.

36. Explain how you would write the number 3.1×10^{9} in standard form.

For Exercises 37–52, write the numbers in standard form. **(See Example 3.)**

37. 5×10^{-5}

38. 2×10^{-7}

39. 2.8×10^{3}

40. 9.1×10^{6}

41. 6.03×10^{-4}

42. 7.01×10^{-3}

43. 2.4×10^{6}

44. 3.1×10^{4}

45. 1.9×10^{-2}

46. 2.8×10^{-6}

47. 7.032×10^{3}

48. 8.205×10^{2}

49. One picogram (pg) is equal to 1×10^{-12} g.

50. A nanometer (nm) is approximately 3.94×10^{-8} in.

51. A normal diet contains between 1.6×10^{3} Cal and 2.8×10^{3} Cal per day.

52. The total land area of Texas is approximately 2.62×10^{5} square miles.

Concept 3: Multiplying and Dividing Numbers in Scientific Notation

For Exercises 53–72, multiply or divide as indicated. Write the answers in scientific notation. **(See Example 4.)**

53. $(2.5 \times 10^{6})(2 \times 10^{-2})$

54. $(2 \times 10^{-7})(3 \times 10^{13})$

55. $(1.2 \times 10^{4})(3 \times 10^{7})$

56. $(3.2 \times 10^{-3})(2.5 \times 10^{8})$

57. $\dfrac{7.7 \times 10^{6}}{3.5 \times 10^{2}}$

58. $\dfrac{9.5 \times 10^{11}}{1.9 \times 10^{3}}$

59. $\dfrac{9 \times 10^{-6}}{4 \times 10^{7}}$

60. $\dfrac{7 \times 10^{-2}}{5 \times 10^{9}}$

61. $80,000,000,000 \times 4000$

62. 0.0006×0.03

63. $(3.2 \times 10^{-4})(7.6 \times 10^{-7})$

64. $(5.9 \times 10^{12})(3.6 \times 10^{9})$

65. $\dfrac{210,000,000,000}{0.007}$

66. $\dfrac{160,000,000,000,000}{0.00008}$

67. $\dfrac{5.7 \times 10^{-2}}{9.5 \times 10^{-8}}$

68. $\dfrac{2.72 \times 10^{-6}}{6.8 \times 10^{-4}}$

69. $6,000,000,000 \times 0.0000000023$

70. $0.000055 \times 40,000$

71. $\dfrac{0.0000000003}{6000}$

72. $\dfrac{420,000}{0.0000021}$

Mixed Exercises

73. If a piece of paper is 3×10^{-3} in. thick, how thick is a stack of 1.25×10^{3} pieces of paper?

74. A box of staples contains 5×10^{3} staples and weighs 15 oz. How much does one staple weigh? Write your answer in scientific notation.

75. Bill Gates owned approximately 1,100,000,000 shares of Microsoft stock. If the stock price was $27 per share, how much was Bill Gates's stock worth?

76. A state lottery had a jackpot of 5.2×10^7. This week the winner was a group of office employees that included 13 people. How much would each person receive?

77. Dinosaurs became extinct about 65 million years ago.

    a. Write the number 65 million in scientific notation.

    b. How many days is 65 million years?

    c. How many hours is 65 million years?

    d. How many seconds is 65 million years?

78. The Earth is 150,000,000 km from the Sun.

    a. Write the number 150,000,000 in scientific notation.

    b. There are 1000 m in a kilometer. How many meters is the Earth from the Sun?

    c. There are 100 cm in a meter. How many centimeters is the Earth from the Sun?

Section 5.5   Addition and Subtraction of Polynomials

Concepts

1. Introduction to Polynomials
2. Addition of Polynomials
3. Subtraction of Polynomials
4. Polynomials and Applications to Geometry

1. Introduction to Polynomials

One commonly used algebraic expression is called a polynomial. A **polynomial** in one variable, x, is defined as a single term or a sum of terms of the form ax^n, where a is a real number and the exponent, n, is a nonnegative integer. For each term, a is called the **coefficient**, and n is called the **degree of the term**. For example:

Term (Expressed in the Form ax^n)	Coefficient	Degree
$-12z^7$	-12	7
$x^3 \rightarrow$ rewrite as $1x^3$	1	3
$10w \rightarrow$ rewrite as $10w^1$	10	1
$7 \rightarrow$ rewrite as $7x^0$	7	0

If a polynomial has exactly one term, it is categorized as a **monomial**. A two-term polynomial is called a **binomial**, and a three-term polynomial is called a **trinomial**. A polynomial in one variable is written in **descending order** if the term with highest degree is written first, followed by the term of next highest degree and so on. The term with highest degree is called the **leading term**, and its coefficient is called the **leading coefficient**. The **degree of a polynomial** is the greatest degree of all of its terms. Thus, for a polynomial written in descending order, the leading term determines the degree of the polynomial.

	Expression	Descending Order	Leading Coefficient	Degree of Polynomial
Monomials	$-3x^4$	$-3x^4$	-3	4
	17	17	17	0
Binomials	$4y^3 - 6y^5$	$-6y^5 + 4y^3$	-6	5
	$\dfrac{1}{2} - \dfrac{1}{4}c$	$-\dfrac{1}{4}c + \dfrac{1}{2}$	$-\dfrac{1}{4}$	1
Trinomials	$4p - 3p^3 + 8p^6$	$8p^6 - 3p^3 + 4p$	8	6
	$7a^4 - 1.2a^8 + 3a^3$	$-1.2a^8 + 7a^4 + 3a^3$	-1.2	8

Example 1 Identifying the Parts of a Polynomial

Given: $3a - 2a^4 + 6 - a^3$

a. List the terms of the polynomial, and state the coefficient and degree of each term.

b. Write the polynomial in descending order.

c. State the degree of the polynomial and the leading coefficient.

d. Evaluate the polynomial for $a = -2$.

Skill Practice

a. Write the polynomial in descending order; b. State the degree of the polynomial; c. State the coefficient of the leading term; d. Evaluate the polynomial for $x = -1$.

1. $5x^3 - x + 8x^4 + 3x^2$

Solution:

a. term: $3a$ coefficient: 3   degree: 1

    term: $-2a^4$ coefficient: -2 degree: 4

    term: 6   coefficient: 6   degree: 0

    term: $-a^3$ coefficient: -1 degree: 3

b. $-2a^4 - a^3 + 3a + 6$

c. The degree of the polynomial is 4 and the leading coefficient is -2.

d. $-2a^4 - a^3 + 3a + 6$

$= -2(-2)^4 - (-2)^3 + 3(-2) + 6$ Substitute -2 for the variable, a. Remember to use parentheses when replacing a variable.

$= -2(16) - (-8) + 3(-2) + 6$ Simplify exponents first.

$= -32 - (-8) + (-6) + 6$ Perform multiplication before addition and subtraction.

$= -24$ Simplify.

Polynomials may have more than one variable. In such a case, the degree of a term is the sum of the exponents of the variables contained in the term. For example, the term, $32x^2y^5z$, has degree 8 because the exponents applied to x, y, and z are 2, 5, and 1, respectively. The following polynomial has a degree of 11 because the highest degree of its terms is 11.

$$32x^2y^5z \quad - \quad 2x^3y \quad + \quad 2x^2yz^8 \quad + \quad 7$$

    ↑   ↑   ↑   ↑

degree   degree   degree   degree

8   4   11   0

Answers

1. a. $8x^4 + 5x^3 + 3x^2 - x$

   b. 4   c. 8   d. 7

2. Addition of Polynomials

Recall that two terms are *like* terms if they each have the same variables, and the corresponding variables are raised to the same powers.

Same exponents   Same exponents

Like Terms: $3x^2, -7x^2$ $-5yz^3, yz^3$

Same variables   Same variables

Different exponents

Unlike Terms: $9z^2, 12z^6$ $\frac{1}{3}w^6, \frac{2}{5}p^6$ $4y, 7$

Different variables   Different variables

Recall that the distributive property is used to add or subtract *like* terms. For example,

$3x^2 + 9x^2 - 2x^2$

$\quad = (3 + 9 - 2)x^2$ Apply the distributive property.

$\quad = (10)x^2$ Simplify.

$\quad = 10x^2$

Skill Practice

Add the polynomials.
  2. $13a^2b^3 + 2a^2b^3$

Example 2   **Adding Polynomials**

Add the polynomials. $3x^2y + 5x^2y$

Solution:

$3x^2y + 5x^2y$

$\quad = (3 + 5)x^2y$ Apply the distributive property.

$\quad = (8)x^2y$

$\quad = 8x^2y$ Simplify.

It is the distributive property that enables us to add *like* terms. We shorten the process by adding the coefficients of *like* terms.

Skill Practice

Add the polynomials.
  3. $(7q^2 - 2q + 4) +$
      $(5q^2 + 6q - 9)$

Example 3   **Adding Polynomials**

Add the polynomials. $(-3c^3 + 5c^2 - 7c) + (11c^3 + 6c^2 + 3)$

Solution:

$(-3c^3 + 5c^2 - 7c) + (11c^3 + 6c^2 + 3)$

$\quad = -3c^3 + 11c^3 + 5c^2 + 6c^2 - 7c + 3$ Clear parentheses, and group
                                                    like terms.

$\quad = 8c^3 + 11c^2 - 7c + 3$ Combine *like* terms.

Avoiding Mistakes

When *adding* like terms, the exponents do not change.

Answers
2. $15a^2b^3$ **3.** $12q^2 + 4q - 5$

> **TIP:** Polynomials can also be added by combining *like* terms in columns.
> The sum of the polynomials from Example 3 is shown here.
>
> $$\begin{array}{r} -3c^3 + 5c^2 - 7c + 0 \\ + \; 11c^3 + 6c^2 + 0c + 3 \\ \hline 8c^3 + 11c^2 - 7c + 3 \end{array}$$
> Place holders such as 0 and $0c$ may be used to help line up *like* terms.

Example 4 Adding Polynomials

Add the polynomials. $(4w^2 - 2x) + (3w^2 - 4x^2 + 6x)$

Solution:

$(4w^2 - 2x) + (3w^2 - 4x^2 + 6x)$

$= 4w^2 + 3w^2 - 4x^2 - 2x + 6x$ Clear parentheses and group *like* terms.

$= 7w^2 - 4x^2 + 4x$

> **TIP:** To add these polynomials vertically, align *like* terms in the same column.
>
> $$\begin{array}{r} 4w^2 \qquad\; - 2x \\ + \; 3w^2 - 4x^2 + 6x \\ \hline 7w^2 - 4x^2 + 4x \end{array}$$

Skill Practice

Add the polynomials.

4. $(5x^2 - 4xy + y^2) + (-3x^2 - 5y^2)$

3. Subtraction of Polynomials

Subtraction of two polynomials requires us to find the opposite of the polynomial being subtracted. To find the opposite of a polynomial, take the opposite of each term. This is equivalent to multiplying the polynomial by -1.

Example 5 Finding the Opposite of a Polynomial

Find the opposite of the polynomials.

a. $5x$ **b.** $3a - 4b - c$ **c.** $5.5y^4 - 2.4y^3 + 1.1y$

Solution:

Expression	**Opposite**	**Simplified Form**
a. $5x$	$-(5x)$	$-5x$
b. $3a - 4b - c$	$-(3a - 4b - c)$	$-3a + 4b + c$
c. $5.5y^4 - 2.4y^3 + 1.1y$	$-(5.5y^4 - 2.4y^3 + 1.1y)$	$-5.5y^4 + 2.4y^3 - 1.1y$

Skill Practice

Find the opposite of the polynomials.

5. $x - 3$
6. $3y^2 - 2xy + 6x + 2$
7. $-2.1w^3 + 4.9w^2 - 1.9w$

> **TIP:** Notice that the sign of each term is changed when finding the opposite of a polynomial.

Answers

4. $2x^2 - 4xy - 4y^2$
5. $-x + 3$
6. $-3y^2 + 2xy - 6x - 2$
7. $2.1w^3 - 4.9w^2 + 1.9w$

Subtraction of two polynomials is similar to subtracting real numbers. Add the opposite of the second polynomial to the first polynomial.

> **Subtraction of Polynomials**
> If A and B are polynomials, then $A - B = A + (-B)$.

Skill Practice

Subtract the polynomials.
8. $(x^2 + 3x - 2)$
$\quad - (4x^2 + 6x + 1)$

Example 6   Subtracting Polynomials

Subtract the polynomials. $(-4p^4 + 5p^2 - 3) - (11p^2 + 4p - 6)$

Solution:

$(-4p^4 + 5p^2 - 3) - (11p^2 + 4p - 6)$

$= (-4p^4 + 5p^2 - 3) + (-11p^2 - 4p + 6)$ Add the opposite of the second polynomial.

$= -4p^4 + 5p^2 - 11p^2 - 4p - 3 + 6$ Group *like* terms.

$= -4p^4 - 6p^2 - 4p + 3$ Combine *like* terms.

> **TIP:** Two polynomials can also be subtracted in columns by adding the opposite of the second polynomial to the first polynomial. Place holders (shown in red) may be used to help line up *like* terms.
>
> $-4p^4 + 0p^3 + 5p^2 + 0p - 3$
> $-(0p^4 + 0p^3 + 11p^2 + 4p - 6)$ Add the opposite
>
> $-4p^4 + 0p^3 + 5p^2 + 0p - 3$
> $+ \underline{-0p^4 - 0p^3 - 11p^2 - 4p + 6}$
> $-4p^4 \qquad - 6p^2 - 4p + 3$
>
> The difference of the polynomials is $-4p^4 - 6p^2 - 4p + 3$.

Skill Practice

Subtract the polynomials.
9. $(-3y^2 + xy + 2x^2)$
$\quad - (-2y^2 - 3xy - 8x^2)$

Example 7   Subtracting Polynomials

Subtract the polynomials. $(a^2 - 2ab + 7b^2) - (-8a^2 - 6ab + 2b^2)$

Solution:

$(a^2 - 2ab + 7b^2) - (-8a^2 - 6ab + 2b^2)$

$= (a^2 - 2ab + 7b^2) + (8a^2 + 6ab - 2b^2)$ Add the opposite of the second polynomial.

$= a^2 + 8a^2 - 2ab + 6ab + 7b^2 - 2b^2$ Group *like* terms.

$= 9a^2 + 4ab + 5b^2$ Combine *like* terms.

Concept Connections

Determine if the polynomial is equivalent to $-(a - b)$.
10. $a + b$ **11.** $-a + b$
12. $b - a$ **13.** $-a - b$

Answers
8. $-3x^2 - 3x - 3$
9. $-y^2 + 4xy + 10x^2$
10. No   **11.** Yes
12. Yes   **13.** No

Example 8 Subtracting Polynomials

Subtract $\frac{1}{3}t^4 + \frac{1}{2}t^2$ from $t^2 - 4$, and simplify the result.

Solution:

To subtract a from b, we write $b - a$. Thus, to subtract $\overbrace{\frac{1}{3}t^4 + \frac{1}{2}t^2}^{a}$ from $\overbrace{t^2 - 4}^{b}$, we have

$$\overset{b}{(t^2 - 4)} \overset{-}{-} \overset{a}{\left(\frac{1}{3}t^4 + \frac{1}{2}t^2\right)}$$

$$= t^2 - 4 - \frac{1}{3}t^4 - \frac{1}{2}t^2 \qquad \text{Apply the distributive property.}$$

$$= -\frac{1}{3}t^4 + t^2 - \frac{1}{2}t^2 - 4 \qquad \text{Group } like \text{ terms in descending order.}$$

$$= -\frac{1}{3}t^4 + \frac{2}{2}t^2 - \frac{1}{2}t^2 - 4 \qquad \text{The } t^2 \text{ terms are the only } like \text{ terms.}$$
$$\qquad\qquad\qquad\qquad\qquad\qquad \text{Find a common denominator for the } t^2 \text{ terms.}$$

$$= -\frac{1}{3}t^4 + \frac{1}{2}t^2 - 4 \qquad \text{Add } like \text{ terms.}$$

4. Polynomials and Applications to Geometry

Example 9 Subtracting Polynomials in Geometry

If the perimeter of the triangle in Figure 5-1 can be represented by the polynomial $2x^2 + 5x + 6$, find a polynomial that represents the length of the missing side.

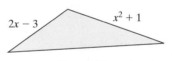
$2x - 3$ $\quad x^2 + 1$

Figure 5-1

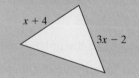
Solution:

The missing side of the triangle can be found by subtracting the sum of the two known sides from the perimeter.

$$\begin{pmatrix} \text{Length} \\ \text{of missing} \\ \text{side} \end{pmatrix} = (\text{perimeter}) - \begin{bmatrix} \text{sum of the} \\ \text{two known sides} \end{bmatrix}$$

$$\begin{pmatrix} \text{Length} \\ \text{of missing} \\ \text{side} \end{pmatrix} = (2x^2 + 5x + 6) - [(2x - 3) + (x^2 + 1)]$$

$$= 2x^2 + 5x + 6 - [2x - 3 + x^2 + 1] \qquad \text{Clear inner parentheses.}$$

$$= 2x^2 + 5x + 6 - (x^2 + 2x - 2) \qquad \text{Combine } like \text{ terms within } [\ \ ].$$

$$= 2x^2 + 5x + 6 - x^2 - 2x + 2 \qquad \text{Apply the distributive property.}$$

$$= 2x^2 - x^2 + 5x - 2x + 6 + 2 \qquad \text{Group } like \text{ terms.}$$

$$= x^2 + 3x + 8 \qquad \text{Combine } like \text{ terms.}$$

The polynomial $x^2 + 3x + 8$ represents the length of the missing side.

Section 5.5 Practice Exercises

Vocabulary and Key Concepts

1. **a.** A _____ is a single term or a sum of terms of the form ax^n where n is a nonegative integer.

   b. For the term ax^n, a is called the _____ and n is called the _____ of the term.

   c. Given the term x, the coefficient of the term is _____.

   d. A monomial is a polynomial with exactly _____ term(s).

   e. A _____ is a polynomial with exactly two terms.

   f. A _____ is a polynomial with exactly three terms.

   g. The term with the highest degree is called the _____ term and its coefficient is called the

   _____ _____.

   h. The degree of a polynomial is the _____ degree of all of its terms.

   i. The degree of a nonzero constant such as 5 is _____.

Review Exercises

For Exercises 2–7, simplify the expression.

2. $\dfrac{p^3 \cdot 4p}{p^2}$

3. $(3x)^2(5x^{-4})$

4. $(6y^{-3})(2y^9)$

5. $\dfrac{8t^{-6}}{4t^{-2}}$

6. $\dfrac{8^3 \cdot 8^{-4}}{8^{-2} \cdot 8^6}$

7. $\dfrac{3^4 \cdot 3^{-8}}{3^{12} \cdot 3^{-4}}$

8. Explain the difference between 3×10^7 and 3^7.

9. Explain the difference between 4×10^{-2} and 4^{-2}.

Concept 1: Introduction to Polynomials

For Exercises 10–12,

   a. write the polynomial in descending order.

   b. identify the leading coefficient.

   c. identify the degree of the polynomial. **(See Example 1.)**

10. $10 - 8a - a^3 + 2a^2 + a^5$

11. $6 + 7x^2 - 7x^5 + 9x$

12. $\dfrac{1}{2}y + y^2 - 12y^4 + y^3 - 6$

For Exercises 13–22, categorize each expression as a monomial, a binomial, or a trinomial. Then evaluate the polynomial given $x = -3$, $y = 2$, and $z = -1$. **(See Example 1.)**

13. $10x^2 + 5x$

14. $7z + 13z^2 - 15$

15. $6x^2$

16. 9

17. $2y - y^4$

18. $7x + 2$

19. $2y^4 - 3y + 1$

20. 23

21. $-32xyz$

22. $y^4 - x^2$

Concept 2: Addition of Polynomials

23. Explain why the terms $3x$ and $3x^2$ are not *like* terms.

24. Explain why the terms $4w^3$ and $4z^3$ are not *like* terms.

For Exercises 25–42, add the polynomials. **(See Examples 2–4.)**

25. $23x^2y + 12x^2y$

26. $-5ab^3 + 17ab^3$

27. $3b^5d^2 + (5b^5d^2 - 9d)$

28. $4c^2d^3 + (3cd - 10c^2d^3)$

29. $(7y^2 + 2y - 9) + (-3y^2 - y)$

30. $(-3w^2 + 4w - 6) + (5w^2 + 2)$

31. $(5x + 3x^2 - x^3) + (2x^2 + 4x - 10)$

32. $(t^2 - 4t + t^4) + (3t^4 + 2t + 6)$

33. $(6.1y + 3.2x) + (4.8y - 3.2x)$

34. $(2.7m - 0.5h) + (-3.2m + 0.2h)$

35. $\begin{aligned}& 6a + 2b - 5c \\ + \; & {-2a - 2b - 3c}\end{aligned}$

36. $\begin{aligned}& -13x + 5y + 10z \\ + \; & {-3x - 3y + \; 2z}\end{aligned}$

37. $\left(\dfrac{2}{5}a + \dfrac{1}{4}b - \dfrac{5}{6}\right) + \left(\dfrac{3}{5}a - \dfrac{3}{4}b - \dfrac{7}{6}\right)$

38. $\left(\dfrac{5}{9}x + \dfrac{1}{10}y\right) + \left(-\dfrac{4}{9}x + \dfrac{3}{10}y\right)$

39. $\left(z - \dfrac{8}{3}\right) + \left(\dfrac{4}{3}z^2 - z + 1\right)$

40. $\left(-\dfrac{7}{5}r + 1\right) + \left(-\dfrac{3}{5}r^2 + \dfrac{7}{5}r + 1\right)$

41. $\begin{aligned}& 7.9t^3 \qquad\quad + 2.6t - 1.1 \\ + \; & \qquad {-3.4t^2 + 3.4t - 3.1}\end{aligned}$

42. $\begin{aligned}& 0.34y^2 \qquad\; + 1.23 \\ + \; & \qquad 3.42y - 7.56\end{aligned}$

Concept 3: Subtraction of Polynomials

For Exercises 43–48, find the opposite of each polynomial. **(See Example 5.)**

43. $4h - 5$

44. $5k - 12$

45. $-2m^2 + 3m - 15$

46. $-n^2 - 6n + 9$

47. $3v^3 + 5v^2 + 10v + 22$

48. $7u^4 + 3v^2 + 17$

For Exercises 49–68, subtract the polynomials. **(See Examples 6 and 7.)**

49. $4a^3b^2 - 12a^3b^2$

50. $5yz^4 - 14yz^4$

51. $-32x^3 - 21x^3$

52. $-23c^5 - 12c^5$

53. $(7a - 7) - (12a - 4)$

54. $(4x + 3v) - (-3x + v)$

55. $\begin{aligned}& 4k + 3 \\ - \; & {(-12k - 6)}\end{aligned}$

56. $\begin{aligned}& 3h - 15 \\ - \; & {(8h + 13)}\end{aligned}$

57. $25s - (23s + 14)$

58. $3x^2 - (-x^2 - 12)$

59. $(5t^2 - 3t - 2) - (2t^2 + t + 1)$

60. $(k^2 + 2k + 1) - (3k^2 - 6k + 2)$

61. $\begin{aligned}& 10r - 6s + 2t \\ - \; & {(12r - 3s - \; t)}\end{aligned}$

62. $\begin{aligned}& a - 14b + 7c \\ - \; & {(-3a - \; 8b + 2c)}\end{aligned}$

63. $\left(\frac{7}{8}x + \frac{2}{3}y - \frac{3}{10}\right) - \left(\frac{1}{8}x + \frac{1}{3}y\right)$

64. $\left(r - \frac{1}{12}s\right) - \left(\frac{1}{2}r - \frac{5}{12}s - \frac{4}{11}\right)$

65. $\left(\frac{2}{3}h^2 - \frac{1}{5}h - \frac{3}{4}\right) - \left(\frac{4}{3}h^2 - \frac{4}{5}h + \frac{7}{4}\right)$

66. $\left(\frac{3}{8}p^3 - \frac{5}{7}p^2 - \frac{2}{5}\right) - \left(\frac{5}{8}p^3 - \frac{2}{7}p^2 + \frac{7}{5}\right)$

67.
$$4.5x^4 - 3.1x^2 \qquad\quad - 6.7$$
$$- (2.1x^4 \qquad\quad + 4.4x \qquad)$$

68.
$$1.3c^3 \qquad\qquad + 4.8$$
$$- (\qquad 4.3c^2 - 2c - 2.2)$$

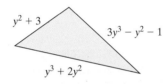 **69.** Find the difference of $(4b^3 + 6b - 7)$ and $(-12b^2 + 11b + 5)$.

70. Find the difference of $(-5y^2 + 3y - 21)$ and $(-4y^2 - 5y + 23)$.

71. Subtract $(3x^3 - 5x + 10)$ from $(-2x^2 + 6x - 21)$.
(See Example 8.)

72. Subtract $(7a^5 - 2a^3 - 5a)$ from $(3a^5 - 9a^2 + 3a - 8)$.

Concept 4: Polynomials and Applications to Geometry

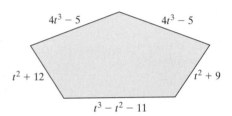 **73.** Find a polynomial that represents the perimeter of the figure.

74. Find a polynomial that represents the perimeter of the figure.

75. If the perimeter of the figure can be represented by the polynomial $5a^2 - 2a + 1$, find a polynomial that represents the length of the missing side. **(See Example 9.)**

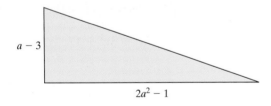

76. If the perimeter of the figure can be represented by the polynomial $6w^3 - 2w - 3$, find a polynomial that represents the length of the missing side.

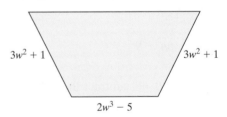

Mixed Exercises

For Exercises 77–92, perform the indicated operation.

77. $(2ab^2 + 9a^2b) + (7ab^2 - 3ab + 7a^2b)$

78. $(8x^2y - 3xy - 6xy^2) + (3x^2y - 12xy)$

79.
$$4z^5 \qquad + z^3 - 3z + 13$$
$$- (\quad - z^4 - 8z^3 \qquad + 15)$$

80.
$$-15t^4 \qquad - 23t^2 + 16t$$
$$- (\qquad 21t^3 + 18t^2 + \quad t)$$

81. $(9x^4 + 2x^3 - x + 5) + (9x^3 - 3x^2 + 8x + 3) - (7x^4 - x + 12)$

82. $(-6y^3 - 9y^2 + 23) - (7y^2 + 2y - 11) + (3y^3 - 25)$

83. $(0.2w^2 + 3w + 1.3) - (w^3 - 0.7w + 2)$

84. $(8.1u^3 - 5.2u^2 + 4) + (2.8u^3 + 6.3u - 7)$

85. $(7p^2q - 3pq^2) - (8p^2q + pq) + (4pq - pq^2)$

86. $(12c^2d - 2cd + 8cd^2) - (-c^2d + 4cd) - (5cd - 2cd^2)$

87. $(5x - 2x^3) + (2x^3 - 5x)$

88. $(p^2 - 4p + 2) - (2 + p^2 - 4p)$

89. $2a^2b - 4ab + ab^2$
    $- (2a^2b + ab - 5ab^2)$

90. $-3xy + 7xy^2 + 5x^2y$
    $+ -8xy - 11xy^2 + 3x^2y$

91. $[(3y^2 - 5y) - (2y^2 + y - 1)] + (10y^2 - 4y - 5)$

92. $(12c^3 - 5c^2 - 2c) + [(7c^3 - 2c^2 + c) - (4c^3 + 4c)]$

Expanding Your Skills

93. Write a binomial of degree 3. (Answers may vary.)

94. Write a trinomial of degree 6. (Answers may vary.)

95. Write a monomial of degree 5. (Answers may vary.)

96. Write a monomial of degree 1. (Answers may vary.)

97. Write a trinomial with the leading coefficient -6. (Answers may vary.)

98. Write a binomial with the leading coefficient 13. (Answers may vary.)

Multiplication of Polynomials and Special Products

Section 5.6

1. Multiplication of Polynomials

The properties of exponents covered in Sections 5.1–5.3 can be used to simplify many algebraic expressions including the multiplication of monomials. To multiply monomials, first use the associative and commutative properties of multiplication to group coefficients and like bases. Then simplify the result by using the properties of exponents.

Concepts

1. Multiplication of Polynomials
2. Special Case Products: Difference of Squares and Perfect Square Trinomials
3. Applications to Geometry

Example 1   **Multiplying Monomials**

Multiply.

a. $(3x^4)(4x^2)$ **b.** $(-4c^5d)(2c^2d^3e)$ **c.** $\left(\dfrac{1}{3}a^4b^3\right)\left(\dfrac{3}{4}b^7\right)$

Solution:

a. $(3x^4)(4x^2)$

    $= (3 \cdot 4)(x^4x^2)$ Group coefficients and like bases.

    $= 12x^6$ Multiply the coefficients and add the exponents on x.

b. $(-4c^5d)(2c^2d^3e)$

    $= (-4 \cdot 2)(c^5c^2)(dd^3)(e)$ Group coefficients and like bases.

    $= -8c^7d^4e$ Simplify.

c. $\left(\dfrac{1}{3}a^4b^3\right)\left(\dfrac{3}{4}b^7\right)$

    $= \left(\dfrac{1}{3} \cdot \dfrac{3}{4}\right)(a^4)(b^3b^7)$ Group coefficients and like bases.

    $= \dfrac{1}{4}a^4b^{10}$ Simplify.

Skill Practice

Multiply.
1. $-5y(6y^3)$
2. $7x^2y(-2x^3y^4)$
3. $\left(\dfrac{2}{5}w^5z^3\right)\left(\dfrac{15}{4}w^4\right)$

Answers
1. $-30y^4$
2. $-14x^5y^5$
3. $\dfrac{3}{2}w^9z^3$

The distributive property is used to multiply polynomials: $a(b + c) = ab + ac$.

Example 2 **Multiplying a Polynomial by a Monomial**

Multiply.

a. $2t(4t - 3)$ **b.** $-3a^2\left(-4a^2 + 2a - \dfrac{1}{3}\right)$

Solution:

a. $2t(4t - 3)$ Multiply each term of the binomial by $2t$.

$= (2t)(4t) + 2t(-3)$ Apply the distributive property.

$= 8t^2 - 6t$ Simplify each term.

b. $-3a^2\left(-4a^2 + 2a - \dfrac{1}{3}\right)$ Multiply each term of the trinomial by $-3a^2$.

$= (-3a^2)(-4a^2) + (-3a^2)(2a) + (-3a^2)\left(-\dfrac{1}{3}\right)$ Apply the distributive property.

$= 12a^4 - 6a^3 + a^2$ Simplify each term.

Thus far, we have illustrated polynomial multiplication involving monomials. Next, the distributive property will be used to multiply polynomials with more than one term.

$(x + 3)(x + 5) = x(x + 5) + 3(x + 5)$ Apply the distributive property.

$= x(x + 5) + 3(x + 5)$ Apply the distributive property again.

$= (x)(x) + (x)(5) + (3)(x) + (3)(5)$

$= x^2 + 5x + 3x + 15$

$= x^2 + 8x + 15$ Combine *like* terms.

Note: Using the distributive property results in multiplying each term of the first polynomial by each term of the second polynomial.

$(x + 3)(x + 5) = (x)(x) + (x)(5) + (3)(x) + (3)(5)$

$= x^2 + 5x + 3x + 15$

$= x^2 + 8x + 15$

Example 3 **Multiplying a Polynomial by a Polynomial**

Multiply the polynomials. $(c - 7)(c + 2)$

Solution:

$(c - 7)(c + 2)$ Multiply each term in the first polynomial by each term in the second. That is, apply the distributive property.

$= (c)(c) + (c)(2) + (-7)(c) + (-7)(2)$

$= c^2 + 2c - 7c - 14$ Simplify.

$= c^2 - 5c - 14$ Combine *like* terms.

TIP: Notice that the product of two *binomials* equals the sum of the products of the **F**irst terms, the **O**uter terms, the **I**nner terms, and the **L**ast terms. The acronym **FOIL** (First Outer Inner Last) can be used as a memory device to multiply two binomials.

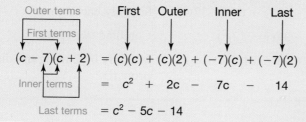

Outer terms

First terms

First · Outer · Inner · Last

$(c - 7)(c + 2) = (c)(c) + (c)(2) + (-7)(c) + (-7)(2)$

Inner terms

$= c^2 + 2c - 7c - 14$

Last terms $= c^2 - 5c - 14$

Example 4 **Multiplying a Polynomial by a Polynomial**

Multiply the polynomials. $(y - 2)(3y^2 + y - 5)$

Solution:

$(y - 2)(3y^2 + y - 5)$ Multiply each term in the first polynomial by each term in the second.

$= (y)(3y^2) + (y)(y) + (y)(-5) + (-2)(3y^2) + (-2)(y) + (-2)(-5)$

$= 3y^3 + y^2 - 5y - 6y^2 - 2y + 10$ Simplify each term.

$= 3y^3 - 5y^2 - 7y + 10$ Combine *like* terms.

TIP: Multiplication of polynomials can be performed vertically by a process similar to column multiplication of real numbers. For example,

$$\begin{array}{r} 235 \\ \times\ 21 \\ \hline 235 \\ 4700 \\ \hline 4935 \end{array}$$

$$\begin{array}{r} 3y^2 + y - 5 \\ \times\ \quad y - 2 \\ \hline -6y^2 - 2y + 10 \\ 3y^3 + y^2 - 5y + \ 0 \\ \hline 3y^3 - 5y^2 - 7y + 10 \end{array}$$

Note: When multiplying by the column method, it is important to *align like* terms vertically before adding terms.

Example 5 **Multiplying Polynomials**

Multiply the polynomials. $2(10x + 3y)(2x - 4y)$

Solution:

$2(10x + 3y)(2x - 4y)$ — In this case, we are multiplying three polynomials—a monomial times two binomials. The associative property of multiplication allows us to choose which two polynomials to multiply first.

$= 2[(10x + 3y)(2x - 4y)]$ — First we will multiply the binomials. Multiply each term in the first binomial by each term in the second binomial. That is, apply the distributive property.

$= 2[(10x)(2x) + (10x)(-4y) + (3y)(2x) + (3y)(-4y)]$

$= 2[20x^2 - 40xy + 6xy - 12y^2]$ — Simplify each term.

$= 2(20x^2 - 34xy - 12y^2)$ — Combine *like* terms.

$= 40x^2 - 68xy - 24y^2$ — Multiply by 2 using the distributive property.

2. Special Case Products: Difference of Squares and Perfect Square Trinomials

In some cases the product of two binomials takes on a special pattern.

I. The first special case occurs when multiplying the sum and difference of the same two terms. For example:

$(2x + 3)(2x - 3)$ — Notice that the middle terms are opposites. This leaves only the difference between the square of the first term and the square of the second term. For this reason, the product is called a *difference of squares*.

$= 4x^2 - 6x + 6x - 9$

$= 4x^2 - 9$

Note: The binomials $2x + 3$ and $2x - 3$ are called **conjugates**. In one expression, $2x$ and 3 are added, and in the other, $2x$ and 3 are subtracted.

II. The second special case involves the square of a binomial. For example:

$(3x + 7)^2$ — When squaring a binomial, the product will be a trinomial called a *perfect square trinomial*. The first and third terms are formed by squaring each term of the binomial. The middle term equals twice the product of the terms in the binomial.

$= (3x + 7)(3x + 7)$

$= 9x^2 + 21x + 21x + 49$

$= 9x^2 + 42x + 49$

$= (3x)^2 + 2(3x)(7) + (7)^2$

Note: The expression $(3x - 7)^2$ also expands to a perfect square trinomial, but the middle term will be negative:

$$(3x - 7)(3x - 7) = 9x^2 - 21x - 21x + 49 = 9x^2 - 42x + 49$$

Special Case Product Formulas

1. $(a + b)(a - b) = a^2 - b^2$ The product is called a **difference of squares**.

2. $(a + b)^2 = a^2 + 2ab + b^2$ $\Big\}$ The product is called a **perfect square**
$ (a - b)^2 = a^2 - 2ab + b^2$ **trinomial**.

You should become familiar with these special case products because they will be used again in Chapter 6 to factor polynomials.

Example 6   Finding Special Products

Multiply the conjugates.

a. $(x - 9)(x + 9)$ **b.** $\left(\dfrac{1}{2}p + 6\right)\left(\dfrac{1}{2}p - 6\right)$

Solution:

a. $(x - 9)(x + 9)$ Apply the formula:
$(a + b)(a - b) = a^2 - b^2.$

$\overset{a^2 - b^2}{}$

$= (x)^2 - (9)^2$ Substitute $a = x$ and
$b = 9$.

$= x^2 - 81$

b. $\left(\dfrac{1}{2}p + 6\right)\left(\dfrac{1}{2}p - 6\right)$ Apply the formula: $(a + b)(a - b) = a^2 - b^2$.

$\overset{a^2 - b^2}{}$

$= \left(\dfrac{1}{2}p\right)^2 - (6)^2$ Substitute $a = \dfrac{1}{2}p$ and $b = 6$.

$= \dfrac{1}{4}p^2 - 36$ Simplify each term.

> **TIP:** The product of two conjugates can be checked by applying the distributive property:
>
> $(x - 9)(x + 9)$
>
> $= x^2 + 9x - 9x - 81$
>
> $= x^2 - 81$

Skill Practice

Multiply the conjugates.

9. $(a + 7)(a - 7)$

10. $\left(\dfrac{4}{5}x - 10\right)\left(\dfrac{4}{5}x + 10\right)$

Example 7   Finding Special Products

Square the binomials.

a. $(3w - 4)^2$ **b.** $(5x^2 + 2)^2$

Solution:

a. $(3w - 4)^2$ Apply the formula:
$(a - b)^2 = a^2 - 2ab + b^2.$

$\overset{a^2 - 2ab + b^2}{}$

$= (3w)^2 - 2(3w)(4) + (4)^2$ Substitute $a = 3w$, $b = 4$.

$= 9w^2 - 24w + 16$ Simplify each term.

Skill Practice

Square the binomials.

11. $(2x + 3)^2$

12. $(5c^2 - 6)^2$

Answers

9. $a^2 - 49$

10. $\dfrac{16}{25}x^2 - 100$

11. $4x^2 + 12x + 9$

12. $25c^4 - 60c^2 + 36$

Avoiding Mistakes

The property for squaring two factors is different than the property for squaring two terms:
$(ab)^2 = a^2b^2$ but
$(a + b)^2 = a^2 + 2ab + b^2$

b. $(5x^2 + 2)^2$
Apply the formula:
$(a + b)^2 = a^2 + 2ab + b^2.$

$\overset{a^2\ +\ 2ab\ +\ b^2}{}$

$= (5x^2)^2 + 2(5x^2)(2) + (2)^2$ Substitute $a = 5x^2, b = 2.$

$= 25x^4 + 20x^2 + 4$ Simplify each term.

3. Applications to Geometry

Example 8 Using Special Case Products in an Application of Geometry

Find a polynomial that represents the volume of the cube (Figure 5-2).

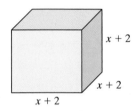

$x + 2$

$x + 2$

$x + 2$

Figure 5-2

Skill Practice

13. Find the polynomial that represents the volume of the cube.

$x - 1$

$x - 1$

$x - 1$

Solution:

$$\text{Volume} = (\text{length})(\text{width})(\text{height})$$
$$V = (x + 2)(x + 2)(x + 2) \quad \text{or} \quad V = (x + 2)^3$$

To expand $(x + 2)(x + 2)(x + 2)$, multiply the first two factors. Then multiply the result by the last factor.

$V = \underbrace{(x + 2)(x + 2)}(x + 2)$

$= (x^2 + 4x + 4)(x + 2)$ ⟵

TIP: $(x + 2)(x + 2) = (x + 2)^2$ and results in a perfect square trinomial.

$(x + 2)^2 = (x)^2 + 2(x)(2) + (2)^2$
$= x^2 + 4x + 4$

$= (x^2)(x) + (x^2)(2) + (4x)(x) + (4x)(2) + (4)(x) + (4)(2)$ Apply the distributive property.

$= x^3 + 2x^2 + 4x^2 + 8x + 4x + 8$ Group *like* terms.

$= x^3 + 6x^2 + 12x + 8$ Combine *like* terms.

The volume of the cube can be represented by

$$V = (x + 2)^3 = x^3 + 6x^2 + 12x + 8.$$

Answer

13. The volume of the cube can be represented by
$x^3 - 3x^2 + 3x - 1.$

Section 5.6 Practice Exercises

Vocabulary and Key Concepts

1. a. The conjugate of $5 + 2x$ is _____.

  b. When two conjugates are multiplied the resulting binomial is a difference of _____. This is given by the formula $(a + b)(a - b) =$ _____.

  c. When a binomial is squared, the resulting trinomial is a _____ square trinomial. This is given by the formula $(a + b)^2 =$ _____.

Review Exercises

For Exercises 2–9, simplify the expressions (if possible).

2. $4x + 5x$

3. $2y^2 - 4y^2$

4. $(4x)(5x)$

5. $(2y^2)(-4y^2)$

6. $-5a^3b - 2a^3b$

7. $7uvw^2 + uvw^2$

8. $(-5a^3b)(-2a^3b)$

9. $(7uvw^2)(uvw^2)$

Concept 1: Multiplication of Polynomials

For Exercises 10–18, multiply the expressions. **(See Example 1.)**

10. $8(4x)$

11. $-2(6y)$

12. $-10(5z)$

13. $7(3p)$

14. $(x^{10})(4x^3)$

15. $(a^{13}b^4)(12ab^4)$

16. $(4m^3n^7)(-3m^6n)$

17. $(2c^7d)(-c^3d^{11})$

18. $(-5u^2v)(-8u^3v^2)$

For Exercises 19–54, multiply the polynomials. **(See Examples 2–5.)**

19. $8pq(2pq - 3p + 5q)$

20. $5ab(2ab + 6a - 3b)$

21. $(k^2 - 13k - 6)(-4k)$

22. $(h^2 + 5h - 12)(-2h)$

23. $-15pq(3p^2 + p^3q^2 - 2q)$

24. $-4u^2v(2u - 5uv^3 + v)$

25. $(y + 10)(y + 9)$

26. $(x + 5)(x + 6)$

27. $(m - 12)(m - 2)$

28. $(n - 7)(n - 2)$

29. $(3p - 2)(4p + 1)$

30. $(7q + 11)(q - 5)$

31. $(8 - 4w)(-3w + 2)$

32. $(-6z + 10)(4 - 2z)$

33. $(p - 3w)(p - 11w)$

34. $(y - 7x)(y - 10x)$

35. $(6x - 1)(2x + 5)$

36. $(3x + 7)(x - 8)$

37. $(4a - 9)(1.5a - 2)$

38. $(2.1y - 0.5)(y + 3)$

39. $(3t - 7)(1 + 3t^2)$

40. $(2 - 5w)(2w^2 - 5)$

41. $3(3m + 4n)(m + 2n)$

42. $2(7y + z)(3y + 5z)$

43. $(5s + 3)(s^2 + s - 2)$

44. $(t - 4)(2t^2 - t + 6)$

45. $(3w - 2)(9w^2 + 6w + 4)$

46. $(z + 5)(z^2 - 5z + 25)$

47. $(p^2 + p - 5)(p^2 + 4p - 1)$

48. $(-x^2 - 2x + 4)(x^2 + 2x - 6)$

49. $\left(\dfrac{1}{2}x + \dfrac{3}{4}\right)\left(\dfrac{3}{2}x - \dfrac{1}{4}\right)$

50. $\left(\dfrac{5}{6}y - \dfrac{1}{3}\right)\left(\dfrac{1}{6}y - \dfrac{2}{3}\right)$

51. $\begin{array}{r} 3a^2 - 4a + 9 \\ \times \underline{\quad\quad 2a - 5} \end{array}$

52. $\begin{array}{r} 7x^2 - 3x - 4 \\ \times \underline{\quad\quad 5x + 1} \end{array}$

53. $\begin{array}{r} 4x^2 - 12xy + 9y^2 \\ \times \underline{\quad\quad 2x - 3y} \end{array}$

54. $\begin{array}{r} 25a^2 + 10ab + b^2 \\ \times \underline{\quad\quad 5a + b} \end{array}$

Concept 2: Special Case Products: Difference of Squares and Perfect Square Trinomials

For Exercises 55–66, multiply the conjugates. **(See Example 6.)**

55. $(3a - 4b)(3a + 4b)$

56. $(5y + 7x)(5y - 7x)$

57. $(9k + 6)(9k - 6)$

58. $(2h - 5)(2h + 5)$

59. $\left(\dfrac{1}{2} - t\right)\left(\dfrac{1}{2} + t\right)$

60. $\left(r + \dfrac{1}{4}\right)\left(r - \dfrac{1}{4}\right)$

61. $(u^3 + 5v)(u^3 - 5v)$

62. $(8w^2 - x)(8w^2 + x)$

63. $(2 - 3a)(2 + 3a)$

64. $(1 - 4x^2)(1 + 4x^2)$

65. $\left(\dfrac{2}{3} - p\right)\left(\dfrac{2}{3} + p\right)$

66. $\left(\dfrac{1}{8} - q\right)\left(\dfrac{1}{8} + q\right)$

For Exercises 67–78, square the binomials. **(See Example 7.)**

67. $(a + 5)^2$

68. $(a - 3)^2$

69. $(x - y)^2$

70. $(x + y)^2$

71. $(2c + 5)^2$

72. $(5d - 9)^2$

73. $(3t^2 - 4s)^2$

74. $(u^2 + 4v)^2$

75. $(7 - t)^2$

76. $(4 + w)^2$

77. $(3 + 4q)^2$

78. $(2 - 3b)^2$

79. a. Evaluate $(2 + 4)^2$ by working within the parentheses first.

    b. Evaluate $2^2 + 4^2$.

    c. Compare the answers to parts (a) and (b) and make a conjecture about $(a + b)^2$ and $a^2 + b^2$.

80. a. Evaluate $(6 - 5)^2$ by working within the parentheses first.

    b. Evaluate $6^2 - 5^2$.

    c. Compare the answers to parts (a) and (b) and make a conjecture about $(a - b)^2$ and $a^2 - b^2$.

Concept 3: Applications to Geometry

81. Find a polynomial expression that represents the area of the rectangle shown in the figure.

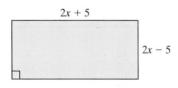

82. Find a polynomial expression that represents the area of the rectangle shown in the figure.

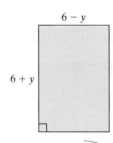

83. Find a polynomial expression that represents the area of the square shown in the figure.

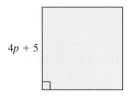

$4p + 5$

84. Find a polynomial expression that represents the area of the square shown in the figure.

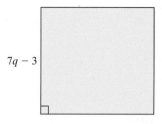

$7q - 3$

85. Find a polynomial that represents the volume of the cube shown in the figure. **(See Example 8.)**
(Recall: $V = s^3$)

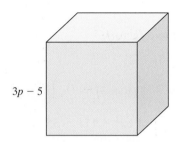

$3p - 5$

86. Find a polynomial that represents the volume of the rectangular solid shown in the figure.
(Recall: $V = lwh$)

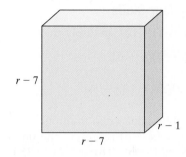

$r - 7$

$r - 1$

$r - 7$

87. Find a polynomial that represents the area of the triangle shown in the figure.
(Recall: $A = \frac{1}{2}bh$)

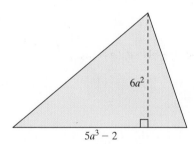

$6a^2$

$5a^3 - 2$

88. Find a polynomial that represents the area of the triangle shown in the figure.

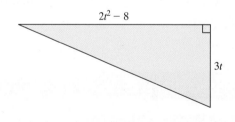

$2t^2 - 8$

$3t$

Mixed Exercises

For Exercises 89–118, multiply the expressions.

89. $(7x + y)(7x - y)$

90. $(9w - 4z)(9w + 4z)$

91. $(5s + 3t)^2$

92. $(5s - 3t)^2$

93. $(7x - 3y)(3x - 8y)$

94. $(5a - 4b)(2a - b)$

95. $\left(\frac{2}{3}t + 2\right)(3t + 4)$

96. $\left(\frac{1}{5}s + 6\right)(5s - 3)$

97. $-5(3x + 5)(2x - 1)$

98. $-4(2k - 5)(4k - 3)$

99. $(3a - 2)(5a + 1 + 2a^2)$

100. $(u + 4)(2 - 3u + u^2)$

101. $(y^2 + 2y + 4)(y - 5)$ **102.** $(w^2 - w + 6)(w + 2)$ **103.** $\left(\dfrac{1}{3}m - n\right)^2$

104. $\left(\dfrac{2}{5}p - q\right)^2$ **105.** $6w^2(7w - 14)$ **106.** $4v^3(v + 12)$

107. $(4y - 8.1)(4y + 8.1)$ **108.** $(2h + 2.7)(2h - 2.7)$ **109.** $(3c^2 + 4)(7c^2 - 8)$

110. $(5k^3 - 9)(k^3 - 2)$ **111.** $(3.1x + 4.5)^2$ **112.** $(2.5y + 1.1)^2$

113. $(k - 4)^3$ **114.** $(h + 3)^3$ **115.** $(5x + 3)^3$

116. $(2a - 4)^3$ **117.** $(y^2 + 2y + 1)(2y^2 - y + 3)$ **118.** $(2w^2 - w - 5)(3w^2 + 2w + 1)$

Expanding Your Skills

For Exercises 119–122, multiply the expressions containing more than two factors.

119. $2a(3a - 4)(a + 5)$ **120.** $5x(x + 2)(6x - 1)$

121. $(x - 3)(2x + 1)(x - 4)$ **122.** $(y - 2)(2y - 3)(y + 3)$

123. What binomial when multiplied by $(3x + 5)$ will produce a product of $6x^2 - 11x - 35$? [*Hint:* Let the quantity $(a + b)$ represent the unknown binomial. Then find a and b such that $(3x + 5)(a + b) = 6x^2 - 11x - 35$.]

124. What binomial when multiplied by $(2x - 4)$ will produce a product of $2x^2 + 8x - 24$?

For Exercises 125–127, determine what values of k would create a perfect square trinomial.

125. $x^2 + kx + 25$ **126.** $w^2 + kw + 9$ **127.** $a^2 + ka + 16$

Section 5.7   Division of Polynomials

Concepts

1. Division by a Monomial
2. Long Division

Division of polynomials will be presented in this section as two separate cases: The first case illustrates division by a monomial divisor. The second case illustrates long division by a polynomial with two or more terms.

1. Division by a Monomial

To divide a polynomial by a monomial, divide each individual term in the polynomial by the divisor and simplify the result.

> **Dividing a Polynomial by a Monomial**
> If a, b, and c are polynomials such that $c \neq 0$, then
>
> $$\frac{a + b}{c} = \frac{a}{c} + \frac{b}{c} \qquad \text{Similarly,} \qquad \frac{a - b}{c} = \frac{a}{c} - \frac{b}{c}$$

Example 1 Dividing a Polynomial by a Monomial

Divide the polynomials.

a. $\dfrac{5a^3 - 10a^2 + 20a}{5a}$ **b.** $(12y^2z^3 - 15yz^2 + 6y^2z) \div (-6y^2z)$

Solution:

a. $\dfrac{5a^3 - 10a^2 + 20a}{5a}$

$= \dfrac{5a^3}{5a} - \dfrac{10a^2}{5a} + \dfrac{20a}{5a}$ Divide each term in the numerator by $5a$.

$= a^2 - 2a + 4$ Simplify each term using the properties of exponents.

b. $(12y^2z^3 - 15yz^2 + 6y^2z) \div (-6y^2z)$

$= \dfrac{12y^2z^3 - 15yz^2 + 6y^2z}{-6y^2z}$

$= \dfrac{12y^2z^3}{-6y^2z} - \dfrac{15yz^2}{-6y^2z} + \dfrac{6y^2z}{-6y^2z}$ Divide each term by $-6y^2z$.

$= -2z^2 + \dfrac{5z}{2y} - 1$ Simplify each term.

Skill Practice

Divide the polynomials.
1. $(36a^4 - 48a^3 + 12a^2) \div (6a^3)$

2. $\dfrac{-15x^3y^4 + 25x^2y^3 - 5xy^2}{-5xy^2}$

2. Long Division

If the divisor has two or more terms, a *long division* process similar to the division of real numbers is used. Take a minute to review the long division process for real numbers by dividing 2273 by 5.

$$
\begin{array}{r}
454 \leftarrow \text{Quotient} \\
5\overline{)2273} \\
-20 \\
\hline
27 \\
-25 \\
\hline
23 \\
-20 \\
\hline
3 \leftarrow \text{Remainder}
\end{array}
$$

Therefore, $2273 \div 5 = 454\frac{3}{5}$

A similar procedure is used for long division of polynomials as shown in Example 2.

Answers

1. $6a - 8 + \dfrac{2}{a}$

2. $3x^2y^2 - 5xy + 1$

Example 2 Using Long Division to Divide Polynomials

Divide the polynomials using long division. $(2x^2 - x + 3) \div (x - 3)$

Solution:

$x - 3\overline{)2x^2 - x + 3}$ Divide the leading term in the dividend by the leading term in the divisor.

$$\frac{2x^2}{x} = 2x$$

This is the first term in the quotient.

$$
\begin{array}{r}
2x \\
x - 3\overline{)2x^2 - x + 3} \\
-(2x^2 - 6x)
\end{array}
$$
Multiply $2x$ by the divisor $2x(x - 3) = 2x^2 - 6x$ and subtract the result.

$$
\begin{array}{r}
2x \\
x - 3\overline{)2x^2 - x + 3} \\
-2x^2 + 6x \\
\hline
5x
\end{array}
$$
Subtract the quantity $2x^2 - 6x$. To do this, add the opposite.

$$
\begin{array}{r}
2x + 5 \\
x - 3\overline{)2x^2 - x + 3} \\
-2x^2 + 6x \downarrow \\
\hline
5x + 3
\end{array}
$$
Bring down the next column, and repeat the process.
Divide the leading term by x: $(5x)/x = 5$.
Place 5 in the quotient.

$$
\begin{array}{r}
2x + 5 \\
x - 3\overline{)2x^2 - x + 3} \\
-2x^2 + 6x \\
\hline
5x + 3 \\
-(5x - 15)
\end{array}
$$
Multiply the divisor by 5: $5(x - 3) = 5x - 15$ and subtract the result.

$$
\begin{array}{r}
2x + 5 \\
x - 3\overline{)2x^2 - x + 3} \\
-2x^2 + 6x \\
\hline
5x + 3 \\
-5x + 15 \\
\hline
18
\end{array}
$$
Subtract the quantity $5x - 15$ by adding the opposite.
The remainder is 18.

Summary:

The quotient is	$2x + 5$
The remainder is	18
The divisor is	$x - 3$
The dividend is	$2x^2 - x + 3$

The solution to a long division problem is usually written in the form:

$$\text{quotient} + \frac{\text{remainder}}{\text{divisor}}$$

Hence

$$(2x^2 - x + 3) \div (x - 3) = 2x + 5 + \frac{18}{x - 3}$$

The division of polynomials can be checked in the same fashion as the division of real numbers. To check Example 2, we use the **division algorithm**:

$$\text{Dividend} = (\text{divisor})(\text{quotient}) + \text{remainder}$$

$$2x^2 - x + 3 \stackrel{?}{=} (x - 3)(2x + 5) + (18)$$

$$\stackrel{?}{=} 2x^2 + 5x - 6x - 15 + (18)$$

$$= 2x^2 - x + 3 \ ✔$$

Example 3   Using Long Division to Divide Polynomials

Divide the polynomials using long division: $(2w^3 + 8w^2 - 16) \div (2w + 4)$

Solution:

First note that the dividend has a missing power of w and can be written as $2w^3 + 8w^2 + 0w - 16$. The term $0w$ is a place holder for the missing term. It is helpful to use the place holder to keep the powers of w lined up.

$$\begin{array}{r} w^2 \\ 2w + 4\overline{)2w^3 + 8w^2 + 0w - 16} \\ -(2w^3 + 4w^2) \end{array}$$

Divide $2w^3 \div 2w = w^2$. This is the first term of the quotient.
Then multiply $w^2(2w + 4) = 2w^3 + 4w^2$.

$$\begin{array}{r} w^2 \\ 2w + 4\overline{)2w^3 + 8w^2 + 0w - 16} \\ -2w^3 - 4w^2 \\ \hline 4w^2 + 0w \end{array}$$

Subtract by adding the opposite.

Bring down the next column, and repeat the process.

$$\begin{array}{r} w^2 + 2w \\ 2w + 4\overline{)2w^3 + 8w^2 + 0w - 16} \\ -2w^3 - 4w^2 \\ \hline 4w^2 + 0w \\ -(4w^2 + 8w) \end{array}$$

Divide $4w^2$ by the leading term in the divisor. $4w^2 \div 2w = 2w$. Place $2w$ in the quotient.
Multiply $2w(2w + 4) = 4w^2 + 8w$.

$$\begin{array}{r} w^2 + 2w \\ 2w + 4\overline{)2w^3 + 8w^2 + 0w - 16} \\ -2w^3 - 4w^2 \\ \hline 4w^2 + 0w \\ -4w^2 - 8w \\ \hline -8w - 16 \end{array}$$

Subtract by adding the opposite.

Bring down the next column and repeat.

$$\begin{array}{r} w^2 + 2w - 4 \\ 2w + 4\overline{)2w^3 + 8w^2 + 0w - 16} \\ -2w^3 - 4w^2 \\ \hline 4w^2 + 0w \\ -4w^2 - 8w \\ \hline -8w - 16 \\ -(-8w - 16) \end{array}$$

Divide $-8w$ by the leading term in the divisor. $-8w \div 2w = -4$. Place -4 in the quotient.
Multiply $-4(2w + 4) = -8w - 16$.

$$\begin{array}{r} w^2 + 2w - 4 \\ 2w + 4\overline{)2w^3 + 8w^2 + 0w - 16} \\ -2w^3 - 4w^2 \\ \hline 4w^2 + 0w \\ -4w^2 - 8w \\ \hline -8w - 16 \\ 8w + 16 \\ \hline 0 \end{array}$$

Subtract by adding the opposite.

The remainder is 0.

The quotient is $w^2 + 2w - 4$, and the remainder is 0.

Answer

4. $3x^2 - 2x + 5$

In Example 3, the remainder is zero. Therefore, we say that $2w + 4$ divides *evenly* into $2w^3 + 8w^2 - 16$. For this reason, the divisor and quotient are factors of $2w^3 + 8w^2 - 16$. To check, we have

$$\text{Dividend} = (\text{divisor})(\text{quotient}) + \text{remainder}$$

$$2w^3 + 8w^2 - 16 \overset{?}{=} (2w + 4)(w^2 + 2w - 4) + 0$$

$$\overset{?}{=} 2w^3 + 4w^2 - 8w + 4w^2 + 8w - 16$$

$$= 2w^3 + 8w^2 - 16 ✔$$

Skill Practice

Divide the polynomials using long division.

5. $(4 - x^2 + x^3) \div (2 + x^2)$

Example 4   Using Long Division to Divide Polynomials

Divide the polynomials using long division.

$$\frac{2y + y^4 - 5}{1 + y^2}$$

Solution:

First note that both the dividend and divisor should be written in descending order:

$$\frac{y^4 + 2y - 5}{y^2 + 1}$$

Also note that the dividend and the divisor have missing powers of y. Use place holders.

$$y^2 + 0y + 1 \overline{)y^4 + 0y^3 + 0y^2 + 2y - 5}$$

$$y^2 + 0y + 1 \overline{)\begin{array}{c} y^2 \\ y^4 + 0y^3 + 0y^2 + 2y - 5 \\ -(y^4 + 0y^3 + y^2) \end{array}}$$

Divide $y^4 \div y^2 = y^2$. This is the first term of the quotient.

Multiply $y^2(y^2 + 0y + 1) = y^4 + 0y^3 + y^2$.

$$y^2 + 0y + 1 \overline{)\begin{array}{c} y^2 \\ y^4 + 0y^3 + 0y^2 + 2y - 5 \\ \underline{-y^4 - 0y^3 - y^2} \\ -y^2 + 2y - 5 \end{array}}$$

Subtract by adding the opposite.

Bring down the next columns.

$$y^2 + 0y + 1 \overline{)\begin{array}{c} y^2 \qquad -1 \\ y^4 + 0y^3 + 0y^2 + 2y - 5 \\ \underline{-y^4 - 0y^3 - y^2} \\ -y^2 + 2y - 5 \\ -(-y^2 - 0y - 1) \end{array}}$$

Divide $-y^2 \div y^2 = -1$.

Multiply $-1(y^2 + 0y + 1) = -y^2 - 0y - 1$.

$$y^2 + 0y + 1 \overline{)\begin{array}{c} y^2 \qquad -1 \\ y^4 + 0y^3 + 0y^2 + 2y - 5 \\ \underline{-y^4 - 0y^3 - y^2} \\ -y^2 + 2y - 5 \\ \underline{y^2 + 0y + 1} \\ 2y - 4 \end{array}}$$

Subtract by adding the opposite.

Remainder

Answer

5. $x - 1 + \dfrac{-2x + 6}{x^2 + 2}$

Therefore, $\dfrac{y^4 + 2y - 5}{y^2 + 1} = y^2 - 1 + \dfrac{2y - 4}{y^2 + 1}$

Example 5 Determining Whether Long Division Is Necessary

Determine whether long division is necessary for each division of polynomials.

a. $\dfrac{2p^5 - 8p^4 + 4p - 16}{p^2 - 2p + 1}$

b. $\dfrac{2p^5 - 8p^4 + 4p - 16}{2p^2}$

c. $(3z^3 - 5z^2 + 10) \div (15z^3)$

d. $(3z^3 - 5z^2 + 10) \div (3z + 1)$

Solution:

a. $\dfrac{2p^5 - 8p^4 + 4p - 16}{p^2 - 2p + 1}$ The divisor has three terms. Use long division.

b. $\dfrac{2p^5 - 8p^4 + 4p - 16}{2p^2}$ The divisor has one term. No long division.

c. $(3z^3 - 5z^2 + 10) \div (15z^3)$ The divisor has one term. No long division.

d. $(3z^3 - 5z^2 + 10) \div (3z + 1)$ The divisor has two terms. Use long division.

TIP: Recall that
- Long division is used when the divisor has *two or more terms*.
- If the divisor has *one term*, then divide each term in the dividend by the monomial divisor.

Skill Practice

Divide the polynomials using the appropriate method of division.

6. $\dfrac{6x^3 - x^2 + 3x - 5}{2x + 3}$

7. $\dfrac{9w^3 - 18w^2 + 6w + 12}{3w}$

Answers

6. $3x^2 - 5x + 9 + \dfrac{-32}{2x + 3}$

7. $3w^2 - 6w + 2 + \dfrac{4}{w}$

Section 5.7 Practice Exercises

Vocabulary and Key Concepts

1. The _____ algorithm states that: Dividend = (divisor)(_____) + (_____)

Review Exercises

For Exercises 2–11, perform the indicated operations.

2. $(7a^2 + a - 6) + (2a^2 + 5a + 11)$

3. $(6z^5 - 2z^3 + z - 6) - (10z^4 + 2z^3 + z^2 + z)$

4. $8b^2(2b^2 - 5b + 12)$

5. $(10x + y)(x - 3y)$

6. $(2w^3 + 5)^2$

7. $(10x + y) + (x - 3y)$

8. $\left(\dfrac{7}{8}w - 1\right)\left(\dfrac{7}{8}w + 1\right)$

9. $\left(\dfrac{4}{3}y^2 - \dfrac{1}{2}y + \dfrac{3}{8}\right) - \left(\dfrac{1}{3}y^2 + \dfrac{1}{4}y - \dfrac{1}{8}\right)$

10. $(2x + 1)(5x - 3)$

11. $(a + 3)(a^2 - 3a + 9)$

Concept 1: Division by a Monomial

12. There are two methods for dividing polynomials. Explain when long division is used.

13. a. Divide: $\dfrac{15t^3 + 18t^2}{3t}$

    b. Check by multiplying the quotient by the divisor.

14. a. Divide: $(-9y^4 + 6y^2 - y) \div (3y)$

    b. Check by multiplying the quotient by the divisor.

For Exercises 15–30, divide the polynomials. **(See Example 1.)**

15. $(6a^2 + 4a - 14) \div (2)$

16. $\dfrac{4b^2 + 16b - 12}{4}$

17. $\dfrac{-5x^2 - 20x + 5}{-5}$

18. $\dfrac{-3y^3 + 12y - 6}{-3}$

19. $\dfrac{3p^3 - p^2}{p}$

20. $(7q^4 + 5q^2) \div q$

21. $(4m^2 + 8m) \div 4m^2$

22. $\dfrac{n^2 - 8}{n}$

23. $\dfrac{14y^4 - 7y^3 + 21y^2}{-7y^2}$

24. $(25a^5 - 5a^4 + 15a^3 - 5a) \div (-5a)$

25. $(4x^3 - 24x^2 - x + 8) \div (4x)$

26. $\dfrac{20w^3 + 15w^2 - w + 5}{10w}$

27. $\dfrac{-a^3b^2 + a^2b^2 - ab^3}{-a^2b^2}$

28. $(3x^4y^3 - x^2y^2 - xy^3) \div (-x^2y^2)$

29. $(6t^4 - 2t^3 + 3t^2 - t + 4) \div (2t^3)$

30. $\dfrac{2y^3 - 2y^2 + 3y - 9}{2y^2}$

Concept 2: Long Division

31. a. Divide $(z^2 + 7z + 11) \div (z + 5)$

    b. Check by multiplying the quotient by the divisor and adding the remainder.

32. a. Divide $\dfrac{2w^2 - 7w + 3}{w - 4}$

    b. Check by multiplying the quotient by the divisor and adding the remainder.

For Exercises 33–58, divide the polynomials. **(See Examples 2–4.)**

33. $\dfrac{t^2 + 4t + 5}{t + 1}$

34. $(3x^2 + 8x + 5) \div (x + 2)$

35. $(7b^2 - 3b - 4) \div (b - 1)$

36. $\dfrac{w^2 - w - 2}{w - 2}$

37. $\dfrac{5k^2 - 29k - 6}{5k + 1}$

38. $(4y^2 + 25y - 21) \div (4y - 3)$

39. $(4p^3 + 12p^2 + p - 12) \div (2p + 3)$

40. $\dfrac{12a^3 - 2a^2 - 17a - 5}{3a + 1}$

41. $\dfrac{-k - 6 + k^2}{1 + k}$

42. $(1 + h^2 + 3h) \div (2 + h)$

43. $(4x^3 - 8x^2 + 15x - 16) \div (2x - 3)$

44. $\dfrac{3b^3 + b^2 + 17b - 49}{3b - 5}$

45. $\dfrac{3y^3 + 5y^2 + y + 1}{3y - 1}$

46. $\dfrac{4t^3 + 4t^2 - 9t + 3}{2t + 3}$

47. $\dfrac{9 + a^2}{a + 3}$

48. $(3 + m^2) \div (m + 3)$

49. $(4x^3 - 3x - 26) \div (x - 2)$

50. $(4y^3 + y + 1) \div (2y + 1)$

51. $(w^4 + 5w^3 - 5w^2 - 15w + 7) \div (w^2 - 3)$

52. $\dfrac{p^4 - p^3 - 4p^2 - 2p - 15}{p^2 + 2}$

53. $\dfrac{2n^4 + 5n^3 - 11n^2 - 20n + 12}{2n^2 + 3n - 2}$

54. $(6y^4 - 5y^3 - 8y^2 + 16y - 8) \div (2y^2 - 3y + 2)$

55. $(5x^3 - 4x - 9) \div (5x^2 + 5x + 1)$

56. $\dfrac{3a^3 - 5a + 16}{3a^2 - 6a + 7}$

57. $\dfrac{3y^4 + 2y + 3}{y^2 + 1}$

58. $\dfrac{2x^4 + 6x + 4}{x^2 + 2}$

59. Show that $(x^3 - 8) \div (x - 2)$ is *not* $(x^2 + 4)$.

60. Explain why $(y^3 + 27) \div (y + 3)$ is *not* $(y^2 + 9)$.

Mixed Exercises

For Exercises 61–72, determine which method to use to divide the polynomials: monomial division or long division. Then use that method to divide the polynomials. **(See Example 5.)**

61. $\dfrac{9a^3 + 12a^2}{3a}$

62. $\dfrac{3y^2 + 17y - 12}{y + 6}$

63. $(p^3 + p^2 - 4p - 4) \div (p^2 - p - 2)$

64. $(q^3 + 1) \div (q + 1)$

65. $\dfrac{t^4 + t^2 - 16}{t + 2}$

66. $\dfrac{-8m^5 - 4m^3 + 4m^2}{-2m^2}$

67. $(w^4 + w^2 - 5) \div (w^2 - 2)$

68. $(2k^2 + 9k + 7) \div (k + 1)$

69. $\dfrac{n^3 - 64}{n - 4}$

70. $\dfrac{15s^2 + 34s + 28}{5s + 3}$

71. $(9r^3 - 12r^2 + 9) \div (-3r^2)$

72. $(6x^4 - 16x^3 + 15x^2 - 5x + 10) \div (3x + 1)$

Expanding Your Skills

For Exercises 73–80, divide the polynomials and note any patterns.

73. $(x^2 - 1) \div (x - 1)$

74. $(x^3 - 1) \div (x - 1)$

75. $(x^4 - 1) \div (x - 1)$

76. $(x^5 - 1) \div (x - 1)$

77. $x^2 \div (x - 1)$

78. $x^3 \div (x - 1)$

79. $x^4 \div (x - 1)$

80. $x^5 \div (x - 1)$

Problem Recognition Exercises

Operations on Polynomials

For Exercises 1–40, perform the indicated operations and simplify.

1. a. $6x^2 + 2x^2$
  b. $(6x^2)(2x^2)$

2. a. $8y^3 + y^3$
  b. $(8y^3)(y^3)$

3. a. $(4x + y)^2$
  b. $(4xy)^2$

4. a. $(2a + b)^2$
  b. $(2ab)^2$

5. a. $(2x + 3) + (4x - 2)$
  b. $(2x + 3)(4x - 2)$

6. a. $(5m^2 + 1) + (m^2 + m)$
  b. $(5m^2 + 1)(m^2 + m)$

7. a. $(3z + 2)^2$
  b. $(3z + 2)(3z - 2)$

8. a. $(6y - 7)^2$
  b. $(6y - 7)(6y + 7)$

9. a. $(2x - 4)(x^2 - 2x + 3)$
  b. $(2x - 4) + (x^2 - 2x + 3)$

10. a. $(3y^2 + 8)(-y^2 - 4)$
  b. $(3y^2 + 8) - (-y^2 - 4)$

11. a. $x + x$
  b. $x \cdot x$

12. a. $2c + 2c$
  b. $2c \cdot 2c$

13. $(4xy)^2$

14. $(2ab)^2$

15. $(-2x^4 - 6x^3 + 8x^2) \div (2x^2)$

16. $(-15m^3 + 12m^2 - 3m) \div (-3m)$

17. $(m^3 - 4m^2 - 6) - (3m^2 + 7m) + (-m^3 - 9m + 6)$

18. $(n^4 + 2n^2 - 3n) + (4n^2 + 2n - 1) - (4n^5 + 6n - 3)$

19. $(8x^3 + 2x + 6) \div (x - 2)$

20. $(-4x^3 + 2x^2 - 5) \div (x - 3)$

21. $(2x - y)(3x^2 + 4xy - y^2)$

22. $(3a + b)(2a^2 - ab + 2b^2)$

23. $(x + y^2)(x^2 - xy^2 + y^4)$

24. $(m^2 + 1)(m^4 - m^2 + 1)$

25. $(a^2 + 2b) - (a^2 - 2b)$ **26.** $(y^3 - 6z) - (y^3 + 6z)$

27. $(a^3 + 2b)(a^3 - 2b)$

28. $(y^3 - 6z)(y^3 + 6z)$

29. $\dfrac{8p^2 + 4p - 6}{2p - 1}$

30. $\dfrac{4v^2 - 8v + 8}{2v + 3}$

31. $\dfrac{12x^3y^7}{3xy^5}$

32. $\dfrac{-18p^2q^4}{2pq^3}$

33. $\left(\dfrac{3}{7}x - \dfrac{1}{2}\right)\left(\dfrac{3}{7}x + \dfrac{1}{2}\right)$ **34.** $\left(\dfrac{2}{5}y + \dfrac{4}{3}\right)\left(\dfrac{2}{5}y - \dfrac{4}{3}\right)$

35. $\left(\dfrac{1}{9}x^3 + \dfrac{2}{3}x^2 + \dfrac{1}{6}x - 3\right) - \left(\dfrac{4}{3}x^3 + \dfrac{1}{9}x^2 + \dfrac{2}{3}x + 1\right)$

36. $\left(\dfrac{1}{10}y^2 - \dfrac{3}{5}y - \dfrac{1}{15}\right) - \left(\dfrac{7}{5}y^2 + \dfrac{3}{10}y - \dfrac{1}{3}\right)$

37. $(0.05x^2 - 0.16x - 0.75) + (1.25x^2 - 0.14x + 0.25)$

38. $(1.6w^3 + 2.8w + 6.1) + (3.4w^3 - 4.1w^2 - 7.3)$

39. $(3x^2y)(-2xy^5)$

40. $(10ab^4)(5a^3b^2)$

Group Activity

The Pythagorean Theorem and a Geometric "Proof"

Estimated Time: 25–30 minutes

Group Size: 2

Right triangles occur in many applications of mathematics. By definition, a right triangle is a triangle that contains a 90° angle. The two shorter sides in a right triangle are referred to as the "legs," and the longest side is called the "hypotenuse." In the triangle, the legs are labeled as a and b, and the hypotenuse is labeled as c.

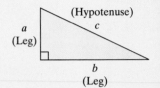

   Right triangles have an important property that the sum of the squares of the two legs of a right triangle equals the square of the hypotenuse. This fact is referred to as the Pythagorean theorem. In symbols, the Pythagorean theorem is stated as:

$$a^2 + b^2 = c^2$$

1. The following triangles are right triangles. Verify that $a^2 + b^2 = c^2$. (The units may be left off when performing these calculations.)

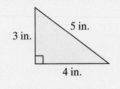

$a = 3$

$b = 4$

$c = 5$

$a^2 + b^2 = c^2$

$(3)^2 + (4)^2 \overset{?}{=} (5)^2$

$9 + 16 = 25$ ✔

$a = \underline{\hspace{1cm}}$

$b = \underline{\hspace{1cm}}$

$c = \underline{\hspace{1cm}}$

$a^2 + b^2 = c^2$

$(\underline{\hspace{0.5cm}})^2 + (\underline{\hspace{0.5cm}})^2 \overset{?}{=} (\underline{\hspace{0.5cm}})^2$

$\underline{\hspace{0.5cm}} + \underline{\hspace{0.5cm}} = \underline{\hspace{0.5cm}}$ ✔

2. The following geometric "proof" of the Pythagorean theorem uses addition, subtraction, and multiplication of polynomials. Consider the square figure. The length of each side of the large outer square is $(a + b)$. Therefore, the area of the large outer square is $(a + b)^2$.

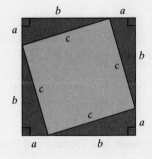

   The area of the large outer square can also be found by adding the area of the inner square (pictured in light gray) plus the area of the four right triangles (pictured in dark gray).

Area of inner square: c^2 Area of the four right triangles: $4 \cdot (\frac{1}{2}\, a\, b)$

½ Base · Height

3. Now equate the two expressions representing the area of the large outer square:

$$\left(\begin{array}{c}\text{Area of outer} \\ \text{square}\end{array}\right) = \left(\begin{array}{c}\text{area of inner} \\ \text{square}\end{array}\right) + \left(\begin{array}{c}\text{4 times the area} \\ \text{of the right triangles}\end{array}\right)$$

$\underline{\hspace{2cm}} = \underline{\hspace{2cm}} + \underline{\hspace{2.5cm}}$

$\underline{\hspace{2cm}} = \underline{\hspace{2cm}} + \underline{\hspace{2.5cm}}$ ←——Clear parentheses on both sides of the equation.

$\underline{\hspace{2cm}} = \underline{\hspace{2cm}}$ ←——Subtract $2ab$ from both sides.

Chapter 5   Summary

Section 5.1   Multiplying and Dividing Expressions with Common Bases

Key Concepts	**Examples**

Definition

$b^n = \underbrace{b \cdot b \cdot b \cdot b \cdot \ldots b}_{n \text{ factors of } b}$ b is the base, n is the exponent

Example 1

$3^4 = 3 \cdot 3 \cdot 3 \cdot 3 = 81$ 3 is the base

                                                   4 is the exponent

Example 2

Compare: $(-5)^2$ versus -5^2

versus
$$(-5)^2 = (-5)(-5) = 25$$
$$-5^2 = -1(5^2) = -1(5)(5) = -25$$

Multiplying Expressions with Like Bases

$b^m b^n = b^{m+n}$ (m, n positive integers)

Example 3

Simplify: $x^3 \cdot x^4 \cdot x^2 \cdot x = x^{10}$

Dividing Expressions with Like Bases

$\dfrac{b^m}{b^n} = b^{m-n}$ ($b \neq 0, m, n,$ positive integers)

Example 4

Simplify: $\dfrac{c^4 d^{10}}{cd^5} = c^{4-1}d^{10-5} = c^3 d^5$

Section 5.2   More Properties of Exponents

Key Concepts	**Examples**

Power Rule for Exponents

$(b^m)^n = b^{mn}$ ($b \neq 0, m, n$ positive integers)

Example 1

Simplify: $(x^4)^5 = x^{20}$

Power of a Product and Power of a Quotient

Assume m and n are positive integers and a and b are real numbers where $b \neq 0$.
Then,

$(ab)^m = a^m b^m$ and $\left(\dfrac{a}{b}\right)^m = \dfrac{a^m}{b^m}$

Example 2

Simplify: $(4uv^2)^3 = 4^3 u^3 (v^2)^3 = 64u^3 v^6$

Example 3

Simplify: $\left(\dfrac{p^5 q^3}{5pq^2}\right)^2 = \left(\dfrac{p^{5-1}q^{3-2}}{5}\right)^2 = \left(\dfrac{p^4 q}{5}\right)^2$

$$= \dfrac{p^8 q^2}{25}$$

Section 5.3   Definitions of b^0 and b^{-n}

Key Concepts

Definitions

If b is a nonzero real number and n is an integer, then:

1. $b^0 = 1$

2. $b^{-n} = \left(\dfrac{1}{b}\right)^n = \dfrac{1}{b^n}$

Examples

Example 1

Simplify: $4^0 = 1$

Example 2

Simplify: $y^{-7} = \dfrac{1}{y^7}$

Example 3

Simplify: $\dfrac{8a^0b^{-2}}{c^{-5}d}$

$$= \dfrac{8(1)c^5}{b^2d} = \dfrac{8c^5}{b^2d}$$

Section 5.4   Scientific Notation

Key Concepts

A positive number written in **scientific notation** is expressed in the form:

$a \times 10^n$ where $1 \le a < 10$ and n is an integer.

Examples

Example 1

Write the numbers in scientific notation:

$35{,}000 = 3.5 \times 10^4$

$0.000\ 000\ 548 = 5.48 \times 10^{-7}$

Example 2

Multiply: $(3.5 \times 10^4)(2 \times 10^{-6})$

$$= 7 \times 10^{-2}$$

Example 3

Divide: $\dfrac{8.4 \times 10^{-9}}{2.1 \times 10^3} = 4 \times 10^{-9-3} = 4 \times 10^{-12}$

Section 5.5 Addition and Subtraction of Polynomials

Key Concepts

A **polynomial** in one variable is a sum of terms of the form ax^n, where a is a real number and the exponent, n, is a nonnegative integer. For each term, a is called the **coefficient** of the term and n is the **degree of the term**. For a polynomial written in **descending order**, the term with highest degree is the **leading term**, and its coefficient is called the **leading coefficient**. The **degree of the polynomial** is the largest degree of all its terms.

To add or subtract polynomials, add or subtract *like* terms.

Examples

Example 1

Given: $4x^5 - 8x^3 + 9x - 5$

Coefficients of each term: $4, -8, 9, -5$

Degree of each term: $\quad\quad 5, 3, 1, 0$

Leading term: $\quad\quad\quad\quad 4x^5$

Leading coefficient: $\quad\quad 4$

Degree of polynomial: $\quad 5$

Example 2

Perform the indicated operations:

$$(2x^4 - 5x^3 + 1) - (x^4 + 3) + (x^3 - 4x - 7)$$
$$= 2x^4 - 5x^3 + 1 - x^4 - 3 + x^3 - 4x - 7$$
$$= 2x^4 - x^4 - 5x^3 + x^3 - 4x + 1 - 3 - 7$$
$$= x^4 - 4x^3 - 4x - 9$$

Section 5.6 Multiplication of Polynomials and Special Products

Key Concepts

Multiplying Monomials

Use the commutative and associative properties of multiplication to group coefficients and like bases.

Multiplying Polynomials

Multiply each term in the first polynomial by each term in the second polynomial.

Product of Conjugates

Results in a **difference of squares**

$$(a + b)(a - b) = a^2 - b^2$$

Square of a Binomial

Results in a **perfect square trinomial**

$$(a + b)^2 = a^2 + 2ab + b^2$$
$$(a - b)^2 = a^2 - 2ab + b^2$$

Examples

Example 1

Multiply: $(5a^2b)(-2ab^3)$

$$= (5 \cdot -2)(a^2a)(bb^3)$$
$$= -10a^3b^4$$

Example 2

Multiply: $(x - 2)(3x^2 - 4x + 11)$

$$= 3x^3 - 4x^2 + 11x - 6x^2 + 8x - 22$$
$$= 3x^3 - 10x^2 + 19x - 22$$

Example 3

Multiply: $(3w - 4v)(3w + 4v)$

$$= (3w)^2 - (4v)^2$$
$$= 9w^2 - 16v^2$$

Example 4

Multiply: $(5c - 8d)^2$

$$= (5c)^2 - 2(5c)(8d) + (8d)^2$$
$$= 25c^2 - 80cd + 64d^2$$

Section 5.7   Division of Polynomials

Key Concepts

Division of Polynomials

1. Division by a monomial, use the properties:

$$\frac{a + b}{c} = \frac{a}{c} + \frac{b}{c} \quad \text{and} \quad \frac{a - b}{c} = \frac{a}{c} - \frac{b}{c}$$

2. If the divisor has more than one term, use long division.

Examples

Example 1

Divide: $\dfrac{-3x^2 - 6x + 9}{-3x}$

$$= \frac{-3x^2}{-3x} - \frac{6x}{-3x} + \frac{9}{-3x}$$

$$= x + 2 - \frac{3}{x}$$

Example 2

Divide: $(3x^2 - 5x + 1) \div (x + 2)$

$$\begin{array}{r} 3x - 11 \\ x + 2 \overline{) 3x^2 - 5x + 1} \\ -(3x^2 + 6x) \\ \hline -11x + 1 \\ -(-11x - 22) \\ \hline 23 \end{array}$$

$$3x - 11 + \frac{23}{x + 2}$$

Chapter 5   Review Exercises

Section 5.1

For Exercises 1–4, identify the base and the exponent.

1. 5^3 **2.** x^4 **3.** $(-2)^0$ **4.** y

5. Evaluate the expressions.

    a. 6^2 **b.** $(-6)^2$ **c.** -6^2

6. Evaluate the expressions.

    a. 4^3 **b.** $(-4)^3$ **c.** -4^3

For Exercises 7–18, simplify and write the answers in exponent form. Assume that all variables represent nonzero real numbers.

7. $5^3 \cdot 5^{10}$ **8.** $a^7 a^4$

9. $x \cdot x^6 \cdot x^2$ **10.** $6^3 \cdot 6 \cdot 6^5$

11. $\dfrac{10^7}{10^4}$ **12.** $\dfrac{y^{14}}{y^8}$

13. $\dfrac{b^9}{b}$ **14.** $\dfrac{7^8}{7}$

15. $\dfrac{k^2 k^3}{k^4}$ **16.** $\dfrac{8^4 \cdot 8^7}{8^{11}}$

17. $\dfrac{2^8 \cdot 2^{10}}{2^3 \cdot 2^7}$ **18.** $\dfrac{q^3 q^{12}}{q q^8}$

19. Explain why $2^2 \cdot 4^4$ does *not* equal 8^6.

20. Explain why $\frac{10^5}{5^2}$ does *not* equal 2^3.

For Exercises 21 and 22, use the formula

$$A = P(1 + r)^t$$

21. Find the amount in an account after 3 yr if the initial investment is \$6000, invested at 6% interest compounded annually.

22. Find the amount in an account after 2 yr if the initial investment is \$20,000, invested at 5% interest compounded annually.

Section 5.2

For Exercises 23–40, simplify the expressions. Write the answers in exponent form. Assume all variables represent nonzero real numbers.

23. $(7^3)^4$

24. $(c^2)^6$

25. $(p^4p^2)^3$

26. $(9^5 \cdot 9^2)^4$

27. $\left(\dfrac{a}{b}\right)^2$

28. $\left(\dfrac{1}{3}\right)^4$

29. $\left(\dfrac{5}{c^2d^5}\right)^2$

30. $\left(-\dfrac{m^2}{4n^6}\right)^5$

31. $(2ab^2)^4$

32. $(-x^7y)^2$

33. $\left(\dfrac{-3x^3}{5y^2z}\right)^3$

34. $\left(\dfrac{r^3}{s^2t^6}\right)^5$

35. $\dfrac{a^4(a^2)^8}{(a^3)^3}$

36. $\dfrac{(8^3)^4 \cdot 8^{10}}{(8^4)^5}$

37. $\dfrac{(4h^2k)^2(h^3k)^4}{(2hk^3)^2}$

38. $\dfrac{(p^3q)^3(2p^2q^4)^4}{(8p)(pq^3)^2}$

39. $\left(\dfrac{2x^4y^3}{4xy^2}\right)^2$

40. $\left(\dfrac{a^4b^6}{ab^4}\right)^3$

Section 5.3

For Exercises 41–62, simplify the expressions. Write the answers with positive exponents. Assume all variables represent nonzero real numbers.

41. 8^0

42. $(-b)^0$

43. $-x^0$

44. 1^0

45. $2y^0$

46. $(2y)^0$

47. z^{-5}

48. 10^{-4}

49. $(6a)^{-2}$

50. $6a^{-2}$

51. $4^0 + 4^{-2}$

52. $9^{-1} + 9^0$

53. $t^{-6}t^{-2}$

54. r^8r^{-9}

55. $\dfrac{12x^{-2}y^3}{6x^4y^{-4}}$

56. $\dfrac{8ab^{-3}c^0}{10a^{-5}b^{-4}c^{-1}}$

57. $(-2m^2n^{-4})^{-4}$

58. $(3u^{-5}v^2)^{-3}$

59. $\dfrac{(k^{-6})^{-2}(k^3)}{5k^{-6}k^0}$

60. $\dfrac{(3h)^{-2}(h^{-5})^{-3}}{h^{-4}h^8}$

61. $2 \cdot 3^{-1} - 6^{-1}$

62. $2^{-1} - 2^{-2} + 2^0$

Section 5.4

63. Write the numbers in scientific notation.

  a. In a recent year there were 97,400,000 packages of M&Ms sold in the United States.

  b. The thickness of a piece of paper is 0.0042 in.

64. Write the numbers in standard form.

  a. A pH of 10 means the hydrogen ion concentration is 1×10^{-10} units.

  b. A fund-raising event for neurospinal research raised 2.56×10^5.

For Exercises 65–68, perform the indicated operations. Write the answers in scientific notation.

65. $(4.1 \times 10^{-6})(2.3 \times 10^{11})$

66. $\dfrac{9.3 \times 10^3}{6.0 \times 10^{-7}}$

67. $\dfrac{2000}{0.000008}$

68. $(0.000078)(21,000,000)$

69. Use your calculator to evaluate 5^{20}. Why is scientific notation necessary on your calculator to express the answer?

70. Use your calculator to evaluate $(0.4)^{30}$. Why is scientific notation necessary on your calculator to express the answer?

71. The average distance between the Earth and Sun is 9.3×10^7 mi.

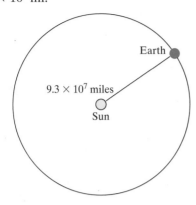

a. If the Earth's orbit is approximated by a circle, find the total distance the Earth travels around the Sun in one orbit. (*Hint:* The circumference of a circle is given by $C = 2\pi r$.) Express the answer in scientific notation.

b. If the Earth makes one complete trip around the Sun in 1 yr (365 days = 8.76×10^3 hr), find the average speed that the Earth travels around the Sun in miles per hour. Express the answer in scientific notation.

72. The average distance between the planet Mercury and the Sun is 3.6×10^7 mi.

a. If Mercury's orbit is approximated by a circle, find the total distance Mercury travels around the Sun in one orbit. (*Hint:* The circumference of a circle is given by $C = 2\pi r$.) Express the answer in scientific notation.

b. If Mercury makes one complete trip around the Sun in 88 days (2.112×10^3 hr), find the average speed that Mercury travels around the Sun in miles per hour. Express the answer in scientific notation.

Section 5.5

73. For the polynomial $7x^4 - x + 6$

a. Classify as a monomial, a binomial, or a trinomial.

b. Identify the degree of the polynomial.

c. Identify the leading coefficient.

74. For the polynomial $2y^3 - 5y^7$

a. Classify as a monomial, a binomial, or a trinomial.

b. Identify the degree of the polynomial.

c. Identify the leading coefficient.

For Exercises 75–80, add or subtract as indicated.

75. $(4x + 2) + (3x - 5)$

76. $(7y^2 - 11y - 6) - (8y^2 + 3y - 4)$

77. $(9a^2 - 6) - (-5a^2 + 2a)$

78. $\left(5x^3 - \dfrac{1}{4}x^2 + \dfrac{5}{8}x + 2\right) + \left(\dfrac{5}{2}x^3 + \dfrac{1}{2}x^2 - \dfrac{1}{8}x\right)$

79. $\begin{array}{l} 8w^4 - 6w + 3 \\ + \ 2w^4 + 2w^3 - w + 1 \end{array}$

80. $\begin{array}{l} -0.02b^5 + b^4 - 0.7b + 0.3 \\ + 0.03b^5 - 0.1b^3 + b + 0.03 \end{array}$

81. Subtract $(9x^2 + 4x + 6)$ from $(7x^2 - 5x)$.

82. Find the difference of $(x^2 - 5x - 3)$ and $(6x^2 + 4x + 9)$.

83. Write a trinomial of degree 2 with a leading coefficient of -5. (Answers may vary.)

84. Write a binomial of degree 5 with leading coefficient 6. (Answers may vary.)

85. Find a polynomial that represents the perimeter of the given rectangle.

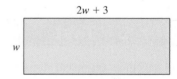

Section 5.6

For Exercises 86–103, multiply the expressions.

86. $(25x^4y^3)(-3x^2y)$ **87.** $(9a^6)(2a^2b^4)$

88. $5c(3c^3 - 7c + 5)$ **89.** $(x^2 + 5x - 3)(-2x)$

90. $(5k - 4)(k + 1)$ **91.** $(4t - 1)(5t + 2)$

92. $(q + 8)(6q - 1)$ **93.** $(2a - 6)(a + 5)$

94. $\left(7a + \dfrac{1}{2}\right)^2$ **95.** $(b - 4)^2$

96. $(4p^2 + 6p + 9)(2p - 3)$

97. $(2w - 1)(-w^2 - 3w - 4)$

98. $\begin{array}{r} 2x^2 - 3x + 4 \\ \times \ 2x - 1 \\ \hline \end{array}$

99.
$$4a^2 + a - 5$$
$$\times \quad 3a + 2$$

100. $(b - 4)(b + 4)$

101. $\left(\frac{1}{3}r^4 - s^2\right)\left(\frac{1}{3}r^4 + s^2\right)$

102. $(-7z^2 + 6)^2$

103. $(2h + 3)(h^4 - h^3 + h^2 - h + 1)$

104. Find a polynomial that represents the area of the given rectangle.

$2x - 5$

$x + 4$

Section 5.7

For Exercises 105–117, divide the polynomials.

105. $\dfrac{20y^3 - 10y^2}{5y}$

106. $(18a^3b^2 - 9a^2b - 27ab^2) \div 9ab$

107. $(12x^4 - 8x^3 + 4x^2) \div (-4x^2)$

108. $\dfrac{10z^7w^4 - 15z^3w^2 - 20zw}{-20z^2w}$

109. $\dfrac{x^2 + 7x + 10}{x + 5}$

110. $(2t^2 + t - 10) \div (t - 2)$

111. $(2p^2 + p - 16) \div (2p + 7)$

112. $\dfrac{5a^2 + 27a - 22}{5a - 3}$

113. $\dfrac{b^3 - 125}{b - 5}$

114. $(z^3 + 4z^2 + 5z + 20) \div (5 + z^2)$

115. $(y^4 - 4y^3 + 5y^2 - 3y + 2) \div (y^2 + 3)$

116. $(3t^4 - 8t^3 + t^2 - 4t - 5) \div (3t^2 + t + 1)$

117. $\dfrac{2w^4 + w^3 + 4w - 3}{2w^2 - w + 3}$

Chapter 5 Test

Assume all variables represent nonzero real numbers.

1. Expand the expression using the definition of exponents, then simplify: $\dfrac{3^4 \cdot 3^3}{3^6}$

For Exercises 2–13, simplify the expression. Write the answer with positive exponents only.

2. $9^5 \cdot 9$

3. $\dfrac{q^{10}}{q^2}$

4. $(-7)^0$

5. c^{-3}

6. $3^0 + 2^{-1} - 4^{-1}$

7. $4 \cdot 8^{-1} + 16^0$

8. $(3a^2b)^3$

9. $\left(\dfrac{2x}{y^3}\right)^4$

10. $\dfrac{14^3 \cdot 14^9}{14^{10} \cdot 14}$

11. $\dfrac{(s^2t)^3(7s^4t)^4}{(7s^2t^3)^2}$

12. $(2a^0b^{-6})^2$

13. $\left(\dfrac{6a^{-5}b}{8ab^{-2}}\right)^{-2}$

14. a. Write the number in scientific notation: 43,000,000,000

b. Write the number in standard form: 5.6×10^{-6}

15. Multiply: $(1.2 \times 10^6)(7 \times 10^{-15})$

16. Divide: $\dfrac{60,000}{0.008}$

17. The average amount of water flowing over Niagara Falls is 1.68×10^5 m^3/min.

   a. How many cubic meters of water flow over the falls in one day?

   b. How many cubic meters of water flow over the falls in one year?

18. Write the polynomial in descending order: $4x + 5x^3 - 7x^2 + 11$

   a. Identify the degree of the polynomial.

   b. Identify the leading coefficient of the polynomial.

For Exercises 19–28, perform the indicated operations.

19. $(5t^4 - 2t^2 - 17) + (12t^3 + 2t^2 + 7t - 2)$

20. $(7w^2 - 11w - 6) + (8w^2 + 3w + 4) - (-9w^2 - 5w + 2)$

21. $-2x^3(5x^2 + x - 15)$ **22.** $(4a - 3)(2a - 1)$

23. $(4y - 5)(y^2 - 5y + 3)$ **24.** $(2 + 3b)(2 - 3b)$

25. $(5z - 6)^2$ **26.** $(5x + 3)(3x - 2)$

27. $(2x^2 + 5x) - (6x^2 - 7)$

28. $(y^2 - 5y + 2)(y - 6)$

29. Subtract $(3x^2 - 5x^3 + 2x)$ from $(10x^3 - 4x^2 + 1)$.

30. Find the perimeter and the area of the rectangle shown in the figure.

$5x + 2$

$x - 3$

For Exercises 31–35, divide:

31. $(-12x^8 + x^6 - 8x^3) \div (4x^2)$

32. $\dfrac{16a^3b - 2a^2b^2 + 8ab}{-4ab}$

33. $\dfrac{2y^2 - 13y + 21}{y - 3}$

34. $(-5w^2 + 2w^3 - 2w + 5) \div (2w + 3)$

35. $\dfrac{3x^4 + x^3 + 4x - 33}{x^2 + 4}$

Chapters 1–5   Cumulative Review Exercises

For Exercises 1 and 2, simplify completely.

1. $-5 - \dfrac{1}{2}[4 - 3(-7)]$ **2.** $|-3^2 + 5|$

3. Translate the phrase into a mathematical expression and simplify:

The difference of the square of five and the square root of four

4. Solve for x: $\dfrac{1}{2}(x - 6) + \dfrac{2}{3} = \dfrac{1}{4}x$

5. Solve for y: $-2y - 3 = -5(y - 1) + 3y$

6. For a point in a rectangular coordinate system, in which quadrant are both the x- and y-coordinates negative?

7. For a point in a rectangular coordinate system, on which axis is the x-coordinate zero and the y-coordinate nonzero?

8. In a triangle, one angle measures 23° more than the smallest angle. The third angle measures 10° more than the sum of the other two angles. Find the measure of each angle.

9. A snow storm lasts for 9 hr and dumps snow at a rate of $1\frac{1}{2}$ in./hr. If there was already 6 in. of snow on the ground before the storm, the snow depth is given by the equation:

$y = \dfrac{3}{2}x + 6$ where y is the snow depth in inches and $x \geq 0$ is the time in hours.

a. Find the snow depth after 4 hr.

b. Find the snow depth at the end of the storm.

c. How long had it snowed when the total depth of snow was $14\frac{1}{4}$ in.?

10. Solve the system of equations.

$$5x + 3y = -3$$
$$3x + 2y = -1$$

11. Solve the inequality. Graph the solution set on the real number line and express the solution in interval notation. $2 - 3(2x + 4) \leq -2x - (x - 5)$

For Exercises 12–15, perform the indicated operations.

12. $(2x^2 + 3x - 7) - (-3x^2 + 12x + 8)$

13. $(2y + 3z)(-y - 5z)$

14. $(4t - 3)^2$

15. $\left(\dfrac{2}{5}a + \dfrac{1}{3}\right)\left(\dfrac{2}{5}a - \dfrac{1}{3}\right)$

For Exercises 16 and 17, divide the polynomials.

16. $(12a^4b^3 - 6a^2b^2 + 3ab) \div (-3ab)$

17. $\dfrac{4m^3 - 5m + 2}{m - 2}$

For Exercises 18 and 19, use the properties of exponents to simplify the expressions. Write the answers with positive exponents only. Assume all variables represent nonzero real numbers.

18. $\left(\dfrac{2c^2d^4}{8cd^6}\right)^2$

19. $\dfrac{10a^{-2}b^{-3}}{5a^0b^{-6}}$

20. Perform the indicated operations, and write the final answer in scientific notation.

$$\dfrac{8.2 \times 10^{-2}}{2 \times 10^{-5}}$$

Factoring Polynomials

6

CHAPTER OUTLINE

Chapter 6

Chapter 6 is devoted to a mathematical operation called factoring. The applications of factoring are far-reaching, and in this chapter, we use factoring as a tool to solve a type of equation called a quadratic equation.

Review Your Skills

Along the way, we will need the skill of recognizing perfect squares and perfect cubes. A perfect square is a number that is a square of a rational number. For example, 49 is a perfect square because $49 = 7^2$. We also will need to recognize perfect cubes. A perfect cube is a number that is a cube of a rational number. For example, 125 is a perfect cube because $125 = 5^3$.

   To complete the puzzle, first answer the questions and fill in the appropriate box. Then fill the grid so that every row, every column, and every 2 × 3 box contains the digits 1 through 6.

A. What number squared is 1?

B. What number squared is 16?

C. What number cubed is 1?

D. What number squared is 36?

E. What number squared is 25?

F. What number cubed is 64?

G. What number cubed is 8?

H. What number cubed is 27?

I. What number squared is 4?

J. What number squared is 9?

Section 6.1 — Greatest Common Factor and Factoring by Grouping

1. Identifying the Greatest Common Factor

Chapter 6 is devoted to a mathematical operation called **factoring**. To factor an integer means to write the integer as a product of two or more integers. To factor a polynomial means to express the polynomial as a product of two or more polynomials.

In the product $2 \cdot 5 = 10$, for example, 2 and 5 are factors of 10.

In the product $(3x + 4)(2x - 1) = 6x^2 + 5x - 4$, the quantities $(3x + 4)$ and $(2x - 1)$ are factors of $6x^2 + 5x - 4$.

We begin our study of factoring by factoring integers. The number 20, for example, can be factored as $1 \cdot 20$ or $2 \cdot 10$ or $4 \cdot 5$ or $2 \cdot 2 \cdot 5$. The product $2 \cdot 2 \cdot 5$ (or equivalently $2^2 \cdot 5$) consists only of prime numbers and is called the **prime factorization**.

The **greatest common factor** (denoted **GCF**) of two or more integers is the largest factor common to each integer. To find the greatest common factor of two or more integers, it is often helpful to express the numbers as a product of prime factors as shown in the next example.

Example 1   Identifying the GCF

Find the greatest common factor.

a. 24 and 36   **b.** 105, 40, and 60

Solution:

First find the prime factorization of each number. Then find the product of common factors.

a.
$$\begin{array}{ll} 2\,|\,24 & 2\,|\,36 \\ 2\,|\,12 & 2\,|\,18 \\ 2\,|\,6 & 3\,|\,9 \\ 3 & 3 \end{array}$$

Factors of 24 = $2 \cdot 2 \cdot 2 \cdot 3$ ⟵ Common factors are circled.
Factors of 36 = $2 \cdot 2 \cdot 3 \cdot 3$

The numbers 24 and 36 share two factors of 2 and one factor of 3. Therefore, the greatest common factor is $2 \cdot 2 \cdot 3 = 12$.

b.
$$\begin{array}{lll} 5\,|\,105 & 5\,|\,40 & 5\,|\,60 \\ 3\,|\,21 & 2\,|\,8 & 3\,|\,12 \\ 7 & 2\,|\,4 & 2\,|\,4 \\ & 2 & 2 \end{array}$$

Factors of 105 = $3 \cdot 7 \cdot 5$

Factors of 40 = $2 \cdot 2 \cdot 2 \cdot 5$

Factors of 60 = $2 \cdot 2 \cdot 3 \cdot 5$

The greatest common factor is 5.

In Example 2, we find the greatest common factor of two or more variable terms.

Example 2 Identifying the Greatest Common Factor

Find the GCF among each group of terms.

a. $7x^3, 14x^2, 21x^4$ **b.** $15a^4b, 25a^3b^2$

Solution:

List the factors of each term.

a. $7x^3 = \boxed{7 \cdot x \cdot x} \cdot x$

$14x^2 = 2 \cdot \boxed{7 \cdot x \cdot x}$

$21x^4 = 3 \cdot \boxed{7 \cdot x \cdot x} \cdot x \cdot x$

The GCF is $7x^2$.

b. $15a^4b = 3 \cdot \boxed{5 \cdot a \cdot a \cdot a} \cdot a \cdot \boxed{b}$

$25a^3b^2 = 5 \cdot \boxed{5 \cdot a \cdot a \cdot a} \cdot b \cdot \boxed{b}$

The GCF is $5a^3b$.

> **TIP:** Notice in Example 2(b) the expressions $15a^4b$ and $25a^3b^2$ share factors of 5, a, and b. The GCF is the product of the common factors, where each factor is raised to the lowest power to which it occurs in all the original expressions.
>
> $15a^4b = 3 \cdot 5a^4b$ Lowest power of 5 is 1: 5^1
>
> $25a^3b^2 = 5^2a^3b^2$ Lowest power of a is 3: a^3 The GCF is $5a^3b$.
>
> Lowest power of b is 1: b^1

Skill Practice

Find the GCF.

3. $10z^3, 15z^5, 40z$

4. $6w^3y^5, 21w^4y^2$

Example 3 Identifying the Greatest Common Factor

Find the GCF of the terms $8c^2d^7e$ and $6c^3d^4$.

Solution:

$8c^2d^7e = 2^3c^2d^7e$

$6c^3d^4 = 2 \cdot 3c^3d^4$ The common factors are 2, c, and d.

The lowest power of 2 is 1: 2^1

The lowest power of c is 2: c^2 The GCF is $2c^2d^4$.

The lowest power of d is 4: d^4

Skill Practice

Find the GCF.

5. $9m^2np^8, 15n^4p^5$

Sometimes polynomials share a common binomial factor, as shown in Example 4.

Example 4 Identifying the Greatest Common Binomial Factor

Find the greatest common factor between the terms $3x(a + b)$ and $2y(a + b)$.

Solution:

$3x(a + b)$ The only common factor is the binomial $(a + b)$.

$2y(a + b)$ The GCF is $(a + b)$.

Skill Practice

Find the GCF.

6. $a(x + 2)$ and $b(x + 2)$

Answers

3. $5z$ **4.** $3w^3y^2$

5. $3np^5$ **6.** $(x + 2)$

2. Factoring out the Greatest Common Factor

The process of factoring a polynomial is the reverse process of multiplying polynomials. Both operations use the distributive property: $ab + ac = a(b + c)$.

Multiply

$$5y(y^2 + 3y + 1) = 5y(y^2) + 5y(3y) + 5y(1)$$
$$= 5y^3 + 15y^2 + 5y$$

Factor

$$5y^3 + 15y^2 + 5y = 5y(y^2) + 5y(3y) + 5y(1)$$
$$= 5y(y^2 + 3y + 1)$$

Factoring out the Greatest Common Factor

Step 1 Identify the GCF of all terms of the polynomial.

Step 2 Write each term as the product of the GCF and another factor.

Step 3 Use the distributive property to remove the GCF.

Note: To check the factorization, multiply the polynomials to remove parentheses.

Skill Practice

Factor out the GCF.
  7. $6w + 18$
  8. $21m^3 - 7m$

Example 5 **Factoring out the Greatest Common Factor**

Factor out the GCF.

a. $4x - 20$ **b.** $6w^2 + 3w$

Solution:

a. $4x - 20$ The GCF is 4.

$= 4(x) - 4(5)$ Write each term as the product of the GCF and another factor.

$= 4(x - 5)$ Use the distributive property to factor out the GCF.

TIP: Any factoring problem can be checked by multiplying the factors:

Check: $4(x - 5) = 4x - 20$ ✔

Avoiding Mistakes

In Example 5(b), the GCF, $3w$, is equal to one of the terms of the polynomial. In such a case, you must leave a 1 in place of that term after the GCF is factored out.

b. $6w^2 + 3w$ The GCF is $3w$.

$= 3w(2w) + 3w(1)$ Write each term as the product of $3w$ and another factor.

$= 3w(2w + 1)$ Use the distributive property to factor out the GCF.

Check: $3w(2w + 1) = 6w^2 + 3w$ ✔

Answers

7. $6(w + 3)$ **8.** $7m(3m^2 - 1)$

Example 6 Factoring out the Greatest Common Factor

Factor out the GCF.

a. $15y^3 + 12y^4$ **b.** $9a^4b - 18a^5b + 27a^6b$

Solution:

a. $15y^3 + 12y^4$ The GCF is $3y^3$.

$= 3y^3(5) + 3y^3(4y)$ Write each term as the product of $3y^3$ and another factor.

$= 3y^3(5 + 4y)$ Use the distributive property to factor out the GCF.

Check: $3y^3(5 + 4y) = 15y^3 + 12y^4$ ✔

TIP: When factoring out the GCF from a polynomial, the terms within parentheses are found by dividing the original terms by the GCF. For example:

$15y^3 + 12y^4$ The GCF is $3y^3$.

$$\frac{15y^3}{3y^3} = 5 \quad \text{and} \quad \frac{12y^4}{3y^3} = 4y$$

Thus, $15y^3 + 12y^4 = 3y^3(5 + 4y)$

---

b. $9a^4b - 18a^5b + 27a^6b$ The GCF is $9a^4b$.

$= 9a^4b(1) - 9a^4b(2a) + 9a^4b(3a^2)$ Write each term as the product of $9a^4b$ and another factor.

$= 9a^4b(1 - 2a + 3a^2)$ Use the distributive property to factor out the GCF.

Check: $9a^4b(1 - 2a + 3a^2)$
$= 9a^4b - 18a^5b + 27a^6b$ ✔

Skill Practice

Factor out the GCF.
9. $9y^2 - 6y^5$
10. $50s^3t - 40st^2 + 10st$

The greatest common factor of the polynomial $2x + 5y$ is 1. If we factor out the GCF, we have $1(2x + 5y)$. A polynomial whose only factors are itself and 1 is called a **prime polynomial**. A prime polynomial cannot be factored further.

3. Factoring out a Negative Factor

Usually it is advantageous to factor out the *opposite* of the GCF when the leading coefficient of the polynomial is negative. This is demonstrated in Example 7. Notice that this *changes the signs* of the remaining terms inside the parentheses.

Answers
9. $3y^2(3 - 2y^3)$
10. $10st(5s^2 - 4t + 1)$

Example 7 **Factoring out a Negative Factor**

Factor out -3 from the polynomial $-3x^2 + 6x - 33$.

Solution:

$-3x^2 + 6x - 33$ The GCF is 3. However, in this case, we will factor out the *opposite* of the GCF, -3.

$= -3(x^2) + (-3)(-2x) + (-3)(11)$ Write each term as the product of -3 and another factor.

$= -3[x^2 + (-2x) + 11]$ Factor out -3.

$= -3(x^2 - 2x + 11)$ Simplify. Notice that each sign within the trinomial has changed.

Check: $-3(x^2 - 2x + 11) = -3x^2 + 6x - 33$ ✔

Example 8 **Factoring out a Negative Factor**

Factor out the quantity $-4pq$ from the polynomial $-12p^3q - 8p^2q^2 + 4pq^3$.

Solution:

$-12p^3q - 8p^2q^2 + 4pq^3$ The GCF is $4pq$. However, in this case, we will factor out the *opposite* of the GCF, $-4pq$.

$= -4pq(3p^2) + (-4pq)(2pq) + (-4pq)(-q^2)$ Write each term as the product of $-4pq$ and another factor.

$= -4pq[3p^2 + 2pq + (-q^2)]$ Factor out $-4pq$. Notice that each sign within the trinomial has changed.

$= -4pq(3p^2 + 2pq - q^2)$ To verify that this is the correct factorization and that the signs are correct, multiply the factors.

Check: $-4pq(3p^2 + 2pq - q^2) = -12p^3q - 8p^2q^2 + 4pq^3$ ✔

4. Factoring out a Binomial Factor

The distributive property can also be used to factor out a common factor that consists of more than one term as shown in Example 9.

Example 9 **Factoring out a Binomial Factor**

Factor out the GCF. $2w(x + 3) - 5(x + 3)$

Solution:

$2w(x + 3) - 5(x + 3)$ The greatest common factor is the quantity $(x + 3)$.

$= (x + 3)(2w) - (x + 3)(5)$ Write each term as the product of $(x + 3)$ and another factor.

$= (x + 3)(2w - 5)$ Use the distributive property to factor out the GCF.

5. Factoring by Grouping

When two binomials are multiplied, the product before simplifying contains four terms. For example:

$$(x + 4)(3a + 2b) = (x + 4)(3a) + (x + 4)(2b)$$
$$= (x + 4)(3a) + (x + 4)(2b)$$
$$= 3ax + 12a + 2bx + 8b$$

In Example 10, we learn how to reverse this process. That is, given a four-term polynomial, we will factor it as a product of two binomials. The process is called *factoring by grouping*.

> **Factoring by Grouping**
>
> To factor a four-term polynomial by grouping:
>
> **Step 1** Identify and factor out the GCF from all four terms.
> **Step 2** Factor out the GCF from the first pair of terms. Factor out the GCF from the second pair of terms. (Sometimes it is necessary to factor out the opposite of the GCF.)
> **Step 3** If the two terms share a common binomial factor, factor out the binomial factor.

Example 10 **Factoring by Grouping**

Factor by grouping. $3ax + 12a + 2bx + 8b$

Solution:

$3ax + 12a + 2bx + 8b$ **Step 1:** Identify and factor out the GCF from all four terms. In this case, the GCF is 1.

$= 3ax + 12a + 2bx + 8b$ Group the first pair of terms and the second pair of terms.

$= 3a(x + 4) + 2b(x + 4)$ **Step 2:** Factor out the GCF from each pair of terms. *Note:* The two terms now share a common binomial factor of $(x + 4)$.

$= (x + 4)(3a + 2b)$ **Step 3:** Factor out the common binomial factor.

Check: $(x + 4)(3a + 2b) = 3ax + 2bx + 12a + 8b$ ✔

Note: Step 2 results in two terms with a common binomial factor. If the two binomials are different, step 3 cannot be performed. In such a case, the original polynomial may not be factorable by grouping, or different pairs of terms may need to be grouped and inspected.

> **Skill Practice**
>
> Factor by grouping.
> **14.** $5x + 10y + ax + 2ay$

TIP: One frequently asked question when factoring is whether the order can be switched between the factors. The answer is yes. Because multiplication is commutative, the order in which the factors are written does not matter.

$$(x + 4)(3a + 2b) = (3a + 2b)(x + 4)$$

Answer
14. $(x + 2y)(5 + a)$

Example 11 **Factoring by Grouping**

Factor by grouping. $ax + ay - x - y$

Solution:

$ax + ay - x - y$ **Step 1:** Identify and factor out the GCF from all four terms. In this case, the GCF is 1.

$= ax + ay \mid - x - y$ Group the first pair of terms and the second pair of terms.

$= a(x + y) - 1(x + y)$ **Step 2:** Factor out a from the first pair of terms.

Factor out -1 from the second pair of terms. (This causes sign changes within the second parentheses.) The terms in parentheses now match.

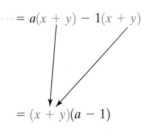

$= (x + y)(a - 1)$ **Step 3:** Factor out the common binomial factor.

$\underline{\text{Check:}}\ (x + y)(a - 1) = x(a) + x(-1) + y(a) + y(-1)$

$= ax - x + ay - y\ ✔$

Example 12 **Factoring by Grouping**

Factor by grouping. $16w^4 - 40w^3 - 12w^2 + 30w$

Solution:

$16w^4 - 40w^3 - 12w^2 + 30w$ **Step 1:** Identify and factor out the GCF from all four terms. In this case, the GCF is $2w$.

$= 2w[8w^3 - 20w^2 - 6w + 15]$

$= 2w[8w^3 - 20w^2 \mid - 6w + 15]$ Group the first pair of terms and the second pair of terms.

$= 2w[4w^2(2w - 5) - 3(2w - 5)]$ **Step 2:** Factor out $4w^2$ from the first pair of terms.

Factor out -3 from the second pair of terms. (This causes sign changes within the second parentheses. The terms in parentheses now match.)

$= 2w[(2w - 5)(4w^2 - 3)]$ **Step 3:** Factor out the common binomial factor.

$= 2w(2w - 5)(4w^2 - 3)$

Section 6.1 Practice Exercises

Study Skills Exercise

The final exam is just around the corner. Your old tests and quizzes provide good material to study for the final exam. Use your old tests to make a list of the chapters on which you need to concentrate. Ask your professor for help if there are still concepts that you do not understand.

Vocabulary and Key Concepts

1. **a.** Factoring a polynomial means to write it as a _____ of two or more polynomials.

   b. The prime factorization of a number consists of only _____ factors.

   c. The _____ _____ _____ (GCF) of two or more integers is the largest whole number that is a factor of each integer.

   d. A polynomial whose only factors are 1 and itself is called a _____ polynomial.

   e. The first step toward factoring a polynomial is to factor out the _____ _____ _____.

   f. To factor a four-term polynomial, we try the process of factoring by _____.

Concept 1: Identifying the Greatest Common Factor

2. List all the factors of 24.

For Exercises 3–14, identify the greatest common factor. **(See Examples 1–4.)**

3. $28, 63$

4. $24, 40$

5. $42, 30, 60$

6. $20, 52, 32$

7. $3xy, 7y$

8. $10mn, 11n$

9. $12w^3z, 16w^2z$

10. $20cd, 15c^3d$

11. $8x^3y^4z^2, 12xy^5z^4, 6x^2y^8z^3$

12. $15r^2s^2t^5, 5r^3s^4t^3, 30r^4s^3t^2$

13. $7(x - y), 9(x - y)$

14. $(2a - b), 3(2a - b)$

Concept 2: Factoring out the Greatest Common Factor

15. **a.** Use the distributive property to multiply $3(x - 2y)$.

    b. Use the distributive property to factor $3x - 6y$.

16. **a.** Use the distributive property to multiply $a^2(5a + b)$.

    b. Use the distributive property to factor $5a^3 + a^2b$.

For Exercises 17–36, factor out the GCF. **(See Examples 5 and 6.)**

17. $4p + 12$

18. $3q - 15$

19. $5c^2 - 10c + 15$

20. $16d^3 + 24d^2 + 32d$

21. $x^5 + x^3$

22. $y^2 - y^3$

23. $t^4 - 4t + 8t^2$

24. $7r^3 - r^5 + r^4$

25. $2ab + 4a^3b$

26. $5u^3v^2 - 5uv$

27. $38x^2y - 19x^2y^4$

28. $100a^5b^3 + 16a^2b$

29. $6x^3y^5 - 18xy^9z$

30. $15mp^7q^4 + 12m^4q^3$

31. $5 + 7y^3$

32. $w^3 - 5u^3v^2$

33. $42p^3q^2 + 14pq^2 - 7p^4q^4$

34. $8m^2n^3 - 24m^2n^2 + 4m^3n$

35. $t^5 + 2rt^3 - 3t^4 + 4r^2t^2$

36. $u^2v + 5u^3v^2 - 2u^2 + 8uv$

Concept 3: Factoring out a Negative Factor

37. For the polynomial $-2x^3 - 4x^2 + 8x$

    a. Factor out $-2x$.   **b.** Factor out $2x$.

38. For the polynomial $-9y^5 + 3y^3 - 12y$

    a. Factor out $-3y$.   **b.** Factor out $3y$.

39. Factor out -1 from the polynomial $-8t^2 - 9t - 2$.

40. Factor out -1 from the polynomial $-6x^3 - 2x - 5$.

For Exercises 41–46, factor out the opposite of the greatest common factor. **(See Examples 7 and 8.)**

41. $-15p^3 - 30p^2$

42. $-24m^3 - 12m^4$

43. $-q^4 + 2q^2 - 9q$

44. $-r^3 + 9r^2 - 5r$

45. $-7x - 6y - 2z$

46. $-4a + 5b - c$

Concept 4: Factoring out a Binomial Factor

For Exercises 47–52, factor out the GCF. **(See Example 9.)**

47. $13(a + 6) - 4b(a + 6)$

48. $7(x^2 + 1) - y(x^2 + 1)$

49. $8v(w^2 - 2) + (w^2 - 2)$

50. $t(r + 2) + (r + 2)$

51. $21x(x + 3) + 7x^2(x + 3)$

52. $5y^3(y - 2) - 15y(y - 2)$

Concept 5: Factoring by Grouping

For Exercises 53–72, factor by grouping. **(See Examples 10 and 11.)**

53. $8a^2 - 4ab + 6ac - 3bc$

54. $4x^3 + 3x^2y + 4xy^2 + 3y^3$

55. $3q + 3p + qr + pr$

56. $xy - xz + 7y - 7z$

57. $6x^2 + 3x + 4x + 2$

58. $4y^2 + 8y + 7y + 14$

59. $2t^2 + 6t - t - 3$

60. $2p^2 - p - 2p + 1$

61. $6y^2 - 2y - 9y + 3$

62. $5a^2 + 30a - 2a - 12$

63. $b^4 + b^3 - 4b - 4$

64. $8w^5 + 12w^2 - 10w^3 - 15$

65. $3j^2k + 15k + j^2 + 5$

66. $2ab^2 - 6ac + b^2 - 3c$

67. $14w^6x^6 + 7w^6 - 2x^6 - 1$

68. $18p^4x - 4x - 9p^5 + 2p$

69. $ay + bx + by + ax$

    (*Hint:* Rearrange the terms.)

70. $2c + 3ay + ac + 6y$

71. $vw^2 - 3 + w - 3wv$

72. $2x^2 + 6m + 12 + x^2m$

Mixed Exercises

For Exercises 73–78, factor out the GCF first. Then factor by grouping. **(See Example 12.)**

73. $15x^4 + 15x^2y^2 + 10x^3y + 10xy^3$

74. $2a^3b - 4a^2b + 32ab - 64b$

75. $4abx - 4b^2x - 4ab + 4b^2$

76. $p^2q - pq^2 - rp^2q + rpq^2$

77. $6st^2 - 18st - 6t^4 + 18t^3$

78. $15j^3 - 10j^2k - 15j^2k^2 + 10jk^3$

79. The formula $P = 2l + 2w$ represents the perimeter, P, of a rectangle given the length, l, and the width, w. Factor out the GCF, and write an equivalent formula in factored form.

80. The formula $P = 2a + 2b$ represents the perimeter, P, of a parallelogram given the base, b, and an adjacent side, a. Factor out the GCF, and write an equivalent formula in factored form.

81. The formula $S = 2\pi r^2 + 2\pi rh$ represents the surface area, S, of a cylinder with radius, r, and height, h. Factor out the GCF, and write an equivalent formula in factored form.

82. The formula $A = P + Prt$ represents the total amount of money, A, in an account that earns simple interest at a rate, r, for t years. Factor out the GCF, and write an equivalent formula in factored form.

Expanding Your Skills

83. Factor out $\dfrac{1}{7}$ from $\dfrac{1}{7}x^2 + \dfrac{3}{7}x - \dfrac{5}{7}$.

84. Factor out $\dfrac{1}{5}$ from $\dfrac{6}{5}y^2 - \dfrac{4}{5}y + \dfrac{1}{5}$.

85. Factor out $\dfrac{1}{4}$ from $\dfrac{5}{4}w^2 + \dfrac{3}{4}w + \dfrac{9}{4}$.

86. Factor out $\dfrac{1}{6}$ from $\dfrac{1}{6}p^2 - \dfrac{3}{6}p + \dfrac{5}{6}$.

87. Write a polynomial that has a GCF of $3x$. (Answers may vary.)

88. Write a polynomial that has a GCF of $7y$. (Answers may vary.)

89. Write a polynomial that has a GCF of $4p^2q$. (Answers may vary.)

90. Write a polynomial that has a GCF of $2ab^2$. (Answers may vary.)

Factoring Trinomials of the Form $x^2 + bx + c$ Section 6.2

1. Factoring Trinomials with a Leading Coefficient of 1

Concept

1. Factoring Trinomials with a Leading Coefficient of 1

In Section 5.6, we learned how to multiply two binomials. We also saw that such a product often results in a trinomial. For example,

$$\underset{\substack{\text{Sum of products of inner} \\ \text{terms and outer terms}}}{(x + 3)(x + 7) = \overset{\substack{\text{Product of} \\ \text{first terms}}}{x^2} + \underbrace{7x + 3x}_{} + \overset{\substack{\text{Product of} \\ \text{last terms}}}{21} = x^2 + 10x + 21}$$

In this section, we want to reverse the process. That is, given a trinomial, we want to *factor* it as a product of two binomials. In particular, we begin our study with the case in which a trinomial has a leading coefficient of 1.

Consider the quadratic trinomial $x^2 + bx + c$. To produce a leading term of x^2, we can construct binomials of the form $(x + \quad)(x + \quad)$. The remaining terms can be obtained from two integers, p and q, whose product is c and whose sum is b.

$$x^2 + bx + c = (x + p)(x + q) = x^2 + qx + px + pq$$
$$= x^2 + \underbrace{(q + p)}_{\text{Sum} = b}x + \underbrace{pq}_{\text{Product} = c}$$

This process is demonstrated in Example 1.

Example 1 Factoring a Trinomial of the Form $x^2 + bx + c$

Factor: $w^2 - 15w + 50$

Solution:

$w^2 - 15w + 50 = (w + \square)(w + \square)$ The product $w \cdot w = w^2$.

Find two integers whose product is 50 and whose sum is -15. To form a positive product, the factors must be either both positive or both negative. The sum must be negative, so we will choose negative factors of 50.

Product $= 50$	Sum
$(-1)(-50)$	-51
$(-2)(-25)$	-27
$(-5)(-10)$	-15

$$w^2 - 15w + 50 = (w + \square)(w + \square)$$
$$= (w + (-5))(w + (-10))$$
$$= (w - 5)(w - 10) \quad \text{Factored form}$$

Check:

$$(w - 5)(w - 10) = w^2 - 10w - 5w + 50$$
$$= w^2 - 15w + 50 \ \checkmark$$

One frequently asked question is whether the order of factors can be reversed. The answer is yes because multiplication of polynomials is a commutative operation. Therefore, in Example 1, we can express the factorization as $(w - 5)(w - 10)$ or as $(w - 10)(w - 5)$.

Example 2 Factoring a Trinomial of the Form $x^2 + bx + c$

Factor: $x^2 + 4x - 45$

Solution:

$x^2 + 4x - 45 = (x + \square)(x + \square)$ The product of the first terms in the binomials must equal the leading term of the trinomial $x \cdot x = x^2$.

We must fill in the blanks with two integers whose product is -45 and whose sum is 4. The factors must have opposite signs to produce a negative product. The possible factorizations of -45 are:

Product $= -45$	Sum
$-1 \cdot 45$	44
$-3 \cdot 15$	12
$-5 \cdot 9$	4
$-9 \cdot 5$	-4
$-15 \cdot 3$	-12
$-45 \cdot 1$	-44

$$x^2 + 4x - 45 = (x + \square)(x + \square)$$

$$= (x + (-5))(x + 9) \qquad \text{Fill in the blanks with } -5 \text{ and } 9.$$

$$= (x - 5)(x + 9) \qquad \text{Factored form}$$

Check:
$$(x - 5)(x + 9) = x^2 + 9x - 5x - 45$$

$$= x^2 + 4x - 45 \checkmark$$

TIP: Practice will help you become proficient in factoring polynomials. As you do your homework, keep these important guidelines in mind:

- To factor a trinomial, write the trinomial in descending order such as $x^2 + bx + c$.
- For all factoring problems, always factor out the GCF from all terms first.

Furthermore, we offer the following rules for determining the signs within the binomial factors.

Sign Rules for Factoring Trinomials

Given the trinomial $x^2 + bx + c$, the signs within the binomial factors are determined as follows:

Case 1 If c is *positive*, then the signs in the binomials must be the same (either both positive or both negative). The correct choice is determined by the middle term. If the middle term is positive, then both signs must be positive. If the middle term is negative, then both signs must be negative.

c is positive.
$$x^2 + 6x + 8$$
$$(x + 2)(x + 4)$$
Same signs

c is positive.
$$x^2 - 6x + 8$$
$$(x - 2)(x - 4)$$
Same signs

Case 2 If c is *negative*, then the signs in the binomials must be different.

c is negative.
$$x^2 + 2x - 35$$
$$(x + 7)(x - 5)$$
Different signs

c is negative.
$$x^2 - 2x - 35$$
$$(x - 7)(x + 5)$$
Different signs

Skill Practice

Factor.

3. $-5w + w^2 - 6$

4. $30y^3 + 2y^4 + 112y^2$

Example 3 Factoring Trinomials

Factor. **a.** $-8p - 48 + p^2$ **b.** $-40t - 30t^2 + 10t^3$

Solution:

a. $-8p - 48 + p^2$

$= p^2 - 8p - 48$ Write in descending order.

$= (p \quad \square)(p \quad \square)$ Find two integers whose product is -48 and whose sum is -8. The numbers are -12 and 4.

$= (p - 12)(p + 4)$ Factored form

b. $-40t - 30t^2 + 10t^3$

$= 10t^3 - 30t^2 - 40t$ Write in descending order.

$= 10t(t^2 - 3t - 4)$ Factor out the GCF.

$= 10t(t \quad \square)(t \quad \square)$ Find two integers whose product is -4 and whose sum is -3. The numbers are -4 and 1.

$= 10t(t - 4)(t + 1)$ Factored form

Example 4 Factoring Trinomials

Factor. **a.** $-a^2 + 6a - 8$ **b.** $-2c^2 - 22cd - 60d^2$

Solution:

a. $-a^2 + 6a - 8$

It is generally easier to factor a trinomial with a *positive* leading coefficient. Therefore, we will factor out -1 from all terms.

$= -1(a^2 - 6a + 8)$

$= -1(a \quad \square)(a \quad \square)$ Find two integers whose product is 8 and whose sum is -6. The numbers are -4 and -2.

$= -1(a - 4)(a - 2)$

$= -(a - 4)(a - 2)$

Skill Practice

Factor.

5. $-x^2 + x + 12$

6. $-3a^2 + 15ab - 12b^2$

Avoiding Mistakes

Recall that factoring out -1 from a polynomial changes the signs of all terms within parentheses.

b. $-2c^2 - 22cd - 60d^2$

$= -2(c^2 + 11cd + 30d^2)$ Factor out -2.

$= -2(c \quad \square d)(c \quad \square d)$ Notice that the second pair of terms has a factor of d. This will produce a product of d^2.

$= -2(c + 5d)(c + 6d)$ Find two integers whose product is 30 and whose sum is 11. The numbers are 5 and 6.

To factor a trinomial of the form $x^2 + bx + c$, we must find two integers whose product is c and whose sum is b. If no such integers exist, then the trinomial is prime.

Answers

3. $(w - 6)(w + 1)$

4. $2y^2(y + 8)(y + 7)$

5. $-(x - 4)(x + 3)$

6. $-3(a - b)(a - 4b)$

Example 5 Factoring Trinomials

Factor: $x^2 - 13x + 8$

Solution:

$x^2 - 13x + 8$ The trinomial is in descending order. The GCF is 1.

$= (x \quad \square)(x \quad \square)$ Find two integers whose product is 8 and whose sum is -13. No such integers exist.

The trinomial $x^2 - 13x + 8$ is prime.

Section 6.2 Practice Exercises

Vocabulary and Key Concepts

1. a. Given a trinomial $x^2 + bx + c$, if c is positive, then the signs in the binomial factors are either both _____ or both negative.

b. Given a trinomial $x^2 + bx + c$, if c is negative, then the signs in the binomial factors are (choose one: both positive, both negative, different).

c. Which is the correct factored form of $x^2 - 7x - 44$? The product $(x + 4)(x - 11)$ or $(x - 11)(x + 4)$?

d. Which is the complete factorization of $3x^2 + 24x + 36$? The product $(3x + 6)(x + 6)$ or $3(x + 6)(x + 2)$?

Review Exercises

For Exercises 2–6, factor completely.

2. $9a^6b^3 - 27a^3b^6 - 3a^2b^2$

3. $3t(t - 5) - 6(t - 5)$

4. $4(3x - 2) + 8x(3x - 2)$

5. $ax + 2bx - 5a - 10b$

6. $m^2 - mx - 3pm + 3px$

Concept 1: Factoring Trinomials with a Leading Coefficient of 1

For Exercises 7–20, factor completely. **(See Examples 1, 2, and 5.)**

7. $x^2 + 10x + 16$

8. $y^2 + 18y + 80$

9. $z^2 - 11z + 18$

10. $w^2 - 7w + 12$

11. $z^2 - 3z - 18$

12. $w^2 + 4w - 12$

13. $p^2 - 3p - 40$

14. $a^2 - 10a + 9$

15. $t^2 + 6t - 40$

16. $m^2 - 12m + 11$

17. $x^2 - 3x + 20$

18. $y^2 + 6y + 18$

19. $n^2 + 8n + 16$

20. $v^2 + 10v + 25$

For Exercises 21–24, assume that b and c represent positive integers.

21. When factoring a polynomial of the form $x^2 + bx + c$, pick an appropriate combination of signs.

    a. $(\ +\ )(\ +\ )$ **b.** $(\ -\ )(\ -\ )$ **c.** $(\ +\ )(\ -\ )$

22. When factoring a polynomial of the form $x^2 + bx - c$, pick an appropriate combination of signs.

    a. $(\ +\ )(\ +\ )$ **b.** $(\ -\ )(\ -\ )$ **c.** $(\ +\ )(\ -\ )$

23. When factoring a polynomial of the form $x^2 - bx - c$, pick an appropriate combination of signs.

    a. $(\ +\ )(\ +\ )$ **b.** $(\ -\ )(\ -\ )$ **c.** $(\ +\ )(\ -\ )$

24. When factoring a polynomial of the form $x^2 - bx + c$, pick an appropriate combination of signs.

    a. $(\ +\ )(\ +\ )$ **b.** $(\ -\ )(\ -\ )$ **c.** $(\ +\ )(\ -\ )$

25. Which is the correct factorization of $y^2 - y - 12$? Explain. $(y - 4)(y + 3)$ or $(y + 3)(y - 4)$

26. Which is the correct factorization of $x^2 + 14x + 13$? Explain. $(x + 13)(x + 1)$ or $(x + 1)(x + 13)$

27. Which is the correct factorization of $w^2 + 2w + 1$? Explain. $(w + 1)(w + 1)$ or $(w + 1)^2$

28. Which is the correct factorization of $z^2 - 4z + 4$? Explain. $(z - 2)(z - 2)$ or $(z - 2)^2$

29. In what order should a trinomial be written before attempting to factor it?

30. Referring to page 437, write two important guidelines to follow when factoring trinomials.

For Exercises 31–66, factor completely. Be sure to factor out the GCF when necessary. **(See Examples 3 and 4.)**

31. $-13x + x^2 - 30$

32. $12y - 160 + y^2$

33. $-18w + 65 + w^2$

34. $17t + t^2 + 72$

35. $22t + t^2 + 72$

36. $10q - 1200 + q^2$

37. $3x^2 - 30x - 72$

38. $2z^2 + 4z - 198$

39. $8p^3 - 40p^2 + 32p$

40. $5w^4 - 35w^3 + 50w^2$

41. $y^4z^2 - 12y^3z^2 + 36y^2z^2$

42. $t^4u^2 + 6t^3u^2 + 9t^2u^2$

43. $-x^2 + 10x - 24$

44. $-y^2 - 12y - 35$

45. $-m^2 + m + 6$

46. $-n^2 + 5n + 6$

47. $-4 - 2c^2 - 6c$

48. $-40d - 30 - 10d^2$

49. $x^3y^3 - 19x^2y^3 + 60xy^3$

50. $y^2z^5 + 17yz^5 + 60z^5$

51. $12p^2 - 96p + 84$

52. $5w^2 - 40w - 45$

53. $-2m^2 + 22m - 20$

54. $-3x^2 - 36x - 81$

55. $c^2 + 6cd + 5d^2$

56. $x^2 + 8xy + 12y^2$

57. $a^2 - 9ab + 14b^2$

58. $m^2 - 15mn + 44n^2$

59. $a^2 + 4a + 18$

60. $b^2 - 6a + 15$

61. $2q + q^2 - 63$

62. $-32 - 4t + t^2$

63. $x^2 + 20x + 100$

64. $z^2 - 24z + 144$

65. $t^2 + 18t - 40$

66. $d^2 + 2d - 99$

67. A student factored a trinomial as $(2x - 4)(x - 3)$. The instructor did not give full credit. Why?

68. A student factored a trinomial as $(y + 2)(5y - 15)$. The instructor did not give full credit. Why?

69. What polynomial factors as $(x - 4)(x + 13)$?

70. What polynomial factors as $(q - 7)(q + 10)$?

71. Raul purchased a parcel of land in the country. The given expressions represent the lengths of the boundary lines of his property.

    a. Write the perimeter of the land as a polynomial in simplified form.

    b. Write the polynomial from part (a) in factored form.

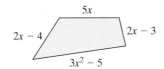

72. Jamison painted a mural in the shape of a triangle on the wall of a building. The given expressions represent the lengths of the sides of the triangle.

    a. Write the perimeter of the triangle as a polynomial in simplified form.

    b. Write the polynomial in factored form.

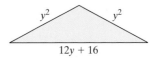

Expanding Your Skills

For Exercises 73–76, factor completely.

73. $x^4 + 10x^2 + 9$ **74.** $y^4 + 4y^2 - 21$ **75.** $w^4 + 2w^2 - 15$ **76.** $p^4 - 13p^2 + 40$

77. Find all integers, b, that make the trinomial $x^2 + bx + 6$ factorable.

78. Find all integers, b, that make the trinomial $x^2 + bx + 10$ factorable.

79. Find a value of c that makes the trinomial $x^2 + 6x + c$ factorable.

80. Find a value of c that makes the trinomial $x^2 + 8x + c$ factorable.

Factoring Trinomials: Trial-and-Error Method

Section 6.3

In Section 6.2, we learned how to factor trinomials of the form $x^2 + bx + c$. These trinomials had a leading coefficient of 1. In this section and the next, we will consider the more general case in which the leading coefficient may be *any* nonzero integer. That is, we will factor quadratic trinomials of the form $ax^2 + bx + c$ (where $a \neq 0$). The method presented in this section is called the trial-and-error method.

Concept

1. Factoring Trinomials by the Trial-and-Error Method

1. Factoring Trinomials by the Trial-and-Error Method

To understand the basis of factoring trinomials of the form $ax^2 + bx + c$, first consider the multiplication of two binomials:

Product of $2 \cdot 1$ Product of $3 \cdot 2$

$$(2x + 3)(1x + 2) = 2x^2 + \mathbf{4x + 3x} + 6 = 2x^2 + 7x + 6$$

Sum of products of inner terms and outer terms

To factor the trinomial, $2x^2 + 7x + 6$, this operation is reversed.

$$\overbrace{2x^2 + 7x + 6 = (\square x \quad \square)(\square x \quad \square)}^{\text{Factors of 2}}$$
$$\underbrace{}_{\text{Factors of 6}}$$

We need to fill in the blanks so that the product of the first terms in the binomials is $2x^2$ and the product of the last terms in the binomials is 6. Furthermore, the factors of $2x^2$ and 6 must be chosen so that the sum of the products of the inner terms and outer terms equals $7x$.

To produce the product $2x^2$, we might try the factors $2x$ and x within the binomials:

$$(2x \quad \square)(x \quad \square)$$

To produce a product of 6, the remaining terms in the binomials must either both be positive or both be negative. To produce a positive middle term, we will try positive factors of 6 in the remaining blanks until the correct product is found. The possibilities are $1 \cdot 6, 2 \cdot 3, 3 \cdot 2,$ and $6 \cdot 1$.

$(2x + 1)(x + 6) = 2x^2 + 12x + 1x + 6 = 2x^2 + 13x + 6$ Wrong middle term

$(2x + 2)(x + 3) = 2x^2 + 6x + 2x + 6 = 2x^2 + 8x + 6$ Wrong middle term

$(2x + 6)(x + 1) = 2x^2 + 2x + 6x + 6 = 2x^2 + 8x + 6$ Wrong middle term

$(2x + 3)(x + 2) = 2x^2 + 4x + 3x + 6 = 2x^2 + 7x + 6$ Correct!

The correct factorization of $2x^2 + 7x + 6$ is $(2x + 3)(x + 2)$. ✔

As this example shows, we factor a trinomial of the form $ax^2 + bx + c$ by shuffling the factors of a and c within the binomials until the correct product is obtained. However, sometimes it is not necessary to test all the possible combinations of factors. In the previous example, the GCF of the original trinomial is 1. Therefore, any binomial factor whose terms share a common factor *greater than 1* does not need to be considered. In this case, the possibilities $(2x + 2)(x + 3)$ and $(2x + 6)(x + 1)$ cannot work.

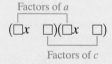

$\underbrace{(2x + 2)}(x + 3) \qquad \underbrace{(2x + 6)}(x + 1)$
Common   Common
factor of 2   factor of 2

Trial-and-Error Method to Factor $ax^2 + bx + c$

Step 1 Factor out the GCF.

Step 2 List all pairs of positive factors of a and all pairs of factors of c. Consider the reverse order for one of the lists of factors.

Step 3 Construct two binomials of the form:

$$\overbrace{(\square x \quad \square)(\square x \quad \square)}^{\text{Factors of } a}$$
$$\underbrace{}_{\text{Factors of } c}$$

Step 4 Test each combination of factors and signs until the correct product is found.

Step 5 If no combination of factors produces the correct product, the trinomial cannot be factored further and is a *prime polynomial*.

Before we begin Example 1, keep these two important guidelines in mind:

- For any factoring problem you encounter, always factor out the GCF from all terms first.
- To factor a trinomial, write the trinomial in the form $ax^2 + bx + c$.

Example 1 **Factoring a Trinomial by the Trial-and-Error Method**

Factor the trinomial by the trial-and-error method. $10x^2 + 11x + 1$

Solution:

$10x^2 + 11x + 1$ **Step 1:** Factor out the GCF from all terms. In this case, the GCF is 1.

The trinomial is written in the form $ax^2 + bx + c$.

To factor $10x^2 + 11x + 1$, two binomials must be constructed in the form:

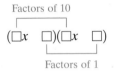

Factors of 10

$(\square x \quad \square)(\square x \quad \square)$

Factors of 1

Step 2: To produce the product $10x^2$, we might try $5x$ and $2x$, or $10x$ and $1x$. To produce a product of 1, we will try the factors $(1)(1)$ and $(-1)(-1)$.

Step 3: Construct all possible binomial factors using different combinations of the factors of $10x^2$ and 1.

$(5x + 1)(2x + 1) = 10x^2 + 5x + 2x + 1 = 10x^2 + 7x + 1$ Wrong middle term

$(5x - 1)(2x - 1) = 10x^2 - 5x - 2x + 1 = 10x^2 - 7x + 1$ Wrong middle term

Because the factors of 1 did not produce the correct trinomial when coupled with $5x$ and $2x$, try using $10x$ and $1x$.

$(10x - 1)(1x - 1) = 10x^2 - 10x - 1x + 1 = 10x^2 - 11x + 1$ Wrong sign on the middle term

$(10x + 1)(1x + 1) = 10x^2 + 10x + 1x + 1 = 10x^2 + 11x + 1$ Correct!

Therefore, $10x^2 + 11x + 1 = (10x + 1)(x + 1)$.

Skill Practice

Factor using the trial-and-error method.

1. $3b^2 + 8b + 4$

In Example 1, the factors of 1 must have the same signs to produce a positive product. Therefore, the binomial factors must both be sums or both be differences. Determining the correct signs is an important aspect of factoring trinomials. We suggest the following guidelines:

Answer

1. $(3b + 2)(b + 2)$

Sign Rules for the Trial-and-Error Method

Given the trinomial $ax^2 + bx + c, (a > 0)$, the signs can be determined as follows:

- If *c is positive*, then the signs in the binomials must be the same (either both positive or both negative). The correct choice is determined by the middle term. If the middle term is positive, then both signs must be positive. If the middle term is negative, then both signs must be negative.

$$\overset{\displaystyle c\text{ is positive}}{\underset{\downarrow}{20x^2 + 43x + 21}} \qquad \overset{\displaystyle c\text{ is positive}}{\underset{\downarrow}{20x^2 - 43x + 21}}$$

$$\underbrace{(4x + 3)(5x + 7)}_{\text{Same signs}} \qquad \underbrace{(4x - 3)(5x - 7)}_{\text{Same signs}}$$

TIP: Look at the sign on the third term. If it is a sum, the signs will be the same in the two binomials. If it is a difference, the signs in the two binomials will be different: sum—same sign; difference—different signs.

- If *c is negative*, then the signs in the binomial must be different. The middle term in the trinomial determines which factor gets the positive sign and which gets the negative sign.

$$\overset{\displaystyle c\text{ is negative}}{\underset{\downarrow}{x^2 + 3x - 28}} \qquad \overset{\displaystyle c\text{ is negative}}{\underset{\downarrow}{x^2 - 3x - 28}}$$

$$\underbrace{(x + 7)(x - 4)}_{\text{Different signs}} \qquad \underbrace{(x - 7)(x + 4)}_{\text{Different signs}}$$

Skill Practice

Factor.

2. $-25w + 6w^2 + 4$

Example 2   Factoring a Trinomial by the Trial-and-Error Method

Factor the trinomial: $13y - 6 + 8y^2$

Solution:

$13y - 6 + 8y^2$

$= 8y^2 + 13y - 6$ Write the polynomial in descending order.

$(\square y \ \ \square)(\square y \ \ \square)$ **Step 1:** The GCF is 1.

Factors of 8	Factors of 6
$1 \cdot 8$	$1 \cdot 6$
$2 \cdot 4$	$2 \cdot 3$
	$3 \cdot 2 \atop 6 \cdot 1$ (reverse order)

Step 2: List the positive factors of 8 and positive factors of 6. Consider the reverse order in one list of factors.

$$\left.\begin{array}{l}(1y \ \ 1)(8y \ \ 6) \\ (1y \ \ 3)(8y \ \ 2) \\ (2y \ \ 1)(4y \ \ 6) \\ (2y \ \ 2)(4y \ \ 3) \\ (2y \ \ 3)(4y \ \ 2) \\ (2y \ \ 6)(4y \ \ 1)\end{array}\right\}$$

Step 3: Construct all possible binomial factors using different combinations of the factors of 8 and 6.

Without regard to signs, these factorizations cannot work because the terms in the binomials share a common factor greater than 1.

Answer

2. $(6w - 1)(w - 4)$

Test the remaining factorizations. Keep in mind that to produce a product of -6, the signs within the parentheses must be opposite (one positive and one negative). Also, the sum of the products of the inner terms and outer terms must be combined to form $13y$.

$(1y \quad 6)(8y \quad 1)$ *Incorrect.* Wrong middle term.
Regardless of the signs, the product of inner terms, $48y$, and the product of outer terms, $1y$, cannot be combined to form the middle term $13y$.

$(1y \quad 2)(8y \quad 3)$ *Correct.* The terms $16y$ and $3y$ can be combined to form the middle term $13y$, provided the signs are applied correctly. We require $+16y$ and $-3y$.

The correct factorization of $8y^2 + 13y - 6$ is $(y + 2)(8y - 3)$.

Remember that the first step in any factoring problem is to remove the GCF. By removing the GCF, the remaining terms of the trinomial will be simpler and may have smaller coefficients.

Example 3 Factoring a Trinomial by the Trial-and-Error Method

Factor the trinomial by the trial-and-error method: $40x^3 - 104x^2 + 10x$

Solution:

$40x^3 - 104x^2 + 10x$

$= 2x(20x^2 - 52x + 5)$ **Step 1:** The GCF is $2x$.

$= 2x(\Box x \quad \Box)(\Box x \quad \Box)$ **Step 2:** List the factors of 20 and factors of 5. Consider the reverse order in one list of factors.

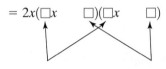

Factors of 20	Factors of 5
$1 \cdot 20$	$1 \cdot 5$
$2 \cdot 10$	$5 \cdot 1$
$4 \cdot 5$	

Step 3: Construct all possible binomial factors using different combinations of the factors of 20 and factors of 5. The signs in the parentheses must both be negative.

$= 2x(1x - 1)(20x - 5)$
$= 2x(2x - 1)(10x - 5)$ *Incorrect.* Once the GCF has been removed from the original polynomial, the binomial factors cannot contain a GCF greater than 1.
$= 2x(4x - 1)(5x - 5)$

$= 2x(1x - 5)(20x - 1)$ *Incorrect.* Wrong middle term.
$2x(x - 5)(20x - 1)$
$= 2x(20x^2 - 1x - 100x + 5)$
$= 2x(20x^2 - 101x + 5)$

$= 2x(4x - 5)(5x - 1)$ *Incorrect.* Wrong middle term.
$2x(4x - 5)(5x - 1)$
$= 2x(20x^2 - 4x - 25x + 5)$
$= 2x(20x^2 - 29x + 5)$

$= 2x(2x - 5)(10x - 1)$ *Correct.* $2x(2x - 5)(10x - 1)$
$= 2x(20x^2 - 2x - 50x + 5)$
$= 2x(20x^2 - 52x + 5)$
$= 40x^3 - 104x^2 + 10x$

The correct factorization is $2x(2x - 5)(10x - 1)$.

Often it is easier to factor a trinomial when the leading coefficient is positive. If the leading coefficient is negative, consider factoring out the opposite of the GCF.

Example 4 **Factoring a Trinomial by the Trial-and-Error Method**

Factor: $-45x^2 - 3xy + 18y^2$

Solution:

$-45x^2 - 3xy + 18y^2$

$= -3(15x^2 + xy - 6y^2)$ **Step 1:** Factor out -3 to make the leading coefficient positive.

$= -3(\square x \quad \square y)(\square x \quad \square y)$ **Step 2:** List the factors of 15 and 6.

Factors of 15	Factors of 6
$1 \cdot 15$	$1 \cdot 6$
$3 \cdot 5$	$2 \cdot 3$
	$3 \cdot 2$
	$6 \cdot 1$

Step 3: We will construct all binomial combinations, without regard to signs first.

$\left.\begin{array}{l} -3(x \quad y)(15x \quad 6y) \\ -3(x \quad 2y)(15x \quad 3y) \\ -3(3x \quad 3y)(5x \quad 2y) \\ -3(3x \quad 6y)(5x \quad y) \end{array}\right\}$ *Incorrect.* The binomials contain a common factor.

Test the remaining factorizations. The signs within parentheses must be opposite to produce a product of $-6y^2$. Also, the sum of the products of the inner terms and outer terms must be combined to form $1xy$.

$-3(x \quad 3y)(15x \quad 2y)$ *Incorrect.* Regardless of signs, $45xy$ and $2xy$ cannot be combined to equal xy.

$-3(x \quad 6y)(15x \quad y)$ *Incorrect.* Regardless of signs, $90xy$ and xy cannot be combined to equal xy.

$-3(3x \quad y)(5x \quad 6y)$ *Incorrect.* Regardless of signs, $5xy$ and $18xy$ cannot be combined to equal xy.

$-3(3x \quad 2y)(5x \quad 3y)$ *Correct.* The terms $10xy$ and $9xy$ can be combined to form xy provided that the signs are applied correctly. We require $10xy$ and $-9xy$.

$-3(3x + 2y)(5x - 3y)$ Factored form

Recall that a prime polynomial is a polynomial whose only factors are itself and 1. Not every trinomial is factorable by the methods presented in this text.

Example 5 Factoring a Trinomial by the Trial-and-Error Method

Factor the trinomial by the trial-and-error method: $2p^2 - 8p + 3$

Solution:

$2p^2 - 8p + 3$ **Step 1:** The GCF is 1.

$= (1p \;\; \square)(2p \;\; \square)$ **Step 2:** List the factors of 2 and the factors of 3.

Factors of 2	Factors of 3
$1 \cdot 2$	$1 \cdot 3$
	$3 \cdot 1$

Step 3: Construct all possible binomial factors using different combinations of the factors of 2 and 3. Because the third term in the trinomial is positive, both signs in the binomial must be the same. Because the middle term coefficient is negative, both signs will be negative.

$(p - 1)(2p - 3) = 2p^2 - 3p - 2p + 3$

$\qquad\qquad\qquad = 2p^2 - 5p + 3$ *Incorrect.*   Wrong middle term.

$(p - 3)(2p - 1) = 2p^2 - p - 6p + 3$

$\qquad\qquad\qquad = 2p^2 - 7p + 3$ *Incorrect.*   Wrong middle term.

None of the combinations of factors results in the correct product. Therefore, the polynomial $2p^2 - 8p + 3$ is prime and cannot be factored further.

Skill Practice

Factor.

5. $3a^2 + a + 4$

In Example 6, we use the trial-and-error method to factor a higher degree trinomial into two binomial factors.

Example 6 Factoring a Higher Degree Trinomial

Factor the trinomial: $3x^4 + 8x^2 + 5$

Solution:

$3x^4 + 8x^2 + 5$ **Step 1:** The GCF is 1.

$= (\square x^2 + \square)(\square x^2 + \square)$ **Step 2:** To produce the product $3x^4$, we must use $3x^2$, and $1x^2$. To produce a product of 5, we will try the factors $(1)(5)$ and $(5)(1)$.

Step 3: Construct all possible binomial factors using the combinations of factors of $3x^4$ and 5.

$(3x^2 + 1)(x^2 + 5) = 3x^4 + 15x^2 + 1x^2 + 5 = 3x^4 + 16x^2 + 5$ Wrong middle term

$(3x^2 + 5)(x^2 + 1) = 3x^4 + 3x^2 + 5x^2 + 5 = 3x^4 + 8x^2 + 5$ Correct!

Therefore, $3x^4 + 8x^2 + 5 = (3x^2 + 5)(x^2 + 1)$.

Skill Practice

Factor.

6. $2y^4 - y^2 - 15$

Answers

5. Prime   **6.** $(y^2 - 3)(2y^2 + 5)$

Section 6.3 Practice Exercises

Vocabulary and Key Concepts

1. **a.** Which is the correct factored form of $2x^2 - 5x - 12$? The product $(2x + 3)(x - 4)$ or $(x - 4)(2x + 3)$?

   b. Which is the complete factorization of $6x^2 - 4x - 10$? The product $(3x - 5)(2x + 2)$ or $2(3x - 5)(x + 1)$?

Review Exercises

For Exercises 2–6, factor completely.

2. $5uv^2 - 10u^2v + 25u^2v^2$

3. $mn - m - 2n + 2$

4. $5x - 10 - xy + 2y$

5. $6a^2 - 30a - 84$

6. $10b^2 + 20b - 240$

Concept 1: Factoring Trinomials by the Trial-and-Error Method

For Exercises 7–10, assume a, b, and c represent positive integers.

7. When factoring a polynomial of the form $ax^2 + bx + c$, pick an appropriate combination of signs.

   a. (+)(+)

   b. (−)(−)

   c. (+)(−)

8. When factoring a polynomial of the form $ax^2 - bx - c$, pick an appropriate combination of signs.

   a. (+)(+)

   b. (−)(−)

   c. (+)(−)

9. When factoring a polynomial of the form $ax^2 - bx + c$, pick an appropriate combination of signs.

   a. (+)(+)

   b. (−)(−)

   c. (+)(−)

10. When factoring a polynomial of the form $ax^2 + bx - c$, pick an appropriate combination of signs.

    a. (+)(+)

    b. (−)(−)

    c. (+)(−)

For Exercises 11–28, factor completely by using the trial-and-error method. **(See Examples 1, 2, and 5.)**

11. $3n^2 + 13n + 4$

12. $2w^2 + 5w - 3$

13. $2y^2 - 3y - 2$

14. $2a^2 + 7a + 6$

15. $5x^2 - 14x - 3$

16. $7y^2 + 9y - 10$

17. $12c^2 - 5c - 2$

18. $6z^2 + z - 12$

19. $-12 + 10w^2 + 37w$

20. $-10 + 10p^2 + 21p$

21. $-5q - 6 + 6q^2$

22. $17a - 2 + 3a^2$

23. $6b - 23 + 4b^2$

24. $8 + 7x^2 - 18x$

25. $-8 + 25m^2 - 10m$

26. $8q^2 + 31q - 4$

27. $6y^2 + 19xy - 20x^2$

28. $12y^2 - 73yz + 6z^2$

For Exercises 29–36, factor completely. Be sure to factor out the GCF first. **(See Examples 3 and 4.)**

29. $2m^2 - 12m - 80$

30. $3c^2 - 33c + 72$

31. $2y^5 + 13y^4 + 6y^3$

32. $3u^8 - 13u^7 + 4u^6$

33. $-a^2 - 15a + 34$

34. $-x^2 - 7x - 10$

35. $80m^2 - 100mp - 30p^2$

36. $60w^2 + 550wz - 500z^2$

For Exercises 37–42, factor the higher degree polynomial. **(See Example 6.)**

37. $x^4 + 10x^2 + 9$

38. $y^4 + 4y^2 - 21$

39. $w^4 + 2w^2 - 15$

40. $p^4 - 13p^2 + 40$

41. $2x^4 - 7x^2 - 15$

42. $5y^4 + 11y^2 + 2$

Mixed Exercises

For Exercises 43–82, factor the trinomial completely.

43. $20z - 18 - 2z^2$

44. $25t - 5t^2 - 30$

45. $42 - 13q + q^2$

46. $-5w - 24 + w^2$

47. $6t^2 + 7t - 3$

48. $4p^2 - 9p + 2$

49. $4m^2 - 20m + 25$

50. $16r^2 + 24r + 9$

51. $5c^2 - c + 2$

52. $7s^2 + 2s + 9$

53. $6x^2 - 19xy + 10y^2$

54. $15p^2 + pq - 2q^2$

55. $12m^2 + 11mn - 5n^2$

56. $4a^2 + 5ab - 6b^2$

57. $30r^2 + 5r - 10$

58. $36x^2 - 18x - 4$

59. $4s^2 - 8st + t^2$

60. $6u^2 - 10uv + 5v^2$

61. $10t^2 - 23t - 5$

62. $16n^2 + 14n + 3$

63. $14w^2 + 13w - 12$

64. $12x^2 - 16x + 5$

65. $a^2 - 10a - 24$

66. $b^2 + 6b - 7$

67. $x^2 + 9xy + 20y^2$

68. $p^2 - 13pq + 36q^2$

69. $a^2 + 21ab + 20b^2$

70. $x^2 - 17xy - 18y^2$

71. $t^2 - 10t + 21$

72. $z^2 - 15z + 36$

73. $5d^3 + 3d^2 - 10d$

74. $3y^3 - y^2 + 12y$

75. $4b^3 - 4b^2 - 80b$

76. $2w^2 + 20w + 42$

77. $x^2y^2 - 13xy^2 + 30y^2$

78. $p^2q^2 - 14pq^2 + 33q^2$

79. $-12u^3 - 22u^2 + 20u$

80. $-18z^4 + 15z^3 + 12z^2$

81. $8x^4 + 14x^2 + 3$

82. $6y^4 - 5y^2 - 4$

83. A rock is thrown straight upward from the top of a 40-ft building. Its height in feet after t seconds is given by the polynomial $-16t^2 + 12t + 40$.

   a. Calculate the height of the rock after 1 s. $(t = 1)$

   b. Write $-16t^2 + 12t + 40$ in factored form. Then evaluate the factored form of the polynomial for $t = 1$. Is the result the same as from part (a)?

84. A baseball is thrown straight downward from the top of a 120-ft building. Its height in feet after t seconds is given by $-16t^2 - 8t + 120$.

   a. Calculate the height of the ball after 2 s. $(t = 2)$

   b. Write $-16t^2 - 8t + 120$ in factored form. Then evaluate the factored form of the polynomial for $t = 2$. Is the result the same as from part (a)?

Expanding Your Skills

For Exercises 85–88, each pair of trinomials looks similar but differs by one sign. Factor each trinomial, and see how their factored forms differ.

85 **a.** $x^2 - 10x - 24$

   b. $x^2 - 10x + 24$

86. **a.** $x^2 - 13x - 30$

   b. $x^2 - 13x + 30$

87. **a.** $x^2 - 5x - 6$

   b. $x^2 - 5x + 6$

88. **a.** $x^2 - 10x + 9$

   b. $x^2 + 10x + 9$

Section 6.4 Factoring Trinomials: AC-Method

Concept

1. Factoring Trinomials by the AC-Method

In Section 6.2, we factored trinomials with a leading coefficient of 1. In Section 6.3, we learned the trial-and-error method to factor the more general case in which the leading coefficient is any integer. In this section, we provide an alternative method to factor trinomials, called the ac-method.

1. Factoring Trinomials by the AC-Method

The product of two binomials results in a four-term expression that can sometimes be simplified to a trinomial. To factor the trinomial, we want to reverse the process.

Multiply:

$$\underset{\text{Multiply the binomials.}}{(2x + 3)(x + 2)} = \longrightarrow \underset{\text{Add the middle terms.}}{2x^2 + 4x + 3x + 6} = \longrightarrow 2x^2 + 7x + 6$$

Factor:

$$2x^2 + 7x + 6 = \longrightarrow 2x^2 + 4x + 3x + 6 = \longrightarrow (2x + 3)(x + 2)$$

$$\underset{\text{Rewrite the middle term as a sum or difference of terms.}}{} \qquad \underset{\text{Factor by grouping.}}{}$$

To factor a quadratic trinomial, $ax^2 + bx + c$, by the ac-method, we rewrite the middle term, bx, as a sum or difference of terms. The goal is to produce a four-term polynomial that can be factored by grouping. The process is outlined as follows.

AC-Method: Factoring $ax^2 + bx + c$ ($a \neq 0$)

Step 1 Factor out the GCF from all terms.

Step 2 Multiply the coefficients of the first and last terms (ac).

Step 3 Find two integers whose product is ac and whose sum is b. (If no pair of integers can be found, then the trinomial cannot be factored further and is a *prime polynomial*.)

Step 4 Rewrite the middle term, bx, as the sum of two terms whose coefficients are the integers found in step 3.

Step 5 Factor the polynomial by grouping.

The ac-method for factoring trinomials is illustrated in Example 1. However, before we begin, keep these two important guidelines in mind:

- For any factoring problem you encounter, always factor out the GCF from all terms first.
- To factor a trinomial, write the trinomial in the form $ax^2 + bx + c$.

Example 1 **Factoring a Trinomial by the AC-Method**

Factor the trinomial by the ac-method: $2x^2 + 7x + 6$

Solution:

$2x^2 + 7x + 6$

Step 1: Factor out the GCF from all terms. In this case, the GCF is 1. The trinomial is written in the form $ax^2 + bx + c$.

$a = 2, b = 7, c = 6$

Step 2: Find the product $ac = (2)(6) = 12$.

$\underline{12}$	$\underline{12}$
$1 \cdot 12$	$(-1)(-12)$
$2 \cdot 6$	$(-2)(-6)$
$3 \cdot 4$	$(-3)(-4)$

Step 3: List all factors of ac and search for the pair whose sum equals the value of b. That is, list the factors of 12 and find the pair whose sum equals 7.

The numbers 3 and 4 satisfy both conditions: $3 \cdot 4 = 12$ and $3 + 4 = 7$.

$2x^2 + 7x + 6$

$= 2x^2 + 3x + 4x + 6$

Step 4: Write the middle term of the trinomial as the sum of two terms whose coefficients are the selected pair of numbers: 3 and 4.

$= 2x^2 + 3x \mid + 4x + 6$ **Step 5:** Factor by grouping.

$= x(2x + 3) + 2(2x + 3)$

$= (2x + 3)(x + 2)$

Check: $(2x + 3)(x + 2) = 2x^2 + 4x + 3x + 6$

$= 2x^2 + 7x + 6$ ✔

Skill Practice

Factor by the ac-method.

1. $2x^2 + 5x + 3$

TIP: One frequently asked question is whether the order matters when we rewrite the middle term of the trinomial as two terms (step 4). The answer is no. From the previous example, the two middle terms in step 4 could have been reversed to obtain the same result:

$$2x^2 + 7x + 6$$
$$= 2x^2 + 4x + 3x + 6$$
$$= 2x(x + 2) + 3(x + 2)$$
$$= (x + 2)(2x + 3)$$

This example also points out that the order in which two factors are written does not matter. The expression $(x + 2)(2x + 3)$ is equivalent to $(2x + 3)(x + 2)$ because multiplication is a commutative operation.

Answer

1. $(x + 1)(2x + 3)$

Example 2 Factoring a Trinomial by the AC-Method

Factor the trinomial by the ac-method: $-2x + 8x^2 - 3$

Solution:

$-2x + 8x^2 - 3$ First rewrite the polynomial in the form $ax^2 + bx + c$.

$= 8x^2 - 2x - 3$ **Step 1:** The GCF is 1.

$a = 8, b = -2, c = -3$ **Step 2:** Find the product $ac = (8)(-3) = -24$.

-24	-24
$-1 \cdot 24$	$-24 \cdot 1$
$-2 \cdot 12$	$-12 \cdot 2$
$-3 \cdot 8$	$-8 \cdot 3$
$-4 \cdot 6$	$-6 \cdot 4$

Step 3: List all the factors of -24 and find the pair of factors whose sum equals -2.

The numbers -6 and 4 satisfy both conditions: $(-6)(4) = -24$ and $-6 + 4 = -2$.

$= 8x^2 - 2x - 3$ **Step 4:** Write the middle term of the trinomial as two terms whose coefficients are the selected pair of numbers, -6 and 4.

$= 8x^2 - 6x + 4x - 3$

$= 8x^2 - 6x \ \vdots + 4x - 3$ **Step 5:** Factor by grouping.

$= 2x(4x - 3) + 1(4x - 3)$

$= (4x - 3)(2x + 1)$

Check: $(4x - 3)(2x + 1) = 8x^2 + 4x - 6x - 3$

$= 8x^2 - 2x - 3$ ✔

Example 3 Factoring a Trinomial by the AC-Method

Factor the trinomial by the ac-method: $10x^3 - 85x^2 + 105x$

Solution:

$10x^3 - 85x^2 + 105x$ **Step 1:** Factor out the GCF of $5x$.

$= 5x(2x^2 - 17x + 21)$ The trinomial is in the form $ax^2 + bx + c$.

$a = 2, b = -17, c = 21$ **Step 2:** Find the product $ac = (2)(21) = 42$.

42	42
$1 \cdot 42$	$(-1)(-42)$
$2 \cdot 21$	$(-2)(-21)$
$3 \cdot 14$	$(-3)(-14)$
$6 \cdot 7$	$(-6)(-7)$

Step 3: List all the factors of 42 and find the pair whose sum equals -17.

The numbers -3 and -14 satisfy both conditions: $(-3)(-14) = 42$ and $-3 + (-14) = -17$.

Answers

2. $(2w + 3)(3w + 2)$
3. $3y(3y - 4)(y - 2)$

$= 5x(2x^2 - 17x + 21)$

Step 4: Write the middle term of the trinomial as two terms whose coefficients are the selected pair of numbers, -3 and -14.

$= 5x(2x^2 - 3x - 14x + 21)$

$= 5x(2x^2 - 3x \mid - 14x + 21)$ **Step 5:** Factor by grouping.

$= 5x[x(2x - 3) - 7(2x - 3)]$

$= 5x(2x - 3)(x - 7)$

Avoiding Mistakes

Remember to bring down the GCF in each successive step as you factor.

TIP: Notice when the GCF is removed from the original trinomial, the new trinomial has smaller coefficients. This makes the factoring process simpler because the product ac is smaller. It is much easier to list the factors of 42 than the factors of 1050.

Original trinomial	**With the GCF factored out**
$10x^3 - 85x^2 + 105x$	$5x(2x^2 - 17x + 21)$
$ac = (10)(105) = 1050$	$ac = (2)(21) = 42$

In most cases, it is easier to factor a trinomial with a positive leading coefficient.

Example 4   Factoring a Trinomial by the AC-Method

Factor: $-18x^2 + 21xy + 15y^2$

Solution:

$-18x^2 + 21xy + 15y^2$ **Step 1:** Factor out the GCF.

$= -3(6x^2 - 7xy - 5y^2)$ Factor out -3 to make the leading term positive.

                               Step 2: The product $ac = (6)(-5) = -30$.

                               Step 3: The numbers -10 and 3 have a product of -30 and a sum of -7.

$= -3[6x^2 - 10xy + 3xy - 5y^2]$ **Step 4:** Rewrite the middle term, $-7xy$ as $-10xy + 3xy$.

$= -3[6x^2 - 10xy \mid + 3xy - 5y^2]$ **Step 5:** Factor by grouping.

$= -3[2x(3x - 5y) + y(3x - 5y)]$

$= -3(3x - 5y)(2x + y)$ Factored form

Skill Practice

Factor.

4. $-8x^2 - 8xy + 30y^2$

Recall that a prime polynomial is a polynomial whose only factors are itself and 1. It also should be noted that not every trinomial is factorable by the methods presented in this text.

Answer

4. $-2(2x - 3y)(2x + 5y)$

Example 5 **Factoring a Trinomial by the AC-Method**

Factor the trinomial by the ac-method: $2p^2 - 8p + 3$

Solution:

$2p^2 - 8p + 3$ **Step 1:** The GCF is 1.

                Step 2: The product $ac = 6$.

$\underline{6}$	$\underline{6}$
$1 \cdot 6$	$(-1)(-6)$
$2 \cdot 3$	$(-2)(-3)$

Step 3: List the factors of 6. Notice that no pair of factors has a sum of -8. Therefore, the trinomial cannot be factored.

The trinomial $2p^2 - 8p + 3$ is a prime polynomial.

In Example 6, we use the ac-method to factor a higher degree trinomial.

Example 6 **Factoring a Higher Degree Trinomial**

Factor the trinomial. $2x^4 + 5x^2 + 2$

Solution:

$2x^4 + 5x^2 + 2$ **Step 1:** The GCF is 1.

$a = 2, b = 5, c = 2$ **Step 2:** Find the product $ac = (2)(2) = 4$.

                Step 3: The numbers 1 and 4 have a product of 4 and a sum of 5.

$= 2x^4 + x^2 + 4x^2 + 2$ **Step 4:** Rewrite the middle term, $5x^2$, as $x^2 + 4x^2$.

$= 2x^4 + x^2 + 4x^2 + 2$ **Step 5:** Factor by grouping.

$= x^2(2x^2 + 1) + 2(2x^2 + 1)$

$= (2x^2 + 1)(x^2 + 2)$ Factored form.

Section 6.4   Practice Exercises

Vocabulary and Key Concepts

1. a. Which is the correct factored form of $10x^2 - 13x - 3$? The product $(5x + 1)(2x - 3)$ or $(2x - 3)(5x + 1)$?

   b. Which is the complete factorization of $12x^2 - 15x - 18$? The product $(4x + 3)(3x - 6)$ or $3(4x + 3)(x - 2)$?

Review Exercises

For Exercises 2–4, factor completely.

2. $5x(x - 2) - 2(x - 2)$ **3.** $8(y + 5) + 9y(y + 5)$

4. $6ab + 24b - 12a - 48$

Concept 1: Factoring Trinomials by the AC-Method

For Exercises 5–12, find the pair of integers whose product and sum are given.

5. Product: 12   Sum: 13

6. Product: 12   Sum: 7

7. Product: 8   Sum: -9

8. Product: -4 Sum: -3

9. Product: -20 Sum: 1

10. Product: -6 Sum: -1

11. Product: -18 Sum: 7

12. Product: -72 Sum: -6

For Exercises 13–30, factor the trinomials using the ac-method. **(See Examples 1, 2, and 5.)**

13. $3x^2 + 13x + 4$

14. $2y^2 + 7y + 6$

15. $4w^2 - 9w + 2$

16. $2p^2 - 3p - 2$

17. $x^2 + 7x - 18$

18. $y^2 - 6y - 40$

19. $2m^2 + 5m - 3$

20. $6n^2 + 7n - 3$

21. $8k^2 - 6k - 9$

22. $9h^2 - 3h - 2$

23. $4k^2 - 20k + 25$

24. $16h^2 + 24h + 9$

25. $5x^2 + x + 7$

26. $4y^2 - y + 2$

27. $10 + 9z^2 - 21z$

28. $13x + 4x^2 - 12$

29. $12y^2 + 8yz - 15z^2$

30. $20a^2 + 3ab - 9b^2$

For Exercises 31–38, factor completely. Be sure to factor out the GCF first. **(See Examples 3 and 4.)**

31. $50y + 24 + 14y^2$

32. $-24 + 10w + 4w^2$

33. $-15w^2 + 22w + 5$

34. $-16z^2 + 34z + 15$

35. $-12x^2 + 20xy - 8y^2$

36. $-6p^2 - 21pq - 9q^2$

37. $18y^3 + 60y^2 + 42y$

38. $8t^3 - 4t^2 - 40t$

For Exercises 39–44, factor the higher degree polynomial. **(See Example 6.)**

39. $a^4 + 5a^2 + 6$

40. $y^4 - 2y^2 - 35$

41. $6x^4 - x^2 - 15$

42. $8t^4 + 2t^2 - 3$

43. $8p^4 + 37p^2 - 15$

44. $2a^4 + 11a^2 + 14$

Mixed Exercises

For Exercises 45–80, factor completely.

45. $20p^2 - 19p + 3$

46. $4p^2 + 5pq - 6q^2$

47. $6u^2 - 19uv + 10v^2$

48. $15m^2 + mn - 2n^2$

49. $12a^2 + 11ab - 5b^2$

50. $3r^2 - rs - 14s^2$

51. $3h^2 + 19hk - 14k^2$

52. $2u^2 + uv - 15v^2$

53. $2x^2 - 13xy + y^2$

54. $3p^2 + 20pq - q^2$

55. $3 - 14z + 16z^2$

56. $10w + 1 + 16w^2$

57. $b^2 + 16 - 8b$

58. $1 + q^2 - 2q$

59. $25x - 5x^2 - 30$

60. $20a - 18 - 2a^2$

61. $-6 - t + t^2$

62. $-6 + m + m^2$

63. $v^2 + 2v + 15$

64. $x^2 - x - 1$

65. $72x^2 + 18x - 2$

66. $20y^2 - 78y - 8$

67. $p^3 - 6p^2 - 27p$

68. $w^5 - 11w^4 + 28w^3$

69. $3x^3 + 10x^2 + 7x$

70. $4r^3 + 3r^2 - 10r$

71. $2p^3 - 38p^2 + 120p$

72. $4q^3 - 4q^2 - 80q$

73. $x^2y^2 + 14x^2y + 33x^2$

74. $a^2b^2 + 13ab^2 + 30b^2$

75. $-k^2 - 7k - 10$

76. $-m^2 - 15m + 34$

77. $-3n^2 - 3n + 90$

78. $-2h^2 + 28h - 90$

79. $x^4 - 7x^2 + 10$

80. $m^4 + 10m^2 + 21$

81. Is the expression $(2x + 4)(x - 7)$ factored completely? Explain why or why not.

82. Is the expression $(3x + 1)(5x - 10)$ factored completely? Explain why or why not.

83. Colleen noticed that the number of tables placed in her restaurant affects the number of customers who eat at the restaurant. The number of customers each night is given by $-2x^2 + 40x - 72$, where x is the number of tables set up in the room, and $2 \le x \le 18$.

   a. Calculate the number of customers when there are 10 tables set up. $(x = 10)$

   b. Write $-2x^2 + 40x - 72$ in factored form. Then evaluate the factored form of the polynomial for $x = 10$. Is the result the same as from part (a)?

84. Roland sells skins for smartphones online. He noticed that for every dollar he discounts the price, he sells two more skins per week. His income in dollars each week is given by $-2d^2 + 30d + 200$, where d is the dollar amount of discount in price.

   a. Calculate his income if his discount is $2. $(d = 2)$

   b. Write $-2d^2 + 30d + 200$ in factored form. Then evaluate the factored form of the polynomial for $d = 2$. Is the result the same as from part (a)?

85. A formula for finding the sum of the first n even integers is given by $n^2 + n$.

   a. Find the sum of the first 6 even integers $(2 + 4 + 6 + 8 + 10 + 12)$ by evaluating the expression for $n = 6$.

   b. Write the polynomial in factored form. Then evaluate the factored form of the expression for $n = 6$. Is the result the same as part (a)?

86. A formula for finding the sum of the squares of the first n integers is given by $\dfrac{2n^3 + 3n^2 + n}{6}$.

   a. Find the sum of the squares of the first 4 integers $(1^2 + 2^2 + 3^2 + 4^2)$ by evaluating the expression for $n = 4$.

   b. Write the polynomial in the numerator of the expression in factored form. Then evaluate the factored form of the expression for $n = 4$. Is the result the same as part (a)?

Section 6.5   Difference of Squares and Perfect Square Trinomials

Concepts

1. Factoring a Difference of Squares
2. Factoring Perfect Square Trinomials

1. Factoring a Difference of Squares

Up to this point, we have learned several methods of factoring, including:

- Factoring out the greatest common factor from a polynomial
- Factoring a four-term polynomial by grouping
- Factoring trinomials by the ac-method or by the trial-and-error method

In this section, we begin by factoring a special binomial called a difference of squares. Recall from Section 5.6 that the product of two conjugates results in a **difference of squares**:

$$(a + b)(a - b) = a^2 - b^2$$

Therefore, to factor a difference of squares, the process is reversed. Identify a and b and construct the conjugate factors.

Factored Form of a Difference of Squares

$$a^2 - b^2 = (a + b)(a - b)$$

To help recognize a difference of squares, we recommend that you become familiar with the first several perfect squares.

Perfect Squares	Perfect Squares	Perfect Squares
$1 = (1)^2$	$36 = (6)^2$	$121 = (11)^2$
$4 = (2)^2$	$49 = (7)^2$	$144 = (12)^2$
$9 = (3)^2$	$64 = (8)^2$	$169 = (13)^2$
$16 = (4)^2$	$81 = (9)^2$	$196 = (14)^2$
$25 = (5)^2$	$100 = (10)^2$	$225 = (15)^2$

It is also important to recognize that a variable expression is a perfect square if its exponent is a multiple of 2. For example:

Perfect Squares

$$x^2 = (x)^2$$
$$x^4 = (x^2)^2$$
$$x^6 = (x^3)^2$$
$$x^8 = (x^4)^2$$
$$x^{10} = (x^5)^2$$

Example 1 **Factoring Differences of Squares**

Factor the binomials.

a. $y^2 - 25$ **b.** $49s^2 - 4t^4$ **c.** $18w^2z - 2z$

Solution:

a. $y^2 - 25$ 　　　　　　　　The binomial is a difference of squares.

$\quad = (y)^2 - (5)^2$ 　　　　　Write in the form: $a^2 - b^2$, where $a = y, b = 5$.

$\quad = (y + 5)(y - 5)$ 　　　　Factor as $(a + b)(a - b)$.

b. $49s^2 - 4t^4$ 　　　　　　The binomial is a difference of squares.

$\quad = (7s)^2 - (2t^2)^2$ 　　　　Write in the form $a^2 - b^2$, where $a = 7s$ and $b = 2t^2$.

$\quad = (7s + 2t^2)(7s - 2t^2)$ 　　Factor as $(a + b)(a - b)$.

c. $18w^2z - 2z$ The GCF is $2z$.

$= 2z(9w^2 - 1)$ $(9w^2 - 1)$ is a difference of squares.

$= 2z[(3w)^2 - (1)^2]$ Write in the form: $a^2 - b^2$, where $a = 3w, b = 1$.

$= 2z(3w + 1)(3w - 1)$ Factor as $(a + b)(a - b)$.

The difference of squares $a^2 - b^2$ factors as $(a + b)(a - b)$. However, the *sum* of squares is not factorable.

> ## Sum of Squares
> Suppose a and b have no common factors. Then the **sum of squares** $a^2 + b^2$ is *not* factorable over the real numbers.
>
> That is, $a^2 + b^2$ is prime over the real numbers.

To see why $a^2 + b^2$ is not factorable, consider the product of binomials:

$$(a + b)(a - b) = a^2 - b^2 \qquad \text{Wrong sign}$$
$$(a + b)(a + b) = a^2 + 2ab + b^2 \qquad \text{Wrong middle term}$$
$$(a - b)(a - b) = a^2 - 2ab + b^2 \qquad \text{Wrong middle term}$$

After exhausting all possibilities, we see that if a and b share no common factors, then the sum of squares $a^2 + b^2$ is a prime polynomial.

Example 2   Factoring Binomials

Factor the binomials, if possible.   **a.** $p^2 - 9$ **b.** $p^2 + 9$

Solution:

a. $p^2 - 9$ Difference of squares

$= (p - 3)(p + 3)$ Factor as $a^2 - b^2 = (a - b)(a + b)$.

b. $p^2 + 9$ Sum of squares

     Prime (cannot be factored)

Skill Practice

Factor the binomials, if possible.
4. $t^2 - 144$
5. $t^2 + 144$

Some factoring problems require several steps. Always be sure to factor completely.

Example 3   Factoring the Difference of Squares

Factor completely. $w^4 - 81$

Solution:

$w^4 - 81$ The GCF is 1. $w^4 - 81$ is a difference of squares.

$= (w^2)^2 - (9)^2$ Write in the form: $a^2 - b^2$, where $a = w^2, b = 9$.

$= (w^2 + 9)(w^2 - 9)$ Factor as $(a + b)(a - b)$.

$= (w^2 + 9)(w + 3)(w - 3)$ Note that $w^2 - 9$ can be factored further as a difference of squares. (The binomial $w^2 + 9$ is a sum of squares and cannot be factored further.)

Skill Practice

Factor completely.
6. $y^4 - 1$

Answers
4. $(t - 12)(t + 12)$
5. Prime
6. $(y + 1)(y - 1)(y^2 + 1)$

Example 4 Factoring a Polynomial

Factor completely. $y^3 - 5y^2 - 4y + 20$

Solution:

$y^3 - 5y^2 - 4y + 20$ The GCF is 1. The polynomial has four terms. Factor by grouping.

$= y^3 - 5y^2 \mid - 4y + 20$

$= y^2(y - 5) - 4(y - 5)$

$= (y - 5)(y^2 - 4)$ The expression $y^2 - 4$ is a difference of squares and can be factored further as $(y - 2)(y + 2)$.

$= (y - 5)(y - 2)(y + 2)$

Check: $(y - 5)(y - 2)(y + 2) = (y - 5)(y^2 - 2y + 2y - 4)$

$= (y - 5)(y^2 - 4)$

$= (y^3 - 4y - 5y^2 + 20)$

$= y^3 - 5y^2 - 4y + 20$ ✔

Skill Practice

Factor completely.

7. $p^3 + 7p^2 - 9p - 63$

2. Factoring Perfect Square Trinomials

Recall from Section 5.6 that the square of a binomial always results in a **perfect square trinomial**.

$$(a + b)^2 = (a + b)(a + b) \xrightarrow{\text{Multiply.}} = a^2 + 2ab + b^2$$

$$(a - b)^2 = (a - b)(a - b) \xrightarrow{\text{Multiply.}} = a^2 - 2ab + b^2$$

For example, $(3x + 5)^2 = (3x)^2 + 2(3x)(5) + (5)^2$

$$= 9x^2 + 30x + 25 \text{ (perfect square trinomial)}$$

We now want to reverse this process by factoring a perfect square trinomial. The trial-and-error method or the ac-method can always be used; however, if we recognize the pattern for a perfect square trinomial, we can use one of the following formulas to reach a quick solution.

Factored Form of a Perfect Square Trinomial

$$a^2 + 2ab + b^2 = (a + b)^2$$

$$a^2 - 2ab + b^2 = (a - b)^2$$

For example, $4x^2 + 36x + 81$ is a perfect square trinomial with $a = 2x$ and $b = 9$. Therefore, it factors as

$$4x^2 + 36x + 81 = (2x)^2 + 2(2x)(9) + (9)^2 = (2x + 9)^2$$

$$a^2 \ + 2 \ (a) \ (b) + (b)^2 = \ (a \ + \ b)^2$$

Answer

7. $(p - 3)(p + 3)(p + 7)$

To apply the formula to factor a perfect square trinomial, we must first be sure that the trinomial is indeed a perfect square trinomial.

Checking for a Perfect Square Trinomial

Step 1   Determine whether the first and third terms are both perfect squares and have positive coefficients.

Step 2   If this is the case, identify a and b, and determine if the middle term equals $2ab$ or $-2ab$.

Example 5   Factoring Perfect Square Trinomials

Factor the trinomials completely.

a. $x^2 + 14x + 49$ **b.** $25y^2 - 20y + 4$

Solution:

a. $x^2 + 14x + 49$ The GCF is 1.

- The first and third terms are positive.
- The first term is a perfect square: $x^2 = (x)^2$.

Perfect squares

$x^2 + 14x + 49$

- The third term is a perfect square: $49 = (7)^2$.
- The middle term is twice the product of x and 7: $14x = 2(x)(7)$.

$= (x)^2 + 2(x)(7) + (7)^2$ The trinomial is in the form $a^2 + 2ab + b^2$, where $a = x$ and $b = 7$.

$= (x + 7)^2$ Factor as $(a + b)^2$.

b. $25y^2 - 20y + 4$ The GCF is 1.

Perfect squares

$25y^2 - 20y + 4$

- The first and third terms are positive.
- The first term is a perfect square: $25y^2 = (5y)^2$.
- The third term is a perfect square: $4 = (2)^2$.

$= (5y)^2 - 2(5y)(2) + (2)^2$ •   In the middle: $20y = 2(5y)(2)$

$= (5y - 2)^2$ Factor as $(a - b)^2$.

Example 6 **Factoring Perfect Square Trinomials**

Factor the trinomials completely.

a. $18c^3 - 48c^2d + 32cd^2$　　　**b.** $5w^2 + 50w + 45$

Solution:

a. $18c^3 - 48c^2d + 32cd^2$

$= 2c(9c^2 - 24cd + 16d^2)$　　　The GCF is $2c$.

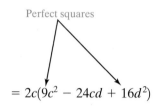

$= 2c(9c^2 - 24cd + 16d^2)$

$= 2c[(3c)^2 - 2(3c)(4d) + (4d)^2]$

$= 2c(3c - 4d)^2$

- The first and third terms are positive.
- The first term is a perfect square: $9c^2 = (3c)^2$.
- The third term is a perfect square: $16d^2 = (4d)^2$.
- In the middle: $24cd = 2(3c)(4d)$

Factor as $(a - b)^2$.

b. $5w^2 + 50w + 45$

$= 5(w^2 + 10w + 9)$　　　The GCF is 5.

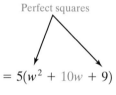

$= 5(w^2 + 10w + 9)$

The first and third terms are perfect squares.

$$w^2 = (w)^2 \quad \text{and} \quad 9 = (3)^2$$

However, the middle term is not 2 times the product of w and 3. Therefore, this is not a perfect square trinomial.

$$10w \neq 2(w)(3)$$

$= 5(w + 9)(w + 1)$　　　To factor, use the trial-and-error method.

TIP: If you do not recognize that a trinomial is a perfect square trinomial, you can still use the trial-and-error method or ac-method to factor it.

Answers
10. $5z(z + 2w)^2$
11. $10(4x + 9)(x + 1)$

Section 6.5 Practice Exercises

Vocabulary and Key Concepts

1. a. The binomial $x^2 - 16$ is an example of a _____ of squares. After factoring out the GCF, we factor a difference of squares $a^2 - b^2$ as _____.

b. The binomial $y^2 + 121$ is an example of a _____ of squares.

c. A sum of squares with greatest common factor 1 (is/is not) factorable over the real numbers.

d. The square of a binomial always results in a perfect _____ trinomial.

e. A perfect square trinomial $a^2 + 2ab + b^2$ factors as _____. Likewise, $a^2 - 2ab + b^2$ factors as _____.

Review Exercises

For Exercises 2–10, factor completely.

2. $3x^2 + x - 10$

3. $6x^2 - 17x + 5$

4. $6a^2b + 3a^3b$

5. $15x^2y^5 - 10xy^6$

6. $5p^2q + 20p^2 - 3pq - 12p$

7. $ax + ab - 6x - 6b$

8. $-6x + 5 + x^2$

9. $6y - 40 + y^2$

10. $a^2 + 7a + 1$

Concept 1: Factoring a Difference of Squares

11. What binomial factors as $(x - 5)(x + 5)$?

12. What binomial factors as $(n - 3)(n + 3)$?

13. What binomial factors as $(2p - 3q)(2p + 3q)$?

14. What binomial factors as $(7x - 4y)(7x + 4y)$?

For Exercises 15–38, factor the binomials completely. **(See Examples 1–3.)**

15. $x^2 - 36$

16. $r^2 - 81$

17. $3w^2 - 300$

18. $t^3 - 49t$

19. $4a^2 - 121b^2$

20. $9x^2 - y^2$

21. $49m^2 - 16n^2$

22. $100a^2 - 49b^2$

23. $9q^2 + 16$

24. $36 + s^2$

25. $y^2 - 4z^2$

26. $b^2 - 144c^2$

27. $a^2 - b^4$

28. $y^4 - x^2$

29. $25p^2q^2 - 1$

30. $81s^2t^2 - 1$

31. $c^2 - \dfrac{1}{25}$

32. $z^2 - \dfrac{1}{4}$

33. $50 - 32t^2$

34. $63 - 7h^2$

35. $z^4 - 16$

36. $y^4 - 625$

37. $16 - z^4$

38. $81 - a^4$

For Exercises 39–46, factor each polynomial completely. **(See Example 4.)**

39. $x^3 + 5x^2 - 9x - 45$

40. $y^3 + 6y^2 - 4y - 24$

41. $c^3 - c^2 - 25c + 25$

42. $t^3 + 2t^2 - 16t - 32$

43. $2x^2 - 18 + x^2y - 9y$

44. $5a^2 - 5 + a^2b - b$

45. $x^2y^2 - 9x^2 - 4y^2 + 36$

46. $w^2z^2 - w^2 - 25z^2 + 25$

Concept 2: Factoring Perfect Square Trinomials

47. Multiply. $(3x + 5)^2$

48. Multiply. $(2y - 7)^2$

49. a. Which trinomial is a perfect square trinomial? $x^2 + 4x + 4$ or $x^2 + 5x + 4$

b. Factor the trinomials from part (a).

50. a. Which trinomial is a perfect square trinomial? $x^2 + 13x + 36$ or $x^2 + 12x + 36$

b. Factor the trinomials from part (a).

For Exercises 51–68, factor completely. (*Hint:* Look for the pattern of a perfect square trinomial.) **(See Examples 5 and 6.)**

51. $x^2 + 18x + 81$

52. $y^2 - 8y + 16$

53. $25z^2 - 20z + 4$

54. $36p^2 + 60p + 25$

55. $49a^2 + 42ab + 9b^2$

56. $25m^2 - 30mn + 9n^2$

57. $-2y + y^2 + 1$

58. $4 + w^2 - 4w$

59. $80z^2 + 120zw + 45w^2$

60. $36p^2 - 24pq + 4q^2$

61. $9y^2 + 78y + 25$

62. $4y^2 + 20y + 9$

63. $2a^2 - 20a + 50$

64. $3t^2 + 18t + 27$

65. $4x^2 + x + 9$

66. $c^2 - 4c + 16$

67. $4x^2 + 4xy + y^2$

68. $100y^2 + 20yz + z^2$

69. The volume of the box shown is given as $3x^3 - 6x^2 + 3x$. Write the polynomial in factored form.

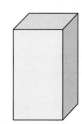

70. The volume of the box shown is given as $20y^3 + 20y^2 + 5y$. Write the polynomial in factored form.

Expanding Your Skills

For Exercises 71–78, factor the difference of squares.

71. $(y - 3)^2 - 9$

72. $(x - 2)^2 - 4$

73. $(2p + 1)^2 - 36$

74. $(4q + 3)^2 - 25$

75. $16 - (t + 2)^2$

76. $81 - (a + 5)^2$

77. $(2a - 5)^2 - 100b^2$

78. $(3k + 7)^2 - 49m^2$

79. a. Write a polynomial that represents the area of the shaded region in the figure.

    b. Factor the expression from part (a).

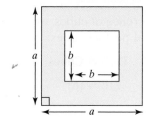

80. a. Write a polynomial that represents the area of the shaded region in the figure.

    b. Factor the expression from part (a).

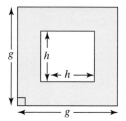

Sum and Difference of Cubes

Section 6.6

1. Factoring a Sum or Difference of Cubes

Concepts

1. Factoring a Sum or Difference of Cubes

2. Factoring Binomials: A Summary

A binomial $a^2 - b^2$ is a difference of squares and can be factored as $(a - b)(a + b)$. Furthermore, if a and b share no common factors, then a sum of squares $a^2 + b^2$ is not factorable over the real numbers. In this section, we will learn that both a difference of cubes, $a^3 - b^3$, and a sum of cubes, $a^3 + b^3$, are factorable.

Factored Form of a Sum or Difference of Cubes

Sum of Cubes: $\qquad a^3 + b^3 = (a + b)(a^2 - ab + b^2)$

Difference of Cubes: $\quad a^3 - b^3 = (a - b)(a^2 + ab + b^2)$

Multiplication can be used to confirm the formulas for factoring a sum or difference of cubes:

$$(a + b)(a^2 - ab + b^2) = a^3 - a^2b + ab^2 + a^2b - ab^2 + b^3 = a^3 + b^3 \ ✔$$

$$(a - b)(a^2 + ab + b^2) = a^3 + a^2b + ab^2 - a^2b - ab^2 - b^3 = a^3 - b^3 \ ✔$$

To help you remember the formulas for factoring a sum or difference of cubes, keep the following guidelines in mind:

- The factored form is the product of a binomial and a trinomial.
- The first and third terms in the trinomial are the squares of the terms within the binomial factor.
- Without regard to signs, the middle term in the trinomial is the product of the terms in the binomial factor.

Square the first term of the binomial.   Product of terms in the binomial

$$x^3 + 8 = (x)^3 + (2)^3 = (x + 2)[(x)^2 - (x)(2) + (2)^2]$$

Square the last term of the binomial.

- The sign within the binomial factor is the same as the sign of the original binomial.
- The first and third terms in the trinomial are always positive.
- The sign of the middle term in the trinomial is opposite the sign within the binomial.

Same sign   Positive

$$x^3 + 8 = (x)^3 + (2)^3 = (x + 2)[(x)^2 - (x)(2) + (2)^2]$$

Opposite signs

TIP: To help remember the placement of the signs in factoring the sum or difference of cubes, remember SOAP: **S**ame sign, **O**pposite signs, **A**lways **P**ositive.

To help you recognize a sum or difference of cubes, we recommend that you familiarize yourself with the first several perfect cubes:

Perfect Cubes	**Perfect Cubes**
$1 = (1)^3$	$216 = (6)^3$
$8 = (2)^3$	$343 = (7)^3$
$27 = (3)^3$	$512 = (8)^3$
$64 = (4)^3$	$729 = (9)^3$
$125 = (5)^3$	$1000 = (10)^3$

It is also helpful to recognize that a variable expression is a perfect cube if its exponent is a multiple of 3. For example:

Perfect Cubes

$$x^3 = (x)^3$$
$$x^6 = (x^2)^3$$
$$x^9 = (x^3)^3$$
$$x^{12} = (x^4)^3$$

Skill Practice

Factor.

1. $p^3 + 125$

Answer

1. $(p + 5)(p^2 - 5p + 25)$

Example 1   **Factoring a Sum of Cubes**

Factor: $w^3 + 64$

Solution:

$w^3 + 64$	w^3 and 64 are perfect cubes.
$= (w)^3 + (4)^3$	Write as $a^3 + b^3$, where $a = w, b = 4$.
$a^3 + b^3 = (a + b)(a^2 - ab + b^2)$	Apply the formula for a sum of cubes.
$(w)^3 + (4)^3 = (w + 4)[(w)^2 - (w)(4) + (4)^2]$	
$= (w + 4)(w^2 - 4w + 16)$	Simplify.

Example 2 Factoring a Difference of Cubes

Factor: $27p^3 - 1000q^3$

Solution:

$27p^3 - 1000q^3$ $27p^3$ and $1000q^3$ are perfect cubes.

$(3p)^3 - (10q)^3$ Write as $a^3 - b^3$, where $a = 3p$, $b = 10q$.

$\qquad a^3 - b^3 = (a - b)(a^2 + ab + b^2)$ Apply the formula for a difference of cubes.

$(3p)^3 - (10q)^3 = (3p - 10q)[(3p)^2 + (3p)(10q) + (10q)^2]$

$\qquad\qquad\qquad = (3p - 10q)(9p^2 + 30pq + 100q^2)$ Simplify.

Skill Practice

Factor.

2. $8y^3 - 27z^3$

2. Factoring Binomials: A Summary

After removing the GCF, the next step in any factoring problem is to recognize what type of pattern it follows. Exponents that are divisible by 2 are perfect squares and those divisible by 3 are perfect cubes. The formulas for factoring binomials are summarized in the following box:

Factored Forms of Binomials

Difference of Squares: $a^2 - b^2 = (a + b)(a - b)$

Difference of Cubes: $a^3 - b^3 = (a - b)(a^2 + ab + b^2)$

Sum of Cubes: $a^3 + b^3 = (a + b)(a^2 - ab + b^2)$

Example 3 Factoring Binomials

Factor completely.

a. $27y^3 + 1$ **b.** $m^2 - \dfrac{1}{4}$ **c.** $z^6 - 8w^3$

Solution:

a. $27y^3 + 1$ Sum of cubes: $27y^3 = (3y)^3$ and $1 = (1)^3$.

$= (3y)^3 + (1)^3$ Write as $a^3 + b^3$, where $a = 3y$ and $b = 1$.

$= (3y + 1)[(3y)^2 - (3y)(1) + (1)^2]$ Apply the formula $a^3 + b^3 = (a + b)(a^2 - ab + b^2)$.

$= (3y + 1)(9y^2 - 3y + 1)$ Simplify.

b. $m^2 - \dfrac{1}{4}$ Difference of squares

$= (m)^2 - \left(\dfrac{1}{2}\right)^2$ Write as $a^2 - b^2$, where $a = m$ and $b = \frac{1}{2}$.

$= \left(m + \dfrac{1}{2}\right)\left(m - \dfrac{1}{2}\right)$ Apply the formula $a^2 - b^2 = (a + b)(a - b)$.

Skill Practice

Factor completely.

3. $1000x^3 + 1$

4. $25p^2 - \dfrac{1}{9}$

5. $27a^6 - b^3$

Answers

2. $(2y - 3z)(4y^2 + 6yz + 9z^2)$

3. $(10x + 1)(100x^2 - 10x + 1)$

4. $\left(5p - \dfrac{1}{3}\right)\left(5p + \dfrac{1}{3}\right)$

5. $(3a^2 - b)(9a^4 + 3a^2b + b^2)$

c. $z^6 - 8w^3$ Difference of cubes: $z^6 = (z^2)^3$ and $8w^3 = (2w)^3$

$= (z^2)^3 - (2w)^3$ Write as $a^3 - b^3$, where $a = z^2$ and $b = 2w$.

$= (z^2 - 2w)[(z^2)^2 + (z^2)(2w) + (2w)^2]$ Apply the formula $a^3 - b^3 = (a - b)(a^2 + ab + b^2)$.

$= (z^2 - 2w)(z^4 + 2z^2w + 4w^2)$ Simplify.

Each of the factorizations in Example 3 can be checked by multiplying.

Some factoring problems require more than one method of factoring. In general, when factoring a polynomial, be sure to factor completely.

Skill Practice

Factor completely.

6. $2x^4 - 2$

Example 4   **Factoring Polynomials**

Factor completely. $3y^4 - 48$

Solution:

$3y^4 - 48$

$= 3(y^4 - 16)$ Factor out the GCF. The binomial is a difference of squares.

$= 3[(y^2)^2 - (4)^2]$ Write as $a^2 - b^2$, where $a = y^2$ and $b = 4$.

$= 3(y^2 + 4)(y^2 - 4)$ Apply the formula $a^2 - b^2 = (a + b)(a - b)$.

$y^2 + 4$ is a sum of squares and cannot be factored.

$= 3(y^2 + 4)(y + 2)(y - 2)$ $y^2 - 4$ is a difference of squares and can be factored further.

Skill Practice

Factor completely.

7. $x^3 + 6x^2 - 4x - 24$

Example 5   **Factoring Polynomials**

Factor completely. $4x^3 + 4x^2 - 25x - 25$

Solution:

$4x^3 + 4x^2 - 25x - 25$ The GCF is 1.

$= 4x^3 + 4x^2 - 25x - 25$ The polynomial has four terms. Factor by grouping.

$= 4x^2(x + 1) - 25(x + 1)$

$= (x + 1)(4x^2 - 25)$ $4x^2 - 25$ is a difference of squares.

$= (x + 1)(2x + 5)(2x - 5)$

Answers

6. $2(x^2 + 1)(x - 1)(x + 1)$
7. $(x + 6)(x + 2)(x - 2)$

Example 6	Factoring Binomials

Factor the binomial $x^6 - y^6$ as

a. A difference of cubes   **b.** A difference of squares

Notice that the expressions x^6 and y^6 are both perfect squares and perfect cubes because both exponents are multiples of 2 and of 3. Consequently, $x^6 - y^6$ can be factored initially as either the difference of squares or as the difference of cubes.

Skill Practice

Factor completely.

8. $z^6 - 64$

Solution:

a. $x^6 - y^6$

Difference of cubes

$= (x^2)^3 - (y^2)^3$

Write as $a^3 - b^3$, where $a = x^2$ and $b = y^2$.

$= (x^2 - y^2)[(x^2)^2 + (x^2)(y^2) + (y^2)^2]$

Apply the formula $a^3 - b^3 = (a - b)(a^2 + ab + b^2)$.

$= (x^2 - y^2)(x^4 + x^2y^2 + y^4)$

Factor $x^2 - y^2$ as a difference of squares.

$= (x + y)(x - y)(x^4 + x^2y^2 + y^4)$

b. $x^6 - y^6$

Difference of squares

$= (x^3)^2 - (y^3)^2$

Write as $a^2 - b^2$, where $a = x^3$ and $b = y^3$.

$= (x^3 + y^3)(x^3 - y^3)$

Apply the formula $a^2 - b^2 = (a + b)(a - b)$.

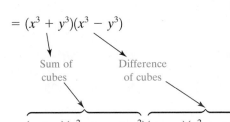

Sum of cubes   Difference of cubes

Factor $x^3 + y^3$ as a sum of cubes.

Factor $x^3 - y^3$ as a difference of cubes.

$= (x + y)(x^2 - xy + y^2)(x - y)(x^2 + xy + y^2)$

In a case such as this, it is recommended that you factor the expression as a difference of squares first because it factors more completely into polynomials of lower degree.

$$x^6 - y^6 = (x + y)(x^2 - xy + y^2)(x - y)(x^2 + xy + y^2)$$

Answer

8. $(z + 2)(z - 2)(z^2 + 2z + 4)$
$(z^2 - 2z + 4)$

Section 6.6   Practice Exercises

Vocabulary and Key Concepts

1. **a.** The binomial $x^3 + 27$ is an example of a _____ of _____.

    b. The binomial $c^3 - 8$ is an example of a _____ of _____.

    c. A difference of cubes $a^3 - b^3$ factors as $($ $)($ $)$.

    d. A sum of cubes $a^3 + b^3$ factors as $($ $)($ $)$.

Review Exercises

For Exercises 2–10, factor completely.

2. $600 - 6x^2$

3. $20 - 5t^2$

4. $ax + bx + 5a + 5b$

5. $2t + 2u + st + su$

6. $5y^2 + 13y - 6$

7. $3v^2 + 5v - 12$

8. $40a^3b^3 - 16a^2b^2 + 24a^3b$

9. $-c^2 - 10c - 25$

10. $-z^2 + 6z - 9$

Concept 1: Factoring a Sum or Difference of Cubes

11. Identify the expressions that are perfect cubes:
    $x^3, 8, 9, y^6, a^4, b^2, 3p^3, 27q^3, w^{12}, r^3s^6$

12. Identify the expressions that are perfect cubes:
    $z^9, -81, 30, 8, 6x^3, y^{15}, 27a^3, b^2, p^3q^2, -1$

13. Identify the expressions that are perfect cubes:
    $36, t^3, -1, 27, a^3b^6, -9, 125, -8x^2, y^6, 25$

14. Identify the expressions that are perfect cubes:
    $343, 15b^3, z^3, w^{12}, -p^9, -1000, a^2b^3, 3x^3, -8, 60$

For Exercises 15–30, factor the sums or differences of cubes. **(See Examples 1 and 2.)**

15. $y^3 - 8$

16. $x^3 + 27$

17. $1 - p^3$

18. $q^3 + 1$

19. $w^3 + 64$

20. $8 - t^3$

21. $x^3 - 1000y^3$

22. $8r^3 - 27t^3$

23. $64t^3 + 1$

24. $125r^3 + 1$

25. $1000a^3 + 27$

26. $216b^3 - 125$

27. $n^3 - \dfrac{1}{8}$

28. $\dfrac{8}{27} + m^3$

29. $125x^3 + 8y^3$

30. $27t^3 + 64u^3$

Concept 2: Factoring Binomials: A Summary

For Exercises 31–66, factor completely. **(See Examples 3–6.)**

31. $x^4 - 4$

32. $b^4 - 25$

33. $a^2 + 9$

34. $w^2 + 36$

35. $t^3 + 64$

36. $u^3 + 27$

37. $g^3 - 4$

38. $h^3 - 25$

39. $4b^3 + 108$

40. $3c^3 - 24$

41. $5p^2 - 125$

42. $2q^4 - 8$

43. $\dfrac{1}{64} - 8h^3$

44. $\dfrac{1}{125} + k^6$

45. $x^4 - 16$

46. $p^4 - 81$

47. $\dfrac{4}{9}x^2 - w^2$ $\qquad$ **48.** $\dfrac{16}{25}y^2 - x^2$ $\qquad$ **49.** $q^6 - 64$ $\qquad$ **50.** $a^6 - 1$

$\qquad\qquad\qquad\qquad\qquad\qquad\qquad\qquad\qquad\qquad\qquad$ (*Hint:* Factor using the difference of squares first.)

51. $x^9 + 64y^3$ $\qquad$ **52.** $125w^3 - z^9$ $\qquad$ **53.** $2x^3 + 3x^2 - 2x - 3$ $\qquad$ **54.** $3x^3 + x^2 - 12x - 4$

55. $16x^4 - y^4$ $\qquad$ **56.** $1 - t^4$ $\qquad$ **57.** $81y^4 - 16$ $\qquad$ **58.** $u^5 - 256u$

59. $a^3 + b^6$ $\qquad$ **60.** $u^6 - v^3$ $\qquad$ **61.** $x^4 - y^4$ $\qquad$ **62.** $a^4 - b^4$

63. $k^3 + 4k^2 - 9k - 36$ $\qquad$ **64.** $w^3 - 2w^2 - 4w + 8$ $\qquad$ **65.** $2t^3 - 10t^2 - 2t + 10$ $\qquad$ **66.** $9a^3 + 27a^2 - 4a - 12$

Expanding Your Skills

For Exercises 67–70, factor completely.

67. $\dfrac{64}{125}p^3 - \dfrac{1}{8}q^3$ $\qquad$ **68.** $\dfrac{1}{1000}r^3 + \dfrac{8}{27}s^3$ $\qquad$ **69.** $a^{12} + b^{12}$ $\qquad$ **70.** $a^9 - b^9$

Use Exercises 71 and 72 to investigate the relationship between division and factoring.

71. a. Use long division to divide $x^3 - 8$ by $(x - 2)$.

$\quad$ **b.** Factor $x^3 - 8$.

72. a. Use long division to divide $y^3 + 27$ by $(y + 3)$.

$\quad$ **b.** Factor $y^3 + 27$.

73. What trinomial multiplied by $(x - 4)$ gives a difference of cubes?

74. What trinomial multiplied by $(p + 5)$ gives a sum of cubes?

75. Write a binomial that when multiplied by $(4x^2 - 2x + 1)$ produces a sum of cubes.

76. Write a binomial that when multiplied by $(9y^2 + 15y + 25)$ produces a difference of cubes.

Problem Recognition Exercises

Factoring Strategy

Step 1 Factor out the GCF (Section 6.1).

Step 2 Identify whether the polynomial has two terms, three terms, or more than three terms.

Step 3 If the polynomial has more than three terms, try factoring by grouping (Section 6.1).

Step 4 If the polynomial has three terms, check first for a perfect square trinomial. Otherwise, factor the trinomial with the trial-and-error method or the ac-method (Sections 6.3 or 6.4).

Step 5 If the polynomial has two terms, determine if it fits the pattern for
- A difference of squares: $a^2 - b^2 = (a - b)(a + b)$ (Section 6.5)
- A sum of squares: $a^2 + b^2$ is prime.
- A difference of cubes: $a^3 - b^3 = (a - b)(a^2 + ab + b^2)$ (Section 6.6)
- A sum of cubes: $a^3 + b^3 = (a + b)(a^2 - ab + b^2)$ (Section 6.6)

Step 6 Be sure to factor the polynomial completely.

Step 7 Check by multiplying.

1. What is meant by a prime polynomial?

2. What is the first step in factoring any polynomial?

3. When factoring a binomial, what patterns can you look for?

4. What technique should be considered when factoring a four-term polynomial?

For Exercises 5–73,

a. Factor out the GCF from each polynomial. Then identify the category in which the remaining polynomial best fits. Choose from
   - difference of squares
   - sum of squares
   - difference of cubes
   - sum of cubes
   - trinomial (perfect square trinomial)
   - trinomial (nonperfect square trinomial)
   - four terms-grouping
   - none of these

b. Factor the polynomial completely.

5. $2a^2 - 162$

6. $y^2 + 4y + 3$

7. $6w^2 - 6w$

8. $16z^4 - 81$

9. $3t^2 + 13t + 4$

10. $5r^3 + 5$

11. $3ac + ad - 3bc - bd$

12. $x^3 - 125$

13. $y^3 + 8$

14. $7p^2 - 29p + 4$

15. $3q^2 - 9q - 12$

16. $-2x^2 + 8x - 8$

17. $18a^2 + 12a$

18. $54 - 2y^3$

19. $4t^2 - 100$

20. $4t^2 - 31t - 8$

21. $10c^2 + 10c + 10$

22. $2xw - 10x + 3yw - 15y$

23. $x^3 + 0.001$

24. $4q^2 - 9$

25. $64 + 16k + k^2$

26. $s^2t + 5t + 6s^2 + 30$

27. $2x^2 + 2x - xy - y$

28. $w^3 + y^3$

29. $a^3 - c^3$

30. $3y^2 + y + 1$

31. $c^2 + 8c + 9$

32. $a^2 + 2a + 1$

33. $b^2 + 10b + 25$

34. $-t^2 - 4t + 32$

35. $-p^3 - 5p^2 - 4p$

36. $x^2y^2 - 49$

37. $6x^2 - 21x - 45$

38. $20y^2 - 14y + 2$

39. $5a^2bc^3 - 7abc^2$

40. $8a^2 - 50$

41. $t^2 + 2t - 63$

42. $b^2 + 2b - 80$

43. $ab + ay - b^2 - by$

44. $6x^3y^4 + 3x^2y^5$

45. $14u^2 - 11uv + 2v^2$

46. $9p^2 - 36pq + 4q^2$

47. $4q^2 - 8q - 6$

48. $9w^2 + 3w - 15$

49. $9m^2 + 16n^2$

50. $5b^2 - 30b + 45$

51. $6r^2 + 11r + 3$

52. $4s^2 + 4s - 15$

53. $16a^4 - 1$

54. $p^3 + p^2c - 9p - 9c$

55. $81u^2 - 90uv + 25v^2$

56. $4x^2 + 16$

57. $x^2 - 5x - 6$

58. $q^2 + q - 7$

59. $2ax - 6ay + 4bx - 12by$

60. $8m^3 - 10m^2 - 3m$

61. $21x^4y + 41x^3y + 10x^2y$

62. $2m^4 - 128$

63. $8uv - 6u + 12v - 9$

64. $4t^2 - 20t + st - 5s$

65. $12x^2 - 12x + 3$

66. $p^2 + 2pq + q^2$

67. $6n^3 + 5n^2 - 4n$

68. $4k^3 + 4k^2 - 3k$

69. $64 - y^2$

70. $36b - b^3$

71. $b^2 - 4b + 10$

72. $y^2 + 6y + 8$

73. $c^4 - 12c^2 + 20$

Solving Equations Using the Zero Product Rule   Section 6.7

1. Definition of a Quadratic Equation

In Section 2.1, we solved linear equations in one variable. These are equations of the form $ax + b = c\,(a \neq 0)$. A linear equation in one variable is sometimes called a first-degree polynomial equation because the highest degree of all its terms is 1. A second-degree polynomial equation in one variable is called a quadratic equation.

> **Concepts**
>
> 1. Definition of a Quadratic Equation
> 2. Zero Product Rule
> 3. Solving Equations by Factoring

A Quadratic Equation in One Variable

If a, b, and c are real numbers such that $a \neq 0$, then a **quadratic equation** is an equation that can be written in the form

$$ax^2 + bx + c = 0.$$

The following equations are quadratic because they can each be written in the form $ax^2 + bx + c = 0$, $(a \neq 0)$.

$-4x^2 + 4x = 1$	$x(x - 2) = 3$	$(x - 4)(x + 4) = 9$
$-4x^2 + 4x - 1 = 0$	$x^2 - 2x = 3$	$x^2 - 16 = 9$
	$x^2 - 2x - 3 = 0$	$x^2 - 25 = 0$
		$x^2 + 0x - 25 = 0$

2. Zero Product Rule

One method for solving a quadratic equation is to factor and apply the zero product rule. The **zero product rule** states that if the product of two factors is zero, then one or both of its factors is zero.

Zero Product Rule

$$\text{If } ab = 0, \text{ then } a = 0 \text{ or } b = 0.$$

Example 1 Applying the Zero Product Rule

Solve the equation by using the zero product rule. $(x - 4)(x + 3) = 0$

Solution:

$(x - 4)(x + 3) = 0$ Apply the zero product rule.

$x - 4 = 0$ or $x + 3 = 0$ Set each factor equal to zero.

     $x = 4$ or $x = -3$ Solve each equation for x.

$\underline{\text{Check: } x = 4}$ $\underline{\text{Check: } x = -3}$

$(4 - 4)(4 + 3) \overset{?}{=} 0$ $(-3 - 4)(-3 + 3) \overset{?}{=} 0$

           $(0)(7) \overset{?}{=} 0 ✔$ $(-7)(0) \overset{?}{=} 0 ✔$

The solutions are 4 and -3.

Example 2 Applying the Zero Product Rule

Solve the equation by using the zero product rule. $(x + 8)(4x + 1) = 0$

Solution:

$(x + 8)(4x + 1) = 0$ Apply the zero product rule.

$x + 8 = 0$ or $4x + 1 = 0$ Set each factor equal to zero.

     $x = -8$ or $4x = -1$ Solve each equation for x.

     $x = -8$ or $x = -\dfrac{1}{4}$

The solutions -8 and $-\dfrac{1}{4}$ check in the original equation.

Example 3 Applying the Zero Product Rule

Solve the equation using the zero product rule. $x(3x - 7) = 0$

Solution:

$x(3x - 7) = 0$ Apply the zero product rule.

$x = 0$ or $3x - 7 = 0$ Set each factor equal to zero.

$x = 0$ or $3x = 7$ Solve each equation for x.

$x = 0$ or $x = \dfrac{7}{3}$

The solutions 0 and $\dfrac{7}{3}$ check in the original equation.

3. Solving Equations by Factoring

Quadratic equations, like linear equations, arise in many applications in mathematics, science, and business. The following steps summarize the factoring method for solving a quadratic equation.

Solving a Quadratic Equation by Factoring

Step 1 Write the equation in the form: $ax^2 + bx + c = 0$.

Step 2 Factor the quadratic expression completely.

Step 3 Apply the zero product rule. That is, set each factor equal to zero, and solve the resulting equations.

Note: The solution(s) found in step 3 may be checked by substitution in the original equation.

Example 4 Solving a Quadratic Equation

Solve the quadratic equation. $2x^2 - 9x = 5$

Solution:

$$2x^2 - 9x = 5$$

$$2x^2 - 9x - 5 = 0 \qquad \text{Write the equation in the form}$$
$$ax^2 + bx + c = 0.$$

$$(2x + 1)(x - 5) = 0 \qquad \text{Factor the polynomial completely.}$$

$$2x + 1 = 0 \quad \text{or} \quad x - 5 = 0 \qquad \text{Set each factor equal to zero.}$$

$$2x = -1 \quad \text{or} \quad x = 5 \qquad \text{Solve each equation.}$$

$$x = -\frac{1}{2} \quad \text{or} \quad x = 5$$

Check: $x = -\dfrac{1}{2}$ $\qquad\qquad$ Check: $x = 5$

$$2x^2 - 9x = 5 \qquad\qquad 2x^2 - 9x = 5$$

$$2\left(-\frac{1}{2}\right)^2 - 9\left(-\frac{1}{2}\right) \stackrel{?}{=} 5 \qquad 2(5)^2 - 9(5) \stackrel{?}{=} 5$$

$$2\left(\frac{1}{4}\right) + \frac{9}{2} \stackrel{?}{=} 5 \qquad\qquad 2(25) - 45 \stackrel{?}{=} 5$$

$$\frac{1}{2} + \frac{9}{2} \stackrel{?}{=} 5 \qquad\qquad\qquad 50 - 45 \stackrel{?}{=} 5 \checkmark$$

$$\frac{10}{2} \stackrel{?}{=} 5 \checkmark$$

The solutions are $-\dfrac{1}{2}$ and 5.

Skill Practice

Solve the equation.

4. $2y^2 + 19y = -24$

Answer

4. $-8, -\dfrac{3}{2}$

Skill Practice

Solve the equation.

5. $5s^2 = 45$

Example 5 Solving a Quadratic Equation

Solve the quadratic equation. $4x^2 + 24x = 0$

Solution:

$4x^2 + 24x = 0$ The equation is already in the form $ax^2 + bx + c = 0$. (Note that $c = 0$.)

$4x(x + 6) = 0$ Factor completely.

$4x = 0 \quad$ or $\quad x + 6 = 0$ Set each factor equal to zero.

$x = 0 \quad$ or $\quad x = -6$

The solutions are 0 and -6. They both check in the original equation.

Skill Practice

Solve the equation.

6. $4z(z + 3) = 4z + 5$

Example 6 Solving a Quadratic Equation

Solve the quadratic equation. $5x(5x + 2) = 10x + 9$

Solution:

$5x(5x + 2) = 10x + 9$

$25x^2 + 10x = 10x + 9$ Clear parentheses.

$25x^2 + 10x - 10x - 9 = 0$ Set the equation equal to zero.

$25x^2 - 9 = 0$ The equation is in the form $ax^2 + bx + c = 0$. (Note that $b = 0$.)

$(5x - 3)(5x + 3) = 0$ Factor completely.

$5x - 3 = 0 \quad$ or $\quad 5x + 3 = 0$ Set each factor equal to zero.

$5x = 3 \quad$ or $\quad 5x = -3$ Solve each equation.

$\dfrac{5x}{5} = \dfrac{3}{5} \quad$ or $\quad \dfrac{5x}{5} = \dfrac{-3}{5}$

$x = \dfrac{3}{5} \quad$ or $\quad x = -\dfrac{3}{5}$

The solutions are $\dfrac{3}{5}$ and $-\dfrac{3}{5}$. They both check in the original equation.

The zero product rule can be used to solve higher degree polynomial equations provided the equations can be set to zero and written in factored form.

Answers

5. 3, -3 **6.** $-\dfrac{5}{2}, \dfrac{1}{2}$

Example 7 Solving Higher Degree Polynomial Equations

Solve the equation. $-6(y + 3)(y - 5)(2y + 7) = 0$

Solution:

$-6(y + 3)(y - 5)(2y + 7) = 0$ The equation is already in factored form and equal to zero.

Set each factor equal to zero.

Solve each equation for y.

$-6 \neq 0$	or	$y + 3 = 0$	or	$y - 5 = 0$	or	$2y + 7 = 0$

No solution,		$y = -3$	or	$y = 5$	or	$y = -\dfrac{7}{2}$

Notice that when the constant factor is set equal to zero, the result is a contradiction, $-6 = 0$. The constant factor does not produce a solution to the equation. Therefore, the only solutions are $-3, 5$, and $-\frac{7}{2}$. Each solution can be checked in the original equation.

Skill Practice

Solve the equation.

7. $5(p - 4)(p + 7)(2p - 9) = 0$

Example 8 Solving a Higher Degree Polynomial Equation

Solve the equation. $w^3 + 5w^2 - 9w - 45 = 0$

Solution:

$w^3 + 5w^2 - 9w - 45 = 0$ This is a higher degree polynomial equation.

$w^3 + 5w^2 \mid - 9w - 45 = 0$ The equation is already set equal to zero. Now factor.

$w^2(w + 5) - 9(w + 5) = 0$ Because there are four terms, try factoring
$(w + 5)(w^2 - 9) = 0$ by grouping.

$(w + 5)(w - 3)(w + 3) = 0$ $w^2 - 9$ is a difference of squares and can be factored further.

$w + 5 = 0$	or	$w - 3 = 0$	or	$w + 3 = 0$	Set each factor equal to zero.

$w = -5$	or	$w = 3$	or	$w = -3$	Solve each equation.

The solutions are $-5, -3$, and 3. Each solution checks in the original equation.

Skill Practice

Solve the equation.

8. $x^3 + 3x^2 - 4x - 12 = 0$

Answers

7. $4, -7, \dfrac{9}{2}$ **8.** $-2, -3, 2$

Section 6.7 Practice Exercises

Vocabulary and Key Concepts

1. a. An equation that can be written in the form $ax^2 + bx + c = 0, a \neq 0$, is called a _____ equation.

b. The zero product rule states that if $ab = 0$, then $a =$ _____ or $b =$ _____.

Review Exercises

For Exercises 2–7, factor completely.

2. $6a - 8 - 3ab + 4b$

3. $4b^2 - 44b + 120$

4. $8u^2v^2 - 4uv$

5. $3x^2 + 10x - 8$

6. $3h^2 - 75$

7. $4x^2 + 16y^2$

Concept 1: Definition of a Quadratic Equation

For Exercises 8–13, identify the equations as linear, quadratic, or neither.

8. $4 - 5x = 0$

9. $5x^3 + 2 = 0$

10. $3x - 6x^2 = 0$

11. $1 - x + 2x^2 = 0$

12. $7x^4 + 8 = 0$

13. $3x + 2 = 0$

Concept 2: Zero Product Rule

For Exercises 14–22, solve the equations using the zero product rule. **(See Examples 1–3.)**

14. $(x - 5)(x + 1) = 0$

15. $(x + 3)(x - 1) = 0$

16. $(3x - 2)(3x + 2) = 0$

17. $(2x - 7)(2x + 7) = 0$

18. $2(x - 7)(x - 7) = 0$

19. $3(x + 5)(x + 5) = 0$

20. $(3x - 2)(2x - 3) = 0$

21. $x(5x - 1) = 0$

22. $x(3x + 8) = 0$

23. For a quadratic equation of the form $ax^2 + bx + c = 0$, what must be done before applying the zero product rule?

24. What are the requirements needed to use the zero product rule to solve a quadratic equation or higher degree polynomial equation?

Concept 3: Solving Equations by Factoring

For Exercises 25–72, solve the equations. **(See Examples 4–8.)**

25. $p^2 - 2p - 15 = 0$

26. $y^2 - 7y - 8 = 0$

27. $z^2 + 10z - 24 = 0$

28. $w^2 - 10w + 16 = 0$

29. $2q^2 - 7q = 4$

30. $4x^2 - 11x = 3$

31. $0 = 9x^2 - 4$

32. $4a^2 - 49 = 0$

33. $2k^2 - 28k + 96 = 0$

34. $0 = 2t^2 + 20t + 50$

35. $0 = 2m^3 - 5m^2 - 12m$

36. $3n^3 + 4n^2 + n = 0$

37. $5(3p + 1)(p - 3)(p + 6) = 0$

38. $4(2x - 1)(x - 10)(x + 7) = 0$

39. $x(x - 4)(2x + 3) = 0$

40. $x(3x + 1)(x + 1) = 0$

41. $-5x(2x + 9)(x - 11) = 0$

42. $-3x(x + 7)(3x - 5) = 0$

43. $x^3 - 16x = 0$

44. $t^3 - 36t = 0$

45. $3x^2 + 18x = 0$

46. $2y^2 - 20y = 0$

47. $16m^2 = 9$

48. $9n^2 = 1$

49. $2y^3 + 14y^2 = -20y$

50. $3d^3 - 6d^2 = 24d$

51. $5t - 2(t - 7) = 0$

52. $8h = 5(h - 9) + 6$

53. $2c(c - 8) = -30$

54. $3q(q - 3) = 12$

55. $b^3 = -4b^2 - 4b$

56. $x^3 + 36x = 12x^2$

57. $3(a^2 + 2a) = 2a^2 - 9$

58. $9(k - 1) = -4k^2$

59. $2n(n + 2) = 6$

60. $3p(p - 1) = 18$

61. $x(2x + 5) - 1 = 2x^2 + 3x + 2$

62. $3z(z - 2) - z = 3z^2 + 4$

63. $27q^2 = 9q$

64. $21w^2 = 14w$

65. $3(c^2 - 2c) = 0$

66. $2(4d^2 + d) = 0$

67. $y^3 - 3y^2 - 4y + 12 = 0$

68. $t^3 + 2t^2 - 16t - 32 = 0$

69. $(x - 1)(x + 2) = 18$

70. $(w + 5)(w - 3) = 20$

71. $(p + 2)(p + 3) = 1 - p$

72. $(k - 6)(k - 1) = -k - 2$

Problem Recognition Exercises

Polynomial Expressions versus Polynomial Equations

For Exercises 1–36, factor each expression and solve each equation.

1. **a.** $x^2 + 6x - 7$
b. $x^2 + 6x - 7 = 0$

2. **a.** $c^2 + 8c + 12$
b. $c^2 + 8c + 12 = 0$

3. **a.** $2y^2 + 7y + 3$
b. $2y^2 + 7y + 3 = 0$

4. **a.** $3x^2 - 8x + 5$
b. $3x^2 - 8x + 5 = 0$

5. **a.** $5q^2 + q - 4 = 0$
b. $5q^2 + q - 4$

6. **a.** $6a^2 - 7a - 3 = 0$
b. $6a^2 - 7a - 3$

7. **a.** $a^2 - 64 = 0$
b. $a^2 - 64$

8. **a.** $v^2 - 100 = 0$
b. $v^2 - 100$

9. **a.** $4b^2 - 81$
b. $4b^2 - 81 = 0$

10. **a.** $36t^2 - 49$
b. $36t^2 - 49 = 0$

11. **a.** $8x^2 + 16x + 6 = 0$
b. $8x^2 + 16x + 6$

12. **a.** $12y^2 + 40y + 32 = 0$
b. $12y^2 + 40y + 32$

13. **a.** $x^3 - 8x^2 - 20x$
b. $x^3 - 8x^2 - 20x = 0$

14. **a.** $k^3 + 5k^2 - 14k$
b. $k^3 + 5k^2 - 14k = 0$

15. **a.** $b^3 + b^2 - 9b - 9 = 0$
b. $b^3 + b^2 - 9b - 9$

16. $x^3 - 8x^2 - 4x + 32 = 0$

17. $2s^2 - 6s + rs - 3r$

18. $6t^2 + 3t + 10tu + 5u$

19. $8x^3 - 2x = 0$

20. $2b^3 - 50b = 0$

21. $2x^3 - 4x^2 + 2x = 0$

22. $3t^3 + 18t^2 + 27t = 0$

23. $7c^2 - 2c + 3 = 7(c^2 + c)$

24. $3z(2z + 4) = -7 + 6z^2$

25. $8w^3 + 27$

26. $1000q^3 - 1$

27. $5z^2 + 2z = 7$

28. $4h^2 + 25h = -6$

29. $3b(b + 6) = b - 10$

30. $3y^2 + 1 = y(y - 3)$

31. $5(2x - 3) - 2(3x + 1) = 4 - 3x$

32. $11 - 6a = -4(2a - 3) - 1$

33. $4s^2 = 64$

34. $81v^2 = 36$

35. $(x - 3)(x - 4) = 6$

36. $(x + 5)(x + 9) = 21$

Section 6.8	Applications of Quadratic Equations

1. Applications of Quadratic Equations

In this section we solve applications using the Problem-Solving Strategies outlined in Section 2.4.

Example 1   Translating to a Quadratic Equation

The product of two consecutive integers is 14 more than 6 times the smaller integer.

Solution:

Let x represent the first (smaller) integer.

Then $x + 1$ represents the second (larger) integer.   Label the unknowns.

(Smaller integer)(larger integer) $= 6 \cdot$ (smaller integer) $+ 14$ Verbal model

$$x(x + 1) = 6(x) + 14 \qquad \text{Algebraic equation}$$

$$x^2 + x = 6x + 14 \qquad \text{Simplify.}$$

$$x^2 + x - 6x - 14 = 0 \qquad \text{Set one side of the equation equal to zero.}$$

$$x^2 - 5x - 14 = 0$$

$$(x - 7)(x + 2) = 0 \qquad \text{Factor.}$$

$$x - 7 = 0 \quad \text{or} \quad x + 2 = 0 \qquad \text{Set each factor equal to zero.}$$

$$x = 7 \quad \text{or} \quad x = -2 \qquad \text{Solve for } x.$$

Recall that x represents the smaller integer. Therefore, there are two possibilities for the pairs of consecutive integers.

If $x = 7$, then the larger integer is $x + 1$ or $7 + 1 = 8$.

If $x = -2$, then the larger integer is $x + 1$ or $-2 + 1 = -1$.

The integers are 7 and 8, or -2 and -1.

Example 2   Using a Quadratic Equation in a Geometry Application

A rectangular sign has an area of 40 ft^2. If the width is 3 feet shorter than the length, what are the dimensions of the sign?

Solution:

Let x represent the length of the sign.   Label the variables.
Then $x - 3$ represents the width (Figure 6-1).

The problem gives information about the length of the sides and about the area. Therefore, we can form a relationship by using the formula for the area of a rectangle.

$x - 3$

x

Figure 6-1

$A = l \cdot w$	Area equals length times width.
$40 = x(x - 3)$	Set up an algebraic equation.
$40 = x^2 - 3x$	Clear parentheses.
$0 = x^2 - 3x - 40$	Write the equation in the form, $ax^2 + bx + c = 0$.
$0 = (x - 8)(x + 5)$	Factor.
$0 = x - 8$ or $0 = x + 5$	Set each factor equal to zero.
$8 = x$ or $-5 \cancel{=} x$	Because x represents the length of a rectangle, reject the negative solution.

The variable x represents the length of the sign. The length is 8 ft.

The expression $x - 3$ represents the width. The width is 8 ft $-$ 3 ft, or 5 ft.

Avoiding Mistakes

When solving an application, remember to check that your answer is reasonable.

Example 3 Using a Quadratic Equation in an Application

A large boulder breaks off a 64-ft cliff and falls into the ocean below. The height of the boulder above sea level is given by the equation

$h = -16t^2 + 64$ where h is the boulder's height in feet, and t is the time in seconds.

Find the time required for the boulder to hit the water.

64 ft

Skill Practice

3. An object is launched into the air from the ground and its height is given by $h = -16t^2 + 144t$, where h is the height in feet after t seconds. Find the time required for the object to hit the ground.

Animation

Solution:

When the boulder hits the water, its height is zero. Therefore, substitute $h = 0$ into the equation.

$h = -16t^2 + 64$	The equation is quadratic.
$0 = -16t^2 + 64$	Substitute $h = 0$.
$0 = -16(t^2 - 4)$	Factor out the GCF.
$0 = -16(t - 2)(t + 2)$	Factor as a difference of squares.
$-16 \cancel{=} 0$ or $t - 2 = 0$ or $t + 2 = 0$	Set each factor to zero.
No solution, $t = 2$ or $t \cancel{=} -2$	Solve for t.

The negative value of t is rejected because the boulder cannot fall for a negative time. Therefore, the boulder hits the water after 2 seconds.

Answer

3. 9 seconds

2. Pythagorean Theorem

Recall that a right triangle is a triangle that contains a 90° angle. Furthermore, the sum of the squares of the two legs (the shorter sides) of a right triangle equals the square of the hypotenuse (the longest side). This important fact is known as the Pythagorean theorem. The Pythagorean theorem is an enduring landmark of mathematical history from which many mathematical ideas have been built. Although the theorem is named after Pythagoras (sixth century B.C.E.), a Greek mathematician and philosopher, it is thought that the ancient Babylonians were familiar with the principle more than a thousand years earlier.

For the right triangle shown in Figure 6-2, the **Pythagorean theorem** is stated as:

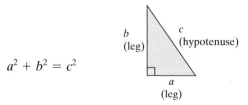

$$a^2 + b^2 = c^2$$

Figure 6-2

In this formula, a and b are the legs of the right triangle and c is the hypotenuse. Notice that the hypotenuse is the longest side of the right triangle and is opposite the 90° angle.

The triangle shown below is a right triangle. Notice that the lengths of the sides satisfy the Pythagorean theorem.

The shorter sides are labeled as a and b.

Label the sides.

The longest side is the hypotenuse. It is always labeled as c.

$a^2 + b^2 = c^2$	Apply the Pythagorean theorem.
$(4)^2 + (3)^2 = (5)^2$	Substitute $a = 4$, $b = 3$, and $c = 5$.
$16 + 9 = 25$	
$25 = 25$ ✔	

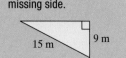
Example 4 Applying the Pythagorean Theorem

Find the length of the missing side of the right triangle.

Solution:

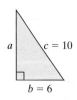

Label the triangle.

$a^2 + b^2 = c^2$	Apply the Pythagorean theorem.
$a^2 + 6^2 = 10^2$	Substitute $b = 6$ and $c = 10$.

Answer

4. The length of the third side is 12 m.

$$a^2 + 36 = 100$$ Simplify.

The equation is quadratic. Set one side of the equation equal to zero.

$$a^2 + 36 - 100 = 100 - 100$$ Subtract 100 from both sides.

$$a^2 - 64 = 0$$

$$(a + 8)(a - 8) = 0$$ Factor.

$$a + 8 = 0 \quad \text{or} \quad a - 8 = 0$$ Set each factor equal to zero.

$$a \cancel{=} -8 \quad \text{or} \quad a = 8$$ Because x represents the length of a side of a triangle, reject the negative solution.

The length of the third side is 8 ft.

Example 5 Using a Quadratic Equation in an Application

A 13-ft board is used as a ramp to unload furniture off a loading platform. If the distance between the top of the board and the ground is 7 ft less than the distance between the bottom of the board and the base of the platform, find both distances.

Solution:

Let x represent the distance between the bottom of the board and the base of the platform. Then $x - 7$ represents the distance between the top of the board and the ground (Figure 6-3).

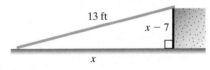

Figure 6-3

$$a^2 + b^2 = c^2$$ Pythagorean theorem

$$x^2 + (x - 7)^2 = (13)^2$$

$$x^2 + (x)^2 - 2(x)(7) + (7)^2 = 169$$

$$x^2 + x^2 - 14x + 49 = 169$$

$$2x^2 - 14x + 49 = 169$$ Combine *like* terms.

$$2x^2 - 14x + 49 - 169 = 169 - 169$$ Set the equation equal to zero.

$$2x^2 - 14x - 120 = 0$$ Write the equation in the form $ax^2 + bx + c = 0$.

$$2(x^2 - 7x - 60) = 0$$ Factor.

$$2(x - 12)(x + 5) = 0$$

$$2 \cancel{=} 0 \quad \text{or} \quad x - 12 = 0 \quad \text{or} \quad x + 5 = 0$$ Set each factor equal to zero.

$$x = 12 \quad \text{or} \quad x \cancel{=} -5$$ Solve both equations for x.

Recall that x represents the distance between the bottom of the board and the base of the platform. We reject the negative value of x because a distance cannot be negative. Therefore, the distance between the bottom of the board and the base of the platform is 12 ft. The distance between the top of the board and the ground is $x - 7 = 5$ ft.

Skill Practice

5. A 5-yd ladder leans against a wall. The distance from the bottom of the wall to the top of the ladder is 1 yd more than the distance from the bottom of the wall to the bottom of the ladder. Find both distances.

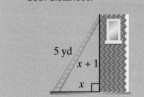

Avoiding Mistakes

Recall that the square of a binomial results in a perfect square trinomial.

$$(a - b)^2 = a^2 - 2ab + b^2$$

Don't forget the middle term.

Answer

5. The distance along the wall to the top of the ladder is 4 yd. The distance on the ground from the ladder to the wall is 3 yd.

Section 6.8 Practice Exercises

Vocabulary and Key Concepts

1. a. If x is the smaller of two consecutive integers, then _____ represents the next greater integer.

   b. If x is the smaller of two consecutive odd integers, then _____ represents the next greater odd integer.

   c. If x is the smaller of two consecutive even integers, then _____ represents the next greater even integer.

   d. The area of a rectangle of length l and width w is given by $A =$ _____.

   e. The area of a triangle with base b and height h is given by the formula $A =$ _____.

   f. Given a right triangle with legs a and b and hypotenuse c, the Pythagorean theorem is stated as _____.

Review Exercises

For Exercises 2–7, solve the quadratic equations.

2. $(6x + 1)(x + 4) = 0$ **3.** $9x(3x + 2) = 0$ **4.** $4x^2 - 1 = 0$

5. $x^2 - 5x = 6$ **6.** $x(x - 20) = -100$ **7.** $6x^2 - 7x - 10 = 0$

8. Explain what is wrong with the following problem: $(x - 3)(x + 2) = 5$
$x - 3 = 5$ or $x + 2 = 5$

Concept 1: Applications of Quadratic Equations

9. If eleven is added to the square of a number, the result is sixty. Find all such numbers.

10. If a number is added to two times its square, the result is thirty-six. Find all such numbers.

 11. If twelve is added to six times a number, the result is twenty-eight less than the square of the number. Find all such numbers.

12. The square of a number is equal to twenty more than the number. Find all such numbers.

13. The product of two consecutive odd integers is sixty-three. Find all such integers. **(See Example 1.)**

14. The product of two consecutive even integers is forty-eight. Find all such integers.

15. The sum of the squares of two consecutive integers is one more than ten times the larger number. Find all such integers.

16. The sum of the squares of two consecutive integers is nine less than ten times the sum of the integers. Find all such integers.

17. *Las Meninas* (Spanish for *The Maids of Honor*) is a famous painting by Spanish painter Diego Velazquez. This work is regarded as one of the most important paintings in western art history. The height of the painting is approximately 2 ft more than its width. If the total area is 99 ft², determine the dimensions of the painting. **(See Example 2.)**

18. The width of a rectangular painting is 2 in. less than the length. The area is 120 in.². Find the length and width.

19. The width of a rectangular slab of concrete is 3 m less than the length. The area is 28 m².

   a. What are the dimensions of the rectangle?

   b. What is the perimeter of the rectangle?

20. The width of a rectangular picture is 7 in. less than the length. The area of the picture is 78 in.².

   a. What are the dimensions of the picture?

   b. What is the perimeter of the picture?

21. The base of a triangle is 3 ft more than the height. If the area is 14 ft², find the base and the height.

22. The height of a triangle is 15 cm more than the base. If the area is 125 cm², find the base and the height.

23. The height of a triangle is 7 cm less than 3 times the base. If the area is 20 cm², find the base and the height.

24. The base of a triangle is 2 ft less than 4 times the height. If the area is 6 ft², find the base and the height.

25. In a physics experiment, a ball is dropped off a 144-ft platform. The height of the ball above the ground is given by the equation

$h = -16t^2 + 144$ where h is the ball's height in feet, and t is the time in seconds after the ball is dropped ($t \geq 0$).

Find the time required for the ball to hit the ground. (*Hint:* Let $h = 0$.) **(See Example 3.)**

26. A stone is dropped off a 256-ft cliff. The height of the stone above the ground is given by the equation

$h = -16t^2 + 256$ where h is the stone's height in feet, and t is the time in seconds after the stone is dropped ($t \geq 0$).

Find the time required for the stone to hit the ground.

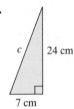

27. An object is shot straight up into the air from ground level with an initial speed of 24 ft/sec. The height of the object (in feet) is given by the equation

$h = -16t^2 + 24t$ where t is the time in seconds after launch ($t \geq 0$).

Find the time(s) when the object is at ground level.

28. A rocket is launched straight up into the air from the ground with initial speed of 64 ft/sec. The height of the rocket (in feet) is given by the equation

$h = -16t^2 + 64t$ where t is the time in seconds after launch ($t \geq 0$).

Find the time(s) when the rocket is at ground level.

Concept 2: Pythagorean Theorem

29. Sketch a right triangle and label the sides with the words *leg* and *hypotenuse*.

30. State the Pythagorean theorem.

For Exercises 31–34, find the length of the missing side of the right triangle. **(See Example 4.)**

31.
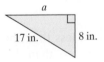

32.

33.

34.
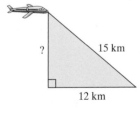

35. Find the length of the supporting brace.

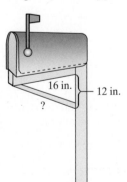

36. Find the height of the airplane above the ground.

37. Darcy holds the end of a kite string 3 ft (1 yd) off the ground and wants to estimate the height of the kite. Her friend Jenna is 24 yd away from her, standing directly under the kite as shown in the figure. If Darcy has 30 yd of string out, find the height of the kite (ignore the sag in the string).

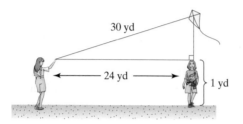

38. Two cars leave the same point at the same time, one traveling north and the other traveling east. After an hour, one car has traveled 48 mi and the other has traveled 64 mi. How many miles apart were they at that time?

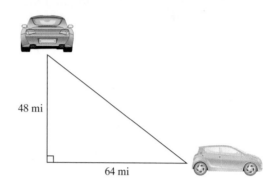

39. A 17-ft ladder rests against the side of a house. The distance between the top of the ladder and the ground is 7 ft more than the distance between the base of the ladder and the bottom of the house. Find both distances. **(See Example 5.)**

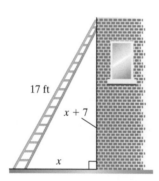

40. Two boats leave a marina. One travels east, and the other travels south. After 30 min, the second boat has traveled 1 mi farther than the first boat and the distance between the boats is 5 mi. Find the distance each boat traveled.

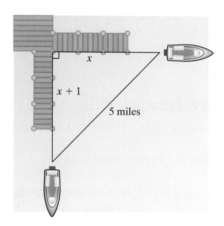

41. One leg of a right triangle is 4 m less than the hypotenuse. The other leg is 2 m less than the hypotenuse. Find the length of the hypotenuse.

42. The longer leg of a right triangle is 1 cm less than twice the shorter leg. The hypotenuse is 1 cm greater than twice the shorter leg. Find the length of the shorter leg.

Group Activity

Building a Factoring Test

Estimated Time: 30–45 minutes

Group Size: 3

In this activity, each group will make a test for this chapter. Then the groups will trade papers and take the test by factoring the polynomials or solving the equations.

For Exercises 1–8, write a polynomial that satisfies the given conditions. Do not use reference materials such as the textbook or your notes.

1. A trinomial with a GCF not equal to 1. The GCF should include a constant and at least one variable.

1. _____

2. A four-term polynomial that is factorable by grouping.

2. _____

3. A factorable trinomial with a leading coefficient of 1. (The trinomial should factor as a product of two binomials.)

3. _____

4. A factorable trinomial with a leading coefficient not equal to 1. (The trinomial should factor as a product of two binomials.)

4. _____

5. A trinomial that requires the GCF to be removed. The resulting trinomial should factor as a product of two binomials.

5. _____

6. A difference of squares.

6. _____

7. A difference of cubes.

7. _____

8. A sum of cubes.

8. _____

9. Write a quadratic *equation* that has solutions $x = 4$ and $x = -7$.

9. _____

10. Write a quadratic *equation* that has solutions $x = 0$ and $x = -\dfrac{2}{3}$.

10. _____

Chapter 6 Summary

Section 6.1 Greatest Common Factor and Factoring by Grouping

Key Concepts

The **greatest common factor** (GCF) is the greatest factor common to all terms of a polynomial. To factor out the GCF from a polynomial, use the distributive property.

A four-term polynomial may be factorable by grouping.

Steps to Factoring by Grouping

1. Identify and factor out the GCF from all four terms.
2. Factor out the GCF from the first pair of terms. Factor out the GCF or its opposite from the second pair of terms.
3. If the two terms share a common binomial factor, factor out the binomial factor.

Examples

Example 1

$3x(a + b) - 5(a + b)$ Greatest common factor is $(a + b)$.

$= (a + b)(3x - 5)$

Example 2

$60xa - 30xb - 80ya + 40yb$

$= 10[6xa - 3xb - 8ya + 4yb]$ Factor out GCF.

$= 10[3x(2a - b) - 4y(2a - b)]$ Factor by grouping.

$= 10(2a - b)(3x - 4y)$

Section 6.2 Factoring Trinomials of the Form $x^2 + bx + c$

Key Concepts

Factoring a Trinomial with a Leading Coefficient of 1

A trinomial of the form $x^2 + bx + c$ factors as

$$x^2 + bx + c = (x \ \Box)(x \ \Box)$$

where the remaining terms are given by two integers whose product is c and whose sum is b.

Examples

Example 1

Factor: $x^2 - 14x + 45$

$x^2 - 14x + 45$ The integers -5 and -9 have a product of 45

$= (x \ \Box)(x \ \Box)$ and a sum of -14.

$= (x - 5)(x - 9)$

Section 6.3   Factoring Trinomials: Trial-and-Error Method

Key Concepts

Trial-and-Error Method for Factoring Trinomials in the Form $ax^2 + bx + c$ (where $a \neq 0$)

1. Factor out the GCF from all terms.
2. List the pairs of factors of a and the pairs of factors of c. Consider the reverse order in one of the lists.
3. Construct two binomials of the form

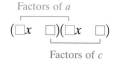

4. Test each combination of factors and signs until the product forms the correct trinomial.
5. If no combination of factors produces the correct product, then the trinomial is prime.

Examples

Example 1

$10y^2 + 35y - 20$

$= 5(2y^2 + 7y - 4)$

The pairs of factors of 2 are: $2 \cdot 1$
The pairs of factors of -4 are:

$$-1(4) \qquad 1(-4)$$
$$-2(2) \qquad 2(-2)$$
$$-4(1) \qquad 4(-1)$$

$(2y - 2)(y + 2) = 2y^2 + 2y - 4$	No
$(2y - 4)(y + 1) = 2y^2 - 2y - 4$	No
$(2y + 1)(y - 4) = 2y^2 - 7y - 4$	No
$(2y + 2)(y - 2) = 2y^2 - 2y - 4$	No
$(2y + 4)(y - 1) = 2y^2 + 2y - 4$	No
$(2y - 1)(y + 4) = 2y^2 + 7y - 4$	Yes

$10y^2 + 35y - 20 = 5(2y - 1)(y + 4)$

Section 6.4   Factoring Trinomials: AC-Method

Key Concepts

AC-Method for Factoring Trinomials of the Form $ax^2 + bx + c$ (where $a \neq 0$)

1. Factor out the GCF from all terms.
2. Multiply the coefficients of the first and last terms (ac).
3. Find two integers whose product is ac and whose sum is b. (If no pair of integers can be found, then the trinomial is prime.)
4. Rewrite the middle term (bx) as the sum of two terms whose coefficients are the numbers found in step 3.
5. Factor the polynomial by grouping.

Examples

Example 1

$10y^2 + 35y - 20$

$= 5(2y^2 + 7y - 4)$ First factor out the GCF.

Identify the product $ac = (2)(-4) = -8$.

Find two integers whose product is -8 and whose sum is 7. The numbers are 8 and -1.

$5[2y^2 + 8y - 1y - 4]$

$= 5[2y(y + 4) - 1(y + 4)]$

$= 5(y + 4)(2y - 1)$

| **Section 6.5** | **Difference of Squares and Perfect Square Trinomials** |

Key Concepts

Factoring a Difference of Squares

$$a^2 - b^2 = (a - b)(a + b)$$

Factoring a Perfect Square Trinomial

The factored form of a **perfect square trinomial** is the square of a binomial:

$$a^2 + 2ab + b^2 = (a + b)^2$$
$$a^2 - 2ab + b^2 = (a - b)^2$$

Examples

Example 1

$$25z^2 - 4y^2$$
$$= (5z - 2y)(5z + 2y)$$

Example 2

Factor: $25y^2 + 10y + 1$
$$= (5y)^2 + 2(5y)(1) + (1)^2$$
$$= (5y + 1)^2$$

| **Section 6.6** | **Sum and Difference of Cubes** |

Key Concepts

Factoring a Sum or Difference of Cubes

$$a^3 + b^3 = (a + b)(a^2 - ab + b^2)$$

$$a^3 - b^3 = (a - b)(a^2 + ab + b^2)$$

Examples

Example 1

$$x^6 + 8y^3$$
$$= (x^2)^3 + (2y)^3$$
$$= (x^2 + 2y)(x^4 - 2x^2y + 4y^2)$$

Example 2

$$m^3 - 64$$
$$= (m)^3 - (4)^3$$
$$= (m - 4)(m^2 + 4m + 16)$$

Section 6.7   Solving Equations Using the Zero Product Rule

Key Concepts

An equation of the form $ax^2 + bx + c = 0$, where $a \neq 0$, is a **quadratic equation**.

The **zero product rule** states that if $ab = 0$, then $a = 0$ or $b = 0$. The zero product rule can be used to solve a quadratic equation or a higher degree polynomial equation that is factored and set equal to zero.

Examples

Example 1

The equation $2x^2 - 17x + 30 = 0$ is a quadratic equation.

Example 2

$3w(w - 4)(2w + 1) = 0$

$3w = 0$ or $w - 4 = 0$ or $2w + 1 = 0$

$w = 0$ or $w = 4$ or $w = -\dfrac{1}{2}$

The solutions are 0, 4, and $-\dfrac{1}{2}$.

Example 3

$4x^2 = 34x - 60$

$4x^2 - 34x + 60 = 0$

$2(2x^2 - 17x + 30) = 0$

$2(2x - 5)(x - 6) = 0$

$2 \neq 0$ or $2x - 5 = 0$ or $x - 6 = 0$

$x = \dfrac{5}{2}$ or $x = 6$

The solutions are $\dfrac{5}{2}$ and 6.

Section 6.8 Applications of Quadratic Equations

Key Concepts

Use the zero product rule to solve applications.

Some applications involve the **Pythagorean theorem**.

$$a^2 + b^2 = c^2$$

Examples

Example 1

Find two consecutive integers such that the sum of their squares is 61.

Let x represent one integer.
Let $x + 1$ represent the next consecutive integer.

$$x^2 + (x + 1)^2 = 61$$
$$x^2 + x^2 + 2x + 1 = 61$$
$$2x^2 + 2x - 60 = 0$$
$$2(x^2 + x - 30) = 0$$
$$2(x - 5)(x + 6) = 0$$
$$x = 5 \quad \text{or} \quad x = -6$$

If $x = 5$, then the next consecutive integer is 6.
If $x = -6$, then the next consecutive integer is -5.
The integers are 5 and 6, or -6 and -5.

Example 2

Find the length of the missing side.

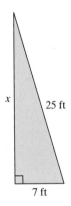

$$x^2 + (7)^2 = (25)^2$$
$$x^2 + 49 = 625$$
$$x^2 - 576 = 0$$
$$(x - 24)(x + 24) = 0$$
$$x = 24 \quad \text{or} \quad x \cancel{=} -24$$

The length of the side is 24 ft.

Chapter 6   Review Exercises

Section 6.1

For Exercises 1–4, identify the greatest common factor for each group of terms.

1. $15a^2b^4, 30a^3b, 9a^5b^3$

2. $3(x + 5), x(x + 5)$

3. $2c^3(3c - 5), 4c(3c - 5)$

4. $-2wyz, -4xyz$

For Exercises 5–10, factor out the greatest common factor.

5. $6x^2 + 2x^4 - 8x$

6. $11w^3y^3 - 44w^2y^5$

7. $-t^2 + 5t$

8. $-6u^2 - u$

9. $3b(b + 2) - 7(b + 2)$

10. $2(5x + 9) + 8x(5x + 9)$

For Exercises 11–14, factor by grouping.

11. $7w^2 + 14w + wb + 2b$

12. $b^2 - 2b + yb - 2y$

13. $60y^2 - 45y - 12y + 9$

14. $6a - 3a^2 - 2ab + a^2b$

Section 6.2

For Exercises 15–24, factor completely.

15. $x^2 - 10x + 21$

16. $y^2 - 19y + 88$

17. $-6z + z^2 - 72$

18. $-39 + q^2 - 10q$

19. $3p^2w + 36pw + 60w$

20. $2m^4 + 26m^3 + 80m^2$

21. $-t^2 + 10t - 16$

22. $-w^2 - w + 20$

23. $a^2 + 12ab + 11b^2$

24. $c^2 - 3cd - 18d^2$

Section 6.3

For Exercises 25–28, let a, b, and c represent positive integers.

25. When factoring a polynomial of the form $ax^2 - bx - c$, should the signs of the binomials be both positive, both negative, or different?

26. When factoring a polynomial of the form $ax^2 - bx + c$ should the signs of the binomials be both positive, both negative, or different?

27. When factoring a polynomial of the form $ax^2 + bx + c$, should the signs of the binomials be both positive, both negative, or different?

28. When factoring a polynomial of the form $ax^2 + bx - c$, should the signs of the binomials be both positive, both negative, or different?

For Exercises 29–42, factor the trinomial using the trial-and-error method.

29. $2y^2 - 5y - 12$

30. $4w^2 - 5w - 6$

31. $10z^2 + 29z + 10$

32. $8z^2 + 6z - 9$

33. $2p^2 - 5p + 1$

34. $5r^2 - 3r + 7$

35. $10w^2 - 60w - 270$

36. $-3y^2 + 18y + 48$

37. $9c^2 - 30cd + 25d^2$

38. $x^2 + 12x + 36$

39. $6g^2 + 7gh + 2h^2$

40. $12m^2 - 32mn + 5n^2$

41. $v^4 - 2v^2 - 3$

42. $x^4 + 7x^2 + 10$

Section 6.4

For Exercises 43 and 44, find a pair of integers whose product and sum are given.

43. Product: -5 sum: 4

44. Product: 15   sum: -8

For Exercises 45–58, factor the trinomial using the ac-method.

45. $3c^2 - 5c - 2$

46. $4y^2 + 13y + 3$

47. $t^2 + 13t + 12$

48. $4x^3 + 17x^2 - 15x$

49. $w^4 + 7w^2 + 10$

50. $p^2 - 8pq + 15q^2$

51. $-40v^2 - 22v + 6$

52. $40s^2 + 30s - 100$

53. $a^3b - 10a^2b^2 + 24ab^3$ **54.** $2z^6 + 8z^5 - 42z^4$

55. $m + 9m^2 - 2$ **56.** $2 + 6p^2 + 19p$

57. $49x^2 + 140x + 100$ **58.** $9w^2 - 6wz + z^2$

Section 6.5

For Exercises 59 and 60, write the formula to factor each binomial, if possible.

59. $a^2 - b^2$ **60.** $a^2 + b^2$

For Exercises 61–76, factor completely.

61. $a^2 - 49$ **62.** $d^2 - 64$

63. $100 - 81t^2$ **64.** $4 - 25k^2$

65. $x^2 + 16$ **66.** $y^2 + 121$

67. $y^2 + 12y + 36$ **68.** $t^2 + 16t + 64$

69. $9a^2 - 12a + 4$ **70.** $25x^2 - 40x + 16$

71. $-3v^2 - 12v - 12$ **72.** $-2x^2 + 20x - 50$

73. $2c^4 - 18$ **74.** $72x^2 - 2y^2$

75. $p^3 + 3p^2 - 16p - 48$ **76.** $4k - 8 - k^3 + 2k^2$

Section 6.6

For Exercises 77 and 78, write the formula to factor each binomial, if possible.

77. $a^3 + b^3$ **78.** $a^3 - b^3$

For Exercises 79–92, factor completely using the factoring strategy found on page 469.

79. $64 + a^3$ **80.** $125 - b^3$

81. $p^6 + 8$ **82.** $q^6 - \dfrac{1}{27}$

83. $6x^3 - 48$ **84.** $7y^3 + 7$

85. $x^3 - 36x$ **86.** $q^4 - 64q$

87. $8h^2 + 20$ **88.** $m^2 - 8m$

89. $x^3 + 4x^2 - x - 4$ **90.** $5p^4q - 20q^3$

91. $8n + n^4$ **92.** $14m^3 - 14$

Section 6.7

93. For which of the following equations can the zero product rule be applied directly? Explain.

$(x - 3)(2x + 1) = 0$ or $(x - 3)(2x + 1) = 6$

For Exercises 94–109, solve the equation using the zero product rule.

94. $(4x - 1)(3x + 2) = 0$

95. $(a - 9)(2a - 1) = 0$

96. $3w(w + 3)(5w + 2) = 0$

97. $6u(u - 7)(4u - 9) = 0$

98. $7k^2 - 9k - 10 = 0$

99. $4h^2 - 23h - 6 = 0$

100. $q^2 - 144 = 0$ **101.** $r^2 = 25$

102. $5v^2 - v = 0$ **103.** $x(x - 6) = -8$

104. $36t^2 + 60t = -25$ **105.** $9s^2 + 12s = -4$

106. $3(y^2 + 4) = 20y$ **107.** $2(p^2 - 66) = -13p$

108. $2y^3 - 18y^2 = -28y$ **109.** $x^3 - 4x = 0$

Section 6.8

110. The base of a parallelogram is 1 ft longer than twice the height. If the area is 78 ft², what are the base and height of the parallelogram?

111. A ball is tossed into the air from ground level with initial speed of 16 ft/sec. The height of the ball is given by the equation

$h = -16t^2 + 16t$ $(t \geq 0)$ where h is the ball's height in feet, and t is the time in seconds.

Find the time(s) when the ball is at ground level.

112. Find the length of the ramp.

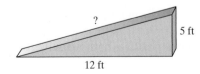

?   5 ft

12 ft

113. A right triangle has one leg that is 2 ft longer than the other leg. The hypotenuse is 2 ft less than twice the shorter leg. Find the lengths of all sides of the triangle.

114. If the square of a number is subtracted from 60, the result is -4. Find all such numbers.

115. The product of two consecutive integers is 44 more than 14 times their sum.

116. The base of a triangle is 1 m longer than twice the height. If the area of the triangle is 18 m^2, find the base and height.

Chapter 6   Test

1. Factor out the GCF: $15x^4 - 3x + 6x^3$

2. Factor by grouping: $7a - 35 - a^2 + 5a$

3. Factor the trinomial: $6w^2 - 43w + 7$

4. Factor the difference of squares: $169 - p^2$

5. Factor the perfect square trinomial: $q^2 - 16q + 64$

6. Factor the sum of cubes: $8 + t^3$

For Exercises 7–26, factor completely.

7. $a^2 + 12a + 32$

8. $x^2 + x - 42$

9. $2y^2 - 17y + 8$

10. $6z^2 + 19z + 8$

11. $9t^2 - 100$

12. $v^2 - 81$

13. $3a^2 + 27ab + 54b^2$

14. $c^4 - 1$

15. $xy - 7x + 3y - 21$

16. $49 + p^2$

17. $-10u^2 + 30u - 20$

18. $12t^2 - 75$

19. $5y^2 - 50y + 125$

20. $21q^2 + 14q$

21. $2x^3 + x^2 - 8x - 4$

22. $y^3 - 125$

23. $m^2n^2 - 81$

24. $16a^2 - 64b^2$

25. $64x^3 - 27y^6$

26. $3x^2y - 6xy - 24y$

For Exercises 27–31, solve the equation.

27. $(2x - 3)(x + 5) = 0$

28. $x^2 - 7x = 0$

29. $x^2 - 6x = 16$

30. $x(5x + 4) = 1$

31. $y^3 + 10y^2 - 9y - 90 = 0$

32. A tennis court has an area of 312 yd^2. If the length is 2 yd more than twice the width, find the dimensions of the court.

33. The product of two consecutive odd integers is 35. Find the integers.

34. The height of a triangle is 5 in. less than the length of the base. The area is 42 in.^{2}. Find the length of the base and the height of the triangle.

35. The hypotenuse of a right triangle is 2 ft less than three times the shorter leg. The longer leg is 3 ft less than three times the shorter leg. Find the length of the shorter leg.

36. A stone is dropped off a 144-ft cliff. The height of the stone above the ground is given in the equation

$h = -16t^2 + 144$ where h is the stone's height in feet, and t is the time in seconds after the stone is dropped ($t \geq 0$).

Find the time required for the stone to hit the ground.

Chapters 1–6   Cumulative Review Exercises

1. Simplify. $\dfrac{|4 - 25 \div (-5) \cdot 2|}{\sqrt{8^2 + 6^2}}$

2. Solve. $5 - 2(t + 4) = 3t + 12$

3. Solve for y. $3x - 2y = 8$

4. A child's piggy bank contains 17 coins in quarters and dimes. The number of dimes is three less than the number of quarters. How many of each type of coin is in the piggy bank?

5. Solve the inequality. Graph the solution on a number line and write the solution set in interval notation.

$$-\frac{5}{12}x \le \frac{5}{3}$$ ⟶

6. Given the equation $y = x + 4$

  a. Is the equation linear?

  b. Identify the slope.

  c. Identify the y-intercept.

  d. Identify the x-intercept.

  e. Graph the line.

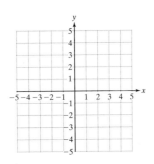

7. Consider the equation, $x = 5$.

  a. Does the equation present a horizontal or vertical line?

  b. Determine the slope of the line, if it exists.

  c. Identify the x-intercept, if it exists.

  d. Identify the y-intercept, if it exists.

8. Find an equation of the line passing through the point $(-3, 5)$ and having a slope of 3. Write the final answer in slope-intercept form.

9. Solve the system. $\begin{aligned} 2x - 3y &= 4 \\ 5x - 6y &= 13 \end{aligned}$

For Exercises 10–13, perform the indicated operations.

10. $2\left(\dfrac{1}{3}y^3 - \dfrac{3}{2}y^2 - 7\right) - \left(\dfrac{2}{3}y^3 + \dfrac{1}{2}y^2 + 5y\right)$

11. $(4p^2 - 5p - 1)(2p - 3)$

12. $(2w - 7)^2$

13. $(r^4 + 2r^3 - 5r + 1) \div (r - 3)$

14. Simplify. $\dfrac{c^{12}c^{-5}}{c^3}$

15. Simplify. $\left(\dfrac{6a^2b^{-4}}{2a^4b^{-5}}\right)^{-2}$

16. Divide. Write the final answer in scientific notation: $\dfrac{8 \times 10^{-3}}{5 \times 10^{-6}}$

For Exercises 17–19, factor completely.

17. $w^4 - 16$

18. $2ax + 10bx - 3ya - 15yb$

19. $4x^2 - 8x - 5$

20. Solve. $4x(2x - 1)(x + 5) = 0$

Rational Expressions and Equations

7

CHAPTER OUTLINE

Chapter 7

In this chapter, we define a rational expression as a ratio of two polynomials. Then we perform operations on rational expressions and solve rational equations.

Review Your Skills

You may find it helpful to review operations with fractions before you begin this chapter. (See Section R.2.) Complete the matching problems, then record the letter of the answer in the spaces below to complete the sentence.

1. Add. $\dfrac{7}{4} + \dfrac{5}{3} + \dfrac{1}{2}$ **2.** Multiply. $\dfrac{5}{3} \cdot \dfrac{11}{4}$

3. Fraction that is not in lowest terms.

4. In this problem, a common denominator is not required.

5. Fractions can be eliminated from this problem by multiplying by the LCD.

a. $\dfrac{7}{8}x + \dfrac{2}{3} = \dfrac{1}{2}$ **t.** $\dfrac{45}{12}$

r. $\dfrac{47}{12}$ **p.** $\dfrac{34}{3} \cdot \dfrac{1}{4}$

n. $\dfrac{7}{8} + \dfrac{1}{3} - \dfrac{1}{2}$ **o.** $\dfrac{55}{12}$

The enemy of a good student is $\underset{4}{\_\_}\,\underset{1}{\_\_}\,\underset{2}{\_\_}\,\overset{c}{\_\_}\,\underset{1}{\_\_}\,\underset{5}{\_\_}\,\overset{s}{\_\_}\,\underset{3}{\_\_}\,\overset{i}{\_\_}\,\overset{n}{\_\_}\,\underset{5}{\_\_}\,\underset{3}{\_\_}\,\overset{i}{\_\_}\,\underset{2}{\_\_}\,\overset{n}{\_\_}.$

Introduction to Rational Expressions

1. Definition of a Rational Expression

In Section 1.1, we defined a rational number as the ratio of two integers, $\frac{p}{q}$, where $q \neq 0$.

$$\text{Examples of rational numbers: } \frac{2}{3}, -\frac{1}{5}, 9$$

In a similar way, we define a **rational expression** as the ratio of two polynomials, $\frac{p}{q}$, where $q \neq 0$.

$$\text{Examples of rational expressions: } \frac{3x-6}{x^2-4}, \quad \frac{3}{4}, \quad \frac{6r^5+2r}{7}$$

2. Evaluating Rational Expressions

Example 1   **Evaluating Rational Expressions**

Evaluate the rational expression for the given values of x. $\dfrac{x}{x-3}$

a. $x = 6$ **b.** $x = -3$ **c.** $x = 0$ **d.** $x = 3$

Solution:

Substitute the given value for the variable. Use order of operations to simplify.

a. $\dfrac{x}{x-3}$

$\dfrac{(6)}{(6)-3}$ Substitute $x = 6$.

$= \dfrac{6}{3}$

$= 2$

b. $\dfrac{x}{x-3}$

$\dfrac{(-3)}{(-3)-3}$ Substitute $x = -3$.

$= \dfrac{-3}{-6}$

$= \dfrac{1}{2}$

c. $\dfrac{x}{x-3}$

$\dfrac{(0)}{(0)-3}$ Substitute $x = 0$.

$= \dfrac{0}{-3}$

$= 0$

d. $\dfrac{x}{x-3}$

$\dfrac{(3)}{(3)-3}$ Substitute $x = 3$.

$= \dfrac{3}{0}$ Undefined.

Recall that division by zero is undefined.

Skill Practice

Evaluate the expression for the given values of x.

$$\frac{x-3}{x+5}$$

1. $x = 2$
2. $x = 0$
3. $x = 3$
4. $x = -5$

Avoiding Mistakes

The numerator is 0, therefore the fraction is equal to 0.

Avoiding Mistakes

The denominator is 0, therefore the fraction is undefined.

Answers

1. $-\dfrac{1}{7}$ 2. $-\dfrac{3}{5}$
3. 0   4. Undefined

3. Restricted Values of a Rational Expression

From Example 1 we see that not all values of x can be substituted into a rational expression. The values that make the denominator zero must be restricted.

The expression $\dfrac{x}{x-3}$ is undefined for $x = 3$, so we call $x = 3$ a restricted value.

Restricted values of a rational expression are all values that make the expression undefined, that is, make the denominator equal to zero.

Finding the Restricted Values of a Rational Expression

- Set the denominator equal to zero and solve the resulting equation.
- The restricted values are the solutions to the equation.

Example 2 **Finding the Restricted Values of Rational Expressions**

Identify the restricted values for each expression.

a. $\dfrac{y-3}{2y+7}$ **b.** $\dfrac{-5}{x}$

Solution:

a. $\dfrac{y-3}{2y+7}$

$2y + 7 = 0$ Set the denominator equal to zero.

$2y = -7$ Solve the equation.

$\dfrac{2y}{2} = \dfrac{-7}{2}$

$y = -\dfrac{7}{2}$ The restricted value is $y = -\dfrac{7}{2}$.

b. $\dfrac{-5}{x}$

$x = 0$ Set the denominator equal to zero.

The restricted value is $x = 0$.

Skill Practice

Identify the restricted values.

8. $\dfrac{w - 4}{w^2 - 9}$

9. $\dfrac{8}{z^4 + 1}$

Example 3 **Finding the Restricted Values of Rational Expressions**

Identify the restricted values for each expression.

a. $\dfrac{a + 10}{a^2 - 25}$ **b.** $\dfrac{2x^3 + 5}{x^2 + 9}$

Solution:

a. $\dfrac{a + 10}{a^2 - 25}$

$a^2 - 25 = 0$ Set the denominator equal to zero. The equation is quadratic.

$(a - 5)(a + 5) = 0$ Factor.

$a - 5 = 0$ or $a + 5 = 0$ Set each factor equal to zero.

$a = 5$ or $a = -5$

The restricted values are $a = 5$ and $a = -5$.

b. $\dfrac{2x^3 + 5}{x^2 + 9}$

The quantity x^2 cannot be negative for any real number, x, so the denominator $x^2 + 9$ cannot equal zero. Therefore, there are no restricted values.

4. Simplifying Rational Expressions

In many cases, it is advantageous to simplify or reduce a fraction to lowest terms. The same is true for rational expressions.

The method for simplifying rational expressions mirrors the process for simplifying fractions. In each case, factor the numerator and denominator. Common factors in the numerator and denominator form a ratio of 1 and can be reduced.

Simplifying a fraction: $\dfrac{21}{35} \xrightarrow{\text{Factor}} \dfrac{3 \cdot \overset{1}{\cancel{7}}}{5 \cdot \cancel{7}} = \dfrac{3}{5} \cdot (1) = \dfrac{3}{5}$

Simplifying a rational expression: $\dfrac{2x - 6}{x^2 - 9} \xrightarrow{\text{Factor}} \dfrac{2\overset{1}{\cancel{(x - 3)}}}{(x + 3)\cancel{(x - 3)}} = \dfrac{2}{(x + 3)}(1) = \dfrac{2}{x + 3}$

Informally, to simplify a rational expression to lowest terms, we simplify the ratio of common factors to 1. Formally, this is accomplished by applying the fundamental principle of rational expressions.

> **Fundamental Principle of Rational Expressions**
> Let p, q, and r represent polynomials where $q \neq 0$ and $r \neq 0$. Then
> $$\frac{pr}{qr} = \frac{p}{q} \cdot \frac{r}{r} = \frac{p}{q} \cdot 1 = \frac{p}{q}$$

Answers

8. $w = 3, w = -3$
9. There are no restricted values.

Example 4 Simplifying a Rational Expression

Given the expression $\dfrac{2p - 14}{p^2 - 49}$

a. Factor the numerator and denominator.

b. Identify the restricted values.

c. Simplify the rational expression.

Solution:

a. $\dfrac{2p - 14}{p^2 - 49}$ Factor out the GCF in the numerator.

$\quad = \dfrac{2(p - 7)}{(p + 7)(p - 7)}$ Factor the denominator as a difference of squares.

b. $(p + 7)(p - 7) = 0$ To find the restricted values, set the denominator equal to zero. The equation is quadratic.

$\quad p + 7 = 0 \quad$ or $\quad p - 7 = 0$ Set each factor equal to 0.

$\quad p = -7 \quad$ or $\quad p = 7$ The restricted values are -7 and 7.

c. $\dfrac{2(p \overset{1}{\cancel{-7}})}{(p + 7)(p \cancel{-7})}$ Simplify the ratio of common factors to 1.

$\quad = \dfrac{2}{p + 7} \quad$ (provided $p \neq 7$ and $p \neq -7$)

Skill Practice

Given: $\dfrac{5z + 25}{z^2 + 3z - 10}$

10. Factor the numerator and the denominator.

11. Identify the restricted values.

12. Simplify the rational expression.

Avoiding Mistakes

The restricted values of a rational expression are always determined *before* simplifying the expression to lowest terms.

In Example 4, it is important to note that the expressions

$$\frac{2p - 14}{p^2 - 49} \quad \text{and} \quad \frac{2}{p + 7}$$

are equal for all values of p that make each expression a real number. Therefore,

$$\frac{2p - 14}{p^2 - 49} = \frac{2}{p + 7}$$

for all values of p except $p = 7$ and $p = -7$. (At $p = 7$ and $p = -7$, the original expression is undefined.) This is why the restricted values are always determined before the expression is simplified.

From this point forward, we will write statements of equality between two rational expressions with the assumption that they are equal for all values of the variable for which each expression is defined.

Answers

10. $\dfrac{5(z + 5)}{(z + 5)(z - 2)}$

11. $z = -5, z = 2$

12. $\dfrac{5}{z - 2} (z \neq 2, z \neq -5)$

Example 5 Simplifying a Rational Expression

Simplify the rational expression. $\dfrac{18a^4}{9a^5}$

Solution:

$$\dfrac{18a^4}{9a^5}$$

$$= \dfrac{2 \cdot 3 \cdot 3 \cdot a \cdot a \cdot a \cdot a}{3 \cdot 3 \cdot a \cdot a \cdot a \cdot a \cdot a} \qquad \text{Factor the numerator and denominator.}$$

$$= \dfrac{2 \cdot (3 \cdot 3 \cdot a \cdot a \cdot a \cdot a)}{(3 \cdot 3 \cdot a \cdot a \cdot a \cdot a) \cdot a} \qquad \text{Simplify common factors.}$$

$$= \dfrac{2}{a}$$

> **TIP:** The expression $\dfrac{18a^4}{9a^5}$ can also be simplified using the properties of exponents.
>
> $$\dfrac{18a^4}{9a^5} = 2a^{4-5} = 2a^{-1} = \dfrac{2}{a}$$

Example 6 Simplifying a Rational Expression

Simplify the rational expression. $\dfrac{2c - 8}{10c^2 - 80c + 160}$

Solution:

$$\dfrac{2c - 8}{10c^2 - 80c + 160}$$

$$= \dfrac{2(c - 4)}{10(c^2 - 8c + 16)} \qquad \text{Factor out the GCF.}$$

$$= \dfrac{2(c - 4)}{10(c - 4)^2} \qquad \text{Factor the denominator.}$$

$$= \dfrac{2(c - 4)}{2 \cdot 5(c - 4)(c - 4)} \qquad \text{Simplify the ratio of common factors to 1.}$$

$$= \dfrac{1}{5(c - 4)}$$

Avoiding Mistakes

Given the expression

$$\dfrac{2c - 8}{10c^2 - 80c + 160}$$

do not be tempted to reduce before factoring. The terms $2c$ and $10c^2$ cannot be "canceled" because they are *terms* not factors.

The numerator and denominator must be in factored form before simplifying.

The process to simplify a rational expression is based on the identity property of multiplication. Therefore, this process applies only to factors (remember that factors are multiplied). For example:

Answers

13. $\dfrac{5q}{3}$ **14.** $\dfrac{x - 1}{2x - 3}$

$$\frac{3x}{3y} = \frac{\overset{1}{\cancel{3}} \cdot x}{\cancel{3} \cdot y} = 1 \cdot \frac{x}{y} = \frac{x}{y}$$

$\uparrow$ Simplify

Terms that are added or subtracted cannot be reduced to lowest terms. For example:

$$\frac{x + 3}{y + 3}$$

$\uparrow$ Cannot be simplified

The objective of simplifying a rational expression to lowest terms is to create an equivalent expression that is simpler to use. Consider the rational expression from Example 6 in its original form and in its reduced form. If we substitute a value for c into each expression, we see that the reduced form is easier to evaluate. For example, substitute $c = 3$:

Original Expression	**Simplified Expression**
$\dfrac{2c - 8}{10c^2 - 80c + 160}$	$\dfrac{1}{5(c - 4)}$

Substitute $c = 3$

$$= \frac{2(3) - 8}{10(3)^2 - 80(3) + 160} \qquad = \frac{1}{5(3 - 4)}$$

$$= \frac{6 - 8}{10(9) - 240 + 160} \qquad = \frac{1}{5(-1)}$$

$$= \frac{-2}{90 - 240 + 160} \qquad\qquad = -\frac{1}{5}$$

$$= \frac{-2}{10} \quad \text{or} \quad -\frac{1}{5}$$

5. Simplifying a Ratio of -1

When two factors are identical in the numerator and denominator, they form a ratio of 1 and can be reduced. Sometimes we encounter two factors that are opposites and form a ratio of -1. For example:

Simplified Form **Details/Notes**

$\dfrac{-5}{5} = -1$ The ratio of a number and its opposite is -1.

$\dfrac{100}{-100} = -1$ The ratio of a number and its opposite is -1.

$\dfrac{x + 7}{-x - 7} = -1$ $\dfrac{x + 7}{-x - 7} = \dfrac{x + 7}{-1(x + 7)} = \dfrac{\overset{1}{\cancel{x + 7}}}{-1(\cancel{x + 7})} = \dfrac{1}{-1} = -1$

$\overset{\curvearrowright}{\text{factor out } -1}$

$\dfrac{2 - x}{x - 2} = -1$ $\dfrac{2 - x}{x - 2} = \dfrac{-1(-2 + x)}{x - 2} = \dfrac{-1(\overset{1}{\cancel{x - 2}})}{\cancel{x - 2}} = \dfrac{-1}{1} = -1$

Recognizing factors that are opposites is useful when simplifying rational expressions.

Avoiding Mistakes

While the expression $2 - x$ and $x - 2$ are opposites, the expressions $2 - x$ and $2 + x$ are *not*.

Therefore $\dfrac{2 - x}{2 + x}$ does not simplify to -1.

Example 7 Simplifying a Rational Expression

Simplify the rational expression. $\quad \dfrac{3c - 3d}{d - c}$

Solution:

$\dfrac{3c - 3d}{d - c}$

$= \dfrac{3(c - d)}{d - c}$ Factor the numerator and denominator.

Notice that $(c - d)$ and $(d - c)$ are opposites and form a ratio of -1.

$= \dfrac{3(\overset{-1}{\cancel{c - d}})}{\cancel{d - c}}$ $\quad$ Details: $\dfrac{3(c - d)}{d - c} = \dfrac{3(c - d)}{-1(-d + c)} = \dfrac{3(c - d)}{-1(c - d)}$

$= 3(-1)$ $\qquad\qquad\qquad\qquad\qquad\qquad\qquad = \dfrac{3}{-1} = -3$

$= -3$

TIP: It is important to recognize that a rational expression can be written in several equivalent forms. In particular, two numbers with opposite signs form a negative quotient. Therefore, a number such as $-\frac{3}{4}$ can be written as:

$$-\dfrac{3}{4} \quad \text{or} \quad \dfrac{-3}{4} \quad \text{or} \quad \dfrac{3}{-4}$$

The negative sign can be written in the numerator, in the denominator, or out in front of the fraction. We demonstrate this concept in Example 8.

Example 8 Simplifying a Rational Expression

Simplify the rational expression. $\quad \dfrac{5 - y}{y^2 - 25}$

Solution:

$\dfrac{5 - y}{y^2 - 25}$

$= \dfrac{5 - y}{(y - 5)(y + 5)}$ Factor the numerator and denominator.

Notice that $5 - y$ and $y - 5$ are opposites and form a ratio of -1.

$= \dfrac{\overset{-1}{\cancel{5 - y}}}{(\cancel{y - 5})(y + 5)}$ $\quad$ Details: $\dfrac{5 - y}{(y - 5)(y + 5)} = \dfrac{-1(-5 + y)}{(y - 5)(y + 5)}$

$\qquad\qquad\qquad\qquad\qquad\qquad = \dfrac{-1(y - 5)}{(y - 5)(y + 5)} = \dfrac{-1}{y + 5}$

$= \dfrac{-1}{y + 5} \quad \text{or} \quad \dfrac{1}{-(y + 5)} \quad \text{or} \quad -\dfrac{1}{y + 5}$

Section 7.1   Practice Exercises

Study Skills Exercise

Review Section R.2 in this text. Write an example of how to simplify (reduce) a fraction, multiply two fractions, divide two fractions, add two fractions, and subtract two fractions. Then as you learn about rational expressions, compare the operations on rational expressions with those on fractions. This is a great place to use 3×5 cards again. Write an example of an operation with fractions on one side and the same operation with rational expressions on the other side.

Vocabulary and Key Concepts

1. a. A _____ expression is the ratio of two polynomials, $\dfrac{p}{q}$, where $q \neq 0$.

b. Restricted values of a rational expression are all values that make the _____ equal to _____.

c. For polynomials p, q, and r, where $q \neq 0$ and $r \neq 0$, $\dfrac{pr}{qr} = $ _____.

d. The ratio $\dfrac{a-b}{a-b} = $ _____ whereas the ratio $\dfrac{a-b}{b-a} = $ _____ provided that $a \neq b$.

Concept 2: Evaluating Rational Expressions

For Exercises 2–10, substitute the given number into the expression and simplify (if possible). **(See Example 1.)**

2. $\dfrac{5}{y-4}$; $y = 6$

3. $\dfrac{t-2}{t^2-4t+8}$; $t = 2$

4. $\dfrac{4x}{x-7}$; $x = 8$

5. $\dfrac{1}{x-6}$; $x = -2$

6. $\dfrac{w-10}{w+6}$; $w = 0$

7. $\dfrac{w-4}{2w+8}$; $w = 0$

8. $\dfrac{y-8}{2y^2+y-1}$; $y = 8$

9. $\dfrac{(a-7)(a+1)}{(a-2)(a+5)}$; $a = 2$

10. $\dfrac{(a+4)(a+1)}{(a-4)(a-1)}$; $a = 1$

11. A bicyclist rides 24 mi against a wind and returns 24 mi with the same wind. His average speed for the return trip traveling with the wind is 8 mph faster than his speed going out against the wind. If x represents the bicyclist's speed going out against the wind, then the total time, t, required for the round trip is given by

$$t = \dfrac{24}{x} + \dfrac{24}{x+8} \qquad \text{where } t \text{ is measured in hours.}$$

a. Find the time required for the round trip if the cyclist rides 12 mph against the wind.

b. Find the time required for the round trip if the cyclist rides 24 mph against the wind.

12. The manufacturer of mountain bikes has a fixed cost of $56,000, plus a variable cost of $140 per bike. The average cost per bike, y (in dollars), is given by the equation:

$$y = \dfrac{56{,}000 + 140x}{x} \qquad \text{where } x \text{ represents the number of bikes produced.}$$

a. Find the average cost per bike if the manufacturer produces 1000 bikes.

b. Find the average cost per bike if the manufacturer produces 2000 bikes.

c. Find the average cost per bike if the manufacturer produces 10,000 bikes.

Concept 3: Restricted Values of a Rational Expression

For Exercises 13–24, identify the restricted values. **(See Examples 2 and 3.)**

13. $\dfrac{5}{k + 2}$

14. $\dfrac{-3}{h - 4}$

15. $\dfrac{x + 5}{(2x - 5)(x + 8)}$

16. $\dfrac{4y + 1}{(3y + 7)(y + 3)}$

17. $\dfrac{m + 12}{m^2 + 5m + 6}$

18. $\dfrac{c - 11}{c^2 - 5c - 6}$

19. $\dfrac{x - 4}{x^2 + 9}$

20. $\dfrac{x + 1}{x^2 + 4}$

21. $\dfrac{y^2 - y - 12}{12}$

22. $\dfrac{z^2 + 10z + 9}{9}$

23. $\dfrac{t - 5}{t}$

24. $\dfrac{2w + 7}{w}$

25. Construct a rational expression that is undefined for $x = 2$. (Answers will vary.)

26. Construct a rational expression that is undefined for $x = 5$. (Answers will vary.)

27. Construct a rational expression that is undefined for $x = -3$ and $x = 7$. (Answers will vary.)

28. Construct a rational expression that is undefined for $x = -1$ and $x = 4$. (Answers will vary.)

29. Evaluate the expressions for $x = -1$.

   a. $\dfrac{3x^2 - 2x - 1}{6x^2 - 7x - 3}$ **b.** $\dfrac{x - 1}{2x - 3}$

30. Evaluate the expressions for $x = 4$.

   a. $\dfrac{(x + 5)^2}{x^2 + 6x + 5}$ **b.** $\dfrac{x + 5}{x + 1}$

31. Evaluate the expressions for $x = 1$.

   a. $\dfrac{5x + 5}{x^2 - 1}$ **b.** $\dfrac{5}{x - 1}$

32. Evaluate the expressions for $x = -3$.

   a. $\dfrac{2x^2 - 4x - 6}{2x^2 - 18}$ **b.** $\dfrac{x + 1}{x + 3}$

Concept 4: Simplifying Rational Expressions

For Exercises 33–42,

   a. Identify the restricted values.   **b.** Simplify the rational expression. **(See Example 4.)**

33. $\dfrac{3y + 6}{6y + 12}$

34. $\dfrac{8x - 8}{4x - 4}$

35. $\dfrac{t^2 - 1}{t + 1}$

36. $\dfrac{r^2 - 4}{r - 2}$

37. $\dfrac{7w}{21w^2 - 35w}$

38. $\dfrac{12a^2}{24a^2 - 18a}$

39. $\dfrac{9x^2 - 4}{6x + 4}$

40. $\dfrac{8n - 20}{4n^2 - 25}$

41. $\dfrac{a^2 + 3a - 10}{a^2 + a - 6}$

42. $\dfrac{t^2 + 3t - 10}{t^2 + t - 20}$

For Exercises 43–72, simplify the rational expression. **(See Examples 5 and 6.)**

43. $\dfrac{7b^2}{21b}$

44. $\dfrac{15c^3}{3c^5}$

45. $\dfrac{-24x^2y^5z}{8xy^4z^3}$

46. $\dfrac{60rs^4t^2}{-12r^4s^2t^3}$

47. $\dfrac{(p - 3)(p + 5)}{(p + 5)(p + 4)}$

48. $\dfrac{(c + 4)(c - 1)}{(c + 4)(c + 2)}$

49. $\dfrac{m + 11}{4(m + 11)(m - 11)}$

50. $\dfrac{n - 7}{9(n + 2)(n - 7)}$

51. $\dfrac{x(2x+1)^2}{4x^3(2x+1)}$

52. $\dfrac{(p+2)(p-3)^4}{(p+2)^2(p-3)^2}$

53. $\dfrac{5}{20a-25}$

54. $\dfrac{7}{14c-21}$

55. $\dfrac{3x^2-6x}{9xy+18x}$

56. $\dfrac{6p^2+12p}{2pq-4p}$

57. $\dfrac{2x+4}{x^2-3x-10}$

58. $\dfrac{5z+15}{z^2-4z-21}$

59. $\dfrac{a^2-49}{a-7}$

60. $\dfrac{b^2-64}{b-8}$

61. $\dfrac{q^2+25}{q+5}$

62. $\dfrac{r^2+36}{r+6}$

63. $\dfrac{y^2+6y+9}{2y^2+y-15}$

64. $\dfrac{h^2+h-6}{h^2+2h-8}$

65. $\dfrac{5q^2+5}{q^4-1}$

66. $\dfrac{4t^2+16}{t^4-16}$

67. $\dfrac{ac-ad+2bc-2bd}{2ac+ad+4bc+2bd}$ (*Hint:* Factor by grouping.)

68. $\dfrac{3pr-ps-3qr+qs}{3pr-ps+3qr-qs}$ (*Hint:* Factor by grouping.)

69. $\dfrac{5x^3+4x^2-45x-36}{x^2-9}$

70. $\dfrac{x^2-1}{ax^3-bx^2-ax+b}$

71. $\dfrac{2x^2-xy-3y^2}{2x^2-11xy+12y^2}$

72. $\dfrac{2c^2+cd-d^2}{5c^2+3cd-2d^2}$

Concept 5: Simplifying a Ratio of −1

73. What is the relationship between $x-2$ and $2-x$?

74. What is the relationship between $w+p$ and $-w-p$?

For Exercises 75–86, simplify the rational expressions. **(See Examples 7 and 8.)**

75. $\dfrac{x-5}{5-x}$

76. $\dfrac{8-p}{p-8}$

77. $\dfrac{-4-y}{4+y}$

78. $\dfrac{z+10}{-z-10}$

79. $\dfrac{3y-6}{12-6y}$

80. $\dfrac{4q-4}{12-12q}$

81. $\dfrac{k+5}{5-k}$

82. $\dfrac{2+n}{2-n}$

83. $\dfrac{10x-12}{10x+12}$

84. $\dfrac{4t-16}{16+4t}$

85. $\dfrac{x^2-x-12}{16-x^2}$

86. $\dfrac{49-b^2}{b^2-10b+21}$

Mixed Exercises

For Exercises 87–100, simplify the rational expressions.

87. $\dfrac{3x^2+7x-6}{x^2+7x+12}$

88. $\dfrac{y^2-5y-14}{2y^2-y-10}$

89. $\dfrac{3(m-2)}{6(2-m)}$

90. $\dfrac{8(1-x)}{4(x-1)}$

91. $\dfrac{w^2-4}{8-4w}$

92. $\dfrac{15-3x}{x^2-25}$

93. $\dfrac{18st^5}{12st^3}$

94. $\dfrac{20a^4b^2}{25ab^2}$

95. $\dfrac{4r^2-4rs+s^2}{s^2-4r^2}$

96. $\dfrac{y^2-9z^2}{3z^2+2yz-y^2}$

97. $\dfrac{3y-3x}{2x^2-4xy+2y^2}$

98. $\dfrac{49p^2-28pq+4q^2}{4q-14p}$

99. $\dfrac{2t^2-3t}{2t^4-13t^3+15t^2}$

100. $\dfrac{4m^3+3m^2}{4m^3+7m^2+3m}$

Expanding Your Skills

For Exercises 101–104, factor and simplify.

101. $\dfrac{w^3 - 8}{w^2 + 2w + 4}$ **102.** $\dfrac{y^3 + 27}{y^2 - 3y + 9}$ **103.** $\dfrac{z^2 - 16}{z^3 - 64}$ **104.** $\dfrac{x^2 - 25}{x^3 + 125}$

The restricted values of a rational expression are the values for the variable that make the expression undefined. Since it is always important to be aware of what values can and cannot be substituted for the variable, another important concept is that of the **domain** of a rational expression. The restricted values are the values that *cannot* be used for the variable whereas the domain is the set of values that *can* be used for the variable. For example in the expression $\dfrac{4}{x - 5}$, the restricted value is 5, which means the domain is all real numbers except 5. Set-builder notation is often used to express this set: $\{x \mid x \text{ is a real number}, x \neq 5\}$. The domain of a rational expression is the set of all real numbers except any restricted values.

For Exercises 105–110,

    a. Identify the restricted values for the rational expression.

    b. Write the domain of the rational expression using set-builder notation.

105. $\dfrac{5}{x + 12}$ **106.** $\dfrac{-6}{y - 8}$

107. $\dfrac{a + 2}{a^2 - a}$ **108.** $\dfrac{c - 6}{c^2 + 10c}$

109. $\dfrac{z^2}{z^2 + 4z + 3}$ **110.** $\dfrac{x^2}{x^2 - x - 6}$

Section 7.2   Multiplication and Division of Rational Expressions

Concepts

1. Multiplication of Rational Expressions
2. Division of Rational Expressions

1. Multiplication of Rational Expressions

Recall from Section R.2 that to multiply fractions, we multiply the numerators and multiply the denominators. The same is true for multiplying rational expressions.

> **Multiplication of Rational Expressions**
>
> Let p, q, r, and s represent polynomials, such that $q \neq 0, s \neq 0$. Then,
>
> $$\frac{p}{q} \cdot \frac{r}{s} = \frac{pr}{qs}$$

For example:

Multiply the Fractions	**Multiply the Rational Expressions**
$\dfrac{2}{3} \cdot \dfrac{5}{7} = \dfrac{10}{21}$	$\dfrac{2x}{3y} \cdot \dfrac{5z}{7} = \dfrac{10xz}{21y}$

Sometimes it is possible to simplify a ratio of common factors to 1 *before* multiplying. To do so, we must first factor the numerators and denominators of each fraction.

$$\frac{15}{14} \cdot \frac{21}{10} = \frac{3 \cdot \overset{1}{\cancel{5}}}{2 \cdot \cancel{7}} \cdot \frac{3 \cdot \overset{1}{\cancel{7}}}{2 \cdot \cancel{5}} = \frac{9}{4}$$

The same process is also used to multiply rational expressions.

> ## Multiplying Rational Expressions
> **Step 1** Factor the numerators and denominators of all rational expressions.
> **Step 2** Simplify the ratios of common factors to 1.
> **Step 3** Multiply the remaining factors in the numerator, and multiply the remaining factors in the denominator.

Example 1 Multiplying Rational Expressions

Multiply. $\dfrac{5a^2b}{2} \cdot \dfrac{6a}{10b}$

Solution:

$$\frac{5a^2b}{2} \cdot \frac{6a}{10b}$$

$$= \frac{5 \cdot a \cdot a \cdot b}{2} \cdot \frac{2 \cdot 3 \cdot a}{2 \cdot 5 \cdot b} \qquad \text{Factor into prime factors.}$$

$$= \frac{\overset{1}{\cancel{5}} \cdot a \cdot a \cdot \overset{1}{\cancel{b}}}{2} \cdot \frac{\overset{1}{\cancel{2}} \cdot 3 \cdot a}{\cancel{2} \cdot \cancel{5} \cdot \cancel{b}} \qquad \text{Simplify.}$$

$$= \frac{3a^3}{2} \qquad \text{Multiply remaining factors.}$$

Example 2 Multiplying Rational Expressions

Multiply. $\dfrac{3c - 3d}{6c} \cdot \dfrac{2}{c^2 - d^2}$

Solution:

$$\frac{3c - 3d}{6c} \cdot \frac{2}{c^2 - d^2}$$

$$= \frac{3(c - d)}{2 \cdot 3 \cdot c} \cdot \frac{2}{(c - d)(c + d)} \qquad \text{Factor.}$$

$$= \frac{\overset{1}{\cancel{3}}(\overset{1}{\cancel{c - d}})}{\cancel{2} \cdot \cancel{3} \cdot c} \cdot \frac{\overset{1}{\cancel{2}}}{(\cancel{c - d})(c + d)} \qquad \text{Simplify.}$$

$$= \frac{1}{c(c + d)} \qquad \text{Multiply remaining factors.}$$

Avoiding Mistakes

If all the factors in the numerator reduce to a ratio of 1, a factor of 1 is left in the numerator

Example 3 Multiplying Rational Expressions

Multiply. $\dfrac{35 - 5x}{5x + 5} \cdot \dfrac{x^2 + 5x + 4}{x^2 - 49}$

Solution:

$$\dfrac{35 - 5x}{5x + 5} \cdot \dfrac{x^2 + 5x + 4}{x^2 - 49}$$

$$= \dfrac{5(7 - x)}{5(x + 1)} \cdot \dfrac{(x + 4)(x + 1)}{(x - 7)(x + 7)}$$ 　Factor the numerators and denominators completely.

$$= \dfrac{\overset{1}{\cancel{5}}(\overset{-1}{\cancel{7 - x}})}{\cancel{5}(\cancel{x + 1})} \cdot \dfrac{(x + 4)(\overset{1}{\cancel{x + 1}})}{(\cancel{x - 7})(x + 7)}$$ 　Simplify the ratios of common factors to 1 or -1.

$$= \dfrac{-1(x + 4)}{x + 7}$$ 　Multiply remaining factors.

$$= \dfrac{-(x + 4)}{x + 7} \quad \text{or} \quad \dfrac{x + 4}{-(x + 7)} \quad \text{or} \quad -\dfrac{x + 4}{x + 7}$$

TIP: The ratio $\dfrac{7 - x}{x - 7} = -1$ because $7 - x$ and $x - 7$ are opposites.

2. Division of Rational Expressions

Recall that to divide two fractions, multiply the first fraction by the reciprocal of the second.

$$\dfrac{21}{10} \div \dfrac{49}{15} \xrightarrow[\text{of the second fraction}]{\text{multiply by the reciprocal}} \dfrac{21}{10} \cdot \dfrac{15}{49} \xrightarrow{\text{factor}} \dfrac{3 \cdot \overset{1}{\cancel{7}}}{2 \cdot \cancel{5}} \cdot \dfrac{3 \cdot \overset{1}{\cancel{5}}}{\cancel{7} \cdot 7} = \dfrac{9}{14}$$

The same process is used to divide rational expressions.

> **Division of Rational Expressions**
>
> Let p, q, r, and s represent polynomials, such that $q \neq 0$, $r \neq 0$, $s \neq 0$. Then,
>
> $$\dfrac{p}{q} \div \dfrac{r}{s} = \dfrac{p}{q} \cdot \dfrac{s}{r} = \dfrac{ps}{qr}$$

Example 4 Dividing Rational Expressions

Divide. $\dfrac{5t - 15}{2} \div \dfrac{t^2 - 9}{10}$

Solution:

$$\dfrac{5t - 15}{2} \div \dfrac{t^2 - 9}{10}$$

$$= \dfrac{5t - 15}{2} \cdot \dfrac{10}{t^2 - 9}$$ 　Multiply the first fraction by the reciprocal of the second.

$$= \dfrac{5(t - 3)}{2} \cdot \dfrac{2 \cdot 5}{(t - 3)(t + 3)}$$ 　Factor each polynomial.

$$= \dfrac{5(\overset{1}{\cancel{t - 3}})}{\cancel{2}} \cdot \dfrac{\overset{1}{\cancel{2}} \cdot 5}{(\cancel{t - 3})(t + 3)}$$ 　Simplify the ratio of common factors to 1.

$$= \dfrac{25}{t + 3}$$

Avoiding Mistakes

When dividing rational expressions, take the reciprocal of the second fraction and change to multiplication *before* reducing like factors.

Answers

3. $\dfrac{-(p + 1)}{5}$ or $\dfrac{p + 1}{-5}$ or $-\dfrac{p + 1}{5}$

4. $\dfrac{14}{y + 4}$

Example 5 Dividing Rational Expressions

Divide. $\dfrac{p^2 - 11p + 30}{10p^2 - 250} \div \dfrac{30p - 5p^2}{2p + 4}$

Solution:

$\dfrac{p^2 - 11p + 30}{10p^2 - 250} \div \dfrac{30p - 5p^2}{2p + 4}$

$= \dfrac{p^2 - 11p + 30}{10p^2 - 250} \cdot \dfrac{2p + 4}{30p - 5p^2}$

Multiply the first fraction by the reciprocal of the second.

Factor the trinomial.
$p^2 - 11p + 30 = (p - 5)(p - 6)$

$= \dfrac{(p - 5)(p - 6)}{2 \cdot 5(p - 5)(p + 5)} \cdot \dfrac{2(p + 2)}{5p(6 - p)}$

Factor out the GCF.
$2p + 4 = 2(p + 2)$

Factor out the GCF. Then factor the difference of squares.
$10p^2 - 250 = 10(p^2 - 25)$
$ = 2 \cdot 5(p - 5)(p + 5)$

Factor out the GCF.
$30p - 5p^2 = 5p(6 - p)$

$= \dfrac{\overset{1}{\cancel{(p - 5)}}\overset{-1}{\cancel{(p - 6)}}}{\cancel{2} \cdot 5\cancel{(p - 5)}(p + 5)} \cdot \dfrac{\overset{1}{\cancel{2}}(p + 2)}{5p\cancel{(6 - p)}}$

Simplify the ratio of common factors to 1 or −1.

$= -\dfrac{(p + 2)}{25p(p + 5)}$

Example 6 Dividing Rational Expressions

Divide. $\dfrac{\dfrac{3x}{4y}}{\dfrac{5x}{6y}}$

Solution:

$\dfrac{\dfrac{3x}{4y}}{\dfrac{5x}{6y}}$ ⟵ This fraction bar denotes division (÷).

$= \dfrac{3x}{4y} \div \dfrac{5x}{6y}$

$= \dfrac{3x}{4y} \cdot \dfrac{6y}{5x}$

Multiply by the reciprocal of the second fraction.

$= \dfrac{3 \cdot \overset{1}{\cancel{x}}}{\cancel{2} \cdot 2 \cdot \cancel{y}} \cdot \dfrac{\overset{1}{\cancel{2}} \cdot 3 \cdot \overset{1}{\cancel{y}}}{5 \cdot \cancel{x}}$

Simplify the ratio of common factors to 1.

$= \dfrac{9}{10}$

Sometimes multiplication and division of rational expressions appear in the same problem. In such a case, apply the order of operations by multiplying or dividing in order from left to right.

Example 7 **Multiplying and Dividing Rational Expressions**

Perform the indicated operations. $\dfrac{4}{c^2-9} \div \dfrac{6}{c-3} \cdot \dfrac{3c}{8}$

Solution:

In this example, division occurs first, before multiplication. Parentheses may be inserted to reinforce the proper order.

$$\left(\dfrac{4}{c^2-9} \div \dfrac{6}{c-3}\right) \cdot \dfrac{3c}{8}$$

$$= \left(\dfrac{4}{c^2-9} \cdot \dfrac{c-3}{6}\right) \cdot \dfrac{3c}{8}$$

Multiply the first fraction by the reciprocal of the second.

$$= \left(\dfrac{2 \cdot 2}{(c-3)(c+3)} \cdot \dfrac{c-3}{2 \cdot 3}\right) \cdot \dfrac{3 \cdot c}{2 \cdot 2 \cdot 2}$$

Now that each operation is written as multiplication, factor the polynomials and reduce the common factors.

$$= \dfrac{\overset{1}{2} \cdot \overset{1}{2}}{(\cancel{c-3})(c+3)} \cdot \dfrac{\overset{1}{(\cancel{c-3})}}{2 \cdot \cancel{3}} \cdot \dfrac{\overset{1}{\cancel{3}} \cdot c}{2 \cdot 2 \cdot 2}$$

$$= \dfrac{c}{4(c+3)}$$

Simplify.

TIP: When multiplying more than two fractions, the ratio of common factors in any numerator and any denominator can be simplified. In Example 7, the factors of 2 in the numerator of the first fraction form a ratio of 1 with the factors of 2 in the denominator of the third fraction.

$$\dfrac{\overset{1}{2} \cdot \overset{1}{2}}{(c-3)(c+3)} \cdot \dfrac{(c-3)}{2 \cdot 3} \cdot \dfrac{3 \cdot c}{\cancel{2} \cdot \cancel{2} \cdot 2}$$

Section 7.2 Practice Exercises

Review Exercises

For Exercises 1–8, multiply or divide the fractions.

1. $\dfrac{3}{5} \cdot \dfrac{1}{2}$

2. $\dfrac{6}{7} \cdot \dfrac{5}{12}$

3. $\dfrac{3}{4} \div \dfrac{3}{8}$

4. $\dfrac{18}{5} \div \dfrac{2}{5}$

5. $6 \cdot \dfrac{5}{12}$

6. $\dfrac{7}{25} \cdot 5$

7. $\dfrac{\frac{21}{4}}{\frac{7}{5}}$

8. $\dfrac{\frac{9}{2}}{\frac{3}{4}}$

Concept 1: Multiplication of Rational Expressions

For Exercises 9–24, multiply. **(See Examples 1–3.)**

9. $\dfrac{2xy}{5x^2} \cdot \dfrac{15}{4y}$

10. $\dfrac{7s}{t^2} \cdot \dfrac{t^2}{14s^2}$

11. $\dfrac{6x^3}{9x^6y^2} \cdot \dfrac{18x^4y^7}{4y}$

12. $\dfrac{10a^2b}{15b^2} \cdot \dfrac{30b}{2a^3}$

13. $\dfrac{4x - 24}{20x} \cdot \dfrac{5x}{8}$

14. $\dfrac{5a + 20}{a} \cdot \dfrac{3a}{10}$

15. $\dfrac{3y + 18}{y^2} \cdot \dfrac{4y}{6y + 36}$

16. $\dfrac{2p - 4}{6p} \cdot \dfrac{4p^2}{8p - 16}$

17. $\dfrac{10}{2 - a} \cdot \dfrac{a - 2}{16}$

18. $\dfrac{w - 3}{6} \cdot \dfrac{20}{3 - w}$

19. $\dfrac{b^2 - a^2}{a - b} \cdot \dfrac{a}{a^2 - ab}$

20. $\dfrac{(x - y)^2}{x^2 + xy} \cdot \dfrac{x}{y - x}$

21. $\dfrac{y^2 + 2y + 1}{5y - 10} \cdot \dfrac{y^2 - 3y + 2}{y^2 - 1}$

22. $\dfrac{6a^2 - 6}{a^2 + 6a + 5} \cdot \dfrac{a^2 + 5a}{12a}$

23. $\dfrac{10x}{2x^2 + 3x + 1} \cdot \dfrac{x^2 + 7x + 6}{5x}$

24. $\dfrac{p - 3}{p^2 + p - 12} \cdot \dfrac{4p + 16}{p + 1}$

Concept 2: Division of Rational Expressions

For Exercises 25–38, divide. **(See Examples 4–6.)**

25. $\dfrac{4x}{7y} \div \dfrac{2x^2}{21xy}$

26. $\dfrac{6cd}{5d^2} \div \dfrac{8c^3}{10d}$

27. $\dfrac{\dfrac{8m^4n^5}{5n^6}}{\dfrac{24mn}{15m^3}}$

28. $\dfrac{\dfrac{10a^3b}{3a}}{\dfrac{5b}{9ab}}$

29. $\dfrac{4a + 12}{6a - 18} \div \dfrac{3a + 9}{5a - 15}$

30. $\dfrac{8b - 16}{3b + 3} \div \dfrac{5b - 10}{2b + 2}$

31. $\dfrac{3x - 21}{6x^2 - 42x} \div \dfrac{7}{12x}$

32. $\dfrac{4a^2 - 4a}{9a - 9} \div \dfrac{5}{12a}$

33. $\dfrac{m^2 - n^2}{9} \div \dfrac{3n - 3m}{27m}$

34. $\dfrac{9 - b^2}{15b + 15} \div \dfrac{b - 3}{5b}$

35. $\dfrac{3p + 4q}{p^2 + 4pq + 4q^2} \div \dfrac{4}{p + 2q}$

36. $\dfrac{x^2 + 2xy + y^2}{2x - y} \div \dfrac{x + y}{5}$

37. $\dfrac{p^2 - 2p - 3}{p^2 - p - 6} \div \dfrac{p^2 - 1}{p^2 + 2p}$

38. $\dfrac{4t^2 - 1}{t^2 - 5t} \div \dfrac{2t^2 + 5t + 2}{t^2 - 3t - 10}$

Mixed Exercises

For Exercises 39–64, multiply or divide as indicated.

39. $(w + 3) \cdot \dfrac{w}{2w^2 + 5w - 3}$

40. $\dfrac{5t + 1}{5t^2 - 31t + 6} \cdot (t - 6)$

41. $(r - 5) \cdot \dfrac{4r}{2r^2 - 7r - 15}$

42. $\dfrac{q + 1}{5q^2 - 28q - 12} \cdot (5q + 2)$

43. $\dfrac{\dfrac{5t - 10}{12}}{\dfrac{4t - 8}{8}}$

44. $\dfrac{\dfrac{6m + 6}{5}}{\dfrac{3m + 3}{10}}$

45. $\dfrac{2a^2 + 13a - 24}{8a - 12} \div (a + 8)$

46. $\dfrac{3y^2 + 20y - 7}{5y + 35} \div (3y - 1)$

47. $\dfrac{y^2 + 5y - 36}{y^2 - 2y - 8} \cdot \dfrac{y + 2}{y - 6}$

48. $\dfrac{z^2 - 11z + 28}{z - 1} \cdot \dfrac{z + 1}{z^2 - 6z - 7}$

49. $\dfrac{2t^2 + t - 1}{t^2 + 3t + 2} \cdot \dfrac{t + 2}{2t - 1}$

50. $\dfrac{3p^2 - 2p - 8}{3p^2 - 5p - 12} \cdot \dfrac{p - 3}{p - 2}$

51. $(5t - 1) \div \dfrac{5t^2 + 9t - 2}{3t + 8}$

52. $(2q - 3) \div \dfrac{2q^2 + 5q - 12}{q - 7}$

53. $\dfrac{x^2 + 2x - 3}{x^2 - 3x + 2} \cdot \dfrac{x^2 + 2x - 8}{x^2 + 4x + 3}$

54. $\dfrac{y^2 + y - 12}{y^2 - y - 20} \cdot \dfrac{y^2 + y - 30}{y^2 - 2y - 3}$

55. $\dfrac{\dfrac{w^2 - 6w + 9}{8}}{\dfrac{9 - w^2}{4w + 12}}$

56. $\dfrac{\dfrac{p^2 - 6p + 8}{24}}{\dfrac{16 - p^2}{6p + 6}}$

57. $\dfrac{5k^2 + 7k + 2}{k^2 + 5k + 4} \div \dfrac{5k^2 + 17k + 6}{k^2 + 10k + 24}$

58. $\dfrac{4h^2 - 5h + 1}{h^2 + h - 2} \div \dfrac{6h^2 - 7h + 2}{2h^2 + 3h - 2}$

59. $\dfrac{ax + a + bx + b}{2x^2 + 4x + 2} \cdot \dfrac{4x + 4}{a^2 + ab}$

60. $\dfrac{3my + 9m + ny + 3n}{9m^2 + 6mn + n^2} \cdot \dfrac{30m + 10n}{5y^2 + 15y}$

61. $\dfrac{y^4 - 1}{2y^2 - 3y + 1} \div \dfrac{2y^2 + 2}{8y^2 - 4y}$

62. $\dfrac{x^4 - 16}{6x^2 + 24} \div \dfrac{x^2 - 2x}{3x}$

63. $\dfrac{x^2 - xy - 2y^2}{x + 2y} \div \dfrac{x^2 - 4xy + 4y^2}{x^2 - 4y^2}$

64. $\dfrac{4m^2 - 4mn - 3n^2}{8m^2 - 18n^2} \div \dfrac{3m + 3n}{6m^2 + 15mn + 9n^2}$

For Exercises 65–72, multiply or divide as indicated. **(See Example 7.)**

65. $\dfrac{z^2 + 2z + 1}{3z + 6} \cdot \dfrac{z^2 - 4}{z + 1} \cdot \dfrac{z}{z^2 - z - 2}$

66. $\dfrac{c^2 + 3c}{c^2 + 5c - 6} \cdot \dfrac{c^2 - 4}{c^2 + c - 6} \cdot \dfrac{c + 6}{c}$

67. $\dfrac{y^3 - 3y^2 + 4y - 12}{y^4 - 16} \cdot \dfrac{3y^2 + 5y - 2}{3y^2 - 10y + 3} \div \dfrac{3}{6y - 12}$

68. $\dfrac{x^2 - 25}{3x^2 + 3xy} \cdot \dfrac{x^2 + 4x + xy + 4y}{x^2 + 9x + 20} \div \dfrac{x - 5}{x}$

69. $\dfrac{a^2 - 5a}{a^2 + 7a + 12} \div \dfrac{a^3 - 7a^2 + 10a}{a^2 + 9a + 18} \div \dfrac{a + 6}{a + 4}$

70. $\dfrac{t^2 + t - 2}{t^2 + 5t + 6} \div \dfrac{t - 1}{t} \div \dfrac{5t - 5}{t + 3}$

71. $\dfrac{p^3 - q^3}{p - q} \cdot \dfrac{p + q}{2p^2 + 2pq + 2q^2}$

72. $\dfrac{r^3 + s^3}{r - s} \div \dfrac{r^2 + 2rs + s^2}{r^2 - s^2}$

Section 7.3 | Least Common Denominator

Concepts

1. Least Common Denominator
2. Writing Rational Expressions with the Least Common Denominator

1. Least Common Denominator

In Sections 7.1 and 7.2, we learned how to simplify, multiply, and divide rational expressions. Our next goal is to add and subtract rational expressions. As with fractions, rational expressions may be added or subtracted only if they have the same denominator.

The **least common denominator (LCD)** of two or more rational expressions is defined as the least common multiple of the denominators. For example, consider the fractions $\frac{1}{20}$ and $\frac{1}{8}$. By inspection, you can probably see that the least common denominator is 40. To understand why, find the prime factorization of both denominators:

$$20 = 2^2 \cdot 5 \quad \text{and} \quad 8 = 2^3$$

A common multiple of 20 and 8 must be a multiple of 5, a multiple of 2^2, and a multiple of 2^3. However, any number that is a multiple of $2^3 = 8$ is automatically a multiple of $2^2 = 4$. Therefore, it is sufficient to construct the least common denominator as the product of unique prime factors, in which each factor is raised to its highest power.

$$\text{The LCD of } \frac{1}{20} \text{ and } \frac{1}{8} \text{ is } 2^3 \cdot 5 = 40.$$

Finding the Least Common Denominator of Two or More Rational Expressions

Step 1 Factor all denominators completely.

Step 2 The LCD is the product of unique prime factors from the denominators, in which each factor is raised to the highest power to which it appears in any denominator.

Example 1 Finding the Least Common Denominator of Rational Expressions

Find the LCD of the rational expressions.

a. $\dfrac{5}{14}; \dfrac{3}{49}; \dfrac{1}{8}$ **b.** $\dfrac{5}{3x^2z}; \dfrac{7}{x^5y^3}$

Solution:

a. $\dfrac{5}{14}; \dfrac{3}{49}; \dfrac{1}{8}$

$= \dfrac{5}{2 \cdot 7}; \dfrac{3}{7^2}; \dfrac{1}{2^3}$ Factor the denominators.

The LCD is $7^2 \cdot 2^3 = 392$.   The LCD is the product of unique factors, each raised to its highest power.

b. $\dfrac{5}{3x^2z}; \dfrac{7}{x^5y^3}$

$= \dfrac{5}{3 \cdot x^2 \cdot z^1}; \dfrac{7}{x^5 \cdot y^3}$ The denominators are in factored form.

The LCD is the product of $3 \cdot x^5 \cdot y^3 \cdot z^1$ or simply $3x^5y^3z$.

Example 2 Finding the Least Common Denominator of Rational Expressions

Find the LCD for each pair of rational expressions.

a. $\dfrac{a+b}{a^2-25}; \dfrac{1}{2a-10}$ **b.** $\dfrac{x-5}{x^2-2x}; \dfrac{1}{x^2-4x+4}$

Skill Practice

Find the LCD for each set of expressions.

1. $\dfrac{3}{8}; \dfrac{7}{10}; \dfrac{1}{15}$

2. $\dfrac{1}{5a^3b^2}; \dfrac{1}{10a^4b}$

Skill Practice

Find the LCD.

3. $\dfrac{x}{x^2-16}; \dfrac{2}{3x+12}$

4. $\dfrac{6}{t^2+5t-14};$

$\dfrac{8}{t^2-3t+2}$

Answers

1. 120   **2.** $10a^4b^2$

3. $3(x-4)(x+4)$

4. $(t+7)(t-2)(t-1)$

Solution:

a. $\dfrac{a+b}{a^2-25}; \dfrac{1}{2a-10}$

$= \dfrac{a+b}{(a-5)(a+5)}; \dfrac{1}{2(a-5)}$ Factor the denominators.

The LCD is $2(a-5)(a+5)$.   The LCD is the product of unique factors, each raised to its highest power.

b. $\dfrac{x-5}{x^2-2x}; \dfrac{1}{x^2-4x+4}$

$= \dfrac{x-5}{x(x-2)}; \dfrac{1}{(x-2)^2}$ Factor the denominators.

The LCD is $x(x-2)^2$.   The LCD is the product of unique factors, each raised to its highest power.

Concept Connections

5. Nadia thought that the LCD for the rational expressions $\frac{5}{x}$ and $\frac{1}{x+3}$ should be $x+3$. Explain why this is not the LCD. What is the correct LCD?

2. Writing Rational Expressions with the Least Common Denominator

To add or subtract two rational expressions, the expressions must have the same denominator. Therefore, we must first practice the skill of converting each rational expression into an equivalent expression with the LCD as its denominator.

Writing Equivalent Fractions with Common Denominators
Step 1 Identify the LCD for the expressions.
Step 2 Multiply the numerator and denominator of each fraction by the factors from the LCD that are missing from the original denominators.

Skill Practice

For each pair of expressions, find the LCD, and then convert each expression to an equivalent fraction with the denominator equal to the LCD.

6. $\dfrac{2}{rs^2}; \dfrac{-1}{r^3s}$

7. $\dfrac{5}{x-3}; \dfrac{x}{x+1}$

Example 3   **Converting to the Least Common Denominator**

Find the LCD of each pair of rational expressions. Then convert each expression to an equivalent fraction with the denominator equal to the LCD.

a. $\dfrac{3}{2ab}; \dfrac{6}{5a^2}$ **b.** $\dfrac{4}{x+1}; \dfrac{7}{x-4}$

Solution:

a. $\dfrac{3}{2ab}; \dfrac{6}{5a^2}$ The LCD is $10a^2b$.

$\dfrac{3}{2ab} = \dfrac{3\cdot 5a}{2ab\cdot 5a} = \dfrac{15a}{10a^2b}$ The first expression is missing the factor $5a$ from the denominator.

$\dfrac{6}{5a^2} = \dfrac{6\cdot 2b}{5a^2\cdot 2b} = \dfrac{12b}{10a^2b}$ The second expression is missing the factor $2b$ from the denominator.

Answers

5. The unique factors that appear in the denominators are x and $x+3$, both of which are needed in the LCD. The correct LCD is $x(x+3)$.

6. $\dfrac{2}{rs^2} = \dfrac{2r^2}{r^3s^2}; \dfrac{-1}{r^3s} = \dfrac{-s}{r^3s^2}$

7. $\dfrac{5}{x-3} = \dfrac{5x+5}{(x-3)(x+1)}$

$\dfrac{x}{x+1} = \dfrac{x^2-3x}{(x+1)(x-3)}$

b. $\dfrac{4}{x+1}; \dfrac{7}{x-4}$ The LCD is $(x+1)(x-4)$.

$\dfrac{4}{x+1} = \dfrac{4(x-4)}{(x+1)(x-4)} = \dfrac{4x-16}{(x+1)(x-4)}$ ◄ The first expression is missing the factor $(x-4)$ from the denominator.

$\dfrac{7}{x-4} = \dfrac{7(x+1)}{(x-4)(x+1)} = \dfrac{7x+7}{(x-4)(x+1)}$ ◄ The second expression is missing the factor $(x+1)$ from the denominator.

Example 4 Converting to the Least Common Denominator

Find the LCD of the pair of rational expressions. Then convert each expression to an equivalent fraction with the denominator equal to the LCD.

$$\frac{w+2}{w^2-w-12}; \frac{1}{w^2-9}$$

Solution:

$\dfrac{w+2}{w^2-w-12}; \dfrac{1}{w^2-9}$ To find the LCD, factor each denominator.

$\dfrac{w+2}{(w-4)(w+3)}; \dfrac{1}{(w-3)(w+3)}$ The LCD is $(w-4)(w+3)(w-3)$.

$\dfrac{w+2}{(w-4)(w+3)} = \dfrac{(w+2)(w-3)}{(w-4)(w+3)(w-3)}$ The first expression is missing the factor $(w-3)$ from the denominator.

$= \dfrac{w^2-w-6}{(w-4)(w+3)(w-3)}$ ◄

$\dfrac{1}{(w-3)(w+3)} = \dfrac{1(w-4)}{(w-3)(w+3)(w-4)}$ The second expression is missing the factor $(w-4)$ from the denominator.

$= \dfrac{w-4}{(w-3)(w+3)(w-4)}$ ◄

Example 5 Converting to the Least Common Denominator

Convert each expression to an equivalent expression with the denominator equal to the LCD. $\dfrac{3}{x-7}$ and $\dfrac{1}{7-x}$

Solution:

Notice that the expressions $x-7$ and $7-x$ are opposites and differ by a factor of -1. Therefore, we may use either $x-7$ or $7-x$ as a common denominator. Each case is shown below.

Converting to the Denominator $x - 7$

$$\frac{3}{x - 7}; \frac{1}{7 - x}$$

Leave the first fraction unchanged because it has the desired LCD.

TIP: In Example 5, the expressions $$\frac{3}{x - 7} \text{ and } \frac{1}{7 - x}$$ have opposite factors in the denominators. In such a case, you do not need to include *both* factors in the LCD.	

$$\frac{1}{7 - x} = \frac{(-1)1}{(-1)(7 - x)}$$

Multiply the *second* rational expression by the ratio $\frac{-1}{-1}$ to change its denominator to $x - 7$.

$$= \frac{-1}{-7 + x}$$

Apply the distributive property.

$$= \frac{-1}{x - 7}$$

Converting to the Denominator $7 - x$

$$\frac{3}{x - 7}; \frac{1}{7 - x}$$

Leave the second fraction unchanged because it has the desired LCD.

$$\frac{3}{x - 7} = \frac{(-1)3}{(-1)(x - 7)};$$

Multiply the *first* rational expression by the ratio $\frac{-1}{-1}$ to change its denominator to $7 - x$.

$$= \frac{-3}{-x + 7}$$

Apply the distributive property.

$$= \frac{-3}{7 - x}$$

Section 7.3 Practice Exercises

Vocabulary and Key Concepts

1. The least common denominator (LCD) of two rational expressions is defined as the least common _____ of the _____.

Review Exercises

2. Evaluate the expression for the given values of x. $\dfrac{2x}{x + 5}$

   a. $x = 1$ **b.** $x = 5$ **c.** $x = -5$

For Exercises 3 and 4, identify the restricted values. Then simplify the expression.

3. $\dfrac{3x + 3}{5x^2 - 5}$

4. $\dfrac{x + 2}{x^2 - 3x - 10}$

For Exercises 5–8, multiply or divide as indicated.

5. $\dfrac{a + 3}{a + 7} \cdot \dfrac{a^2 + 3a - 10}{a^2 + a - 6}$

6. $\dfrac{6(a + 2b)}{2(a - 3b)} \cdot \dfrac{4(a + 3b)(a - 3b)}{9(a + 2b)(a - 2b)}$

7. $\dfrac{16y^2}{9y + 36} \div \dfrac{8y^3}{3y + 12}$

8. $\dfrac{5b^2 + 6b + 1}{b^2 + 5b + 6} \div (5b + 1)$

9. Which of the expressions are equivalent to $-\dfrac{5}{x - 3}$? Circle all that apply.

a. $\dfrac{-5}{x - 3}$

b. $\dfrac{5}{-x + 3}$

c. $\dfrac{5}{3 - x}$

d. $\dfrac{5}{-(x - 3)}$

10. Which of the expressions are equivalent to $\dfrac{4 - a}{6}$? Circle all that apply.

a. $\dfrac{a - 4}{-6}$

b. $\dfrac{a - 4}{6}$

c. $\dfrac{-(4 - a)}{-6}$

d. $-\dfrac{a - 4}{6}$

Concept 1: Least Common Denominator

11. Explain why the least common denominator of $\frac{1}{x^3}$, $\frac{1}{x^5}$, and $\frac{1}{x^4}$ is x^5.

12. Explain why the least common denominator of $\frac{2}{y^3}$, $\frac{9}{y^6}$, and $\frac{4}{y^5}$ is y^6.

For Exercises 13–30, identify the LCD. **(See Examples 1 and 2.)**

13. $\dfrac{4}{15}$; $\dfrac{5}{9}$

14. $\dfrac{7}{12}$; $\dfrac{1}{18}$

15. $\dfrac{1}{16}$; $\dfrac{1}{4}$; $\dfrac{1}{6}$

16. $\dfrac{1}{2}$; $\dfrac{11}{12}$; $\dfrac{3}{8}$

17. $\dfrac{1}{7}$; $\dfrac{2}{9}$

18. $\dfrac{2}{3}$; $\dfrac{5}{8}$

19. $\dfrac{1}{3x^2y}$; $\dfrac{8}{9xy^3}$

20. $\dfrac{5}{2a^4b^2}$; $\dfrac{1}{8ab^3}$

21. $\dfrac{6}{w^2}$; $\dfrac{7}{y}$

22. $\dfrac{2}{r}$; $\dfrac{3}{s^2}$

23. $\dfrac{p}{(p + 3)(p - 1)}$; $\dfrac{2}{(p + 3)(p + 2)}$

24. $\dfrac{6}{(q + 4)(q - 4)}$; $\dfrac{q^2}{(q + 1)(q + 4)}$

25. $\dfrac{7}{3t(t + 1)}$; $\dfrac{10t}{9(t + 1)^2}$

26. $\dfrac{13x}{15(x - 1)^2}$; $\dfrac{5}{3x(x - 1)}$

27. $\dfrac{y}{y^2 - 4}$; $\dfrac{3y}{y^2 + 5y + 6}$

28. $\dfrac{4}{w^2 - 3w + 2}$; $\dfrac{w}{w^2 - 4}$

29. $\dfrac{5}{3 - x}$; $\dfrac{7}{x - 3}$

30. $\dfrac{4}{x - 6}$; $\dfrac{9}{6 - x}$

31. Explain why a common denominator of

$$\dfrac{b + 1}{b - 1} \quad \text{and} \quad \dfrac{b}{1 - b}$$

could be either $(b - 1)$ or $(1 - b)$.

32. Explain why a common denominator of

$$\dfrac{1}{6 - t} \quad \text{and} \quad \dfrac{t}{t - 6}$$

could be either $(6 - t)$ or $(t - 6)$.

Concept 2: Writing Rational Expressions with the Least Common Denominator

For Exercises 33–56, find the LCD. Then convert each expression to an equivalent expression with the denominator equal to the LCD. **(See Examples 3–5.)**

33. $\dfrac{6}{5x^2}; \dfrac{1}{x}$

34. $\dfrac{3}{y}; \dfrac{7}{9y^2}$

35. $\dfrac{4}{5x^2}; \dfrac{y}{6x^3}$

36. $\dfrac{3}{15b^2}; \dfrac{c}{3b^2}$

37. $\dfrac{5}{6a^2b}; \dfrac{a}{12b}$

38. $\dfrac{x}{15y^2}; \dfrac{y}{5xy}$

39. $\dfrac{6}{m + 4}; \dfrac{3}{m - 1}$

40. $\dfrac{3}{n - 5}; \dfrac{7}{n + 2}$

41. $\dfrac{6}{2x - 5}; \dfrac{1}{x + 3}$

42. $\dfrac{4}{m + 3}; \dfrac{-3}{5m + 1}$

43. $\dfrac{6}{(w + 3)(w - 8)}; \dfrac{w}{(w - 8)(w + 1)}$

44. $\dfrac{t}{(t + 2)(t + 12)}; \dfrac{18}{(t - 2)(t + 2)}$

45. $\dfrac{6p}{p^2 - 4}; \dfrac{3}{p^2 + 4p + 4}$

46. $\dfrac{5}{q^2 - 6q + 9}; \dfrac{q}{q^2 - 9}$

47. $\dfrac{1}{a - 4}; \dfrac{a}{4 - a}$

48. $\dfrac{3b}{2b - 5}; \dfrac{2b}{5 - 2b}$

49. $\dfrac{4}{x - 7}; \dfrac{y}{14 - 2x}$

50. $\dfrac{4}{3x - 15}; \dfrac{z}{5 - x}$

51. $\dfrac{1}{a + b}; \dfrac{6}{-a - b}$

52. $\dfrac{p}{-q - 8}; \dfrac{1}{q + 8}$

53. $\dfrac{-3}{24y + 8}; \dfrac{5}{18y + 6}$

54. $\dfrac{r}{10r + 5}; \dfrac{2}{16r + 8}$

55. $\dfrac{3}{5z}; \dfrac{1}{z + 4}$

56. $\dfrac{-1}{4a - 8}; \dfrac{5}{4a}$

Expanding Your Skills

For Exercises 57–60, find the LCD. Then convert each expression to an equivalent expression with the denominator equal to the LCD.

57. $\dfrac{z}{z^2 + 9z + 14}; \dfrac{-3z}{z^2 + 10z + 21}; \dfrac{5}{z^2 + 5z + 6}$

58. $\dfrac{6}{w^2 - 3w - 4}; \dfrac{1}{w^2 + 6w + 5}; \dfrac{-9w}{w^2 + w - 20}$

59. $\dfrac{3}{p^3 - 8}; \dfrac{p}{p^2 - 4}; \dfrac{5p}{p^2 + 2p + 4}$

60. $\dfrac{7}{q^3 + 125}; \dfrac{q}{q^2 - 25}; \dfrac{12}{q^2 - 5q + 25}$

Addition and Subtraction of Rational Expressions | Section 7.4

1. Addition and Subtraction of Rational Expressions with the Same Denominator

To add or subtract rational expressions, the expressions must have the same denominator. As with fractions, we add or subtract rational expressions with the same denominator by combining the terms in the numerator and then writing the result over the common denominator. Then, if possible, we simplify the expression.

Concepts

1. Addition and Subtraction of Rational Expressions with the Same Denominator
2. Addition and Subtraction of Rational Expressions with Different Denominators
3. Using Rational Expressions in Translations

Addition and Subtraction of Rational Expressions

Let p, q, and r represent polynomials where $q \neq 0$. Then,

1. $\dfrac{p}{q} + \dfrac{r}{q} = \dfrac{p+r}{q}$ **2.** $\dfrac{p}{q} - \dfrac{r}{q} = \dfrac{p-r}{q}$

Example 1 **Adding and Subtracting Rational Expressions with the Same Denominator**

Add or subtract as indicated. **a.** $\dfrac{1}{12} + \dfrac{7}{12}$ **b.** $\dfrac{2}{5p} - \dfrac{7}{5p}$

Solution:

a. $\dfrac{1}{12} + \dfrac{7}{12}$ The fractions have the same denominator.

$= \dfrac{1+7}{12}$ Add the terms in the numerators, and write the result over the denominator.

$= \dfrac{8}{12}$

$= \dfrac{2}{3}$ Simplify.

b. $\dfrac{2}{5p} - \dfrac{7}{5p}$ The rational expressions have the same denominator.

$= \dfrac{2-7}{5p}$ Subtract the terms in the numerators, and write the result over the denominator.

$= \dfrac{-5}{5p}$

$= \dfrac{\overset{-1}{(-\cancel{5})}}{\cancel{5}p}$ Simplify.

$= -\dfrac{1}{p}$

Skill Practice

Add or subtract as indicated.

1. $\dfrac{3}{14} + \dfrac{4}{14}$

2. $\dfrac{2}{7d} - \dfrac{9}{7d}$

Answers

1. $\dfrac{1}{2}$ **2.** $-\dfrac{1}{d}$

Example 2 Adding and Subtracting Rational Expressions with the Same Denominator

Add or subtract as indicated.

a. $\dfrac{2}{3d + 5} + \dfrac{7d}{3d + 5}$

b. $\dfrac{x^2}{x - 3} - \dfrac{-5x + 24}{x - 3}$

Solution:

a. $\dfrac{2}{3d + 5} + \dfrac{7d}{3d + 5}$ The rational expressions have the same denominator.

$= \dfrac{2 + 7d}{3d + 5}$ Add the terms in the numerators, and write the result over the denominator.

$= \dfrac{7d + 2}{3d + 5}$ Because the numerator and denominator share no common factors, the expression is in lowest terms.

b. $\dfrac{x^2}{x - 3} - \dfrac{-5x + 24}{x - 3}$ The rational expressions have the same denominator.

$= \dfrac{x^2 - (-5x + 24)}{x - 3}$ Subtract the terms in the numerators, and write the result over the denominator.

$= \dfrac{x^2 + 5x - 24}{x - 3}$ Simplify the numerator.

$= \dfrac{(x + 8)(x - 3)}{(x - 3)}$ Factor the numerator and denominator to determine if the rational expression can be simplified.

$= \dfrac{(x + 8)\overset{1}{(\cancel{x - 3})}}{\cancel{(x - 3)}}$ Simplify.

$= x + 8$

2. Addition and Subtraction of Rational Expressions with Different Denominators

To add or subtract two rational expressions with unlike denominators, we must convert the expressions to equivalent expressions with the same denominator. For example, consider adding

$$\frac{1}{10} + \frac{12}{5y}$$

The LCD is $10y$. For each expression, identify the factors from the LCD that are missing from the denominator. Then multiply the numerator and denominator of the expression by the missing factor(s).

$$\underset{\substack{\text{Missing} \\ y}}{\frac{1}{10}} + \underset{\substack{\text{Missing} \\ 2}}{\frac{12}{5y}}$$

$$= \frac{1 \cdot y}{10 \cdot y} + \frac{12 \cdot 2}{5y \cdot 2}$$

$$= \frac{y}{10y} + \frac{24}{10y}$$ The rational expressions now have the same denominators.

$$= \frac{y + 24}{10y}$$ Add the numerators.

After successfully adding or subtracting two rational expressions, always check to see if the final answer is simplified. If necessary, factor the numerator and denominator, and reduce common factors. The expression

$$\frac{y + 24}{10y}$$

is in lowest terms because the numerator and denominator do not share any common factors.

Adding or Subtracting Rational Expressions

Step 1 Factor the denominators of each rational expression.

Step 2 Identify the LCD.

Step 3 Rewrite each rational expression as an equivalent expression with the LCD as its denominator.

Step 4 Add or subtract the numerators, and write the result over the common denominator.

Step 5 Simplify.

Example 3 **Subtracting Rational Expressions with Different Denominators**

Subtract. $\dfrac{4}{7k} - \dfrac{3}{k^2}$

Solution:

$\dfrac{4}{7k} - \dfrac{3}{k^2}$

Step 1: The denominators are already factored.

Step 2: The LCD is $7k^2$.

$= \dfrac{4 \cdot k}{7k \cdot k} - \dfrac{3 \cdot 7}{k^2 \cdot 7}$ **Step 3:** Write each expression with the LCD.

$= \dfrac{4k}{7k^2} - \dfrac{21}{7k^2}$

$= \dfrac{4k - 21}{7k^2}$ **Step 4:** Subtract the numerators, and write the result over the LCD.

Step 5: The expression is in lowest terms because the numerator and denominator share no common factors.

Example 4 Subtracting Rational Expressions with Different Denominators

Subtract. $\dfrac{2q-4}{3} - \dfrac{q+1}{2}$

Solution:

$\dfrac{2q-4}{3} - \dfrac{q+1}{2}$ **Step 1:** The denominators are already factored.

Step 2: The LCD is 6.

$= \dfrac{2(2q-4)}{2 \cdot 3} - \dfrac{3(q+1)}{3 \cdot 2}$ **Step 3:** Write each expression with the LCD.

$= \dfrac{2(2q-4) - 3(q+1)}{6}$ **Step 4:** Subtract the numerators, and write the result over the LCD.

$= \dfrac{4q - 8 - 3q - 3}{6}$

$= \dfrac{q - 11}{6}$ **Step 5:** The expression is in lowest terms because the numerator and denominator share no common factors.

Example 5 Adding Rational Expressions with Different Denominators

Add. $\dfrac{1}{x-5} + \dfrac{-10}{x^2-25}$

Solution:

$\dfrac{1}{x-5} + \dfrac{-10}{x^2-25}$

$= \dfrac{1}{x-5} + \dfrac{-10}{(x-5)(x+5)}$ **Step 1:** Factor the denominators.

Step 2: The LCD is $(x-5)(x+5)$.

$= \dfrac{1(x+5)}{(x-5)(x+5)} + \dfrac{-10}{(x-5)(x+5)}$ **Step 3:** Write each expression with the LCD.

$= \dfrac{1(x+5) + (-10)}{(x-5)(x+5)}$ **Step 4:** Add the numerators, and write the result over the LCD.

$= \dfrac{x+5-10}{(x-5)(x+5)}$

$= \dfrac{\overset{1}{\cancel{x-5}}}{\cancel{(x-5)}(x+5)}$ **Step 5:** Simplify.

$= \dfrac{1}{x+5}$

Example 6 **Subtracting Rational Expressions with Different Denominators**

Subtract. $\dfrac{p+2}{p-1} - \dfrac{2}{p+6} - \dfrac{14}{p^2+5p-6}$

Solution:

$\dfrac{p+2}{p-1} - \dfrac{2}{p+6} - \dfrac{14}{p^2+5p-6}$

$= \dfrac{p+2}{p-1} - \dfrac{2}{p+6} - \dfrac{14}{(p-1)(p+6)}$ **Step 1:** Factor the denominators.

Step 2: The LCD is $(p-1)(p+6)$.

Step 3: Write each expression with the LCD.

$= \dfrac{(p+2)(p+6)}{(p-1)(p+6)} - \dfrac{2(p-1)}{(p+6)(p-1)} - \dfrac{14}{(p-1)(p+6)}$

$= \dfrac{(p+2)(p+6) - 2(p-1) - 14}{(p-1)(p+6)}$ **Step 4:** Combine the numerators, and write the result over the LCD.

$= \dfrac{p^2+6p+2p+12-2p+2-14}{(p-1)(p+6)}$ **Step 5:** Clear parentheses in the numerator.

$= \dfrac{p^2+6p}{(p-1)(p+6)}$ Combine *like* terms.

$= \dfrac{p(p+6)}{(p-1)(p+6)}$ Factor the numerator to determine if the expression is in lowest terms.

$= \dfrac{p\overset{1}{(p+6)}}{(p-1)(p+6)}$ Simplify.

$= \dfrac{p}{p-1}$

When the denominators of two rational expressions are opposites, we can produce identical denominators by multiplying one of the expressions by the ratio $\frac{-1}{-1}$. This is demonstrated in Example 7.

Skill Practice

Subtract.

8. $\dfrac{2y}{y-1} - \dfrac{1}{y} - \dfrac{2y+1}{y^2-y}$

Answer

8. $\dfrac{2y-3}{y-1}$

Example 7 **Adding Rational Expressions with Different Denominators**

Add the rational expressions. $\dfrac{1}{d-7} + \dfrac{5}{7-d}$

Solution:

$\dfrac{1}{d-7} + \dfrac{5}{7-d}$ The expressions $d-7$ and $7-d$ are opposites and differ by a factor of -1. Therefore, multiply the numerator and denominator of *either* expression by -1 to obtain a common denominator.

$= \dfrac{1}{d-7} + \dfrac{(-1)5}{(-1)(7-d)}$ Note that $-1(7-d) = -7 + d$ or $d - 7$.

$= \dfrac{1}{d-7} + \dfrac{-5}{d-7}$ Simplify.

$= \dfrac{1+(-5)}{d-7}$ Add the terms in the numerators, and write the result over the common denominator.

$= \dfrac{-4}{d-7}$

3. Using Rational Expressions in Translations

Example 8 **Using Rational Expressions in Translations**

Translate the English phrase into a mathematical expression. Then simplify by combining the rational expressions.

The difference of the reciprocal of n and the quotient of n and 3

Solution:

The difference of the reciprocal of n and the quotient of n and 3

$$\underset{\substack{\text{The reciprocal} \\ \text{of } n}}{\left(\dfrac{1}{n}\right)} \overset{\substack{\text{The difference of}}}{-} \underset{\substack{\text{The quotient} \\ \text{of } n \text{ and } 3}}{\left(\dfrac{n}{3}\right)}$$

$\dfrac{1}{n} - \dfrac{n}{3}$ The LCD is $3n$.

$= \dfrac{3 \cdot 1}{3 \cdot n} - \dfrac{n \cdot n}{3 \cdot n}$ Write each expression with the LCD.

$= \dfrac{3 - n^2}{3n}$ Subtract the numerators.

Section 7.4 Practice Exercises

Review Exercises

1. For the rational expression $\dfrac{x^2 - 4x - 5}{x^2 - 7x + 10}$

  a. Find the value of the expression (if possible) when $x = 0, 1, -1, 2,$ and 5.

  b. Factor the denominator and identify the restricted values.

  c. Simplify the expression.

2. For the rational expression $\dfrac{a^2 + a - 2}{a^2 - 4a - 12}$

  a. Find the value of the expression (if possible) when $a = 0, 1, -2, 2,$ and 6.

  b. Factor the denominator, and identify the restricted values.

  c. Simplify the expression.

For Exercises 3 and 4, multiply or divide as indicated.

3. $\dfrac{2b^2 - b - 3}{2b^2 - 3b - 9} \div \dfrac{b^2 - 1}{4b + 6}$

4. $\dfrac{6t - 1}{5t - 30} \cdot \dfrac{10t - 25}{2t^2 - 3t - 5}$

Concept 1: Addition and Subtraction of Rational Expressions with the Same Denominator

For Exercises 5–26, add or subtract the expressions with like denominators as indicated. **(See Examples 1 and 2.)**

5. $\dfrac{7}{8} + \dfrac{3}{8}$

6. $\dfrac{1}{3} + \dfrac{7}{3}$

7. $\dfrac{9}{16} - \dfrac{3}{16}$

8. $\dfrac{14}{15} - \dfrac{4}{15}$

9. $\dfrac{5a}{a + 2} - \dfrac{3a - 4}{a + 2}$

10. $\dfrac{2b}{b - 3} - \dfrac{b - 9}{b - 3}$

11. $\dfrac{5c}{c + 6} + \dfrac{30}{c + 6}$

12. $\dfrac{12}{2 + d} + \dfrac{6d}{2 + d}$

13. $\dfrac{5}{t - 8} - \dfrac{2t + 1}{t - 8}$

14. $\dfrac{7p + 1}{2p + 1} - \dfrac{p - 4}{2p + 1}$

15. $\dfrac{9x^2}{3x - 7} - \dfrac{49}{3x - 7}$

16. $\dfrac{4w^2}{2w - 1} - \dfrac{1}{2w - 1}$

17. $\dfrac{m^2}{m + 5} + \dfrac{10m + 25}{m + 5}$

18. $\dfrac{k^2}{k - 3} - \dfrac{6k - 9}{k - 3}$

19. $\dfrac{2a}{a + 2} + \dfrac{4}{a + 2}$

20. $\dfrac{5b}{b + 4} + \dfrac{20}{b + 4}$

21. $\dfrac{x^2}{x + 5} - \dfrac{25}{x + 5}$

22. $\dfrac{y^2}{y - 7} - \dfrac{49}{y - 7}$

23. $\dfrac{r}{r^2 + 3r + 2} + \dfrac{2}{r^2 + 3r + 2}$

24. $\dfrac{x}{x^2 - x - 12} - \dfrac{4}{x^2 - x - 12}$

25. $\dfrac{1}{3y^2 + 22y + 7} - \dfrac{-3y}{3y^2 + 22y + 7}$

26. $\dfrac{5}{2x^2 + 13x + 20} + \dfrac{2x}{2x^2 + 13x + 20}$

For Exercises 27 and 28, find an expression that represents the perimeter of the figure (assume that $x > 0$, $y > 0$, and $t > 0$).

27.

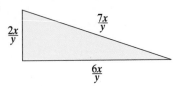

28.

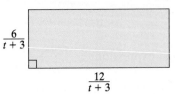

Concept 2: Addition and Subtraction of Rational Expressions with Different Denominators

For Exercises 29–70, add or subtract the expressions with unlike denominators as indicated. **(See Examples 3–7.)**

29. $\dfrac{5}{4} + \dfrac{3}{2a}$

30. $\dfrac{11}{6p} + \dfrac{-7}{4p}$

31. $\dfrac{4}{5xy^3} + \dfrac{2x}{15y^2}$

32. $\dfrac{5}{3a^2b} + \dfrac{-7}{6b^2}$

33. $\dfrac{2}{s^3t^3} - \dfrac{3}{s^4t}$

34. $\dfrac{1}{p^2q} - \dfrac{2}{pq^3}$

35. $\dfrac{z}{3z - 9} - \dfrac{z - 2}{z - 3}$

36. $\dfrac{3w - 8}{2w - 4} - \dfrac{w - 3}{w - 2}$

37. $\dfrac{5}{a + 1} + \dfrac{4}{3a + 3}$

38. $\dfrac{2}{c - 4} + \dfrac{1}{5c - 20}$

39. $\dfrac{k}{k^2 - 9} - \dfrac{4}{k - 3}$

40. $\dfrac{7}{h + 2} - \dfrac{2h - 3}{h^2 - 4}$

41. $\dfrac{3a - 7}{6a + 10} - \dfrac{10}{3a^2 + 5a}$

42. $\dfrac{k + 2}{8k} - \dfrac{3 - k}{12k}$

43. $\dfrac{x}{x - 4} + \dfrac{3}{x + 1}$.

44. $\dfrac{4}{y - 3} + \dfrac{y}{y - 5}$

45. $\dfrac{3x}{x^2 + 6x + 9} + \dfrac{x}{x^2 + 5x + 6}$

46. $\dfrac{7x}{x^2 + 2xy + y^2} + \dfrac{3x}{x^2 + xy}$

47. $\dfrac{p}{3} - \dfrac{4p - 1}{-3}$

48. $\dfrac{r}{7} - \dfrac{r - 5}{-7}$

49. $\dfrac{8}{x - 3} - \dfrac{1}{3 - x}$

50. $\dfrac{5y}{y - 1} - \dfrac{3y}{1 - y}$

51. $\dfrac{4n}{n - 8} - \dfrac{2n - 1}{8 - n}$

52. $\dfrac{m}{m - 2} - \dfrac{3m + 1}{2 - m}$

53. $\dfrac{5}{x} + \dfrac{3}{x + 2}$

54. $\dfrac{6}{y - 1} + \dfrac{9}{y}$

55. $\dfrac{y}{4y + 2} + \dfrac{3y}{6y + 3}$

56. $\dfrac{4}{q^2 - 2q} - \dfrac{5}{3q - 6}$

57. $\dfrac{4w}{w^2 + 2w - 3} + \dfrac{2}{1 - w}$

58. $\dfrac{z - 23}{z^2 - z - 20} - \dfrac{2}{5 - z}$

59. $\dfrac{3a - 8}{a^2 - 5a + 6} + \dfrac{a + 2}{a^2 - 6a + 8}$

60. $\dfrac{3b + 5}{b^2 + 4b + 3} + \dfrac{-b + 5}{b^2 + 2b - 3}$

61. $\dfrac{4x}{x^2 + 4x - 5} - \dfrac{x}{x^2 + 10x + 25}$

62. $\dfrac{x}{x^2 + 5x + 4} - \dfrac{2x}{x^2 + 8x + 16}$

63. $\dfrac{3y}{2y^2 - y - 1} - \dfrac{4y}{2y^2 - 7y - 4}$

64. $\dfrac{5}{6y^2 - 7y - 3} + \dfrac{4y}{3y^2 + 4y + 1}$

65. $\dfrac{3}{2p - 1} - \dfrac{4p + 4}{4p^2 - 1}$

66. $\dfrac{1}{3q - 2} - \dfrac{6q + 4}{9q^2 - 4}$

67. $\dfrac{m}{m + n} - \dfrac{m}{m - n} + \dfrac{1}{m^2 - n^2}$

68. $\dfrac{x}{x + y} - \dfrac{2xy}{x^2 - y^2} + \dfrac{y}{x - y}$

69. $\dfrac{2}{a + b} + \dfrac{2}{a - b} - \dfrac{4a}{a^2 - b^2}$

70. $\dfrac{-2x}{x^2 - y^2} + \dfrac{1}{x + y} - \dfrac{1}{x - y}$

For Exercises 71 and 72, find an expression that represents the perimeter of the figure (assume that $x > 0$ and $t > 0$).

71.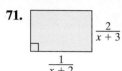

72.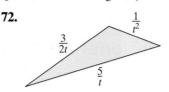

Concept 3: Using Rational Expressions in Translations

73. Let a number be represented by n. Write the reciprocal of n.

74. Write the reciprocal of the sum of a number and 6.

75. Write the quotient of 5 and the sum of a number and 2.

76. Write the quotient of 12 and p.

For Exercises 77–80, translate the English phrases into algebraic expressions. Then simplify by combining the rational expressions. **(See Example 8.)**

77. The sum of a number and the quantity seven times the reciprocal of the number.

78. The sum of a number and the quantity five times the reciprocal of the number.

79. The difference of the reciprocal of n and the quotient of 2 and n.

80. The difference of the reciprocal of m and the quotient of $3m$ and 7.

Expanding Your Skills

For Exercises 81–86, perform the indicated operations.

81. $\dfrac{-3}{w^3 + 27} - \dfrac{1}{w^2 - 9}$

82. $\dfrac{m}{m^3 - 1} + \dfrac{1}{(m - 1)^2}$

83. $\dfrac{2p}{p^2 + 5p + 6} - \dfrac{p + 1}{p^2 + 2p - 3} + \dfrac{3}{p^2 + p - 2}$

84. $\dfrac{3t}{8t^2 + 2t - 1} - \dfrac{5t}{2t^2 - 9t - 5} + \dfrac{2}{4t^2 - 21t + 5}$

85. $\dfrac{3m}{m^2 + 3m - 10} + \dfrac{5}{4 - 2m} - \dfrac{1}{m + 5}$

86. $\dfrac{2n}{3n^2 - 8n - 3} + \dfrac{1}{6 - 2n} - \dfrac{3}{3n + 1}$

For Exercises 87–90, simplify by applying the order of operations.

87. $\left(\dfrac{2}{k + 1} + 3\right)\left(\dfrac{k + 1}{4k + 7}\right)$

88. $\left(\dfrac{p + 1}{3p + 4}\right)\left(\dfrac{1}{p + 1} + 2\right)$

89. $\left(\dfrac{1}{10a} - \dfrac{b}{10a^2}\right) \div \left(\dfrac{1}{10} - \dfrac{b}{10a}\right)$

90. $\left(\dfrac{1}{2m} + \dfrac{n}{2m^2}\right) \div \left(\dfrac{1}{4} + \dfrac{n}{4m}\right)$

Problem Recognition Exercises

Operations on Rational Expressions

In Sections 7.1–7.4, we learned how to simplify, add, subtract, multiply, and divide rational expressions. The procedure for each operation is different, and it takes considerable practice to determine the correct method to apply for a given problem. The following review exercises give you the opportunity to practice the specific techniques for simplifying rational expressions.

For Exercises 1–20, perform any indicated operations and simplify the expression.

1. $\dfrac{5}{3x + 1} - \dfrac{2x - 4}{3x + 1}$

2. $\dfrac{\dfrac{w + 1}{w^2 - 16}}{\dfrac{w + 1}{w + 4}}$

3. $\dfrac{3}{y} \cdot \dfrac{y^2 - 5y}{6y - 9}$

4. $\dfrac{-1}{x + 3} + \dfrac{2}{2x - 1}$

5. $\dfrac{x - 9}{9x - x^2}$

6. $\dfrac{1}{p} - \dfrac{3}{p^2 + 3p} + \dfrac{p}{3p + 9}$

7. $\dfrac{c^2 + 5c + 6}{c^2 + c - 2} \div \dfrac{c}{c - 1}$

8. $\dfrac{2x^2 - 5x - 3}{x^2 - 9} \cdot \dfrac{x^2 + 6x + 9}{10x + 5}$

9. $\dfrac{6a^2b^3}{72ab^7c}$

10. $\dfrac{2a}{a + b} - \dfrac{b}{a - b} - \dfrac{-4ab}{a^2 - b^2}$

11. $\dfrac{p^2 + 10pq + 25q^2}{p^2 + 6pq + 5q^2} \div \dfrac{10p + 50q}{2p^2 - 2q^2}$

12. $\dfrac{3k - 8}{k - 5} + \dfrac{k - 12}{k - 5}$

13. $\dfrac{20x^2 + 10x}{4x^3 + 4x^2 + x}$

14. $\dfrac{w^2 - 81}{w^2 + 10w + 9} \cdot \dfrac{w^2 + w + 2zw + 2z}{w^2 - 9w + zw - 9z}$

15. $\dfrac{8x^2 - 18x - 5}{4x^2 - 25} \div \dfrac{4x^2 - 11x - 3}{3x - 9}$

16. $\dfrac{xy + 7x + 5y + 35}{x^2 + ax + 5x + 5a}$

17. $\dfrac{a}{a^2 - 9} - \dfrac{3}{6a - 18}$

18. $\dfrac{4}{y^2 - 36} + \dfrac{2}{y^2 - 4y - 12}$

19. $(t^2 + 5t - 24)\left(\dfrac{t + 8}{t - 3}\right)$

20. $\dfrac{6b^2 - 7b - 10}{b - 2}$

Complex Fractions

1. Simplifying Complex Fractions (Method I)

A **complex fraction** is an expression containing one or more fractions in the numerator, denominator, or both. For example,

$$\frac{\dfrac{1}{ab}}{\dfrac{2}{b}} \quad \text{and} \quad \frac{1 + \dfrac{3}{4} - \dfrac{1}{6}}{\dfrac{1}{2} + \dfrac{1}{3}}$$

are complex fractions.

Two methods will be presented to simplify complex fractions. The first method (Method I) follows the order of operations to simplify the numerator and denominator separately before dividing. The process is summarized as follows.

Concepts

1. Simplifying Complex Fractions (Method I)
2. Simplifying Complex Fractions (Method II)

Simplifying a Complex Fraction (Method I)

Step 1 Simplify the expression in the numerator to form a single fraction. Simplify the expression in the denominator to form a single fraction.

Step 2 Divide the rational expressions from step 1 by multiplying the numerator of the complex fraction by the reciprocal of the denominator of the complex fraction.

Step 3 Simplify to lowest terms if possible.

Example 1 Simplifying Complex Fractions (Method I)

Simplify the expression. $\dfrac{\dfrac{1}{ab}}{\dfrac{2}{b}}$

Solution:

Step 1: The numerator and denominator of the complex fraction are already single fractions.

$$\frac{\dfrac{1}{ab}}{\dfrac{2}{b}} \longleftarrow \quad \text{This fraction bar denotes division } (\div).$$

$$= \frac{1}{ab} \div \frac{2}{b}$$

$$= \frac{1}{ab} \cdot \frac{b}{2} \qquad \textbf{Step 2:} \quad \text{Multiply the numerator of the complex fraction by the reciprocal of } \tfrac{2}{b}, \text{ which is } \tfrac{b}{2}.$$

$$= \frac{1}{a\cancel{b}} \cdot \frac{\overset{1}{\cancel{b}}}{2} \qquad \textbf{Step 3:} \quad \text{Reduce common factors and simplify.}$$

$$= \frac{1}{2a}$$

Skill Practice

Simplify the expression.

1. $\dfrac{\dfrac{6x}{y}}{\dfrac{9}{2y}}$

Answer

1. $\dfrac{4x}{3}$

Sometimes it is necessary to simplify the numerator and denominator of a complex fraction before the division can be performed. This is illustrated in Example 2.

Example 2 Simplifying Complex Fractions (Method I)

Simplify the expression. $\dfrac{1 + \dfrac{3}{4} - \dfrac{1}{6}}{\dfrac{1}{2} + \dfrac{1}{3}}$

Solution:

$$\dfrac{1 + \dfrac{3}{4} - \dfrac{1}{6}}{\dfrac{1}{2} + \dfrac{1}{3}}$$

Step 1: Combine fractions in the numerator and denominator separately.

$$= \dfrac{1 \cdot \dfrac{12}{12} + \dfrac{3}{4} \cdot \dfrac{3}{3} - \dfrac{1}{6} \cdot \dfrac{2}{2}}{\dfrac{1}{2} \cdot \dfrac{3}{3} + \dfrac{1}{3} \cdot \dfrac{2}{2}}$$

The LCD in the numerator is 12. The LCD in the denominator is 6.

$$= \dfrac{\dfrac{12}{12} + \dfrac{9}{12} - \dfrac{2}{12}}{\dfrac{3}{6} + \dfrac{2}{6}}$$

$$= \dfrac{\dfrac{19}{12}}{\dfrac{5}{6}}$$

Form a single fraction in the numerator and in the denominator.

$$= \dfrac{19}{\overset{2}{\cancel{12}}} \cdot \dfrac{\overset{1}{\cancel{6}}}{5}$$

Step 2: Multiply the numerator by the reciprocal of the denominator.

$$= \dfrac{19}{10}$$

Step 3: Simplify.

Example 3 Simplifying Complex Fractions (Method I)

Simplify the expression. $\dfrac{\dfrac{1}{x} + \dfrac{1}{y}}{x - \dfrac{y^2}{x}}$

Solution:

$\dfrac{\dfrac{1}{x} + \dfrac{1}{y}}{x - \dfrac{y^2}{x}}$

The LCD in the numerator is xy. The LCD in the denominator is x.

$= \dfrac{\dfrac{1 \cdot y}{x \cdot y} + \dfrac{1 \cdot x}{y \cdot x}}{\dfrac{x \cdot x}{1 \cdot x} - \dfrac{y^2}{x}}$

Rewrite the expressions using common denominators.

$= \dfrac{\dfrac{y}{xy} + \dfrac{x}{xy}}{\dfrac{x^2}{x} - \dfrac{y^2}{x}}$

$= \dfrac{\dfrac{y + x}{xy}}{\dfrac{x^2 - y^2}{x}}$

Form single fractions in the numerator and denominator.

$= \dfrac{y + x}{xy} \cdot \dfrac{x}{x^2 - y^2}$

Multiply the numerator by the reciprocal of the denominator.

$= \dfrac{\overset{1}{\cancel{y + x}}}{\cancel{x}y} \cdot \dfrac{\overset{1}{\cancel{x}}}{\cancel{(x + y)}(x - y)}$

Factor and reduce. Note that $(y + x) = (x + y)$.

$= \dfrac{1}{y(x - y)}$

Simplify.

2. Simplifying Complex Fractions (Method II)

We will now simplify the expressions from Examples 2 and 3 again using a second method to simplify complex fractions (Method II). Recall that multiplying the numerator and denominator of a rational expression by the same quantity does not change the value of the expression because we are multiplying by a number equivalent to 1. This is the basis for Method II.

Simplifying a Complex Fraction (Method II)

Step 1 Multiply the numerator and denominator of the complex fraction by the LCD of *all* individual fractions within the expression.

Step 2 Apply the distributive property, and simplify the numerator and denominator.

Step 3 Simplify to lowest terms if possible.

Example 4 Simplifying Complex Fractions (Method II)

Simplify the expression. $\quad \dfrac{1 + \dfrac{3}{4} - \dfrac{1}{6}}{\dfrac{1}{2} + \dfrac{1}{3}}$

Solution:

$$\dfrac{1 + \dfrac{3}{4} - \dfrac{1}{6}}{\dfrac{1}{2} + \dfrac{1}{3}}$$

The LCD of the expressions $1, \frac{3}{4}, \frac{1}{6}, \frac{1}{2},$ and $\frac{1}{3}$ is 12.

$$= \dfrac{12\left(1 + \dfrac{3}{4} - \dfrac{1}{6}\right)}{12\left(\dfrac{1}{2} + \dfrac{1}{3}\right)}$$

Step 1: Multiply the numerator and denominator of the complex fraction by 12.

$$= \dfrac{12 \cdot 1 + 12 \cdot \dfrac{3}{4} - 12 \cdot \dfrac{1}{6}}{12 \cdot \dfrac{1}{2} + 12 \cdot \dfrac{1}{3}}$$

Step 2: Apply the distributive property.

$$= \dfrac{12 \cdot 1 + \overset{3}{\cancel{12}} \cdot \dfrac{3}{4} - \overset{2}{\cancel{12}} \cdot \dfrac{1}{\cancel{6}}}{\overset{6}{\cancel{12}} \cdot \dfrac{1}{2} + \overset{4}{\cancel{12}} \cdot \dfrac{1}{\cancel{3}}}$$

Simplify each term.

$$= \dfrac{12 + 9 - 2}{6 + 4}$$

$$= \dfrac{19}{10}$$

Step 3: Simplify.

Example 5 Simplifying a Complex Fraction (Method II)

Simplify the expression. $\quad \dfrac{\dfrac{1}{x} + \dfrac{1}{y}}{x - \dfrac{y^2}{x}}$

Solution:

$$\dfrac{\dfrac{1}{x} + \dfrac{1}{y}}{x - \dfrac{y^2}{x}}$$

The LCD of the expressions $\frac{1}{x}, \frac{1}{y}, x,$ and $\frac{y^2}{x}$ is xy.

$$= \dfrac{xy\left(\dfrac{1}{x} + \dfrac{1}{y}\right)}{xy\left(x - \dfrac{y^2}{x}\right)}$$

Step 1: Multiply numerator and denominator of the complex fraction by xy.

$$= \frac{xy \cdot \dfrac{1}{x} + xy \cdot \dfrac{1}{y}}{xy \cdot x - xy \cdot \dfrac{y^2}{x}}$$

Step 2: Apply the distributive property, and simplify each term.

$$= \frac{y + x}{x^2y - y^3}$$

$$= \frac{y + x}{y(x^2 - y^2)}$$

Step 3: Factor completely, and reduce common factors.

$$= \frac{\overset{1}{\cancel{y + x}}}{y\cancel{(x + y)}(x - y)}$$

Note that $(y + x) = (x + y)$.

$$= \frac{1}{y(x - y)}$$

| **Example 6** | **Simplifying a Complex Fraction (Method II)** |

Simplify the expression.

$$\frac{\dfrac{1}{k + 1} - 1}{\dfrac{1}{k + 1} + 1}$$

Solution:

$$\frac{\dfrac{1}{k + 1} - 1}{\dfrac{1}{k + 1} + 1}$$

The LCD of $\dfrac{1}{k + 1}$ and 1 is $(k + 1)$.

$$= \frac{(k + 1)\left(\dfrac{1}{k + 1} - 1\right)}{(k + 1)\left(\dfrac{1}{k + 1} + 1\right)}$$

Step 1: Multiply numerator and denominator of the complex fraction by $(k + 1)$.

$$= \frac{\overset{1}{\cancel{(k + 1)}} \cdot \dfrac{1}{\cancel{(k + 1)}} - (k + 1) \cdot 1}{\overset{1}{\cancel{(k + 1)}} \cdot \dfrac{1}{\cancel{(k + 1)}} + (k + 1) \cdot 1}$$

Step 2: Apply the distributive property.

$$= \frac{1 - (k + 1)}{1 + (k + 1)}$$

Simplify.

$$= \frac{1 - k - 1}{1 + k + 1}$$

$$= \frac{-k}{k + 2}$$

Step 3: The expression is already in lowest terms.

Skill Practice

Simplify the expression.

6. $\dfrac{\dfrac{4}{p - 3} + 1}{1 + \dfrac{2}{p - 3}}$

Answer

6. $\dfrac{p + 1}{p - 1}$

Section 7.5 Practice Exercises

Vocabulary and Key Concepts

1. A _____ fraction is an expression containing one or more fractions in the numerator, denominator, or both.

Review Exercises

For Exercises 2 and 3, simplify the expression.

2. $\dfrac{y(2y + 9)}{y^2(2y + 9)}$

3. $\dfrac{a + 5}{2a^2 + 7a - 15}$

For Exercises 4–6, perform the indicated operations.

4. $\dfrac{2}{w - 2} + \dfrac{3}{w}$

5. $\dfrac{6}{5} - \dfrac{3}{5k - 10}$

6. $\dfrac{x^2 - 2xy + y^2}{x^4 - y^4} \div \dfrac{3x^2y - 3xy^2}{x^2 + y^2}$

Concepts 1 and 2: Simplifying Complex Fractions (Methods I and II)

For Exercises 7–34, simplify the complex fractions. **(See Examples 1–6.)**

7. $\dfrac{\frac{7}{18y}}{\frac{2}{9}}$

8. $\dfrac{\frac{a^2}{2a - 3}}{\frac{5a}{8a - 12}}$

9. $\dfrac{\frac{3x + 2y}{2y}}{\frac{6x + 4y}{2}}$

10. $\dfrac{\frac{2x - 10}{4}}{\frac{x^2 - 5x}{3x}}$

11. $\dfrac{\frac{8a^4b^3}{3c}}{\frac{a^7b^2}{9c}}$

12. $\dfrac{\frac{12x^2}{5y}}{\frac{8x^6}{9y^2}}$

13. $\dfrac{\frac{4r^3s}{t^5}}{\frac{2s^7}{r^2t^9}}$

14. $\dfrac{\frac{5p^4q}{w^4}}{\frac{10p^2}{qw^2}}$

15. $\dfrac{\frac{1}{8} + \frac{4}{3}}{\frac{1}{2} - \frac{5}{12}}$

16. $\dfrac{\frac{8}{9} - \frac{1}{3}}{\frac{7}{6} + \frac{1}{9}}$

17. $\dfrac{\frac{1}{h} + \frac{1}{k}}{\frac{1}{hk}}$

18. $\dfrac{\frac{1}{b} + 1}{\frac{1}{b}}$

19. $\dfrac{\frac{n + 1}{n^2 - 9}}{\frac{2}{n + 3}}$

20. $\dfrac{\frac{5}{k - 5}}{\frac{k + 1}{k^2 - 25}}$

21. $\dfrac{2 + \frac{1}{x}}{4 + \frac{1}{x}}$

22. $\dfrac{6 + \frac{6}{k}}{1 + \frac{1}{k}}$

23. $\dfrac{\frac{m}{7} - \frac{7}{m}}{\frac{1}{7} + \frac{1}{m}}$

24. $\dfrac{\frac{2}{p} + \frac{p}{2}}{\frac{p}{3} - \frac{3}{p}}$

25. $\dfrac{\frac{1}{5} - \frac{1}{y}}{\frac{7}{10} + \frac{1}{y^2}}$

26. $\dfrac{\frac{1}{m^2} + \frac{2}{3}}{\frac{1}{m} - \frac{5}{6}}$

27. $\dfrac{\frac{8}{a + 4} + 2}{\frac{12}{a + 4} - 2}$

28. $\dfrac{\frac{2}{w + 1} + 3}{\frac{3}{w + 1} + 4}$

29. $\dfrac{1 - \frac{4}{t^2}}{1 - \frac{2}{t} - \frac{8}{t^2}}$

30. $\dfrac{1 - \frac{9}{p^2}}{1 - \frac{1}{p} - \frac{6}{p^2}}$

31. $\dfrac{t + 4 + \frac{3}{t}}{t - 4 - \frac{5}{t}}$

32. $\dfrac{\frac{9}{4m} + \frac{9}{2m^2}}{\frac{3}{2} + \frac{3}{m}}$

33. $\dfrac{\frac{1}{k - 6} - 1}{\frac{2}{k - 6} - 2}$

34. $\dfrac{\frac{3}{y - 3} + 4}{8 + \frac{6}{y - 3}}$

For Exercises 35–38, translate the English phrases into algebraic expressions. Then simplify the expressions.

35. The sum of one-half and two-thirds, divided by five.

36. The quotient of ten and the difference of two-fifths and one-fourth.

37. The quotient of three and the sum of two-thirds and three-fourths.

38. The difference of three-fifths and one-half, divided by four.

39. In electronics, resistors oppose the flow of current. For two resistors in parallel, the total resistance is given by

$$R = \dfrac{1}{\dfrac{1}{R_1} + \dfrac{1}{R_2}}$$

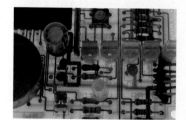

a. Find the total resistance if $R_1 = 2\ \Omega$ (ohms) and $R_2 = 3\ \Omega$.

b. Find the total resistance if $R_1 = 10\ \Omega$ and $R_2 = 15\ \Omega$.

40. Suppose that Joëlle makes a round trip to a location that is d miles away. If the average rate going to the location is r_1 and the average rate on the return trip is given by r_2, the average rate of the entire trip, R, is given by

$$R = \dfrac{2d}{\dfrac{d}{r_1} + \dfrac{d}{r_2}}$$

a. Find the average rate of a trip to a destination 30 mi away when the average rate going there was 60 mph and the average rate returning home was 45 mph. (Round to the nearest tenth of a mile per hour.)

b. Find the average rate of a trip to a destination that is 50 mi away if the driver travels at the same rates as in part (a). (Round to the nearest tenth of a mile per hour.)

c. Compare your answers from parts (a) and (b) and explain the results in the context of the problem.

Expanding Your Skills

For Exercises 41–50, simplify the complex fractions using either method.

41. $\dfrac{x^{-1} - y^{-1}}{x^{-2} - y^{-2}}$

42. $\dfrac{a^{-2} - 1}{a^{-1} - 1}$

43. $\dfrac{2x^{-1} + 8y^{-1}}{4x^{-1}}$

$\left(Hint: 2x^{-1} = \dfrac{2}{x}\right)$

44. $\dfrac{6a^{-1} + 4b^{-1}}{8b^{-1}}$

45. $\dfrac{(mn)^{-2}}{m^{-2} + n^{-2}}$

46. $\dfrac{(xy)^{-1}}{2x^{-1} + 3y^{-1}}$

47. $\dfrac{\dfrac{1}{z^2 - 9} + \dfrac{2}{z + 3}}{\dfrac{3}{z - 3}}$

48. $\dfrac{\dfrac{5}{w^2 - 25} - \dfrac{3}{w + 5}}{\dfrac{4}{w - 5}}$

49. $\dfrac{\dfrac{2}{x - 1} + 2}{\dfrac{2}{x + 1} - 2}$

50. $\dfrac{\dfrac{1}{y - 3} + 1}{\dfrac{2}{y + 3} - 1}$

For Exercises 51 and 52, simplify the complex fractions. (*Hint:* Use the order of operations and begin with the expression on the lower right.)

51. $1 + \dfrac{1}{1 + 1}$

52. $1 + \dfrac{1}{1 + \dfrac{1}{1 + 1}}$

Section 7.6 Rational Equations

1. Introduction to Rational Equations

Thus far we have studied two specific types of equations in one variable: linear equations and quadratic equations. Recall,

$$ax + b = c, \text{ where } a \neq 0, \text{ is a } \textbf{linear equation}$$

$$ax^2 + bx + c = 0, \text{ where } a \neq 0, \text{ is a } \textbf{quadratic equation}.$$

We will now study another type of equation called a rational equation.

> **Definition of a Rational Equation**
> An equation with one or more rational expressions is called a **rational equation**.

The following equations are rational equations:

$$\frac{1}{x} + \frac{1}{3} = \frac{5}{6} \qquad \frac{6}{t^2 - 7t + 12} + \frac{2t}{t - 3} = \frac{3t}{t - 4}$$

To understand the process of solving a rational equation, first review the process of clearing fractions from Section 2.3. We can clear the fractions in an equation by multiplying both sides of the equation by the LCD of all terms.

Example 1 Solving an Equation Containing Fractions

Solve. $\dfrac{y}{2} + \dfrac{y}{4} = 6$

Skill Practice

Solve the equation.

1. $\dfrac{t}{5} - \dfrac{t}{4} = 2$

Solution:

$$\frac{y}{2} + \frac{y}{4} = 6 \qquad \text{The LCD of all terms in the equation is } 4.$$

$$4\left(\frac{y}{2} + \frac{y}{4}\right) = 4(6) \qquad \text{Multiply both sides of the equation by 4 to clear fractions.}$$

$$\overset{2}{4} \cdot \frac{y}{2} + \overset{1}{4} \cdot \frac{y}{4} = 4(6) \qquad \text{Apply the distributive property.}$$

$$2y + y = 24 \qquad \text{Clear fractions.}$$

$$3y = 24 \qquad \text{Solve the resulting equation (linear).}$$

$$y = 8$$

$$\underline{\text{Check:}} \quad \frac{y}{2} + \frac{y}{4} = 6$$

$$\frac{(8)}{2} + \frac{(8)}{4} \overset{?}{=} 6$$

$$4 + 2 \overset{?}{=} 6$$

The solution is 8.

$$6 \overset{?}{=} 6 \checkmark \text{ (True)}$$

2. Solving Rational Equations

The same process of clearing fractions is used to solve rational equations when variables are present in the denominator. Variables in the denominator make it necessary to take note of restricted values.

Example 2 **Solving a Rational Equation**

Solve the equation. $\dfrac{x+1}{x} + \dfrac{1}{3} = \dfrac{5}{6}$

Solution:

$$\frac{x+1}{x} + \frac{1}{3} = \frac{5}{6}$$

The LCD of all the expressions is $6x$. The restricted value is $x = 0$.

$$6x \cdot \left(\frac{x+1}{x} + \frac{1}{3}\right) = 6x \cdot \left(\frac{5}{6}\right)$$

Multiply by the LCD.

$$\overset{1}{6x} \cdot \left(\frac{x+1}{x}\right) + \overset{2}{6x} \cdot \left(\frac{1}{3}\right) = \overset{1}{6x} \cdot \left(\frac{5}{6}\right)$$

Apply the distributive property.

$$6(x+1) + 2x = 5x$$

Clear fractions.

$$6x + 6 + 2x = 5x$$

Solve the resulting equation.

$$8x + 6 = 5x$$

$$3x = -6$$

$$x = -2$$

-2 is not a restricted value.

Check: $\dfrac{x+1}{x} + \dfrac{1}{3} = \dfrac{5}{6}$

$$\frac{(-2)+1}{(-2)} + \frac{1}{3} \overset{?}{=} \frac{5}{6}$$

$$\frac{-1}{-2} + \frac{1}{3} \overset{?}{=} \frac{5}{6}$$

$$\frac{1}{2} + \frac{1}{3} \overset{?}{=} \frac{5}{6}$$

$$\frac{3}{6} + \frac{2}{6} \overset{?}{=} \frac{5}{6}$$

$$\frac{5}{6} \overset{?}{=} \frac{5}{6} \ \checkmark \ (\text{True})$$

The solution is -2.

Avoiding Mistakes

When solving an equation we can multiply both sides of the equation by the LCD to clear fractions. When adding or subtracting fractions, we cannot clear fractions in this way.

Answer

2. -4

Example 3 Solving a Rational Equation

Solve the equation. $\qquad 1 + \dfrac{3a}{a-2} = \dfrac{6}{a-2}$

Solution:

$$1 + \dfrac{3a}{a-2} = \dfrac{6}{a-2}$$

The LCD of all the expressions is $a - 2$. The restricted value is $a = 2$.

$$(a-2)\left(1 + \dfrac{3a}{a-2}\right) = (a-2)\left(\dfrac{6}{a-2}\right)$$

Multiply by the LCD.

$$(a-2)1 + (a\overset{1}{-}2)\left(\dfrac{3a}{a-2}\right) = (a\overset{1}{-}2)\left(\dfrac{6}{a-2}\right)$$

Apply the distributive property.

$$a - 2 + 3a = 6$$

$$4a - 2 = 6$$

Solve the resulting equation (linear).

$$4a = 8$$

$$a = 2$$

2 is a restricted value.

Check: $1 + \dfrac{3a}{a-2} = \dfrac{6}{a-2}$

$$1 + \dfrac{3(2)}{(2)-2} \overset{?}{=} \dfrac{6}{(2)-2}$$

$$1 + \dfrac{6}{0} \overset{?}{=} \dfrac{6}{0}$$

The denominator is 0 when $a = 2$.

Because the value $a = 2$ makes the denominator zero in one (or more) of the rational expressions within the equation, the equation is undefined for $a = 2$. No other potential solutions exist for the equation.

The equation $1 + \dfrac{3a}{a-2} = \dfrac{6}{a-2}$ has no solution.

Examples 1–3 show that the steps to solve a rational equation mirror the process of clearing fractions from Section 2.3. However, there is one significant difference. The solutions of a rational equation must not make the denominator equal to zero for any expression within the equation.

Answer

3. No solution (The value -1 does not check.)

The steps to solve a rational equation are summarized as follows.

Solving a Rational Equation

Step 1 Factor the denominators of all rational expressions. Identify the restricted values.

Step 2 Identify the LCD of all expressions in the equation.

Step 3 Multiply both sides of the equation by the LCD.

Step 4 Solve the resulting equation.

Step 5 Check potential solutions in the original equation.

After multiplying by the LCD and then simplifying, the rational equation will be either a linear equation or higher degree equation.

Example 4 Solving a Rational Equation

Solve the equation. $\quad 1 - \dfrac{4}{p} = -\dfrac{3}{p^2}$

Solution:

$$1 - \frac{4}{p} = -\frac{3}{p^2}$$

Step 1: The denominators are already factored. The restricted value is $p = 0$.

Step 2: The LCD of all expressions is p^2.

$$p^2\left(1 - \frac{4}{p}\right) = p^2\left(-\frac{3}{p^2}\right)$$

Step 3: Multiply by the LCD.

$$p^2(1) - \overset{p}{\cancel{p^2}}\left(\frac{4}{\cancel{p}}\right) = \overset{1}{\cancel{p^2}}\left(-\frac{3}{\cancel{p^2}}\right)$$

Apply the distributive property.

$$p^2 - 4p = -3$$

Step 4: Solve the resulting quadratic equation.

$$p^2 - 4p + 3 = 0$$

Set the equation equal to zero and factor.

$$(p - 3)(p - 1) = 0$$

$$p - 3 = 0 \quad \text{or} \quad p - 1 = 0$$

Set each factor equal to zero.

$$p = 3 \quad \text{or} \quad p = 1$$

Step 5: Check: $p = 3$ Check: $p = 1$

3 and 1 are not restricted values.

$$1 - \frac{4}{p} = -\frac{3}{p^2} \qquad 1 - \frac{4}{p} = -\frac{3}{p^2}$$

$$1 - \frac{4}{(3)} \overset{?}{=} -\frac{3}{(3)^2} \qquad 1 - \frac{4}{(1)} \overset{?}{=} -\frac{3}{(1)^2}$$

$$\frac{3}{3} - \frac{4}{3} \overset{?}{=} -\frac{3}{9} \qquad 1 - 4 \overset{?}{=} -3$$

The solutions are 3 and 1.

$$-\frac{1}{3} \overset{?}{=} -\frac{1}{3} ✔ \qquad -3 \overset{?}{=} -3 ✔$$

Skill Practice

Solve the equation.

4. $\dfrac{z}{2} - \dfrac{1}{2z} = \dfrac{12}{z}$

Answer

4. $5, -5$

Example 5 **Solving a Rational Equation**

Solve the equation. $\qquad \dfrac{6}{t^2 - 7t + 12} + \dfrac{2t}{t - 3} = \dfrac{3t}{t - 4}$

Solution:

$$\dfrac{6}{t^2 - 7t + 12} + \dfrac{2t}{t - 3} = \dfrac{3t}{t - 4}$$

$$\dfrac{6}{(t - 3)(t - 4)} + \dfrac{2t}{t - 3} = \dfrac{3t}{t - 4}$$

Step 1: Factor the denominators. The restricted values are $t = 3$ and $t = 4$.

Step 2: The LCD is $(t - 3)(t - 4)$.

Step 3: Multiply by the LCD on both sides.

$$(t - 3)(t - 4)\left(\dfrac{6}{(t - 3)(t - 4)} + \dfrac{2t}{t - 3}\right) = (t - 3)(t - 4)\left(\dfrac{3t}{t - 4}\right)$$

$$(t-3)(t-4)\left(\dfrac{6}{(t-3)(t-4)}\right) + (t-3)(t - 4)\left(\dfrac{2t}{t-3}\right) = (t - 3)(t-4)\left(\dfrac{3t}{t-4}\right)$$

$$6 + 2t(t - 4) = 3t(t - 3)$$

$$6 + 2t^2 - 8t = 3t^2 - 9t$$

Step 4: Solve the resulting equation.

$$0 = 3t^2 - 2t^2 - 9t + 8t - 6$$

Because the resulting equation is quadratic, set the equation equal to zero and factor.

$$0 = t^2 - t - 6$$

$$0 = (t - 3)(t + 2)$$

$$t - 3 = 0 \quad \text{or} \quad t + 2 = 0 \qquad \text{Set each factor equal to zero.}$$

$$t = 3 \quad \text{or} \quad t = -2$$

3 is a restricted value, but -2 is not restricted.

Step 5: Check the potential solutions in the original equation.

Check: $t = 3$

3 cannot be a solution to the equation because it will make the denominator zero in the original equation.

$$\dfrac{6}{t^2 - 7t + 12} + \dfrac{2t}{t - 3} = \dfrac{3t}{t - 4}$$

$$\dfrac{6}{(3)^2 - 7(3) + 12} + \dfrac{2(3)}{(3) - 3} \overset{?}{=} \dfrac{3(3)}{(3) - 4}$$

$$\dfrac{6}{0} + \dfrac{6}{0} \overset{?}{=} \dfrac{9}{-1}$$

Zero in the denominator

The only solution is -2.

Check: $t = -2$

$$\dfrac{6}{t^2 - 7t + 12} + \dfrac{2t}{t - 3} = \dfrac{3t}{t - 4}$$

$$\dfrac{6}{(-2)^2 - 7(-2) + 12} + \dfrac{2(-2)}{(-2) - 3} \overset{?}{=} \dfrac{3(-2)}{(-2) - 4}$$

$$\dfrac{6}{4 + 14 + 12} + \dfrac{-4}{-5} \overset{?}{=} \dfrac{-6}{-6}$$

$$\dfrac{6}{30} + \dfrac{4}{5} \overset{?}{=} 1$$

$$\dfrac{1}{5} + \dfrac{4}{5} = 1 \; ✔ \; \text{(True)}$$

$$t = -2 \text{ is a solution.}$$

Example 6 Translating to a Rational Equation

Ten times the reciprocal of a number is added to four. The result is equal to the quotient of twenty-two and the number. Find the number.

Solution:

Let x represent the number.

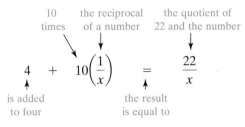

$$4 + \frac{10}{x} = \frac{22}{x}$$
Step 1: The denominators are already factored. The restricted value is $x = 0$.

Step 2: The LCD is x.

$$x\left(4 + \frac{10}{x}\right) = x\left(\frac{22}{x}\right)$$
Step 3: Multiply both sides by the LCD.

$$4x + 10 = 22$$
Apply the distributive property.

$$4x = 12$$
Step 4: Solve the resulting linear equation.

$x = 3$ is a potential solution.

Step 5: 3 is not a restricted value. Substituting $x = 3$ into the original equation verifies that it is a solution.

The number is 3.

> **Skill Practice**
>
> **7.** The quotient of ten and a number is two less than four times the reciprocal of the number. Find the number.

3. Solving Formulas Involving Rational Expressions

A rational equation may have more than one variable. To solve for a specific variable within a rational equation, we can still apply the principle of clearing fractions.

Example 7 Solving Formulas Involving Rational Equations

Solve for k. $F = \frac{ma}{k}$

Solution:

To solve for k, we must clear fractions so that k no longer appears in the denominator.

$$F = \frac{ma}{k}$$
The LCD is k.

$$k \cdot (F) = k \cdot \left(\frac{ma}{k}\right)$$
Multiply both sides of the equation by the LCD.

$$kF = ma$$
Clear fractions.

$$\frac{kF}{F} = \frac{ma}{F}$$
Divide both sides by F.

$$k = \frac{ma}{F}$$

> **Skill Practice**
>
> **8.** Solve for t.
>
> $$C = \frac{rt}{d}$$

> **Answers**
>
> **7.** The number is -3.
>
> **8.** $t = \dfrac{Cd}{r}$

Example 8 Solving Formulas Involving Rational Equations

A formula to find the height of a trapezoid given its area and the lengths of the two parallel sides is $h = \dfrac{2A}{B + b}$. Solve for b, the length of one of the parallel sides.

Solution:

To solve for b, we must clear fractions so that b no longer appears in the denominator.

$$h = \frac{2A}{B + b}$$ The LCD is $(B + b)$.

$$h(B + b) = \left(\frac{2A}{B + b}\right) \cdot (B + b)$$ Multiply both sides of the equation by the LCD.

$$hB + hb = 2A$$ Apply the distributive property.

$$hb = 2A - hB$$ Subtract hB from both sides to isolate the b term.

$$\frac{hb}{h} = \frac{2A - hB}{h}$$ Divide by h.

$$b = \frac{2A - hB}{h}$$

TIP: The solution to Example 8 can be written in several forms. The quantity

$$\frac{2A - hB}{h}$$

can be left as a single rational expression or can be split into two fractions and simplified.

$$b = \frac{2A - hB}{h} = \frac{2A}{h} - \frac{hB}{h} = \frac{2A}{h} - B$$

Example 9 Solving Formulas Involving Rational Expressions

Solve for z. $y = \dfrac{x - z}{x + z}$

Solution:

To solve for z, we must clear fractions so that z no longer appears in the denominator.

$$y = \frac{x - z}{x + z}$$ LCD is $(x + z)$.

$$y(x + z) = \left(\frac{x - z}{x + z}\right)(x + z)$$ Multiply both sides of the equation by the LCD.

$$yx + yz = x - z$$ Apply the distributive property.

$$yz + z = x - yx$$ Collect z terms on one side of the equation and collect terms not containing z on the other side.

$$z(y + 1) = x - yx$$ Factor out z.

$$z = \frac{x - yx}{y + 1}$$ Divide by $y + 1$ to solve for z.

Section 7.6 Practice Exercises

Vocabulary and Key Concepts

1. a. The equation $4x + 7 = -18$ is an example of a _____ equation, whereas $3y^2 - 4y - 7 = 0$ is an example of a _____ equation.

b. The equation $\dfrac{6}{x + 2} + \dfrac{1}{4} = \dfrac{2}{3}$ is an example of a _____ equation.

c. After solving a rational equation, check each potential solution to determine if it makes the _____ equal to zero in one or more of the rational expressions. If so, that potential solution is not a solution to the equation.

Review Exercises

For Exercises 2–7, perform the indicated operations.

2. $\dfrac{2}{x - 3} - \dfrac{3}{x^2 - x - 6}$

3. $\dfrac{2x - 6}{4x^2 + 7x - 2} \div \dfrac{x^2 - 5x + 6}{x^2 - 4}$

4. $\dfrac{2y}{y - 3} + \dfrac{4}{y^2 - 9}$

5. $\dfrac{h - \dfrac{1}{h}}{\dfrac{1}{5} - \dfrac{1}{5h}}$

6. $\dfrac{w - 4}{w^2 - 9} \cdot \dfrac{w - 3}{w^2 - 8w + 16}$

7. $1 + \dfrac{1}{x} - \dfrac{12}{x^2}$

Concept 1: Introduction to Rational Equations

For Exercises 8–13, solve the equations by first clearing the fractions. **(See Example 1.)**

8. $\dfrac{1}{3}z + \dfrac{2}{3} = -2z + 10$

9. $\dfrac{5}{2} + \dfrac{1}{2}b = 5 - \dfrac{1}{3}b$

10. $\dfrac{3}{2}p + \dfrac{1}{3} = \dfrac{2p - 3}{4}$

11. $\dfrac{5}{3} - \dfrac{1}{6}k = \dfrac{3k + 5}{4}$

12. $\dfrac{2x - 3}{4} + \dfrac{9}{10} = \dfrac{x}{5}$

13. $\dfrac{4y + 2}{3} - \dfrac{7}{6} = -\dfrac{y}{6}$

Concept 2: Solving Rational Equations

14. For the equation

$$\dfrac{1}{w} - \dfrac{1}{2} = -\dfrac{1}{4}$$

a. Identify the restricted values.

b. Identify the LCD of the fractions in the equation.

c. Solve the equation.

15. For the equation

$$\dfrac{3}{z} - \dfrac{4}{5} = -\dfrac{1}{5}$$

a. Identify the restricted values.

b. Identify the LCD of the fractions in the equation.

c. Solve the equation.

16. Identify the LCD of all the denominators in the equation.

$$\dfrac{x + 1}{x^2 + 2x - 3} = \dfrac{1}{x + 3} - \dfrac{1}{x - 1}$$

For Exercises 17–46, solve the equations. **(See Examples 2–5.)**

17. $\dfrac{1}{8} = \dfrac{3}{5} + \dfrac{5}{y}$

18. $\dfrac{2}{7} - \dfrac{1}{x} = \dfrac{2}{3}$

19. $\dfrac{7}{4a} = \dfrac{3}{a - 5}$

20. $\dfrac{2}{x + 4} = \dfrac{5}{3x}$

21. $\dfrac{5}{6x} + \dfrac{7}{x} = 1$

22. $\dfrac{14}{3x} - \dfrac{5}{x} = 2$

23. $1 - \dfrac{2}{y} = \dfrac{3}{y^2}$

24. $1 - \dfrac{2}{m} = \dfrac{8}{m^2}$

25. $\dfrac{a+1}{a} = 1 + \dfrac{a-2}{2a}$

26. $\dfrac{7b-4}{5b} = \dfrac{9}{5} - \dfrac{4}{b}$

27. $\dfrac{w}{5} - \dfrac{w+3}{w} = -\dfrac{3}{w}$

28. $\dfrac{t}{12} + \dfrac{t+3}{3t} = \dfrac{1}{t}$

29. $\dfrac{2}{m+3} = \dfrac{5}{4m+12} - \dfrac{3}{8}$

30. $\dfrac{2}{4n-4} - \dfrac{7}{4} = \dfrac{-3}{n-1}$

31. $\dfrac{p}{p-4} - 5 = \dfrac{4}{p-4}$

32. $\dfrac{-5}{q+5} = \dfrac{q}{q+5} + 2$

33. $\dfrac{2t}{t+2} - 2 = \dfrac{t-8}{t+2}$

34. $\dfrac{4w}{w-3} - 3 = \dfrac{3w-1}{w-3}$

35. $\dfrac{x^2-x}{x-2} = \dfrac{12}{x-2}$

36. $\dfrac{x^2+9}{x+4} = \dfrac{-10x}{x+4}$

37. $\dfrac{x^2+3x}{x-1} = \dfrac{4}{x-1}$

38. $\dfrac{2x^2-21}{2x-3} = \dfrac{-11x}{2x-3}$

39. $\dfrac{2x}{x+4} - \dfrac{8}{x-4} = \dfrac{2x^2+32}{x^2-16}$

40. $\dfrac{4x}{x+3} - \dfrac{12}{x-3} = \dfrac{4x^2+36}{x^2-9}$

41. $\dfrac{x}{x+6} = \dfrac{72}{x^2-36} + 4$

42. $\dfrac{y}{y+4} = \dfrac{32}{y^2-16} + 3$

43. $\dfrac{5}{3x-3} - \dfrac{2}{x-2} = \dfrac{7}{x^2-3x+2}$

44. $\dfrac{6}{5a+10} - \dfrac{1}{a-5} = \dfrac{4}{a^2-3a-10}$

45. $\dfrac{w}{w-3} = \dfrac{17}{w^2-7w+12} + \dfrac{1}{w-4}$

46. $\dfrac{y}{y+6} = \dfrac{-6}{y^2+7y+6} + \dfrac{2}{y+1}$

For Exercises 47–50, translate to a rational equation and solve. **(See Example 6.)**

47. The reciprocal of a number is added to three. The result is the quotient of 25 and the number. Find the number.

48. The difference of three and the reciprocal of a number is equal to the quotient of 20 and the number. Find the number.

49. If a number added to five is divided by the difference of the number and two, the result is three-fourths. Find the number.

50. If twice a number added to three is divided by the number plus one, the result is three-halves. Find the number.

Concept 3: Solving Formulas Involving Rational Expressions

For Exercises 51–68, solve for the indicated variable. **(See Examples 7–9.)**

51. $K = \dfrac{ma}{F}$ for m

52. $K = \dfrac{ma}{F}$ for a

53. $K = \dfrac{IR}{E}$ for E

54. $K = \dfrac{IR}{E}$ for R

55. $I = \dfrac{E}{R+r}$ for R

56. $I = \dfrac{E}{R+r}$ for r

57. $h = \dfrac{2A}{B+b}$ for B

58. $\dfrac{C}{\pi r} = 2$ for r

59. $\dfrac{V}{\pi h} = r^2$ for h

60. $\dfrac{V}{lw} = h$ for w

61. $x = \dfrac{at+b}{t}$ for t

62. $\dfrac{T+mf}{m} = g$ for m

63. $\dfrac{x-y}{xy}=z$ for x

64. $\dfrac{w-n}{wn}=P$ for w

65. $a+b=\dfrac{2A}{h}$ for h

66. $1+rt=\dfrac{A}{P}$ for P

67. $\dfrac{1}{R}=\dfrac{1}{R_1}+\dfrac{1}{R_2}$ for R

68. $\dfrac{b+a}{ab}=\dfrac{1}{f}$ for b

Problem Recognition Exercises

Comparing Rational Equations and Rational Expressions

Often adding or subtracting rational expressions is confused with solving rational equations. When adding rational expressions, we combine the terms to simplify the expression. When solving an equation, we clear the fractions and find numerical solutions, if possible. Both processes begin with finding the LCD, but the LCD is used differently in each process. Compare these two examples.

Example 1:

Add. $\dfrac{4}{x}+\dfrac{x}{3}$ (The LCD is $3x$.)

$$=\dfrac{3}{3}\cdot\left(\dfrac{4}{x}\right)+\left(\dfrac{x}{3}\right)\cdot\dfrac{x}{x}$$

$$=\dfrac{12}{3x}+\dfrac{x^2}{3x}$$

$$=\dfrac{12+x^2}{3x}\qquad\text{The final answer is a rational expression.}$$

Example 2:

Solve. $\dfrac{4}{x}+\dfrac{x}{3}=-\dfrac{8}{3}$ (The LCD is $3x$.)

$$\dfrac{3x}{1}\left(\dfrac{4}{x}+\dfrac{x}{3}\right)=\dfrac{3x}{1}\left(-\dfrac{8}{3}\right)$$

$$12+x^2=-8x$$

$$x^2+8x+12=0$$

$$(x+2)(x+6)=0$$

$$x+2=0\text{ or }x+6=0$$

$x=-2$ or $x=-6$ The final answers are numbers. The solutions -2 and -6 both check in the original equation.

For Exercises 1–20, solve the equation or simplify the expression by combining the terms.

1. $\dfrac{y}{2y+4}-\dfrac{2}{y^2+2y}$

2. $\dfrac{1}{x+2}+2=\dfrac{x+11}{x+2}$

3. $\dfrac{5t}{2}-\dfrac{t-2}{3}=5$

4. $3-\dfrac{2}{a-5}$

5. $\dfrac{7}{6p^2}+\dfrac{2}{9p}+\dfrac{1}{3p^2}$

6. $\dfrac{3b}{b+1}-\dfrac{2b}{b-1}$

7. $4+\dfrac{2}{h-3}=5$

8. $\dfrac{2}{w+1}+\dfrac{3}{(w+1)^2}$

9. $\dfrac{1}{x-6}-\dfrac{3}{x^2-6x}=\dfrac{4}{x}$

10. $\dfrac{3}{m}-\dfrac{6}{5}=-\dfrac{3}{m}$

11. $\dfrac{7}{2x+2}+\dfrac{3x}{4x+4}$

12. $\dfrac{10}{2t-1}-1=\dfrac{t}{2t-1}$

13. $\dfrac{3}{5x}+\dfrac{7}{2x}=1$

14. $\dfrac{7}{t^2-5t}-\dfrac{3}{t-5}$

15. $\dfrac{5}{2a-1}+4$

16. $p-\dfrac{5p}{p-2}=-\dfrac{10}{p-2}$

17. $\dfrac{3}{u}+\dfrac{12}{u^2-3u}=\dfrac{u+1}{u-3}$

18. $\dfrac{5}{4k}-\dfrac{2}{6k}$

19. $\dfrac{-2h}{h^2-9}+\dfrac{3}{h-3}$

20. $\dfrac{3y}{y^2-5y+4}=\dfrac{2}{y-4}+\dfrac{3}{y-1}$

Section 7.7 | Applications of Rational Equations and Proportions

1. Solving Proportions

In this section, we look at how rational equations can be used to solve a variety of applications. The first type of rational equation that will be applied is called a proportion.

Definition of Ratio and Proportion

1. The **ratio** of a to b is $\dfrac{a}{b}$ ($b \neq 0$) and can also be expressed as $a{:}b$ or $a \div b$.

2. An equation that equates two ratios or rates is called a **proportion**. Therefore, if $b \neq 0$ and $d \neq 0$, then $\dfrac{a}{b} = \dfrac{c}{d}$ is a proportion.

A proportion can be solved by multiplying both sides of the equation by the LCD and clearing fractions.

Skill Practice

Solve the proportion.

1. $\dfrac{10}{b} = \dfrac{2}{33}$

Example 1 Solving a Proportion

Solve the proportion. $\qquad \dfrac{3}{11} = \dfrac{123}{w}$

Solution:

$$\frac{3}{11} = \frac{123}{w} \qquad \text{The LCD is } 11w.$$

$$\cancel{11}w\left(\frac{3}{\cancel{11}}\right) = 11\cancel{w}\left(\frac{123}{\cancel{w}}\right) \qquad \text{Multiply by the LCD and clear fractions.}$$

$$3w = 11 \cdot 123 \qquad \text{Solve the resulting equation (linear).}$$

$$3w = 1353$$

$$\frac{3w}{3} = \frac{1353}{3}$$

$$w = 451$$

$$\underline{\text{Check: } w = 451}$$

$$\frac{3}{11} = \frac{123}{w}$$

$$\frac{3}{11} \overset{?}{=} \frac{123}{(451)}$$

The solution is 451. $\qquad \dfrac{3}{11} \overset{?}{=} \dfrac{3}{11}$ ✔ (True) $\qquad$ Simplify to lowest terms.

Answer

1. 165

2. Applications of Proportions and Similar Triangles

Example 2 Using a Proportion in an Application

For a recent year, the population of Alabama was approximately 4.2 million. At that time, Alabama had seven representatives in the U.S. House of Representatives. In the same year, North Carolina had a population of approximately 7.2 million. If representation in the House is based on population in equal proportions for each state, how many representatives did North Carolina have?

Solution:

Let x represent the number of representatives for North Carolina.

Set up a proportion by writing two equivalent ratios.

$$\boxed{\frac{\text{Population of Alabama}}{\text{number of representatives}}} \longrightarrow \frac{4.2}{7} = \frac{7.2}{x} \longleftarrow \boxed{\frac{\text{Population of North Carolina}}{\text{number of representatives}}}$$

$$\frac{4.2}{7} = \frac{7.2}{x}$$

$$7x \cdot \frac{4.2}{7} = 7x \cdot \frac{7.2}{x} \qquad \text{Multiply by the LCD, } 7x.$$

$$4.2x = (7.2)(7) \qquad \text{Solve the resulting linear equation.}$$

$$4.2x = 50.4$$

$$\frac{4.2x}{4.2} = \frac{50.4}{4.2}$$

$$x = 12 \qquad \text{North Carolina had 12 representatives.}$$

Skill Practice

2. A university has a ratio of students to faculty of 105 to 2. If the student population at the university is 15,750, how many faculty members are needed?

TIP: The equation from Example 2 could have been solved by first equating the cross products:

$$\frac{4.2}{7} \diagup\hspace{-1em}\diagdown \frac{7.2}{x}$$

$$4.2x = (7.2)(7)$$

$$4.2x = 50.4$$

$$x = 12$$

Proportions are used in geometry with **similar triangles**. Two triangles are similar if their angles have equal measure. In such a case, the lengths of the corresponding sides are proportional. In Figure 7-1, triangle ABC is similar to triangle XYZ. Therefore, the following ratios are equivalent.

$$\frac{a}{x} = \frac{b}{y} = \frac{c}{z}$$

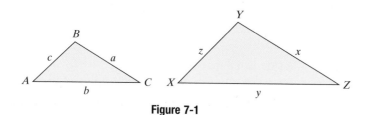

Figure 7-1

Answer

2. 300

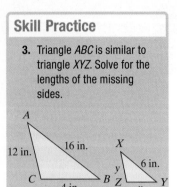
Example 3 **Using Similar Triangles to Find an Unknown Side in a Triangle**

In Figure 7-2, triangle *XYZ* is similar to triangle *ABC*.

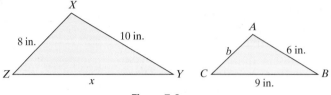

Figure 7-2

a. Solve for *x*.　　**b.** Solve for *b*.

Solution:

a. The lengths of the upper right sides of the triangles are given. These form a known ratio of $\frac{10}{6}$. Because the triangles are similar, the ratio of the other corresponding sides must be equal to $\frac{10}{6}$. To solve for *x*, we have

| Bottom side from large triangle | → | x | $=$ | 10 in. | ← | Right side from large triangle |
| bottom side from small triangle | → | 9 in. | | 6 in. | ← | right side from small triangle |

$$\frac{x}{9} = \frac{10}{6} \qquad \text{The LCD is 18.}$$

$$\overset{2}{\cancel{18}} \cdot \left(\frac{x}{9}\right) = \overset{3}{\cancel{18}} \cdot \left(\frac{10}{6}\right) \qquad \text{Multiply by the LCD.}$$

$$2x = 30 \qquad \text{Clear fractions.}$$

$$x = 15 \qquad \text{Divide by 2.}$$

The length of the side is 15 in.

b. To solve for *b*, the ratio of the upper left sides of the triangles must equal $\frac{10}{6}$.

| Left side from large triangle | → | 8 in. | $=$ | 10 in. | ← | Right side from large triangle |
| left side from small triangle | → | b | | 6 in. | ← | right side from small triangle |

$$\frac{8}{b} = \frac{10}{6} \qquad \text{The LCD is } 6b.$$

$$\cancel{6b} \cdot \left(\frac{8}{\cancel{b}}\right) = \cancel{6}b \cdot \left(\frac{10}{\cancel{6}}\right) \qquad \text{Multiply by the LCD.}$$

$$48 = 10b \qquad \text{Clear fractions.}$$

$$\frac{48}{10} = \frac{10b}{10}$$

$$4.8 = b$$

The length of the side is 4.8 in.

Example 4 **Using Similar Triangles in an Application**

A tree that is 20 ft from a house is to be cut down. Use the following information and similar triangles to find the height of the tree to determine if it will hit the house.

The shadow cast by a yardstick is 2 ft long. The shadow cast by a tree is 11 ft long. Find the height of the tree.

Solution:

Let x represent the height of the tree.

Step 1: Read the problem.

Step 2: Label the unknown.

We will assume that the measurements were taken at the same time of day. Therefore, the angle of the Sun is the same on both objects, and we can set up similar triangles (Figure 7-3).

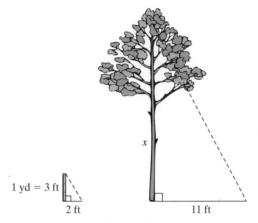

1 yd = 3 ft

2 ft   11 ft

Figure 7-3

Step 3: Create a verbal model.

Height of yardstick	→	3 ft	2 ft	←	Length of yardstick's shadow
height of tree	→	x	11 ft	←	length of tree's shadow

$$\frac{3}{x} = \frac{2}{11}$$

Step 4: Write a mathematical equation.

$$11x\left(\frac{3}{x}\right) = \left(\frac{2}{11}\right)11x$$

Step 5: Multiply by the LCD.

$$33 = 2x$$

Solve the equation.

$$\frac{33}{2} = \frac{2x}{2}$$

$$16.5 = x$$

Step 6: Interpret the results and write the answer in words.

The tree is 16.5 ft high. Since the height is less than 20 ft it will not hit the house.

3. Distance, Rate, and Time Applications

In Sections 2.7 and 4.4 we presented applications involving the relationship among the variables distance, rate, and time. Recall that $d = rt$.

Example 5   **Using a Rational Equation in a Distance, Rate, and Time Application**

A small plane flies 440 mi with the wind from Memphis, TN, to Oklahoma City, OK. In the same amount of time, the plane flies 340 miles against the wind from Oklahoma City to Little Rock, AR (see Figure 7-4). If the wind speed is 30 mph, find the speed of the plane in still air.

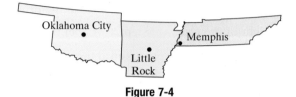

Figure 7-4

Solution:

Let x represent the speed of the plane in still air.

Then $x + 30$ is the speed of the plane with the wind.

$x - 30$ is the speed of the plane against the wind.

Organize the given information in a chart.

	Distance	Rate	Time
With the wind	440	$x + 30$	$\dfrac{440}{x + 30}$
Against the wind	340	$x - 30$	$\dfrac{340}{x - 30}$

Because $d = rt$, then $t = \dfrac{d}{r}$

TIP: The equation

$$\frac{440}{x + 30} = \frac{340}{x - 30}$$

is a proportion. The fractions can also be cleared by equating the cross products.

$$\frac{440}{x + 30} \bowtie \frac{340}{x - 30}$$

$$440(x - 30) = 340(x + 30)$$

The plane travels with the wind for the same amount of time as it travels against the wind, so we can equate the two expressions for time.

$$\left(\begin{array}{c}\text{Time with} \\ \text{the wind}\end{array}\right) = \left(\begin{array}{c}\text{time against} \\ \text{the wind}\end{array}\right)$$

$$\frac{440}{x + 30} = \frac{340}{x - 30} \qquad \text{The LCD is } (x + 30)(x - 30).$$

$$(x + 30)(x - 30) \cdot \frac{440}{x + 30} = (x + 30)(x - 30) \cdot \frac{340}{x - 30}$$

$$440(x - 30) = 340(x + 30)$$

$$440x - 13{,}200 = 340x + 10{,}200 \qquad \text{Solve the resulting linear equation.}$$

$$100x = 23{,}400$$

$$x = 234$$

The plane's speed in still air is 234 mph.

Answer

5. 6 mph

Example 6 Using a Rational Equation in a Distance, Rate, and Time Application

A motorist drives 100 mi between two cities in a bad rainstorm. For the return trip in sunny weather, she averages 10 mph faster and takes $\frac{1}{2}$ hr less time. Find the average speed of the motorist in the rainstorm and in sunny weather.

Solution:

Let x represent the motorist's speed during the rain.

Then $x + 10$ represents the speed in sunny weather.

	Distance	Rate	Time
Trip during rainstorm	100	x	$\dfrac{100}{x}$
Trip during sunny weather	100	$x + 10$	$\dfrac{100}{x + 10}$

Because $d = rt$, then $t = \dfrac{d}{r}$

Because the same distance is traveled in $\frac{1}{2}$ hr less time, the difference between the time of the trip during the rainstorm and the time during sunny weather is $\frac{1}{2}$ hr.

$$\left(\begin{matrix} \text{Time during} \\ \text{the rainstorm} \end{matrix} \right) - \left(\begin{matrix} \text{time during} \\ \text{sunny weather} \end{matrix} \right) = \left(\frac{1}{2}\,\text{hr} \right) \qquad \text{Verbal model}$$

$$\frac{100}{x} - \frac{100}{x + 10} = \frac{1}{2} \qquad \begin{matrix} \text{Mathematical} \\ \text{equation} \end{matrix}$$

$$2x(x + 10)\left(\frac{100}{x} - \frac{100}{x + 10} \right) = 2x(x + 10)\left(\frac{1}{2} \right) \qquad \begin{matrix} \text{Multiply by} \\ \text{the LCD.} \end{matrix}$$

$$2x(x + 10)\left(\frac{100}{x} \right) - 2x(x+10)\left(\frac{100}{x+10} \right) = 2x(x + 10)\left(\frac{1}{2} \right) \qquad \begin{matrix} \text{Apply the} \\ \text{distributive} \\ \text{property.} \end{matrix}$$

$$200(x + 10) - 200x = x(x + 10) \qquad \text{Clear fractions.}$$

$$200x + 2000 - 200x = x^2 + 10x \qquad \begin{matrix} \text{Solve the} \\ \text{resulting} \\ \text{equation} \\ \text{(quadratic).} \end{matrix}$$

$$2000 = x^2 + 10x$$

$$0 = x^2 + 10x - 2000 \qquad \begin{matrix} \text{Set the} \\ \text{equation equal} \\ \text{to zero.} \end{matrix}$$

$$0 = (x - 40)(x + 50) \qquad \text{Factor.}$$

$$x = 40 \quad \text{or} \quad x = -50$$

Because a rate of speed cannot be negative, reject $x = -50$. Therefore, the speed of the motorist in the rainstorm is 40 mph. Because $x + 10 = 40 + 10 = 50$, the average speed for the return trip in sunny weather is 50 mph.

Skill Practice

6. Harley rode his mountain bike 12 mi to the top of the mountain and the same distance back down. His speed going up was 8 mph slower than coming down. The ride up took 2 hr longer than the ride coming down. Find his speeds.

Avoiding Mistakes

The equation

$$\frac{100}{x} - \frac{100}{x + 10} = \frac{1}{2}$$

is not a proportion because the left-hand side has more than one fraction. Do not try to multiply the cross products. Instead, multiply by the LCD to clear fractions.

Answer

6. Uphill speed was 4 mph; downhill speed was 12 mph.

4. Work Applications

Example 7 demonstrates how work rates are related to a portion of a job that can be completed in one unit of time.

Example 7 **Using a Rational Equation in a Work Problem**

A new printing press can print the morning edition in 2 hr, whereas the old printer required 4 hr. How long would it take to print the morning edition if both printers were working together?

Solution:

One method to solve this problem is to add rates.

Let x represent the time required for both printers working together to complete the job.

$$\left(\begin{array}{c}\text{Rate}\\\text{of old printer}\end{array}\right) + \left(\begin{array}{c}\text{rate}\\\text{of new printer}\end{array}\right) = \left(\begin{array}{c}\text{rate of}\\\text{both working together}\end{array}\right)$$

$$\frac{1 \text{ job}}{4 \text{ hr}} \quad + \quad \frac{1 \text{ job}}{2 \text{ hr}} \quad = \quad \frac{1 \text{ job}}{x \text{ hr}}$$

$$\frac{1}{4} + \frac{1}{2} = \frac{1}{x}$$

$$4x\left(\frac{1}{4} + \frac{1}{2}\right) = 4x\left(\frac{1}{x}\right) \qquad \text{The LCD is } 4x.$$

$$\overset{1}{\cancel{4x}} \cdot \frac{1}{\cancel{4}} + \overset{2}{\cancel{4x}} \cdot \frac{1}{\cancel{2}} = \overset{1}{\cancel{4x}} \cdot \frac{1}{\cancel{x}} \qquad \text{Apply the distributive property.}$$

$$x + 2x = 4 \qquad \text{Solve the resulting linear equation.}$$

$$3x = 4$$

$$x = \frac{4}{3} \qquad \text{The time required to print the morning edition using both printers is } 1\frac{1}{3} \text{ hr.}$$

An alternative approach to Example 7 is to determine the portion of the job that each printer can complete in 1 hr and extend that rate to the portion of the job completed in x hours.

- The old printer can perform the job in 4 hr. Therefore, it completes $\frac{1}{4}$ of the job in 1 hr and $\frac{1}{4}x$ jobs in x hours.
- The new printer can perform the job in 2 hr. Therefore, it completes $\frac{1}{2}$ of the job in 1 hr and $\frac{1}{2}x$ jobs in x hours.

The sum of the portions of the job completed by each printer must equal one whole job.

$$\begin{pmatrix} \text{Portion of job} \\ \text{completed by} \\ \text{old printer} \end{pmatrix} + \begin{pmatrix} \text{portion of job} \\ \text{completed by} \\ \text{new printer} \end{pmatrix} = \begin{pmatrix} 1 \\ \text{whole} \\ \text{job} \end{pmatrix}$$

$\dfrac{1}{4}x + \dfrac{1}{2}x = 1$ The LCD is 4.

$4\left(\dfrac{1}{4}x + \dfrac{1}{2}x\right) = 4(1)$ Multiply by the LCD.

$x + 2x = 4$ Solve the resulting linear equation.

$3x = 4$

$x = \dfrac{4}{3}$ The time required using both printers is $1\frac{1}{3}$ hr.

Section 7.7 Practice Exercises

Vocabulary and Key Concepts

1. a. An equation that equates two ratios is called a _____.

   b. Given similar triangles, the lengths of corresponding sides are _____.

Review Exercises

For Exercises 2–7, determine whether each of the following is an equation or an expression. If it is an equation, solve it. If it is an expression, perform the indicated operation.

2. $\dfrac{b}{5} + 3 = 9$

3. $\dfrac{m}{m-1} - \dfrac{2}{m+3}$

4. $\dfrac{2}{a+5} + \dfrac{5}{a^2-25}$

5. $\dfrac{3y+6}{20} \div \dfrac{4y+8}{8}$

6. $\dfrac{z^2+z}{24} \cdot \dfrac{8}{z+1}$

7. $\dfrac{3}{p+3} = \dfrac{12p+19}{p^2+7p+12} - \dfrac{5}{p+4}$

8. Determine whether 1 is a solution to the equation. $\dfrac{1}{x-1} + \dfrac{1}{2} = \dfrac{2}{x^2-1}$

Concept 1: Solving Proportions

For Exercises 9–22, solve the proportions. **(See Example 1.)**

9. $\dfrac{8}{5} = \dfrac{152}{p}$

10. $\dfrac{6}{7} = \dfrac{96}{y}$

11. $\dfrac{19}{76} = \dfrac{z}{4}$

12. $\dfrac{15}{135} = \dfrac{w}{9}$

13. $\dfrac{5}{3} = \dfrac{a}{8}$

14. $\dfrac{b}{14} = \dfrac{3}{8}$

15. $\dfrac{2}{1.9} = \dfrac{x}{38}$

16. $\dfrac{16}{1.3} = \dfrac{30}{p}$

17. $\dfrac{y+1}{2y} = \dfrac{2}{3}$

18. $\dfrac{w-2}{4w} = \dfrac{1}{6}$

19. $\dfrac{9}{2z-1} = \dfrac{3}{z}$

20. $\dfrac{1}{t} = \dfrac{1}{4-t}$

21. $\dfrac{8}{9a-1} = \dfrac{5}{3a+2}$

22. $\dfrac{4p+1}{3} = \dfrac{2p-5}{6}$

23. Charles's law describes the relationship between the initial and final temperature and volume of a gas held at a constant pressure.

$$\dfrac{V_i}{V_f} = \dfrac{T_i}{T_f}$$

  a. Solve the equation for V_f.

  b. Solve the equation for T_f.

24. The relationship between the area, height, and base of a triangle is given by the proportion

$$\dfrac{A}{b} = \dfrac{h}{2}$$

  a. Solve the equation for A.

  b. Solve the equation for b.

Concept 2: Applications of Proportions and Similar Triangles

For Exercises 25–32, solve using proportions.

25. Toni drives her Honda Civic 132 mi on the highway on 4 gal of gas. At this rate how many miles can she drive on 9 gal of gas? **(See Example 2.)**

26. Tim takes his pulse for 10 sec and counts 12 beats. How many beats per minute is this?

27. It is recommended that 7.8 mL of Grow-It-Right plant food be mixed with 2 L of water for feeding house plants. How much plant food should be mixed with 1 gal of water to maintain the same concentration? (1 gal $\approx$ 3.8 L.) Express the answer in milliliters.

28. According to the website for the state of Virginia, 0.8 million tons of clothing is reused or recycled out of 7 million tons of clothing discarded. If 17.5 million tons of clothing is discarded, how many tons will be reused or recycled?

29. Andrew is on a low-carbohydrate diet. If his diet book tells him that an 8-oz serving of pineapple contains 19.2 g of carbohydrate, how many grams of carbohydrate does a 5-oz serving contain?

30. Cooking oatmeal requires 1 cup of water for every $\frac{1}{2}$ cup of oats. How many cups of water will be required for $\frac{3}{4}$ cup of oats?

31. According to a building code, a wheelchair ramp must be at least 12 ft long for each foot of height. If the height of a newly constructed ramp is to be $1\frac{2}{3}$ ft, find the minimum acceptable length.

32. A map has a scale of 50 mi/in. If two cities measure 6.5 in. apart, how many miles does this represent?

For Exercises 33–36, triangle ABC is similar to triangle XYZ. Solve for x and y. **(See Example 3.)**

33.

34.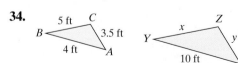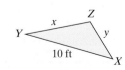

35.

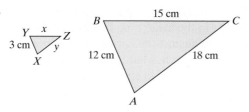

36.

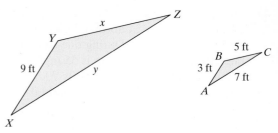

37. To estimate the height of a light pole, a mathematics student measures the length of a shadow cast by a meterstick and the length of the shadow cast by the light pole. Find the height of the light pole. **(See Example 4.)**

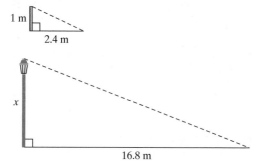

38. To estimate the height of a building, a student measures the length of a shadow cast by a yardstick and the length of the shadow cast by the building. Find the height of the building.

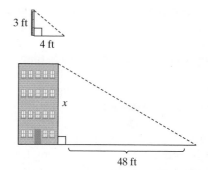

39. A 6-ft-tall man standing 54 ft from a light post casts an 18-ft shadow. What is the height of the light post?

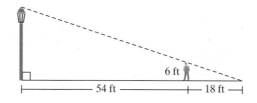

40. For a science project at school, a student must measure the height of a tree. The student measures the length of the shadow of the tree and then measures the length of the shadow cast by a yardstick. Use similar triangles to find the height of the tree.

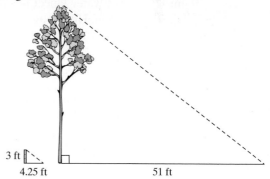

Concept 3: Distance, Rate, and Time Applications

41. A boat travels 54 mi upstream against the current in the same amount of time it takes to travel 66 mi downstream with the current. If the current is 2 mph, what is the speed of the boat in still water? (Use $t = \frac{d}{r}$ to complete the table.) **(See Example 5.)**

	Distance	Rate	Time
With the current (downstream)			
Against the current (upstream)			

42. A plane flies 630 mi with the wind in the same time that it takes to fly 455 mi against the wind. If this plane flies at the rate of 217 mph in still air, what is the speed of the wind? (Use $t = \frac{d}{r}$ to complete the table.)

	Distance	Rate	Time
With the wind			
Against the wind			

43. The jet stream is a fast flowing air current found in the atmosphere at around 36,000 ft above the surface of the Earth. During one summer day, the speed of the jet stream is 35 mph. A plane flying with the jet stream can fly 700 mi in the same amount of time that it would take to fly 500 mi against the jet stream. What is the speed of the plane in still air?

44. A fisherman travels 9 mi downstream with the current in the same time that he travels 3 mi upstream against the current. If the speed of the current is 6 mph, what is the speed at which the fisherman travels in still water?

45. An athlete in training rides his bike 20 mi and then immediately follows with a 10-mi run. The total workout takes him 2.5 hr. He also knows that he bikes about twice as fast as he runs. Determine his biking speed and his running speed.

46. Devon can cross-country ski 5 km/hr faster than his sister Shanelle. Devon skis 45 km in the same time Shanelle skis 30 km. Find their speeds.

47. Floyd can walk 2 mph faster than his wife, Rachel. It takes Rachel 3 hr longer than Floyd to hike a 12-mi trail through the park. Find their speeds. **(See Example 6.)**

48. Janine bikes 3 mph faster than her sister, Jessica. Janine can ride 36 mi in 1 hr less time than Jessica can ride the same distance. Find each of their speeds.

49. Sergio rode his bike 4 mi. Then he got a flat tire and had to walk back 4 mi. It took him 1 hr longer to walk than it did to ride. If his rate walking was 9 mph less than his rate riding, find the two rates.

50. Amber jogs 10 km in $\frac{3}{4}$ hr less than she can walk the same distance. If her walking rate is 3 km/hr less than her jogging rate, find her rates jogging and walking (in km/hr).

Concept 4: Work Applications

51. If the cold-water faucet is left on, the sink will fill in 10 min. If the hot-water faucet is left on, the sink will fill in 12 min. How long would it take to fill the sink if both faucets are left on? **(See Example 7.)**

52. The CUT-IT-OUT lawn mowing company consists of two people: Tina and Bill. If Tina cuts a lawn by herself, she can do it in 4 hr. If Bill cuts the same lawn himself, it takes him an hour longer than Tina. How long would it take them if they worked together?

53. A manuscript needs to be printed. One printer can do the job in 50 min, and another printer can do the job in 40 min. How long would it take if both printers were used?

54. A pump can empty a small pond in 4 hr. Another more efficient pump can do the job in 3 hr. How long would it take to empty the pond if both pumps were used?

55. A pipe can fill a reservoir in 16 hr. A drainage pipe can drain the reservoir in 24 hr. How long would it take to fill the reservoir if the drainage pipe were left open by mistake? (*Hint:* The rate at which water drains should be negative.)

56. A hole in the bottom of a child's plastic swimming pool can drain the pool in 60 min. If the pool had no hole, a hose could fill the pool in 40 min. How long would it take the hose to fill the pool with the hole?

57. Tim and Al are bricklayers. Tim can construct an outdoor grill in 5 days. If Al helps Tim, they can build it in only 2 days. How long would it take Al to build the grill alone?

58. Norma is a new and inexperienced secretary. It takes her 3 hr to prepare a mailing. If her boss helps her, the mailing can be completed in 1 hr. How long would it take the boss to do the job by herself?

Expanding Your Skills

For Exercises 59–62, solve using proportions.

59. The ratio of smokers to nonsmokers in a restaurant is 2 to 7. There are 100 more nonsmokers than smokers. How many smokers and nonsmokers are in the restaurant?

60. The ratio of fiction to nonfiction books sold in a bookstore is 5 to 3. One week there were 180 more fiction books sold than nonfiction. Find the number of fiction and nonfiction books sold during that week.

61. There are 440 students attending a biology lecture. The ratio of male to female students at the lecture is 6 to 5. How many men and women are attending the lecture?

62. The ratio of dogs to cats at the humane society is 5 to 8. The total number of dogs and cats is 650. How many dogs and how many cats are at the humane society?

Variation

1. Definition of Direct and Inverse Variation

In this section, we introduce the concept of variation. Direct and inverse variation models can show how one quantity varies in proportion to another.

> **Definition of Direct and Inverse Variation**
>
> Let k be a nonzero constant real number. Then,
>
> **1.** y varies **directly** as x.
> y is directly proportional to x. $\Big\}$ is equivalent to $y = kx$
>
> **2.** y varies **inversely** as x.
> y is inversely proportional to x. $\Big\}$ is equivalent to $y = \dfrac{k}{x}$
>
> *Note:* The value of k is called the constant of variation.

For a car traveling 30 mph, the equation $d = 30t$ indicates that the distance traveled is *directly proportional* to the time of travel. For positive values of k, when two values are directly related, as one value increases, the other will also increase. Likewise, if one value decreases, the other will decrease. In the equation $d = 30t$, the longer the time of the trip, the greater the distance traveled. The shorter the time of the trip, the shorter the distance traveled.

For positive values of k, when two positive values are *inversely related*, as one value increases, the other will decrease, and vice versa. Consider a car traveling between Toronto and Montreal, a distance of 500 km. The time required to make the trip is inversely proportional to the speed of travel: $t = 500/r$. As the rate of speed, r, increases, the quotient $500/r$ will decrease. Thus the time will decrease. Similarly, as the rate of speed decreases, the trip will take longer.

2. Translations Involving Variation

The first step in using a variation model is to translate an English phrase into an equivalent mathematical equation.

Example 1 Translating to a Variation Model

Translate each expression into an equivalent mathematical model.

a. The circumference of a circle varies directly as the radius.

b. At a constant temperature, the volume of a gas varies inversely as the pressure.

c. The length of time of a meeting is directly proportional to the *square* of the number of people present.

Solution:

a. Let C represent circumference and r represent radius. The variables are directly related, so use the model $C = kr$.

b. Let V represent volume and P represent pressure. Because the variables are inversely related, use the model $V = k/P$.

c. Let t represent time, and let N be the number of people present at a meeting. Because t is directly related to N^2, use the model $t = kN^2$.

Sometimes a value varies directly as the product of two or more other values. In this case, we have joint variation.

> ## Joint Variation
>
> Let k be a nonzero constant real number. Then the following statements are equivalent:
>
> $$\left.\begin{array}{l} y \text{ varies } \textbf{jointly} \text{ as } w \text{ and } z. \\ y \text{ is jointly proportional to } w \text{ and } z. \end{array}\right\} \quad y = kwz$$

Example 2 Translating to a Variation Model

Translate each expression into an equivalent mathematical model.

a. y varies jointly as u and the square root of v.

b. The gravitational force of attraction between two planets varies jointly as the product of their masses and inversely as the square of the distance between them.

Solution:

a. $y = ku\sqrt{v}$

b. Let m_1 and m_2 represent the masses of the two planets. Let F represent the gravitational force of attraction and d represent the distance between the planets.

The variation model is $$F = \frac{km_1m_2}{d^2}$$

3. Applications of Variation

Consider the variation models $y = kx$ and $y = k/x$. In either case, if values for x and y are known, we can solve for k. Once k is known, we can use the variation equation to find y if x is known, or to find x if y is known. This concept is the basis for solving many problems involving variation.

Finding a Variation Model

Step 1 Write a general variation model that relates the values given in the problem. Let k represent the constant of variation.

Step 2 Solve for k by substituting known values of the variables into the model from step 1.

Step 3 Substitute the value of k into the original variation model from step 1.

Example 3   Solving an Application Involving Direct Variation

The variable z varies directly as w. When w is 16, z is 56.

a. Write a variation model for this situation. Use k as the constant of variation.

b. Solve for the constant of variation.

c. Find the value of z when w is 84.

Solution:

a. $z = kw$

b. $z = kw$

   $56 = k(16)$ Substitute known values for z and w. Then solve for the unknown value of k.

   $\dfrac{56}{16} = \dfrac{k(16)}{16}$ To isolate k, divide both sides by 16.

   $\dfrac{7}{2} = k$ Simplify $\dfrac{56}{16}$ to $\dfrac{7}{2}$.

c. With the value of k known, the variation model can now be written as $z = \dfrac{7}{2}w$.

   $z = \dfrac{7}{2}(84)$ To find z when $w = 84$, substitute $w = 84$ into the equation.

   $z = 294$

Example 4   Solving an Application Involving Direct Variation

The speed of a racing canoe in still water varies directly as the square root of the length of the canoe.

a. If a 16-ft canoe can travel 6.2 mph in still water, find a variation model that relates the speed of a canoe to its length.

b. Find the speed of a 25-ft canoe.

Solution:

a. Let s represent the speed of the canoe and L represent the length. The general variation model is $s = k\sqrt{L}$. To solve for k, substitute the known values for s and L.

Skill Practice

The variable t varies directly as the square of v. When v is 8, t is 32.

6. Write a variation model for this relationship.

7. Solve for the constant of variation.

8. Find t when $v = 10$.

Skill Practice

9. The amount of water needed by a mountain hiker varies directly as the time spent hiking. The hiker needs 2.4 L for a 4-hr hike. How much water will be needed for a 5-hr hike?

Answers

6. $t = kv^2$ **7.** $\dfrac{1}{2}$

8. 50   **9.** 3 L

$$s = k\sqrt{L}$$

$$6.2 = k\sqrt{16} \qquad \text{Substitute } s = 6.2 \text{ mph and } L = 16 \text{ ft.}$$

$$6.2 = k \cdot 4$$

$$\frac{6.2}{4} = \frac{4k}{4} \qquad \text{Solve for } k.$$

$$k = 1.55$$

$$s = 1.55\sqrt{L} \qquad \text{Substitute } k = 1.55 \text{ into the model } s = k\sqrt{L}.$$

b. $s = 1.55\sqrt{L}$

$$= 1.55\sqrt{25} \qquad \text{Find the speed when } L = 25 \text{ ft.}$$

$$= 7.75 \text{ mph} \qquad \text{The speed is 7.75 mph.}$$

Skill Practice

10. The yield on a bond varies inversely as the price. The yield on a particular bond is 5% when the price is $100. Find the yield when the price is $125.

| Example 5 | **Solving an Application Involving Inverse Variation** |

The loudness of sound measured in decibels varies inversely as the square of the distance between the listener and the source of the sound. If the loudness of sound is 17.92 decibels at a distance of 10 ft from a home theater speaker, what is the decibel level 20 ft from the speaker?

Solution:

Let L represent the loudness of sound in decibels and d represent the distance in feet. The inverse relationship between decibel level and the square of the distance is modeled by

$$L = \frac{k}{d^2}$$

$$17.92 = \frac{k}{(10)^2} \qquad \text{Substitute } L = 17.92 \text{ decibels and } d = 10 \text{ ft.}$$

$$17.92 = \frac{k}{100}$$

$$(17.92)100 = \frac{k}{100} \cdot 100 \qquad \text{Solve for } k \text{ (clear fractions).}$$

$$k = 1792$$

$$L = \frac{1792}{d^2} \qquad \text{Substitute } k = 1792 \text{ into the original model } L = \frac{k}{d^2}.$$

With the value of k known, we can find L for any value of d.

$$L = \frac{1792}{(20)^2} \qquad \text{Find the loudness when } d = 20 \text{ ft.}$$

$$= 4.48 \text{ decibels} \qquad \text{The loudness is 4.48 decibels.}$$

Notice that the loudness of sound is 17.92 decibels at a distance 10 ft from the speaker. When the distance from the speaker is increased to 20 ft, the decibel level decreases to 4.48 decibels. This is consistent with an inverse relationship. For $k > 0$, as one variable is increased, the other is decreased. It also seems reasonable that the further one moves away from the source of a sound, the softer the sound becomes.

Answer

10. 4%

| Example 6 | Solving an Application Involving Joint Variation |

The kinetic energy of an object varies jointly as the weight of the object at sea level and as the square of its velocity. During a hurricane, a 0.5-lb stone traveling at 60 mph has 81 J (joules) of kinetic energy. Suppose the wind speed doubles to 120 mph. Find the kinetic energy.

Solution:

Let E represent the kinetic energy, let w represent the weight, and let v represent the velocity of the stone. The variation model is

$$E = kwv^2$$

$$81 = k(0.5)(60)^2 \qquad \text{Substitute } E = 81 \text{ J}, w = 0.5 \text{ lb, and } v = 60 \text{ mph.}$$

$$81 = k(0.5)(3600) \qquad \text{Simplify exponents.}$$

$$81 = k(1800)$$

$$\frac{81}{1800} = \frac{k(1800)}{1800} \qquad \text{Divide by 1800.}$$

$$0.045 = k \qquad \text{Solve for } k.$$

With the value of k known, the model $E = kwv^2$ can now be written as $E = 0.045wv^2$. We now find the kinetic energy of a 0.5-lb stone traveling at 120 mph.

$$E = 0.045(0.5)(120)^2$$

$$= 324$$

The kinetic energy of a 0.5-lb stone traveling at 120 mph is 324 J.

In Example 6, when the velocity increased by 2 times, the kinetic energy increased by 4 times (note that 324 J = 4 · 81 J). This factor of 4 occurs because the kinetic energy is proportional to the *square* of the velocity. When the velocity increased by 2 times, the kinetic energy increased by 2^2 times.

Skill Practice

11. The amount of simple interest earned in an account varies jointly as the interest rate and time of the investment. An account earns $72 in 4 years at 2% interest. How much interest would be earned in 3 years at a rate of 5%?

Answer
11. $135

Section 7.8 Practice Exercises

Vocabulary and Key Concepts

1. a. Let k be a nonzero constant. If y varies directly as x, then $y = $ _____ where k is the constant of variation.

b. Let k be a nonzero constant. If y varies inversely as x, then $y = $ _____ where k is the constant of variation.

c. Let k be a nonzero constant. If y varies jointly as x and w, then $y = $ _____ where k is the constant of variation.

Review Exercises

For Exercises 2–7, perform the indicated operation or solve the equation.

2. $\dfrac{5p}{p+2} + \dfrac{10}{p+2}$

3. $\dfrac{2y}{3} - \dfrac{3y-1}{5} = 1$

4. $\dfrac{3}{q-1} \cdot \dfrac{2q^2 + 3q - 5}{6q + 24}$

5. $\dfrac{a}{4} + \dfrac{3}{a} = 2$

6. $\dfrac{3}{b^2 + 5b - 14} - \dfrac{2}{b^2 - 49}$

7. $\dfrac{a + \dfrac{a}{b}}{\dfrac{a}{b} - a}$

Concept 1: Definition of Direct and Inverse Variation

8. In the equation $r = kt$, does r vary directly or inversely with t?

9. In the equation $w = \dfrac{k}{v}$, does w vary directly or inversely with v?

10. In the equation $P = \dfrac{k \cdot c}{v}$, does P vary directly or inversely as v?

Concept 2: Translations Involving Variation

For Exercises 11–22, write a variation model. Use k as the constant of variation. **(See Examples 1 and 2.)**

11. T varies directly as q.

12. W varies directly as z.

13. b varies inversely as c.

14. m varies inversely as t.

15. Q is directly proportional to x and inversely proportional to y.

16. d is directly proportional to p and inversely proportional to n.

17. c varies jointly as s and t.

18. w varies jointly as p and f.

19. L varies jointly as w and the square root of v.

20. q varies jointly as v and the square root of w.

21. x varies directly as the square of y and inversely as z.

22. a varies directly as n and inversely as the square of d.

Concept 3: Applications of Variation

For Exercises 23–28, find the constant of variation, k. **(See Example 3.)**

23. y varies directly as x and when x is 4, y is 18.

24. m varies directly as x and when x is 8, m is 22.

25. p varies inversely as q and when q is 16, p is 32.

26. T varies inversely as x and when x is 40, T is 200.

27. y varies jointly as w and v. When w is 50 and v is 0.1, y is 8.75.

28. N varies jointly as t and p. When t is 1 and p is 7.5, N is 330.

Solve Exercises 29–40 using the steps found on page 559. **(See Example 3.)**

29. x varies directly as p. If $x = 50$ when $p = 10$, find x when p is 14.

30. y is directly proportional to z. If $y = 12$ when $z = 36$, find y when z is 21.

31. b is inversely proportional to c. If b is 4 when c is 3, find b when $c = 2$.

32. q varies inversely as w. If q is 8 when w is 50, find q when w is 125.

33. Z varies directly as the square of w. If $Z = 14$ when $w = 4$, find Z when $w = 8$.

34. m varies directly as the square of x. If $m = 200$ when $x = 20$, find m when x is 32.

35. Q varies inversely as the square of p. If $Q = 4$ when $p = 3$, find Q when $p = 2$.

36. z is inversely proportional to the square of t. If $z = 15$ when $t = 4$, find z when $t = 10$.

37. L varies jointly as a and the square root of b. If $L = 72$ when $a = 8$ and $b = 9$, find L when $a = \frac{1}{2}$ and $b = 36$.

38. Y varies jointly as the cube of x and the square root of w. $Y = 128$ when $x = 2$ and $w = 16$. Find Y when $x = \frac{1}{2}$ and $w = 64$.

39. B varies directly as m and inversely as n. $B = 20$ when $m = 10$ and $n = 3$. Find B when $m = 15$ and $n = 12$.

40. R varies directly as s and inversely as t. $R = 14$ when $s = 2$ and $t = 9$. Find R when $s = 4$ and $t = 3$.

For Exercises 41–58, use a variation model to solve for the unknown value. (See Examples 4–6.)

41. The weight of a person's heart varies directly as the person's actual weight. For a 150-lb man, his heart would weigh 0.75 lb.

   a. Approximate the weight of a 184-lb man's heart.

   b. How much does your heart weigh?

42. The number of calories, C, in beer varies directly with the number of fluid ounces, n. If 12 fl oz of beer contains 153 calories, how many calories are in 40 fl oz of beer?

43. The amount of medicine that a physician prescribes for a patient varies directly as the weight of the patient. A physician prescribes 3 g of a medicine for a 150-lb person.

   a. How many grams should be prescribed for a 180-lb person?

   b. How many grams should be prescribed for a 225-lb person?

   c. How many grams should be prescribed for a 120-lb person?

44. The number of turkeys needed for a banquet is directly proportional to the number of guests that must be fed. Master Chef Rico knows that he needs to cook 3 turkeys to feed 42 guests.

   a. How many turkeys should he cook to feed 70 guests?

   b. How many turkeys should he cook to feed 140 guests?

   c. How many turkeys should be cooked to feed 700 guests at an inaugural ball?

   d. How many turkeys should be cooked for a wedding with 100 guests?

45. The unit cost of producing CDs is inversely proportional to the number of CDs produced. If 5000 CDs are produced, the cost per CD is $0.48.

   a. What would be the unit cost if 6000 CDs were produced?

   b. What would be the unit cost if 8000 CDs were produced?

   c. What would be the unit cost if 2400 CDs were produced?

46. An author self-publishes a book and finds that the number of books she can sell per month varies inversely as the price of the book. The author can sell 1500 books per month when the price is set at $8 per book.

   a. How many books would she expect to sell if the price were $12?

   b. How many books would she expect to sell if the price were $15?

   c. How many books would she expect to sell if the price were $6?

47. The amount of pollution entering the atmosphere over a given time varies directly as the number of people living in an area. If 80,000 people cause 56,800 tons of pollutants, how many tons enter the atmosphere in a city with a population of 500,000?

48. The area of a picture projected on a wall varies directly as the square of the distance from the projector to the wall. If a 10-ft distance produces a 16-ft^2 picture, what is the area of a picture produced when the projection unit is moved to a distance 20 ft from the wall?

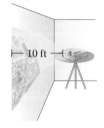

49. The stopping distance of a car varies directly as the square of the speed of the car. If a car traveling at 40 mph has a stopping distance of 109 ft, find the stopping distance of a car that is traveling at 25 mph. (Round your answer to one decimal place.)

50. The intensity of a light source varies inversely as the square of the distance from the source. If the intensity of a lightbulb is 400 lumens/m^2 (lux) at a distance of 5 m, determine the intensity at 8 m.

51. The power in an electric circuit varies jointly as the current and the square of the resistance. If the power is 144 W (watts) when the current is 4 A (amperes) and the resistance is 6 Ω (ohms), find the power when the current is 3 A and the resistance is 10 Ω.

52. Some body-builders claim that, within safe limits, the number of repetitions that a person can complete on a given weight-lifting exercise is inversely proportional to the amount of weight lifted. Roxanne can bench press 45 lb for 15 repetitions.

   a. How many repetitions can Roxanne bench with 60 lb of weight?

   b. How many repetitions can Roxanne bench with 75 lb of weight?

   c. How many repetitions can Roxanne bench with 100 lb of weight?

53. The current in a wire varies directly as the voltage and inversely as the resistance. If the current is 9 A (amperes) when the voltage is 90 V (volts) and the resistance is 10 Ω (ohms), find the current when the voltage is 185 V and the resistance is 10 Ω.

54. The resistance of a wire varies directly as its length and inversely as the square of its diameter. A 40-ft wire 0.1 in. in diameter has a resistance of 4 Ω. What is the resistance of a 50-ft wire with a diameter of 0.2 in.?

55. The weight of a medicine ball varies directly as the cube of its radius. A ball with a radius of 3 in. weighs 4.32 lb. How much would a medicine ball weigh if its radius is 5 in.?

56. The surface area of a cube varies directly as the square of the length of an edge. The surface area is 24 ft^2 when the length of an edge is 2 ft. Find the surface area of a cube with an edge that is 5 ft.

57. The amount of simple interest earned in an account varies jointly as the amount of principal invested and the amount of time the money is invested. If $2500 in principal earns $500 in interest after 4 years, then how much interest will be earned on $7000 invested for 10 years?

58. The amount of simple interest earned in an account varies jointly as the amount of principal invested and the amount of time the money is invested. If $6000 in principal earns $840 in interest after 2 years, then how much interest will be earned on $4500 invested for 8 years?

Group Activity

Computing Monthly Mortgage Payments

Materials: A calculator

Estimated Time: 15–20 minutes

Group Size: 3

When a person borrows money to buy a house, the bank usually requires a down payment of between 0% and 20% of the cost of the house. The bank then issues a loan for the remaining balance on the house. The loan to buy a house is called a *mortgage*. Monthly payments are made to pay off the mortgage over a period of years.

A formula to calculate the monthly payment, P, for a loan is given by the complex fraction:

$$P = \frac{\dfrac{Ar}{12}}{1 - \dfrac{1}{\left(1 + \dfrac{r}{12}\right)^{12t}}} \qquad \text{where}$$

P is the monthly payment
A is the original amount of the mortgage
r is the annual interest rate
t is the term of the loan in years

Suppose a person wants to buy a $200,000 house. The bank requires a down payment of 20%, and the loan is issued at 7.5% interest for 30 yr.

1. Find the amount of the down payment. _____

2. Find the amount of the mortgage. _____

3. Find the monthly payment (to the nearest cent). _____

4. Multiply the monthly payment found in question 3 by the total number of months in a 30-yr period. Interpret what this value means in the context of the problem.

5. How much total interest was paid on the loan for the house? _____

6. What was the total amount paid for the house (include the down payment)? _____

Chapter 7   Summary

Section 7.1   Introduction to Rational Expressions

Key Concepts

A **rational expression** is a ratio of the form $\frac{p}{q}$ where p and q are polynomials and $q \neq 0$.

Restricted values of a rational expression are those values that, when substituted for the variable, make the expression undefined. To find restricted values, set the denominator equal to 0 and solve the equation.

Simplifying a Rational Expression to Lowest Terms

Factor the numerator and denominator completely, and reduce factors whose ratio is equal to 1 or to -1. A rational expression written in lowest terms will still have the same restrictions on the variable as the original expression.

Examples

Example 1

$$\frac{x + 2}{x^2 - 5x - 14} \quad \text{is a rational expression.}$$

Example 2

To find the restricted values of $\dfrac{x + 2}{x^2 - 5x - 14}$ factor the

denominator: $\dfrac{x + 2}{(x + 2)(x - 7)}$

The restricted values are $x = -2$ and $x = 7$.

Example 3

Simplify to lowest terms. $\dfrac{x + 2}{x^2 - 5x - 14}$

$\dfrac{\overset{1}{\cancel{x + 2}}}{\cancel{(x + 2)}(x - 7)}$ Simplify.

$= \dfrac{1}{x - 7}$ (provided $x \neq 7$, $x \neq -2$).

Section 7.2   Multiplication and Division of Rational Expressions

Key Concepts

Multiplication of Rational Expressions

Multiply the numerators and multiply the denominators. That is, if $q \neq 0$ and $s \neq 0$, then

$$\frac{p}{q} \cdot \frac{r}{s} = \frac{pr}{qs}$$

Factor the numerator and denominator completely. Then reduce factors whose ratio is 1 or -1.

Examples

Example 1

Multiply. $\dfrac{b^2 - a^2}{a^2 - 2ab + b^2} \cdot \dfrac{a^2 - 3ab + 2b^2}{2a + 2b}$

$= \dfrac{\overset{-1}{\cancel{(b - a)}}\overset{1}{\cancel{(b + a)}}}{(a - b)\cancel{(a - b)}} \cdot \dfrac{(a - 2b)\overset{1}{\cancel{(a - b)}}}{2\cancel{(a + b)}}$

$= -\dfrac{a - 2b}{2} \quad \text{or} \quad \dfrac{2b - a}{2}$

Division of Rational Expressions

Multiply the first expression by the reciprocal of the second expression. That is, for $q \neq 0$, $r \neq 0$, and $s \neq 0$,

$$\frac{p}{q} \div \frac{r}{s} = \frac{p}{q} \cdot \frac{s}{r} = \frac{ps}{qr}$$

Example 2

Divide. $\dfrac{x - 2}{15} \div \dfrac{x^2 + 2x - 8}{20x}$

$$= \frac{x - 2}{15} \cdot \frac{20x}{x^2 + 2x - 8}$$

$$= \frac{\overset{1}{\cancel{(x - 2)}}}{15} \cdot \frac{\overset{4}{\cancel{20x}}}{\cancel{(x - 2)}(x + 4)}$$
$$\underset{3}{} \qquad \underset{1}{}$$

$$= \frac{4x}{3(x + 4)}$$

Section 7.3   Least Common Denominator

Key Concepts

Converting a Rational Expression to an Equivalent Expression with a Different Denominator

Multiply numerator and denominator of the rational expression by the missing factors necessary to create the desired denominator.

Finding the Least Common Denominator (LCD) of Two or More Rational Expressions

1. Factor all denominators completely.
2. The LCD is the product of unique factors from the denominators, where each factor is raised to its highest power.

Examples

Example 1

Convert $\dfrac{-3}{x - 2}$ to an equivalent expression with the indicated denominator:

$$\frac{-3}{x - 2} = \frac{}{5(x - 2)(x + 2)}$$

Multiply numerator and denominator by the missing factors from the denominator.

$$\frac{-3 \cdot 5(x + 2)}{(x - 2) \cdot 5(x + 2)} = \frac{-15x - 30}{5(x - 2)(x + 2)}$$

Example 2

Identify the LCD. $\dfrac{1}{8x^3y^2z}; \dfrac{5}{6xy^4}$

1. Write the denominators as a product of prime factors:

$$\frac{1}{2^3x^3y^2z}; \frac{5}{2 \cdot 3xy^4}$$

2. The LCD is $2^3 3 x^3 y^4 z$ or $24x^3y^4z$.

Section 7.4 — Addition and Subtraction of Rational Expressions

Key Concepts

To add or subtract rational expressions, the expressions must have the same denominator.

Steps to Add or Subtract Rational Expressions

1. Factor the denominators of each rational expression.
2. Identify the LCD.
3. Rewrite each rational expression as an equivalent expression with the LCD as its denominator.
4. Add or subtract the numerators, and write the result over the common denominator.
5. Simplify.

Examples

Example 1

Subtract. $\dfrac{c}{2c-8} - \dfrac{14}{c^2-c-12}$

$$= \frac{c}{2(c-4)} - \frac{14}{(c-4)(c+3)}$$

The LCD is $2(c-4)(c+3)$.

$$= \frac{c(c+3)}{2(c-4)(c+3)} - \frac{2 \cdot 14}{2(c-4)(c+3)}$$

$$= \frac{c^2+3c-28}{2(c-4)(c+3)}$$

$$= \frac{(c-4)(c+7)}{2(c-4)(c+3)} = \frac{(c+7)}{2(c+3)}$$

Section 7.5 — Complex Fractions

Key Concepts

Complex fractions can be simplified by using Method I or Method II.

Method I

1. Add or subtract expressions in the numerator to form a single fraction. Add or subtract expressions in the denominator to form a single fraction.
2. Divide the rational expressions from step 1 by multiplying the numerator of the complex fraction by the reciprocal of the denominator of the complex fraction.
3. Simplify to lowest terms, if possible.

Examples

Example 1

Simplify. $\dfrac{1 - \dfrac{4}{w^2}}{1 - \dfrac{1}{w} - \dfrac{6}{w^2}} = \dfrac{\dfrac{w^2}{w^2} - \dfrac{4}{w^2}}{\dfrac{w^2}{w^2} - \dfrac{w}{w^2} - \dfrac{6}{w^2}}$

$$= \frac{\dfrac{w^2-4}{w^2}}{\dfrac{w^2-w-6}{w^2}} = \frac{w^2-4}{w^2} \cdot \frac{w^2}{w^2-w-6}$$

$$= \frac{(w-2)(w+2)}{w^2} \cdot \frac{\overset{1}{w^2}}{(w-3)(w+2)}$$

$$= \frac{w-2}{w-3}$$

Method II

1. Multiply the numerator and denominator of the complex fraction by the LCD of all individual fractions within the expression.
2. Apply the distributive property, and simplify the result.
3. Simplify to lowest terms, if possible.

Example 2

Simplify. $\dfrac{1 - \dfrac{4}{w^2}}{1 - \dfrac{1}{w} - \dfrac{6}{w^2}} = \dfrac{w^2\left(1 - \dfrac{4}{w^2}\right)}{w^2\left(1 - \dfrac{1}{w} - \dfrac{6}{w^2}\right)}$

$= \dfrac{w^2 - 4}{w^2 - w - 6} = \dfrac{(w - 2)\overset{1}{\cancel{(w + 2)}}}{(w - 3)\cancel{(w + 2)}}$

$= \dfrac{w - 2}{w - 3}$

Section 7.6   Rational Equations

Key Concepts

An equation with one or more rational expressions is called a **rational equation**.

Steps to Solve a Rational Equation

1. Factor the denominators of all rational expressions. Identify the restricted values.
2. Identify the LCD of all expressions in the equation.
3. Multiply both sides of the equation by the LCD.
4. Solve the resulting equation.
5. Check each potential solution in the original equation.

Examples

Example 1

Solve. $\dfrac{1}{w} - \dfrac{1}{2w - 1} = \dfrac{-2w}{2w - 1}$

The restricted values are $w = 0$ and $w = \dfrac{1}{2}$.

The LCD is $w(2w - 1)$.

$\cancel{w}(2w - 1)\dfrac{1}{\cancel{w}} - w\cancel{(2w - 1)}\dfrac{1}{\cancel{2w - 1}}$

$= w\cancel{(2w - 1)}\dfrac{-2w}{\cancel{2w - 1}}$

$(2w - 1)(1) - w(1) = w(-2w)$

$2w - 1 - w = -2w^2$ Quadratic equation

$2w^2 + w - 1 = 0$

$(2w - 1)(w + 1) = 0$

$w \cancel{=} \dfrac{1}{2}$ or $w = -1$

   Does not check.   Checks.

Example 2

Solve for I. $q = \dfrac{VQ}{I}$

$I \cdot q = \dfrac{VQ}{I} \cdot I$

$Iq = VQ$

$I = \dfrac{VQ}{q}$

Section 7.7 Applications of Rational Equations and Proportions

Key Concepts and Examples

Solving Proportions

An equation that equates two rates or ratios is called a **proportion**:

$$\frac{a}{b} = \frac{c}{d} \quad (b \neq 0, d \neq 0)$$

To solve a proportion, multiply both sides of the equation by the LCD.

Examples

Example 1

A 90-g serving of a particular ice cream contains 10 g of fat. How much fat does 400 g of the same ice cream contain?

$$\frac{10 \text{ g fat}}{90 \text{ g ice cream}} = \frac{x \text{ grams fat}}{400 \text{ g ice cream}}$$

$$\frac{10}{90} = \frac{x}{400}$$

$$\overset{40}{3600} \cdot \left(\frac{10}{90}\right) = \left(\frac{x}{400}\right) \cdot \overset{9}{3600}$$

$$400 = 9x$$

$$x = \frac{400}{9} \approx 44.4 \text{ g}$$

The fat content in 440 g of the ice cream is approximately 44.4 g.

Examples 2 and 3 give applications of rational equations.

Example 2

Two cars travel from Los Angeles to Las Vegas. One car travels an average of 8 mph faster than the other car. If the faster car travels 189 mi in the same time as the slower car travels 165 mi, what is the average speed of each car?

Let r represent the speed of the slower car.
Let $r + 8$ represent the speed of the faster car.

	Distance	Rate	Time
Slower car	165	r	$\frac{165}{r}$
Faster car	189	$r + 8$	$\frac{189}{r + 8}$

$$\frac{165}{r} = \frac{189}{r + 8}$$

$$165(r + 8) = 189r$$

$$165r + 1320 = 189r$$

$$1320 = 24r$$

$$55 = r$$

The slower car travels 55 mph, and the faster car travels $55 + 8 = 63$ mph.

Example 3

Beth and Cecelia have a house cleaning business. Beth can clean a particular house in 5 hr by herself. Cecelia can clean the same house in 4 hr. How long would it take if they cleaned the house together?

Let x be the number of hours it takes for both Beth and Cecelia to clean the house.

Beth's rate is $\dfrac{1 \text{ job}}{5 \text{ hr}}$. Cecelia's rate is $\dfrac{1 \text{ job}}{4 \text{ hr}}$.

The rate together is $\dfrac{1 \text{ job}}{x \text{ hr}}$.

$$\frac{1}{5} + \frac{1}{4} = \frac{1}{x} \qquad \text{Add the rates.}$$

$$20x\left(\frac{1}{5} + \frac{1}{4}\right) = 20x\left(\frac{1}{x}\right)$$

$$4x + 5x = 20$$

$$9x = 20$$

$$x = \frac{20}{9}$$

It takes $\dfrac{20}{9}$ hr or $2\dfrac{2}{9}$ hr working together.

Section 7.8   Variation

Key Concepts

Direct Variation

y varies directly as x.
y is directly proportional to x. $\left.\right\}$ $y = kx$

Inverse Variation

y varies inversely as x.
y is inversely proportional to x. $\left.\right\}$ $y = \dfrac{k}{x}$

Joint Variation

y varies jointly as w and z.
y is jointly proportional to w and z. $\left.\right\}$ $y = kwz$

Steps to Find a Variation Model

1. Write a general variation model that relates the variables given in the problem. Let k represent the constant of variation.
2. Solve for k by substituting known values of the variables into the model from step 1.
3. Substitute the value of k into the original variation model from step 1.

Examples

Example 1

t varies directly as the square root of x.

$t = k\sqrt{x}$

Example 2

W is inversely proportional to the cube of x.

$W = \dfrac{k}{x^3}$

Example 3

y is jointly proportional to x and the square of z.

$y = kxz^2$

Example 4

C varies directly as the square root of d and inversely as t. If $C = 12$ when d is 9 and t is 6, find C if d is 16 and t is 12.

Step 1. $C = \dfrac{k\sqrt{d}}{t}$

Step 2. $12 = \dfrac{k\sqrt{9}}{6} \Rightarrow 12 = \dfrac{k \cdot 3}{6} \Rightarrow k = 24$

Step 3. $C = \dfrac{24\sqrt{d}}{t} \Rightarrow C = \dfrac{24\sqrt{16}}{12} \Rightarrow C = 8$

Chapter 7   Review Exercises

Section 7.1

1. For the rational expression $\dfrac{t - 2}{t + 9}$

    a. Evaluate the expression (if possible) for $t = 0, 1, 2, -3, -9$

    b. Identify the restricted values.

2. For the rational expression $\dfrac{k + 1}{k - 5}$

    a. Evaluate the expression for $k = 0, 1, 5, -1, -2$

    b. Identify the restricted values.

3. Which of the rational expressions are equal to -1?

a. $\dfrac{2 - x}{x - 2}$

b. $\dfrac{x - 5}{x + 5}$

c. $\dfrac{-x - 7}{x + 7}$

d. $\dfrac{x^2 - 4}{4 - x^2}$

For Exercises 4–13, identify the restricted values. Then simplify the expressions.

4. $\dfrac{x - 3}{(2x - 5)(x - 3)}$

5. $\dfrac{h + 7}{(3h + 1)(h + 7)}$

6. $\dfrac{4a^2 + 7a - 2}{a^2 - 4}$

7. $\dfrac{2w^2 + 11w + 12}{w^2 - 16}$

8. $\dfrac{z^2 - 4z}{8 - 2z}$

9. $\dfrac{15 - 3k}{2k^2 - 10k}$

10. $\dfrac{2b^2 + 4b - 6}{4b + 12}$

11. $\dfrac{3m^2 - 12m - 15}{9m + 9}$

12. $\dfrac{n + 3}{n^2 + 6n + 9}$

13. $\dfrac{p + 7}{p^2 + 14p + 49}$

Section 7.2

For Exercises 14–27, multiply or divide as indicated.

14. $\dfrac{3y^3}{3y - 6} \cdot \dfrac{y - 2}{y}$

15. $\dfrac{2u + 10}{u} \cdot \dfrac{u^3}{4u + 20}$

16. $\dfrac{11}{v - 2} \cdot \dfrac{2v^2 - 8}{22}$

17. $\dfrac{8}{x^2 - 25} \cdot \dfrac{3x + 15}{16}$

18. $\dfrac{4c^2 + 4c}{c^2 - 25} \div \dfrac{8c}{c^2 - 5c}$

19. $\dfrac{q^2 - 5q + 6}{2q + 4} \div \dfrac{2q - 6}{q + 2}$

20. $\left(\dfrac{-2t}{t + 1}\right)(t^2 - 4t - 5)$ **21.** $(s^2 - 6s + 8)\left(\dfrac{4s}{s - 2}\right)$

22. $\dfrac{\dfrac{a^2 + 5a + 1}{7a - 7}}{\dfrac{a^2 + 5a + 1}{a - 1}}$

23. $\dfrac{\dfrac{n^2 + n + 1}{n^2 - 4}}{\dfrac{n^2 + n + 1}{n + 2}}$

24. $\dfrac{5h^2 - 6h + 1}{h^2 - 1} \div \dfrac{16h^2 - 9}{4h^2 + 7h + 3} \cdot \dfrac{3 - 4h}{30h - 6}$

25. $\dfrac{3m - 3}{6m^2 + 18m + 12} \cdot \dfrac{2m^2 - 8}{m^2 - 3m + 2} \div \dfrac{m + 3}{m + 1}$

26. $\dfrac{x - 2}{x^2 - 3x - 18} \cdot \dfrac{6 - x}{x^2 - 4}$

27. $\dfrac{4y^2 - 1}{1 + 2y} \div \dfrac{y^2 - 4y - 5}{5 - y}$

Section 7.3

28. Determine the LCD.

$$\dfrac{6}{n^2 - 9}; \dfrac{5}{n^2 - n - 6}$$

29. Determine the LCD.

$$\dfrac{8}{m^2 - 16}; \dfrac{7}{m^2 - m - 12}$$

30. State two possible LCDs that could be used to add the fractions.

$$\dfrac{7}{c - 2} + \dfrac{4}{2 - c}$$

31. State two possible LCDs that could be used to subtract the fractions.

$$\dfrac{10}{3 - x} - \dfrac{5}{x - 3}$$

For Exercises 32–37, write each fraction as an equivalent fraction with the LCD as its denominator.

32. $\dfrac{2}{5a}; \dfrac{3}{10b}$

33. $\dfrac{7}{4x}; \dfrac{11}{6y}$

34. $\dfrac{1}{x^2y^4}; \dfrac{3}{xy^5}$

35. $\dfrac{5}{ab^3}; \dfrac{3}{ac^2}$

36. $\dfrac{5}{p + 2}; \dfrac{p}{p - 4}$

37. $\dfrac{6}{q}; \dfrac{1}{q + 8}$

Section 7.4

For Exercises 38–49, add or subtract as indicated.

38. $\dfrac{h + 3}{h + 1} + \dfrac{h - 1}{h + 1}$

39. $\dfrac{b - 6}{b - 2} + \dfrac{b + 2}{b - 2}$

40. $\dfrac{a^2}{a - 5} - \dfrac{25}{a - 5}$

41. $\dfrac{x^2}{x + 7} - \dfrac{49}{x + 7}$

42. $\dfrac{y}{y^2 - 81} + \dfrac{2}{9 - y}$

43. $\dfrac{3}{4 - t^2} + \dfrac{t}{2 - t}$

44. $\dfrac{4}{3m} - \dfrac{1}{m + 2}$

45. $\dfrac{5}{2r + 12} - \dfrac{1}{r}$

46. $\dfrac{4p}{p^2 + 6p + 5} - \dfrac{3p}{p^2 + 5p + 4}$

47. $\dfrac{3q}{q^2 + 7q + 10} - \dfrac{2q}{q^2 + 6q + 8}$

48. $\dfrac{1}{h} + \dfrac{h}{2h + 4} - \dfrac{2}{h^2 + 2h}$

49. $\dfrac{x}{3x + 9} - \dfrac{3}{x^2 + 3x} + \dfrac{1}{x}$

Section 7.5

For Exercises 50–57, simplify the complex fractions.

50. $\dfrac{\dfrac{a - 4}{3}}{\dfrac{a - 2}{3}}$

51. $\dfrac{\dfrac{z + 5}{z}}{\dfrac{z - 5}{3}}$

52. $\dfrac{\dfrac{2 - 3w}{2}}{\dfrac{2}{w} - 3}$

53. $\dfrac{\dfrac{2}{y} + 6}{\dfrac{3y + 1}{4}}$

54. $\dfrac{\dfrac{y}{x} - \dfrac{x}{y}}{\dfrac{1}{x} + \dfrac{1}{y}}$

55. $\dfrac{\dfrac{b}{a} - \dfrac{a}{b}}{\dfrac{1}{b} - \dfrac{1}{a}}$

56. $\dfrac{\dfrac{6}{p + 2} + 4}{\dfrac{8}{p + 2} - 4}$

57. $\dfrac{\dfrac{25}{k + 5} + 5}{\dfrac{5}{k + 5} - 5}$

Section 7.6

For Exercises 58–65, solve the equations.

58. $\dfrac{2}{x} + \dfrac{1}{2} = \dfrac{1}{4}$

59. $\dfrac{1}{y} + \dfrac{3}{4} = \dfrac{1}{4}$

60. $\dfrac{w}{w - 1} = \dfrac{3}{w + 1} + 1$

61. $\dfrac{t + 1}{3} - \dfrac{t - 1}{6} = \dfrac{1}{6}$

62. $\dfrac{4p - 4}{p^2 + 5p - 14} + \dfrac{2}{p + 7} = \dfrac{1}{p - 2}$

63. $\dfrac{w + 1}{w - 3} - \dfrac{3}{w} = \dfrac{12}{w^2 - 3w}$

64. $\dfrac{1}{z + 2} = \dfrac{4}{z^2 - 4} - \dfrac{1}{z - 2}$

65. $\dfrac{y + 1}{y + 3} = \dfrac{y^2 - 11y}{y^2 + y - 6} - \dfrac{y - 3}{y - 2}$

66. Four times a number is added to 5. The sum is then divided by 6. The result is $\frac{7}{2}$. Find the number.

67. Solve the formula $\dfrac{V}{h} = \dfrac{\pi r^2}{3}$ for h.

68. Solve the formula $\dfrac{A}{b} = \dfrac{h}{2}$ for b.

Section 7.7

For Exercises 69 and 70, solve the proportions.

69. $\dfrac{m + 2}{8} = \dfrac{m}{3}$

70. $\dfrac{12}{a} = \dfrac{5}{8}$

71. A bag of popcorn states that it contains 4 g of fat per serving. If a serving is 2 oz, how many grams of fat are in a 5-oz bag?

72. Bud goes 10 mph faster on his Harley Davidson motorcycle than Ed goes on his Honda motorcycle. If Bud travels 105 mi in the same time that Ed travels 90 mi, what are the rates of the two bikers?

73. There are two pumps set up to fill a small swimming pool. One pump takes 24 min by itself to fill the pool, but the other takes 56 min by itself. How long would it take if both pumps work together?

74. Triangle XYZ is similar to triangle ABC. Find the values of x and b.

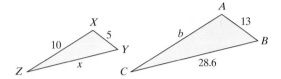

Section 7.8

75. The force applied to a spring varies directly with the distance that the spring is stretched.

   a. Write a variation model using k as the constant of variation.

   b. When 6 lb of force is applied, the spring stretches 2 ft. Find k.

   c. How much force is required to stretch the spring 4.2 ft?

76. Suppose y varies inversely with the cube of x, and $y = 9$ when $x = 2$. Find y when $x = 3$.

77. Suppose y varies jointly with x and the square root of z, and $y = 3$ when $x = 3$ and $z = 4$. Find y when $x = 8$ and $z = 9$.

 78. The distance, d, that one can see to the horizon varies directly as the square root of the height above sea level. If a person 25 m above sea level can see 30 km, how far can a person see if she is 64 m above sea level?

Chapter 7   Test

For Exercises 1 and 2,

   a. Identify the restricted values.

   b. Simplify the rational expression.

1. $\dfrac{5(x - 2)(x + 1)}{30(2 - x)}$

2. $\dfrac{7a^2 - 42a}{a^3 - 4a^2 - 12a}$

3. Identify the rational expressions that are equal to -1.

   a. $\dfrac{x + 4}{x - 4}$

   b. $\dfrac{7 - 2x}{2x - 7}$

   c. $\dfrac{9x^2 + 16}{-9x^2 - 16}$

   d. $-\dfrac{x + 5}{x + 5}$

4. Find the LCD of the pairs of rational expressions.

   a. $\dfrac{x}{3(x + 3)}; \dfrac{7}{5(x + 3)}$

   b. $\dfrac{-2}{3x^2y}; \dfrac{4}{xy^2}$

For Exercises 5–11, perform the indicated operation.

5. $\dfrac{2}{y^2 + 4y + 3} + \dfrac{1}{3y + 9}$

6. $\dfrac{9 - b^2}{5b + 15} \div \dfrac{b - 3}{b + 3}$

7. $\dfrac{w^2 - 4w}{w^2 - 8w + 16} \cdot \dfrac{w - 4}{w^2 + w}$

8. $\dfrac{t}{t - 2} - \dfrac{8}{t^2 - 4}$

9. $\dfrac{1}{x + 4} + \dfrac{2}{x^2 + 2x - 8} + \dfrac{x}{x - 2}$

10. $\dfrac{2y}{y - 6} - \dfrac{7}{6 - y}$

11. $\dfrac{1 - \dfrac{4}{m}}{m - \dfrac{16}{m}}$

For Exercises 12–16, solve the equation.

12. $\dfrac{3}{a} + \dfrac{5}{2} = \dfrac{7}{a}$

13. $\dfrac{p}{p-1} + \dfrac{1}{p} = \dfrac{p^2+1}{p^2-p}$

14. $\dfrac{3}{c-2} - \dfrac{1}{c+1} = \dfrac{7}{c^2-c-2}$

15. $\dfrac{4x}{x-4} = 3 + \dfrac{16}{x-4}$

16. $\dfrac{y^2+7y}{y-2} - \dfrac{36}{2y-4} = 4$

17. Solve the formula $\dfrac{C}{2} = \dfrac{A}{r}$ for r.

18. Solve the proportion.

$$\dfrac{y+7}{-4} = \dfrac{1}{4}$$

19. A recipe for vegetable soup calls for $\frac{1}{2}$ cup of carrots for six servings. How many cups of carrots are needed to prepare 15 servings?

20. A motorboat can travel 28 mi downstream in the same amount of time as it can travel 18 mi upstream. Find the speed of the current if the boat can travel 23 mph in still water.

21. Two printers working together can complete a job in 2 hr. If one printer requires 6 hr to do the job alone, how many hours would the second printer need to complete the job alone?

22. Triangle XYZ is similar to triangle ABC. Find the values of a and b.

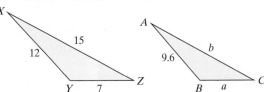

23. The amount of medication prescribed for a patient varies directly as the patient's weight. If a 160-lb person is prescribed 6 mL of a medicine, then how much medicine would be prescribed to a 220-lb person?

24. The number of drinks sold at a concession stand varies inversely as price. If the price is set at $1.25 per drink, then 400 drinks are sold. If the price is set at $2.50 per drink, then how many drinks are sold?

Chapters 1–7 Cumulative Review Exercises

For Exercises 1 and 2, simplify completely.

1. $\left(\dfrac{1}{2}\right)^{-4} + 2^4$

2. $|3-5| + |-2+7|$

3. Solve. $\dfrac{1}{2} - \dfrac{3}{4}(y-1) = \dfrac{5}{12}$

4. Complete the table.

Set-Builder Notation	Graph	Interval Notation
$\{x \mid x \geq -1\}$		
		$(-\infty, 5)$

5. The perimeter of a rectangular swimming pool is 104 m. The length is 1 m more than twice the width. Find the length and width.

6. The height of a triangle is 2 in. less than the base. The area is 40 in.^{2}. Find the base and height of the triangle.

7. Simplify. $\left(\dfrac{4x^{-1}y^{-2}}{z^4}\right)^{-2}(2y^{-1}z^3)^3$

8. The length and width of a rectangle are given in terms of x.

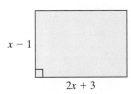

a. Write a polynomial that represents the perimeter of the rectangle.

b. Write a polynomial that represents the area of the rectangle.

9. Factor completely. $25x^2 - 30x + 9$

10. Factor. $10cd + 5d - 6c - 3$

11. Identify the restricted values of the expression.

$$\frac{x + 3}{(x - 5)(2x + 1)}$$

12. Solve the system.

$$x + 2y = -7$$
$$6x + 3y = -6$$

13. Divide. $\dfrac{2x - 6}{x^2 - 16} \div \dfrac{10x^2 - 90}{x^2 - x - 12}$

14. Simplify.

$$\frac{\dfrac{3}{4} - \dfrac{1}{x}}{\dfrac{1}{3x} - \dfrac{1}{4}}$$

15. Solve.

$$\frac{7}{y^2 - 4} = \frac{3}{y - 2} + \frac{2}{y + 2}$$

16. Solve the proportion.

$$\frac{2b - 5}{6} = \frac{4b}{7}$$

17. Determine the x- and y-intercepts.

   a. $-2x + 4y = 8$ **b.** $y = 5x$

18. Determine the slope

   a. of the line containing the points $(0, -6)$ and $(-5, 1)$.

   b. of the line $y = -\dfrac{2}{3}x - 6$.

   c. of a line parallel to a line having a slope of 4.

   d. of a line perpendicular to a line having a slope of 4.

19. Find an equation of a line passing through the point $(1, 2)$ and having a slope of 5. Write the answer in slope-intercept form.

20. A group of teenagers buys 2 large popcorns and 6 drinks at the movie theater for $27. A couple buys 1 large popcorn and 2 drinks for $10.50. Find the price for 1 large popcorn and the price for 1 drink.

Radicals

8

Chapter 8

Chapter 8 is devoted to the study of radicals and their applications. We first present the techniques to add, subtract, multiply, and divide radical expressions.

Review Your Skills

The skill of multiplying radicals is similar to multiplying polynomials. This puzzle will help you practice multiplying polynomials.

   Circle the correct response. Write the corresponding letters in the box below to complete the sentence.

1. $2xy(2x - 4y + xy)$

   ANT $4x^2y - 8xy^2 + 2x^2y^2$

   ENT $4x^2y - 8xy^2 + 2xy$

2. $(2x - y)(3x + 4y)$

   HAG $6x^2 + 5xy - 4y^2$

   HOG $6x^2 - 5xy - 4y^2$

3. $(2x + 3y)^2$

   ING $4x^2 + 9y^2$

   REM $4x^2 + 12xy + 9y^2$

4. $(5x - y)(5x + y)$

   THE $5x^2 - y^2$

   ORE $25x^2 - y^2$

5. $(x^2 - 3y)(x + y)$

   RAD $x^3 - 2xy - 3y^2$

   PYT $x^3 + x^2y - 3xy - 3y^2$

6. $(8x^2y^3)(-3xy^4)$

   HEO $-24x^3y^7$

   HOE $-24x^2y^{12}$

One application in which square roots are used is with the

		5			2			4			1			6			3	

577

Section 8.1 | Introduction to Roots and Radicals

1. Definition of a Square Root

Recall that to square a number means to multiply the number by itself: $b^2 = b \cdot b$. To find a square root of a number, we reverse the process of squaring a number. For example, finding a square root of 49 is equivalent to asking: "What number when squared equals 49?"

One obvious answer to this question is 7 because $(7)^2 = 49$. But -7 will also work because $(-7)^2 = 49$.

Definition of a Square Root

b is a **square root** of a if $b^2 = a$.

Skill Practice

Identify the square roots of the numbers.

1. 64   2. -36

3. 36   4. $\dfrac{25}{16}$

Example 1 Identifying the Square Roots of a Number

Identify the square roots of

a. 9   **b.** 121   **c.** 0   **d.** -4

Solution:

a. 3 is a square root of 9 because $(3)^2 = 9$.
   -3 is a square root of 9 because $(-3)^2 = 9$.

b. 11 is a square root of 121 because $(11)^2 = 121$.
   -11 is a square root of 121 because $(-11)^2 = 121$.

c. 0 is a square root of 0 because $(0)^2 = 0$.

d. There are no real numbers that when squared will equal a negative number. Therefore, there are no real-valued square roots of -4.

TIP: All positive real numbers have two real-valued square roots: one positive and one negative. Zero has only one square root, which is 0 itself. Finally, for any negative real number, there are no real-valued square roots.

Recall from Section 1.2 that the positive square root of a real number can be denoted with a radical sign, $\sqrt{}$.

Notation for Positive and Negative Square Roots

Let a represent a positive real number. Then,

1. $\sqrt{a}$ is the **positive square root** of a.   Example: $\sqrt{100} = 10$
   The positive square root is also called
   the **principal square root**.
2. $-\sqrt{a}$ is the **negative square root** of a.   Example: $-\sqrt{100} = -10$
3. $\sqrt{0} = 0$

Answers

1. $8; -8$
2. There are no real-valued square roots.
3. $6; -6$ 4. $\dfrac{5}{4}; -\dfrac{5}{4}$

Example 2 **Simplifying Square Roots**

Simplify the square roots.

a. $\sqrt{36}$ b. $\sqrt{225}$ c. $\sqrt{1}$ d. $\sqrt{\dfrac{9}{4}}$ e. $\sqrt{0.49}$

Solution:

a. $\sqrt{36}$ denotes the positive square root of 36. $\sqrt{36} = 6$

b. $\sqrt{225}$ denotes the positive square root of 225. $\sqrt{225} = 15$

c. $\sqrt{1}$ denotes the positive square root of 1. $\sqrt{1} = 1$

d. $\sqrt{\dfrac{9}{4}}$ denotes the positive square root of $\dfrac{9}{4}$. $\sqrt{\dfrac{9}{4}} = \dfrac{3}{2}$

e. $\sqrt{0.49}$ denotes the positive square root. $\sqrt{0.49} = 0.7$

The numbers 36, 225, 1, $\frac{9}{4}$, and 0.49 are **perfect squares** because their square roots are rational numbers. Radicals that cannot be simplified to rational numbers are irrational numbers. Recall that an irrational number cannot be written as a terminating or repeating decimal. For example, the symbol $\sqrt{13}$ is used to represent the exact value of the square root of 13. The symbol $\sqrt{42}$ is used to represent the exact value of the square root of 42. These values are irrational numbers but can be approximated by rational numbers by using a calculator.

$$\sqrt{13} \approx 3.605551275 \qquad \sqrt{42} \approx 6.480740698$$

Note: The only way to denote the *exact* values of the square root of 13 and the square root of 42 is $\sqrt{13}$ and $\sqrt{42}$.

A negative number cannot have a real number as a square root because no real number when squared is negative. For example, $\sqrt{-25}$ is *not a real number* because there is no real number, b, for which $(b)^2 = -25$.

TIP: Before using a calculator to evaluate a square root, try estimating the value first.

$\sqrt{13}$ must be a number between 3 and 4 because $\sqrt{9} < \sqrt{13} < \sqrt{16}$.

$\sqrt{42}$ must be a number between 6 and 7 because $\sqrt{36} < \sqrt{42} < \sqrt{49}$.

Example 3 **Simplifying Square Roots if Possible**

Simplify the square roots if possible.

a. $\sqrt{-100}$ b. $-\sqrt{100}$ c. $\sqrt{-64}$

Solution:

a. $\sqrt{-100}$ Not a real number

b. $-\sqrt{100}$

$-1 \cdot \sqrt{100}$ The expression $-\sqrt{100}$ is equivalent to $-1 \cdot \sqrt{100}$.

$-1 \cdot 10 = -10$

c. $\sqrt{-64}$ Not a real number

2. Definition of an *n*th-Root

To find a square root of a number, we reverse the process of squaring a number. This concept can be extended to finding a third root (called a cube root), a fourth root, and in general, an *n*th-root.

> ### Definition of an *n*th-Root
>
> b is an **nth-root** of a if $b^n = a$.

Concept Connections

13. Identify the index and radicand.

$\sqrt[3]{2xy}$

The radical sign, $\sqrt{}$, is used to denote the principal square root of a number. The symbol, $\sqrt[n]{}$, is used to denote the *n*th-root of a number.

In the expression $\sqrt[n]{a}$, n is called the **index** of the radical, and a is called the **radicand**. For a square root, the index is 2, but it is usually not written ($\sqrt[2]{a}$ is denoted simply as $\sqrt{a}$). A radical with an index of 3 is called a **cube root**, $\sqrt[3]{a}$.

> ### Definition of $\sqrt[n]{a}$
>
> **1.** If n is a positive *even* integer and $a > 0$, then $\sqrt[n]{a}$ is the principal (positive) *n*th-root of a.
>
> Example: $\sqrt[4]{81} = 3$
>
> **2.** If $n > 1$ is an *odd* integer, then $\sqrt[n]{a}$ is the *n*th-root of a.
>
> Example: $\sqrt[3]{-125} = -5$
>
> **3.** If $n > 1$ is an integer, then $\sqrt[n]{0} = 0$.
>
> Example: $\sqrt[6]{0} = 0$

For the purpose of simplifying radicals, it is helpful to know the following patterns:

Perfect cubes	Perfect fourth powers	Perfect fifth powers
$1^3 = 1$	$1^4 = 1$	$1^5 = 1$
$2^3 = 8$	$2^4 = 16$	$2^5 = 32$
$3^3 = 27$	$3^4 = 81$	$3^5 = 243$
$4^3 = 64$	$4^4 = 256$	$4^5 = 1024$
$5^3 = 125$	$5^4 = 625$	$5^5 = 3125$

Skill Practice

Simplify the expressions if possible.

14. $\sqrt[3]{27}$ **15.** $\sqrt[4]{1}$

16. $\sqrt[3]{216}$ **17.** $\sqrt[5]{-32}$

18. $\sqrt[4]{\dfrac{16}{625}}$ **19.** $\sqrt{0.25}$

20. $\sqrt[4]{-1}$

Example 4   Simplifying *n*th-Roots

Simplify the expressions, if possible.

a. $\sqrt[3]{8}$ **b.** $\sqrt[4]{16}$ **c.** $\sqrt[5]{32}$ **d.** $\sqrt[3]{-64}$

e. $\sqrt[3]{\dfrac{125}{27}}$ **f.** $\sqrt{0.01}$ **g.** $\sqrt[4]{-81}$

Solution:

a. $\sqrt[3]{8} = 2$ Because $(2)^3 = 8$

b. $\sqrt[4]{16} = 2$ Because $(2)^4 = 16$

c. $\sqrt[5]{32} = 2$ Because $(2)^5 = 32$

d. $\sqrt[3]{-64} = -4$ Because $(-4)^3 = -64$

e. $\sqrt[3]{\dfrac{125}{27}} = \dfrac{5}{3}$ Because $\left(\dfrac{5}{3}\right)^3 = \dfrac{125}{27}$

> **TIP:** Even-indexed roots of negative numbers are not real numbers. Odd-indexed roots of negative numbers are negative.

Answers

13. Index: 3; radicand: $2xy$

14. 3   **15.** 1   **16.** 6

17. -2 **18.** $\dfrac{2}{5}$ **19.** 0.5

20. Not a real number.

f. $\sqrt{0.01} = 0.1$ Because $(0.1)^2 = 0.01$

Note: $\sqrt{0.01}$ is equivalent to $\sqrt{\dfrac{1}{100}} = \dfrac{1}{10}$, or 0.1.

g. $\sqrt[4]{-81}$ is not a real number because no real number raised to the fourth power equals -81.

Example 4(g) illustrates that an nth-root of a negative number is not a real number if the index is even because no real number raised to an even power is negative.

Finding an nth-root of a variable expression is similar to finding an nth-root of a numerical expression. However, for roots with an even index, particular care must be taken to obtain a nonnegative value.

Definition of $\sqrt[n]{a^n}$

1. If $n > 1$ is an odd integer,   Example: cube root $\sqrt[3]{a^3} = a$
then $\sqrt[n]{a^n} = a$

2. If n is a positive even integer,   Example: square root $\sqrt{a^2} = |a|$
then $\sqrt[n]{a^n} = |a|$

The absolute value bars are necessary for roots with an even index because the variable, a, may represent a positive quantity or a negative quantity. By using absolute value bars, we ensure that $\sqrt[n]{a^n} = |a|$ is nonnegative and represents the principal nth-root of a.

If n is an even integer, then $\sqrt[n]{a^n} = |a|$. However, if the variable a is assumed to be nonnegative, then the absolute value bars may be omitted, that is, $\sqrt[n]{a^n} = a$ provided $a \geq 0$. In the following examples and exercises, we will make the assumption that the variables within a radical expression are positive real numbers. In such a case, the absolute value bars are not needed to evaluate $\sqrt[n]{a^n}$.

It is helpful to become familiar with the patterns associated with perfect squares and perfect cubes involving variable expressions.

The following powers of x are perfect squares:

Perfect squares

$(x^1)^2 = x^2$
$(x^2)^2 = x^4$
$(x^3)^2 = x^6$
$(x^4)^2 = x^8$
$\ldots$

TIP: Any expression raised to an even power (multiple of 2) is a perfect square.

The following powers of x are perfect cubes:

Perfect cubes

$(x^1)^3 = x^3$
$(x^2)^3 = x^6$
$(x^3)^3 = x^9$
$(x^4)^3 = x^{12}$
$\ldots$

TIP: Any expression raised to a power that is a multiple of 3 is a perfect cube.

Example 5   Simplifying *n*th-Roots

Simplify the expressions. Assume that the variables are positive real numbers.

     a. $\sqrt{c^6}$ **b.** $\sqrt[3]{d^{15}}$ **c.** $\sqrt{a^2b^2}$ **d.** $\sqrt[3]{64z^6}$

Solution:

     a. $\sqrt{c^6}$ The expression c^6 is a perfect square.

         $\sqrt{c^6} = c^3$ This is because $\sqrt{(c^3)^2} = c^3$.

     b. $\sqrt[3]{d^{15}}$ The expression d^{15} is a perfect cube.

         $\sqrt[3]{d^{15}} = d^5$ This is because $\sqrt[3]{(d^5)^3} = d^5$.

     c. $\sqrt{a^2b^2} = ab$ This is because $\sqrt{a^2b^2} = \sqrt{(ab)^2} = ab$.

     d. $\sqrt[3]{64z^6} = 4z^2$ This is because $\sqrt[3]{(4z^2)^3} = 4z^2$.

3. Translations Involving *n*th-Roots

It is important to understand the vocabulary and language associated with *n*th-roots. For instance, you must be able to distinguish between the square of a number and the square *root* of a number. Example 6 offers practice translating between English form and algebraic form.

Example 6   Writing an English Phrase in Algebraic Form

Translate each English phrase into an algebraic expression.

     a. The difference of the square of *x* and the principal square root of 7

     b. The quotient of 1 and the cube root of *z*

Solution:

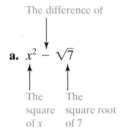

a. $x^2 - \sqrt{7}$

The   The
square   square root
of *x*   of 7

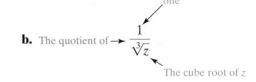

b. The quotient of → $\dfrac{1}{\sqrt[3]{z}}$

one

The cube root of *z*

4. Pythagorean Theorem

Recall that the **Pythagorean theorem** relates the lengths of the three sides of a right triangle (Figure 8-1).

$$a^2 + b^2 = c^2$$

The principal square root can be used to solve for an unknown side of a right triangle if the lengths of the other two sides are known.

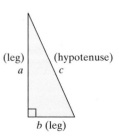

(leg) a (hypotenuse) c

b (leg)

Figure 8-1

Example 7	Applying the Pythagorean Theorem

Use the Pythagorean theorem and the definition of the principal square root of a number to find the length of the unknown side.

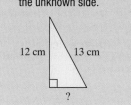

Solution:

Label the sides of the triangle.

$a^2 + b^2 = c^2$

$a^2 + (8)^2 = (10)^2$ Apply the Pythagorean theorem.

$a^2 + 64 = 100$ Simplify.

$a^2 = 36$ This equation is quadratic. One method for solving the equation is to set the equation equal to zero, factor, and apply the zero product rule. However, we can also use the definition of a square root to solve for a.

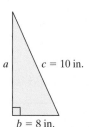

$a = \sqrt{36}$ or $a = -\sqrt{36}$ By definition, a must be one of the square roots of 36 (either 6 or -6). However, because a represents a distance, choose the *positive* (principal) square root of 36.

$a = 6$

The third side is 6 in. long.

Example 8	Applying the Pythagorean Theorem

A bridge across a river is 600 yd long. A boat ramp at point R is 200 yd due north of point P on the bridge, such that the line segments $\overline{PQ}$ and $\overline{PR}$ form a right angle (Figure 8-2). How far does a kayak travel if it leaves from the boat ramp and paddles to point Q?

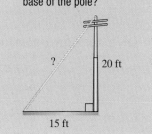

Figure 8-2

Solution:

Label the triangle:

$a^2 + b^2 = c^2$

$(200)^2 + (600)^2 = c^2$ Apply the Pythagorean theorem. The distance traveled is c.

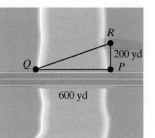

$40{,}000 + 360{,}000 = c^2$ Simplify.

$400{,}000 = c^2$ By definition, c must be one of the square roots of 400,000. Because the value of c is a distance, choose the positive square root of 400,000.

$c = \sqrt{400{,}000}$

$c \approx 632$ A calculator can be used to approximate the positive square root of 400,000.

The kayak must travel approximately 632 yd.

Answers

27. 5 cm   **28.** The wire is 25 ft long.

Calculator Connections

Topic: Evaluating Square Roots and Higher Order Roots on a Calculator

A calculator can be used to approximate the value of a radical expression. To evaluate a square root, use the $\sqrt{\ }$ key. For example, evaluate: $\sqrt{25}$, $\sqrt{60}$, $\sqrt{\frac{13}{3}}$

Scientific Calculator

Enter: 25 $\boxed{\sqrt{x}}$	**Result:** $\boxed{5}$
Enter: 60 $\boxed{\sqrt{x}}$	**Result:** $\boxed{7.745966692}$
Enter: 13 $\boxed{\div}$ 3 $\boxed{=}$ $\boxed{\sqrt{x}}$	**Result:** $\boxed{2.081665999}$

Graphing Calculator

On the graphing calculator, the radicand is enclosed in parentheses.

```
√(25)
              5
√(60)
     7.745966692
√(13/3)
     2.081665999
```

TIP: The values $\sqrt{60}$ and $\sqrt{\frac{13}{3}}$ are approximated on the calculator to 10 digits. However, $\sqrt{60}$ and $\sqrt{\frac{13}{3}}$ are actually irrational numbers. Their decimal forms are nonterminating and nonrepeating. The only way to represent the exact answers is by writing the radical forms, $\sqrt{60}$ and $\sqrt{\frac{13}{2}}$.

To evaluate cube roots, your calculator may have a $\boxed{\sqrt[3]{\ }}$ key. Otherwise, for cube roots and roots of higher index (fourth roots, fifth roots, and so on), try using the $\boxed{\sqrt[x]{y}}$ key or $\boxed{\sqrt[x]{\ }}$ key. For example, evaluate $\sqrt[3]{64}$, $\sqrt[4]{81}$, and $\sqrt[3]{162}$:

Scientific Calculator

Enter: 64 $\boxed{2^{nd}}$ $\boxed{\sqrt[x]{y}}$ 3 $\boxed{=}$	**Result:** $\boxed{4}$
Enter: 81 $\boxed{2^{nd}}$ $\boxed{\sqrt[x]{y}}$ 4 $\boxed{=}$	**Result:** $\boxed{3}$
Enter: 162 $\boxed{2^{nd}}$ $\boxed{\sqrt[x]{y}}$ 3 $\boxed{=}$	**Result:** $\boxed{5.451361778}$

Graphing Calculator

On a graphing calculator, the index is usually entered first.

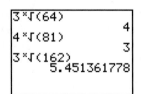

```
3*√(64)
              4
4*√(81)
              3
3*√(162)
     5.451361778
```

Calculator Exercises

Estimate the value of each radical. Then use a calculator to approximate the radical to three decimal places. **(See the Tip on page 579.)**

1. $\sqrt{5}$	**2.** $\sqrt{17}$	**3.** $\sqrt{50}$	**4.** $\sqrt{96}$
5. $\sqrt{33}$	**6.** $\sqrt{145}$	**7.** $\sqrt{80}$	**8.** $\sqrt{170}$
9. $\sqrt[3]{7}$	**10.** $\sqrt[3]{28}$	**11.** $\sqrt[3]{65}$	**12.** $\sqrt[3]{124}$

Section 8.1 Practice Exercises

Vocabulary and Key Concepts

1. a. If $b^2 = a$, then _____ is a square root of _____.

   b. The symbol $\sqrt{a}$ denotes the _____ or positive square root of a.

   c. A number is a perfect square if its square root is a _____ number.

   d. b is an nth root of a if _____ = _____.

   e. Given the symbol $\sqrt[n]{a}$, n is called the _____ and a is called the _____.

   f. The symbol $\sqrt[3]{a}$ denotes the _____ root of a.

   g. The expression $\sqrt{-4}$ (is/is not) a real number. The expression $-\sqrt{4}$ (is/is not) a real number.

   h. The expression $\sqrt[n]{a^n} = |a|$ if n is (even/odd). The expression $\sqrt[n]{a^n} = a$ if n is (even/odd).

   i. Given a right triangle with legs a and b and hypotenuse c, the Pythagorean theorem is stated as _____.

Concept 1: Definition of a Square Root

For Exercises 2–9, determine the square roots. **(See Example 1.)**

2. 4

3. 144

4. -64

5. -49

6. 81

7. 0

8. $\dfrac{16}{9}$

9. $\dfrac{1}{25}$

10. a. What is the principal square root of 64?

   b. What is the negative square root of 64?

11. a. What is the principal square root of 169?

   b. What is the negative square root of 169?

12. Does every number have two square roots? Explain.

13. Which number has only one square root?

14. Which of the following are perfect squares?

   $\{0, 1, 4, 15, 30, 49, 72, 81, 144, 300, 625, 900\}$

15. Which of the following are perfect squares?

   $\{8, 9, 12, 16, 25, 36, 42, 64, 95, 121, 140, 169\}$

For Exercises 16–31, simplify the square roots. **(See Example 2.)**

16. $\sqrt{16}$

17. $\sqrt{4}$

18. $\sqrt{81}$

19. $\sqrt{49}$

20. $\sqrt{0.25}$

21. $\sqrt{0.16}$

22. $\sqrt{0.64}$

23. $\sqrt{0.09}$

24. $\sqrt{\dfrac{1}{9}}$

25. $\sqrt{\dfrac{25}{16}}$

26. $\sqrt{\dfrac{49}{121}}$

27. $\sqrt{\dfrac{1}{144}}$

28. $\sqrt{64 + 36}$

29. $\sqrt{16 + 9}$

30. $\sqrt{169 - 144}$

31. $\sqrt{225 - 144}$

32. Explain the difference between $\sqrt{-16}$ and $-\sqrt{16}$.

33. Using the definition of a square root, explain why $\sqrt{-16}$ does not have a real-valued square root.

34. Evaluate. $-\sqrt{|-25|}$

For Exercises 35–46, simplify the square roots, if possible. **(See Example 3.)**

35. $-\sqrt{4}$

36. $-\sqrt{1}$

37. $\sqrt{-4}$

38. $\sqrt{-1}$

39. $\sqrt{-\dfrac{4}{49}}$

40. $-\sqrt{-\dfrac{9}{25}}$

41. $-\sqrt{-\dfrac{1}{36}}$

42. $-\sqrt{\dfrac{1}{36}}$

43. $-\sqrt{400}$

44. $-\sqrt{121}$

45. $\sqrt{-900}$

46. $\sqrt{-169}$

Concept 2: Definition of an *n*th-Root

47. Which of the following are perfect cubes?

0, 1, 3, 9, 27, 36, 42, 90, 125

48. Which of the following are perfect cubes?

6, 8, 16, 20, 30, 64, 111, 150, 216

49. Does -27 have a real-valued cube root?

50. Does -8 have a real-valued cube root?

For Exercises 51–66, simplify the *n*th roots, if possible. **(See Example 4.)**

51. $\sqrt[3]{27}$

52. $\sqrt[3]{-27}$

53. $\sqrt[3]{64}$

54. $\sqrt[3]{-64}$

55. $-\sqrt[4]{16}$

56. $-\sqrt[4]{81}$

57. $\sqrt[4]{-1}$

58. $\sqrt[4]{0}$

59. $\sqrt[4]{-256}$

60. $\sqrt[4]{-625}$

61. $\sqrt[5]{-\dfrac{1}{32}}$

62. $-\sqrt[5]{\dfrac{1}{32}}$

63. $-\sqrt[6]{1}$

64. $\sqrt[6]{64}$

65. $\sqrt[6]{0}$

66. $\sqrt[6]{-1}$

67. Determine which of the expressions are perfect squares. Then state a rule for determining perfect squares based on the exponent of the expression.

$x^2,\ a^3,\ y^4,\ z^5,\ (ab)^6,\ (pq)^7,\ w^8x^8,\ c^9d^9,\ m^{10},\ n^{11}$

68. Determine which of the expressions are perfect cubes. Then state a rule for determining perfect cubes based on the exponent of the expression.

$a^2,\ b^3,\ c^4,\ d^5,\ e^6,\ (xy)^7,\ (wz)^8,\ (pq)^9,\ t^{10}s^{10},\ m^{11}n^{11},\ u^{12}v^{12}$

For Exercises 69–88, simplify the expressions. Assume the variables represent positive real numbers. **(See Example 5.)**

69. $\sqrt{(4)^2}$

70. $\sqrt{(8)^2}$

71. $\sqrt[3]{(5)^3}$

72. $\sqrt[3]{(7)^3}$

73. $\sqrt{y^{12}}$

74. $\sqrt{z^{20}}$

75. $\sqrt{a^8b^{30}}$

76. $\sqrt{t^{50}s^{60}}$

77. $\sqrt[3]{q^{24}}$

78. $\sqrt[3]{x^{33}}$

79. $\sqrt[3]{8w^6}$

80. $\sqrt[3]{-27x^{27}}$

81. $\sqrt{(5x)^2}$

82. $\sqrt{(6w)^2}$

83. $-\sqrt{25x^2}$

84. $-\sqrt{36w^2}$

85. $\sqrt[3]{(5p^2)^3}$

86. $\sqrt[3]{(2k^4)^3}$

87. $\sqrt[3]{125p^6}$

88. $\sqrt[3]{8k^{12}}$

Concept 3: Translations Involving *n*th-Roots

For Exercises 89–92, translate the English phrase to an algebraic expression. **(See Example 6.)**

89. The sum of the principal square root of q and the square of p

90. The product of the principal square root of 11 and the cube of x

91. The quotient of 6 and the cube root of x

92. The difference of the square of y and 1

Concept 4: Pythagorean Theorem

For Exercises 93–98, find the length of the third side of each triangle using the Pythagorean theorem. Round the answer to the nearest tenth if necessary. **(See Example 7.)**

93.

15 cm

12 cm

94.

8 in.

6 in.

95.

12 ft   13 ft

96.

5 m

4 m

97.

6.5 cm

2.4 cm

98.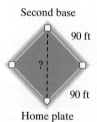

14.8 ft

9.2 ft

99. Find the length of the diagonal of the square tile shown in the figure. Round the answer to the nearest tenth of an inch.

12 in.

12 in.

100. A baseball diamond is 90 ft on a side. Find the distance between home plate and second base. Round the answer to the nearest tenth of a foot.

Second base

90 ft

?

Home plate

90 ft

101. A new plasma television is listed as being 42 in. This distance is the diagonal distance across the screen. If the screen measures 28 inches in height, what is the actual width of the screen? Round to the nearest tenth of an inch.
(See Example 8.)

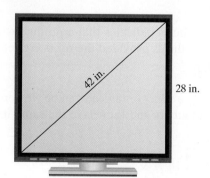

42 in.

28 in.

102. A marine biologist wants to track the migration of a pod of whales. He receives a radio signal from a tagged humpback whale and determines that the whale is 21 mi east and 37 mi north of his laboratory. Find the direct distance between the whale and the laboratory. Round to the nearest tenth of a mile.

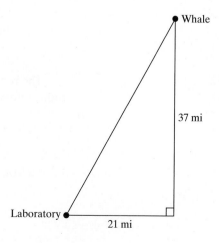

Whale

37 mi

Laboratory

21 mi

103. On a map, the cities Asheville, North Carolina, Roanoke, Virginia, and Greensboro, North Carolina, form a right triangle (see the figure). The distance between Asheville and Roanoke is 300 km. The distance between Roanoke and Greensboro is 134 km. How far is it from Greensboro to Asheville? Round the answer to the nearest kilometer.

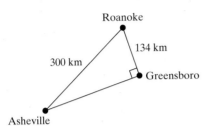

104. Jackson, Mississippi, is west of Meridian, Mississippi, a distance of 141 km. Tupelo, Mississippi, is north of Meridian, a distance of 209 km. How far is it from Jackson to Tupelo? Round the answer to the nearest kilometer.

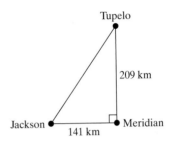

Expanding Your Skills

105. For what values of x will $\sqrt{x}$ be a real number?

106. For what values of x will $\sqrt{-x}$ be a real number?

107. Under what conditions will $\sqrt{a-b}$ be a real number?

108. Under what conditions will $\sqrt{m-n}$ be a real number?

Section 8.2   Simplifying Radicals

Concepts

1. Multiplication Property of Radicals
2. Simplifying Radicals Using the Order of Operations
3. Simplifying Cube Roots

1. Multiplication Property of Radicals

You may have already recognized certain properties of radicals involving a product.

> **Multiplication Property of Radicals**
> Let a and b represent real numbers such that $\sqrt[n]{a}$ and $\sqrt[n]{b}$ are both real. Then,
> $$\sqrt[n]{ab} = \sqrt[n]{a} \cdot \sqrt[n]{b} \qquad \textbf{Multiplication property of radicals}$$

The multiplication property of radicals indicates that a product within a radicand can be written as a product of radicals provided the roots are real numbers.

$$\sqrt{100} = \sqrt{25} \cdot \sqrt{4}$$

The reverse process is also true. A product of radicals can be written as a single radical provided the roots are real numbers and they have the same indices.

$$\overset{\text{Same index}}{\sqrt{2} \cdot \sqrt{18}} = \sqrt{36}$$

In algebra, it is customary to simplify radical expressions as much as possible.

Simplified Form of a Radical

Consider any radical expression where the radicand is written as a product of prime factors. The expression is in **simplified form** if all of the following conditions are met:

1. The radicand has no factor raised to a power greater than or equal to the index.
2. There are no radicals in the denominator of a fraction.
3. The radicand does not contain a fraction.

The expression $\sqrt{x^2}$ is not simplified because it fails condition 1. Because x^2 is a perfect square, $\sqrt{x^2}$ is easily simplified.

$$\sqrt{x^2} = x \quad (\text{for } x \ge 0)$$

However, how is an expression such as $\sqrt{x^7}$ simplified? This and many other radical expressions can be simplified using the multiplication property of radicals. This is illustrated in Examples 1–3.

Example 1 Using the Multiplication Property to Simplify a Radical Expression

Use the multiplication property of radicals to simplify the expression $\sqrt{x^7}$. Assume $x \ge 0$.

Solution:

The expression $\sqrt{x^7}$ is equivalent to $\sqrt{x^6 \cdot x}$. By applying the multiplication property of radicals, we have

$$\sqrt{x^6 \cdot x} = \sqrt{x^6} \cdot \sqrt{x} \qquad x^6 \text{ is a perfect square because } (x^3)^2 = x^6.$$

$$= x^3 \cdot \sqrt{x} \qquad \text{Simplify.}$$

$$= x^3\sqrt{x}$$

In Example 1, the expression x^7 is not a perfect square. Therefore, to simplify $\sqrt{x^7}$, it was necessary to write the radicand as the product of the largest perfect square factor and a remaining, or "leftover," factor: $\sqrt{x^7} = \sqrt{x^6 \cdot x}$.

Example 2 Using the Multiplication Property to Simplify Radicals

Use the multiplication property of radicals to simplify the expressions. Assume the variables represent positive real numbers.

a. $\sqrt{a^{15}}$ b. $\sqrt{x^2y^5}$ c. $\sqrt{s^9t^{11}}$

Solution:

The goal is to rewrite each radicand as the product of the largest perfect square factor and a leftover factor.

a. $\sqrt{a^{15}}$

$\quad = \sqrt{a^{14} \cdot a} \qquad a^{14}$ is the largest perfect square factor in the radicand.

$\quad = \sqrt{a^{14}} \cdot \sqrt{a} \qquad$ Apply the multiplication property of radicals.

$\quad = a^7\sqrt{a} \qquad$ Simplify.

b. $\sqrt{x^2y^5}$

$$= \sqrt{x^2y^4 \cdot y} \qquad\quad x^2y^4 \text{ is the largest perfect square factor in the radicand.}$$

$$= \sqrt{x^2y^4} \cdot \sqrt{y} \qquad \text{Apply the multiplication property of radicals.}$$

$$= xy^2\sqrt{y} \qquad\quad \text{Simplify.}$$

c. $\sqrt{s^9t^{11}}$

$$= \sqrt{s^8t^{10} \cdot st} \qquad\quad s^8t^{10} \text{ is the largest perfect square factor in the radicand.}$$

$$= \sqrt{s^8t^{10}} \cdot \sqrt{st} \qquad \text{Apply the multiplication property of radicals.}$$

$$= s^4t^5\sqrt{st} \qquad\quad \text{Simplify.}$$

Each expression in Example 2 involves a radicand that is a product of variable factors. If a numerical factor is present, sometimes it is necessary to factor the coefficient before simplifying the radical.

Skill Practice

Simplify the expressions. Assume the variables represent positive real numbers.

8. $\sqrt{12}$ **9.** $\sqrt{60x^2}$

10. $7\sqrt{18t^{10}}$

> **Example 3**   **Using the Multiplication Property to Simplify Radicals**

Use the multiplication property of radicals to simplify the expressions. Assume the variables represent positive real numbers.

   a. $\sqrt{50}$ **b.** $5\sqrt{24a^6}$ **c.** $-\sqrt{81x^4y^3}$

Solution:

The goal is to rewrite each radicand as the product of the largest perfect square factor and a leftover factor.

   a. Write the radicand as a product of prime factors. From the prime factorization, the largest perfect square is easily identified.

TIP: The expression $\sqrt{50}$ can also be written as:

$$\sqrt{25 \cdot 2}$$
$$= \sqrt{25} \cdot \sqrt{2}$$
$$= 5\sqrt{2}$$

$$\sqrt{50} = \sqrt{5^2 \cdot 2} \qquad \text{Factor the radicand.} \qquad\qquad 2\overline{)50}$$
$$\qquad\qquad 5^2 \text{ is the largest perfect square factor.} \quad 5\overline{)25}$$
$$\qquad\qquad\qquad\qquad\qquad\qquad\qquad\qquad\qquad 5$$

$$= \sqrt{5^2} \cdot \sqrt{2} \qquad \text{Apply the multiplication property of radicals.}$$

$$= 5\sqrt{2} \qquad\qquad \text{Simplify.}$$

   b. $5\sqrt{24a^6} = 5\sqrt{2^3 \cdot 3 \cdot a^6} \qquad \text{Write the radicand as a product of prime factors: } 24 = 2^3 \cdot 3.$

$$= 5\sqrt{2^2a^6 \cdot 2 \cdot 3} \qquad 2^2a^6 \text{ is the largest perfect square factor in the radicand.}$$

$$= 5\sqrt{2^2a^6} \cdot \sqrt{2 \cdot 3} \qquad \text{Apply the multiplication property of radicals.}$$

$$= 5 \cdot 2a^3\sqrt{6} \qquad \text{Simplify the radical.}$$

$$= 10a^3\sqrt{6} \qquad \text{Simplify the coefficient of the radical.}$$

Answers

 8. $2\sqrt{3}$ **9.** $2x\sqrt{15}$
10. $21t^5\sqrt{2}$

c. $-\sqrt{81x^4y^3} = -\sqrt{3^4x^4y^3}$

Write the radical as a product of prime factors. *Note:* $81 = 3^4$.

$= -\sqrt{3^4x^4y^2 \cdot y}$

$3^4x^4y^2$ is the largest perfect square factor in the radicand.

$= -\sqrt{3^4x^4y^2} \cdot \sqrt{y}$

Apply the multiplication property of radicals.

$= -3^2x^2y \cdot \sqrt{y}$

Simplify the radical.

$= -9x^2y\sqrt{y}$

Simplify the coefficient of the radical.

Avoiding Mistakes

The multiplication property of radicals enables us to simplify a product within a radical. That is,
$$\sqrt{x^2y^2} = \sqrt{x^2} \cdot \sqrt{y^2} = xy \quad \text{(for } x \geq 0 \text{ and } y \geq 0)$$
However, this rule does not apply to *terms* that are added or subtracted *within* the radical. That is,
$$\sqrt{x^2 + y^2} \neq \sqrt{x^2} + \sqrt{y^2} \quad \text{and} \quad \sqrt{x^2 - y^2} \neq \sqrt{x^2} - \sqrt{y^2}$$
For example: $\sqrt{(16) \cdot (9)} = 4 \cdot 3$, however, $\sqrt{16 + 9} \neq 4 + 3$.

---

2. Simplifying Radicals Using the Order of Operations

Often a radical can be simplified by applying the order of operations. In Example 4, the first step will be to simplify the expression within the radicand.

Example 4 Simplifying Radicals Using the Order of Operations

Simplify the expressions. Assume the variables represent positive real numbers.

a. $\sqrt{\dfrac{a^5}{a^3}}$ 　　**b.** $\sqrt{\dfrac{6}{96}}$ 　　**c.** $\sqrt{\dfrac{27x^5}{3x}}$

Solution:

a. $\sqrt{\dfrac{a^5}{a^3}}$

The radical contains a fraction. However, the fraction can be simplified.

$= \sqrt{a^2}$

Reduce the fraction to lowest terms.

$= a$

Simplify the radical.

b. $\sqrt{\dfrac{6}{96}}$

The radical contains a fraction that can be simplified.

$= \sqrt{\dfrac{1}{16}}$

Reduce the fraction to lowest terms.

$= \dfrac{1}{4}$

Simplify.

c. $\sqrt{\dfrac{27x^5}{3x}}$

The fraction within the radicand can be simplified.

$= \sqrt{9x^4}$

Reduce to lowest terms.

$= 3x^2$

Simplify.

Answers

11. y^4 　**12.** $\dfrac{2}{5}$ 　**13.** $4z$

Example 5 Simplifying Radical Expressions

Simplify the expressions.

a. $\dfrac{5\sqrt{20}}{2}$ **b.** $\dfrac{2 - \sqrt{36}}{12}$

Solution:

a. $\dfrac{5\sqrt{20}}{2} = \dfrac{5\sqrt{4 \cdot 5}}{2}$ Following the order of operations, first simplify the radical. 4 is the largest perfect square factor in the radicand.

$= \dfrac{5\sqrt{4} \cdot \sqrt{5}}{2}$ Apply the multiplication property of radicals.

$= \dfrac{5 \cdot 2\sqrt{5}}{2}$ Simplify the radical.

$= \dfrac{\overset{5}{\cancel{10}}\sqrt{5}}{2}$ Simplify to lowest terms.

$= 5\sqrt{5}$

b. $\dfrac{2 - \sqrt{36}}{12}$

$= \dfrac{2 - 6}{12}$ Following the order of operations, first simplify the radical.

$= \dfrac{-4}{12}$ Next, simplify the numerator.

$= -\dfrac{1}{3}$ Reduce the fraction to lowest terms.

3. Simplifying Cube Roots

Example 6 Simplifying Cube Roots

Use the multiplication property of radicals to simplify the expressions.

a. $\sqrt[3]{z^5}$ **b.** $\sqrt[3]{-80}$

Solution:

a. $\sqrt[3]{z^5}$

$= \sqrt[3]{z^3 \cdot z^2}$ z^3 is the largest perfect cube factor in the radicand.

$= \sqrt[3]{z^3} \cdot \sqrt[3]{z^2}$ Apply the multiplication property of radicals.

$= z\sqrt[3]{z^2}$ Simplify.

b. $\sqrt[3]{-80}$

$= \sqrt[3]{-1 \cdot 8 \cdot 10}$ Factor the radicand. -1 and 8 are perfect cubes.

$= \sqrt[3]{-1} \cdot \sqrt[3]{8} \cdot \sqrt[3]{10}$ Apply the multiplication property of radicals.

$= -1 \cdot 2 \cdot \sqrt[3]{10}$ Simplify.

$= -2\sqrt[3]{10}$

Example 7 Simplifying Cube Roots

Simplify the expressions.

a. $\sqrt[3]{\dfrac{a^{16}}{a}}$ **b.** $\sqrt[3]{\dfrac{2}{16}}$

Solution:

a. $\sqrt[3]{\dfrac{a^{16}}{a}}$ The radical contains a fraction that can be simplified.

$= \sqrt[3]{a^{15}}$ Reduce to lowest terms.

$= a^5$ Simplify.

b. $\sqrt[3]{\dfrac{2}{16}}$ The radical contains a fraction that can be simplified.

$= \sqrt[3]{\dfrac{1}{8}}$ Reduce to lowest terms.

$= \dfrac{1}{2}$ Simplify.

Calculator Connections

Topic: Verifying Simplified Radicals

A calculator can support the multiplication property of radicals. For example, use a calculator to evaluate $\sqrt{50}$ and its simplified form $5\sqrt{2}$.

Scientific Calculator

Enter: 50 $\boxed{\sqrt{x}}$ **Result:** 7.071067812

Enter: 2 $\boxed{\sqrt{x}}$ $\boxed{\times}$ 5 $\boxed{=}$ **Result:** 7.071067812

Graphing Calculator
```
√(50)
        7.071067812
5*√(2)
        7.071067812
```

TIP: The decimal approximation for $\sqrt{50}$ and $5\sqrt{2}$ agree for the first 10 digits. This in itself does not make $\sqrt{50} = 5\sqrt{2}$. It is the multiplication property of radicals that guarantees that the expressions are equal.

Calculator Exercises

Simplify the radical expressions algebraically. Then use a calculator to approximate the original expression and its simplified form.

1. $\sqrt{125}$ **2.** $\sqrt{18}$ **3.** $\sqrt[3]{54}$ **4.** $\sqrt[3]{108}$

Section 8.2 Practice Exercises

Vocabulary and Key Concepts

1. **a.** The multiplication property of radicals indicates that if both $\sqrt[n]{a}$ and $\sqrt[n]{b}$ are real numbers, then $\sqrt[n]{ab} = $ _____ $\cdot \sqrt[n]{b}$.

    b. Explain why the radical is not in simplified form. $\sqrt{x^3}$

    c. On a calculator, $\sqrt{2}$ is given as 1.414213562. Is this decimal number the exact value of $\sqrt{2}$?

Review Exercises

2. Which of the following are perfect squares? 2, 4, 6, 16, 20, 25, x^2, x^3, x^{15}, x^{20}, x^{25}

3. Which of the following are perfect cubes? 3, 6, 8, 9, 12, 27, y^3, y^8, y^9, y^{12}, y^{27}

4. Which of the following are perfect fourth powers? 4, 16, 20, 25, 81, w^4, w^{16}, w^{20}, w^{25}, w^{81}

For Exercises 5–12, simplify the expressions, if possible. Assume the variables represent positive real numbers.

5. $-\sqrt{25}$

6. $\sqrt{-25}$

7. $-\sqrt[3]{27}$

8. $\sqrt[3]{-27}$

9. $\sqrt{a^8}$

10. $\sqrt[3]{b^{15}}$

11. $\sqrt{4x^2y^4}$

12. $\sqrt{9p^{10}}$

13. On a map, Seattle, Washington, is 378 km west of Spokane, Washington. Portland, Oregon, is 236 km south of Seattle. Approximate the distance between Portland and Spokane to the nearest kilometer.

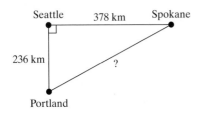

14. A new roof is needed on a shed. How many square feet of tar paper would be needed to cover the top of the roof?

Concept 1: Multiplication Property of Radicals

For Exercises 15–50, use the multiplication property of radicals to simplify the expressions. Assume the variables represent positive real numbers. **(See Examples 1–3.)**

15. $\sqrt{18}$

16. $\sqrt{75}$

17. $\sqrt{28}$

18. $\sqrt{40}$

19. $6\sqrt{20}$

20. $10\sqrt{27}$

21. $-2\sqrt{50}$

22. $-11\sqrt{8}$

23. $\sqrt{a^5}$

24. $\sqrt{b^9}$

25. $\sqrt{w^{22}}$

26. $\sqrt{p^{18}}$

27. $\sqrt{m^4n^5}$

28. $\sqrt{c^2d^9}$

29. $x\sqrt{x^{13}y^{10}}$

30. $v\sqrt{u^{10}v^7}$

31. $3\sqrt{t^{10}}$

32. $-4\sqrt{m^8n^4}$

33. $\sqrt{8x^3}$

34. $\sqrt{27y^5}$

35. $\sqrt{16z^3}$

36. $\sqrt{9y^5}$

37. $-\sqrt{45w^6}$

38. $-\sqrt{56v^8}$

39. $\sqrt{z^{25}}$ **40.** $\sqrt{25p^{49}}$ **41.** $-\sqrt{15z^{11}}$ **42.** $-\sqrt{6k^{15}}$

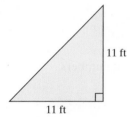 **43.** $5\sqrt{104a^2b^7}$ **44.** $3\sqrt{88m^4n^{11}}$ **45.** $\sqrt{26pq}$ **46.** $\sqrt{15a}$

47. $m\sqrt{m^{10}n^{16}}$ **48.** $c^2\sqrt{c^4d^{12}}$ **49.** $-\sqrt{48a^3b^5c^4}$ **50.** $-\sqrt{18xy^4z^3}$

Concept 2: Simplifying Radicals Using the Order of Operations

For Exercises 51–70, use the order of operations, if necessary, to simplify the expressions. Assume the variables represent positive real numbers. **(See Examples 4 and 5.)**

51. $\sqrt{\dfrac{a^9}{a}}$ **52.** $\sqrt{\dfrac{x^5}{x}}$ **53.** $\sqrt{\dfrac{y^{15}}{y^5}}$ **54.** $\sqrt{\dfrac{c^{31}}{c^{11}}}$

55. $\sqrt{\dfrac{5}{20}}$ **56.** $\sqrt{\dfrac{3}{75}}$ **57.** $\sqrt{\dfrac{40}{10}}$ **58.** $\sqrt{\dfrac{80}{5}}$

59. $\sqrt{\dfrac{32x^3}{8x}}$ **60.** $\sqrt{\dfrac{200b^{11}}{2b^5}}$ 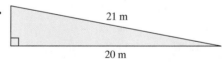 **61.** $\sqrt{\dfrac{50p^7}{2p}}$ **62.** $\sqrt{\dfrac{45t^9}{5t^5}}$

63. $\dfrac{3\sqrt{20}}{2}$ **64.** $\dfrac{5\sqrt{18}}{3}$ **65.** $\dfrac{5\sqrt{24}}{10}$ **66.** $\dfrac{2\sqrt{27}}{6}$

67. $\dfrac{10+\sqrt{4}}{3}$ **68.** $\dfrac{-1+\sqrt{25}}{4}$ **69.** $\dfrac{20-\sqrt{36}}{2}$ **70.** $\dfrac{3-\sqrt{81}}{3}$

For Exercises 71–74, find the exact length of the third side of each triangle using the Pythagorean theorem. Write the answer as a simplified radical.

71.

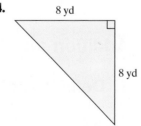

11 ft

11 ft

72.

21 m

20 m

73.

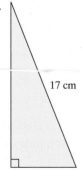

17 cm

5 cm

74.

8 yd

8 yd

Concept 3: Simplifying Cube Roots

For Exercises 75–86, simplify the cube roots.   **(See Examples 6 and 7.)**

75. $\sqrt[3]{a^8}$

76. $\sqrt[3]{8v^3}$

77. $7\sqrt[3]{16z^3}$

78. $5\sqrt[3]{54t^6}$

79. $\sqrt[3]{16a^5b^6}$

80. $\sqrt[3]{81p^9q^{11}}$

81. $\sqrt[3]{\dfrac{z^4}{z}}$

82. $\sqrt[3]{\dfrac{w^8}{w^2}}$

83. $\sqrt[3]{-\dfrac{32}{4}}$

84. $\sqrt[3]{-\dfrac{128}{2}}$

85. $-\sqrt[3]{40}$

86. $-\sqrt[3]{54}$

Mixed Exercises

For Exercises 87–110, simplify the expressions. Assume the variables represent positive real numbers.

87. $\sqrt{\dfrac{3}{27}}$

88. $\sqrt{\dfrac{5}{125}}$

89. $\sqrt{16a^3}$

90. $\sqrt{125x^6}$

91. $\sqrt{\dfrac{4x^3}{x}}$

92. $\sqrt{\dfrac{9z^5}{z}}$

93. $\sqrt{8p^2q}$

94. $\sqrt{6cd^3}$

95. $-\sqrt{32}$

96. $-\sqrt{64}$

97. $\sqrt{52u^4v^7}$

98. $\sqrt{44p^8q^{10}}$

99. $\sqrt{216}$

100. $\sqrt{250}$

101. $\sqrt[3]{216}$

102. $\sqrt[3]{250}$

103. $\sqrt[3]{16a^3}$

104. $\sqrt[3]{125x^6}$

105. $\sqrt[3]{\dfrac{x^5}{x^2}}$

106. $\sqrt[3]{\dfrac{y^{11}}{y^2}}$

107. $\dfrac{-6\sqrt{20}}{12}$

108. $\dfrac{-5\sqrt{32}}{10}$

▶️ **109.** $\dfrac{-4-\sqrt{25}}{18}$

110. $\dfrac{8-\sqrt{100}}{2}$

Expanding Your Skills

For Exercises 111–114, simplify the expressions. Assume the variables represent positive real numbers.

111. $\sqrt{(-2-5)^2+(-4+3)^2}$

112. $\sqrt{(-1-7)^2+[1-(-1)]^2}$

113. $\sqrt{x^2+10x+25}$

114. $\sqrt{x^2+6x+9}$

Section 8.3   Addition and Subtraction of Radicals

Concepts

1. Definition of *Like* Radicals
2. Addition and Subtraction of Radicals

1. Definition of *Like* Radicals

Definition of *Like* Radicals

Two radical terms are said to be *like* **radicals** if they have the same index and the same radicand.

The following are pairs of *like* radicals:

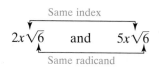

Indices and radicands are the same.
Both indices are 2. Both radicands are 6.

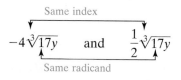

Indices and radicands are the same.
Both indices are 3. Both radicands are $17y$.

These pairs are *not like* radicals:

Different indices

$9\sqrt{3}$ and $9\sqrt[3]{3}$ Radicals have different indices.

$8ab\sqrt{5}$ and $ab\sqrt{10}$ Radicals have different radicands.

Different radicands

2. Addition and Subtraction of Radicals

Like radicals can be added or subtracted by using the distributive property.

Same index

Distributive property

$$9\sqrt{2y} + 4\sqrt{2y} = (9 + 4)\sqrt{2y} = 13\sqrt{2y}$$

Same radicand

Example 1 **Adding and Subtracting Radicals**

Add or subtract the radicals as indicated. Assume all variables represent positive real numbers.

a. $\sqrt{5} + \sqrt{5}$ **b.** $6\sqrt[3]{15} + 3\sqrt[3]{15} + \sqrt[3]{15}$ **c.** $\sqrt{xy} - 6\sqrt{xy} + 4\sqrt{xy}$

Solution:

a. $\sqrt{5} + \sqrt{5}$

$= 1\sqrt{5} + 1\sqrt{5}$ *Note:* $\sqrt{5} = 1\sqrt{5}$.

$= (1 + 1)\sqrt{5}$ Apply the distributive property.

$= 2\sqrt{5}$ Simplify.

b. $6\sqrt[3]{15} + 3\sqrt[3]{15} + \sqrt[3]{15}$ The radicals have the same radicand and same index.

$= 6\sqrt[3]{15} + 3\sqrt[3]{15} + 1\sqrt[3]{15}$ *Note:* $\sqrt[3]{15} = 1\sqrt[3]{15}$.

$= (6 + 3 + 1)\sqrt[3]{15}$ Apply the distributive property.

$= 10\sqrt[3]{15}$

c. $\sqrt{xy} - 6\sqrt{xy} + 4\sqrt{xy}$ The radicals have the same radicand and same index.

$= 1\sqrt{xy} - 6\sqrt{xy} + 4\sqrt{xy}$ *Note:* $\sqrt{xy} = 1\sqrt{xy}$.

$= (1 - 6 + 4)\sqrt{xy}$ Apply the distributive property.

$= -1\sqrt{xy}$ Simplify.

$= -\sqrt{xy}$

From Example 1, you can see that the process of adding or subtracting *like* radicals is similar to combining *like* terms.

$$x + x \qquad\qquad \text{similarly,} \qquad\qquad \sqrt{5} + \sqrt{5}$$
$$= 1x + 1x \qquad\qquad\qquad\qquad\qquad = 1\sqrt{5} + 1\sqrt{5}$$
$$= 2x \qquad\qquad\qquad\qquad\qquad\qquad = 2\sqrt{5}$$

The end result is that the numerical coefficients are added or subtracted and the radical factor is unchanged.

Sometimes it is necessary to simplify radicals before adding or subtracting.

Example 2   Simplifying Radicals before Adding or Subtracting

Add or subtract the radicals as indicated.

a. $\sqrt{20} + 7\sqrt{5}$ **b.** $\sqrt{50} - \sqrt{8}$

Solution:

a. $\sqrt{20} + 7\sqrt{5}$ Because the radicands are different, try simplifying the radicals first.

$= \sqrt{4 \cdot 5} + 7\sqrt{5}$ Factor the radicand.

$= 2\sqrt{5} + 7\sqrt{5}$ The terms are *like* radicals.

$= (2 + 7)\sqrt{5}$ Apply the distributive property.

$= 9\sqrt{5}$ Simplify.

b. $\sqrt{50} - \sqrt{8}$ Because the radicands are different, try simplifying the radicals first.

$= \sqrt{25 \cdot 2} - \sqrt{4 \cdot 2}$ Factor the radicands.

$= 5\sqrt{2} - 2\sqrt{2}$ The terms are *like* radicals.

$= (5 - 2)\sqrt{2}$ Apply the distributive property.

$= 3\sqrt{2}$ Simplify.

Example 3   Simplifying Radicals before Adding or Subtracting

Add or subtract the radicals as indicated. Assume the variables represent positive real numbers.

a. $-4\sqrt{3x^2} - x\sqrt{27} + 5x\sqrt{3}$ **b.** $a\sqrt{8a^5} + 6\sqrt{2a^7} + \sqrt{9a}$

Skill Practice

Add or subtract the radicals as indicated.

4. $4\sqrt{18} + \sqrt{8}$

5. $\sqrt{50} - \sqrt{98}$

Answers

4. $14\sqrt{2}$ **5.** $-2\sqrt{2}$

Solution:

a. $-4\sqrt{3x^2} - x\sqrt{27} + 5x\sqrt{3}$ Simplify each radical.

$\qquad = -4\sqrt{3x^2} - x\sqrt{9 \cdot 3} + 5x\sqrt{3}$ Factor the radicands.

$\qquad = -4x\sqrt{3} - 3x\sqrt{3} + 5x\sqrt{3}$ The terms are *like* radicals.

$\qquad = (-4x - 3x + 5x)\sqrt{3}$ Apply the distributive property.

$\qquad = -2x\sqrt{3}$ Simplify.

b. $a\sqrt{8a^5} + 6\sqrt{2a^7} + \sqrt{9a}$ Simplify each radical.

$\qquad = a\sqrt{4a^4 \cdot 2a} + 6\sqrt{a^6 \cdot 2a} + \sqrt{9 \cdot a}$ Factor the radicands..

$\qquad = a \cdot 2a^2\sqrt{2a} + 6 \cdot a^3\sqrt{2a} + 3\sqrt{a}$ Simplify the radicals.

$\qquad = 2a^3\sqrt{2a} + 6a^3\sqrt{2a} + 3\sqrt{a}$ The first two terms are *like* radicals.

$\qquad = (2a^3 + 6a^3)\sqrt{2a} + 3\sqrt{a}$ Apply the distributive property.

$\qquad = 8a^3\sqrt{2a} + 3\sqrt{a}$

> **Skill Practice**
>
> Add or subtract the radicals as indicated. Assume the variables represent positive real numbers.
>
> **6.** $4x\sqrt{12} - \sqrt{27x^2}$
> **7.** $\sqrt{28y^3} - y\sqrt{63y} + \sqrt{700}$

It is important to realize that only *like* radicals can be added or subtracted. The next example provides extra practice for recognizing *unlike* radicals.

Example 4   Recognizing *Unlike* Radicals

Explain why the radicals cannot be simplified further by adding or subtracting.

a. $2\sqrt{7} - 5\sqrt{3}$ **b.** $7 + 4\sqrt{5}$

Solution:

a. $2\sqrt{7} - 5\sqrt{3}$ Radicands are not the same.

b. $7 + 4\sqrt{5}$ One term has a radical, and one does not.

> **Skill Practice**
>
> Explain why the radicals cannot be simplified further.
>
> **8.** $12 - 7\sqrt{5}$
> **9.** $2\sqrt{3} - 3\sqrt{2}$

Answers

6. $5x\sqrt{3}$ **7.** $-y\sqrt{7y} + 10\sqrt{7}$
8. One term has a radical and one does not.
9. The radicands are not the same.

Section 8.3 Practice Exercises

Vocabulary and Key Concepts

1. Two radical terms are called *like* radicals if they have the same _____ and the same _____.

Review Exercises

For Exercises 2–9, simplify the expressions. Assume the variables represent positive real numbers.

2. $\sqrt{25w^2}$ **3.** $\sqrt[3]{8y^3}$ **4.** $\sqrt[3]{4z^4}$ **5.** $\sqrt{36x^3}$

6. $\sqrt{\dfrac{9a^6}{a^2}}$ **7.** $\sqrt{\dfrac{12x^3}{3x}}$ **8.** $\dfrac{\sqrt{25c^6}}{16}$ **9.** $\sqrt{-25}$

Concept 1: Definition of *Like* Radicals

10. How do you determine whether two radicals are *like* or *unlike*?

11. Write two radicals that are considered *unlike*.

12. From the three pairs of radicals, identify the pair of *like* radicals:

  a. $2\sqrt{x}$ and $8\sqrt[3]{x}$

  b. $\sqrt{5}$ and $-3\sqrt{5}$

  c. $3a\sqrt{3}$ and $3a\sqrt{2}$

13. From the three pairs of radicals, identify the pair of *like* radicals:

  a. $13\sqrt{5b}$ and $13b\sqrt{5}$

  b. $\sqrt[4]{x^2y}$ and $\sqrt[3]{x^2y}$

  c. $-2\sqrt[3]{y^2}$ and $6\sqrt[3]{y^2}$

Concept 2: Addition and Subtraction of Radicals

For Exercises 14–28, add or subtract the expressions, if possible. Assume the variables represent positive real numbers. **(See Example 1.)**

14. $8\sqrt{6} + 2\sqrt{6}$

15. $3\sqrt{2} + 5\sqrt{2}$

16. $4\sqrt{3} - 2\sqrt{3} + 5\sqrt{3}$

17. $5\sqrt{7} - 3\sqrt{7} + 2\sqrt{7}$

18. $\sqrt[3]{11} + \sqrt[3]{11}$

19. $\sqrt[3]{10} + \sqrt[3]{10}$

20. $12\sqrt{x} - 3\sqrt{x}$

21. $15\sqrt{y} - 4\sqrt{y}$

22. $-3\sqrt{a} + 2\sqrt{a} + \sqrt{a}$

23. $5\sqrt{c} - 6\sqrt{c} + \sqrt{c}$

24. $7x\sqrt{11} - 9x\sqrt{11}$

25. $8y\sqrt{15} - 3y\sqrt{15}$

26. $9\sqrt{2} - 9\sqrt{5}$

27. $x\sqrt{y} - y\sqrt{x}$

28. $a\sqrt{b} + b\sqrt{a}$

Mixed Exercises

For Exercises 29–58, simplify. Then add or subtract the expressions, if possible. Assume the variables represent positive real numbers. **(See Examples 2 and 3.)**

29. $2\sqrt{12} + \sqrt{48}$

30. $5\sqrt{32} + 2\sqrt{50}$

31. $4\sqrt{45} - 6\sqrt{20}$

32. $8\sqrt{54} - 4\sqrt{24}$

33. $\dfrac{1}{2}\sqrt{8} + \dfrac{1}{3}\sqrt{18}$

34. $\dfrac{1}{4}\sqrt{32} - \dfrac{1}{5}\sqrt{50}$

35. $6p\sqrt{20p^2} + p^2\sqrt{80}$

36. $2q\sqrt{48} + \sqrt{27q^2}$

37. $-2\sqrt{2k} + 6\sqrt{8k}$

38. $5\sqrt{27x} - 4\sqrt{12x}$

39. $11\sqrt{a^4b} - a^2\sqrt{b} - 9a\sqrt{a^2b}$

40. $-7\sqrt{x^4y} + 5x^2\sqrt{y} - 6x\sqrt{x^2y}$

41. $4\sqrt{5} - \sqrt{5}$

42. $-3\sqrt{10} - \sqrt{10}$

43. $\dfrac{5}{6}z\sqrt{6} + \dfrac{7}{9}z\sqrt{6}$

44. $\dfrac{3}{4}a\sqrt{b} + \dfrac{1}{6}a\sqrt{b}$

45. $1.1\sqrt{10} - 5.6\sqrt{10} + 2.8\sqrt{10}$

46. $0.25\sqrt{x} + 1.50\sqrt{x} - 0.75\sqrt{x}$

47. $4\sqrt{x^3} - 2x\sqrt{x}$

48. $8\sqrt{y^9} - 2y^2\sqrt{y^5}$

49. $4\sqrt{7} + \sqrt{63} - 2\sqrt{28}$

50. $8\sqrt{3} - 2\sqrt{27} + \sqrt{75}$

51. $\sqrt{16w} + \sqrt{24w} + \sqrt{40w}$

52. $\sqrt{54y} + \sqrt{81y} - \sqrt{12y}$

53. $\sqrt{x^6y} + 5x^2\sqrt{x^2y}$

54. $7\sqrt{a^5b^2} - a^2\sqrt{ab^2}$

55. $4\sqrt{6} + 2\sqrt{3} - 8\sqrt{6}$

56. $-7\sqrt{y} - \sqrt{z} + 2\sqrt{z}$

57. $x\sqrt{8} - 2\sqrt{18x^2} + \sqrt{2x}$

58. $5\sqrt{p^5} - 2p\sqrt{p} + p\sqrt{16p^3}$

For Exercises 59 and 60, find the exact perimeter of each figure.

59.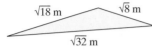
$\sqrt{18}$ m $\sqrt{8}$ m

$\sqrt{32}$ m

60.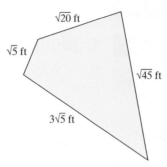
$\sqrt{20}$ ft

$\sqrt{5}$ ft

$\sqrt{45}$ ft

$3\sqrt{5}$ ft

61. Find the exact perimeter of a rectangle whose width is $2\sqrt{3}$ in. and whose length is $3\sqrt{12}$ in.

62. Find the exact perimeter of a square whose side length is $5\sqrt{8}$ cm.

For Exercises 63–68, determine the reason why the radical expressions cannot be combined by addition or subtraction. **(See Example 4.)**

63. $\sqrt{5} + 5\sqrt{2}$

64. $3\sqrt{10} + 10\sqrt{3}$

65. $3 + 5\sqrt{7}$

66. $-2 + 5\sqrt{11}$

67. $5\sqrt{2} + \sqrt[3]{2}$

68. $\sqrt[4]{6} - 3\sqrt{6}$

Expanding Your Skills

69. Find the slope of the line through the points: $(4, 2\sqrt{3})$ and $(1, \sqrt{3})$.

70. Find the slope of the line through the points: $(7, 4\sqrt{5})$ and $(2, 3\sqrt{5})$.

71. A golfer hits a golf ball at an angle of $30°$ with an initial velocity of 46 meters/second (m/sec). The horizontal position of the ball, x (measured in meters), depends on the number of seconds, t, after the ball is struck according to the equation:

$$x = 23t\sqrt{3}$$

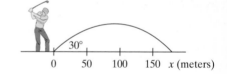

a. What is the horizontal position of the ball after 2 sec? Round the answer to the nearest meter.

b. What is the horizontal position of the ball after 4 sec? Round the answer to the nearest meter.

72. A long-jumper leaves the ground at an angle of $30°$ at a speed of 9 m/sec. The horizontal position of the long jumper, x (measured in meters), depends on the number of seconds, t, after he leaves the ground according to the equation:

$$x = 4.5t\sqrt{3}$$

a. What is the horizontal position of the long-jumper after 0.5 sec? Round the answer to the nearest hundredth of a meter.

b. What is the horizontal position of the long-jumper after 0.75 sec? Round the answer to the nearest hundredth of a meter.

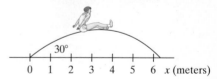

| Section 8.4 | **Multiplication of Radicals** |

Concepts

1. Multiplication Property of Radicals
2. Expressions of the Form $(\sqrt[n]{a})^n$
3. Special Case Products

1. Multiplication Property of Radicals

In this section, we will learn how to multiply radicals that have the same index. Recall from Section 8.2 the multiplication property of radicals.

Multiplication Property of Radicals

Let a and b represent real numbers such that $\sqrt[n]{a}$ and $\sqrt[n]{b}$ are both real. Then,

$$\sqrt[n]{a} \cdot \sqrt[n]{b} = \sqrt[n]{ab}$$

To multiply two radical expressions, use the multiplication property of radicals along with the commutative and associative properties of multiplication.

Skill Practice

Multiply the expressions and simplify the result. Assume the variables represent positive real numbers.

1. $\sqrt{2} \cdot \sqrt{5}$
2. $(-5z\sqrt{6})(4z\sqrt{2})$
3. $(9y\sqrt{x})\left(\frac{1}{3}y\sqrt{xy}\right)$

| **Example 1** | **Multiplying Radical Expressions** |

Multiply the expressions and simplify the result. Assume the variables represent positive real numbers.

a. $\sqrt{3} \cdot \sqrt{2}$　　**b.** $(5\sqrt{3})(2\sqrt{15})$　　**c.** $(6a\sqrt{ab})\left(\frac{1}{3}a\sqrt{a}\right)$

Solution:

a. $\sqrt{3} \cdot \sqrt{2} = \sqrt{6}$　　Multiplication property of radicals

b. $(5\sqrt{3})(2\sqrt{15}) = (5 \cdot 2)(\sqrt{3} \cdot \sqrt{15})$　　Regroup factors.

$\qquad = 10\sqrt{45}$　　Multiplication property of radicals

$\qquad = 10\sqrt{9 \cdot 5}$　　Simplify the radical.

$\qquad = 10 \cdot 3\sqrt{5}$

$\qquad = 30\sqrt{5}$

c. $(6a\sqrt{ab})\left(\frac{1}{3}a\sqrt{a}\right) = \left(6a \cdot \frac{1}{3}a\right)(\sqrt{ab} \cdot \sqrt{a})$　　Regroup factors.

$\qquad = 2a^2\sqrt{a^2b}$　　Multiplication property of radicals

$\qquad = 2a^2 \cdot a\sqrt{b}$　　Simplify the radical.

$\qquad = 2a^3\sqrt{b}$

When multiplying radical expressions with more than one term, we use the distributive property.

Answers

1. $\sqrt{10}$　　2. $-40z^2\sqrt{3}$
3. $3xy^2\sqrt{y}$

Example 2 **Multiplying Radical Expressions with Multiple Terms**

Multiply the expressions. Assume the variables represent positive real numbers.

a. $\sqrt{5}(4 + 3\sqrt{5})$ **b.** $(\sqrt{x} - 10)(\sqrt{y} + 4)$ **c.** $(2\sqrt{3} - \sqrt{5})(\sqrt{3} + 6\sqrt{5})$

Solution:

a. $\sqrt{5}(4 + 3\sqrt{5})$

$= \sqrt{5}(4) + \sqrt{5}(3\sqrt{5})$ Apply the distributive property.

$= 4\sqrt{5} + 3\sqrt{25}$ Multiplication property of radicals

$= 4\sqrt{5} + 3 \cdot 5$ Simplify the radical.

$= 4\sqrt{5} + 15$

b. $(\sqrt{x} - 10)(\sqrt{y} + 4)$

$= \sqrt{x}(\sqrt{y}) + \sqrt{x}(4) - 10(\sqrt{y}) - 10(4)$ Apply the distributive property.

$= \sqrt{xy} + 4\sqrt{x} - 10\sqrt{y} - 40$ Simplify.

c. $(2\sqrt{3} - \sqrt{5})(\sqrt{3} + 6\sqrt{5})$

$= 2\sqrt{3}(\sqrt{3}) + 2\sqrt{3}(6\sqrt{5}) - \sqrt{5}(\sqrt{3}) - \sqrt{5}(6\sqrt{5})$ Apply the distributive property.

$= 2\sqrt{9} + 12\sqrt{15} - \sqrt{15} - 6\sqrt{25}$ Multiplication property of radicals

$= 2 \cdot 3 + 11\sqrt{15} - 6 \cdot 5$ Simplify radicals. Combine *like* radicals.

$= 6 + 11\sqrt{15} - 30$

$= -24 + 11\sqrt{15}$ Combine *like* terms.

Skill Practice

Multiply the expressions and simplify the result. Assume the variables represent positive real numbers.

4. $\sqrt{7}(2\sqrt{7} - 4)$
5. $(\sqrt{x} + 2)(\sqrt{x} - 3)$
6. $(2\sqrt{a} + 4\sqrt{6}) \cdot$ $(\sqrt{a} - 3\sqrt{6})$

2. Expressions of the Form $(\sqrt[n]{a})^n$

The multiplication property of radicals can be used to simplify an expression of the form $(\sqrt{a})^2$, where $a \geq 0$.

$$(\sqrt{a})^2 = \sqrt{a} \cdot \sqrt{a} = \sqrt{a^2} = a$$

This logic can be applied to nth-roots. If $\sqrt[n]{a}$ is a real number, then $(\sqrt[n]{a})^n = a$.

Skill Practice

Simplify the expressions.

7. $(\sqrt{13})^2$
8. $(\sqrt[3]{y})^3$
9. $(2\sqrt{11})^2$

Example 3 **Simplifying Radical Expressions**

Simplify the expressions.

a. $(\sqrt{7})^2$ **b.** $(\sqrt[3]{x})^3$ **c.** $(3\sqrt{2})^2$

Solution:

a. $(\sqrt{7})^2 = 7$ **b.** $(\sqrt[3]{x})^3 = x$ **c.** $(3\sqrt{2})^2 = 3^2 \cdot (\sqrt{2})^2 = 9 \cdot 2 = 18$

Answers

4. $14 - 4\sqrt{7}$
5. $x - \sqrt{x} - 6$
6. $2a - 2\sqrt{6a} - 72$
7. 13   **8.** y **9.** 44

3. Special Case Products

From Example 2, you may have noticed a similarity between multiplying radical expressions and multiplying polynomials.

Recall from Section 5.6 that the square of a binomial results in a perfect square trinomial.

$$(a + b)^2 = a^2 + 2ab + b^2$$

$$(a - b)^2 = a^2 - 2ab + b^2$$

The same patterns occur when squaring a radical expression with two terms.

Example 4 Squaring a Two-Term Radical Expression

Square the radical expression. Assume the variables represent positive real numbers.

$$(\sqrt{x} + \sqrt{y})^2$$

Solution:

$(\sqrt{x} + \sqrt{y})^2$
This expression is in the form $(a + b)^2$, where $a = \sqrt{x}$ and $b = \sqrt{y}$.

$a^2 + 2ab + b^2$

$= (\sqrt{x})^2 + 2(\sqrt{x})(\sqrt{y}) + (\sqrt{y})^2$
Apply the formula $(a + b)^2 = a^2 + 2ab + b^2$.

$= x + 2\sqrt{xy} + y$
Simplify.

TIP: The product $(\sqrt{x} + \sqrt{y})^2$ can also be found using the distributive property.

$$(\sqrt{x} + \sqrt{y})^2 = (\sqrt{x} + \sqrt{y})(\sqrt{x} + \sqrt{y}) = \sqrt{x} \cdot \sqrt{x} + \sqrt{x} \cdot \sqrt{y} + \sqrt{y} \cdot \sqrt{x} + \sqrt{y} \cdot \sqrt{y}$$

$$= \sqrt{x^2} + \sqrt{xy} + \sqrt{xy} + \sqrt{y^2}$$

$$= x + 2\sqrt{xy} + y$$

Example 5 Squaring a Two-Term Radical Expression

Square the radical expression. $(\sqrt{2} - 4\sqrt{3})^2$

Solution:

$(\sqrt{2} - 4\sqrt{3})^2$
This expression is in the form $(a - b)^2$, where $a = \sqrt{2}$ and $b = 4\sqrt{3}$.

$a^2 - 2ab + b^2$

$(\sqrt{2})^2 - 2(\sqrt{2})(4\sqrt{3}) + (4\sqrt{3})^2$
Apply the formula $(a - b)^2 = a^2 - 2ab + b^2$.

$= 2 - 8\sqrt{6} + 16 \cdot 3$
Simplify.

$= 2 - 8\sqrt{6} + 48$

$= 50 - 8\sqrt{6}$

Answers
10. $p + 6\sqrt{p} + 9$
11. $23 - 6\sqrt{10}$

Recall from Section 5.6 that the product of two conjugate binomials results in a difference of squares.

$$(a + b)(a - b) = a^2 - b^2$$

The same pattern occurs when multiplying two conjugate radical expressions.

Example 6 **Multiplying Conjugate Radical Expressions**

Multiply the radical expressions. $(\sqrt{5} + 4)(\sqrt{5} - 4)$

Solution:

$(\sqrt{5} + 4)(\sqrt{5} - 4)$ This expression is in the form $(a + b)(a - b)$, where $a = \sqrt{5}$ and $b = 4$.

$\overset{a^2 - b^2}{}$

$= (\sqrt{5})^2 - (4)^2$ Apply the formula $(a + b)(a - b) = a^2 - b^2$.

$= 5 - 16$ Simplify.

$= -11$

TIP: The product $(\sqrt{5} + 4)(\sqrt{5} - 4)$ can also be found using the distributive property.

$(\sqrt{5} + 4)(\sqrt{5} - 4) = \sqrt{5} \cdot (\sqrt{5}) + \sqrt{5} \cdot (-4) + 4 \cdot (\sqrt{5}) + 4 \cdot (-4)$

$\qquad\qquad\qquad = 5 - 4\sqrt{5} + 4\sqrt{5} - 16$

$\qquad\qquad\qquad = 5 - 16$

$\qquad\qquad\qquad = -11$

Example 7 **Multiplying Conjugate Radical Expressions**

Multiply the radical expressions. Assume the variables represent positive real numbers.

$$(2\sqrt{c} - 3\sqrt{d})(2\sqrt{c} + 3\sqrt{d})$$

Solution:

$(2\sqrt{c} - 3\sqrt{d})(2\sqrt{c} + 3\sqrt{d})$ This expression is in the form $(a - b)(a + b)$, where $a = 2\sqrt{c}$ and $b = 3\sqrt{d}$.

$\overset{a^2 - b^2}{}$

$= (2\sqrt{c})^2 - (3\sqrt{d})^2$ Apply the formula $(a + b)(a - b) = a^2 - b^2$.

$= 4c - 9d$

Section 8.4   Practice Exercises

Vocabulary and Key Concepts

1. **a.** The multiplication property of radicals indicates that $\sqrt[n]{a} \cdot \sqrt[n]{b} = $ _____ provided that both $\sqrt[n]{a}$ and $\sqrt[n]{b}$ are real numbers.

    b. If $\sqrt[n]{a}$ is a real number, then $(\sqrt[n]{a})^n = $ _____.

    c. Two binomials $(x + \sqrt{2})$ and $(x - \sqrt{2})$ are called _____ of each other, and their product is $(x)^2 - (\sqrt{2})^2$.

Review Exercises

For Exercises 2–5, perform the indicated operations and simplify. Assume the variables represent positive real numbers.

2. $\sqrt{25} + \sqrt{16} - \sqrt{36}$ 3. $\sqrt{100} - \sqrt{4} + \sqrt{9}$ 4. $6x\sqrt{18} + 2\sqrt{2x^2}$ 5. $10\sqrt{zw^4} - w^2\sqrt{49z}$

6. What three conditions are needed for a radical expression to be in simplified form?

Concept 1: Multiplication Property of Radicals

For Exercises 7–26, multiply the expressions. Assume the variables represent positive real numbers. **(See Example 1.)**

7. $\sqrt{5} \cdot \sqrt{3}$ 8. $\sqrt{7} \cdot \sqrt{6}$ 9. $\sqrt{47} \cdot \sqrt{47}$ 10. $\sqrt{59} \cdot \sqrt{59}$

11. $\sqrt{b} \cdot \sqrt{b}$ 12. $\sqrt{t} \cdot \sqrt{t}$ 13. $(2\sqrt{15})(3\sqrt{p})$ 14. $(4\sqrt{2})(5\sqrt{q})$

15. $\sqrt{10} \cdot \sqrt{5}$ 16. $\sqrt{2} \cdot \sqrt{10}$ 17. $(-\sqrt{7})(-2\sqrt{14})$ 18. $(-6\sqrt{2})(-\sqrt{22})$

19. $(3x\sqrt{2})(\sqrt{14})$ 20. $(4y\sqrt{3})(\sqrt{6})$ 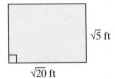 21. $\left(\frac{1}{6}x\sqrt{xy}\right)(24x\sqrt{x})$ 22. $\left(\frac{1}{4}u\sqrt{uv}\right)(8u\sqrt{v})$

23. $(6w\sqrt{5})(w\sqrt{8})$ 24. $(t\sqrt{2})(5\sqrt{6t})$ 25. $(-2\sqrt{3})(4\sqrt{5})$ 26. $(-\sqrt{7})(2\sqrt{3})$

For Exercises 27 and 28, find the exact perimeter and exact area of the rectangles.

27.

$\sqrt{5}$ ft

$\sqrt{20}$ ft

28.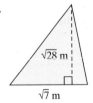

$\sqrt{8}$ in.

$\sqrt{2}$ in.

For Exercises 29 and 30, find the exact area of the triangles.

29.

$\sqrt{12}$ cm

$\sqrt{3}$ cm

30.

$\sqrt{28}$ m

$\sqrt{7}$ m

For Exercises 31–44, multiply the expressions. Assume the variables represent positive real numbers. **(See Example 2.)**

31. $\sqrt{3w} \cdot \sqrt{3w}$

32. $\sqrt{6p} \cdot \sqrt{6p}$

33. $(8\sqrt{5y})(-2\sqrt{2})$

34. $(4\sqrt{5x})(7\sqrt{3})$

35. $\sqrt{2}(\sqrt{6} - \sqrt{3})$

36. $\sqrt{5}(\sqrt{10} + \sqrt{7})$

37. $4\sqrt{x}(\sqrt{x} + 5)$

38. $2\sqrt{y}(3 - \sqrt{y})$

39. $(\sqrt{3} + 2\sqrt{10})(4\sqrt{3} - \sqrt{10})$

40. $(8\sqrt{7} - \sqrt{5})(\sqrt{7} + 3\sqrt{5})$

41. $(\sqrt{a} - 3b)(9\sqrt{a} - b)$

42. $(11\sqrt{m} + 4n)(\sqrt{m} + n)$

43. $(p + 2\sqrt{p})(8p + 3\sqrt{p} - 4)$

44. $(5s - \sqrt{s})(s + 5\sqrt{s} + 6)$

Concept 2: Expressions of the Form $(\sqrt[n]{a})^n$

For Exercises 45–52, simplify the expressions. Assume the variables represent positive real numbers. **(See Example 3.)**

45. $(\sqrt{10})^2$

46. $(\sqrt{23})^2$

47. $(\sqrt[3]{4})^3$

48. $(\sqrt[3]{29})^3$

49. $(\sqrt[4]{t})^4$

50. $(\sqrt[4]{xy})^4$

51. $(4\sqrt{c})^2$

52. $(10\sqrt{2pq})^2$

Concept 3: Special Case Products

For Exercises 53–60, multiply the radical expressions. Assume the variables represent positive real numbers. **(See Examples 4 and 5.)**

53. $(\sqrt{13} + 4)^2$

54. $(6 - \sqrt{11})^2$

55. $(\sqrt{a} - 2)^2$

56. $(\sqrt{p} + 3)^2$

57. $(2\sqrt{a} - 3)^2$

58. $(3\sqrt{w} + 4)^2$

59. $(\sqrt{10} - \sqrt{11})^2$

60. $(\sqrt{3} - \sqrt{2})^2$

For Exercises 61–72, multiply the radical expressions. Assume the variables represent positive real numbers. **(See Examples 6 and 7.)**

61. $(\sqrt{5} + 2)(\sqrt{5} - 2)$

62. $(\sqrt{3} - 4)(\sqrt{3} + 4)$

63. $(\sqrt{x} + \sqrt{y})(\sqrt{x} - \sqrt{y})$

64. $(\sqrt{a} + \sqrt{b})(\sqrt{a} - \sqrt{b})$

65. $(\sqrt{10} - \sqrt{11})(\sqrt{10} + \sqrt{11})$

66. $(\sqrt{3} - \sqrt{2})(\sqrt{3} + \sqrt{2})$

67. $(\sqrt{6} + \sqrt{2})(\sqrt{6} - \sqrt{2})$

68. $(\sqrt{15} - \sqrt{5})(\sqrt{15} + \sqrt{5})$

69. $(8\sqrt{x} - 2\sqrt{y})(8\sqrt{x} + 2\sqrt{y})$

70. $(4\sqrt{s} + 11\sqrt{t})(4\sqrt{s} - 11\sqrt{t})$

71. $(5\sqrt{3} - \sqrt{2})(5\sqrt{3} + \sqrt{2})$

72. $(2\sqrt{7} - 4\sqrt{3})(2\sqrt{7} + 4\sqrt{3})$

Mixed Exercises

For Exercises 73–84, multiply the expressions in parts (a) and (b) and compare the process used. Assume the variables represent positive real numbers.

73. a. $3(x + 2)$
b. $\sqrt{3}(\sqrt{x} + \sqrt{2})$

74. a. $-5(6 + y)$
b. $-\sqrt{5}(\sqrt{6} + \sqrt{y})$

75. a. $(2a + 3)^2$
b. $(2\sqrt{a} + 3)^2$

76. a. $(6 - z)^2$
b. $(\sqrt{6} - z)^2$

77. a. $(b - 5)(b + 5)$
b. $(\sqrt{b} - 5)(\sqrt{b} + 5)$

78. a. $(3w - 1)(3w + 1)$
b. $(3\sqrt{w} - 1)(3\sqrt{w} + 1)$

79. a. $(x - 2y)^2$
b. $(\sqrt{x} - 2\sqrt{y})^2$

80. a. $(5c + 2d)^2$
b. $(5\sqrt{c} + 2\sqrt{d})^2$

81. a. $(p - q)(p + q)$
b. $(\sqrt{p} - \sqrt{q})(\sqrt{p} + \sqrt{q})$

82. a. $(t - 3)(t + 3)$
b. $(\sqrt{t} - \sqrt{3})(\sqrt{t} + \sqrt{3})$

83. a. $(y - 3)^2$
b. $(\sqrt{x - 2} - 3)^2$

84. a. $(p + 4)^2$
b. $(\sqrt{x + 1} + 4)^2$

Section 8.5 | Division of Radicals and Rationalization

1. Simplified Form of a Radical

Recall the conditions for a radical to be simplified.

Simplified Form of a Radical

Consider any radical expression where the radicand is written as a product of prime factors. The expression is in simplified form if all of the following conditions are met:

1. The radicand has no factor raised to a power greater than or equal to the index.
2. There are no radicals in the denominator of a fraction.
3. The radicand does not contain a fraction.

The basis of the second and third conditions, which restrict radicals from the denominator of an expression, are largely historical. In some cases, removing a radical from the denominator of a fraction will create an expression that is computationally simpler.

The process to remove a radical from the denominator is called **rationalizing the denominator**. In this section, we will show three approaches that can be used to achieve the second and third conditions of a simplified radical.

1. Rationalizing by applying the division property of radicals
2. Rationalizing when the denominator contains a single radical term
3. Rationalizing when the denominator contains two terms involving square roots

2. Division Property of Radicals

The multiplication property of radicals enables a product within a radical to be separated and written as a product of radicals. We now state a similar property for radicals involving quotients.

Division Property of Radicals

Let a and b represent real numbers such that $\sqrt[n]{a}$ and $\sqrt[n]{b}$ are both real. Then,

$$\sqrt[n]{\frac{a}{b}} = \frac{\sqrt[n]{a}}{\sqrt[n]{b}} \qquad b \neq 0$$

The division property of radicals indicates that a quotient within a radicand can be written as a quotient of radicals provided the roots are real numbers. For example:

$$\sqrt{\frac{4}{9}} = \frac{\sqrt{4}}{\sqrt{9}}$$

The reverse process is also true. A quotient of radicals can be written as a single radical provided that the roots are real numbers and they have the same indices.

$$\text{same index} \left[\frac{\sqrt[3]{125}}{\sqrt[3]{8}} = \sqrt[3]{\frac{125}{8}} \right.$$

In Examples 1 and 2, we will apply the division property of radicals to simplify radical expressions.

Example 1 **Using the Division Property to Simplify Radicals**

Use the division property of radicals to simplify the expressions. Assume the variables represent positive real numbers.

a. $\sqrt{\dfrac{a^{10}}{b^4}}$ **b.** $\sqrt{\dfrac{20x^3}{9}}$

Solution:

a. $\sqrt{\dfrac{a^{10}}{b^4}}$ The radicand contains an irreducible fraction.

$= \dfrac{\sqrt{a^{10}}}{\sqrt{b^4}}$ Apply the division property to rewrite as a quotient of radicals.

$= \dfrac{a^5}{b^2}$ Simplify the radicals.

b. $\sqrt{\dfrac{20x^3}{9}}$ The radicand contains an irreducible fraction.

$= \dfrac{\sqrt{20x^3}}{\sqrt{9}}$ Apply the division property to rewrite as a quotient of radicals.

$= \dfrac{\sqrt{4 \cdot x^2 \cdot 5 \cdot x}}{\sqrt{9}}$ Factor the radicand in the numerator to simplify the radical.

$= \dfrac{2x\sqrt{5x}}{3}$ Simplify the radicals in the numerator and denominator. The expression is simplified since it now satisfies all conditions.

Skill Practice

Simplify the expressions.

1. $\sqrt{\dfrac{c^4}{49}}$

2. $\sqrt{\dfrac{12b^5}{25}}$

Answers

1. $\dfrac{c^2}{7}$ 2. $\dfrac{2b^2\sqrt{3b}}{5}$

Example 2 Using the Division Property to Simplify Radicals

Use the division property of radicals to simplify the expressions. Assume the variables represent positive real numbers.

a. $\dfrac{\sqrt[3]{9}}{\sqrt[3]{72}}$ 　　 b. $\dfrac{\sqrt{7y^3}}{\sqrt{y}}$

Solution:

a. $\dfrac{\sqrt[3]{9}}{\sqrt[3]{72}}$ 　　 There is a radical in the denominator of the fraction.

$= \sqrt[3]{\dfrac{9}{72}}$ 　　 Apply the division property to write the quotient under a single radical.

$= \sqrt[3]{\dfrac{1}{8}}$ 　　 Reduce to lowest terms.

$= \dfrac{1}{2}$ 　　 Simplify the radical.

b. $\dfrac{\sqrt{7y^3}}{\sqrt{y}}$ 　　 There is a radical in the denominator of the fraction.

$= \sqrt{\dfrac{7y^3}{y}}$ 　　 Apply the division property to write the quotient under a single radical.

$= \sqrt{7y^2}$ 　　 Simplify the fraction.

$= y\sqrt{7}$ 　　 Simplify the radical.

3. Rationalizing the Denominator: One Term

Examples 1 and 2 show that radical expressions can sometimes be simplified by using the division property of radicals. However, there are cases where other methods are needed. For example:

$\dfrac{2}{\sqrt{2}}$ and $\dfrac{2}{\sqrt{5} + \sqrt{3}}$ are two such cases.

To begin the first case, recall that the nth-root of a perfect nth power is easily simplified. For example:

$$\sqrt{x^2} = x \quad x \geq 0$$

Example 3 Rationalizing the Denominator: One Term

Simplify the expression. 　　 $\dfrac{2}{\sqrt{2}}$

Solution:

A square root of a perfect square is needed in the denominator to remove the radical.

$\dfrac{2}{\sqrt{2}} = \dfrac{2}{\sqrt{2}} \cdot \dfrac{\sqrt{2}}{\sqrt{2}}$ 　　 Multiply the numerator and denominator by $\sqrt{2}$ because $\sqrt{2} \cdot \sqrt{2} = \sqrt{2^2}$.

$= \dfrac{2\sqrt{2}}{\sqrt{2^2}}$ 　　 Multiply the radicals.

Answers

3. 5 　　 **4.** $z^4\sqrt{10}$ 　　 **5.** $\dfrac{3\sqrt{5}}{5}$

$$= \frac{2\sqrt{2}}{2} \qquad \text{Simplify.}$$

$$= \frac{2\sqrt{2}}{2} \qquad \text{Reduce the fraction to lowest terms.}$$

$$= \sqrt{2}$$

Example 4 **Rationalizing the Denominator: One Term**

Simplify the expression. Assume x represents a positive real number. $\sqrt{\dfrac{x}{5}}$

Solution:

$$\sqrt{\frac{x}{5}} \qquad \text{The radicand contains an irreducible fraction.}$$

$$= \frac{\sqrt{x}}{\sqrt{5}} \qquad \text{Apply the division property of radicals.}$$

$$= \frac{\sqrt{x}}{\sqrt{5}} \cdot \frac{\sqrt{5}}{\sqrt{5}} \qquad \begin{array}{l}\text{Multiply the numerator and denominator by } \sqrt{5} \\ \text{because } \sqrt{5} \cdot \sqrt{5} = \sqrt{5^2}.\end{array}$$

$$= \frac{\sqrt{5x}}{\sqrt{5^2}} \qquad \text{Multiply the radicals.}$$

$$= \frac{\sqrt{5x}}{5} \qquad \text{Simplify the radicals.}$$

> **Skill Practice**
>
> Simplify the expression by rationalizing the denominator.
>
> **6.** $\sqrt{\dfrac{7}{10}}$

> **Avoiding Mistakes**
>
> In the expression $\dfrac{\sqrt{5x}}{5}$, do not try to "cancel" the factor of $\sqrt{5}$ from the numerator with the factor of 5 in the denominator. $\sqrt{5}$ and 5 are not equal.

Example 5 **Rationalizing the Denominator: One Term**

Simplify the expression. Assume w represents a positive real number.

$$\frac{14\sqrt{w}}{\sqrt{7}}$$

Solution:

$$\frac{14\sqrt{w}}{\sqrt{7}} \qquad \text{Fraction contains a radical in the denominator.}$$

$$= \frac{14\sqrt{w}}{\sqrt{7}} \cdot \frac{\sqrt{7}}{\sqrt{7}} \qquad \begin{array}{l}\text{Multiply the numerator and denominator by } \sqrt{7} \\ \text{because } \sqrt{7} \cdot \sqrt{7} = \sqrt{7^2}.\end{array}$$

$$= \frac{14\sqrt{7w}}{\sqrt{7^2}} \qquad \text{Multiply the radicals.}$$

$$= \frac{14\sqrt{7w}}{7} \qquad \text{Simplify.}$$

$$= \frac{\overset{2}{14}\sqrt{7w}}{\underset{1}{7}} \qquad \text{Reduce to lowest terms.}$$

$$= 2\sqrt{7w}$$

> **Skill Practice**
>
> Simplify the expression by rationalizing the denominator.
>
> **7.** $\dfrac{6y}{\sqrt{3}}$

> **TIP:** In the expression
>
> $$\frac{14\sqrt{7w}}{7}$$
>
> the factor of 14 and the factor of 7 may be reduced because both factors are outside the radical.
>
> $$\frac{14\sqrt{7w}}{7} = \frac{14}{7} \cdot \sqrt{7w}$$
>
> $$= 2\sqrt{7w}$$

Answers

6. $\dfrac{\sqrt{70}}{10}$ **7.** $2y\sqrt{3}$

Example 6 **Rationalizing the Denominator: One Term**

Simplify the expression. Assume w represents a positive real number.

$$\sqrt{\dfrac{w}{12}}$$

Solution:

$\sqrt{\dfrac{w}{12}}$ The radical contains an irreducible fraction.

$= \dfrac{\sqrt{w}}{\sqrt{12}}$ Apply the division property of radicals.

$= \dfrac{\sqrt{w}}{\sqrt{4 \cdot 3}}$ Factor 12 to simplify the radical.

$= \dfrac{\sqrt{w}}{2\sqrt{3}}$ The $\sqrt{3}$ in the denominator needs to be rationalized.

$= \dfrac{\sqrt{w}}{2\sqrt{3}} \cdot \dfrac{\sqrt{3}}{\sqrt{3}}$ Multiply the numerator and denominator by $\sqrt{3}$ because $\sqrt{3} \cdot \sqrt{3} = \sqrt{3^2}$.

$= \dfrac{\sqrt{3w}}{2\sqrt{3^2}}$ Multiply the radicals.

$= \dfrac{\sqrt{3w}}{2 \cdot 3}$ Simplify.

$= \dfrac{\sqrt{3w}}{6}$ This cannot be simplified further because 3 is inside the radical and 6 is not.

4. Rationalizing the Denominator: Two Terms

Recall from the multiplication of polynomials that the product of two conjugates results in a difference of squares.

$$(a + b)(a - b) = a^2 - b^2$$

If either a or b has a square root factor, the expression will simplify without a radical; that is, the expression is rationalized. For example,

$$(\sqrt{5} - \sqrt{3})(\sqrt{5} + \sqrt{3}) = (\sqrt{5})^2 - (\sqrt{3})^2$$
$$= 5 - 3$$
$$= 2$$

Multiplying a binomial by its conjugate is the basis for rationalizing a denominator with two terms involving square roots.

Example 7   Rationalizing the Denominator: Two Terms

Simplify the expression by rationalizing the denominator. $\dfrac{2}{\sqrt{6} + 2}$

Solution:

$\dfrac{2}{\sqrt{6} + 2}$ To rationalize a denominator with two terms, multiply the numerator and denominator by the conjugate of the denominator.

$= \dfrac{2}{(\sqrt{6} + 2)} \cdot \dfrac{(\sqrt{6} - 2)}{(\sqrt{6} - 2)}$

       Conjugates

The denominator is in the form $(a + b)(a - b)$, where $a = \sqrt{6}$ and $b = 2$.

$= \dfrac{2(\sqrt{6} - 2)}{(\sqrt{6})^2 - (2)^2}$ In the denominator, apply the formula $(a + b)(a - b) = a^2 - b^2$.

$= \dfrac{2(\sqrt{6} - 2)}{6 - 4}$ Simplify.

$= \dfrac{2(\sqrt{6} - 2)}{2}$

$= \dfrac{\overset{1}{2}(\sqrt{6} - 2)}{2}$ Simplify to lowest terms.

$= \sqrt{6} - 2$

Skill Practice

Simplify the expression by rationalizing the denominator.

9. $\dfrac{6}{\sqrt{3} - 1}$

Example 8   Rationalizing the Denominator: Two Terms

Simplify the expression by rationalizing the denominator. Assume x represents a positive real number.

$$\dfrac{\sqrt{x} + \sqrt{2}}{\sqrt{x} - \sqrt{2}}$$

Solution:

$\dfrac{\sqrt{x} + \sqrt{2}}{\sqrt{x} - \sqrt{2}} = \dfrac{(\sqrt{x} + \sqrt{2})}{(\sqrt{x} - \sqrt{2})} \cdot \dfrac{(\sqrt{x} + \sqrt{2})}{(\sqrt{x} + \sqrt{2})}$ Multiply the numerator and denominator by the conjugate of the denominator.

       Conjugates

$= \dfrac{(\sqrt{x} + \sqrt{2})^2}{(\sqrt{x} - \sqrt{2})(\sqrt{x} + \sqrt{2})}$

$= \dfrac{(\sqrt{x})^2 + 2(\sqrt{x})(\sqrt{2}) + (\sqrt{2})^2}{(\sqrt{x})^2 - (\sqrt{2})^2}$ Simplify using special case products.

$= \dfrac{x + 2\sqrt{2x} + 2}{x - 2}$ Simplify the radicals.

Skill Practice

Simplify the expression by rationalizing the denominators.

10. $\dfrac{\sqrt{y} - \sqrt{5}}{\sqrt{y} + \sqrt{5}}$

Answers

9. $3\sqrt{3} + 3$

10. $\dfrac{y - 2\sqrt{5y} + 5}{y - 5}$

5. Simplifying Quotients That Contain Radicals

Sometimes a radical expression within a quotient must be reduced to lowest terms. This is demonstrated in the next example.

Skill Practice

Simplify the expression.

11. $\dfrac{6 - \sqrt{24}}{12}$

Avoiding Mistakes

Remember that it is not correct to reduce *terms* within a rational expression. In the expression

$$\dfrac{4 - 2\sqrt{5}}{10}$$

do not try to reduce the 4 and the 10. Only common *factors* can be canceled.

Answer

11. $\dfrac{3 - \sqrt{6}}{6}$

Example 9 Simplifying a Radical Quotient to Lowest Terms

Simplify the expression $\dfrac{4 - \sqrt{20}}{10}$.

Solution:

$\dfrac{4 - \sqrt{20}}{10}$ First, factor 20 to simplify the radical.

$= \dfrac{4 - \sqrt{4 \cdot 5}}{10}$

$= \dfrac{4 - 2\sqrt{5}}{10}$ Simplify the radical.

$= \dfrac{2(2 - \sqrt{5})}{2 \cdot 5}$ Factor out the GCF.

$= \dfrac{2(2 - \sqrt{5})}{2 \cdot 5}$ Reduce to lowest terms.

$= \dfrac{2 - \sqrt{5}}{5}$

Section 8.5 Practice Exercises

Vocabulary and Key Concepts

1. **a.** In the simplified form of a radical, the radicand has no factor raised to a power greater than or equal to the _____ .

   b. In the simplified form of a radical, there are no radicals in the _____ of a fraction.

   c. The process of removing a radical from the denominator of a fraction is called _____ the denominator.

   d. The division property of radicals indicates that $\sqrt[n]{\dfrac{a}{b}} =$ _____ provided that both $\sqrt[n]{a}$ and $\sqrt[n]{b}$ are real numbers and that $b \neq 0$.

   e. To rationalize the denominator for the expression $\dfrac{\sqrt{x} + 3}{\sqrt{x} - 2}$, multiply the numerator and denominator by the conjugate of the _____ .

Review Exercises

For Exercises 2–10, perform the indicated operations. Assume the variables represent positive real numbers.

2. $x\sqrt{45} + 4\sqrt{20x^2}$

3. $(2\sqrt{y} + 3)(3\sqrt{y} + 7)$

4. $(4\sqrt{w} - 2)(2\sqrt{w} - 4)$

5. $4\sqrt{3} + \sqrt{5} \cdot \sqrt{15}$

6. $\sqrt{7} \cdot \sqrt{21} + 2\sqrt{27}$

7. $(5 - \sqrt{a})^2$

8. $(\sqrt{z} + 3)^2$

9. $(\sqrt{2} + \sqrt{7})(\sqrt{2} - \sqrt{7})$

10. $(\sqrt{3} + 5)(\sqrt{3} - 5)$

Concept 2: Division Property of Radicals

For Exercises 11–30, use the division property of radicals, if necessary, to simplify the expressions. Assume the variables represent positive real numbers. **(See Examples 1 and 2.)**

11. $\sqrt{\dfrac{3}{16}}$

12. $\sqrt{\dfrac{7}{25}}$

13. $\sqrt{\dfrac{a^4}{b^4}}$

14. $\sqrt{\dfrac{y^6}{z^2}}$

15. $\sqrt{\dfrac{c^3}{4}}$

16. $\sqrt{\dfrac{d^5}{9}}$

17. $\sqrt[3]{\dfrac{x^2}{27}}$

18. $\sqrt[3]{\dfrac{c^2}{8}}$

19. $\sqrt[3]{\dfrac{y^5}{27y^3}}$

20. $\sqrt[3]{\dfrac{7ac}{64c^4}}$

21. $\sqrt{\dfrac{200}{81}}$

22. $\sqrt{\dfrac{80}{49}}$

23. $\dfrac{\sqrt{8}}{\sqrt{50}}$

24. $\dfrac{\sqrt{21}}{\sqrt{12}}$

25. $\dfrac{\sqrt{p}}{\sqrt{4p^3}}$

26. $\dfrac{\sqrt{9t}}{\sqrt{t^5}}$

27. $\dfrac{\sqrt[3]{z^5}}{\sqrt[3]{z^2}}$

28. $\dfrac{\sqrt[3]{a^7}}{\sqrt[3]{a}}$

29. $\dfrac{\sqrt[3]{24x^5}}{\sqrt[3]{3x^4}}$

30. $\dfrac{\sqrt[3]{2y^8}}{\sqrt[3]{54y^7}}$

Concept 3: Rationalizing the Denominator: One Term

For Exercises 31–50, rationalize the denominators. Assume the variables and the variable expressions represent positive real numbers. **(See Examples 3–6.)**

31. $\dfrac{1}{\sqrt{6}}$

32. $\dfrac{5}{\sqrt{2}}$

33. $\dfrac{15}{\sqrt{5}}$

34. $\dfrac{14}{\sqrt{7}}$

35. $\dfrac{6}{\sqrt{x+1}}$

36. $\dfrac{8}{\sqrt{y-3}}$

37. $\sqrt{\dfrac{6}{x}}$

38. $\sqrt{\dfrac{8}{y}}$

39. $\sqrt{\dfrac{3}{7}}$

40. $\sqrt{\dfrac{5}{11}}$

41. $\dfrac{10}{\sqrt{6y}}$

42. $\dfrac{15}{\sqrt{3w}}$

43. $\dfrac{9}{2\sqrt{6}}$

44. $\dfrac{15}{4\sqrt{10}}$

45. $\sqrt{\dfrac{p}{27}}$

46. $\sqrt{\dfrac{x}{32}}$

47. $\dfrac{5}{\sqrt{20}}$

48. $\dfrac{8}{\sqrt{24}}$

49. $\sqrt{\dfrac{x^2}{y^3}}$

50. $\sqrt{\dfrac{a}{b^5}}$

Concept 4: Rationalizing the Denominator: Two Terms

For Exercises 51 and 52, multiply the conjugates.

51. $(\sqrt{2}+3)(\sqrt{2}-3)$

52. $(\sqrt{3}+\sqrt{7})(\sqrt{3}-\sqrt{7})$

53. What is the conjugate of $\sqrt{5}-\sqrt{3}$? Multiply $\sqrt{5}-\sqrt{3}$ by its conjugate.

54. What is the conjugate of $\sqrt{7}+\sqrt{2}$? Multiply $\sqrt{7}+\sqrt{2}$ by its conjugate.

55. What is the conjugate of $\sqrt{x}+10$? Multiply $\sqrt{x}+10$ by its conjugate.

56. What is the conjugate of $12-\sqrt{y}$? Multiply $12-\sqrt{y}$ by its conjugate.

For Exercises 57–68, rationalize the denominators. Assume the variables represent positive real numbers.
(See Examples 7 and 8.)

57. $\dfrac{4}{\sqrt{2}+3}$

58. $\dfrac{6}{4-\sqrt{3}}$

59. $\dfrac{1}{\sqrt{5}-\sqrt{2}}$

60. $\dfrac{2}{\sqrt{3}+\sqrt{7}}$

61. $\dfrac{\sqrt{8}}{\sqrt{3}+1}$

62. $\dfrac{\sqrt{18}}{1-\sqrt{2}}$

63. $\dfrac{1}{\sqrt{x}-\sqrt{3}}$

64. $\dfrac{1}{\sqrt{y}+\sqrt{5}}$

65. $\dfrac{2-\sqrt{3}}{2+\sqrt{3}}$

66. $\dfrac{\sqrt{3}-\sqrt{2}}{\sqrt{3}+\sqrt{2}}$

67. $\dfrac{\sqrt{5}+4}{2-\sqrt{5}}$

68. $\dfrac{3+\sqrt{2}}{\sqrt{2}-5}$

Concept 5: Simplifying Quotients That Contain Radicals

For Exercises 69–76, simplify the expression. (See Example 9.)

69. $\dfrac{10-\sqrt{50}}{5}$

70. $\dfrac{4+\sqrt{12}}{2}$

71. $\dfrac{21+\sqrt{98}}{14}$

72. $\dfrac{3-\sqrt{18}}{6}$

73. $\dfrac{2-\sqrt{28}}{2}$

74. $\dfrac{5+\sqrt{75}}{5}$

75. $\dfrac{14+\sqrt{72}}{6}$

76. $\dfrac{15-\sqrt{125}}{10}$

Recall that a radical is simplified if

1. The radicand has no factor raised to a power greater than or equal to the index.

2. There are no radicals in the denominator of a fraction.

3. The radicand does not contain a fraction.

For Exercises 77–80, state which condition(s) fails. Then simplify the radical.

77. **a.** $\sqrt{8x^9}$ **b.** $\dfrac{5}{\sqrt{5x}}$ **c.** $\sqrt{\dfrac{1}{3}}$

78. **a.** $\sqrt{\dfrac{7}{2}}$ **b.** $\sqrt{18y^6}$ **c.** $\dfrac{2}{\sqrt{4x}}$

79. **a.** $\dfrac{3}{\sqrt{x}+1}$ **b.** $\sqrt{\dfrac{9w^2}{t}}$ **c.** $\sqrt{24a^5b^9}$

80. **a.** $\sqrt{\dfrac{12}{z^3}}$ **b.** $\dfrac{4}{\sqrt{a}-\sqrt{b}}$ **c.** $\sqrt[3]{27m^3n^7}$

Mixed Exercises

For Exercises 81–96, simplify the radical expressions, if possible. Assume the variables represent positive real numbers.

81. $\sqrt{45}$

82. $-\sqrt{108y^4}$

83. $-\sqrt{\dfrac{18w^2}{25}}$

84. $\sqrt{\dfrac{8a^2}{7}}$

85. $\sqrt{-36}$

86. $\sqrt{54b^5}$

87. $\sqrt{\dfrac{s^2}{t}}$

88. $\dfrac{x+\sqrt{y}}{x-\sqrt{y}}$

89. $\dfrac{\sqrt{2m^5}}{\sqrt{8m}}$

90. $\dfrac{\sqrt{10w}}{\sqrt{5w^3}}$

91. $\sqrt{\dfrac{81}{t^3}}$

92. $-\sqrt{a^3bc^6}$

93. $\dfrac{3}{\sqrt{11} + \sqrt{5}}$

94. $\dfrac{4}{\sqrt{10} + \sqrt{2}}$

95. $\dfrac{\sqrt{a} + \sqrt{b}}{\sqrt{a} - \sqrt{b}}$

96. $\dfrac{\sqrt{x} + 1}{\sqrt{x} - 1}$

Expanding Your Skills

97. Find the slope of the line through the points: $(5\sqrt{2}, 3)$ and $(\sqrt{2}, 6)$.

98. Find the slope of the line through the points: $(4\sqrt{5}, -1)$ and $(6\sqrt{5}, -5)$.

99. Find the slope of the line through the points: $(\sqrt{3}, -1)$ and $(4\sqrt{3}, 0)$.

100. Find the slope of the line through the points: $(-2\sqrt{7}, -5)$ and $(\sqrt{7}, 2)$.

Problem Recognition Exercises

Operations on Radicals

For Exercises 1–10, simplify each expression. Assume that all variables represent positive real numbers.

1. a. $(\sqrt{3})(\sqrt{6})$ **b.** $\sqrt{3} + \sqrt{6}$ **c.** $\dfrac{\sqrt{6}}{\sqrt{3}}$

2. a. $\dfrac{\sqrt{14}}{\sqrt{2}}$ **b.** $(\sqrt{2})(\sqrt{14})$ **c.** $\sqrt{2} + \sqrt{14}$

3. a. $(3\sqrt{z})^2$ **b.** $(3 + \sqrt{z})^2$ **c.** $(3 + \sqrt{z})(3 - \sqrt{z})$

4. a. $(4 - \sqrt{x})^2$ **b.** $(4 - \sqrt{x})(4 + \sqrt{x})$ **c.** $(4\sqrt{x})^2$

5. a. $\dfrac{12}{\sqrt{2x}}$ **b.** $\sqrt{\dfrac{12}{2x}}$ **c.** $\dfrac{12}{\sqrt{2} + x}$

6. a. $\dfrac{15}{3 - \sqrt{y}}$ **b.** $\dfrac{15}{\sqrt{3y}}$ **c.** $\sqrt{\dfrac{15}{3y}}$

7. a. $(2\sqrt{5} + 1) + (\sqrt{5} - 2)$ **b.** $(2\sqrt{5} + 1)(\sqrt{5} - 2)$ **c.** $2\sqrt{5}(\sqrt{5} - 2)$

8. a. $(4\sqrt{3} - 5)(\sqrt{3} + 4)$ **b.** $4\sqrt{3}(\sqrt{3} + 4)$ **c.** $(4\sqrt{3} - 5) - (\sqrt{3} + 4)$

9. a. $\sqrt{16a^{15}}$ **b.** $\sqrt[3]{16a^{15}}$

10. a. $\sqrt[3]{27y^9}$ **b.** $\sqrt{27y^9}$

Section 8.6 Radical Equations

1. Solving Radical Equations

Definition of a Radical Equation

An equation with one or more radicals containing a variable is called a **radical equation**.

For example, $\sqrt{x} = 5$ is a radical equation. Recall that $(\sqrt[n]{a})^n = a$ provided $\sqrt[n]{a}$ is a real number. The basis to solve a radical equation is to eliminate the radical by raising both sides of the equation to a power equal to the index of the radical.

To solve the equation $\sqrt{x} = 5$, square both sides of the equation.

$$\sqrt{x} = 5$$
$$(\sqrt{x})^2 = (5)^2$$
$$x = 25$$

By raising each side of a radical equation to a power equal to the index of the radical, a new equation is produced. However, it is important to note that the new equation may have **extraneous solutions**; that is, some or all of the solutions to the new equation may *not* be solutions to the original radical equation. For this reason, it is necessary to check *all* potential solutions in the original equation. For example, consider the equation $\sqrt{x} = -10$. This equation has no solution because by definition, the principal square root of x must be a nonnegative number. However, if we square both sides of the equation, it appears as though a solution exists.

$$(\sqrt{x})^2 = (-10)^2$$
$$x = 100 \qquad \text{The value 100 does not check in the original}$$

equation $\sqrt{x} = -10$. Therefore, 100 is an extraneous solution.

Solving a Radical Equation

Step 1 Isolate the radical. If an equation has more than one radical, choose one of the radicals to isolate.

Step 2 Raise each side of the equation to a power equal to the index of the radical.

Step 3 Solve the resulting equation.

Step 4 Check the potential solutions in the original equation.*

*In solving radical equations, extraneous solutions *potentially occur* only when each side of the equation is raised to an even power.

Example 1 Solving a Radical Equation

Solve the equation. $\sqrt{2x + 1} + 5 = 8$

Solution:

$\sqrt{2x + 1} + 5 = 8$

$\sqrt{2x + 1} = 8 - 5$ Isolate the radical.

$\sqrt{2x + 1} = 3$

$(\sqrt{2x + 1})^2 = (3)^2$ Raise both sides to a power equal to the index of the radical.

$2x + 1 = 9$ Simplify both sides.

$2x = 8$ Solve the resulting equation (the equation is

$x = 4$ linear).

Check: Check 4 as a potential solution.

$\sqrt{2x + 1} + 5 = 8$

$\sqrt{2(4) + 1} + 5 \stackrel{?}{=} 8$

$\sqrt{8 + 1} + 5 \stackrel{?}{=} 8$

$\sqrt{9} + 5 \stackrel{?}{=} 8$

$3 + 5 \stackrel{?}{=} 8$ ✔   The answer checks.

The solution is 4.

Skill Practice

Solve the equation.
1. $\sqrt{p - 4} - 2 = 4$

Example 2 Solving a Radical Equation

Solve the equation. $8 + \sqrt{x + 2} = 7$

Solution:

$8 + \sqrt{x + 2} = 7$

$\sqrt{x + 2} = 7 - 8$ Isolate the radical.

$\sqrt{x + 2} = -1$

$(\sqrt{x + 2})^2 = (-1)^2$ Raise both sides to a power equal to the index of the radical.

$x + 2 = 1$ Simplify.

$x = -1$ Solve the resulting equation.

Check: Check -1 as a potential solution.

$8 + \sqrt{x + 2} = 7$

$8 + \sqrt{(-1) + 2} \stackrel{?}{=} 7$

$8 + \sqrt{1} \stackrel{?}{=} 7$

$8 + 1 \neq 7$ The value -1 does not check. It is an extraneous solution.

There is no solution to the equation.

Skill Practice

Solve the equation.
2. $\sqrt{2y + 5} + 7 = 4$

TIP: After isolating the radical in Example 2, the equation shows a square root equated to a negative number.

$\sqrt{x + 2} = -1$

By definition, a principal square root of any real number must be nonnegative. Therefore, there can be no solution to this equation.

Answers

1. 40
2. No solution (The value 2 does not check.)

Example 3 **Solving a Radical Equation**

Solve the equation. $p + 4 = \sqrt{p + 6}$

Solution:

$$p + 4 = \sqrt{p + 6}$$ The radical is already isolated.

$$(p + 4)^2 = (\sqrt{p + 6})^2$$ Raise both sides to a power equal to the index.

$$p^2 + 8p + 16 = p + 6$$

$$p^2 + 7p + 10 = 0$$ Solve the resulting equation (the equation is quadratic).

$$(p + 5)(p + 2) = 0$$ Set the equation equal to zero and factor.

$$p + 5 = 0 \quad \text{or} \quad p + 2 = 0$$ Set each factor equal to zero.

$$p = -5 \quad \text{or} \quad p = -2$$ Solve for p.

$\underline{\text{Check: }} p = -5$

$$p + 4 = \sqrt{p + 6}$$

$$(-5) + 4 \overset{?}{=} \sqrt{(-5) + 6}$$

$$-1 \overset{?}{=} \sqrt{1}$$

$$-1 \neq 1 \qquad \text{Does not check.}$$

$\underline{\text{Check: }} p = -2$

$$p + 4 = \sqrt{p + 6}$$

$$(-2) + 4 \overset{?}{=} \sqrt{(-2) + 6}$$

$$2 \overset{?}{=} \sqrt{4}$$

$$2 \overset{?}{=} 2 \quad ✔ \text{ The solution checks.}$$

The only solution is -2. The value -5 does not check.

Example 4 **Solving a Radical Equation**

Solve the equation. $2\sqrt[3]{2x - 3} - \sqrt[3]{x + 6} = 0$

Solution:

$$2\sqrt[3]{2x - 3} - \sqrt[3]{x + 6} = 0$$

$$2\sqrt[3]{2x - 3} = \sqrt[3]{x + 6}$$ Isolate one of the radicals.

$$\left(2\sqrt[3]{2x - 3}\right)^3 = \left(\sqrt[3]{x + 6}\right)^3$$ Raise both sides to a power equal to the index.

$$(2)^3\left(\sqrt[3]{2x - 3}\right)^3 = \left(\sqrt[3]{x + 6}\right)^3$$ On the left-hand side, be sure to cube both factors, $(2)^3$ and $\left(\sqrt[3]{2x - 3}\right)^3$.

$$8(2x - 3) = x + 6$$ Solve the resulting equation.

$$16x - 24 = x + 6$$

$$15x = 30$$

$$x = 2$$

$\underline{\text{Check:}}$

$$2\sqrt[3]{2x - 3} - \sqrt[3]{x + 6} = 0$$ Check the potential solution, 2.

$$2\sqrt[3]{2(2) - 3} - \sqrt[3]{2 + 6} \overset{?}{=} 0$$

$$2\sqrt[3]{4 - 3} - \sqrt[3]{8} \overset{?}{=} 0$$

$$2\sqrt[3]{1} - 2 \overset{?}{=} 0$$

$$2 - 2 \overset{?}{=} 0 \quad ✔$$ The solution checks.

The solution is 2.

2. Translations Involving Radical Equations

Example 5   Translating to a Radical Equation

The principal square root of the sum of a number and three is equal to seven. Find the number.

Solution:

Let x represent the number.   Label the unknown.

$$\sqrt{x + 3} = 7$$

Translate the verbal model into an algebraic equation.

$$(\sqrt{x + 3})^2 = (7)^2$$

The radical is already isolated. Square both sides.

$$x + 3 = 49$$

The resulting equation is linear.

$$x = 46$$

Solve for x.

Check: Check 46 as a potential solution.

$$\sqrt{x + 3} = 7$$

$$\sqrt{46 + 3} \stackrel{?}{=} 7$$

$$\sqrt{49} \stackrel{?}{=} 7$$

$$7 \stackrel{?}{=} 7 ✔ \quad \text{The solution checks.}$$

The number is 46.

3. Applications of Radical Equations

Example 6   Using a Radical Equation in an Application

For a small company, the weekly sales, y, of its product are related to the money spent on advertising, x, according to the equation:

$$y = 100\sqrt{x}$$

a. Find the amount in sales if the company spends $100 on advertising.

b. Find the amount in sales if the company spends $625 on advertising.

c. Find the amount the company spent on advertising if its sales for 1 week totaled $2000.

Solution:

a. $y = 100\sqrt{x}$

$\quad = 100\sqrt{100}$ Substitute $x = 100$.

$\quad = 100(10)$

$\quad = 1000$

The amount in sales is $1000.

b. $y = 100\sqrt{x}$

$\quad = 100\sqrt{625} \qquad$ Substitute $x = 625$.

$\quad = 100(25)$

$\quad = 2500$

The amount in sales is $2500.

c. $\quad y = 100\sqrt{x}$

$\quad 2000 = 100\sqrt{x} \qquad$ Substitute $y = 2000$.

$\quad \dfrac{2000}{100} = \dfrac{\cancel{100}\sqrt{x}}{\cancel{100}} \qquad$ Isolate the radical. Divide both sides by 100.

$\quad 20 = \sqrt{x} \qquad$ Simplify.

$\quad (20)^2 = (\sqrt{x})^2 \qquad$ Raise both sides to a power equal to the index.

$\quad 400 = x \qquad$ Simplify both sides.

$\quad \underline{\text{Check:}} \qquad$ Check 400 as a potential solution.

$\quad y = 100\sqrt{x}$

$\quad 2000 \stackrel{?}{=} 100\sqrt{400}$

$\quad 2000 \stackrel{?}{=} 100(20)$

$\quad 2000 \stackrel{?}{=} 2000 \ ✔ \qquad$ The solution checks.

The amount spent on advertising was $400.

Section 8.6 Practice Exercises

Vocabulary and Key Concepts

1. a. An equation with one or more radicals containing a variable is called a _____ equation.

  b. A potential solution that does not check in the original equation is called a(n) _____ solution.

  c. What is the first step to solve the equation $\sqrt{x + 2} - 3 = 7$?

  d. To solve the equation $\sqrt[3]{x - 4} = 2$, raise both sides of the equation to the _____ power.

Review Exercises

For Exercises 2–5, rationalize the denominators.

2. $\dfrac{1}{\sqrt{3} - \sqrt{7}}$

3. $\dfrac{1}{\sqrt{2} + \sqrt{10}}$

4. $\dfrac{6}{\sqrt{6}}$

5. $\dfrac{2\sqrt{2}}{\sqrt{3}}$

6. Simplify the expression. $\dfrac{10 - \sqrt{75}}{5}$

For Exercises 7–10, square the binomials.

7. $(x + 4)^2$

8. $(3 - y)^2$

9. $(\sqrt{x} + 4)^2$

10. $(\sqrt{3} - \sqrt{y})^2$

For Exercises 11–14, simplify the expressions. Assume the variable expressions represent positive real numbers.

11. $(\sqrt{2x-3})^2$ **12.** $(\sqrt{m+6})^2$ **13.** $(t+1)^2$ **14.** $(y-4)^2$

Concept 1: Solving Radical Equations

For Exercises 15–47, solve the equations. Be sure to check all of the potential answers. **(See Examples 1–4.)**

15. $\sqrt{t} = 6$

16. $\sqrt{p} = 5$

17. $\sqrt{x+1} = 4$

18. $\sqrt{x-3} = 7$

19. $\sqrt{y-4} = -5$

20. $\sqrt{p+6} = -1$

21. $\sqrt{5-t} = 0$

22. $\sqrt{13+m} = 0$

23. $\sqrt{2n+10} = 3$

24. $\sqrt{1-q} = 15$

25. $\sqrt{6w} - 8 = -2$

26. $\sqrt{2z} - 11 = -3$

27. $\sqrt{5a-4} - 2 = 4$

28. $\sqrt{3b+4} - 3 = 2$

29. $\sqrt{2x-3} + 7 = 3$

30. $\sqrt{8y+1} + 5 = 1$

31. $5\sqrt{c} = \sqrt{10c+15}$

32. $4\sqrt{x} = \sqrt{10x+6}$

33. $\sqrt{x^2-x} = \sqrt{12}$

34. $\sqrt{x^2+5x} = \sqrt{150}$

35. $\sqrt{9y^2-8y+1} = 3y+1$

36. $\sqrt{4x^2+2x+20} = 2x$

37. $\sqrt{x^2+4x+16} = x$

38. $\sqrt{x^2+3x-2} = 4$

39. $\sqrt{2k^2-3k-4} = k$

40. $\sqrt{6t+7} = t+2$

41. $\sqrt{y+1} = y+1$

42. $\sqrt{3p+3} + 5 = p$

43. $\sqrt{2m+1} + 7 = m$

44. $\sqrt[3]{3y+7} = \sqrt[3]{2y-1}$

45. $\sqrt[3]{p-5} - \sqrt[3]{2p+1} = 0$

46. $\sqrt[3]{2x-8} - \sqrt[3]{-x+1} = 0$

47. $\sqrt[3]{a-3} = \sqrt[3]{5a+1}$

Concept 2: Translations Involving Radical Equations

For Exercises 48–53, translate the English sentence to a radical equation and solve the equation. **(See Example 5.)**

48. The square root of the sum of a number and 8 equals 12. Find the number.

49. The square root of the sum of a number and 10 equals 1. Find the number.

50. The square root of a number is 2 less than the number. Find the number.

51. The square root of twice a number is 4 less than the number. Find the number.

52. The cube root of the sum of a number and 4 is -5. Find the number.

53. The cube root of the sum of a number and 1 is 2. Find the number.

Concept 3: Applications of Radical Equations

54. Ignoring air resistance, the time, t (in seconds), required for an object to fall x feet is given by the equation:

$$t = \frac{\sqrt{x}}{4}$$

a. Find the time required for an object to fall 64 ft.

b. Find the distance an object will fall in 4 sec.

55. Ignoring air resistance, the velocity, v (in feet per second: ft/sec), of an object in free fall depends on the distance it has fallen, x (in feet), according to the equation:

$$v = 8\sqrt{x}$$

a. Find the velocity of an object that has fallen 100 ft.

b. Find the distance that an object has fallen if its velocity is 136 ft/sec. **(See Example 6.)**

56. The speed of a car, s (in miles per hour), before the brakes were applied can be approximated by the length of its skid marks, x (in feet), according to the equation:

$$s = 4\sqrt{x}$$

a. Find the speed of a car before the brakes were applied if its skid marks are 324 ft long.

b. How long would you expect the skid marks to be if the car had been traveling the speed limit of 60 mph?

57. The height of a sunflower plant, y (in inches), can be determined by the time, t (in weeks), after the seed has germinated according to the equation:

$$y = 8\sqrt{t} \quad 0 \le t \le 40$$

a. Find the height of the plant after 4 weeks.

b. In how many weeks will the plant be 40 in. tall?

Expanding Your Skills

For Exercises 58–61, solve the equations. First isolate one of the radical terms. Then square both sides. The resulting equation will still have a radical. Repeat the process by isolating the radical and squaring both sides again.

58. $\sqrt{t + 8} = \sqrt{t} + 2$

59. $\sqrt{5x - 9} = \sqrt{5x} - 3$

60. $\sqrt{z + 1} + \sqrt{2z + 3} = 1$

61. $\sqrt{2m + 6} = 1 + \sqrt{7 - 2m}$

Section 8.7   Rational Exponents

Concepts

1. Definition of $a^{1/n}$
2. Definition of $a^{m/n}$
3. Converting between Rational Exponents and Radical Notation
4. Properties of Rational Exponents
5. Applications of Rational Exponents

1. Definition of $a^{1/n}$

The properties for simplifying expressions with integer exponents were presented in Sections 5.1–5.3. In this section, the properties are expanded to include expressions with rational exponents. We begin by defining expressions of the form $a^{1/n}$.

> **Definition of $a^{1/n}$**
>
> Let a be a real number, and let n be an integer such that $n > 1$. If $\sqrt[n]{a}$ is a real number, then
>
> $$a^{1/n} = \sqrt[n]{a}$$

Note: $(\sqrt{a})^2 = a$ for $a > 0$ and $(a^{1/2})^2 = a^{2/2} = a$, so $\sqrt{a} = a^{1/2}$.

Example 1 Evaluating Expressions of the Form $a^{1/n}$

Convert the expression to radical notation and simplify, if possible.

a. $9^{1/2}$　　**b.** $125^{1/3}$　　**c.** $16^{1/4}$　　**d.** $-25^{1/2}$　　**e.** $(-25)^{1/2}$　　**f.** $25^{-1/2}$

Solution:

a. $9^{1/2} = \sqrt{9} = 3$

b. $125^{1/3} = \sqrt[3]{125} = 5$

c. $16^{1/4} = \sqrt[4]{16} = 2$

d. $-25^{1/2}$ is equivalent to $-1 \cdot (25^{1/2})$

$\quad = -1 \cdot \sqrt{25}$

$\quad = -5$

e. $(-25)^{1/2}$ is not a real number because $\sqrt{-25}$ is not a real number.

f. $25^{-1/2} = \dfrac{1}{25^{1/2}} = \dfrac{1}{\sqrt{25}} = \dfrac{1}{5}$

Avoiding Mistakes

In Example 1(f), the expression is first rewritten with a positive exponent before it can be simplified.

2. Definition of $a^{m/n}$

If $\sqrt[n]{a}$ is a real number, then we can define an expression of the form $a^{m/n}$ in such a way that the multiplication property of exponents holds true. For example:

$$16^{3/4} \begin{cases} (16^{1/4})^3 = (\sqrt[4]{16})^3 = (2)^3 = 8 \\[2mm] (16^3)^{1/4} = \sqrt[4]{16^3} = \sqrt[4]{4096} = 8 \end{cases}$$

TIP: In simplifying the expression $a^{m/n}$ it is usually easier to take the root first. That is, simplify as $(a^{1/n})^m$.

Definition of $a^{m/n}$

Let a be a real number, and let m and n be positive integers such that m and n share no common factors and $n > 1$. If $\sqrt[n]{a}$ is a real number, then

$$a^{m/n} = (a^{1/n})^m = (\sqrt[n]{a})^m \quad \text{and} \quad a^{m/n} = (a^m)^{1/n} = \sqrt[n]{a^m}$$

The rational exponent in the expression $a^{m/n}$ is essentially performing two operations. The numerator of the exponent raises the base to the mth-power. The denominator takes the nth-root.

Example 2 Evaluating Expressions of the Form $a^{m/n}$

Convert each expression to radical notation and simplify.

a. $125^{2/3}$　　**b.** $100^{-3/2}$　　**c.** $(81)^{3/4}$

Solution:

a. $125^{2/3} = (\sqrt[3]{125})^2$　　Take the cube root of 125, and square the result.

$\quad = (5)^2$　　Simplify.

$\quad = 25$

b. $100^{-3/2} = \dfrac{1}{100^{3/2}}$ Take the reciprocal of the base.

$= \dfrac{1}{(\sqrt{100})^3}$ Take the square root of 100, and cube the result.

$= \dfrac{1}{(10)^3}$ Simplify.

$= \dfrac{1}{1000}$

c. $(81)^{3/4} = (\sqrt[4]{81})^3$ Take the fourth root of 81, and cube the result.

$= (3)^3$ Simplify.

$= 27$

3. Converting between Rational Exponents and Radical Notation

Example 3   Converting Rational Exponents to Radical Notation

Convert the expressions to radical notation. Assume the variables represent positive real numbers.

a. $x^{3/5}$ **b.** $(2a^2)^{1/3}$ **c.** $5y^{1/4}$ **d.** $p^{-1/2}$

Solution:

a. $x^{3/5} = \sqrt[5]{x^3}$ or $(\sqrt[5]{x})^3$

b. $(2a^2)^{1/3} = \sqrt[3]{2a^2}$

c. $5y^{1/4} = 5\sqrt[4]{y}$ The exponent $\frac{1}{4}$ applies only to y.

d. $p^{-1/2} = \dfrac{1}{\sqrt{p}}$

Example 4   Converting Radical Notation to Rational Exponents

Convert each expression to an equivalent expression using rational exponents. Assume that the variables represent positive real numbers.

a. $\sqrt[4]{c^3}$ **b.** $\sqrt{11p}$ **c.** $11\sqrt{p}$

Solution:

a. $\sqrt[4]{c^3} = c^{3/4}$ **b.** $\sqrt{11p} = (11p)^{1/2}$ **c.** $11\sqrt{p} = 11p^{1/2}$

4. Properties of Rational Exponents

The properties of integer exponents found in Sections 5.1–5.3 also apply to rational exponents.

Operations with Exponents

Let a and b be real numbers. Let m and n be rational numbers such that a^m, a^n, and b^n are real numbers. Then,

Description	Property	Example
1. Multiplying *like* bases	$a^m a^n = a^{m+n}$	$x^{1/3} \cdot x^{4/3} = x^{5/3}$
2. Dividing *like* bases	$\dfrac{a^m}{a^n} = a^{m-n}$	$\dfrac{x^{3/5}}{x^{1/5}} = x^{2/5}$
3. The power rule	$(a^m)^n = a^{mn}$	$(2^{1/3})^{1/2} = 2^{1/6}$
4. Power of a product	$(ab)^m = a^m b^m$	$(xy)^{1/2} = x^{1/2} y^{1/2}$
5. Power of a quotient	$\left(\dfrac{a}{b}\right)^m = \dfrac{a^m}{b^m}$ $(b \neq 0)$	$\left(\dfrac{4}{25}\right)^{1/2} = \dfrac{4^{1/2}}{25^{1/2}} = \dfrac{2}{5}$

Negative and Zero Exponents

Description	Definition	Example
1. Negative exponents	$a^{-m} = \left(\dfrac{1}{a}\right)^m = \dfrac{1}{a^m}$ $(a \neq 0)$	$(8)^{-1/3} = \left(\dfrac{1}{8}\right)^{1/3} = \dfrac{1}{2}$
2. Zero exponent	$a^0 = 1$ $(a \neq 0)$	$5^0 = 1$

Example 5 — Simplifying Expressions with Rational Exponents

Use the properties of exponents to simplify the expressions. Write the final answers with positive exponents only. Assume the variables represent positive real numbers.

a. $x^{2/3} x^{1/3}$ **b.** $\dfrac{y^{1/10}}{y^{4/5}}$ **c.** $(z^4)^{1/2}$ **d.** $(s^4 t^8)^{1/4}$

Solution:

a. $x^{2/3} x^{1/3} = x^{(2/3)+(1/3)}$ Add exponents.

$= x^{3/3}$ Simplify.

$= x$

b. $\dfrac{y^{1/10}}{y^{4/5}} = y^{(1/10)-(4/5)}$ Subtract exponents.

$= y^{(1/10)-(8/10)}$ The common denominator is 10.

$= y^{-7/10} = \dfrac{1}{y^{7/10}}$ Simplify and write with a positive exponent.

c. $(z^4)^{1/2} = z^{(4)\cdot(1/2)}$ Multiply exponents.

$= z^2$ Simplify.

d. $(s^4 t^8)^{1/4} = s^{4/4} t^{8/4}$ Multiply exponents.

$= s t^2$

Skill Practice

Use the properties of exponents to simplify the expressions. Write the answers with positive exponents only. Assume the variables represent positive real numbers.

17. $a^{3/4} \cdot a^{5/4}$ **18.** $\dfrac{t^{2/3}}{t^2}$

19. $(w^{1/3})^{-12}$ **20.** $(y^9 z^{15})^{1/3}$

Answers

17. a^2 **18.** $\dfrac{1}{t^{4/3}}$

19. $\dfrac{1}{w^4}$ **20.** $y^3 z^5$

5. Applications of Rational Exponents

21. The formula for finding the radius of a circle given the area is

$$r = \left(\frac{A}{\pi}\right)^{1/2}$$

Find the radius of a circle given that the area is 12.56 in.^{2}. Use 3.14 for π.

Example 6 Using Rational Exponents in an Application

Suppose P dollars in principal is invested in an account that earns interest annually. If after t years the investment grows to A dollars, then the annual rate of return, r, on the investment is given by

$$r = \left(\frac{A}{P}\right)^{1/t} - 1$$

Find the annual rate of return on $8000 that grew to $11,220.41 after 5 years (round to the nearest tenth of a percent).

Solution:

$$r = \left(\frac{A}{P}\right)^{1/t} - 1 \qquad \text{where } A = \$11{,}220.41, P = \$8000, \text{ and } t = 5. \text{ Hence,}$$

$$r = \left(\frac{11220.41}{8000}\right)^{1/5} - 1$$

$$= (1.40255125)^{1/5} - 1$$

$$\approx 1.070 - 1$$

$$\approx 0.070 \text{ or } 7.0\%$$

Answer

21. 2 in.

There is a 7.0% annual rate of return.

Section 8.7 Practice Exercises

For the exercises in this set, assume that the variables represent positive real numbers unless otherwise stated.

Vocabulary and Key Concepts

1. a. If n is an integer greater than 1, then $a^{1/n} =$ _____.

   b. If m and n are positive integers that share no common factors and $n > 1$, then in radical notation $a^{m/n} =$ _____.

Review Exercises

2. Given $\sqrt[3]{125}$

   a. Identify the index.   **b.** Identify the radicand.

For Exercises 3–6, simplify the radicals.

   3. $(\sqrt[4]{81})^3$ **4.** $(\sqrt[4]{16})^3$ **5.** $\sqrt[3]{(a+1)^3}$ **6.** $\sqrt[5]{(x+y)^5}$

Concept 1: Definition of $a^{1/n}$

For Exercises 7–18, simplify the expression. **(See Example 1.)**

   7. $81^{1/2}$ **8.** $25^{1/2}$ **9.** $125^{1/3}$ **10.** $8^{1/3}$

11. $81^{1/4}$ **12.** $16^{1/4}$ **13.** $(-8)^{1/3}$ **14.** $(-9)^{1/2}$

15. $-8^{1/3}$ **16.** $-9^{1/2}$ **17.** $36^{-1/2}$ **18.** $16^{-1/2}$

For Exercises 19–30, write the expressions in radical notation.

19. $x^{1/3}$ **20.** $y^{1/4}$ **21.** $(4a)^{1/2}$ **22.** $(36x)^{1/2}$

23. $(yz)^{1/5}$ **24.** $(cd)^{1/4}$ **25.** $(u^2)^{1/3}$ **26.** $(v^3)^{1/4}$

27. $5q^{1/2}$ **28.** $6p^{1/2}$ **29.** $\left(\dfrac{x}{9}\right)^{1/2}$ **30.** $\left(\dfrac{y}{8}\right)^{1/3}$

Concept 2: Definition of $a^{m/n}$

31. Explain how to interpret the expression $a^{m/n}$ as a radical.

32. Explain why $(\sqrt[3]{8})^4$ is easier to evaluate than $\sqrt[3]{8^4}$.

For Exercises 33–40, convert the expressions to radical form and simplify. **(See Example 2.)**

33. $16^{3/4}$ **34.** $32^{2/5}$ **35.** $27^{-2/3}$ **36.** $4^{-5/2}$

37. $(-8)^{5/3}$ **38.** $(-27)^{2/3}$ **39.** $\left(\dfrac{1}{4}\right)^{-1/2}$ **40.** $\left(\dfrac{1}{9}\right)^{3/2}$

Concept 3: Converting between Rational Exponents and Radical Notation

For Exercises 41–48, convert each expression to radical notation. **(See Example 3.)**

41. $y^{9/2}$ **42.** $b^{4/9}$ **43.** $(c^5d)^{1/3}$ **44.** $(a^2b)^{1/8}$

45. $(qr)^{-1/5}$ **46.** $(3x)^{-1/4}$ **47.** $6y^{2/3}$ **48.** $2q^{5/6}$

For Exercises 49–56, write the expressions using rational exponents rather than radical notation. **(See Example 4.)**

49. $\sqrt[3]{x}$ **50.** $\sqrt[4]{a}$ **51.** $5\sqrt{x}$ **52.** $7\sqrt[3]{z}$

53. $\sqrt[3]{y^2}$ **54.** $\sqrt[5]{b^2}$ **55.** $\sqrt[4]{m^3n}$ **56.** $\sqrt[5]{u^3v^4}$

Concept 4: Properties of Rational Exponents

For Exercises 57–80, simplify the expressions using the properties of rational exponents. Write the final answers with positive exponents only. **(See Example 5.)**

57. $x^{1/4}x^{3/4}$ **58.** $2^{3/5}2^{2/5}$ **59.** $(y^{1/5})^{10}$ **60.** $(x^{1/2})^8$

61. $6^{-1/5}6^{6/5}$ **62.** $a^{-1/3}a^{2/3}$ **63.** $(a^{1/3}a^{1/4})^{12}$ **64.** $(x^{2/3}x^{1/2})^6$

65. $\dfrac{y^{5/3}}{y^{1/3}}$ **66.** $\dfrac{z^2}{z^{1/2}}$ **67.** $\dfrac{2^{4/3}}{2^{1/3}}$ **68.** $\dfrac{5^{6/5}}{5^{1/5}}$

69. $(x^{-2}y^{1/3})^{1/2}$ **70.** $(a^3b^{-4})^{1/3}$ **71.** $\left(\dfrac{w^{-2}}{z^{-4}}\right)^{-3/2}$ **72.** $\left(\dfrac{x^{-8}}{y^{-4}}\right)^{-1/4}$

73. $(5a^2c^{-1/2}d^{1/2})^2$ **74.** $(2x^{-1/3}y^2z^{5/3})^3$ **75.** $\left(\dfrac{x^{-2/3}}{y^{-3/4}}\right)^{12}$ **76.** $\left(\dfrac{m^{-1/4}}{n^{-1/2}}\right)^{-4}$

77. $\left(\dfrac{16w^{-2}z}{2wz^{-8}}\right)^{1/3}$ **78.** $\left(\dfrac{50p^{-1}q}{2pq^{-3}}\right)^{1/2}$ **79.** $(25x^2y^4z^3)^{1/2}$ **80.** $(8a^6b^3c^2)^{2/3}$

Concept 5: Applications of Rational Exponents

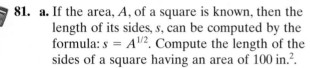

81. a. If the area, A, of a square is known, then the length of its sides, s, can be computed by the formula: $s = A^{1/2}$. Compute the length of the sides of a square having an area of 100 in.^{2}.

  b. Compute the length of the sides of a square having an area of 72 in.^{2}. Round your answer to the nearest 0.01 in.

82. The radius, r, of a sphere of volume, V, is given by

$$r = \left(\dfrac{3V}{4\pi}\right)^{1/3}$$

Find the radius of a spherical ball having a volume of 55 in.^{3}. Round your answer to the nearest 0.01 in.

For Exercises 83 and 84, use the following information.

If P dollars in principal grows to A dollars after t years with annual interest, then the rate of return is given by

$$r = \left(\dfrac{A}{P}\right)^{1/t} - 1$$

83. a. In one account, $10,000 grows to $16,802 after 5 years. Compute the interest rate to the nearest tenth of a percent. **(See Example 6.)**

  b. In another account $10,000 grows to $18,000 after 7 years. Compute the interest rate to the nearest tenth of a percent.

  c. Which account produced a higher average yearly return?

84. a. In one account, $5000 grows to $23,304.79 in 20 years. Compute the interest rate to the nearest whole percent.

  b. In another account, $6000 grows to $34,460.95 in 30 years. Compute the interest rate to the nearest whole percent.

  c. Which account produced a higher average yearly return?

Expanding Your Skills

85. Is $(a + b)^{1/2}$ the same as $a^{1/2} + b^{1/2}$? Explain why or why not by giving an example.

For Exercises 86–91, simplify the expressions. Write the final answer with positive exponents only.

86. $\left(\dfrac{1}{8}\right)^{2/3} + \left(\dfrac{1}{4}\right)^{1/2}$ **87.** $\left(\dfrac{1}{8}\right)^{-2/3} + \left(\dfrac{1}{4}\right)^{-1/2}$ **88.** $\left(\dfrac{1}{16}\right)^{-1/4} - \left(\dfrac{1}{49}\right)^{-1/2}$

89. $\left(\dfrac{1}{16}\right)^{1/4} - \left(\dfrac{1}{49}\right)^{1/2}$ **90.** $\left(\dfrac{x^2y^{-1/3}z^{2/3}}{x^{2/3}y^{1/4}z}\right)^{12}$ **91.** $\left(\dfrac{a^2b^{1/2}c^{-2}}{a^{-3/4}b^0c^{1/8}}\right)^8$

Group Activity

Calculating Standard Deviation

Materials: Pencil, paper, calculator

Estimated Time: 15 minutes

Group Size: 5 or 6

In statistics, the standard deviation of a set of data measures how much the data values differ from the mean of the values. A large standard deviation means that the values are more spread out. A smaller standard deviation means the values are more "clustered" around the mean.

Consider a set of data consisting of the following eight values:
6, 10, 13, 22, 30, 4, 12, 23

1. Calculate the mean (average) of the values.

2. To calculate the standard deviation, first compute the difference of each data point from the mean, and square the result. The process is shown here:

$$(6 - 15)^2 = 81 \qquad (10 - 15)^2 = 25 \qquad (13 - 15)^2 = 4 \qquad (22 - 15)^2 = 49$$

$$(30 - 15)^2 = 225 \qquad (4 - 15)^2 = 121 \qquad (12 - 15)^2 = 9 \qquad (23 - 15)^2 = 64$$

3. Next divide the sum of these values by one less than the number of values. Then take the square root. The result is the standard deviation. Round to the nearest whole number.

$$\sqrt{\frac{81 + 25 + 4 + 49 + 225 + 121 + 9 + 64}{8 - 1}}$$

4. Next, find the standard deviation of the ages of the members of your group. First list the ages. Then follow steps 1–3. Round the standard deviation to the tenths place.

5. Compare the standard deviation of your group of ages to that of several other groups in the class. Which group has ages that are closest to its mean?

Chapter 8 Summary

Key Concepts

b is a **square root** of a if $b^2 = a$.

The expression $\sqrt{a}$ represents the **principal square root** of a.

b is an nth-root of a if $b^n = a$.

1. If n is a positive *even* integer and $a > 0$, then $\sqrt[n]{a}$ is the principal (positive) nth-root of a.
2. If $n > 1$ is a positive *odd* integer, then $\sqrt[n]{a}$ is the nth-root of a.
3. If $n > 1$ is any positive integer, then $\sqrt[n]{0} = 0$.

$\sqrt[n]{a^n} = |a|$ if n is even.

$\sqrt[n]{a^n} = a$ if n is odd.

$\sqrt[n]{a}$ is not a real number if a is *negative* and n is even.

Pythagorean Theorem

$a^2 + b^2 = c^2$

Examples

Example 1

The square roots of 16 are 4 and -4 because $(4)^2 = 16$ and $(-4)^2 = 16$.

$\sqrt{16} = 4$ Because $4^2 = 16$

$\sqrt[3]{125} = 5$ Because $5^3 = 125$

$\sqrt[3]{-8} = -2$ Because $(-2)^3 = -8$

Example 2

$\sqrt{y^2} = |y|$ $\sqrt[3]{y^3} = y$

Example 3

$\sqrt{-16}$ is not a real number.

Example 4

Find the length of the unknown side.

$$a^2 + b^2 = c^2$$
$$(8)^2 + b^2 = (17)^2$$
$$64 + b^2 = 289$$
$$b^2 = 289 - 64$$
$$b^2 = 225$$
$$b = \sqrt{225}$$
$$b = 15$$

Because b denotes a length, b must be the positive square root of 225.

The third side is 15 cm.

Section 8.2   Simplifying Radicals

Key Concepts

Multiplication Property of Radicals

If $\sqrt[n]{a}$ and $\sqrt[n]{b}$ are both real, then

$$\sqrt[n]{ab} = \sqrt[n]{a} \cdot \sqrt[n]{b}$$

Simplifying Radicals

Consider a radical expression whose radicand is written as a product of prime factors. Then the radical is in simplified form if each of the following criteria are met:

1. The radicand has no factor raised to a power greater than or equal to the index.
2. There are no radicals in the denominator of a fraction.
3. The radicand does not contain a fraction.

Examples

Example 1

$$\sqrt{3} \cdot \sqrt{5} = \sqrt{3 \cdot 5} = \sqrt{15}$$

Example 2

$$\sqrt{\frac{b^7}{b^3}} = \sqrt{b^4} = b^2$$

Example 3

$$\sqrt[3]{16x^5y^7} = \sqrt[3]{8x^3y^6 \cdot 2x^2y}$$
$$= \sqrt[3]{8x^3y^6} \cdot \sqrt[3]{2x^2y}$$
$$= 2xy^2\sqrt[3]{2x^2y}$$

Section 8.3   Addition and Subtraction of Radicals

Key Concepts

Two radical terms are *like* radicals if they have the same index and the same radicand.

Use the distributive property to add or subtract *like* radicals.

Examples

Example 1

Like radicals. $\sqrt[3]{5z}, \quad 6\sqrt[3]{5z}$

Example 2

$$3\sqrt{7} - 10\sqrt{7} + \sqrt{7}$$
$$= (3 - 10 + 1)\sqrt{7}$$
$$= -6\sqrt{7}$$

Section 8.4 — Multiplication of Radicals

Key Concepts

Multiplication Property of Radicals

$\sqrt[n]{a} \cdot \sqrt[n]{b} = \sqrt[n]{ab}$ provided $\sqrt[n]{a}$ and $\sqrt[n]{b}$ are both real.

Examples

Example 1

$$(6\sqrt{5})(4\sqrt{3}) = 6 \cdot 4\sqrt{5 \cdot 3}$$
$$= 24\sqrt{15}$$

Example 2

$$3\sqrt{2}(\sqrt{2} + 5\sqrt{7} - \sqrt{6}) = 3\sqrt{4} + 15\sqrt{14} - 3\sqrt{12}$$
$$= 3\sqrt{4} + 15\sqrt{14} - 3\sqrt{4 \cdot 3}$$
$$= 3 \cdot 2 + 15\sqrt{14} - 3 \cdot 2\sqrt{3}$$
$$= 6 + 15\sqrt{14} - 6\sqrt{3}$$

Special Case Products

$(a + b)(a - b) = a^2 - b^2$

$(a + b)^2 = a^2 + 2ab + b^2$

$(a - b)^2 = a^2 - 2ab + b^2$

Example 3

$$(4\sqrt{x} + \sqrt{2})(4\sqrt{x} - \sqrt{2}) = (4\sqrt{x})^2 - (\sqrt{2})^2$$
$$= 16x - 2$$

Example 4

$$(\sqrt{x} - \sqrt{5y})^2 = (\sqrt{x})^2 - 2(\sqrt{x})(\sqrt{5y}) + (\sqrt{5y})^2$$
$$= x - 2\sqrt{5xy} + 5y$$

Section 8.5 — Division of Radicals and Rationalization

Key Concepts

Division Property of Radicals

If $\sqrt[n]{a}$ and $\sqrt[n]{b}$ are both real, then

$$\sqrt[n]{\frac{a}{b}} = \frac{\sqrt[n]{a}}{\sqrt[n]{b}} \quad b \neq 0$$

Rationalizing the Denominator with One Term

Multiply the numerator and denominator by an appropriate expression to create an nth-root of an nth-power in the denominator.

Rationalizing a Two-Term Denominator Involving Square Roots

Multiply the numerator and denominator by the conjugate of the denominator.

Examples

Example 1

$$\sqrt{\frac{w}{16}} = \frac{\sqrt{w}}{\sqrt{16}} = \frac{\sqrt{w}}{4}$$

Example 2

$$\frac{10}{\sqrt{5}} = \frac{10}{\sqrt{5}} \cdot \frac{\sqrt{5}}{\sqrt{5}} = \frac{10\sqrt{5}}{\sqrt{5^2}} = \frac{10\sqrt{5}}{5} = 2\sqrt{5}$$

Example 3

$$\frac{\sqrt{2}}{\sqrt{x} - \sqrt{3}} = \frac{\sqrt{2}}{(\sqrt{x} - \sqrt{3})} \cdot \frac{(\sqrt{x} + \sqrt{3})}{(\sqrt{x} + \sqrt{3})}$$
$$= \frac{\sqrt{2x} + \sqrt{6}}{x - 3}$$

Section 8.6   Radical Equations

Key Concepts

An equation with one or more radicals containing a variable is a **radical equation**.

Steps for Solving a Radical Equation

1. Isolate the radical. If an equation has more than one radical, choose one of the radicals to isolate.
2. Raise each side of the equation to a power equal to the index of the radical.
3. Solve the resulting equation.
4. Check the potential solutions in the original equation.

Note: Raising both sides of an equation to an even power may result in extraneous solutions.

Examples

Example 1

Solve. $\sqrt{2x - 4} + 3 = 7$

Step 1: $\sqrt{2x - 4} = 4$

Step 2: $(\sqrt{2x - 4})^2 = (4)^2$

Step 3: $2x - 4 = 16$

$2x = 20$

$x = 10$

Step 4:

Check:

$$\sqrt{2x - 4} + 3 = 7$$

$$\sqrt{2(10) - 4} + 3 \stackrel{?}{=} 7$$

$$\sqrt{20 - 4} + 3 \stackrel{?}{=} 7$$

$$\sqrt{16} + 3 \stackrel{?}{=} 7$$

$$4 + 3 \stackrel{?}{=} 7 ✔ \qquad \text{The solution checks.}$$

The solution is 10.

Section 8.7   Rational Exponents

Key Concepts

If $\sqrt[n]{a}$ is a real number, then

$a^{1/n} = \sqrt[n]{a}$

$a^{m/n} = (\sqrt[n]{a})^m = \sqrt[n]{a^m}$

Examples

Example 1

$121^{1/2} = \sqrt{121} = 11$

Example 2

$27^{2/3} = (\sqrt[3]{27})^2 = (3)^2 = 9$

Example 3

$8^{-1/3} = \dfrac{1}{8^{1/3}} = \dfrac{1}{\sqrt[3]{8}} = \dfrac{1}{2}$

Chapter 8   Review Exercises

Section 8.1

For Exercises 1–4, state the principal square root and the negative square root.

1. 196

2. 1.44

3. 0.64

4. 225

5. Explain why $\sqrt{-64}$ is *not* a real number.

6. Explain why $\sqrt[3]{-64}$ *is* a real number.

For Exercises 7–18, simplify the expressions, if possible. Assume all variables represent positive real numbers.

7. $-\sqrt{144}$ **8.** $-\sqrt{25}$ **9.** $\sqrt{-144}$

10. $\sqrt{-25}$ **11.** $\sqrt{y^2}$ **12.** $\sqrt[3]{a^3}$

13. $\sqrt[3]{8p^3}$ **14.** $-\sqrt[3]{125}$ **15.** $-\sqrt[4]{625}$

16. $\sqrt[3]{p^{12}}$ **17.** $\sqrt[3]{\dfrac{64}{t^6}}$ **18.** $\sqrt[3]{\dfrac{-27}{w^3}}$

19. The radius, r, of a circle can be found from the area of the circle according to the formula:

$$r = \sqrt{\dfrac{A}{\pi}}$$

   a. What is the radius of a circular garden whose area is 160 m^2? Round to the nearest tenth of a meter.

   b. What is the radius of a circular fountain whose area is 1600 ft^2? Round to the nearest tenth of a foot.

20. Suppose a ball is thrown with an initial velocity of 76 ft/sec at an angle of 30° (see figure). Then the horizontal position of the ball, x (measured in feet), depends on the number of seconds, t, after the ball is thrown according to the equation:

$$x = 38t\sqrt{3}$$

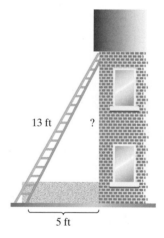

   a. What is the horizontal position of the ball after 1 sec? Round your answer to the nearest tenth of a foot.

   b. What is the horizontal position of the ball after 2 sec? Round your answer to the nearest tenth of a foot.

For Exercises 21 and 22, translate the English phrases into algebraic expressions.

21. The square of b plus the principal square root of 5.

22. The difference of the cube root of y and the fourth root of x.

For Exercises 23 and 24, translate the algebraic expressions into English phrases. (Answers may vary.)

23. $\dfrac{2}{\sqrt{p}}$ **24.** $8\sqrt{q}$

25. A hedge extends 5 ft from the wall of a house. A 13-ft ladder is placed at the edge of the hedge. How far up the house is the tip of the ladder?

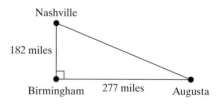

13 ft   ?

5 ft

26. Nashville, Tennessee, is north of Birmingham, Alabama, a distance of 182 miles. Augusta, Georgia, is east of Birmingham, a distance of 277 miles. How far is it from Augusta to Nashville? Round the answer to the nearest mile.

Nashville

182 miles

Birmingham   277 miles   Augusta

Section 8.2

For Exercises 27–32, use the multiplication property of radicals to simplify. Assume the variables represent positive real numbers.

27. $\sqrt{x^{17}}$ **28.** $\sqrt[3]{40}$ **29.** $\sqrt{28}$

30. $5\sqrt{18x^3}$ **31.** $\sqrt[3]{27y^{10}}$ **32.** $2\sqrt{27y^{10}}$

For Exercises 33–42, use order of operations to simplify. Assume the variables represent positive real numbers.

33. $\sqrt{\dfrac{c^5}{c^3}}$ **34.** $\sqrt{\dfrac{t^9}{t^3}}$

35. $\sqrt{\dfrac{200y^5}{2y}}$ **36.** $\sqrt{\dfrac{18x^3}{2x}}$

37. $\sqrt[3]{\dfrac{48x^4}{6x}}$ **38.** $\sqrt[3]{\dfrac{128a^{17}}{2a^2}}$

39. $\dfrac{5\sqrt{12}}{2}$ **40.** $\dfrac{2\sqrt{45}}{6}$

41. $\dfrac{12 - \sqrt{49}}{5}$ **42.** $\dfrac{20 + \sqrt{100}}{5}$

Section 8.3

For Exercises 43–50, add or subtract as indicated. Assume the variables represent positive real numbers.

43. $8\sqrt{6} - \sqrt{6}$

44. $1.6\sqrt{y} - 1.4\sqrt{y} + 0.6\sqrt{y}$

45. $x\sqrt{20} - 2\sqrt{45x^2}$

46. $y\sqrt{64y} + 3\sqrt{y^3}$

47. $3\sqrt{75} - 4\sqrt{28} + \sqrt{7}$

48. $2\sqrt{50} - 4\sqrt{20} - 6\sqrt{2}$

49. $7\sqrt{3x^9} - 3x^4\sqrt{75x}$

50. $3a^2\sqrt{2b^3} - \sqrt{8a^4b^3} + 4a^2b\sqrt{50b}$

51. Find the exact perimeter of the triangle.

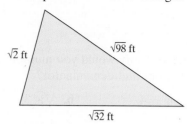

52. Find the exact perimeter of a square whose sides are $3\sqrt{48}$ m.

Section 8.4

For Exercises 53–62, multiply the expressions. Assume the variables represent positive real numbers.

53. $\sqrt{5} \cdot \sqrt{125}$ **54.** $\sqrt{10p} \cdot \sqrt{6}$

55. $(5\sqrt{6})(7\sqrt{2x})$ **56.** $(3\sqrt{y})(-2z\sqrt{11y})$

57. $8\sqrt{m}(\sqrt{m} + 3)$ **58.** $\sqrt{2}(\sqrt{7} + 8)$

59. $(5\sqrt{2} + \sqrt{13})(-\sqrt{2} - 3\sqrt{13})$

60. $(\sqrt{p} + 2\sqrt{q})(4\sqrt{p} - \sqrt{q})$

61. $(8\sqrt{w} - \sqrt{z})(8\sqrt{w} + \sqrt{z})$

62. $(2x - \sqrt{y})^2$

63. Find the exact volume of the box.

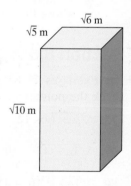

Section 8.5

For Exercises 64–67, use the division property of radicals to write the radicals in simplified form. Assume all variables are positive real numbers.

64. $\dfrac{\sqrt[3]{x^7}}{\sqrt[3]{x^4}}$ **65.** $\dfrac{\sqrt{a^{11}}}{\sqrt{a}}$ **66.** $\dfrac{\sqrt{250c}}{\sqrt{10}}$ **67.** $\dfrac{\sqrt{96y^3}}{\sqrt{6y^2}}$

68. To rationalize the denominator in the expression

$$\dfrac{6}{\sqrt{a} + 5}$$

which quantity would you multiply by in the numerator and denominator?

a. $\sqrt{a} + 5$ **b.** $\sqrt{a} - 5$ **c.** $\sqrt{a}$ **d.** -5

69. To rationalize the denominator in the expression

$$\frac{w}{\sqrt{w} - 4}$$

which quantity would you multiply by in the numerator and denominator?

a. $\sqrt{w} - 4$ **b.** $\sqrt{w} + 4$

c. $\sqrt{w}$ **d.** 4

For Exercises 70–75, rationalize the denominators. Assume the variables represent positive real numbers.

70. $\dfrac{11}{\sqrt{7}}$ **71.** $\sqrt{\dfrac{18}{y}}$ **72.** $\dfrac{\sqrt{24}}{\sqrt{6x^7}}$

73. $\dfrac{10}{\sqrt{7} - \sqrt{2}}$ **74.** $\dfrac{6}{\sqrt{w} + 2}$ **75.** $\dfrac{\sqrt{7} + 3}{\sqrt{7} - 3}$

76. The velocity of an object, v (in meters per second: m/sec) depends on the kinetic energy, E (in joules: J), and mass, m (in kilograms: kg), of the object according to the formula:

$$v = \sqrt{\frac{2E}{m}}$$

    a. What is the exact velocity of a 3-kg object whose kinetic energy is 100 J?

    b. What is the exact velocity of a 5-kg object whose kinetic energy is 162 J?

Section 8.6

For Exercises 77–85, solve the equations. Be sure to check the potential solutions.

77. $\sqrt{p + 6} = 12$ **78.** $\sqrt{k + 1} = -7$

79. $\sqrt{3x - 17} - 10 = 0$

80. $\sqrt{14n + 10} = 4\sqrt{n}$

81. $\sqrt{2z + 2} = \sqrt{3z - 5}$

82. $\sqrt{5y - 5} - \sqrt{4y + 1} = 0$

83. $\sqrt{2m + 5} = m + 1$

84. $\sqrt{3n - 8} - n + 2 = 0$

85. $\sqrt[3]{2y + 13} = -5$

 86. The length of the sides of a cube is related to the volume of the cube according to the formula: $x = \sqrt[3]{V}$.

    a. What is the volume of the cube if the side length is 21 in.?

    b. What is the volume of the cube if the side length is 15 cm?

Section 8.7

For Exercises 87–92, simplify the expressions.

87. $(-27)^{1/3}$ **88.** $121^{1/2}$ **89.** $-16^{1/4}$

90. $(-16)^{1/4}$ **91.** $4^{-3/2}$ **92.** $\left(\dfrac{1}{9}\right)^{-3/2}$

For Exercises 93–96, write the expression in radical notation. Assume the variables represent positive real numbers.

93. $z^{1/5}$ **94.** $q^{2/3}$

95. $(w^3)^{1/4}$ **96.** $\left(\dfrac{b}{121}\right)^{1/2}$

For Exercises 97–100, write the expression using rational exponents rather than radical notation. Assume the variables represent positive real numbers.

97. $\sqrt[5]{a^2}$ **98.** $5\sqrt[3]{m^2}$

99. $\sqrt[5]{a^2 b^4}$ **100.** $\sqrt{6}$

For Exercises 101–106, simplify using the properties of rational exponents. Write the answer with positive exponents only. Assume the variables represent positive real numbers.

101. $y^{2/3} y^{4/3}$ **102.** $a^{1/3} a^{1/2}$

103. $\dfrac{6^{4/5}}{6^{1/5}}$ **104.** $\left(\dfrac{b^4 b^0}{b^{1/4}}\right)^4$

105. $(64a^3 b^6)^{1/3}$ **106.** $(5^{1/2})^{3/2}$

107. The radius, r, of a right circular cylinder can be found if the volume, V, and height, h, are known. The radius is given by

$$r = \left(\frac{V}{\pi h}\right)^{1/2}$$

Find the radius of a right circular cylinder whose volume is 150.8 cm³ and whose height is 12 cm. Round the answer to the nearest tenth of a centimeter.

Chapter 8   Test

1. State the conditions for a radical expression to be in simplified form.

For Exercises 2–7, simplify the radicals, if possible. Assume the variables represent positive real numbers.

2. $\sqrt{242x^2}$

3. $\sqrt[3]{48y^4}$

4. $\sqrt{-64}$

5. $\sqrt{\dfrac{5a^6}{81}}$

6. $\dfrac{9}{\sqrt{6}}$

7. $\dfrac{2}{\sqrt{5}+6}$

8. Translate the English phrases into algebraic expressions and simplify.

   a. The sum of the principal square root of twenty-five and the cube of five.

   b. The difference of the square of four and the principal square root of 16.

 9. A baseball player hits the ball at an angle of 30° with an initial velocity of 112 ft/sec. The horizontal position of the ball, x (measured in feet), depends on the number of seconds, t, after the ball is struck according to the equation

$$x = 56t\sqrt{3}$$

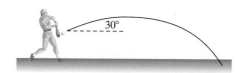

   a. What is the horizontal position of the ball after 1 sec? Round the answer to the nearest foot.

   b. What is the horizontal position of the ball after 3.5 sec? Round the answer to the nearest foot.

For Exercises 10–19, perform the indicated operations. Assume the variables represent positive real numbers.

10. $6\sqrt{z} - 3\sqrt{z} + 5\sqrt{z}$

11. $\sqrt{3}(4\sqrt{2} - 5\sqrt{3})$

12. $\sqrt{50t^2} - t\sqrt{288}$

13. $\sqrt{360} + \sqrt{250} - \sqrt{40}$

14. $(6\sqrt{2} - \sqrt{5})(\sqrt{2} + 4\sqrt{5})$

15. $(3\sqrt{5} - 1)^2$

16. $\dfrac{\sqrt{2m^3n}}{\sqrt{72m^5}}$

17. $(4 - 3\sqrt{x})(4 + 3\sqrt{x})$

18. $\sqrt{\dfrac{2}{11}}$

19. $\dfrac{6}{\sqrt{7} - \sqrt{3}}$

 20. A triathlon consists of a swim, followed by a bike ride, followed by a run. The swim begins on a beach at point A. The swimmers must swim 50 yd to a buoy at point B, then 200 yd to a buoy at point C, and then return to point A on the beach. How far is the distance from point C to point A? (Round to the nearest yard.)

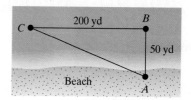

For Exercises 21–23, solve the equations.

21. $\sqrt{2x + 7} + 6 = 2$

22. $\sqrt{1 - 7x} = 1 - x$

23. $\sqrt[3]{x + 6} = \sqrt[3]{2x - 8}$

24. The height, y (in inches), of a tomato plant can be approximated by the time, t (in weeks), after the seed has germinated according to the equation

$$y = 6\sqrt{t}$$

   a. Use the equation to find the height of the plant after 4 weeks.

b. Use the equation to find the time required for the plant to reach a height of 30 in. Verify your answer from the graph.

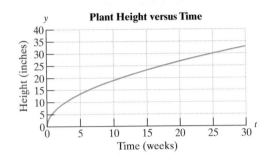

For Exercises 25 and 26, simplify the expression.

25. $10,000^{3/4}$

26. $\left(\dfrac{1}{8}\right)^{-1/3}$

For Exercises 27 and 28, write the expressions in radical notation. Assume the variables represent positive real numbers.

27. $x^{3/5}$

28. $5y^{1/2}$

29. Write the expression using rational exponents: $\sqrt[4]{ab^3}$. (Assume $a \geq 0$ and $b \geq 0$.)

For Exercises 30–32, simplify using the properties of rational exponents. Write the final answer with positive exponents only. Assume the variables represent positive real numbers.

30. $p^{1/4} \cdot p^{2/3}$

31. $\dfrac{5^{4/5}}{5^{1/5}}$

32. $(9m^2n^4)^{1/2}$

Chapters 1–8   Cumulative Review Exercises

1. Simplify. $\dfrac{|-3 - 12 \div 6 + 2|}{\sqrt{5^2 - 4^2}}$

2. Solve.
$2 - 5(2y + 4) - (-3y - 1) = -(y + 5)$

3. Simplify. Write the final answer with positive exponents only.
$$\left(\frac{1}{3}\right)^0 - \left(\frac{1}{4}\right)^{-2}$$

4. Perform the indicated operations:
$2(x - 3) - (3x + 4)(3x - 4)$

5. Divide:
$$\frac{14x^3y - 7x^2y^2 + 28xy^2}{7x^2y^2}$$

6. Factor completely. $50c^2 + 40c + 8$

7. Solve. $10x^2 = x + 2$

8. Perform the indicated operations:
$$\frac{5a^2 + 2ab - 3b^2}{10a + 10b} \div \frac{25a^2 - 9b^2}{50a + 30b}$$

9. Solve for z. $\dfrac{1}{5} + \dfrac{z}{z - 5} = \dfrac{5}{z - 5}$

10. Simplify:
$$\frac{\dfrac{5}{4} + \dfrac{2}{x}}{\dfrac{4}{x} - \dfrac{4}{x^2}}$$

11. Graph. $3y = 6$

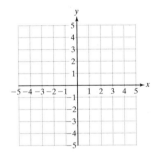

12. The equation $y = 210x + 250$ represents the cost, y (in dollars), of renting office space for x months.

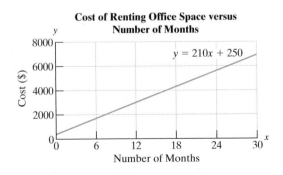

a. Find y when x is 3. Interpret the result in the context of the problem.

b. Find x when y is $2770. Interpret the result in the context of the problem.

c. What is the slope of the line? Interpret the meaning of the slope in the context of the problem.

d. What is the y-intercept? Interpret the meaning of the y-intercept in the context of the problem.

13. Write an equation of the line passing through the points $(2, -1)$ and $(-3, 4)$. Write the answer in slope-intercept form.

14. Solve the system of equations using the addition method. If the system has no solution or infinitely many solutions, so state:

$$3x - 5y = 23$$
$$2x + 4y = -14$$

15. Graph the solution to the inequality:
$-2x - y > 3$

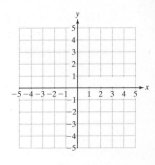

16. How many liters (L) of 20% acid solution must be mixed with a 50% acid solution to obtain 12 L of a 30% acid solution?

17. Simplify. $\sqrt{99}$

18. Perform the indicated operation.
$$5x\sqrt{3} + \sqrt{12x^2}$$

19. Rationalize the denominator. $\dfrac{\sqrt{x}}{\sqrt{x} - \sqrt{y}}$

20. Solve. $\sqrt{2y - 1} - 4 = -1$

More Quadratic Equations

9

CHAPTER OUTLINE

Chapter 9

In earlier chapters, we solved quadratic equations by factoring and applying the zero product rule. In Chapter 9, we present additional techniques to solve quadratic equations. These new techniques can be used to solve quadratic equations even if the equations are not factorable.

Review Your Skills

This puzzle will help you recall the characteristics of a quadratic equation. Circle the number-letter of each true statement. Then write the letter in the matching numbered blank to complete the sentence.

$\boxed{1 - O}$ $m(m + 5) = 8$ is a linear equation.

$\boxed{3 - O}$ $x^2 + 5x + 3 = x(x + 2)$ is a linear equation.

$\boxed{3 - R}$ $x(x^2 - 4x - 1) = 2x^2 + 1$ is a quadratic equation.

$\boxed{2 - W}$ $3(x - 8) = 10x$ is a linear equation.

$\boxed{2 - N}$ $12x(x - 1) + 1 = 6$ is a linear equation.

$\boxed{1 - T}$ $2x^3 + 3x^2 = 2x(x^2 + 4)$ is a quadratic equation.

$\boxed{3 - E}$ $4x(x - 1) = 7x + 10$ is a linear equation.

$\boxed{2 - A}$ $x^2(x^2 + 8) = x(x^2 - 2x + 1)$ is a quadratic equation.

A quadratic equation has at most $\underline{}_{1}\ \underline{}_{2}\ \underline{}_{3}$ solution(s).

Section 9.1 The Square Root Property

1. Review of the Zero Product Rule

In Section 6.7, we learned that an equation that can be written in the form $ax^2 + bx + c = 0$, where $a \neq 0$, is a quadratic equation. One method to solve a quadratic equation is to factor the equation and apply the zero product rule. Recall that the zero product rule states that if $a \cdot b = 0$, then $a = 0$ or $b = 0$. This is reviewed in Examples 1–3.

Skill Practice

Solve the quadratic equation by using the zero product rule.

1. $2x^2 + 3x - 20 = 0$

Example 1   Solving a Quadratic Equation Using the Zero Product Rule

Solve the equation by factoring and applying the zero product rule.

$$2x^2 - 7x - 30 = 0$$

Solution:

$2x^2 - 7x - 30 = 0$	The equation is in the form $ax^2 + bx + c = 0$.
$(2x + 5)(x - 6) = 0$	Factor.
$2x + 5 = 0$ or $x - 6 = 0$	Set each factor equal to zero.
$2x = -5$ or $x = 6$	Solve the resulting equations.
$x = -\dfrac{5}{2}$	

The solutions are $-\dfrac{5}{2}$ and 6.

Skill Practice

Solve the quadratic equation by using the zero product rule.

2. $y(y - 1) = 2y + 10$

Example 2   Solving a Quadratic Equation Using the Zero Product Rule

Solve the equation by factoring and applying the zero product rule.

$$2x(x + 4) = x^2 - 15$$

Solution:

$2x(x + 4) = x^2 - 15$	
$2x^2 + 8x = x^2 - 15$	Clear parentheses and combine like terms.
$x^2 + 8x + 15 = 0$	Set one side of the equation equal to zero. The equation is now in the form $ax^2 + bx + c = 0$.
$(x + 5)(x + 3) = 0$	Factor.

Answers

1. $-4, \dfrac{5}{2}$

2. $5, -2$

$$x + 5 = 0 \quad \text{or} \quad x + 3 = 0 \qquad \text{Set each factor equal to zero.}$$

$$x = -5 \quad \text{or} \qquad x = -3 \qquad \text{Solve each equation.}$$

The solutions are -5 and -3.

TIP: The solutions to an equation can be checked in the original equation.

<u>Check:</u> $x = -5$

$$2x(x + 4) = x^2 - 15$$

$$2(-5)(-5 + 4) \stackrel{?}{=} (-5)^2 - 15$$

$$-10(-1) \stackrel{?}{=} 25 - 15$$

$$10 \stackrel{?}{=} 10 \checkmark$$

<u>Check:</u> $x = -3$

$$2x(x + 4) = x^2 - 15$$

$$2(-3)(-3 + 4) \stackrel{?}{=} (-3)^2 - 15$$

$$-6(1) \stackrel{?}{=} 9 - 15$$

$$-6 \stackrel{?}{=} -6 \checkmark$$

Example 3 **Solving a Quadratic Equation Using the Zero Product Rule**

Solve the equation by factoring and applying the zero product rule.

$$x^2 = 25$$

Solution:

$$x^2 = 25$$

$$x^2 - 25 = 0 \qquad \text{Set one side of the equation equal to zero.}$$

$$(x - 5)(x + 5) = 0 \qquad \text{Factor.}$$

$$x - 5 = 0 \quad \text{or} \quad x + 5 = 0 \qquad \text{Set each factor equal to zero.}$$

$$x = 5 \quad \text{or} \qquad x = -5$$

The solutions are 5 and -5.

Skill Practice

Solve the quadratic equation by using the zero product rule.

3. $t^2 = 49$

2. Solving Quadratic Equations Using the Square Root Property

In Examples 1–3, the quadratic equations were all factorable. In this chapter, we learn techniques to solve *all* quadratic equations, factorable and nonfactorable. The first technique uses the **square root property**.

Square Root Property

For any real number, k, if $x^2 = k$, then $x = \sqrt{k}$ or $x = -\sqrt{k}$.

Note: The solution can also be written as $x = \pm\sqrt{k}$, read as "x equals plus or minus the square root of k."

Answer

3. $7, -7$

Example 4   Solving a Quadratic Equation Using the Square Root Property

Use the square root property to solve the equation.

$$x^2 = 25$$

Solution:

$x^2 = 25$	The equation is in the form $x^2 = k$.
$x = \pm\sqrt{25}$	Apply the square root property.
$x = \pm 5$	

The solutions are 5 and -5. Note that this result is the same as in Example 3.

Example 5   Solving a Quadratic Equation Using the Square Root Property

Use the square root property to solve the equation.

$$2x^2 - 10 = 0$$

Solution:

$2x^2 - 10 = 0$	To apply the square root property, the equation must be in the form $x^2 = k$, that is, we must isolate x^2.
$2x^2 = 10$	Add 10 to both sides.
$x^2 = 5$	Divide both sides by 2. The equation is in the form $x^2 = k$.
$x = \pm\sqrt{5}$	Apply the square root property.

Check: $x = \sqrt{5}$ Check: $x = -\sqrt{5}$

$2x^2 - 10 = 0$ $2x^2 - 10 = 0$

$2(\sqrt{5})^2 - 10 \overset{?}{=} 0$ $2(-\sqrt{5})^2 - 10 \overset{?}{=} 0$

$2(5) - 10 \overset{?}{=} 0$ $2(5) - 10 \overset{?}{=} 0$

$10 - 10 \overset{?}{=} 0 ✔$ $10 - 10 \overset{?}{=} 0 ✔$

The solutions are $\sqrt{5}$ and $-\sqrt{5}$.

In Example 6, we apply the square root property in an equation where the square of a binomial is equal to a constant.

Example 6   Solving a Quadratic Equation Using the Square Root Property

Use the square root property to solve the equation.

$$(t - 4)^2 = 12$$

Solution:

$(t - 4)^2 = 12$	The equation is in the form $x^2 = k$, where $x = (t - 4)$.
$t - 4 = \pm\sqrt{12}$	Apply the square root property.

$$t - 4 = \pm\sqrt{4 \cdot 3} \qquad \text{Simplify the radical.}$$

$$t - 4 = \pm 2\sqrt{3}$$

$$t = 4 \pm 2\sqrt{3} \qquad \text{Solve for } t.$$

<u>Check</u>: $t = 4 + 2\sqrt{3}$ <u>Check</u>: $t = 4 - 2\sqrt{3}$

$$(t - 4)^2 = 12 \qquad\qquad (t - 4)^2 = 12$$

$$(4 + 2\sqrt{3} - 4)^2 \stackrel{?}{=} 12 \qquad (4 - 2\sqrt{3} - 4)^2 \stackrel{?}{=} 12$$

$$(2\sqrt{3})^2 \stackrel{?}{=} 12 \qquad\qquad (-2\sqrt{3})^2 \stackrel{?}{=} 12$$

$$4 \cdot 3 \stackrel{?}{=} 12 \qquad\qquad 4 \cdot 3 \stackrel{?}{=} 12$$

$$12 \stackrel{?}{=} 12 \checkmark \qquad\qquad 12 \stackrel{?}{=} 12 \checkmark$$

The solutions are: $4 + 2\sqrt{3}$ and $4 - 2\sqrt{3}$.

Example 7   **Solving a Quadratic Equation Using the Square Root Property**

Use the square root property to solve the equation.

$$y^2 = -4$$

Solution:

$$y^2 = -4 \qquad \text{The equation is in the form } y^2 = k.$$

$$y = \pm\sqrt{-4}$$

The expression $\sqrt{-4}$ is not a real number. Thus, the equation, $y^2 = -4$, has no real-valued solutions.

Skill Practice

Use the square root property to solve the equation.

7. $z^2 = -9$

Answer

7. The equation has no real-valued solutions.

Section 9.1   Practice Exercises

Vocabulary and Key Concepts

1. a. The zero product rule states that if $ab = 0$, then $a = $ _____ or $b = $ _____.

    b. To apply the zero product rule, one side of the equation must be equal to _____ and the other side must be written in factored form.

    c. The square root property states that for any real number k, if $x^2 = k$, then $x = $ _____ or $x = $ _____.

    d. To apply the square root property to the equation $x^2 + 4 = 13$, first subtract _____ from both sides. The solutions are _____.

Concept 1: Review of the Zero Product Rule

2. Identify the equations as linear or quadratic.

    a. $2x - 5 = 3(x + 2) - 1$

    b. $2x(x - 5) = 3(x + 2) - 1$

    c. $ax^2 + bx + c = 0$
        (a, b, and c are real numbers, and $a \neq 0$)

3. Identify the equations as linear or quadratic.

    a. $ax + b = c$
        (a, b, and c are real numbers, and $a \neq 0$)

    b. $\dfrac{1}{2}p - \dfrac{3}{4}p^2 = 0$

    c. $\dfrac{1}{2}(p - 3) = 5$

For Exercises 4–19, solve using the zero product rule. **(See Examples 1–3.)**

4. $(3z - 2)(4z + 5) = 0$ **5.** $(t + 5)(2t - 1) = 0$ **6.** $r^2 + 7r + 12 = 0$ **7.** $y^2 - 2y - 35 = 0$

8. $10x^2 = 13x - 4$ **9.** $6p^2 = -13p - 2$ **10.** $2m(m - 1) = 3m - 3$ **11.** $2x^2 + 10x = -7(x + 3)$

12. $x^2 = 4$ **13.** $c^2 = 144$ **14.** $(x - 1)^2 = 16$ **15.** $(x - 3)^2 = 25$

16. $3p^2 + 4p = 15$ **17.** $4a^2 + 7a = 2$ **18.** $(x + 2)(x + 3) = 2$ **19.** $(x + 2)(x + 6) = 5$

Concept 2: Solving Quadratic Equations Using the Square Root Property

20. The symbol "±" is read as …

For Exercises 21–44, solve the equations using the square root property. **(See Examples 4–7.)**

21. $x^2 = 49$ **22.** $x^2 = 16$ **23.** $k^2 - 100 = 0$ **24.** $m^2 - 64 = 0$

25. $p^2 = -24$ **26.** $q^2 = -50$ **27.** $3w^2 - 9 = 0$ **28.** $4v^2 - 24 = 0$

29. $(a - 5)^2 = 16$ **30.** $(b + 3)^2 = 1$ **31.** $(y - 5)^2 = 36$ **32.** $(y + 4)^2 = 4$

33. $(x - 11)^2 = 5$ **34.** $(z - 2)^2 = 7$ **35.** $(a + 1)^2 = 18$ **36.** $(b - 1)^2 = 12$

37. $\left(t - \dfrac{1}{4}\right)^2 = \dfrac{7}{16}$ **38.** $\left(t - \dfrac{1}{3}\right)^2 = \dfrac{1}{9}$ **39.** $\left(x - \dfrac{1}{2}\right)^2 + 5 = 20$ **40.** $\left(x + \dfrac{5}{2}\right)^2 - 3 = 18$

41. $(p - 3)^2 = -16$ **42.** $(t + 4)^2 = -9$ **43.** $12t^2 - 20 = 55$ **44.** $8p^2 + 10 = 28$

45. Check the solution $-3 + \sqrt{5}$ in the equation $(x + 3)^2 = 5$.

46. Check the solution $-5 - \sqrt{7}$ in the equation $(p + 5)^2 = 7$.

For Exercises 47 and 48, answer true or false. If a statement is false, explain why.

47. The only solution to the equation $x^2 = 64$ is 8.

48. There are two real solutions to every quadratic equation of the form $x^2 = k$, where $k \geq 0$ is a real number.

49. Ignoring air resistance, the distance, d (in feet), that an object drops in t seconds is given by the equation

$$d = 16t^2$$

a. Find the distance traveled in 2 sec.

b. Find the time required for the object to fall 200 ft. Round to the nearest tenth of a second.

c. Find the time required for an object to fall from the top of the Empire State Building in New York City if the building is 1250 ft high. Round to the nearest tenth of a second.

50. Ignoring air resistance, the distance, d (in meters), that an object drops in t seconds is given by the equation

$$d = 4.9t^2$$

a. Find the distance traveled in 5 sec.

b. Find the time required for the object to fall 50 m. Round to the nearest tenth of a second.

c. Find the time required for an object to fall from the top of the Canada Trust Tower in Toronto, Canada, if the building is 261 m high. Round to the nearest tenth of a second.

51. A right triangle has legs of equal length. If the hypotenuse is 10 m long, find the length (in meters) of each leg. Round the answer to the nearest tenth of a meter.

52. The diagonal of a square computer monitor screen is 24 in. long. Find the length of the sides to the nearest tenth of an inch.

53. The area of a circular wading pool is approximately 200 ft^2. Find the radius to the nearest tenth of a foot.

54. According to the International Swimming Federation, the volume of an eight-lane Olympic size pool should be 2500 m^3. The length of the pool is twice the width, and the depth is 2 m. Use a calculator to find the length and width of the pool.

Completing the Square

1. Completing the Square

In Section 9.1, Example 6, we used the square root property to solve an equation in which the square of a binomial was equal to a constant.

$$\underbrace{(t - 4)^2}_{\substack{\text{Square of a} \\ \text{binomial}}} = \underset{\text{Constant}}{12}$$

Furthermore, any equation $ax^2 + bx + c = 0$ $(a \neq 0)$ can be rewritten as the square of a binomial equal to a constant by using a process called **completing the square**.

We begin our discussion of completing the square with some vocabulary. For a trinomial $ax^2 + bx + c$ $(a \neq 0)$, the term ax^2 is called the **quadratic term**. The term bx is called the **linear term**, and the term c is called the **constant term**.

Next, notice that the square of a binomial is the factored form of a perfect square trinomial.

Concepts

1. Completing the Square
2. Solving Quadratic Equations by Completing the Square

Perfect Square Trinomial	Factored Form
$x^2 + 10x + 25$ ⟶	$(x + 5)^2$
$t^2 - 6t + 9$ ⟶	$(t - 3)^2$
$p^2 - 14p + 49$ ⟶	$(p - 7)^2$

Furthermore, for a perfect square trinomial with a leading coefficient of 1, the constant term is the square of half the coefficient of the linear term. For example:

$$x^2 + 10x + 25 \longleftarrow \qquad t^2 - 6t + 9 \longleftarrow \qquad p^2 - 14p + 49 \longleftarrow$$

$$\left[\frac{1}{2}(10)\right]^2 = [5]^2 = 25 \qquad \left[\frac{1}{2}(-6)\right]^2 = [-3]^2 = 9 \qquad \left[\frac{1}{2}(-14)\right]^2 = [-7]^2 = 49$$

In general, an expression of the form $x^2 + bx$ will result in a perfect square trinomial if the square of half the linear term coefficient, $(\frac{1}{2}b)^2$, is added to the expression.

Skill Practice

Determine the value of n that makes the polynomial a perfect square trinomial. Then factor the expression as the square of a binomial.

1. $q^2 + 8q + n$
2. $t^2 - 10t + n$
3. $v^2 + 3v + n$
4. $y^2 + \frac{1}{4}y + n$

Example 1 **Completing the Square**

Determine the value of n that makes the polynomial a perfect square trinomial. Then factor the expression as the square of a binomial.

a. $x^2 + 12x + n$ **b.** $x^2 - 22x + n$ **c.** $x^2 + 5x + n$ **d.** $x^2 - \frac{3}{5}x + n$

Solution:

The expressions are in the form $x^2 + bx$. Add the square of half the linear term coefficient, $(\frac{1}{2}b)^2$.

a. $x^2 + 12x + n$

$$x^2 + 12x + 36 \qquad n = [\tfrac{1}{2}(12)]^2 = (6)^2 = 36.$$

$$(x + 6)^2 \qquad \text{Factored form}$$

b. $x^2 - 22x + n$

$$x^2 - 22x + 121 \qquad n = [\tfrac{1}{2}(-22)]^2 = (-11)^2 = 121.$$

$$(x - 11)^2 \qquad \text{Factored form}$$

c. $x^2 + 5x + n$

$$x^2 + 5x + \frac{25}{4} \qquad n = \left[\frac{1}{2}(5)\right]^2 = \left(\frac{5}{2}\right)^2 = \frac{25}{4}.$$

$$\left(x + \frac{5}{2}\right)^2 \qquad \text{Factored form}$$

d. $x^2 - \frac{3}{5}x + n$

$$x^2 - \frac{3}{5}x + \frac{9}{100} \qquad n = \left[\frac{1}{2}\left(-\frac{3}{5}\right)\right]^2 = \left(-\frac{3}{10}\right)^2 = \frac{9}{100}$$

$$\left(x - \frac{3}{10}\right)^2 \qquad \text{Factored form}$$

Answers

1. $n = 16; (q + 4)^2$
2. $n = 25; (t - 5)^2$
3. $n = \frac{9}{4}; \left(v + \frac{3}{2}\right)^2$
4. $n = \frac{1}{64}; \left(y + \frac{1}{8}\right)^2$

2. Solving Quadratic Equations by Completing the Square

A quadratic equation can be solved by completing the square and applying the square root property. The following steps outline the procedure.

Solving a Quadratic Equation in the Form $ax^2 + bx + c = 0$ ($a \neq 0$) by Completing the Square and Applying the Square Root Property

Step 1 Divide both sides by a to make the leading coefficient 1.

Step 2 Isolate the variable terms on one side of the equation.

Step 3 Complete the square by adding the square of one-half the linear term coefficient to both sides of the equation. Then factor the resulting perfect square trinomial.

Step 4 Apply the square root property and solve for x.

Example 2 Solving a Quadratic Equation by Completing the Square and Applying the Square Root Property

Solve the quadratic equation by completing the square and applying the square root property.

$$x^2 + 6x - 8 = 0$$

Solution:

$x^2 + 6x - 8 = 0$ The equation is in the form $ax^2 + bx + c = 0$.

     Step 1: The leading coefficient is already 1.

$x^2 + 6x = 8$ **Step 2:** Isolate the variable terms on one side.

$x^2 + 6x + 9 = 8 + 9$ **Step 3:** To complete the square, add $\left[\frac{1}{2}(6)\right]^2 = (3)^2 = 9$ to both sides.

$(x + 3)^2 = 17$ Factor the perfect square trinomial.

$x + 3 = \pm\sqrt{17}$ **Step 4:** Apply the square root property.

$x = -3 \pm \sqrt{17}$ Solve for x.

The solutions are $-3 - \sqrt{17}$ and $-3 + \sqrt{17}$.

Skill Practice

Solve the equation by completing the square and applying the square root property.

5. $t^2 + 4t + 2 = 0$

Answer

5. $-2 \pm \sqrt{2}$

Example 3 Solving a Quadratic Equation by Completing the Square and Applying the Square Root Property

Solve the quadratic equation by completing the square and applying the square root property.

$$2x^2 - 16x - 24 = 0$$

Solution:

$2x^2 - 16x - 24 = 0$ The equation is in the form $ax^2 + bx + c = 0$.

$\dfrac{2x^2}{2} - \dfrac{16x}{2} - \dfrac{24}{2} = \dfrac{0}{2}$ **Step 1:** Divide both sides by the leading coefficient, 2.

$x^2 - 8x - 12 = 0$

$x^2 - 8x = 12$ **Step 2:** Isolate the variable terms on one side.

$x^2 - 8x + 16 = 12 + 16$ **Step 3:** To complete the square, add $[\frac{1}{2}(-8)]^2 = 16$ to both sides of the equation.

$(x - 4)^2 = 28$ Factor the perfect square trinomial.

$x - 4 = \pm\sqrt{28}$ **Step 4:** Apply the square root property.

$x - 4 = \pm 2\sqrt{7}$ Simplify the radical.

$x = 4 \pm 2\sqrt{7}$ Solve for x.

The solutions are $4 + 2\sqrt{7}$ and $4 - 2\sqrt{7}$.

Example 4 Solving a Quadratic Equation by Completing the Square and Applying the Square Root Property

Solve the quadratic equation by completing the square and applying the square root property.

$$x(2x - 5) - 3 = 0$$

Solution:

$x(2x - 5) - 3 = 0$ Clear parentheses.

$2x^2 - 5x - 3 = 0$ The equation is in the form $ax^2 + bx + c = 0$.

$\dfrac{2x^2}{2} - \dfrac{5x}{2} - \dfrac{3}{2} = \dfrac{0}{2}$ **Step 1:** Divide both sides by the leading coefficient, 2.

$x^2 - \dfrac{5}{2}x - \dfrac{3}{2} = 0$

$x^2 - \dfrac{5}{2}x = \dfrac{3}{2}$ **Step 2:** Isolate the variable terms on one side.

Answers

6. $1 \pm 3\sqrt{2}$

7. $\dfrac{3}{5}, -2$

$$x^2 - \frac{5}{2}x + \frac{25}{16} = \frac{3}{2} + \frac{25}{16}$$

Step 3: Add $[\frac{1}{2}(-\frac{5}{2})]^2 = (-\frac{5}{4})^2 = \frac{25}{16}$ to both sides.

$$\left(x - \frac{5}{4}\right)^2 = \frac{24}{16} + \frac{25}{16}$$

Factor the perfect square trinomial. Rewrite the right-hand side with a common denominator and simplify.

$$\left(x - \frac{5}{4}\right)^2 = \frac{49}{16}$$

$$x - \frac{5}{4} = \pm\sqrt{\frac{49}{16}}$$

Step 4: Apply the square root property.

$$x - \frac{5}{4} = \pm\frac{7}{4}$$

Simplify the radical.

$$x = \frac{5}{4} \pm \frac{7}{4}$$

Solve for x.

We have

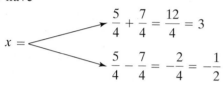

$$x = \begin{cases} \frac{5}{4} + \frac{7}{4} = \frac{12}{4} = 3 \\ \frac{5}{4} - \frac{7}{4} = -\frac{2}{4} = -\frac{1}{2} \end{cases}$$

The solutions are 3 and $-\frac{1}{2}$.

Section 9.2 Practice Exercises

Vocabulary and Key Concepts

1. a. The process to create a perfect square trinomial is called _____ the square.

b. Fill in the blank to complete the square for the trinomial $x^2 + 20x +$ _____.

c. To use completing the square to solve the equation $5x^2 + 3x + 1 = 0$, the first step is to divide both sides of the equation by _____ so that the coefficient on the x^2 term is _____.

d. Given the trinomial $y^2 + 8y + 16$, the coefficient of the linear term is _____.

Review Exercises

For Exercises 2–4, solve the quadratic equation using the square root property.

2. $x^2 = 21$
3. $(x - 5)^2 = 21$
4. $(x - 5)^2 = -21$

Concept 1: Completing the Square

For Exercises 5–16, find the value of n so that the expression is a perfect square trinomial. Then factor the trinomial. **(See Example 1.)**

5. $y^2 + 4y + n$
6. $w^2 - 6w + n$
7. $p^2 - 12p + n$
8. $q^2 + 16q + n$

9. $x^2 - 9x + n$
10. $a^2 - 5a + n$
11. $d^2 + \frac{5}{3}d + n$
12. $t^2 + \frac{1}{4}t + n$

13. $m^2 - \dfrac{1}{5}m + n$ **14.** $x^2 - \dfrac{5}{7}x + n$ **15.** $u^2 + u + n$ **16.** $v^2 - v + n$

Concept 2: Solving Quadratic Equations by Completing the Square

For Exercises 17–36, solve the equations by completing the square and applying the square root property.
(See Examples 2–4.)

17. $x^2 + 4x = 12$ **18.** $x^2 - 2x = 8$ **19.** $y^2 + 6y = -5$ **20.** $t^2 + 10t = 11$

21. $x^2 = 2x + 1$ **22.** $x^2 = 6x - 2$ **23.** $3x^2 - 6x - 15 = 0$ **24.** $5x^2 + 10x - 30 = 0$

25. $4p^2 + 16p = -4$ **26.** $2t^2 - 12t = 12$ **27.** $w^2 + w - 3 = 0$ **28.** $z^2 - 3z - 5 = 0$

29. $x(x + 2) = 40$ **30.** $y(y - 4) = 10$ **31.** $a^2 - 4\underline{a} - 1 = 0$ **32.** $c^2 - 2c - 9 = 0$

33. $2r^2 + 12r + 16 = 0$ **34.** $3p^2 + 12p + 9 = 0$ **35.** $h(h - 11) = -24$ **36.** $k(k - 8) = -7$

Mixed Exercises

For Exercises 37–64, solve the quadratic equation by using the zero product rule or the square root property.
(*Hint:* For some exercises, you may have to factor or complete the square first.)

37. $y^2 = 121$ **38.** $x^2 = 81$ **39.** $(p + 2)^2 = 2$ **40.** $(q - 6)^2 = 3$

41. $(k + 13)(k - 5) = 0$ **42.** $(r - 10)(r + 12) = 0$ **43.** $(x - 13)^2 = 0$ **44.** $(p + 14)^2 = 0$

45. $z^2 - 8z - 20 = 0$ **46.** $b^2 - 14b + 48 = 0$ **47.** $(x - 3)^2 = 16$ **48.** $(x + 2)^2 = 49$

49. $a^2 - 8a + 1 = 0$ **50.** $x^2 + 12x - 4 = 0$ **51.** $2y^2 + 4y = 10$ **52.** $3z^2 - 48z = 6$

53. $x^2 - 9x - 22 = 0$ **54.** $y^2 + 11y + 18 = 0$ **55.** $5h(h - 7) = 0$ **56.** $-2w(w + 9) = 0$

57. $8t^2 + 2t - 3 = 0$ **58.** $18a^2 - 21a + 5 = 0$ **59.** $t^2 = 14$ **60.** $s^2 = 17$

61. $c^2 + 9 = 0$ **62.** $k^2 + 25 = 0$ **63.** $4x^2 - 8x = -4$ **64.** $3x^2 + 12x = -12$

Expanding Your Skills

For Exercises 65 and 66, solve by completing the square.

65. To comply with FAA regulations, a piece of luggage must be checked to the luggage compartment of the plane if its combined linear measurement of length, width, and height is over 45 in. Katie's suitcase has a total volume of 4200 in.^{3}. Its length is 30 in., and its width is 4 in. greater than the height. Find the dimensions of the suitcase. Will this suitcase need to be checked? Explain.

66. Luggage that is checked to the baggage compartment of an airplane must not exceed the dimensional requirements set by the carrier. Most carriers do not allow bags that exceed 30 in. in any dimension. They also require that the combined length, width, and height of the bag not exceed 62 in. Suppose a suitcase has a total volume of 5040 in.^{3}. If the length is 28 in. and the width is 8 in. greater than the height, find the dimensions of the bag. Can this bag be checked to the luggage compartment of the plane? Explain.

Quadratic Formula

Section 9.3

1. Derivation of the Quadratic Formula

Concepts

1. Derivation of the Quadratic Formula
2. Solving Quadratic Equations Using the Quadratic Formula
3. Review of the Methods for Solving a Quadratic Equation
4. Applications of Quadratic Equations

If we solve a general quadratic equation $ax^2 + bx + c = 0 \ (a > 0)$ by completing the square and using the square root property, the result is a formula that gives the solutions for x in terms of a, b, and c.

$$ax^2 + bx + c = 0$$

Begin with a quadratic equation in standard form.

$$\frac{ax^2}{a} + \frac{b}{a}x + \frac{c}{a} = \frac{0}{a}$$

Divide by the leading coefficient.

$$x^2 + \frac{b}{a}x = -\frac{c}{a}$$

Isolate the terms containing x.

$$x^2 + \frac{b}{a}x + \left(\frac{1}{2}\cdot\frac{b}{a}\right)^2 = \left(\frac{1}{2}\cdot\frac{b}{a}\right)^2 - \frac{c}{a}$$

Add the square of $\frac{1}{2}$ the linear term coefficient to both sides of the equation.

$$\left(x + \frac{b}{2a}\right)^2 = \frac{b^2}{4a^2} - \frac{c}{a}$$

Factor the left side as a perfect square.

$$\left(x + \frac{b}{2a}\right)^2 = \frac{b^2}{4a^2} - \frac{c}{a}\cdot\frac{(4a)}{(4a)}$$

On the right side, write the fractions with the common denominator, $4a^2$.

$$\left(x + \frac{b}{2a}\right)^2 = \frac{b^2 - 4ac}{4a^2}$$

Combine the fractions.

$$x + \frac{b}{2a} = \pm\sqrt{\frac{b^2 - 4ac}{4a^2}}$$

Apply the square root property.

$$x + \frac{b}{2a} = \frac{\pm\sqrt{b^2 - 4ac}}{2a}$$

Simplify the denominator.

$$x = -\frac{b}{2a} \pm \frac{\sqrt{b^2 - 4ac}}{2a}$$

Subtract $\frac{b}{2a}$ from both sides.

$$= \frac{-b \pm \sqrt{b^2 - 4ac}}{2a}$$

Combine fractions.

Concept Connections

Write each quadratic equation in the form $ax^2 + bx + c = 0$. Then identify a, b, and c.

1. $4x^2 - 9x + 1 = 0$
2. $3x^2 = 2x + 8$
3. $x(x + 6) = x + 15$

Answers

1. $4x^2 - 9x + 1 = 0$;
   $a = 4; b = -9; c = 1$
2. $3x^2 - 2x - 8 = 0$;
   $a = 3; b = -2; c = -8$
3. $x^2 + 5x - 15 = 0$;
   $a = 1; b = 5; c = -15$

Quadratic Formula

For any quadratic equation of the form $ax^2 + bx + c = 0\ (a \neq 0)$, the solutions are

$$x = \frac{-b \pm \sqrt{b^2 - 4ac}}{2a}$$

2. Solving Quadratic Equations Using the Quadratic Formula

Example 1 **Solving Quadratic Equations Using the Quadratic Formula**

Solve the quadratic equation using the quadratic formula: $3x^2 - 7x = -2$

Skill Practice

Solve by using the quadratic formula.

4. $5x^2 - 9x + 4 = 0$

Solution:

$$3x^2 - 7x = -2$$

$$3x^2 - 7x + 2 = 0 \qquad \text{Write the equation in the form } ax^2 + bx + c = 0.$$

$$a = 3, b = -7, c = 2 \qquad \text{Identify } a, b, \text{ and } c.$$

Avoiding Mistakes

The fraction bar in the quadratic formula extends under both $-b$ and the radical.

$$x = \frac{-b \pm \sqrt{b^2 - 4ac}}{2a}$$

$$x = \frac{-(-7) \pm \sqrt{(-7)^2 - 4(3)(2)}}{2(3)} \qquad \text{Apply the quadratic formula.}$$

$$x = \frac{7 \pm \sqrt{49 - 24}}{6} \qquad \text{Simplify.}$$

$$= \frac{7 \pm \sqrt{25}}{6}$$

$$= \frac{7 \pm 5}{6}$$

There are two rational solutions.

$$x = \begin{cases} \dfrac{7 + 5}{6} = \dfrac{12}{6} = 2 \\ \\ \dfrac{7 - 5}{6} = \dfrac{2}{6} = \dfrac{1}{3} \end{cases}$$

TIP: If the solutions to a quadratic equation are rational numbers, then the original equation could have been solved by factoring and using the zero product rule.

The solutions are 2 and $\dfrac{1}{3}$.

Answer

4. $1, \dfrac{4}{5}$

Example 2 Solving a Quadratic Equation Using the Quadratic Formula

Solve the quadratic equation using the quadratic formula. Then approximate the solutions to three decimal places.

$$2x(x - 1) - 6 = 0$$

Solution:

$2x(x - 1) - 6 = 0$

$2x^2 - 2x - 6 = 0$ Write the equation in the form $ax^2 + bx + c = 0$.

$a = 2, b = -2, c = -6$ Identify a, b, and c.

$x = \dfrac{-b \pm \sqrt{b^2 - 4ac}}{2a}$

$x = \dfrac{-(-2) \pm \sqrt{(-2)^2 - 4(2)(-6)}}{2(2)}$ Apply the quadratic formula.

$= \dfrac{2 \pm \sqrt{4 + 48}}{4}$ Simplify.

$= \dfrac{2 \pm \sqrt{52}}{4}$

$= \dfrac{2 \pm \sqrt{4 \cdot 13}}{4}$ Simplify the radical.

$= \dfrac{2 \pm 2\sqrt{13}}{4}$

$= \dfrac{\overset{1}{2}(1 \pm \sqrt{13})}{\underset{2}{4}}$ Simplify the fraction.

$= \dfrac{1 \pm \sqrt{13}}{2}$

$x = \dfrac{1 + \sqrt{13}}{2} \approx 2.303$

$x = \dfrac{1 - \sqrt{13}}{2} \approx -1.303$

The exact solutions are $\dfrac{1 + \sqrt{13}}{2}$ and $\dfrac{1 - \sqrt{13}}{2}$. The approximate solutions are 2.303 and -1.303.

Answer

5. $-1 \pm \sqrt{6}$;

    $\approx 1.449, \approx -3.449$

Skill Practice

Solve by using the quadratic formula.

6. $\dfrac{1}{2}t^2 + \dfrac{1}{3}t + \dfrac{1}{18} = 0$

Example 3 Solving a Quadratic Equation Using the Quadratic Formula

Solve the quadratic equation using the quadratic formula.

$$\frac{1}{4}w^2 - \frac{1}{2}w + \frac{1}{4} = 0$$

Solution:

$$\frac{1}{4}w^2 - \frac{1}{2}w + \frac{1}{4} = 0$$ Multiply each side of the equation by the LCD, which is 4.

$$4\left(\frac{1}{4}w^2 - \frac{1}{2}w + \frac{1}{4}\right) = 4(0)$$ Use the distributive property to clear fractions.

$$w^2 - 2w + 1 = 0$$ The equation is in the form $ax^2 + bx + c = 0$.

$$a = 1, b = -2, c = 1$$ Identify a, b, and c.

$$w = \frac{-b \pm \sqrt{b^2 - 4ac}}{2a}$$

$$w = \frac{-(-2) \pm \sqrt{(-2)^2 - 4(1)(1)}}{2(1)}$$ Apply the quadratic formula.

$$= \frac{2 \pm \sqrt{4 - 4}}{2}$$ Simplify.

$$= \frac{2 \pm \sqrt{0}}{2}$$

$$= \frac{2 \pm 0}{2}$$ Simplify the radical.

$$= \frac{\overset{1}{2}}{2}$$ Simplify the fraction.

$$= 1$$

The solution is 1.

> **TIP:** When using the quadratic formula, if the radical term results in the square root of zero, there will be only one rational solution.

3. Review of the Methods for Solving a Quadratic Equation

Three methods have been presented for solving quadratic equations.

Methods for Solving a Quadratic Equation
- Factor and use the zero product rule (Section 6.7).
- Use the square root property. Complete the square if necessary (Sections 9.1 and 9.2).
- Use the quadratic formula (Section 9.3).

Answer

6. $-\dfrac{1}{3}$

The zero product rule can be used only if one side of the equation is zero, and the expression on the other side is factorable. The square root property and the quadratic formula can be used to solve any quadratic equation. Before solving a quadratic equation, take a minute to analyze it. Each problem must be examined individually before choosing the most efficient method to find its solutions.

| Example 4 | Solving Quadratic Equations Using Any Method |

Solve the quadratic equations using any method.

a. $(x + 1)^2 = 5$ **b.** $t^2 - t - 30 = 0$ **c.** $2x^2 + 5x + 1 = 0$

Solution:

a. $(x + 1)^2 = 5$ Because the equation is the square of a binomial equal to a constant, the square root property can be applied easily.

$\qquad x + 1 = \pm\sqrt{5}$ Apply the square root property.

$\qquad\qquad x = -1 \pm \sqrt{5}$ Isolate x.

The solutions are $-1 + \sqrt{5}$ and $-1 - \sqrt{5}$.

b. $t^2 - t - 30 = 0$ This equation factors.

$\quad (t - 6)(t + 5) = 0$ Factor and apply the zero product rule.

$\quad t = 6 \quad$ or $\quad t = -5$

The solutions are 6 and -5.

c. $2x^2 + 5x + 1 = 0$ The equation does not factor. Because it is already in the form $ax^2 + bx + c = 0$, use the quadratic formula.

$a = 2, b = 5, c = 1$ Identify a, b, and c.

$$x = \frac{-(5) \pm \sqrt{(5)^2 - 4(2)(1)}}{2(2)}$$ Apply the quadratic formula.

$$x = \frac{-5 \pm \sqrt{25 - 8}}{4}$$ Simplify.

$$x = \frac{-5 \pm \sqrt{17}}{4}$$

The solutions are $\dfrac{-5 + \sqrt{17}}{4}$ and $\dfrac{-5 - \sqrt{17}}{4}$.

Answers

7. $-3, -4$

8. $\dfrac{-7 \pm \sqrt{29}}{10}$

9. $8 \pm \sqrt{3}$

4. Applications of Quadratic Equations

Example 5   **Solving a Quadratic Equation in an Application**

The length of a box is 2 in. longer than the width. The height of the box is 4 in. and the volume of the box is 200 in.³. Find the exact dimensions of the box. Then use a calculator to approximate the dimensions to the nearest tenth of an inch.

Solution:

Label the box as follows (Figure 9-1):

Width $= x$

Length $= x + 2$

Height $= 4$

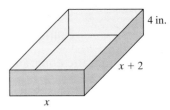

4 in.

$x + 2$

x

Figure 9-1

The volume of a box is given by the formula: $V = lwh$

$$V = l \cdot w \cdot h$$

$$200 = (x + 2)(x)(4) \qquad \text{Substitute } V = 200, l = x + 2, w = x, \text{ and } h = 4.$$

$$200 = (x + 2)4x$$

$$200 = 4x^2 + 8x$$

$$0 = 4x^2 + 8x - 200$$

$$4x^2 + 8x - 200 = 0 \qquad \text{The equation is in the form } ax^2 + bx + c = 0.$$

$$\frac{4x^2}{4} + \frac{8x}{4} - \frac{200}{4} = \frac{0}{4} \qquad \text{The coefficients are all divisible by 4. Dividing by 4 will create smaller values of } a, b, \text{ and } c \text{ to be used in the quadratic formula.}$$

$$x^2 + 2x - 50 = 0 \qquad a = 1, b = 2, c = -50$$

$$x = \frac{-2 \pm \sqrt{(2)^2 - 4(1)(-50)}}{2(1)} \qquad \text{Apply the quadratic formula.}$$

$$= \frac{-2 \pm \sqrt{4 + 200}}{2} \qquad \text{Simplify.}$$

$$= \frac{-2 \pm \sqrt{204}}{2}$$

$$= \frac{-2 \pm 2\sqrt{51}}{2} \qquad \text{Simplify the radical.} \\ \sqrt{204} = \sqrt{4 \cdot 51} = 2\sqrt{51}$$

$$= \frac{\overset{1}{2}(-1 \pm \sqrt{51})}{\underset{1}{2}} \qquad \text{Factor and simplify.}$$

$$= -1 \pm \sqrt{51}$$

Because the width of the box must be positive, use $x = -1 + \sqrt{51}$.

The width is $(-1 + \sqrt{51})$ in. ≈ 6.1 in.

The length is $x + 2$: $(-1 + \sqrt{51} + 2)$ in. or $(1 + \sqrt{51})$ in. ≈ 8.1 in.

The height is 4 in.

Calculator Connections

Topic: Finding Decimal Approximations to the Solutions of a Quadratic Equation

Use the quadratic formula to verify that the solutions to the equation $x(x + 7) + 4 = 0$ are

$$x = \frac{-7 + \sqrt{33}}{2} \quad \text{and} \quad x = \frac{-7 - \sqrt{33}}{2}$$

A calculator can be used to obtain decimal approximations for the irrational solutions of a quadratic equation.

Scientific Calculator

Enter: 7 [+/-] [+] 33 [√] [=] [÷] 2 [=]　　**Result:**　　$\boxed{-0.6277186767}$

Enter: 7 [+/-] [−] 33 [√] [=] [÷] 2 [=]　　**Result:**　　$\boxed{-6.372281323}$

Graphing Calculator

```
(-7+√(33))/2
          -.6277186767
(-7-√(33))/2
          -6.372281323
```

Calculator Exercises

Use a calculator to obtain a decimal approximation of each expression.

1. $\dfrac{-5 + \sqrt{17}}{4}$ and $\dfrac{-5 - \sqrt{17}}{4}$

2. $\dfrac{-40 + \sqrt{1920}}{-32}$ and $\dfrac{-40 - \sqrt{1920}}{-32}$

Section 9.3　Practice Exercises

Vocabulary and Key Concepts

1. a. For the equation $ax^2 + bx + c = 0 \ (a \neq 0)$, the quadratic formula gives the solutions as $x = $ _____ .

　b. To apply the quadratic formula, a quadratic equation must be written in the form _____ , where $a \neq 0$.

　c. To apply the quadratic formula to solve the equation $5x^2 - 24x - 36 = 0$, the value of a is _____ , the value of b is _____ , and the value of c is _____ .

　d. To apply the quadratic formula to solve the equation $2x^2 - 5x - 6 = 0$, the value of $-b$ is _____ and the value of the radicand is _____ .

Review Exercises

For Exercises 2–5, apply the square root property to solve the equation.

2. $z^2 = 169$ 　　　　**3.** $p^2 = 1$ 　　　　**4.** $(x - 4)^2 = 28$ 　　　　**5.** $(y + 3)^2 = 7$

For Exercises 6–8, solve the equations by completing the square.

6. $p^2 + 10p + 2 = 0$ 　　　　**7.** $3a^2 - 12a - 12 = 0$ 　　　　**8.** $x^2 - 5x + 1 = 0$

Concept 1: Derivation of the Quadratic Formula

For Exercises 9–14, write the equations in the form $ax^2 + bx + c = 0$. Then identify the values of a, b, and c.

9. $2x^2 - x = 5$ 　　　　**10.** $5(x^2 + 2) = -3x$ 　　　　**11.** $-3x(x - 4) = -2x$

12. $x(x - 2) = 3(x + 1)$ 　　　　**13.** $x^2 - 9 = 0$ 　　　　**14.** $x^2 + 25 = 0$

Concept 2: Solving Quadratic Equations Using the Quadratic Formula

For Exercises 15–32, solve the equations using the quadratic formula. **(See Examples 1–3.)**

15. $6k^2 - k - 2 = 0$

16. $3n^2 + 5n - 2 = 0$

17. $t^2 + 16t + 64 = 0$

18. $y^2 - 10y + 25 = 0$

19. $5t^2 - t = 3$

20. $2a^2 + 5a = 1$

21. $x(x - 2) = 1$

22. $2y(y - 3) = -1$

23. $2p^2 = -10p - 11$

24. $z^2 = 4z + 1$

25. $-4y^2 - y + 1 = 0$

26. $-5z^2 - 3z + 4 = 0$

27. $2x(x + 1) = 3 - x$

28. $3m(m - 2) = -m + 1$

29. $0.2y^2 = -1.5y - 1$

30. $0.2t^2 = t + 0.5$

31. $\dfrac{2}{3}x^2 + \dfrac{4}{9}x = \dfrac{1}{3}$

32. $\dfrac{1}{2}x^2 + \dfrac{1}{6}x = 1$

Concept 3: Review of the Methods for Solving a Quadratic Equation

For Exercises 33–56, choose any method to solve the quadratic equations. **(See Example 4.)**

33. $16x^2 - 9 = 0$

34. $\dfrac{1}{4}x^2 + 5x + 13 = 0$

35. $(x - 5)^2 = -21$

36. $2x^2 + x + 5 = 0$

37. $\dfrac{1}{9}x^2 + \dfrac{8}{3}x + 11 = 0$

38. $7x^2 = 12x$

39. $2x^2 - 6x - 3 = 0$

40. $4(x + 1)^2 = -15$

41. $9x^2 = 11x$

42. $25x^2 - 4 = 0$

43. $(2y - 3)^2 = 5$

44. $(6z + 1)^2 = 7$

45. $0.4x^2 = 0.2x + 1$

46. $0.6x^2 = 0.1x + 0.8$

47. $9z^2 - z = 0$

48. $16p^2 - p = 0$

49. $r^2 - 52 = 0$

50. $y^2 - 32 = 0$

51. $-2.5t(t - 4) = 1.5$

52. $1.6p(p - 2) = 0.8$

53. $(m - 3)(m + 2) = 9$

54. $(h - 6)(h - 1) = 12$

55. $x^2 + x + 3 = 0$

56. $3x^2 - 20x + 12 = 0$

Concept 4: Applications of Quadratic Equations

57. In a rectangle, the length is 1 m less than twice the width and the area is 100 m². Approximate the dimensions to the nearest tenth of a meter. **(See Example 5.)**

58. In a triangle, the height is 2 cm more than the base. The area is 72 cm². Approximate the base and height to the nearest tenth of a centimeter.

59. The volume of a rectangular storage area is 240 ft³. The length is 2 ft more than the width. The height is 6 ft. Approximate the dimensions to the nearest tenth of a foot.

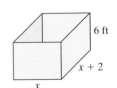

60. In a right triangle, one leg is 2 ft shorter than the other leg. The hypotenuse is 12 ft. Approximate the lengths of the legs to the nearest tenth of a foot.

61. In a rectangle, the length is 4 ft longer than the width. The area is 72 ft². Approximate the dimensions to the nearest tenth of a foot.

62. In a triangle, the base is 4 cm less than twice the height. The area is 60 cm². Approximate the base and height to the nearest tenth of a centimeter.

63. In a right triangle, one leg is 3 m longer than the other leg. The hypotenuse is 13 m. Approximate the lengths of the legs to the nearest tenth of a meter.

64. A bad punter on a football team kicks a football approximately straight upward with an initial velocity of 90 ft/sec. The height h (in feet) of the ball t seconds after being kicked is given by $h = -16t^2 + 90t + 4$. Find the time(s) at which the ball is at a height of 90 ft. Round to one decimal place.

65. NBA basketball legend Michael Jordan had a 48-in. vertical leap. Suppose that Michael jumped from ground level with an initial velocity of 16 ft/sec. Michael's height h (in feet) at a time t seconds after he leaves the ground is given by $h = -16t^2 + 16t$. Use the equation to determine the times at which Michael would be at a height of 1 ft. Round to two decimal places.

Problem Recognition Exercises

Solving Different Types of Equations

For Exercises 1 and 2, solve the equations using each of the three methods.

    a. Factoring and applying the zero product rule

    b. Completing the square and applying the square root property

    c. Applying the quadratic formula

1. $6x^2 + 7x - 3 = 0$ **2.** $y^2 + 14y + 49 = 0$

For Exercises 3–16,

    a. Identify the type of equation as
- linear
- quadratic
- rational
- radical

    b. Solve the equation.

3. $x(x - 8) = 6$ **4.** $2 - 6y = -y^2$

5. $3(k - 6) = 2k - 5$ **6.** $13x + 4 = 5(x - 4)$

7. $8x^2 - 22x + 5 = 0$ **8.** $9w^2 - 15w + 4 = 0$

9. $\dfrac{2}{x - 1} - \dfrac{5}{4} = -\dfrac{1}{x + 1}$ **10.** $\dfrac{5}{p - 2} = 7 - \dfrac{10}{p + 2}$

11. $\sqrt{2y - 2} = y - 1$ **12.** $\sqrt{5p - 1} = p + 1$

13. $(w + 1)^2 = 100$ **14.** $(u - 5)^2 = 64$

15. $\dfrac{2}{x + 1} = \dfrac{5}{4}$ **16.** $\dfrac{7}{t - 1} = \dfrac{21}{2}$

Concepts

1. Definition of a Quadratic Equation in Two Variables
2. Vertex of a Parabola
3. Graphing a Parabola
4. Applications of Quadratic Equations

1. Definition of a Quadratic Equation in Two Variables

In Chapter 3, we learned how to graph the solutions to linear equations in two variables. Now suppose we want to graph the *nonlinear* equation, $y = x^2$. To begin, we create a table of points representing several solutions to the equation (Table 9-1). These points form the curve shown in Figure 9-2.

Table 9-1

x	y
-3	9
-2	4
-1	1
0	0
1	1
2	4
3	9

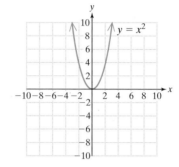

Figure 9-2

The equation $y = x^2$ is a special type of equation called a quadratic equation, and its graph is in the shape of a **parabola**.

Quadratic Equation in Two Variables

Let a, b, and c represent real numbers such that $a \neq 0$. Then an equation of the form $y = ax^2 + bx + c$ is called a **quadratic equation in two variables**.

The graph of a quadratic equation in this form is a parabola that opens upward or downward. The leading coefficient, a, determines the direction of the parabola. For the quadratic equation defined by $y = ax^2 + bx + c$:

Concept Connections

1. Identify the function as linear or quadratic.
   a. $y = 2x + 3$
   b. $y = -3x^2 + x + 4$
   c. $y = 5x^2$
   d. $y = 5x$

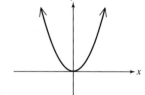

If $a > 0$, the parabola opens *upward*.
For example: $y = x^2$.

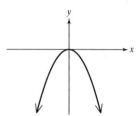

If $a < 0$, the parabola opens *downward*.
For example: $y = -x^2$.

If a parabola opens upward, the **vertex** is the lowest point on the graph. If a parabola opens downward, the **vertex** is the highest point on the graph. For a parabola defind by $y = ax^2 + bx + c$, the **axis of symmetry** is the vertical line that passes through the vertex. Notice that the graph of the parabola is its own mirror image to the left and right of the axis of symmetry.

Answers

1. **a.** Linear   **b.** Quadratic
   c. Quadratic   **d.** Linear

Here are four quadratic equations and their graphs.

$y = 0.5x^2 + 2x + 3$
$a > 0$
Vertex $(-2, 1)$
Axis of symmetry: $x = -2$

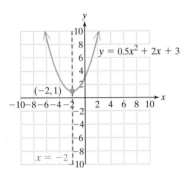

$y = x^2 - 6x + 9$
$a > 0$
Vertex $(3, 0)$
Axis of symmetry: $x = 3$

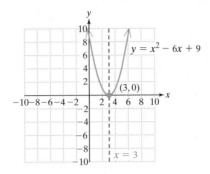

$y = -x^2 + 4x$
$a < 0$
Vertex $(2, 4)$
Axis of symmetry: $x = 2$

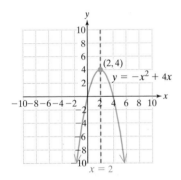

$y = -2x^2 - 4$
$a < 0$
Vertex $(0, -4)$
Axis of symmetry: $x = 0$

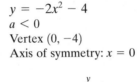
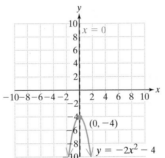

Concept Connections

2. Refer to the graph shown:

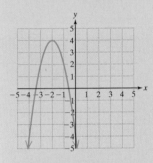

a. Determine the vertex of the parabola.

b. Determine the axis of symmetry of the parabola.

---

2. Vertex of a Parabola

Quadratic equations arise in many applications of mathematics and applied sciences. For example, an object thrown through the air follows a parabolic path. The mirror inside a reflecting telescope is parabolic in shape. In applications, it is often advantageous to analyze the graph of a parabola. In particular, we want to find the location of the x- and y-intercepts and the vertex.

To find the vertex of a parabola defined by $y = ax^2 + bx + c \ (a \neq 0)$, we use the following steps:

Finding the Vertex of a Parabola

Step 1 The x-coordinate of the vertex of the parabola defined by $y = ax^2 + bx + c \ (a \neq 0)$ is given by

$$x = \frac{-b}{2a}$$

Step 2 To find the corresponding y-coordinate of the vertex, substitute the value of the x-coordinate found in step 1 and solve for y.

Answers

2. a. $(-2, 4)$ **b.** $x = -2$

3. Given $y = -x^2 - 4x$, perform parts (a)–(e), as in Example 1.

Example 1   **Analyzing a Parabola**

Given the equation $y = -x^2 + 4x - 3$:

a. Determine whether the parabola opens upward or downward.

b. Find the vertex of the parabola.

c. Find the x-intercept(s).

d. Find the y-intercept.

e. Sketch the parabola.

Solution:

a. The equation $y = -x^2 + 4x - 3$ is written in the form $y = ax^2 + bx + c$, where $a = -1$, $b = 4$, and $c = -3$. Because the value of a is negative, the parabola opens *downward*.

b. The x-coordinate of the vertex is given by $x = \dfrac{-b}{2a}$.

$$x = \frac{-b}{2a} = \frac{-(4)}{2(-1)} \qquad \text{Substitute } b = 4 \text{ and } a = -1.$$

$$= \frac{-4}{-2} \qquad \text{Simplify.}$$

$$= 2$$

The y-coordinate of the vertex is found by substituting $x = 2$ into the equation and solving for y.

$$y = -x^2 + 4x - 3$$

$$= -(2)^2 + 4(2) - 3 \qquad \text{Substitute } x = 2.$$

$$= -4 + 8 - 3$$

$$= 1$$

The vertex is $(2, 1)$.   Because the parabola opens downward, the vertex is the maximum point on the graph of the parabola.

c. To find the x-intercept(s), substitute $y = 0$ and solve for x.

$$y = -x^2 + 4x - 3$$

$$0 = -x^2 + 4x - 3 \qquad \text{Substitute } y = 0. \text{ The resulting equation is quadratic.}$$

$$0 = -1(x^2 - 4x + 3) \qquad \text{Factor out } -1.$$

$$0 = -1(x - 3)(x - 1) \qquad \text{Factor the trinomial.}$$

$$x - 3 = 0 \quad \text{or} \quad x - 1 = 0 \qquad \text{Apply the zero product rule.}$$

$$x = 3 \qquad \text{or} \qquad x = 1$$

The x-intercepts are $(3, 0)$ and $(1, 0)$.

Answers

3. a. downward
   b. $(-2, 4)$
   c. $(0, 0)$ and $(-4, 0)$
   d. $(0, 0)$
   e.

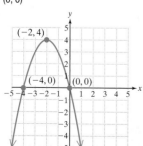

d. To find the y-intercept, substitute $x = 0$ and solve for y.

$$y = -x^2 + 4x - 3$$

$$= -(0)^2 + 4(0) - 3 \qquad \text{Substitute } x = 0.$$

$$= -3$$

The y-intercept is $(0, -3)$.

e. Using the results of parts (a)–(d), we have a parabola that opens downward with vertex $(2, 1)$, x-intercepts at $(3, 0)$ and $(1, 0)$, and y-intercept at $(0, -3)$ (Figure 9-3).

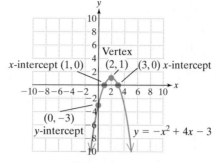

Figure 9-3

3. Graphing a Parabola

To sketch a parabola, determine the vertex and the x- and y-intercepts. Furthermore, notice that the graph of the parabola is symmetric with respect to the axis of symmetry.

To analyze the graph of a parabola, we recommend the following guidelines.

Graphing a Parabola

Given a quadratic equation in the form $y = ax^2 + bx + c$ $(a \neq 0)$, consider the following guidelines to graph the parabola.

Step 1 Determine whether the parabola opens upward or downward.

- If $a > 0$, the parabola opens upward.
- If $a < 0$, the parabola opens downward.

Step 2 Find the vertex.

- The x-coordinate is given by $x = \dfrac{-b}{2a}$

- To find the y-coordinate, substitute the x-coordinate of the vertex into the equation and solve for y.

Step 3 Find the x-intercept(s) by substituting $y = 0$ and solving the equation for x.

- *Note:* If the solutions to the equation in step 3 are not real numbers, then there are no x-intercepts.

Step 4 Find the y-intercept by substituting $x = 0$ and solving the equation for y.

Step 5 Plot the vertex and x- and y-intercepts. If necessary, find and plot additional points near the vertex. Then use the symmetry of the parabola to sketch the curve through the points. (*Note:* The axis of symmetry is the vertical line that passes through the vertex.)

Skill Practice

4. Graph $y = x^2 - 2x + 1$.

Example 2 Graphing a Parabola

Graph $y = x^2 - 6x + 9$.

Solution:

1. The equation $y = x^2 - 6x + 9$ is written in the form $y = ax^2 + bx + c$, where $a = 1, b = -6$, and $c = 9$. Because the value of a is positive, the parabola opens upward.

2. The x-coordinate of the vertex is given by

$$x = \frac{-b}{2a} = \frac{-(-6)}{2(1)} = 3$$

Substituting $x = 3$ into the equation, we have

$$y = (3)^2 - 6(3) + 9$$
$$= 9 - 18 + 9$$
$$= 0$$

The vertex is $(3, 0)$.

3. To find the x-intercept(s), substitute $y = 0$ and solve for x.

$$y = x^2 - 6x + 9 \longrightarrow 0 = x^2 - 6x + 9$$
$$0 = (x - 3)^2 \qquad \text{Factor.}$$
$$x = 3 \qquad \qquad \text{Apply the zero product rule.}$$

The x-intercept is $(3, 0)$.

4. To find the y-intercept, substitute $x = 0$ and solve for y.

$$y = x^2 - 6x + 9 \longrightarrow y = (0)^2 - 6(0) + 9$$
$$= 9$$

The y-intercept is $(0, 9)$.

5. Sketch the parabola through the x- and y-intercepts and vertex (Figure 9-4).

TIP: Using the symmetry of the parabola, we know that the points to the right of the vertex must mirror the points to the left of the vertex.

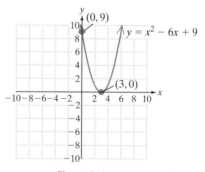

Figure 9-4

Answer

4.

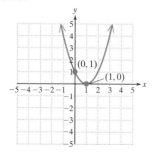

| Example 3 | Graphing a Parabola

Graph $y = -x^2 - 4$.

Solution:

1. The equation $y = -x^2 - 4$ is written in the form $y = ax^2 + bx + c$, where $a = -1, b = 0$, and $c = -4$. Because the value of a is negative, the parabola opens downward.

2. The x-coordinate of the vertex is given by

$$x = \frac{-b}{2a} = \frac{-(0)}{2(-1)} = 0$$

Substituting $x = 0$ into the equation, we have

$$y = -(0)^2 - 4$$
$$= -4$$

The vertex is $(0, -4)$.

3. Substituting $y = 0$ into the equation $y = -x^2 - 4$ results in an equation with no real solutions. Therefore, the graph of $y = -x^2 - 4$ has no x-intercepts.

$$y = -x^2 - 4$$
$$0 = -x^2 - 4$$
$$x^2 = -4$$
$$x = \pm\sqrt{-4} \quad \text{Not a real number}$$

4. The vertex is $(0, -4)$. This is also the y-intercept.

5. Sketch the parabola through the y-intercept and vertex (Figure 9-5).

> **TIP:** The vertex is below the x-axis and the parabola opens downward. Therefore, there can be no x-intercepts. A quick sketch shows this.

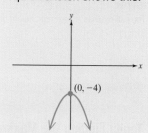

To verify the proper shape of the graph, find additional points to the right or left of the vertex and use the symmetry of the parabola to sketch the curve.

x	y
1	-5
2	-8
3	-13

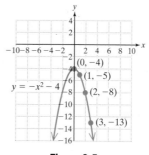

Figure 9-5

4. Applications of Quadratic Equations

| Example 4 | Using a Quadratic Equation in an Application

A golfer hits a ball at an angle of 30°. The height of the ball y (in feet) can be represented by

$$y = -16x^2 + 60x$$

where x is the time in seconds after the ball was hit (Figure 9-6).

Find the maximum height of the ball. In how many seconds will the ball reach its maximum height?

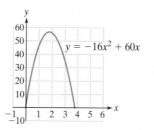

Figure 9-6

Answer

5.

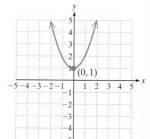

6. A basketball player shoots a basketball at an angle of 45°. The height of the ball y (in feet) is given by $y = -16t^2 + 40t + 6$ where t is time in seconds. Find the maximum height of the ball and the time required to reach that height.

Solution:

The equation is written in the form $y = ax^2 + bx + c$, where $a = -16$, $b = 60$, and $c = 0$. Because a is negative, the parabola opens downward. Therefore, the maximum height of the ball occurs at the vertex of the parabola.

The x-coordinate of the vertex is given by

$$x = \frac{-b}{2a} = \frac{-(60)}{2(-16)} = \frac{-60}{-32} = \frac{15}{8}$$

Substituting $x = \frac{15}{8}$ into the equation, we have

$$y = -16\left(\frac{15}{8}\right)^2 + 60\left(\frac{15}{8}\right)$$

$$= -16\left(\frac{225}{64}\right) + \frac{900}{8}$$

$$= -\frac{225}{4} + \frac{450}{4}$$

$$= \frac{225}{4}$$

The vertex is $\left(\frac{15}{8}, \frac{225}{4}\right)$ or equivalently $(1.875, 56.25)$.

The ball reaches its maximum height of 56.25 ft after 1.875 sec.

Answer

6. The ball reaches a maximum height of 31 ft in 1.25 sec.

Topic: Finding the Maximum or Minimum Point of a Parabola

Some graphing calculators have *Minimum* and *Maximum* features that enable the user to approximate the minimum and maximum values of y. Otherwise, *Zoom* and *Trace* can be used.

For example, the maximum value from Example 4, $y = -16x^2 + 60x$, can be found using the *Maximum* feature.

The minimum value from Example 2, $y = x^2 - 6x + 9$, can be found using the *Minimum* feature.

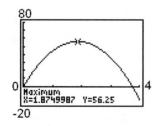

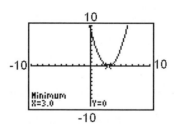

Calculator Exercises

Find the maximum or minimum point for each parabola. Identify the point as a maximum or a minimum.

1. $y = x^2 + 4x + 7$

2. $y = x^2 - 20x + 105$

3. $y = -x^2 - 3x - 4.85$

4. $y = -x^2 + 3.5x - 0.5625$

5. $y = 2x^2 - 10x + \frac{25}{2}$

6. $y = 3x^2 + 16x + \frac{64}{3}$

Section 9.4   Practice Exercises

Vocabulary and Key Concepts

1. **a.** The graph of a quadratic equation, $y = ax^2 + bx + c$, is a _____.

   b. The parabola defined by $y = ax^2 + bx + c$ $(a \neq 0)$ will open upward if a _____ 0 and will open downward if a _____ 0.

   c. If a parabola opens upward, the vertex is the (highest/lowest) point on the graph. If a parabola opens downward, the vertex is the (highest/lowest) point on the graph.

   d. The axis of _____ is a vertical line that passes through the vertex.

   e. The formula, $x = \dfrac{-b}{2a}$, gives the x-coordinate of the _____.

Review Exercises

For Exercises 2–8, solve the quadratic equations using any one of the following methods: factoring, the square root property, or the quadratic formula.

2. $3(y^2 + 1) = 10y$ **3.** $3 + a(a + 2) = 18$ **4.** $4t^2 - 7 = 0$ **5.** $2z^2 + 4z - 10 = 0$

6. $(b + 1)^2 = 6$ **7.** $(x - 2)^2 = 8$ **8.** $3p^2 - 12p - 12 = 0$

Concept 1: Definition of a Quadratic Equation in Two Variables

For Exercises 9–20, identify the equations as linear, quadratic, or neither.

9. $y = -8x + 3$ **10.** $y = 5x - 12$ **11.** $y = 4x^2 - 8x + 22$ **12.** $y = x^2 + 10x - 3$

13. $y = -5x^3 - 8x + 14$ **14.** $y = -3x^4 + 7x - 11$ **15.** $y = 15x$ **16.** $y = -9x$

17. $y = -21x^2$ **18.** $y = 3x^2$ **19.** $y = -x^3 + 1$ **20.** $y = 7x^4 - 4$

Concept 2: Vertex of a Parabola

21. How do you determine whether the parabola defined by $y = ax^2 + bx + c$ $(a \neq 0)$ opens upward or downward?

For Exercises 22–25, identify a and determine if the parabola opens upward or downward. **(See Example 1.)**

22. $y = x^2 - 15$ **23.** $y = 2x^2 + 23$ **24.** $y = -3x^2 + x - 18$ **25.** $y = -10x^2 - 6x - 20$

26. How do you find the vertex of a parabola?

For Exercises 27–34, find the vertex of the parabola. **(See Example 1.)**

27. $y = 2x^2 + 4x - 6$ **28.** $y = x^2 - 4x - 4$ **29.** $y = -x^2 + 2x - 5$ **30.** $y = 2x^2 - 4x - 6$

31. $y = x^2 - 2x + 3$ **32.** $y = -x^2 + 4x - 2$ **33.** $y = 3x^2 - 4$ **34.** $y = 4x^2 - 1$

Concept 3: Graphing a Parabola

For Exercises 35–38, find the x- and y-intercepts. Then match each equation with a graph. **(See Example 1.)**

35. $y = x^2 - 7$ **36.** $y = x^2 - 9$ **37.** $y = x^2 + 6x + 5$ **38.** $y = x^2 - 4x + 3$

a. 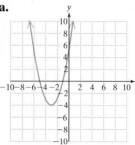   **b.** 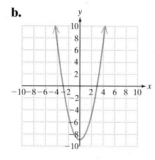   **c.** 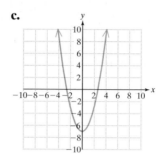   **d.**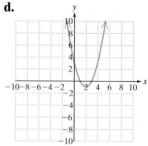

For Exercises 39–50, **(See Examples 1–3.)**

  a. Determine whether the graph of the parabola opens upward or downward.

  b. Find the vertex.

  c. Find the x-intercept(s), if possible.

  d. Find the y-intercept.

  e. Sketch the graph.

39. $y = x^2 - 9$

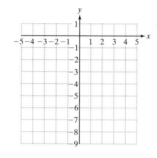

40. $y = x^2 - 4$

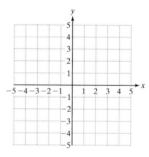

41. $y = x^2 - 2x - 8$

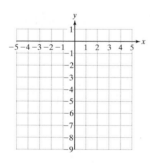

42. $y = x^2 + 2x - 24$

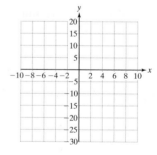

43. $y = -x^2 + 6x - 9$

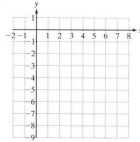

44. $y = -x^2 + 10x - 25$

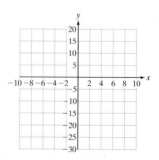

45. $y = -x^2 + 8x - 15$

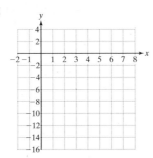

46. $y = -x^2 - 4x + 5$

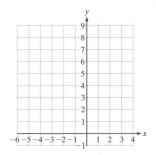

47. $y = x^2 + 6x + 10$

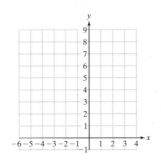

48. $y = x^2 + 4x + 5$

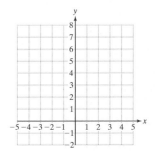

49. $y = -2x^2 - 2$

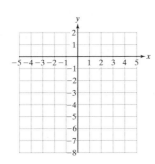

50. $y = -x^2 - 5$

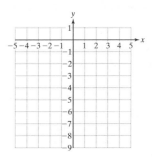

51. True or False: The graph of $y = -5x^2$ has a maximum value but no minimum value.

52. True or False: The graph of $y = -4x^2 + 9x - 6$ opens upward.

53. True or False: The graph of $y = 1.5x^2 - 6x - 3$ opens downward.

54. True or False: The graph of $y = 2x^2 - 5x + 4$ has a maximum value but no minimum value.

Concept 4: Applications of Quadratic Equations

55. A child kicks a ball into the air, and the height of the ball, y (in feet), can be approximated by

$y = -16t^2 + 40t + 3$ where t is the number of seconds after the ball was kicked.

a. Find the maximum height of the ball. **(See Example 4.)**

b. How long will it take the ball to reach its maximum height?

56. A concession stand at the Arthur Ashe Tennis Center sells a hamburger/drink combination dinner for $5. The profit, y (in dollars), can be approximated by

$$y = -0.001x^2 + 3.6x - 400 \qquad \text{where } x \text{ is the number of dinners prepared.}$$

a. Find the number of dinners that should be prepared to maximize profit.

b. What is the maximum profit?

57. For a fund-raising activity, a charitable organization produces calendars to sell in the community. The profit, y (in dollars), can be approximated by

$$y = -\frac{1}{40}x^2 + 10x - 500 \qquad \text{where } x \text{ is the number of calendars produced.}$$

a. Find the number of calendars that should be produced to maximize the profit.

b. What is the maximum profit?

58. The pressure, x, in an automobile tire can affect its wear. Both over-inflated and under-inflated tires can lead to poor performance and poor mileage. For one particular tire, the number of miles that a tire lasts, y (in thousands), is given by

$$y = -0.875x^2 + 57.25x - 900 \qquad \text{where } x \text{ is the tire pressure in pounds per square inch (psi).}$$

a. Find the tire pressure that will yield the maximum number of miles that a tire will last. Round to the nearest whole unit.

b. Find the maximum number of miles that a tire will last if the proper tire pressure is maintained. Round to the nearest thousand miles.

59. Kitesurfing is an extreme sport where athletes are propelled across the water on a board using the power of a kite. Josh loves to kitesurf and the height of one of his jumps can be modeled by $y = -16t^2 + 32t$. In this equation, y represents Josh's height in feet and t represents the time in seconds after launch.

a. How high will Josh be in 0.5 sec?

b. What is Josh's hang time?
(*Hint:* Compute the time required for him to land.)

c. What is Josh's maximum height?

Section 9.5   Introduction to Functions

1. Definition of a Relation

Table 9-2 gives the number of points scored by LeBron James corresponding to the number of minutes that he played per game for six games.

Table 9-2

Minutes Played, x	Number of Points, y		
38	33	$\longrightarrow$	(38, 33)
44	52	$\longrightarrow$	(44, 52)
40	16	$\longrightarrow$	(40, 16)
41	47	$\longrightarrow$	(41, 47)
33	26	$\longrightarrow$	(33, 26)
38	30	$\longrightarrow$	(38, 30)

Each ordered pair from Table 9-2 shows a correspondence, or relationship, between the number of minutes played and the number of points scored by LeBron James. The set of ordered pairs: $\{(38, 33), (44, 52), (40, 16), (41, 47), (33, 26), (38, 30)\}$ defines a relation between the number of minutes played and the number of points scored.

Relation in *x* and *y*

Any set of ordered pairs, (x, y), is called a **relation** in x and y. Furthermore:

- The set of first components in the ordered pairs is called the **domain** of the relation.
- The set of second components in the ordered pairs is called the **range** of the relation.

Example 1 Finding the Domain and Range of a Relation

Find the domain and range of the relation linking the number of minutes played to the number of points scored by James in six games of the season.

$$\{(38, 33), (44, 52), (40, 16), (41, 47), (33, 26), (38, 30)\}$$

Solution:

Domain: $\{38, 44, 40, 41, 33\}$ (Set of first coordinates)

Range: $\{33, 52, 16, 47, 26, 30\}$ (Set of second coordinates)

The domain consists of the number of minutes played. The range represents the corresponding number of points.

Example 2 Finding the Domain and Range of a Relation

The three women represented in Figure 9-7 each have children. Molly has one child, Peggy has two children, and Joanne has three children.

a. If the set of mothers is given as the domain and the set of children is the range, write a set of ordered pairs defining the relation given in Figure 9-7.

b. Write the domain and range of the relation.

Figure 9-7

Solution:

a. $\{$(Molly, Stephen), (Peggy, Brian), (Peggy, Erika), (Joanne, Geoff), (Joanne, Joelle), (Joanne, Julie)$\}$

b. Domain: $\{$Molly, Peggy, Joanne$\}$
Range: $\{$Stephen, Brian, Erika, Geoff, Joelle, Julie$\}$

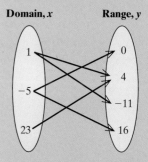

2. Definition of a Function

In mathematics, a special type of relation, called a function, is used extensively.

> ### Definition of a Function
>
> Given a relation in x and y, we say "y is a **function** of x" if for each element x in the domain, there is exactly one value of y in the range.
>
> *Note:* This means that no two ordered pairs may have the same first coordinate and different second coordinates.

In Example 2, the relation linking the set of mothers with their respective children is *not* a function. The domain elements, "Peggy" and "Joanne," each have more than one child. Because these x values in the domain have more than one corresponding y value in the range, the relation is not a function.

To understand the difference between a relation that is a function and one that is not a function, consider Example 3.

Skill Practice

Determine whether the following relations are functions. If the relation is not a function, state why.

4. $\{(0, -7), (4, 9), (-2, -7), \left(\frac{1}{3}, \frac{1}{2}\right), (4, 10)\}$

5. $\{(-8, -3), (4, -3), (-12, 7), (-1, -1)\}$

Example 3 Determining Whether a Relation Is a Function

Determine whether the following relations are functions:

a. $\{(2, -3), (4, 1), (3, -1), (2, 4)\}$ **b.** $\{(-3, 1), (0, 2), (4, -3), (1, 5), (-2, 1)\}$

Solution:

a. This relation is defined by the set of ordered pairs.

$$\text{same } x \text{ values}$$
$$\{(2, -3), (4, 1), (3, -1), (2, 4)\}$$
$$\text{different } y \text{ values}$$

When $x = 2$, there are two possibilities for y: $y = -3$ and $y = 4$.

This relation is *not* a function because for $x = 2$, there is more than one corresponding element in the range.

b. This relation is defined by the set of ordered pairs: $\{(-3, 1), (0, 2), (4, -3), (1, 5), (-2, 1)\}$. Notice that no two ordered pairs have the same value of x but different values of y. Therefore, this relation *is* a function.

3. Vertical Line Test

A relation that is not a function has at least one domain element, x, paired with more than one range element, y. For example, the ordered pairs $(2, 1)$ and $(2, 4)$ do not make a function. On a graph, these two points are aligned vertically in the xy-plane, and a vertical line drawn through one point also intersects the other point (Figure 9-8). Thus, if a vertical line drawn through a graph of a relation intersects the graph in more than one point, the relation cannot be a function. This idea is stated formally as the **vertical line test**.

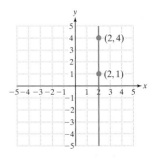

Figure 9-8

Answers

4. Not a function because the domain element, 4, has two different y values: $(4, 9)$ and $(4, 10)$.

5. Function

Using the Vertical Line Test

Consider a relation defined by a set of points (x, y) on a rectangular coordinate system. Then the graph defines y as a function of x if no vertical line intersects the graph in more than one point.

Furthermore, if any vertical line drawn through the graph of a relation intersects the graph in more than one point, then the relation does *not* define y as a function of x.

The vertical line test can be demonstrated by graphing the ordered pairs from the relations in Example 3 (Figure 9-9 and Figure 9-10).

$$\{(2, -3), (4, 1), (3, -1), (2, 4)\} \qquad \{(-3, 1), (0, 2), (4, -3), (1, 5), (-2, 1)\}$$

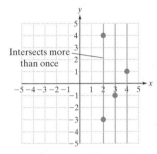

Figure 9-9

Not a Function

A vertical line intersects in
more than one point.

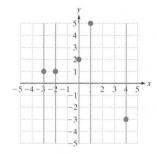

Figure 9-10

Function

No vertical line intersects
more than once.

The relations in Examples 1, 2, and 3 consist of a finite number of ordered pairs. A relation may, however, consist of an *infinite* number of points defined by an equation or by a graph. For example, the equation $y = x + 1$ defines infinitely many ordered pairs whose y-coordinate is one more than its x-coordinate. These ordered pairs cannot all be listed but can be depicted in a graph.

The vertical line test is especially helpful in determining whether a relation is a function based on its graph.

Example 4 Using the Vertical Line Test

Use the vertical line test to determine whether the following relations are functions.

a.
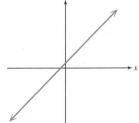

b.
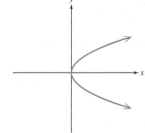

Skill Practice

Use the vertical line test to determine if the following relations are functions.

6.

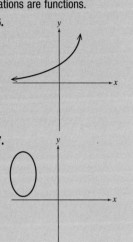

7.

Solution:

a.

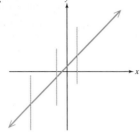

Function
No vertical line intersects more than once.

b.

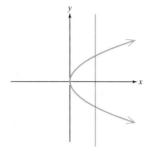

Not a Function
A vertical line intersects in more than one point.

4. Function Notation

A function is defined as a relation with the added restriction that each value of the domain corresponds to only one value in the range. In mathematics, functions are often given by rules or equations to define the relationship between two or more variables. For example, the equation, $y = x + 1$ defines the set of ordered pairs such that the y value is one more than the x value.

When a function is defined by an equation, we often use **function notation**. For example, the equation $y = x + 1$ may be written in function notation as

$$f(x) = x + 1$$

where f is the name of the function, x is an input value from the domain of the function, and $f(x)$ is the function value (or y value) corresponding to x.

The notation $f(x)$ is read as "f of x" or "the value of the function, f, at x."

A function may be evaluated at different values of x by substituting values of x from the domain into the function. For example, for the function defined by $f(x) = x + 1$ we can evaluate f at $x = 3$ by using substitution.

Avoiding Mistakes

The notation $f(x)$ is read as "f of x" and does *not* imply multiplication.

$f(x) = x + 1$

$f(3) = (3) + 1$

$f(3) = 4$ This is read as "f of 3 equals 4."

Thus, when $x = 3$, the corresponding function value is 4. This can also be interpreted as an ordered pair: $(3, 4)$

The names of functions are often given by either lowercase letters or uppercase letters such as f, g, h, p, k, M, and so on.

Skill Practice

Given the function defined by $f(x) = x^2 - 5x$, find the function values.

8. $f(1)$ **9.** $f(0)$

10. $f(-3)$ **11.** $f(2)$

12. $f(-1)$

Example 5   **Evaluating a Function**

Given the function defined by $h(x) = x^2 - 2$, find the function values.

  a. $h(0)$ **b.** $h(1)$ **c.** $h(2)$ **d.** $h(-1)$ **e.** $h(-2)$

Solution:

  a. $h(x) = x^2 - 2$

     $h(0) = (0)^2 - 2$ Substitute $x = 0$ into the function.

     $= 0 - 2$

     $= -2$ $h(0) = -2$ means that when $x = 0$, $y = -2$, yielding the ordered pair $(0, -2)$.

b. $h(x) = x^2 - 2$

$h(1) = (1)^2 - 2$ Substitute $x = 1$ into the function.

     $= 1 - 2$

     $= -1$ $h(1) = -1$ means that when $x = 1$, $y = -1$, yielding the ordered pair $(1, -1)$.

c. $h(x) = x^2 - 2$

$h(2) = (2)^2 - 2$ Substitute $x = 2$ into the function.

     $= 4 - 2$

     $= 2$ $h(2) = 2$ means that when $x = 2$, $y = 2$, yielding the ordered pair $(2, 2)$.

d. $h(x) = x^2 - 2$

$h(-1) = (-1)^2 - 2$ Substitute $x = -1$ into the function.

     $= 1 - 2$

     $= -1$ $h(-1) = -1$ means that when $x = -1$, $y = -1$, yielding the ordered pair $(-1, -1)$.

> **Avoiding Mistakes**
>
> Remember to use parentheses when substituting values into a function. In Example 5(d) for instance, this will ensure that $(-1)^2$ is evaluated rather than -1^2.

e. $h(x) = x^2 - 2$

$h(-2) = (-2)^2 - 2$ Substitute $x = -2$ into the function.

     $= 4 - 2$

     $= 2$ $h(-2) = 2$ means that when $x = -2$, $y = 2$, yielding the ordered pair $(-2, 2)$.

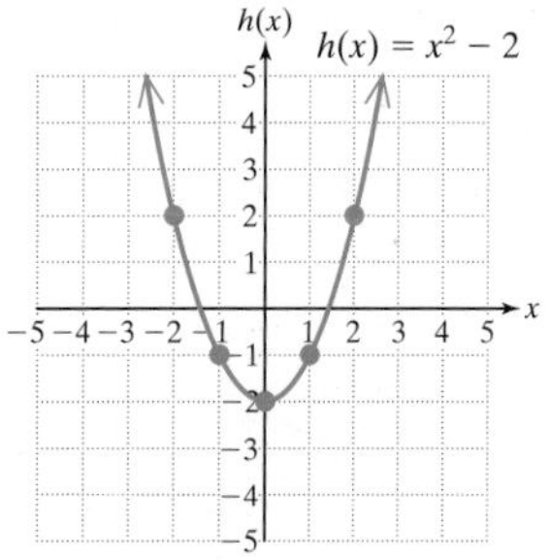

Figure 9-11

The rule $h(x) = x^2 - 2$ is equivalent to the equation $y = x^2 - 2$. The function values $h(0)$, $h(1)$, $h(2)$, $h(-1)$, and $h(-2)$ correspond to the y values in the ordered pairs $(0, -2)$, $(1, -1)$, $(2, 2)$, $(-1, -1)$, and $(-2, 2)$, respectively. These points can be used to sketch a graph of the function (Figure 9-11).

5. Domain and Range of a Function

A function is a relation, and it is often necessary to determine its domain and range. Consider a function defined by the equation $y = f(x)$. The **domain** of f is the set of all x values that when substituted into the function produce a real number. The **range** of f is the set of all y values corresponding to the values of x in the domain.

For Examples 6 and 7, we find the domain and range based on the graph of the function.

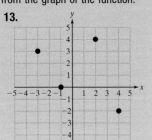

Example 6 Finding the Domain and Range of a Function

Find the domain and the range from the graph of the function.

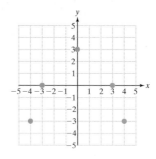

Solution:

From the figure, the function defines the set of ordered pairs:

$$\{(-4, -3), (-3, 0), (0, 3), (3, 0), (4, -3)\}$$

The domain is the set of all x-coordinates: $\{-4, -3, 0, 3, 4\}$

The range is the set of all y-coordinates: $\{-3, 0, 3\}$

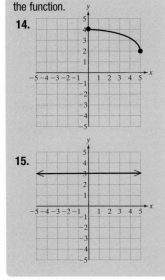
Example 7 Finding the Domain and Range of a Function

Find the domain and range of the functions based on the graph of the function. Express the answers in interval notation.

a.

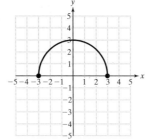

b.

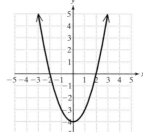

Solution:

a.

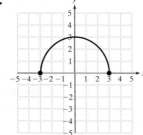

The horizontal "span" of the graph is determined by the x values of the points. This is the domain. In this graph, the x values in the domain are bounded between -3 and 3. (Shown in blue.)

Domain: $[-3, 3]$

The vertical "span" of the graph is determined by the y values of the points. This is the range.

The y values in the range are bounded between 0 and 3. (Shown in red.)

Range: $[0, 3]$

Answers

13. Domain: $\{-3, -1, 2, 4\}$;
range: $\{-2, 0, 3, 4\}$
14. Domain: $[0, 5]$;
range: $[2, 4]$
15. Domain: $(-\infty, \infty)$;
range: $\{3\}$

b.

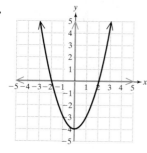

The function extends infinitely far to the left and right. The domain is shown in blue.

Domain: $(-\infty, \infty)$

The y values extend infinitely far in the positive direction, but are bounded below at $y = -4$. (Shown in red.)

Range: $[-4, \infty)$

6. Applications of Functions

Example 8 Using a Function in an Application

The score a student receives on an exam is a function of the number of hours the student spends studying. The function defined by

$$P(x) = \frac{100x^2}{40 + x^2} \quad (x \geq 0)$$

indicates that a student will achieve a score of $P\%$ after studying for x hours.

a. Evaluate $P(0)$, $P(10)$, and $P(20)$.

b. Interpret the function values from part (a) in the context of this problem.

Solution:

a. $P(x) = \dfrac{100x^2}{40 + x^2}$

$$P(0) = \frac{100(0)^2}{40 + (0)^2} \qquad P(10) = \frac{100(10)^2}{40 + (10)^2} \qquad P(20) = \frac{100(20)^2}{40 + (20)^2}$$

$$= \frac{0}{40} \qquad\qquad\qquad = \frac{10,000}{140} \qquad\qquad\quad = \frac{40,000}{440}$$

$$= 0 \qquad\qquad\qquad\quad = \frac{500}{7} \approx 71.4 \qquad\qquad = \frac{1000}{11} \approx 90.9$$

b. $P(0) = 0$ means that for 0 hr spent studying, the student will receive 0% on the exam.

$P(10) \approx 71.4$ means that for 10 hr spent studying, the student will receive approximately 71.4% on the exam.

$P(20) \approx 90.9$ means that for 20 hr spent studying, the student will receive approximately 90.9% on the exam.

The graph of $P(x) = \dfrac{100x^2}{40 + x^2}$ is shown in Figure 9-12.

Student Score (Percent) as a Function of Study Time

$P(20) = 90.9$
$P(10) = 71.4$
$P(0) = 0$

Study Time (hours)

Figure 9-12

Answers

16. 150

17. For a cube 5 in. on a side, the surface area is 150 in.^{2}.

Calculator Connections

Topic: Graphing Functions

A graphing calculator can be used to graph a function. We replace $f(x)$ by y and enter the defining expression into the calculator. For example:

$$f(x) = \frac{1}{4}x^3 - x^2 - x + 4 \quad \text{becomes} \quad y = \frac{1}{4}x^3 - x^2 - x + 4$$

Calculator Exercises

Use a graphing calculator to graph the following functions.

1. $f(x) = x^2 - 5x + 2$

2. $g(x) = -x^2 + 4x + 5$

3. $m(x) = \frac{1}{3}x^3 + x^2 - 3x - 1$

4. $n(x) = x^3 - 9x$

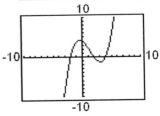

Section 9.5   Practice Exercises

Vocabulary and Key Concepts

1. a. A set of ordered pairs (x, y) is called a _____ in x and y.

   b. The _____ of a relation is the set of first components in the ordered pairs.

   c. The _____ of a relation is the set of second components in the ordered pairs.

   d. Given a relation in x and y, we say that y is a _____ of x if for each element x in the domain, there is exactly one value of y in the range.

   e. If a _____ line intersects the graph of a relation in more than one point, the relation is not a function.

   f. Function notation for the relation $y = 7x - 4$ is $f(x) =$ _____ .

Review Exercises

For Exercises 2–4, find the vertex of each parabola.

2. $y = -3x^2 + 2x + 2$

3. $y = 4x^2 - 2x + 3$

4. $y = x^2 - 5x + 2$

Concept 1: Definition of a Relation

For Exercises 5–14, determine the domain and range of each relation. **(See Examples 1 and 2.)**

5. $\{(4, 2), (3, 7), (4, 1), (0, 6)\}$

6. $\{(-3, -1), (-2, 6), (1, 3), (1, -2)\}$

7. $\{(\frac{1}{2}, 3), (0, 3), (1, 3)\}$

8. $\{(9, 6), (4, 6), (-\frac{1}{3}, 6)\}$

9. $\{(0, 0), (5, 0), (-8, 2), (8, 5)\}$

10. $\{(\frac{1}{2}, -\frac{1}{2}), (-4, 0), (0, -\frac{1}{2}), (\frac{1}{2}, 0)\}$

11.

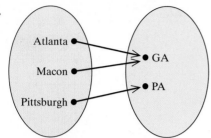

12.

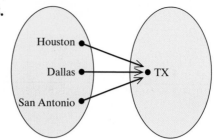

13.

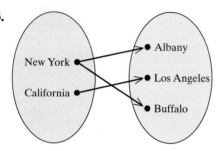

14.

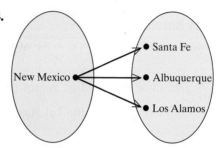

Concept 2: Definition of a Function

15. How can you determine if a set of ordered pairs represents a function?

16. Refer back to Exercises 6, 8, 10, 12, and 14. Identify which relations are functions.

17. Refer back to Exercises 5, 7, 9, 11, and 13. Identify which relations are functions. **(See Example 3.)**

Concept 3: Vertical Line Test

18. How can you tell from the graph of a relation if the relation is a function?

For Exercises 19–27, use the vertical line test to determine if the relation defines y as a function of x. **(See Example 4.)**

19.

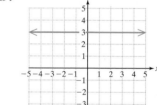

20.

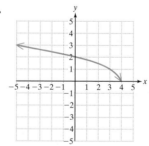

21.

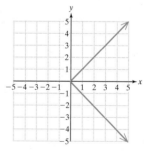

22.

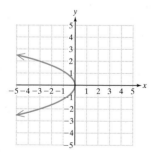

23.

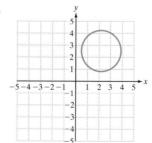

24.

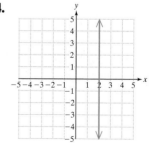

25.

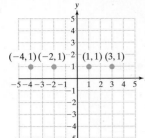

26.

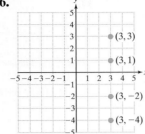

27.

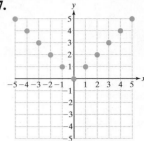

Concept 4: Function Notation

28. Explain how you would evaluate $f(x) = 3x^2$ at $x = -1$.

For Exercises 29–36, determine the function values. **(See Example 5.)**

29. Let $f(x) = 2x - 5$. Find:

   a. $f(0)$

   b. $f(2)$

   c. $f(-3)$

30. Let $g(x) = x^2 + 1$. Find:

   a. $g(0)$

   b. $g(-1)$

   c. $g(3)$

31. Let $h(x) = \dfrac{1}{x + 4}$. Find:

   a. $h(1)$

   b. $h(0)$

   c. $h(-2)$

32. Let $p(x) = \sqrt{x + 4}$. Find:

   a. $p(0)$

   b. $p(-4)$

   c. $p(5)$

33. Let $m(x) = |5x - 7|$. Find:

   a. $m(0)$

   b. $m(1)$

   c. $m(2)$

34. Let $w(x) = |2x - 3|$. Find:

   a. $w(0)$

   b. $w(1)$

   c. $w(2)$

35. Let $n(x) = \sqrt{x - 2}$. Find:

   a. $n(2)$

   b. $n(3)$

   c. $n(6)$

36. Let $t(x) = \dfrac{1}{x - 3}$. Find:

   a. $t(1)$

   b. $t(-1)$

   c. $t(2)$

Concept 5: Domain and Range of a Function

For Exercises 37–40, find the domain and the range from the graphs of the functions. **(See Example 6.)**

37.

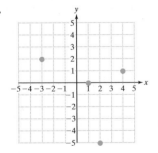

38.

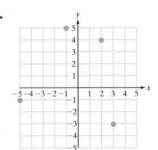

39.

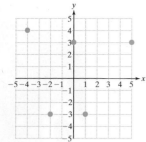

40.

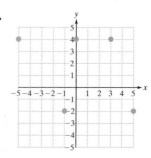

For Exercises 41–44, match the domain and range given with a possible graph.

41. Domain: $(-\infty, \infty)$

Range: $[1, \infty)$

42. Domain: $[-4, 4]$

Range: $[-2, 2]$

43. Domain: $[-2, \infty)$

Range: $(-\infty, \infty)$

44. Domain: $(-\infty, \infty)$

Range: $(-\infty, \infty)$

a.

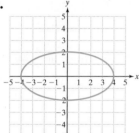

b.

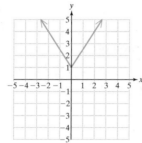

c.

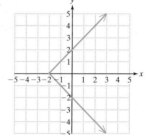

d.

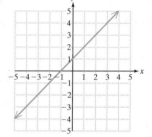

For Exercises 45–48, find the domain and range from the graph of each relation. Express the answers in interval notation. **(See Example 7.)**

45.

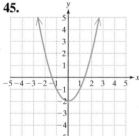

46.

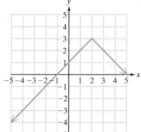

47.

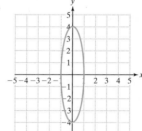

48.

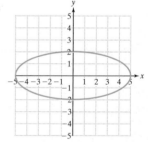

For Exercises 49–52, write each expression as an English phrase.

49. $f(6) = 2$

50. $f(-2) = -14$

51. $g\left(\dfrac{1}{2}\right) = \dfrac{1}{4}$

52. $h(k) = k^2$

53. Consider a function defined by $y = f(x)$. The function value $f(2) = 7$ corresponds to what ordered pair?

54. Consider a function defined by $y = f(x)$. The function value $f(-3) = -4$ corresponds to what ordered pair?

Concept 6: Applications of Functions

55. In the absence of air resistance, the speed, $s(t)$ (in feet per second: ft/sec), of an object in free fall is a function of the number of seconds, t, after it was dropped. **(See Example 8.)**

$$s(t) = 32t$$

a. Find $s(1)$, and interpret the meaning of this function value in terms of speed and time.

b. Find $s(2)$, and interpret the meaning in terms of speed and time.

c. Find $s(10)$, and interpret the meaning in terms of speed and time.

d. A ball dropped from the top of the Willis Tower in Chicago falls for approximately 9.2 sec. How fast was the ball going the instant before it hit the ground?

56. The number of people diagnosed with skin cancer, $N(x)$, can be approximated by $N(x) = 45{,}625(1 + 0.029x)$. For this function, x represents the number of years since 2003. (*Source:* Centers for Disease Control)

a. Evaluate $N(0)$ and interpret its meaning in the context of this problem.

b. Evaluate $N(7)$ and interpret its meaning in the context of this problem. Round to the nearest whole number.

57. A punter kicks a football straight up with an initial velocity of 64 ft/sec. The height of the ball, $h(t)$ (in feet), is a function of the number of seconds, t, after the ball is kicked.

$$h(t) = -16t^2 + 64t + 3$$

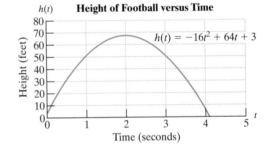

a. Find $h(0)$, and interpret the meaning of the function value in terms of time and height.

b. Find $h(1)$, and interpret the meaning in terms of time and height.

c. Find $h(2)$, and interpret the meaning in terms of time and height.

d. Find $h(4)$, and interpret the meaning in terms of time and height.

58. For people 16 years old and older, the maximum recommended heart rate, $M(x)$ (in beats per minute: beats/min), is a function of a person's age, x (in years).

$$M(x) = 220 - x \text{ for } x \geq 16$$

a. Find $M(16)$, and interpret the meaning in terms of maximum recommended heart rate and age.

b. Find $M(30)$, and interpret the meaning in terms of maximum recommended heart rate and age.

c. Find $M(60)$, and interpret the meaning in terms of maximum recommended heart rate and age.

d. Find your own maximum recommended heart rate.

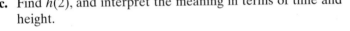

59. An electrician charges $75 to visit, diagnose, and give an estimate for repairing a refrigerator. If Helena decides to have her refrigerator fixed, she will then be charged an additional $50 per hour for labor costs. The equation for the total cost, $C(x)$, of fixing the refrigerator can be modeled by the linear function $C(x) = 75 + 50x$, where x is the number of hours it takes the electrician to fix the refrigerator.

    a. Find the total cost for 3 hr of labor.

    b. If Helena spent $200 on fixing her refrigerator, how many hours of labor was she charged for?

    c. What is the domain of $C(x)$?

    d. What does the y-intercept represent?

Group Activity

Maximizing Volume

Materials: A calculator and a sheet of $8\frac{1}{2}$ by 11 in. paper.

Estimated Time: 25–30 minutes

Group Size: 3

Antonio is going to build a custom gutter system for his house. He plans to use rectangular strips of aluminum that are $8\frac{1}{2}$ in. wide and 72 in. long. Each piece of aluminum will be turned up at a distance of x in. from the sides to form a gutter. See Figure 9-13.

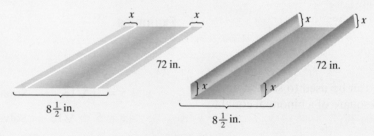

Figure 9-13

Antonio wants to maximize the volume of water that the gutters can hold. To do this, he must determine the distance, x, that should be turned up to form the height of the gutter.

1. To familiarize yourself with this problem, we will simulate the gutter problem using an $8\frac{1}{2}$ by 11 in. piece of paper. For each value of x in the table, turn up the sides of the paper x in. from the edge. Then measure the base, the height, and the length of the paper "gutter," and calculate the volume.

Height, x	Base	Length	Volume
0.5 in.		11 in.	
1.0 in.		11 in.	
1.5 in.		11 in.	
2.0 in.		11 in.	
2.5 in.		11 in.	
3.0 in.		11 in.	
3.5 in.		11 in.	

2. Now follow these steps to find the optimal distance, x, that you should fold the paper to make the greatest volume within the paper gutter.

   a. If the height of the paper gutter is x in., write an expression for the base of the paper gutter.

   b. Write a function for the volume of the paper gutter.

   c. Find the vertex of the parabola defined by the function in part (b).

   d. Interpret the meaning of the vertex from part (c).

3. Use the concept from the paper gutter to write a function for the volume of Antonio's aluminum gutter that is 72 in. long.

4. Now find the optimal distance, x, that he should fold the aluminum sheet to make the greatest volume within the 72-in.-long aluminum gutter. What is the maximum volume?

Chapter 9   Summary

Section 9.1   The Square Root Property

Key Concepts

Square Root Property

If $x^2 = k$, then $x = \pm\sqrt{k}$.

The square root property can be used to solve a quadratic equation written as a square of a binomial equal to a constant.

Examples

Example 1

$$(x - 5)^2 = 13$$

$x - 5 = \pm\sqrt{13}$ Square root property

$x = 5 \pm \sqrt{13}$ Solve for x.

The solutions are $5 + \sqrt{13}$ and $5 - \sqrt{13}$.

Section 9.2　Completing the Square

Key Concepts

Solving a Quadratic Equation of the Form
$ax^2 + bx + c = 0 \ (a \neq 0)$ **by Completing the**
Square and Applying the Square Root Property

1. Divide both sides by a to make the leading coefficient 1.
2. Isolate the variable terms on one side of the equation.
3. Complete the square by adding the square of $\frac{1}{2}$ the linear term coefficient to both sides of the equation. Then factor the resulting perfect square trinomial.
4. Apply the square root property and solve for x.

Examples

Example 1

$$2x^2 - 8x - 6 = 0$$

Step 1:　$\dfrac{2x^2}{2} - \dfrac{8x}{2} - \dfrac{6}{2} = \dfrac{0}{2}$

$$x^2 - 4x - 3 = 0$$

Step 2:　$x^2 - 4x = 3$

Step 3:　$x^2 - 4x + 4 = 3 + 4$　Note that

$$(x - 2)^2 = 7 \qquad [\tfrac{1}{2}(-4)]^2 = (-2)^2 = 4$$

Step 4:　$x - 2 = \pm\sqrt{7}$

$$x = 2 \pm \sqrt{7}$$

The solutions are $2 + \sqrt{7}$ and $2 - \sqrt{7}$.

Section 9.3　Quadratic Formula

Key Concepts

The solutions to a quadratic equation of the form $ax^2 + bx + c = 0 \ (a \neq 0)$ are given by the **quadratic formula**:

$$x = \frac{-b \pm \sqrt{b^2 - 4ac}}{2a}$$

Three Methods for Solving a Quadratic Equation

1. Factoring
2. Completing the square and applying the square root property
3. Using the quadratic formula

Examples

Example 1

$$3x^2 = 2x + 4$$

$$3x^2 - 2x - 4 = 0 \qquad a = 3, b = -2, c = -4$$

$$x = \frac{-(-2) \pm \sqrt{(-2)^2 - 4(3)(-4)}}{2(3)}$$

$$= \frac{2 \pm \sqrt{4 + 48}}{6}$$

$$= \frac{2 \pm \sqrt{52}}{6}$$

$$= \frac{2 \pm 2\sqrt{13}}{6} \qquad \text{Simplify the radical.}$$

$$= \frac{2(1 \pm \sqrt{13})}{6} \qquad \text{Factor.}$$

$$= \frac{1 \pm \sqrt{13}}{3} \qquad \text{Simplify.}$$

The solutions are $\dfrac{1 + \sqrt{13}}{3}$ and $\dfrac{1 - \sqrt{13}}{3}$.

| Section 9.4 | **Graphing Quadratic Equations** |

Key Concepts

Let a, b, and c represent real numbers such that $a \neq 0$. Then a function defined by $y = ax^2 + bx + c$ is called a **quadratic equation in two variables**.

The graph of a quadratic equation is called a **parabola**.

The leading coefficient, a, of a quadratic equation, $y = ax^2 + bx + c$, determines if the parabola will open upward or downward. If $a > 0$, then the parabola opens upward. If $a < 0$, then the parabola opens downward.

Examples

Example 1

$y = x^2 - 4x - 3$ is a quadratic equation. Its graph is in the shape of a parabola.

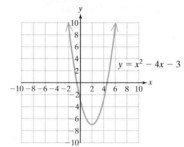

$y = x^2 - 4x - 3$

Finding the Vertex of a Parabola

1. For the equation $y = ax^2 + bx + c$ $(a \neq 0)$, the x-coordinate of the vertex is

$$x = \frac{-b}{2a}$$

2. To find the corresponding y-coordinate of the vertex, substitute the value of the x-coordinate found in step 1 and solve for y.

If a parabola opens upward, the vertex is the lowest point on the graph. If a parabola opens downward, the vertex is the highest point on the graph.

Example 2

Find the vertex of the parabola defined by $y = x^2 - 4x - 3$.

$$x = \frac{-b}{2a} = \frac{-(-4)}{2(1)} = \frac{4}{2} = 2$$

$$y = (2)^2 - 4(2) - 3 = -7 \qquad \text{The vertex is } (2, -7).$$

For the equation $y = x^2 - 4x - 3$, $a > 0$. Therefore, the parabola opens upward. The vertex $(2, -7)$ represents the minimum point on the graph.

Section 9.5   Introduction to Functions

Key Concepts

Any set of ordered pairs, (x, y), is called a **relation** in x and y.

    The **domain** of a relation is the set of first components in the ordered pairs in the relation. The **range** of a relation is the set of second components in the ordered pairs.

    Given a relation in x and y, we say "y is a **function** of x" if for each element x in the domain, there is exactly one value y in the range.

Vertical Line Test for Functions

Consider any relation defined by a set of points (x, y) on a rectangular coordinate system. Then the graph defines y as a function of x if no vertical line intersects the graph in more than one point.

Function Notation

$f(x)$ is the value of the function, f, at x.

Examples

Example 1

Find the domain and range of the relation.

$\{(0, 0), (1, 1), (2, 4), (3, 9), (-1, 1), (-2, 4), (-3, 9)\}$

Domain: $\{0, 1, 2, 3, -1, -2, -3\}$

Range: $\{0, 1, 4, 9\}$

Example 2

Function: $\{(1, 3), (2, 5), (6, 3)\}$

Not a function: $\{(1, 3), (2, 5), (1, -2)\}$

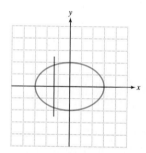

different y values for the same x value

Example 3

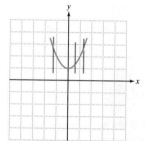

Not a Function
Vertical line intersects more than once.

Function
No vertical line intersects more than once.

Example 4

Given $f(x) = -3x^2 + 5x$, find $f(-2)$.

$f(-2) = -3(-2)^2 + 5(-2)$

$\qquad = -12 - 10$

$\qquad = -22$

Chapter 9   Review Exercises

Section 9.1

For Exercises 1–4, identify the equations as linear or quadratic.

1. $5x - 10 = 3x - 6$ **2.** $(x + 6)^2 = 6$

3. $x(x - 4) = 5x - 2$ **4.** $3(x + 6) = 18(x - 1)$

For Exercises 5–12, solve the equations using the square root property.

5. $x^2 = 25$ **6.** $x^2 - 19 = 0$

7. $x^2 + 49 = 0$ **8.** $x^2 = -48$

9. $(x + 1)^2 = 14$ **10.** $(x - 2)^2 = 60$

11. $\left(x - \dfrac{1}{8}\right)^2 = \dfrac{3}{64}$ **12.** $(2x - 3)^2 = 20$

Section 9.2

For Exercises 13–16, determine the value of n that makes the polynomial a perfect square trinomial.

13. $x^2 + 12x + n$ **14.** $x^2 - 18x + n$

15. $x^2 - 5x + n$ **16.** $x^2 + 7x + n$

For Exercises 17–20, solve the quadratic equations by completing the square and applying the square root property.

17. $x^2 + 8x + 3 = 0$ **18.** $x^2 - 2x - 4 = 0$

19. $2x^2 - 6x - 6 = 0$ **20.** $3x^2 - 7x - 3 = 0$

21. A right triangle has legs of equal length. If the hypotenuse is 15 ft long, find the length of each leg. Round the answer to the nearest tenth of a foot.

22. A can in the shape of a right circular cylinder holds approximately 362 cm³ of liquid. If the height of the can is 12.1 cm, find the radius of the can. Round to the nearest tenth of a centimeter. (*Hint:* The volume of a right circular cylinder is given by: $V = \pi r^2 h$.)

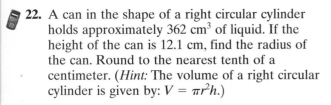

$r = ?$

12.1 cm

Section 9.3

23. Write the quadratic formula from memory.

For Exercises 24–33, find the real solutions for each quadratic equation using the quadratic formula.

24. $5x^2 + x - 7 = 0$ **25.** $x^2 + 4x + 4 = 0$

26. $3x^2 - 2x + 2 = 0$ **27.** $2x^2 - x - 3 = 0$

28. $\dfrac{1}{8}x^2 + x = \dfrac{5}{2}$ **29.** $\dfrac{1}{6}x^2 + x + \dfrac{1}{3} = 0$

30. $1.2x^2 + 6x = 7.2$

31. $0.01x^2 - 0.02x - 0.04 = 0$

32. $(x + 6)(x + 2) = 10$

33. $(x - 1)(x - 7) = -18$

34. One number is two more than another number. Their product is 11.25. Find the numbers.

35. The base of a parallelogram is 1 cm longer than the height, and the area is 24 cm². Find the exact values of the base and height of the parallelogram. Then use a calculator to approximate the values to the nearest tenth of a centimeter.

36. An astronaut on the Moon tosses a rock upward with an initial velocity of 25 ft/sec. The height of the rock, $h(t)$ (in feet), is determined by the number of seconds, t, after the rock is released according to the equation:

$$h(t) = -2.7t^2 + 25t + 5$$

Find the time required for the rock to hit the ground. [*Hint:* At ground level, $h(t) = 0$.] Round to the nearest tenth of a second.

Section 9.4

For Exercises 37–40, identify a and determine if the parabola opens upward or downward.

37. $y = x^2 - 3x + 1$ **38.** $y = -x^2 + 8x + 2$

39. $y = -2x^2 + x - 12$ **40.** $y = 5x^2 - 2x - 6$

For Exercises 41–44, find the vertex for each parabola.

41. $y = 3x^2 + 6x + 4$ **42.** $y = -x^2 + 8x + 3$

43. $y = -2x^2 + 12x - 5$ **44.** $y = 2x^2 + 2x - 1$

For Exercises 45–48,

    a. Determine whether the graph of the parabola opens upward or downward.

    b. Find the vertex.

    c. Find the x-intercept(s) if possible.

    d. Find the y-intercept.

    e. Sketch the graph.

45. $y = x^2 + 2x - 3$

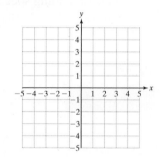

46. $y = x^2 - 2x$

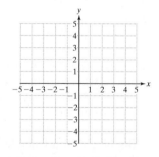

47. $y = -3x^2 + 12x - 9$

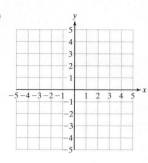

48. $y = -8x^2 - 16x - 12$

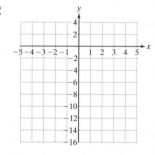

49. An object is launched into the air from ground level with an initial velocity of 256 ft/sec. The height of the object, y (in feet), can be approximated by the function

    $y = -16t^2 + 256t$ where t is the number of seconds after launch.

    a. Find the maximum height of the object.

    b. Find the time required for the object to reach its maximum height.

Section 9.5

For Exercises 50–55, state the domain and range of each relation. Then determine whether the relation is a function.

50. $\{(6, 3), (10, 3), (-1, 3), (0, 3)\}$

51. $\{(2, 0), (2, 1), (2, -5), (2, 2)\}$

52.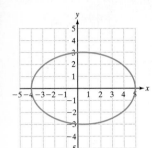

53.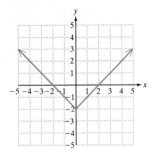

54. $\{(4, 23), (3, -2), (-6, 5), (4, 6)\}$

55. $\{(3, 0), (-4, \frac{1}{2}), (0, 3), (2, -12)\}$

56. Given the function defined by $f(x) = x^3$ find:

   a. $f(0)$ **b.** $f(2)$ **c.** $f(-3)$

   d. $f(-1)$ **e.** $f(4)$

57. Given the function defined by $g(x) = \dfrac{x}{5-x}$. Find:

   a. $g(0)$ **b.** $g(4)$ **c.** $g(-1)$

   d. $g(3)$ **e.** $g(-5)$

 58. The landing distance that a certain plane will travel on a runway is determined by the initial landing speed at the instant the plane touches down. The following function relates landing distance, $D(x)$, to initial landing speed, x, where $x \geq 15$.

$$D(x) = \frac{1}{10}x^2 - 3x + 22$$

where D is in feet and x is in feet per second.

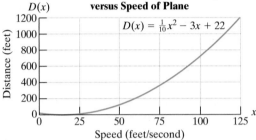

Distance Plane Travels on Runway versus Speed of Plane

   a. Find $D(90)$, and interpret the meaning of the function value in terms of landing speed and length of the runway.

   b. Find $D(110)$, and interpret the meaning in terms of landing speed and length of the runway.

Chapter 9   Test

1. Solve the equation by applying the square root property.

$$(x + 1)^2 = 14$$

2. Solve the equation by completing the square and applying the square root property.

$$x^2 - 8x - 5 = 0$$

3. Solve the equation by using the quadratic formula.

$$3x^2 - 5x = -1$$

For Exercises 4–10, solve the equations using any method.

4. $5x^2 + x - 2 = 0$ **5.** $(c - 12)^2 = 12$

6. $y^2 + 14y - 1 = 0$ **7.** $3t^2 = 30$

8. $4x(3x + 2) = 15$ **9.** $6p^2 - 11p = 0$

10. $\dfrac{1}{4}x^2 - \dfrac{3}{2}x = \dfrac{11}{4}$

 11. The surface area, S, of a sphere is given by the formula $S = 4\pi r^2$, where r is the radius of the sphere. Find the radius of a sphere whose surface area is 201 in.^{2}. Round to the nearest tenth of an inch.

$S = 201$ in.^{2}

 12. The height of a triangle is 2 m longer than twice the base, and the area is 24 m^2. Find the exact values of the base and height. Then use a calculator to approximate the base and height to the nearest tenth of a meter.

13. Explain how to determine if a parabola opens upward or downward.

For Exercises 14–16, find the vertex of the parabola.

14. $y = x^2 - 10x + 25$ **15.** $y = 3x^2 - 6x + 8$

16. $y = -x^2 - 16$

17. Suppose a parabola opens upward and the vertex is located at $(-4, 3)$. How many x-intercepts does the parabola have?

18. Given the parabola, $y = x^2 + 6x + 8$

   a. Determine whether the parabola opens upward or downward.

   b. Find the vertex of the parabola.

   c. Find the x-intercepts.

   d. Find the y-intercept.

   e. Graph the parabola.

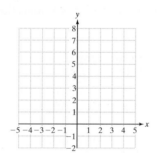

19. Graph the parabola and label the vertex, x-intercepts, and y-intercept.

$$y = -x^2 + 25$$

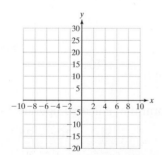

20. The Phelps Arena in Atlanta holds 20,000 seats. If the Atlanta Hawks charge x dollars per ticket for a game, then the total revenue, y (in dollars), can be approximated by

$$y = -400x^2 + 20{,}000x \quad \text{where } x \text{ is the price per ticket.}$$

   a. Find the ticket price that will produce the maximum revenue.

   b. What is the maximum revenue?

21. Write the domain and range for each relation in interval notation. Then determine if the relation is a function.

   a.

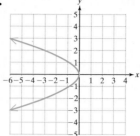

   b.

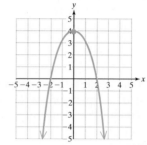

22. For the function defined by $f(x) = \dfrac{1}{x + 2}$, find the function values: $f(0), f(-2), f(6)$.

23. The number of diagonals, $D(x)$, of a polygon is a function of the number of sides, x, of the polygon according to the equation

$$D(x) = \frac{1}{2}x(x - 3)$$

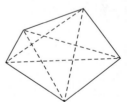

   a. Find $D(5)$ and interpret the meaning of the function value. Verify your answer by counting the number of diagonals in the pentagon in the figure.

   b. Find $D(10)$ and interpret its meaning.

   c. If a polygon has 20 diagonals, how many sides does it have? (*Hint:* Substitute $D(x) = 20$ and solve for x. Try clearing fractions first.)

Chapters 1–9   Cumulative Review Exercises

1. Solve. $3x - 5 = 2(x - 2)$

2. Solve for h. $A = \frac{1}{2}bh$

3. Solve. $\frac{1}{2}y - \frac{5}{6} = \frac{1}{4}y + 2$

4. a. Determine whether 2 is a solution to the inequality. $-3x + 4 < x + 8$

   b. Graph the solution to the inequality: $-3x + 4 < x + 8$. Then write the solution in set-builder notation and in interval notation.

   _____

5. The graph depicts the death rate from 60 U.S. cities versus the median education level of the people living in that city. The death rate, y, is measured in number of deaths per 100,000 people. The median education level, x, is a type of "average" and is measured by grade level. (*Source:* U.S. Bureau of the Census)

   The death rate can be predicted from the median education level according to the equation:

   $y = -37.6x + 1353$ where $9 \le x \le 13$.

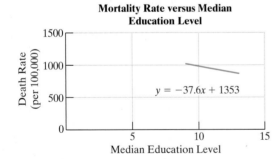

Mortality Rate versus Median Education Level

$y = -37.6x + 1353$

Death Rate (per 100,000)

Median Education Level

   a. From the graph, does it appear that the death rate increases or decreases as the median education level increases?

   b. What is the slope of the line? Interpret the slope in the context of the death rate and education level.

   c. For a city in the United States with a median education level of 12, what would be the expected death rate?

   d. If the death rate of a certain city is 977 per 100,000 people, what would be the approximate median education level?

6. Simplify completely. Write the final answer with positive exponents only.
$$\left(\frac{2a^2b^{-3}}{c}\right)^{-1} \cdot \left(\frac{4a^{-1}}{b^2}\right)^2$$

7. Approximately 5.2×10^7 disposable diapers are thrown into the trash each day in the United States and Canada. How many diapers are thrown away each year?

8. In 1989, the Hipparcos satellite found the distance between Earth and the star, Polaris, to be approximately 2.53×10^{15} mi. If 1 light-year is approximately 5.88×10^{12} miles, how many light-years is Polaris from Earth?

9. Perform the indicated operation.
$(2x - 3)^2 - 4(x - 1)$

10. Divide using long division.
$(2y^4 - 4y^3 + y - 5) \div (y - 2)$

11. Factor. $2x^2 - 9x - 35$

12. Factor completely. $2xy + 8xa - 3by - 12ab$

13. The base of a triangle is 1 m more than the height. If the area is 36 m², find the base and height.

14. Reduce to lowest terms.
$$\frac{5x + 10}{x^2 - 4}$$

15. Multiply. $\dfrac{x^2 + 10x + 9}{x^2 - 81} \cdot \dfrac{18 - 2x}{x^2 + 2x + 1}$

16. Perform the indicated operations.
$$\frac{x^2}{x - 5} - \frac{10x - 25}{x - 5}$$

17. Simplify completely.
$$\frac{\dfrac{1}{x + 1} - \dfrac{1}{x - 1}}{\dfrac{x}{x^2 - 1}}$$

18. Solve. $1 - \dfrac{1}{y} = \dfrac{12}{y^2}$

19. Write an equation of the line passing through the point $(-2, 3)$ and having a slope of $\frac{1}{2}$. Write the final answer in slope-intercept form.

For Exercises 20 and 21,

      a. Find the x-intercept (if it exists).

      b. Find the y-intercept (if it exists).

      c. Find the slope (if it exists).

      d. Graph the line.

20. $2x - 4y = 12$

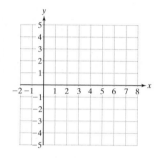

21. $4x + 12 = 0$

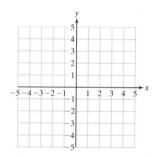

22. Solve the system by using the addition method. If the system has no solution or infinitely many solutions, so state.

$$\frac{1}{2}x - \frac{1}{4}y = \frac{1}{6}$$

$$12x - 3y = 8$$

23. Solve the system by using the substitution method. If the system has no solution or infinitely many solutions, so state.

$$2x - y = 8$$

$$4x - 4y = 3x - 3$$

24. In a right triangle, one acute angle measures $2°$ more than three times the other acute angle. Find the measure of each angle.

25. A bank of 27 coins contains only dimes and quarters. The total value of the coins is $4.80. Find the number of dimes and the number of quarters.

26. Sketch the inequality, $x - y \le 4$.

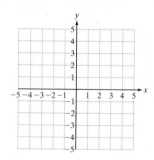

27. Which of the following are irrational numbers? $\{0, -\frac{2}{3}, \pi, \sqrt{7}, 1.2, \sqrt{25}\}$

For Exercises 28 and 29, simplify the radicals.

28. $\sqrt{\dfrac{1}{7}}$

29. $\dfrac{\sqrt{16x^4}}{\sqrt{2x}}$

30. Perform the indicated operation. $(4\sqrt{3} + \sqrt{x})^2$

31. Add the radicals. $-3\sqrt{2x} + \sqrt{50x}$

32. Rationalize the denominator.

$$\frac{4}{2 - \sqrt{a}}$$

33. Solve. $\sqrt{x + 11} = x + 5$

34. Factor completely. $8c^3 - y^3$

35. Which graph defines y as a function of x?

    a.   **b.**

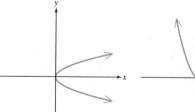
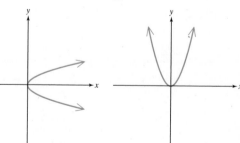

36. Given the functions defined by $f(x) = -\frac{1}{2}x + 4$ and $g(x) = x^2$, find

  a. $f(6)$ **b.** $g(-2)$ **c.** $f(0) + g(3)$

37. Find the domain and range of the function.
$\{(2, 4), (-1, 3), (9, 2), (-6, 8)\}$

38. Find the slope of the line passing through the points $(3, -1)$ and $(-4, -6)$.

39. Find the slope of the line defined by $-4x - 5y = 10$.

40. What value of n would make the expression a perfect square trinomial?

$$x^2 + 10x + n$$

41. Solve the quadratic equation by completing the square and applying the square root property.
$2x^2 + 12x + 6 = 0$

42. Solve the quadratic equation by using the quadratic formula. $2x^2 + 12x + 6 = 0$

43. Graph the parabola defined by the equation. Label the vertex, x-intercepts, and y-intercept.

$$y = x^2 + 4x + 4$$

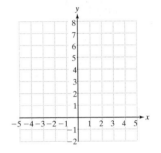

Additional Topics Appendix

Converting Units of Measurement

Section A.1

1. Converting U.S. and Metric Units of Measure

The procedure for multiplying rational expressions and canceling like factors can be applied in converting units of measurement. A conversion factor is a ratio of equivalent measures.

For example, note that 1 ft = 12 in. Therefore, $\dfrac{1 \text{ ft}}{12 \text{ in.}} = 1$ and $\dfrac{12 \text{ in.}}{1 \text{ ft}} = 1$.

These conversion factors are unit ratios or unit fractions because the quotient is 1. To convert from one unit of measure to another, we can multiply by an appropriate conversion factor. We offer these guidelines to determine the proper conversion factor to use.

Concepts

1. Converting U.S. and Metric Units of Measure
2. Converting Units of Measure Involving Temperature

> **Choosing a Conversion Factor**
>
> In a conversion factor,
>
> - The unit of measure in the numerator should be the new unit you want to convert *to*.
> - The unit of measure in the denominator should be the original unit you want to convert *from*.

Table A-1 summarizes some common metric and U.S. customary equivalents. These equivalents can be used to form conversion factors.

Table A-1

Length	Weight/Mass (on Earth)	Capacity
1 in. = 2.54 cm	1 lb ≈ 0.45 kg	1 qt ≈ 0.95 L
1 ft ≈ 0.305 m	1 oz ≈ 28 g	1 fl oz ≈ 30 mL ≈ 30 cc
1 yd ≈ 0.914 m		
1 mi ≈ 1.61 km		

In Example 1 we use a conversion factor to convert from kilometers to miles.

Skill Practice

1. Use the fact that 1 mi ≈ 1.61 km to convert 92 km to miles. Round to one decimal place.

Example 1   Converting Metric Units to U.S. Customary Units

One of the events in the Peachtree Marathon in Atlanta is a 5K race, which means it is 5 km. From Table A-1, use the fact that 1 mi ≈ 1.61 km to convert this distance to miles. Round to one decimal place.

Solution:

The conversion factors that relate miles to kilometers are $\dfrac{1 \text{ mi}}{1.61 \text{ km}} = 1$ or

$\dfrac{1.61 \text{ km}}{1 \text{ mi}} = 1$. We are converting *to* miles *from* kilometers. The conversion factor

with miles in the numerator and kilometers in the denominator is $\dfrac{1 \text{ mi}}{1.61 \text{ km}}$.

$$5 \text{ km} \approx \frac{5 \text{ km}}{1} \cdot \frac{1 \text{ mi}}{1.61 \text{ km}} \qquad \text{Set up a conversion factor to convert kilometers to miles.}$$

$$\approx \frac{5}{1.61} \text{ mi} \qquad \text{Multiply fractions. Like units are canceled.}$$

$$\approx 3.1 \text{ mi} \qquad \text{Divide and round to one decimal place.}$$

The 5K race is approximately 3.1 mi.

Skill Practice

2. Fill in the blank. Round to two decimal places, if necessary.
   a. 170 lb ≈ _____ kg
   b. 10 m ≈ _____ ft
   c. 100 cc ≈ _____ fl oz

Example 2   Converting between U.S. Customary and Metric Measurements

Convert the units as indicated. Round to two decimal places, if necessary.

a. 48 oz ≈ _____ g   b. 200 m ≈ _____ ft

c. 5.2 L ≈ _____ qt

Solution:

a. $48 \text{ oz} \approx \dfrac{48 \text{ oz}}{1} \cdot \dfrac{28 \text{ g}}{1 \text{ oz}}$ From Table A-1 we know that 1 oz ≈ 28 g.

$\approx 48 \cdot 28 \text{ g}$ Multiply. Cancel like units.

$\approx 1344 \text{ g}$

b. $200 \text{ m} \approx \dfrac{200 \text{ m}}{1} \cdot \dfrac{1 \text{ ft}}{0.305 \text{ m}}$ From Table A-1 we know that 1 ft ≈ 0.305 m.

$\approx \dfrac{200}{0.305} \text{ ft}$ Multiply fractions. Cancel like units.

$\approx 655.74 \text{ ft}$ Divide and round to two decimal places.

c. $5.2 \text{ L} \approx \dfrac{5.2 \text{ L}}{1} \cdot \dfrac{1 \text{ qt}}{0.95 \text{ L}}$ From Table A-1 we know that 1 qt ≈ 0.95 L.

$\approx \dfrac{5.2}{0.95} \text{ qt}$ Multiply fractions. Cancel like units.

$\approx 5.47 \text{ qt}$ Divide and round to two decimal places.

Answers

1. 57.1 mi
2. a. 76.5 kg   b. 32.79 ft   c. 3.33 fl oz

2. Converting Units of Measure Involving Temperature

In the United States, the Fahrenheit scale is used most often to measure temperature. The symbol °F stands for "degrees Fahrenheit." Another scale used to measure temperature is the Celsius temperature scale. The symbol °C stands for "degrees Celsius." Use the following formulas to convert back and forth between Fahrenheit and Celsius scales.

Conversions for Temperature Scale

To convert from °C to °F:

$$F = \frac{9}{5}C + 32$$

To convert from °F to °C:

$$C = \frac{5}{9}(F - 32)$$

Example 3 Converting Units of Temperature

a. A warm day in Quebec, Canada, is 25°C. Convert this temperature to °F.

b. A refrigerator should maintain a temperature of not more than 41°F. Convert this temperature to °C.

Solution:

a. To convert from degrees Celsius to degrees Fahrenheit, use the formula $F = \frac{9}{5}C + 32$.

$$F = \frac{9}{5}C + 32$$

$$= \frac{9}{5}(25) + 32 \qquad \text{Substitute } C = 25.$$

$$= 45 + 32 \qquad \text{Perform multiplication first.}$$

$$= 77$$

The temperature in Quebec is equivalent to 77°F.

b. To convert from degrees Fahrenheit to degrees Celsius, use the formula $C = \frac{5}{9}(F - 32)$.

$$C = \frac{5}{9}(F - 32)$$

$$= \frac{5}{9}(41 - 32) \qquad \text{Substitute } F = 41.$$

$$= \frac{5}{9}(9) \qquad \text{Perform the operation within parentheses first.}$$

$$= 5$$

The refrigerator should maintain a temperature of not more than 5°C.

Skill Practice

3. a. Convert 100°F to degrees Celsius. Round to the nearest degree.
   b. Convert −10°C to degrees Fahrenheit.

Answers

3. a. 38°F   b. 14°C

Section A.1   Practice Exercises

Concepts 1 and 2: Converting U.S. and Metric Units of Measurement and Temperature

For Exercises 1–16, convert the units as indicated. Round to one decimal place, if necessary. **(See Examples 1–3.)**

1. 60 m ≈ _____ ft

2. 32 cm = _____ in.

3. 400 ft ≈ _____ m

4. 25 mi ≈ _____ km

5. 0.3 lb ≈ _____ kg

6. 16 oz ≈ _____ g

7. 8.8 g ≈ _____ oz

8. 18 kg ≈ _____ lb

9. 64 fl oz ≈ _____ mL

10. 1.5 qt ≈ _____ L

11. 5.2 L ≈ _____ qt

12. 960 cc ≈ _____ fl oz

13. $-20°C$ = _____ °F

14. 99°C = _____ °F

15. 40°F = _____ °C

16. $-13°F$ = _____ °C

Mixed Exercises

For Exercises 17–32, round answers to one decimal place, if necessary.

17. One of the events in the Winter Olympics is speed skating for a distance of 1500 m. Convert this distance to yards.

18. In a recent ski jump event in the Winter Olympics, the winner jumped a distance of 108 m. Convert this distance to feet.

19. The speed of sound is approximately 1126 ft/sec. Convert this speed to meters per second.

20. A tourist from France notices the speed limit on an interstate highway in the United States is 70 mph. What is the speed limit in km per hour?

21. Tyler works with a nutritionist who recommends that males should consume approximately 3 L of liquids per day. How many quarts per day is this amount?

22. Joanie's nutritionist recommends that females should consume 2.2 L of liquids per day. How many quarts is this amount?

23. A 2-L bottle of juice sells for $1.99. A half-gallon (2-qt) container of juice sells for $1.79. Compare the price per quart to determine which is the better buy.

24. The capacity of an automobile gas tank is 16 gal. Determine the capacity of the tank in L. (*Hint:* 1 gal = 4 qt)

25. The recommended daily intake of protein can vary according to gender, weight, and activity level. The recommended amount for an average male weighing 90 kg is 72 g protein. Determine his weight in lb.

26. A roll of U.S. quarters weighs approximately 227 g. Determine this weight in ounces.

27. One of the smallest miniature horses on record weighed only 20 lb. Convert this weight to kg.

28. On average, a Chihuahua weighs about 5 lb. Convert this weight to kg.

29. In January, the average temperature at the top of Mt. Everest is about $-31°F$. What is the temperature in °C?

30. Jessica set her oven at 185°F to keep her pizza warm. Convert the temperature to °C.

31. Technical information for most iPods states that iPods should not be operated at temperatures above 35°C. What is this temperature in °F?

32. The high temperature in London, England, on a typical September day was 18°C, and the low was 13°C. Convert these temperatures to degrees Fahrenheit.

Student Answer Appendix

Chapter R

Section R.2 Practice Exercises, pp. 16–20

1. a. product **b.** factors **c.** numerator; b **d.** lowest
e. 1; 4 **f.** reciprocals **g.** multiple **h.** least
3. Numerator: 2; denominator: 3; proper
5. Numerator: 6; denominator: 6; improper
7. Numerator: 12; denominator: 1; improper

9. $\frac{3}{4}$ **11.** $\frac{4}{3}$ **13.** $\frac{1}{6}$ **15.** $\frac{2}{2}$

17. $\frac{5}{2}$ or $2\frac{1}{2}$ **19.** $\frac{6}{2}$ or 3

21. The set of whole numbers includes the number 0 and the set of natural numbers does not.

23. For example: $\frac{2}{4}$ **25.** Prime **27.** Composite

29. Composite **31.** Prime **33.** $2 \times 2 \times 3 \times 3$
35. $2 \times 3 \times 7$ **37.** $2 \times 5 \times 11$ **39.** $3 \times 3 \times 3 \times 5$

41. $\frac{1}{5}$ **43.** $\frac{8}{3}$ or $2\frac{2}{3}$ **45.** $\frac{7}{8}$ **47.** $\frac{3}{4}$ **49.** $\frac{5}{8}$

51. $\frac{4}{3}$ or $1\frac{1}{3}$ **53.** False: When adding or subtracting

fractions, it is necessary to have a common denominator.

55. $\frac{4}{3}$ or $1\frac{1}{3}$ **57.** $\frac{2}{3}$ **59.** $\frac{9}{2}$ or $4\frac{1}{2}$ **61.** $\frac{3}{5}$

63. $\frac{5}{3}$ or $1\frac{2}{3}$ **65.** $\frac{90}{13}$ or $6\frac{12}{13}$ **67.** \$1050

69. 35 students **71.** 8 pieces **73.** 8 jars **75.** $\frac{3}{7}$

77. $\frac{1}{2}$ **79.** 30 **81.** 40 **83.** $\frac{7}{8}$ **85.** $\frac{43}{40}$ or $1\frac{3}{40}$

87. $\frac{3}{26}$ **89.** $\frac{29}{36}$ **91.** $\frac{6}{5}$ or $1\frac{1}{5}$ **93.** $\frac{35}{48}$ **95.** $\frac{7}{24}$

97. $\frac{51}{28}$ or $1\frac{23}{28}$ **99.** $\frac{11}{12}$ cup sugar **101.** $\frac{7}{50}$ in.

103. $\frac{46}{5}$ or $9\frac{1}{5}$ **105.** $\frac{1}{6}$ **107.** $\frac{11}{54}$ **109.** $\frac{7}{2}$ or $3\frac{1}{2}$

111. $\frac{13}{8}$ or $1\frac{5}{8}$ **113.** $\frac{59}{12}$ or $4\frac{11}{12}$ **115.** $\frac{1}{8}$ **117.** $8\frac{19}{24}$ in.
119. $1\frac{7}{12}$ hr **121.** $2\frac{1}{4}$ lb **123.** 25 in.

Section R.3 Calculator Connections, p. 26

1. $0.\overline{4}$ **2.** $0.\overline{63}$ **3.** $0.1\overline{36}$ **4.** $0.\overline{384615}$

1.–2.
```
4/9
7/11    .4444444444
        .6363636364
```

3.–4.
```
3/22
5/13    .1363636364
        .3846153846
```

Section R.3 Practice Exercises, pp. 27–29

1. a. tenths; hundredths; thousandths **b.** percent
c. $\frac{1}{100}$; 0.01 **d.** 100% **3.** Hundreds **5.** Tenths

7. Hundredths **9.** No, the symbols I, V, X, and so on each represent certain values but the values are not dependent on the position of the symbol within the number.
11. 0.7 **13.** 0.36 **15.** $1.\overline{2}$ **17.** $0.\overline{21}$ **19.** 214.1

21. 39.268 **23.** 40,000 **25.** 0.73 **27.** $\frac{9}{20}$

29. $\frac{181}{1000}$ **31.** $\frac{51}{25}$ or $2\frac{1}{25}$ **33.** $\frac{13,007}{1000}$ or $13\frac{7}{1000}$

35. $\frac{5}{9}$ **37.** $\frac{10}{9}$ or $1\frac{1}{9}$ **39.** 0.3, $\frac{3}{10}$ **41.** 0.75, $\frac{3}{4}$

43. 0.0375, $\frac{3}{80}$ **45.** 0.157, $\frac{157}{1000}$ **47.** 2.7, $\frac{27}{10}$

49. Multiply by 100%. **51.** 5% **53.** 90%
55. 120% **57.** 750% **59.** 13.5% **61.** 0.3%
63. 6% **65.** 450% **67.** 62.5% **69.** 31.25%
71. $83.\overline{3}$% **73.** $93.\overline{3}$% **75.** \$42 **77.** \$3375
79. 7% **81.** \$792 **83.** \$192 **85.** \$67,500

Section R.4 Practice Exercises, pp. 37–43

1. a. perimeter; circumference **b.** area
c. $C = 2\pi r$; $A = \pi r^2$ **d.** lwh **e.** acute; obtuse
f. complementary; 180° **g.** 180 **h.** right

3. 32 m **5.** 17.2 mi **7.** $11\frac{1}{2}$ in.

9. 31.4 ft **11.** a, f, g **13.** 33 cm^2 **15.** 16.81 m^2
17. 84 in.^{2} **19.** 10.12 km^2 **21.** 13.8474 ft^2
23. 66 in.^{2} **25.** 31.5 ft^2 **27.** c, d, h **29.** 307.72 cm^3
31. 39 in.^{3} **33.** 113.04 cm^3 **35.** 1695.6 cm^3
37. 3052.08 in.^{3} **39.** 113.04 cm^3
41. a. \$0.25/ft^2 **b.** \$104 **43.** Perimeter **45.** 54 ft
47. a. 57,600 ft^2 **b.** 19,200 pieces
49. a. 50.24 in.^{2} **b.** 113.04 in.^{2} **c.** One 12-in. pizza
51. 289.3824 cm^3 **53.** True **55.** True **57.** True
59. Not possible **61.** For example: 100°, 80°
63. a. $\angle 1$ and $\angle 3$, $\angle 2$ and $\angle 4$
b. $\angle 1$ and $\angle 2$, $\angle 2$ and $\angle 3$, $\angle 3$ and $\angle 4$, $\angle 1$ and $\angle 4$
c. $m(\angle 1) = 100°$, $m(\angle 2) = 80°$, $m(\angle 3) = 100°$
65. 57° **67.** 78° **69.** 147° **71.** 58°
73. 7 **75.** 1 **77.** 1 **79.** 5
81. $m(\angle a) = 45°$, $m(\angle b) = 135°$, $m(\angle c) = 45°$, $m(\angle d) = 135°$, $m(\angle e) = 45°$, $m(\angle f) = 135°$, $m(\angle g) = 45°$
83. Scalene **85.** Isosceles **87.** True **89.** 45°
91. No, a 90° angle plus an angle greater than 90° would make the sum of the angles greater than 180°. **93.** 40°
95. 37° **97.** $m(\angle a) = 80°$, $m(\angle b) = 80°$, $m(\angle c) = 100°$, $m(\angle d) = 100°$, $m(\angle e) = 65°$, $m(\angle f) = 115°$, $m(\angle g) = 115°$, $m(\angle h) = 35°$, $m(\angle i) = 145°$, $m(\angle j) = 145°$

99. $m(\angle a) = 70°, m(\angle b) = 65°, m(\angle c) = 65°,$
$m(\angle d) = 110°, m(\angle e) = 70°, m(\angle f) = 110°, m(\angle g) = 115°,$
$m(\angle h) = 115°, m(\angle i) = 65°, m(\angle j) = 70°, m(\angle k) = 65°$
101. 82 ft   **103.** 36 in.^{2} **105.** 15.2464 cm^2

Chapter 1

Chapter Opener Puzzle

Section 1.1 Calculator Connections, p. 54

1. ≈ 3.464101615 **2.** ≈ 9.949874371
3. ≈ 12.56637061 **4.** ≈ 1.772453851

Section 1.1 Practice Exercises, pp. 55–58

1. a. variable   **b.** constants   **c.** set   **d.** inequalities
e. a is less than b **f.** c is greater than or equal to d
g. 5 is not equal to 6   **h.** opposites   **i.** $|a|$; 0

3. 15   **5.** 20   **7.** 12   **9.** 5.3   **11.** $\dfrac{1}{80}$

13. a. \$3.87   **b.** \$10.32   **c.** \$12.90
15. a. 375 calories   **b.** 630 calories   **c.** 270 calories
17.

19. a; rational   **21.** b; rational   **23.** a; rational
25. c; irrational   **27.** a; rational   **29.** a; rational
31. b; rational   **33.** c; irrational
35. For example: $\pi, -\sqrt{2}, \sqrt{3}$
37. For example: $-4, -1, 0$
39. For example: $-\dfrac{3}{4}, \dfrac{1}{2}, 0.206$ **41.** $-\dfrac{3}{2}, -4, 0.\overline{6}, 0, 1$

43. 1   **45.** $-4, 0, 1$ **47. a.** >   **b.** >   **c.** <   **d.** >

49. -18 **51.** 6.1   **53.** $\dfrac{5}{8}$ **55.** $-\dfrac{7}{3}$ **57.** 3

59. $-\dfrac{7}{3}$ **61.** 8   **63.** -72.1 **65.** 2   **67.** 1.5

69. -1.5 **71.** $\dfrac{3}{2}$ **73.** -10 **75.** $-\dfrac{1}{2}$

77. False, $|n|$ is never negative.   **79.** True   **81.** False
83. True   **85.** False   **87.** False   **89.** False
91. True   **93.** True   **95.** False   **97.** True
99. True   **101.** True   **103.** For all $a < 0$

Section 1.2 Calculator Connections, p. 65

1. 2   **2.** 91   **3.** 84   **4.** 12   **5.** 49   **6.** 18
1.–3.   4.–6.

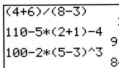

```
(4+6)/(8-3)
                2
110-5*(2+1)-4
                91
100-2*(5-3)^3
                84
```

```
3+(4-1)²
                12
(12-6+1)²
                49
3*8-√(32+2²)
                18
```

7. 4   **8.** 27   **9.** 0.5   7.–9.

```
√(18-2)
                4
(4*3-3*3)^3
                27
(20-3²)/(26-2²)
                .5
```

Section 1.2 Practice Exercises, pp. 66–69

1. a. quotient; product; sum; difference   **b.** base;
exponent; power   **c.** 8^2 **d.** p^4 **e.** radical; square
f. order of operations   **3.** 56   **5.** -14 **7.** -19

9. $\left(\dfrac{1}{6}\right)^4$ **11.** a^3b^2 **13.** $(5c)^5$ **15. a.** x **b.** Yes, 1
17. $x \cdot x \cdot x$ **19.** $2b \cdot 2b \cdot 2b$ **21.** $10 \cdot y \cdot y \cdot y \cdot y \cdot y$

23. $2 \cdot w \cdot z \cdot z$ **25.** 36   **27.** $\dfrac{1}{49}$ **29.** 0.008

31. 64   **33.** 9   **35.** 2   **37.** 12   **39.** 4

41. $\dfrac{1}{3}$ **43.** $\dfrac{5}{9}$ **45.** 20   **47.** 60   **49.** 8   **51.** 78

53. 0   **55.** $\dfrac{7}{6}$ **57.** 45   **59.** 16   **61.** 15   **63.** 19

65. 75   **67.** 3   **69.** 39   **71.** 26   **73.** $\dfrac{5}{12}$ **75.** $\dfrac{5}{2}$

77. a. 0.12   **b.** Yes. $0.12 < 0.20$ **79.** 57,600 ft^2

81. 21 ft^2 **83.** $3x$ **85.** $\dfrac{x}{7}$ or $x \div 7$ **87.** $2 - a$

89. $2y + x$ **91.** $4(x + 12)$ **93.** $3 - Q$

95. $2y^3$; 16   **97.** $|z - 8|$; 2   **99.** $5\sqrt{x}$; 10

101. $yz - x$; 16   **103.** 1   **105.** $\dfrac{1}{4}$

107. a. $36 \div 4 \cdot 3$ Division must be performed before
     $= 9 \cdot 3$ multiplication.
     $= 27$
b. $36 - 4 + 3$ Subtraction must be performed
     $= 32 + 3$ before addition.
     $= 35$
109. This is acceptable, provided division and multiplication
are performed in order from left to right, and subtraction and
addition are performed in order from left to right.

Section 1.3 Practice Exercises, pp. 74–76

1. a. negative   **b.** b **3.** >   **5.** >   **7.** >
9. -6 **11.** 3   **13.** 3   **15.** -3 **17.** -17
19. 7   **21.** -19 **23.** -23 **25.** -5 **27.** -3
29. 0   **31.** 0   **33.** -5 **35.** -3 **37.** 0
39. -23 **41.** -6 **43.** -3 **45.** 21.3

47. $-\dfrac{3}{14}$ **49.** $-\dfrac{1}{6}$ **51.** $-\dfrac{15}{16}$ **53.** $\dfrac{1}{20}$

55. -2.4 or $-\dfrac{12}{5}$ **57.** $\dfrac{1}{4}$ or 0.25 **59.** 0 **61.** $-\dfrac{7}{8}$

63. -1 **65.** $\dfrac{11}{9}$ **67.** -23.08 **69.** -0.002117

71. To add two numbers with different signs, subtract the smaller absolute value from the larger absolute value and apply the sign of the number with the larger absolute value.

73. -1 **75.** 10 **77.** 5 **79.** 1

81. $-6 + (-10); -16$ **83.** $-3 + 8; 5$

85. $-21 + 17; -4$ **87.** $3(-14 + 20); 18$

89. $(-7 + (-2)) + 5; -4$ **91.** $-5 + 13 + (-11); -3°F$

93. $-8 + 1 + 2 + (-5) = -10;$ Amara lost 10 lb.

95. a. $52.23 + (-52.95)$ **b.** Yes

97. a. $100 + 200 + (-500) + 300 + 100 + (-200)$ **b.** $0

Section 1.4 Calculator Connections, p. 82

1. -13 **2.** -2 **3.** 711

1.–3.

```
-8+(-5)
              -13
4+(-5)+(-1)
              -2
627-(-84)
              711
```

4. -0.18 **5.** -17.7 **6.** -990 **7.** -17 **8.** 38

4.–6.

```
-0.06-0.12
              -.18
-3.2+(-14.5)
              -17.7
-472+(-518)
              -990
```

7.–8.

```
-12-9+4
              -17
209-108+(-63)
              38
```

Section 1.4 Practice Exercises, pp. 82–85

1. a. $-b$ **b.** positive   **3.** x^2 **5.** $-b + 2$

7. 9 **9.** -3 **11.** -12 **13.** 4 **15.** -2

17. 8 **19.** -8 **21.** 2 **23.** 6 **25.** 40

27. -40 **29.** 0 **31.** -20 **33.** -24 **35.** 25

37. -5 **39.** $-\dfrac{3}{2}$ **41.** $\dfrac{41}{24}$ **43.** $\dfrac{2}{5}$ **45.** $-\dfrac{2}{3}$

47. 9.2 **49.** -5.72 **51.** -10 **53.** -14

55. -20 **57.** -173.188 **59.** 3.243

61. $6 - (-7); 13$ **63.** $3 - 18; -15$ **65.** $-5 - (-11); 6$

67. $-1 - (-13); 12$ **69.** $-32 - 20; -52$

71. $200 + 400 + 600 + 800 - 1000; \$1000$ **73.** $152°F$

75. $19{,}881$ m   **77.** 13 **79.** -9 **81.** 5 **83.** -25

85. -2 **87.** $-\dfrac{11}{30}$ **89.** $-\dfrac{29}{9}$ **91.** -2 **93.** -11

95. 2 **97.** -7 **99.** 5 **101.** 5 **103.** 3

Chapter 1 Problem Recognition Exercises, p. 85

1. Add their absolute values and apply a negative sign.

2. Subtract the smaller absolute value from the larger absolute value. Apply the sign of the number with the larger absolute value.

3. a. 6 **b.** -6 **c.** -22 **d.** 22 **e.** -22

4. a. -2 **b.** -8 **c.** -8 **d.** -2 **e.** 8 **5. a.** 0 **b.** 0

c. 50 **d.** 0 **e.** -50 **6. a.** $-\dfrac{1}{6}$ **b.** $\dfrac{1}{6}$ **c.** $-\dfrac{7}{6}$

d. $\dfrac{7}{6}$ **e.** $-\dfrac{7}{6}$ **7. a.** -3.6 **b.** 10.6 **c.** 3.6

d. 3.6 **e.** -10.6 **8. a.** 4 **b.** -4 **c.** 6 **d.** 6

9. a. -270 **b.** -110 **c.** -90 **d.** -270

10. a. 402 **b.** -108 **c.** 484 **d.** 24

Section 1.5 Calculator Connections, p. 92

1. -30 **2.** -2 **3.** 625 **4.** 625 **5.** -625 **6.** -5.76

1–3.

```
-6(5)
                -30
-5.2/2.6
                -2
(-5)(-5)(-5)(-5)
                625
```

4–6.

```
(-5)^4
                625
-5^4
                -625
-2.4²
                -5.76
```

7. 5.76 **8.** -1 **9.** 4 **10.** -36

7–8.

```
(-2.4)²
                5.76
(-1)(-1)(-1)
                -1
```

9–10.

```
-8.4/-2.1
                4
90/(-5)(2)
                -36
```

Section 1.5 Practice Exercises, pp. 92–96

1. a. $\dfrac{1}{a}$ **b.** 0 **c.** 0 **d.** undefined   **e.** positive

f. negative   **g.** $1; -\dfrac{3}{2}$ **h.** All of these

3. True   **5.** False   **7.** -56 **9.** 143 **11.** -12.76

13. $\dfrac{3}{4}$ **15.** 36 **17.** -36 **19.** $-\dfrac{27}{125}$ **21.** 0.0016

23. -6 **25.** 10 **27.** 2 **29.** -1 **31.** 1

33. $-\dfrac{1}{5}$ **35.** $(-2)(-7) = 14$ **37.** $-5 \cdot 0 = 0$

39. No number multiplied by zero equals 6.

41. $(-6)(4) = -24$ **43.** 6 **45.** -6 **47.** -8

49. 8 **51.** 0 **53.** Undefined   **55.** 0 **57.** 0

59. $-\dfrac{3}{2}$ **61.** $\dfrac{3}{10}$ **63.** -2 **65.** -7.912 **67.** 0.092

69. -6 **71.** 2.1 **73.** 9 **75.** -9 **77.** $-\dfrac{64}{27}$

79. -14.28 **81.** 340 **83.** $-\dfrac{10}{9}$ **85.** $\dfrac{14}{9}$

87. -30 **89.** 96 **91.** 2 **93.** -1 **95.** $-\dfrac{4}{33}$

97. $-\dfrac{4}{7}$ **99.** -24 **101.** $-\dfrac{1}{20}$ **103.** -23

105. 12 **107.** $\dfrac{9}{7}$ **109.** Undefined   **111.** -48

113. -6 **115.** -1 **117.** 7 **119.** -4

121. -40 **123.** $\dfrac{7}{2}$

125. No. The first expression is equivalent to $10 \div (5x)$. The second is $10 \div 5 \cdot x$.

127. $-3.75(0.3); -1.125$ **129.** $\dfrac{16}{5} \div \left(-\dfrac{8}{9}\right); -\dfrac{18}{5}$

131. $-0.4 + 6(-0.42); -2.92$ **133.** $-\dfrac{1}{4} - 6\left(-\dfrac{1}{3}\right); \dfrac{7}{4}$

135. $3(-2) + 3 = -3$; loss of \$3

137. $2(5) + 3(-3) = 1$; Lorne was 1 sale above quota for the week.

139. $\dfrac{12 + (-15) + 4 + (-9) + 3}{5} = -1$; The average loss was 1 oz.

141. a. -10 **b.** 24 **c.** In part (a), we subtract; in part (b), we multiply.

Chapter 1 Problem Recognition Exercises, p. 96

1. a. -4 **b.** 32 **c.** -12 **d.** 2 **2. a.** 10 **b.** 14
c. -24 **d.** -6 **3. a.** -27 **b.** -324 **c.** -4 **d.** -45
4. a. 30 **b.** 24 **c.** -81 **d.** -9 **5. a.** 50 **b.** -15
c. $\dfrac{1}{2}$ **d.** 5 **6. a.** -5 **b.** -24 **c.** -16 **d.** -80
7. a. 64 **b.** 12 **c.** $\dfrac{1}{4}$ **d.** -20 **8. a.** -7 **b.** -24
c. -63 **d.** -18 **9. a.** -400 **b.** 85 **c.** -16 **d.** 75
10. a. 7 **b.** 294 **c.** $\dfrac{2}{3}$ **d.** -35 **11. a.** 8 **b.** 4
c. 4 **d.** 8 **12. a.** -16 **b.** 2 **c.** -2 **d.** 16

Section 1.6 Practice Exercises, pp. 106–109

1. a. constant   **b.** coefficient   **c.** $1; 1$ **d.** like
3. 7 **5.** 18 **7.** $-\dfrac{27}{5}$ or -5.4 **9.** 0 **11.** $\dfrac{1}{3}$
13. $\dfrac{11}{15}$ **15.** $-8 + 5$ **17.** $x + 8$ **19.** $4(5)$
21. $-12x$ **23.** $x + (-3); -3 + x$
25. $4p + (-9); -9 + 4p$ **27.** $x + (4 + 9); x + 13$
29. $(-5 \cdot 3)x; -15x$ **31.** $\left(\dfrac{6}{11} \cdot \dfrac{11}{6}\right)x; x$
33. $\left(-4 \cdot -\dfrac{1}{4}\right)t; t$ **35.** Reciprocal   **37.** 0
39. $30x + 6$ **41.** $-2a - 16$ **43.** $15c - 3d$
45. $-7y + 14$ **47.** $-\dfrac{2}{3}x + 4$ **49.** $\dfrac{1}{3}m - 1$
51. $-2p - 10$ **53.** $6w + 10z - 16$ **55.** $4x + 8y - 4z$
57. $6w - x + 3y$ **59.** $7 + y$ **61.** $6 + 2x$ **63.** $24z$
65. $50 + r$ **67.** $600 + 20r$ **69.** $600r$ **71.** b   **73.** i
75. g   **77.** d   **79.** h
81.

Term	Coefficient
$2x$	2
$-y$	-1
$18xy$	18
5	5

83.

Term	Coefficient
$-x$	-1
$8y$	8
$-9x^2y$	-9
-3	-3

85. The variable factors are different.
87. The variables are the same and raised to the same power.   **89.** For example: $5y, -2x, 6$ **91.** $2p - 12$
93. $-6y^2 - 7y$ **95.** $7x^3y + xy - 4$ **97.** $3t - \dfrac{7}{5}$
99. $-6x + 22$ **101.** $4w$ **103.** $-3x + 17$
105. $10t - 44w$ **107.** $-18u$ **109.** $-2t + 7$
111. $51a - 27$ **113.** -6 **115.** $4q - \dfrac{1}{3}$

117. $6n$ **119.** $2x + 18$ **121.** $2.2c - 0.32$
123. $-2x - 34$ **125.** $9z - 35$ **127.** Equivalent
129. Not equivalent. The terms are not *like* terms and cannot be combined.   **131.** Not equivalent; subtraction is not commutative.   **133.** Equivalent   **135.** $14\frac{2}{7} + (2\frac{1}{3} + \frac{2}{3})$ is easier.   **137. a.** 55 **b.** 210

Chapter 1 Review Exercises, pp. 115–117

1. a. $7, 1$ **b.** $7, -4, 0, 1$ **c.** $7, 0, 1$ **d.** $7, \frac{1}{3}, -4, 0, -0.\overline{2}, 1$
e. $-\sqrt{3}, \pi$ **f.** $7, \frac{1}{3}, -4, 0, -\sqrt{3}, -0.\overline{2}, \pi, 1$ **2.** $\dfrac{1}{2}$
3. 6 **4.** $\sqrt{7}$ **5.** 0 **6.** False   **7.** False
8. True   **9.** True   **10.** True   **11.** True
12. False   **13.** True   **14.** 0 **15.** 60 **16.** 3
17. 4 **18.** $x \cdot \dfrac{2}{3}$ or $\dfrac{2}{3}x$ **19.** $\dfrac{7}{y}$ or $7 \div y$ **20.** $2 + 3b$
21. $a - 5$ **22.** $5k + 2$ **23.** $13z - 7$ **24.** 216
25. 225 **26.** 6 **27.** $\dfrac{1}{10}$ **28.** $\dfrac{1}{16}$ **29.** $\dfrac{27}{8}$
30. 13 **31.** 11 **32.** 7 **33.** 10 **34.** 2 **35.** 4
36. 15 **37.** -17 **38.** $\dfrac{11}{63}$ **39.** $-\dfrac{5}{22}$ **40.** $-\dfrac{14}{15}$
41. $-\dfrac{27}{10}$ **42.** -2.15 **43.** -4.28 **44.** 3 **45.** 8
46. 4 **47.** When a and b are both negative or when a and b have different signs and the number with the larger absolute value is negative.
48. $-1.9°C$ **49.** -12
50. 33 **51.** -1 **52.** -17 **53.** $-\dfrac{29}{18}$ **54.** $-\dfrac{19}{24}$
55. -1.2 **56.** -4.25 **57.** -10.2 **58.** 12.09
59. $\dfrac{10}{3}$ **60.** $-\dfrac{17}{20}$ **61.** -1 **62.** If $a < b$
63. $-7 - (-18); 11$ **64.** $-6 - 41; -47$
65. $7 - 13; -6$ **66.** $(20 - (-7)) - 5; 22$
67. $(6 + (-12)) - 21; -27$ **68.** $175°F$
69. -170 **70.** -91 **71.** -2 **72.** 3
73. $-\dfrac{1}{6}$ **74.** $-\dfrac{8}{11}$ **75.** 0 **76.** Undefined
77. 0 **78.** 2.25 **79.** $-\dfrac{3}{2}$ **80.** $\dfrac{1}{4}$ **81.** -30
82. 450 **83.** $\dfrac{1}{4}$ **84.** $-\dfrac{1}{7}$ **85.** -2 **86.** $\dfrac{18}{7}$
87. 17 **88.** 6 **89.** $-\dfrac{7}{120}$ **90.** 4.4 **91.** $-\dfrac{1}{3}$
92. -1 **93.** -2 **94.** 11 **95.** 36 **96.** -6
97. 70.6 **98.** True   **99.** False, any nonzero real number raised to an even power is positive.   **100.** True
101. True   **102.** False, the product of two negative numbers is positive.   **103.** True   **104.** True
105. For example: $2 + 3 = 3 + 2$ **106.** For example: $(2 + 3) + 4 = 2 + (3 + 4)$ **107.** For example: $5 + (-5) = 0$ **108.** For example: $7 + 0 = 7$
109. For example: $5 \cdot 2 = 2 \cdot 5$ **110.** For example: $(8 \cdot 2)10 = 8(2 \cdot 10)$ **111.** For example: $3 \cdot \dfrac{1}{3} = 1$
112. For example: $8 \cdot 1 = 8$ **113.** $5x - 2y = 5x + (-2y)$, then use the commutative property of addition.
114. $3a - 9y = 3a + (-9y)$, then use the commutative property of addition.   **115.** $3y, 10x, -12, xy$

116. $3, 10, -12, 1$ **117.** $8a - b - 10$
118. $-7p - 11q + 16$ **119.** $-8z - 18$
120. $20w - 40y + 5$ **121.** $p - 2w$ **122.** $-h + 14m$
123. $-14q - 1$ **124.** $-5.7b + 2.4$ **125.** $4x + 24$
126. $50y + 105$

Chapter 1 Test, pp. 117–118

1. Rational, all repeating decimals are rational numbers.
2.

3. a. False   **b.** True   **c.** True   **d.** True
4. a. $(4x)(4x)(4x)$ **b.** $4 \cdot x \cdot x \cdot x$
5. a. Twice the difference of a and b
b. b subtracted from twice a
6. $\dfrac{\sqrt{c}}{d^2}$ or $\sqrt{c} \div d^2$ **7.** 6 **8.** -19 **9.** -12
10. 28 **11.** $-\dfrac{7}{8}$ **12.** 4.66 **13.** -32 **14.** -12
15. Undefined   **16.** -28 **17.** 0 **18.** 96 **19.** $\dfrac{2}{3}$
20. -8 **21.** 9 **22.** $\dfrac{1}{3}$ **23.** $-\dfrac{3}{5}$
24. Vienna owed \$157.   **25.** Hector's profit was \$6250 more in February.
26. a. Commutative property of multiplication
b. Identity property of addition   **c.** Associative property of addition   **d.** Inverse property of multiplication
e. Associative property of multiplication
27. $-12x + 2y - 4$ **28.** $-12m - 24p + 21$
29. $-6k - 8$ **30.** $-4p - 23$ **31.** $4p - \dfrac{4}{3}$
32. 5 **33.** 18 **34.** -6 **35.** -32
36. $12 - (-4); 16$ **37.** $6 - 8; -2$ **38.** $\dfrac{10}{-12}; -\dfrac{5}{6}$

Chapter 2

Chapter Opener Puzzle

Section 2.1 Practice Exercises, pp. 129–131

1. a. equation   **b.** solution   **c.** linear
3. Expression   **5.** Equation   **7.** Substitute the value into the equation and determine if the right-hand side is equal to the left-hand side.   **9.** No   **11.** Yes

13. Yes   **15.** -1 **17.** 20 **19.** -17 **21.** -16
23. 0 **25.** 1.3 **27.** $\dfrac{11}{2}$ **29.** -2 **31.** -2.13
33. -3.2675 **35.** 9 **37.** -4 **39.** 0 **41.** -15
43. $-\dfrac{4}{5}$ **45.** -10 **47.** 4 **49.** 41 **51.** -127
53. -2.6 **55.** $-8 + x = 42$; The number is 50.
57. $x - (-6) = 18$; The number is 12.
59. $x \cdot 7 = -63$ or $7x = -63$; The number is -9.
61. $\dfrac{x}{12} = \dfrac{1}{3}$; The number is 4.
63. $x + \dfrac{5}{8} = \dfrac{13}{8}$; The number is 1.   **65. a.** 10 **b.** $-\dfrac{1}{9}$
67. a. -12 **b.** $\dfrac{22}{3}$ **69.** -36 **71.** 16 **73.** 2
75. $-\dfrac{7}{4}$ **77.** 11 **79.** -36 **81.** $\dfrac{7}{2}$ **83.** 4
85. 3.6 **87.** 0.4084 **89.** Yes   **91.** No   **93.** Yes
95. Yes   **97.** For example: $y + 9 = 15$ **99.** For example: $2p = -8$ **101.** For example: $5a + 5 = 5$
103. -1 **105.** 7

Section 2.2 Practice Exercises, pp. 137–139

1. a. conditional   **b.** contradiction   **c.** identity
3. $4w + 8$ **5.** $6y - 22$ **7.** 19 **9.** -3
11. -5 **13.** 2 **15.** 6 **17.** $\dfrac{5}{2}$ **19.** -42
21. $-\dfrac{3}{4}$ **23.** 5 **25.** -4 **27.** -26 **29.** 10
31. -8 **33.** $-\dfrac{7}{3}$ **35.** 0 **37.** -3 **39.** -2
41. $\dfrac{9}{2}$ **43.** $-\dfrac{1}{3}$ **45.** 10 **47.** -6 **49.** 0
51. -2 **53.** $-\dfrac{25}{4}$ **55.** $\dfrac{10}{3}$ **57.** -0.25
59. Contradiction; no solution   **61.** Conditional equation; -15 **63.** Identity; all real numbers
65. One solution   **67.** Infinitely many solutions
69. 7 **71.** $\dfrac{1}{2}$ **73.** 0 **75.** All real numbers
77. -46 **79.** 2 **81.** $\dfrac{13}{2}$ **83.** -5
85. No solution   **87.** 2.205 **89.** 10 **91.** -1
93. $a = 15$ **95.** $a = 4$
97. For example: $5x + 2 = 2 + 5x$

Section 2.3 Practice Exercises, pp. 144–146

1. a. clearing fractions   **b.** clearing decimals
3. -2 **5.** -5 **7.** No solution   **9.** $18, 36$
11. $100; 1000; 10,000$ **13.** $30, 60$ **15.** 4 **17.** $-\dfrac{19}{2}$
19. $-\dfrac{15}{4}$ **21.** 8 **23.** 3 **25.** 15
27. No solution   **29.** All real numbers   **31.** 5
33. 2 **35.** -15 **37.** 6 **39.** 107
41. All real numbers   **43.** 67 **45.** 90 **47.** 4
49. 4 **51.** No solution   **53.** -0.25 **55.** -6

57. $\dfrac{8}{3}$ **59.** -11 **61.** $\dfrac{1}{10}$ **63.** -2

65. -1 **67.** 2

Chapter 2 Problem Recognition Exercises, p. 146

1. Expression; $-4b + 18$ **2.** Expression; $20p - 30$

3. Equation; -8 **4.** Equation; -14 **5.** Equation; $\dfrac{1}{3}$

6. Equation; $-\dfrac{4}{3}$ **7.** Expression; $6z - 23$

8. Expression; $-x - 9$ **9.** Equation; $\dfrac{7}{9}$

10. Equation; $-\dfrac{13}{10}$ **11.** Equation; 20

12. Equation; -3 **13.** Equation; $\dfrac{1}{2}$ **14.** Equation; -6

15. Expression; $\dfrac{5}{8}x + \dfrac{7}{4}$ **16.** Expression; $-26t + 18$

17. Equation; no solution   **18.** Equation; no solution

19. Equation; $\dfrac{23}{12}$ **20.** Equation; $\dfrac{5}{8}$

21. Equation; all real numbers
22. Equation; all real numbers

23. Equation; $\dfrac{1}{2}$ **24.** Equation; 0   **25.** Expression; 0

26. Expression; -1 **27.** Expression; $2a + 13$
28. Expression; $8q + 3$ **29.** Equation; 10

30. Equation; $-\dfrac{1}{20}$ **31.** Expression; $-\dfrac{1}{6}y + \dfrac{1}{3}$

32. Expression; $\dfrac{7}{10}x + \dfrac{2}{5}$

Section 2.4 Practice Exercises, pp. 153–157

1. a. consecutive   **b.** even   **c.** odd   **d.** 1   **e.** 2   **f.** 2
3. $x - 5{,}682{,}080$ **5.** $10x$ **7.** $3x - 20$
9. The number is -4.   **11.** The number is -3.
13. The number is 5.   **15.** The number is -5.
17. The number is 3.   **19. a.** $x + 1, x + 2$ **b.** $x - 1, x - 2$
21. The integers are -34 and -33.   **23.** The integers are
13 and 15.   **25.** The sides are 14 in., 15 in., 16 in., 17 in.,
and 18 in.   **27.** The integers are $-54, -52,$ and -50.
29. The integers are 13, 15, and 17.   **31.** The lengths of
the pieces are 33 cm and 53 cm.   **33.** Karen's iPod has
23 playlists and Clarann's iPod has 35 playlists.   **35.** There
were 201 Republicans and 232 Democrats.   **37.** *CSI* had
13.17 million viewers and *Criminal Minds* had 14.23 million
viewers.   **39.** The Congo River is 4370 km long, and the Nile
River is 6825 km.   **41.** The area of Africa is 30,065,000 km^2.
The area of Asia is 44,579,000 km^2.   **43.** They walked 12.3
mi on the first day and 8.2 mi on the second.   **45.** The pieces
are 9 in., 17 in., and 22 in.   **47.** The integers are 42, 43, and 44.
49. Carrie Underwood earned $14 million and Jennifer
Hudson earned $5 million.   **51.** The number is 11.
53. The page numbers are 470 and 471.   **55.** The number
is 10.   **57.** The deepest point in the Arctic Ocean is 5122 m.

59. The number is $\dfrac{7}{16}$.   **61.** The number is 2.5.

Section 2.5 Practice Exercises, pp. 161–163

1. a. simple   **b.** 100   **3.** The numbers are 21 and 22.
5. 12.5%   **7.** 85%   **9.** 0.75   **11.** 1050.8   **13.** 885
15. 2200   **17.** Molly will have to pay $106.99.
19. Approximately 231,000 cases   **21.** 2%
23. Javon's taxable income was $84,000.   **25.** Pam will
earn $420.   **27.** Bob borrowed $1200.   **29.** The rate is 6%.
31. Penny needs to invest $3302.   **33. a.** $20.40
b. $149.60   **35.** The original price was $470.59.
37. The discount rate is 12%.   **39.** The original dosage
was 15 cc.   **41.** The tax rate is 5%.   **43.** The ticket price
was $67.   **45.** The original price was $210,000.
47. Alina made $4600 that month.   **49.** Diane sold $645
over $200 worth of merchandise.

Section 2.6 Calculator Connections, p. 169

1. 140.056   **2.** 31.831   **3.** 1.273   **4.** 0.455

1–2.   3–4.

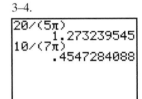

Section 2.6 Practice Exercises, pp. 169–173

1. -5 **3.** 0   **5.** -2 **7.** No solution   **9.** $a = P - b - c$

11. $y = x + z$ **13.** $q = p - 250$ **15.** $b = \dfrac{A}{h}$

17. $t = \dfrac{PV}{nr}$ **19.** $x = 5 + y$ **21.** $y = -3x - 19$

23. $y = \dfrac{-2x + 6}{3}$ or $y = -\dfrac{2}{3}x + 2$

25. $x = \dfrac{y + 9}{-2}$ or $x = -\dfrac{1}{2}y - \dfrac{9}{2}$

27. $y = \dfrac{-4x + 12}{-3}$ or $y = \dfrac{4}{3}x - 4$

29. $y = \dfrac{-ax + c}{b}$ or $y = -\dfrac{a}{b}x + \dfrac{c}{b}$

31. $t = \dfrac{A - P}{Pr}$ or $t = \dfrac{A}{Pr} - \dfrac{1}{r}$

33. $c = \dfrac{a - 2b}{2}$ or $c = \dfrac{a}{2} - b$ **35.** $y = 2Q - x$

37. $a = MS$ **39.** $R = \dfrac{P}{I^2}$

41. The length is 7 ft, and the width is 5 ft.
43. The length is 120 yd and the width is 30 yd.
45. The length is 195 m, and the width is 100 m.
47. The sides are 22 m, 22 m, and 27 m.
49. "Adjacent supplementary angles form a straight angle."
The words *Supplementary* and *Straight* both begin with the
same letter.   **51.** The measures of the angles are 55° and 35°.
53. The measures of the angles are 45° and 135°.
55. $x = 20$; the vertical angles measure 37°.
57. The measures of the angles are 30°, 60°, and 90°.
59. The measures of the angles are 42°, 54°, and 84°.
61. $x = 17$; the measures of the angles are 34° and 56°.

63. a. $A = lw$ **b.** $w = \dfrac{A}{l}$ **c.** The width is 29.5 ft.

65. a. $P = 2l + 2w$ **b.** $l = \dfrac{P - 2w}{2}$ **c.** The length is 103 m.

67. a. $C = 2\pi r$ **b.** $r = \dfrac{C}{2\pi}$ **c.** The radius is approximately 140 ft. **69. a.** 415.48 m² **b.** 10,386.89 m³

Section 2.7 Practice Exercises, pp. 178–182

1. $x = \dfrac{c + by}{a}$ **3.** $y = \dfrac{18 - 7x}{x}$ **5.** 4 **7.** $200 - t$

9. $100 - x$ **11.** $3000 - y$ **13.** 53 tickets were sold at $3 and 28 tickets were sold at $2. **15.** Josh downloaded 17 songs for $0.90 and 8 songs for $1.50. **17.** Angelina purchased 25 bottles of soda and 20 bottles of flavored water.

19. $x + 7$ **21.** $d + 2000$
23. Mix 500 gal of 5% ethanol fuel mixture.
25. The pharmacist needs to use 21 mL of the 1% saline solution. **27.** The contractor needs to mix 6.75 oz of 50% acid solution. **29. a.** 300 mi **b.** $5x$ **c.** $5(x + 12)$ or $5x + 60$
31. She walks 4 mph to the lake. **33.** Bryan hiked 6 mi up the canyon. **35.** The plane travels 600 mph in still air.
37. The slower car travels 48 mph and the faster car travels 52 mph. **39.** The speeds of the vehicles are 40 mph and 50 mph. **41.** Sarah walks 3.5 mph and Jeanette runs 7 mph.
43. a. 2 lb **b.** $0.10x$ **c.** $0.10(x + 3) = 0.10x + 0.30$
45. 10 lb of coffee sold at $12 per pound and 40 lb of coffee sold at $8 per pound. **47.** The boats will meet in $\frac{3}{4}$ hr (45 min).
49. Sam purchased 16 packages of wax and 5 bottles of sunscreen. **51.** 2.5 quarts of 85% chlorine solution
53. 20 L of water **55.** The Japanese bullet train travels 300 km/hr and the Acela Express travels 240 km/hr.

Section 2.8 Practice Exercises, pp. 192–197

1. a. linear inequality **b.** inequality
c. set-builder; interval **3.** -3

5. **7.**

9. **11.**

13. **15.**

Set-Builder Notation	Graph	Interval Notation
17. $\{x \mid x \geq 6\}$		$[6, \infty)$
19. $\{x \mid x \leq 2.1\}$		$(-\infty, 2.1]$
21. $\{x \mid -2 < x \leq 7\}$		$(-2, 7]$

Set-Builder Notation	Graph	Interval Notation
23. $\left\{x \mid x > \dfrac{3}{4}\right\}$		$\left(\dfrac{3}{4}, \infty\right)$
25. $\{x \mid -1 < x < 8\}$		$(-1, 8)$
27. $\{x \mid x \leq -14\}$		$(-\infty, -14]$

Set-Builder Notation	Graph	Interval Notation
29. $\{x \mid x \geq 18\}$		$[18, \infty)$
31. $\{x \mid x < -0.6\}$		$(-\infty, -0.6)$
33. $\{x \mid -3.5 \leq x < 7.1\}$		$[-3.5, 7.1)$

35. a. 3
b. $\{x \mid x > 3\}; (3, \infty)$

37. a. 13
b. $\{p \mid p \leq 13\}; (-\infty, 13]$

39. a. -3
b. $\{c \mid c < -3\}; (-\infty, -3)$

41. a. $-\dfrac{3}{2}$
b. $\left\{z \mid z \geq -\dfrac{3}{2}\right\}; \left[-\dfrac{3}{2}, \infty\right)$

43. $(-1, 4]$

45. $(-3, 5)$

47. $[2, 6]$

49. a. $\{x \mid x \leq 1\}$ **b.** $(-\infty, 1]$

51. a. $\{q \mid q > 10\}$
b. $(10, \infty)$

53. a. $\{x \mid x > 3\}$
b. $(3, \infty)$

55. a. $\{c \mid c > 2\}$
b. $(2, \infty)$

57. a. $\{c \mid c < -2\}$
b. $(-\infty, -2)$

59. a. $\{h \mid h \geq 14\}$
b. $[14, \infty)$

61. a. $\{x \mid x \geq -24\}$
b. $[-24, \infty)$

63. a. $\{p \mid -3 \leq p < 3\}$
b. $[-3, 3)$

65. a. $\left\{h \mid 0 < h < \dfrac{5}{2}\right\}$
b. $\left(0, \dfrac{5}{2}\right)$

67. a. $\{x \mid 10 < x < 12\}$
b. $(10, 12)$

69. a. $\{x \mid -8 \leq x < 24\}$
b. $[-8, 24)$

71. a. $\{y \mid y > -9\}$
b. $(-9, \infty)$

73. a. $\left\{x \mid x \geq -\dfrac{15}{2}\right\}$
b. $\left[-\dfrac{15}{2}, \infty\right)$

75. a. $\{x \mid x < -3\}$
b. $(-\infty, -3)$

77. a. $\left\{b \mid b \geq -\dfrac{1}{3}\right\}$
b. $\left[-\dfrac{1}{3}, \infty\right)$

79. a. $\{n|n > -3\}$
b. $(-3, \infty)$

81. a. $\{x|x < 7\}$
b. $(-\infty, 7)$

83. a. $\{x|x \le -5\}$
b. $(-\infty, -5]$

85. a. $\{z|z \le -2\}$
b. $(-\infty, -2]$

87. a. $\left\{a|a > -\dfrac{2}{3}\right\}$
b. $\left(-\dfrac{2}{3}, \infty\right)$

89. a. $\left\{p|p \le \dfrac{15}{4}\right\}$
b. $\left(-\infty, \dfrac{15}{4}\right]$

91. a. $\{y|y < -9\}$
b. $(-\infty, -9)$

93. a. $\{a|a > -3\}$
b. $(-3, \infty)$

95. a. $\{x|x \le 0\}$ **b.** $(-\infty, 0]$

97. No   **99.** Yes   **101.** $L \ge 10$ **103.** $w > 75$
105. $t \le 72$ **107.** $L \ge 8$ **109.** $2 < h < 5$
111. More than 10.2 in. of rain is needed.   **113.** Trevor needs at least 86 to get a B in the course.   **115. a.** $1539 **b.** 200 birdhouses cost $1440. It is cheaper to purchase 200 birdhouses because the discount is greater.   **117.** If there were more than 145 text messages, the unlimited option would be a better deal.   **119.** Madison needs to babysit a minimum of 39.5 hr.

Chapter 2 Review Exercises, pp. 204–207

1. a. Equation **b.** Expression **c.** Equation
d. Equation   **2.** A linear equation can be written in the
form $ax + b = c, a \ne 0$.   **3. a.** No **b.** Yes **c.** No
d. Yes   **4. a.** No **b.** No **c.** Yes **d.** No   **5.** -8
6. 15   **7.** $\dfrac{21}{4}$ **8.** 70   **9.** $-\dfrac{21}{5}$ **10.** -60
11. $-\dfrac{10}{7}$ **12.** 27   **13.** The number is 60.
14. The number is $\dfrac{7}{24}$.   **15.** The number is -8.
16. The number is -2.   **17.** 1   **18.** $-\dfrac{3}{5}$ **19.** $\dfrac{9}{4}$
20. -6 **21.** -3 **22.** 18   **23.** $\dfrac{3}{4}$ **24.** -3
25. 0   **26.** $\dfrac{1}{8}$ **27.** 2   **28.** 6   **29.** A contradiction
has no solution and an identity is true for all real numbers.
30. Identity   **31.** Conditional equation
32. Contradiction   **33.** Identity   **34.** Contradiction
35. Conditional equation   **36.** 6   **37.** 22   **38.** 13
39. -27 **40.** -10 **41.** -7 **42.** $\dfrac{5}{3}$ **43.** $-\dfrac{9}{4}$
44. 2.5   **45.** -4 **46.** -4.2 **47.** 2.5
48. -312 **49.** 200   **50.** No solution
51. No solution   **52.** All real numbers
53. All real numbers   **54.** The number is 30.
55. The number is 11.   **56.** The number is -7.
57. The number is -10.   **58.** The integers are 66, 68, and 70.   **59.** The integers are 27, 28, and 29.

60. The sides are 25 in., 26 in., and 27 in.
61. The sides are 36 cm, 37 cm, 38 cm, 39 cm, and 40 cm.
62. In 1975 the minimum salary was $16,000.
63. Indiana has 6.2 million people and Kentucky has
4.1 million.   **64.** 23.8   **65.** 28.8   **66.** 12.5%
67. 95%   **68.** 160   **69.** 1750   **70.** The novel
originally cost $29.50.   **71.** The dinner was $40 before tax
and tip.   **72. a.** $840 **b.** $3840   **73.** $12,000
74. $K = C + 273$ **75.** $C = K - 273$
76. $s = \dfrac{P}{4}$ **77.** $s = \dfrac{P}{3}$ **78.** $x = \dfrac{y - b}{m}$
79. $x = \dfrac{c - a}{b}$ **80.** $y = \dfrac{-2x - 2}{5}$
81. $b = \dfrac{Q - 4a}{4}$ or $b = \dfrac{Q}{4} - a$ **82.** The height is 7 m.
83. a. $h = \dfrac{3V}{\pi r^2}$ **b.** The height is 5.1 in.
84. The measures of the angles are $22°, 78°$, and $80°$.
85. The measures of the angles are $50°$ and $40°$.
86. The length is 5 ft, and the width is 4 ft.   **87.** $x = 20$. The
measure of the angles is $65°$.   **88.** The measure of angle
y is $53°$.   **89.** The truck travels 45 km/hr in bad weather
and 60 km/hr in good weather.   **90.** Gus rides 15 mph and
Winston rides 18 mph.   **91.** The cars will be 327.6 mi apart
after 2.8 hr (2 hr and 48 min).   **92.** They meet in 2.25 hr
(2 hr and 15 min).   **93.** 2 lb of 24% fat content beef is
needed.   **94.** 20 lb of the 40% lead solder should be used.
95. $(-2, \infty)$

96. $\left(-\infty, \dfrac{1}{2}\right]$

97. $(-1, 4]$

98. a. $637 **b.** 300 plants cost $1410, and 295 plants cost
$1416. 295 plants cost more.
99. $\{c|c < 17\}; (-\infty, 17)$

100. $\left\{w|w > -\dfrac{1}{3}\right\}; \left(-\dfrac{1}{3}, \infty\right)$

101. $\{x|x \le -6\}; (-\infty, -6]$

102. $\left\{y|y \le -\dfrac{14}{5}\right\}; \left(-\infty, -\dfrac{14}{5}\right]$

103. $\{a|a \ge 49\}; [49, \infty)$

104. $\{t|t < 34.5\}; (-\infty, 34.5)$

105. $\{k|k > 18\}; (18, \infty)$

106. $\left\{h|h \le \dfrac{5}{2}\right\}; \left(-\infty, \dfrac{5}{2}\right]$

107. $\{x|x < -1\}; (-\infty, -1)$

108. $\{b|-3 < b \le 7\}; (-3, 7]$

109. $\{z|-6 \le z \le 5\}; [-6, 5]$

110. More than 2.5 in. is required.
111. Collette can have at most 18 wings.

Chapter 2 Test, pp. 207–208

1. a. b, d   **2. a.** $5x + 7$ **b.** 9   **3.** $\dfrac{7}{3}$ **4.** No solution

5. -16 **6.** $\dfrac{13}{4}$ **7.** 12   **8.** $\dfrac{20}{21}$ **9.** $-\dfrac{16}{9}$ **10.** 15

11. All real numbers   **12.** -3 **13.** -47

14. $y = -3x - 4$ **15.** $r = \dfrac{C}{2\pi}$ **16.** 90

17. a. $(-\infty, 0)$ **b.** $[-2, 5)$

18. $\{x \mid x > -2\}; \ (-2, \infty)$ **19.** $\{x \mid x \le -4\}; \ (-\infty, -4]$

20. $\left\{ y \mid y > -\dfrac{3}{2} \right\}; \left(-\dfrac{3}{2}, \infty \right)$

21. $\{p \mid -5 \le p \le 1\}; \ [-5, 1]$

22. The cost was \$82.00.   **23.** Clarita originally borrowed \$5000.   **24.** The numbers are 18 and 13.   **25.** One family travels 55 mph and the other travels 50 mph. **26.** More than 26.5 in. is required.   **27.** The sides are 61 in., 62 in., 63 in., 64 in., and 65 in.   **28.** Paula needs 30 lb of macadamia nuts.   **29.** Each basketball ticket was \$36.32, and each hockey ticket was \$40.64.   **30.** The measures of the angles are 32° and 58°.   **31.** The field is 110 m long and 75 m wide.   **32.** $y = 30$; The measures of the angles are 30°, 39°, and 111°.

Chapters 1–2 Cumulative Review Exercises, pp. 208–209

1. $\dfrac{1}{2}$ **2.** -7 **3.** $-\dfrac{5}{12}$ **4.** 16   **5.** 4

6. $\sqrt{5^2 - 9}; 4$ **7.** $-14 + 12; -2$ **8.** $-7x^2y, \ 4xy, \ -6$
9. $9x + 13$ **10.** 4   **11.** -7.2

12. All real numbers   **13.** -8 **14.** $-\dfrac{4}{7}$ **15.** -80

16. The numbers are 77 and 79.   **17.** The cost before tax was \$350.00.   **18.** The height is $\frac{41}{6}$ cm or $6\frac{5}{6}$ cm.
19. $\{x \mid x > -2\}; (-2, \infty)$ **20.** $\{x \mid -1 \le x \le 9\}; [-1, 9]$

Chapter 3

Chapter Opener Puzzle

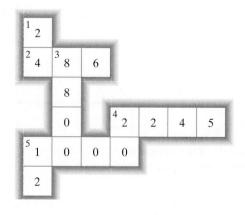

Section 3.1 Practice Exercises, pp. 216–221

1. a. x; y-axis   **b.** ordered   **c.** origin; $(0, 0)$ **d.** quadrants   **e.** negative   **f.** III

3. a. Month 10   **b.** 30   **c.** Between months 3 and 5 and between months 10 and 12   **d.** Months 8 and 9 **e.** Month 3   **f.** 80

5. a. On day 1 the price per share was \$89.25.
b. \$1.75   **c.** $-\$2.75$

7. 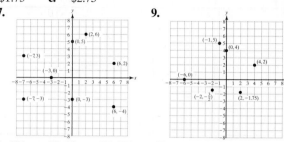   **9.**

11. IV   **13.** II   **15.** III   **17.** I
19. $(0, -5)$ lies on the y-axis.
21. $\left(\frac{7}{8}, 0 \right)$ is located on the x-axis.
23. $A(-4, 2), B(\frac{1}{2}, 4), C(3, -4), D(-3, -4), E(0, -3), F(5, 0)$
25. a. $A(400, 200), B(200, -150), C(-300, -200),$
$D(-300, 250), E(0, 450)$ **b.** 450 m
27. a. $(250, 225), (175, 193), (315, 330), (220, 209),$
$(450, 570), (400, 480), (190, 185)$; the ordered pair $(250, 225)$ means that 250 people produce \$225 in popcorn sales.
b.

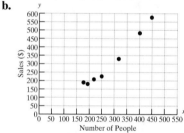

29. a. $(1, -10.2), (2, -9.0), (3, -2.5), (4, 5.7), (5, 13.0), (6, 18.3),$
$(7, 20.9), (8, 19.6), (9, 14.8), (10, 8.7), (11, 2.0), (12, -6.9)$.
b.

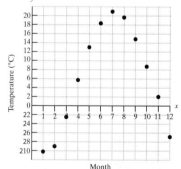

31. a.

Percent of Males/Females with 4 or
More Years of College, United States

Year ($x = 0$ corresponds to 1960)

b. Increasing   **c.** Increasing

Section 3.2 Calculator Connections, pp. 229–230

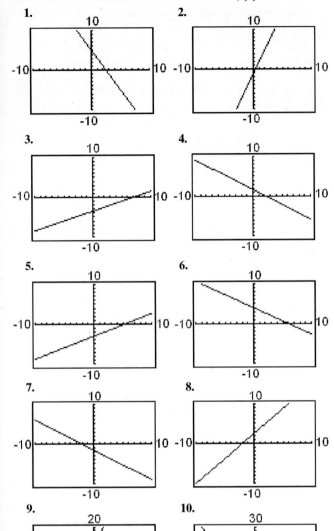

1. **2.** **3.** **4.** **5.** **6.** **7.** **8.** **9.** **10.** **11.** **12.**

19.

x	y
1	−3
−2	0
−3	1
−4	2

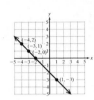

21.

x	y
−2	3
−1	0
−4	9

23.

x	y
0	4
2	0
3	−2

25.

x	y
0	−2
5	−5
10	−8

27.

x	y
0	−2
−3	−2
5	−2

29.

x	y
$\frac{3}{2}$	−1
$\frac{3}{2}$	2
$\frac{3}{2}$	−3

31.

x	y
0	4.6
1	3.4
2	2.2

33. **35.** **37.**

 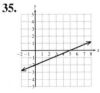 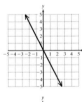

39. **41.** **43.**

Section 3.2 Practice Exercises, pp. 230–236

1. a. $Ax + By = C$ **b.** *x*-intercept   **c.** *y*-intercept
d. vertical   **e.** horizontal   **3.** (−2, −2); Quadrant III
5. (−5, 0); *x*-axis   **7.** (−3, 2); Quadrant II   **9.** Yes
11. Yes   **13.** No   **15.** No   **17.** Yes

45. *y*-axis   **47.** *x*-intercept: (−1, 0); *y*-intercept: (0, −3)
49. *x*-intercept: (−4, 0); *y*-intercept: (0, 1)

51. x-intercept: $\left(-\frac{9}{4}, 0\right)$; y-intercept: $(0, 3)$

53. x-intercept: $\left(\frac{8}{3}, 0\right)$; y-intercept: $(0, 2)$

3. x-intercept: $(6, 0)$; y-intercept: $(0, -2)$

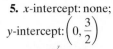

5. x-intercept: none; y-intercept: $\left(0, \frac{3}{2}\right)$

55. x-intercept: $(-4, 0)$; y-intercept: $(0, 8)$

57. x-intercept: $(0, 0)$; y-intercept: $(0, 0)$

7. $m = \frac{1}{3}$ **9.** $m = \frac{6}{11}$ **11.** undefined

13. positive   **15.** Negative   **17.** Zero
19. Undefined   **21.** Positive   **23.** Negative

25. $m = \frac{1}{2}$ **27.** $m = -3$ **29.** $m = 0$

31. The slope is undefined.   **33.** $\frac{1}{3}$ **35.** -3

59. x-intercept: $(10, 0)$; y-intercept: $(0, 5)$

61. x-intercept: $(0, 0)$; y-intercept: $(0, 0)$

37. $\frac{3}{5}$ **39.** Zero   **41.** Undefined   **43.** $\frac{28}{5}$ **45.** $-\frac{9}{2}$

47. $-\frac{7}{8}$ **49.** 3   **51.** -0.45 or $-\frac{9}{20}$

53. -0.15 or $-\frac{3}{20}$ **55. a.** -2 **b.** $\frac{1}{2}$

57. a. 0   **b.** Undefined   **59. a.** $\frac{4}{5}$ **b.** $-\frac{5}{4}$

63. True
67. a. Horizontal
c. no x-intercept;
y-intercept: $(0, -1)$

65. True
69. a. Vertical
c. x-intercept: $(4, 0)$;
no y-intercept

61. Perpendicular   **63.** Parallel   **65.** Neither
67. l_1: $m = 2$, l_2: $m = 2$; parallel

69. l_1: $m = 5$, l_2: $m = -\frac{1}{5}$; perpendicular

71. l_1: $m = \frac{1}{4}$, l_2: $m = 4$; neither   **73.** The average rate of change is $-\$160$ per year.

71. a. Horizontal
c. no x-intercept;
y-intercept $(0, -5)$

73. a. Vertical
c. All points on the y-axis are y-intercepts; x-intercept: $(0, 0)$

75. a. $m = 47$ **b.** The number of male prisoners increased at a rate of 47 thousand per year during this time period.
77. a. 1 mi   **b.** 2 mi   **c.** 3 mi   **d.** $m = 0.2$; The distance between a lightning strike and an observer increases by 0.2 mi for every additional second between seeing lightning and hearing thunder.

79. $m = \frac{3}{4}$ **81.** $m = 0$
83. For example: $(4, -4)$ and $(-2, 0)$

85. For example: $(3, 5)$ and $(1, -1)$

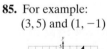
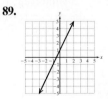

75. A horizontal line may not have an x-intercept. A vertical line may not have a y-intercept.   **77.** a, b, d
79. a. $y = 10{,}068$ **b.** $x = 3$ **c.** $(1, 10068)$ One year after purchase the value of the car is $\$10{,}068$. $(3, 7006)$ Three years after purchase the value of the car is $\$7006$.

Section 3.3 Practice Exercises, pp. 243–249

1. a. slope; $\frac{y_2 - y_1}{x_2 - x_1}$ **b.** parallel   **c.** right   **d.** -1
e. undefined; horizontal

87. For example: $(-3, 1)$ and $(-3, 4)$

89.

91.   **93.**

95. $\dfrac{3m - 3n}{2b}$ or $\dfrac{-3m + 3n}{-2b}$ **97.** $\left(\dfrac{c}{a}, 0\right)$

99. For example: $(7, 1)$

Section 3.4 Calculator Connections, pp. 254–255

1. Perpendicular
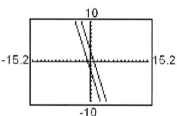

2. Parallel
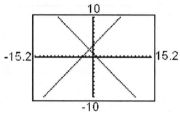

3. Neither
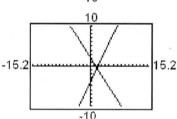

4. The lines may appear parallel; however, they are not parallel because the slopes are different.

5. The lines may appear to coincide on a graph; however, they are not the same line because the y-intercepts are different.

6. The line may appear to be horizontal, but it is not. The slope is 0.001 rather than 0.

Section 3.4 Practice Exercises, pp. 255–259

1. a. $y = mx + b$ **b.** standard

3. x-intercept: $(10, 0)$; y-intercept: $(0, -2)$

5. x-intercept: none; y-intercept: $(0, -3)$

7. x-intercept: $(0, 0)$; y-intercept: $(0, 0)$

9. x-intercept: $(4, 0)$; y-intercept: none

11. $m = -2$; y-intercept: $(0, 3)$ **13.** $m = 1$; y-intercept: $(0, -2)$ **15.** $m = -1$; y-intercept: $(0, 0)$

17. $m = \dfrac{3}{4}$; y-intercept: $(0, -1)$ **19.** $m = \dfrac{2}{5}$; y-intercept: $\left(0, -\dfrac{4}{5}\right)$ **21.** $m = 3$; y-intercept: $(0, -5)$

23. $m = -1$; y-intercept: $(0, 6)$ **25.** Undefined slope; no y-intercept   **27.** $m = 0$; y-intercept: $\left(0, -\dfrac{1}{4}\right)$

29. $m = \dfrac{2}{3}$; y-intercept: $(0, 0)$

31. $m = -3$; y-intercept: $(0, -4)$

33. $m = \dfrac{11}{4}$; y-intercept: $\left(0, -\dfrac{3}{4}\right)$

35.   **37.**

39. b   **41.** e   **43.** c

45. $y = -2x + 9$ **47.** $y = \dfrac{1}{2}x - 3$

49. $y = -\dfrac{1}{2}x + \dfrac{3}{2}$ **51.** $y = -x$

53. $y = \dfrac{4}{5}x$ **55.** $y = -\dfrac{2}{3}$

57. Perpendicular   **59.** Neither   **61.** Parallel

63. Perpendicular   **65.** Parallel   **67.** Perpendicular

69. Neither   **71.** Parallel   **73.** $y = -\dfrac{1}{3}x + 2$

75. $y = 10x - 19$ **77.** $y = 6x - 8$ **79.** $y = \dfrac{1}{2}x - 3$

81. $y = -11$ **83.** $y = 5x$ **85.** $y = -2x + 3$

87. $y = -\dfrac{1}{3}x + 2$ **89.** $y = 4x - 1$

91. a. $m = 1203$; The slope represents the rate of increase in the number of cases of Lyme disease per year.

b. $(0, 10006)$; In the year 1993 there were 10,006 cases reported.   **c.** 30,457 cases   **d.** $x = 22$; the year 2015

93. $y = -\dfrac{A}{B}x + \dfrac{C}{B}$; the slope is $-\dfrac{A}{B}$.   **95.** $m = -\dfrac{6}{7}$

97. $m = \dfrac{11}{8}$

Chapter 3 Problem Recognition Exercises, p. 260

1. a, c, d   **2.** b, f, h   **3.** a   **4.** f   **5.** b, f   **6.** c

7. c, d   **8.** f   **9.** e   **10.** g   **11.** b   **12.** h

13. g   **14.** e   **15.** c   **16.** b, h   **17.** e   **18.** e

19. b, f, h   **20.** c, d

Section 3.5 Practice Exercises, pp. 265–269

1. a. $Ax + By = C$ **b.** horizontal **c.** vertical
d. slope; y-intercept **e.** $y - y_1 = m(x - x_1)$

3.   **5.**

7. 9   **9.** 0   **11.** $y = 3x + 7$ or $3x - y = -7$
13. $y = -4x - 14$ or $4x + y = -14$
15. $y = -\dfrac{1}{2}x - \dfrac{1}{2}$ or $x + 2y = -1$
17. $y = 2x - 2$ or $2x - y = 2$
19. $y = -x - 4$ or $x + y = -4$
21. $y = -0.2x - 2.86$ or $20x + 100y = -286$
23. $y = -2x + 1$
25. $y = 2x + 4$ **27.** $y = \dfrac{1}{2}x - 1$ **29.** $y = 4x + 13$ or
$4x - y = -13$ **31.** $y = -\dfrac{3}{2}x + 6$ or $3x + 2y = 12$
33. $y = -2x - 8$ or $2x + y = -8$ **35.** $y = -\dfrac{1}{5}x - 6$
or $x + 5y = -30$ **37.** iv   **39.** vi   **41.** iii   **43.** $y = 1$
45. $x = 2$ **47.** $y = 2$ **49.** $y = \dfrac{1}{4}x + 8$ or $x - 4y = -32$
51. $y = 3x - 8$ or $3x - y = 8$ **53.** $y = 4.5x - 25.6$ or
$45x - 10y = 256$ **55.** $x = -6$ **57.** $y = -2$
59. $x = -4$ **61.** $y = 2x - 4$ **63.** $y = -\dfrac{1}{2}x + 1$

Section 3.6 Calculator Connections, p. 272

1. 13.3   **2.** −42.3

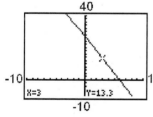   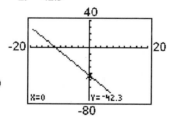

3. 345   **4.** 95

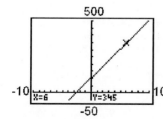   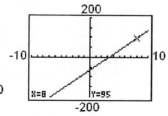

Section 3.6 Practice Exercises, pp. 273–276

1. $m = -\dfrac{5}{2}$ **3.** x-intercept: $(6, 0)$; y-intercept: $(0, 5)$
5. x-intercept: $(-2, 0)$; y-intercept: $(0, -4)$

7. x-intercept: none; y-intercept: $(0, -9)$ **9. a.** $3.00
b. $7.90   **c.** The y-intercept is $(0, 1.6)$. This indicates that the
minimum wage was $1.60 per hour in the year 1970.   **d.** The
slope is 0.14. This indicates that the minimum wage has risen
approximately $0.14 per year during this period.
11. a. $m = \dfrac{2}{7}$ **b.** $m = \dfrac{4}{7}$ **c.** $m = \dfrac{2}{7}$ means that Grindel's
weight increased at a rate of 2 oz in 7 days. $m = \dfrac{4}{7}$ means that
Frisco's weight increased at a rate of 4 oz in 7 days.
d. Frisco gained weight more rapidly.
13. a. $106.95   **b.** $201.95   **c.** $(0, 11.95)$. For 0 kilowatt-
hours used, the cost consists of only the fixed monthly tax of
$11.95.   **d.** $m = 0.095$. The cost increases by $0.095 for each
kilowatt-hour used.   **15. a.** $m = -1.0$
b. $y = -x + 1051$ **c.** The minimum pressure was
approximately 921 mb.   **17. a.** $m = 21.5$
b. The slope means that the consumption of wind energy in
the United States increased by 21.5 trillion Btu per year.
c. $y = 21.5x + 57$ **d.** 272 trillion Btu
19. a. $y = 0.20x + 39.99$ **b.** $47.99
21. a. $y = 90x + 105$ **b.** $1185.00
23. a. $y = 0.8x + 100$ **b.** $260.00

Chapter 3 Review Exercises, pp. 283–287

1.

2. $A(4, -3)$; $B(-3, -2)$; $C(\frac{5}{2}, 5)$; $D(-4, 1)$; $E(-\frac{1}{2}, 0)$; $F(0, -5)$
3. III   **4.** II   **5.** IV   **6.** I   **7.** IV
8. III   **9.** x-axis   **10.** y-axis
11. a. On day 1, the price was $26.25.   **b.** Day 2
c. $2.25   **12. a.** In 2003 (8 years after 1995), there was
only one space shuttle launch. (This was the year that the
Columbia and its crew were lost.)
b.

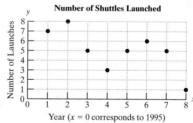

13. No   **14.** No   **15.** Yes   **16.** Yes
17.

x	y
2	1
3	4
1	−2

18.

x	y
0	2
−2	$\frac{7}{3}$
−6	3

19.

x	y
0	−1
3	1
−6	−5

20.

x	y
0	−3
−3	3
1	−5

21.   **22.**   **23.**

24.   **25.** Vertical   **26.** Vertical

27. Horizontal 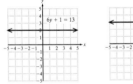 **28.** Horizontal

29. x-intercept: $(-3, 0)$; y-intercept: $\left(0, \dfrac{3}{2}\right)$

30. x-intercept: $(3, 0)$; y-intercept: $(0, 6)$ **31.** x-intercept: $(0, 0)$; y-intercept: $(0, 0)$ **32.** x-intercept: $(0, 0)$; y-intercept: $(0, 0)$ **33.** x-intercept: none; y-intercept: $(0, -4)$ **34.** x-intercept: none; y-intercept: $(0, 2)$

35. x-intercept: $\left(-\dfrac{5}{2}, 0\right)$; y-intercept: none

36. x-intercept: $\left(\dfrac{1}{3}, 0\right)$; y-intercept: none   **37.** $m = \dfrac{12}{5}$

38. -2 **39.** $-\dfrac{2}{3}$ **40.** 8 **41.** Undefined   **42.** 0

43. a. -5 **b.** $\dfrac{1}{5}$ **44. a.** 0 **b.** Undefined

45. $m_1 = \dfrac{2}{3}; m_2 = \dfrac{2}{3}$; parallel   **46.** $m_1 = 8; m_2 = 8$; parallel

47. $m_1 = -\dfrac{5}{12}; m_2 = \dfrac{12}{5}$; perpendicular

48. $m_1 = $ undefined; $m_2 = 0$; perpendicular

49. a. $m = 35$ **b.** The number of kilowatt-hours increased at a rate of 35 kilowatt-hours per day.

50. a. $m = -994$ **b.** The number of new cars sold in Maryland decreased at a rate of 994 cars per year.

51. $y = \dfrac{5}{2}x - 5; m = \dfrac{5}{2}$; y-intercept: $(0, -5)$

52. $y = -\dfrac{3}{4}x + 3; m = -\dfrac{3}{4}$; y-intercept: $(0, 3)$

53. $y = \dfrac{1}{3}x; m = \dfrac{1}{3}$; y-intercept: $(0, 0)$ **54.** $y = \dfrac{12}{5}; m = 0$; y-intercept: $\left(0, \dfrac{12}{5}\right)$ **55.** $y = -\dfrac{5}{2}; m = 0$; y-intercept: $\left(0, -\dfrac{5}{2}\right)$ **56.** $y = x; m = 1$; y-intercept: $(0, 0)$

57. Neither   **58.** Perpendicular   **59.** Parallel
60. Parallel   **61.** Perpendicular   **62.** Neither
63. $y = -\dfrac{4}{3}x - 1$ or $4x + 3y = -3$ **64.** $y = 5x$ or $5x - y = 0$ **65.** $y = -\dfrac{4}{3}x - 6$ or $4x + 3y = -18$
66. $y = 5x - 3$ or $5x - y = 3$ **67.** For example: $y = 3x + 2$ **68.** For example: $5x + 2y = -4$

69. $m = \dfrac{y_2 - y_1}{x_2 - x_1}$ **70.** $y - y_1 = m(x - x_1)$

71. For example: $x = 6$ **72.** For example: $y = -5$

73. $y = -6x + 2$ or $6x + y = 2$ **74.** $y = \dfrac{2}{3}x + \dfrac{5}{3}$ or $2x - 3y = -5$ **75.** $y = \dfrac{1}{4}x - 4$ or $x - 4y = 16$

76. $y = -5$ **77.** $y = \dfrac{6}{5}x + 6$ or $6x - 5y = -30$

78. $y = 4x + 31$ or $4x - y = -31$ **79. a.** 47.8 in.
b. The slope is 2.4 and indicates that the average height for girls increases at a rate of 2.4 in. per year.   **80. a.** $m = 137$
b. The number of prescriptions increased by 137 million per year during this time period.   **c.** $y = 137x + 2825$
d. 4880 million   **81. a.** $y = 20x + 55$ **b.** $235
82. a. $y = 8x + 700$ **b.** $1340

Chapter 3 Test, pp. 287–289

1. a. II **b.** IV **c.** III   **2.** 0 **3.** 0
4. a. $(4, 14)$ After 4 days the bamboo plant is 14 in. tall. $(8, 28), (12, 42), (16, 56), (20, 70)$
b.

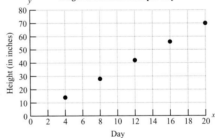

c. Approximately 35 in.
5. a. No **b.** Yes **c.** Yes **d.** Yes
6.

x	y
0	−2
4	−1
6	−½

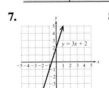

7.   **8.** 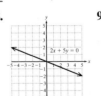 **9.**

10.

11. Horizontal

12. Vertical

13. x-intercept: $\left(-\dfrac{3}{2}, 0\right)$; y-intercept: $(0, 2)$

14. x-intercept: $(0, 0)$; y-intercept: $(0, 0)$ **15.** x-intercept: $(4, 0)$; y-intercept: none   **16.** x-intercept: none; y-intercept: $(0, 3)$

17. $\dfrac{2}{5}$ **18. a.** $\dfrac{1}{3}$ **b.** $\dfrac{4}{3}$ **19. a.** $-\dfrac{1}{4}$ **b.** 4

20. a. Undefined **b.** 0   **21. a.** $m = 0.6$ **b.** The cost of renting a truck increases at a rate of \$0.60 per mile.

22. Parallel

23. Perpendicular   **24.** $y = -\dfrac{1}{3}x + 1$ or $x + 3y = 3$

25. $y = -\dfrac{7}{2}x + 15$ or $7x + 2y = 30$ **26.** $y = \dfrac{1}{4}x + \dfrac{1}{2}$ or $x - 4y = -2$ **27.** $y = 3x + 8$ or $3x - y = -8$

28. $y = -6$ **29.** $y = -x - 3$ or $x + y = -3$

30. a. $y = 1.5x + 10$ **b.** \$25   **31. a.** $m = 20$; The slope indicates that there is an increase of 20 thousand medical doctors per year. **b.** $y = 20x + 414$ **c.** 1114 thousand or, equivalently, 1,114,000

Chapters 1–3 Cumulative Review Exercises, pp. 289–290

1. a. Rational **b.** Rational **c.** Irrational **d.** Rational

2. a. $\dfrac{2}{3}; \dfrac{2}{3}$ **b.** $-5.3; 5.3$ **3.** 69   **4.** -13 **5.** 18

6. $\dfrac{3}{4} \div -\dfrac{7}{8}; -\dfrac{6}{7}$ **7.** $(-2.1)(-6); 12.6$

8. The associative property of addition   **9.** 4   **10.** 5

11. $-\dfrac{9}{2}$ **12.** -2 **13.** 9241 mi^2 **14.** $a = \dfrac{c - b}{3}$

15.

16. x-intercept: $(-2, 0)$; y-intercept: $(0, 1)$

17. $y = -\dfrac{3}{2}x - 6$; slope: $-\dfrac{3}{2}$; y-intercept: $(0, -6)$

18. $2x + 3 = 5$ can be written as $x = 1$, which represents a vertical line. A vertical line of the form $x = k$ ($k \neq 0$) has an x-intercept of $(k, 0)$ and no y-intercept.

19. $y = -3x + 1$ or $3x + y = 1$

20. $y = \frac{2}{3}x + 6$ or $2x - 3y = -18$

Chapter 4

Chapter Opener Puzzle

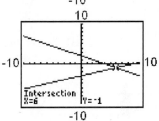

$(1, 1)$ $(7, 7)$ $(4, 9)$ $(4, 0)$ $(1, 7)$
$(7, 1)$ $(0, 4)$ $(9, 4)$

The lines intersect at $(4, 4)$.

Section 4.1 Calculator Connections, pp. 296–297

1. $(2, 1)$

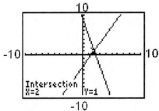

2. $(6, -1)$

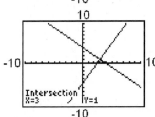

3. $(3, 1)$

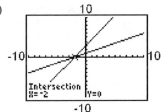

4. $(-2, 0)$

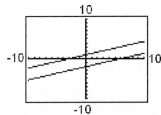

5. No solution

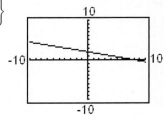

6. $\left\{(x, y) \mid y = -\dfrac{1}{4}x + 2\right\}$

Section 4.1 Practice Exercises, pp. 297–302

1. a. system **b.** solution **c.** intersect **d.** consistent
e. inconsistent **f.** dependent **g.** independent
3. Yes   **5.** No   **7.** Yes   **9.** No   **11.** b   **13.** d
15. a.   **b.**   **c.**

17. c   **19.** a   **21.** a   **23.** b   **25.** c
27. $(3, 1)$ **29.** $(1, -2)$

31. $(1, 4)$ **33.** No solution;
                              inconsistent system

35. Infinitely many solutions;   **37.** $(-3, 6)$
$\{(x, y) \mid -2x + y = 3\}$;
dependent equations

39. $(2, -2)$ **41.** No solution;
                              inconsistent system

43. $(4, 2)$ **45.** $(1, 2)$

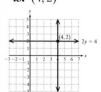

47. Infinitely many solutions;   **49.** $(-3, -1)$
$\{(x, y) \mid y = 0.5x + 2\}$;
dependent equations

51. The same cost occurs when \$2500 of merchandise is
purchased.   **53.** The point of intersection is below the
x-axis and cannot have a positive y-coordinate.   **55.** For
example: $4x + y = 9; -2x - y = -5$ **57.** For example:
$2x + 2y = 1$

Section 4.2 Practice Exercises, pp. 310–311

1. $y = 2x - 4; y = 2x - 4$; coinciding lines
3. $y = -\dfrac{2}{3}x + 2; y = x - 5$; intersecting lines
5. $y = 4x - 4; y = 4x - 13$; parallel lines
7. $(3, -6)$ **9.** $(0, 4)$ **11. a.** y in the second equation
is easiest to isolate because its coefficient is 1.   **b.** $(1, 5)$
13. $(5, 2)$ **15.** $(10, 5)$ **17.** $\left(\dfrac{1}{2}, 3\right)$ **19.** $(5, 3)$
21. $(1, 0)$ **23.** $(1, 4)$ **25.** No solution; inconsistent
system   **27.** Infinitely many solutions;
$\{(x, y) \mid 2x - 6y = -2\}$; dependent equations   **29.** $(5, -7)$
31. $\left(-5, \dfrac{3}{2}\right)$ **33.** $(2, -5)$ **35.** $(-4, 6)$ **37.** $\left(-1, \dfrac{1}{2}\right)$
39. Infinitely many solutions; $\{(x, y) \mid y = 0.25x + 1\}$;
dependent equations   **41.** $(4, 3)$ **43.** No solution;
inconsistent system   **45.** $(-1, 5)$ **47.** $(-6, -4)$
49. The numbers are 48 and 58.   **51.** The numbers are
13 and 39.   **53.** The measures are 165° and 15°.
55. The measures are 70° and 20°.   **57.** The measures
are 42° and 48°.   **59.** For example: $(0, 3), (1, 5), (-1, 1)$

Section 4.3 Practice Exercises, pp. 318–320

1. No   **3.** No   **5.** Yes   **7. a.** True **b.** False,
multiply the second equation by 5.   **9. a.** x would be easier.
b. $(0, -3)$ **11.** $(4, -1)$ **13.** $(4, 3)$ **15.** $(2, 3)$
17. $(1, -4)$ **19.** $(1, -1)$ **21.** $(-4, -6)$ **23.** $\left(\dfrac{7}{9}, \dfrac{5}{9}\right)$
25. The system will have no solution. The lines are parallel.
27. There are infinitely many solutions. The lines coincide.
29. The system will have one solution. The lines intersect at
a point whose x-coordinate is 0.
31. No solution; inconsistent system   **33.** Infinitely many
solutions; $\{(x, y) \mid x + 2y = 2\}$; dependent equations
35. $(1, 4)$ **37.** $(-1, -2)$ **39.** $(2, 1)$
41. No solution; inconsistent system   **43.** $(2, 3)$
45. $(3.5, 2.5)$ **47.** $\left(\dfrac{1}{3}, 2\right)$ **49.** $(-2, 5)$ **51.** $\left(-\dfrac{1}{2}, 1\right)$
53. $(0, 3)$ **55.** No solution   **57.** $(1, 4)$ **59.** $(4, 0)$
61. Infinitely many solutions; $\{(a, b) \mid 9a - 2b = 8\}$
63. $\left(\dfrac{7}{16}, -\dfrac{7}{8}\right)$ **65.** The numbers are 17 and 19.

67. The numbers are −1 and 3.   **69.** The measures are 46° and 134°.   **71.** (1, 3)   **73.** One line within the system of equations would have to "bend" for the system to have exactly two points of intersection. This is not possible.   **75.** $A = -5, B = 2$

Chapter 4 Problem Recognition Exercises, p. 321

1. Infinitely many solutions. The equations represent the same line.   **2.** No solution. The equations represent parallel lines.   **3.** One solution. The equations represent intersecting lines.   **4.** One solution. The equations represent intersecting lines.   **5.** No solution. The equations represent parallel lines.   **6.** Infinitely many solutions. The equations represent the same line.
7. The y variable will easily be eliminated by adding the equations. The solution is $(-3, 1)$.   **8.** The x variable will easily be eliminated by multiplying the second equation by 2 and then adding the equations. The solution is $(3, 4)$.
9. Because the variable x is already isolated in the first equation, the expression $-3y + 4$ can be easily substituted for x in the second equation. The solution is $(-2, 2)$.
10. Because the variable y is already isolated in the second equation, the expression $x - 8$ can be easily substituted for y in the first equation. The solution is $(8, 0)$.   **11.** $(5, 0)$
12. $(1, -7)$ **13.** $(4, -5)$ **14.** $(2, 3)$ **15.** $(2, 0)$
16. $(8, 10)$ **17.** $\left(2, -\dfrac{5}{7}\right)$ **18.** $\left(-\dfrac{14}{3}, -4\right)$
19. No solution; inconsistent system   **20.** No solution; inconsistent system   **21.** $(-1, 0)$ **22.** $(5, 0)$
23. Infinitely many solutions; $\{(x, y)|y = 2x - 14\}$; dependent equations   **24.** Infinitely many solutions; $\{(x, y)|x = 5y - 9\}$; dependent equations
25. $(2200, 1000)$ **26.** $(3300, 1200)$ **27.** $(5, -7)$
28. $(2, -1)$ **29.** $\left(\dfrac{2}{3}, \dfrac{1}{2}\right)$ **30.** $\left(\dfrac{1}{4}, -\dfrac{3}{2}\right)$

Section 4.4 Practice Exercises, pp. 327–331

1. $(-1, 4)$ **3.** $\left(\dfrac{5}{2}, 1\right)$ **5.** The numbers are 4 and 16.
7. The measures are 80° and 10°.   **9.** It costs $8.80 to rent a video game and $5.50 to rent a DVD.   **11.** Technology stock costs $16 per share, and the mutual fund costs $11 per share.
13. Mylee bought forty 46-cent stamps and ten 65-cent stamps.   **15.** Shanelle invested $3500 in the 10% account and $6500 in the 7% account.   **17.** $9000 was borrowed at 6%, and $3000 was borrowed at 9%.   **19.** Invest $12,000 in the bond fund and $18,000 in the stock fund.
21. 15 gal of the 50% mixture should be mixed with 10 gal of the 40% mixture.   **23.** 12 gal of the 45% disinfectant solution should be mixed with 8 gal of the 30% disinfectant solution.   **25.** She should mix 20 mL of the 13% solution with 30 mL of the 18% solution.   **27.** Chad needs 1 L of pure antifreeze and 5 L of 40% solution.   **29.** The speed of the boat in still water is 6 mph, and the speed of the current is 2 mph.   **31.** The speed of the plane in still air is 300 mph, and the wind is 20 mph.   **33.** The speed of the plane in still air is 525 mph and the speed of the wind is 75 mph.
35. There are 17 dimes and 22 nickels.   **37.** 2 qt of water should be mixed.   **39. a.** 835 free throws and 1597 field goals   **b.** 4029 points   **c.** Approximately 50 points per game

41. The speed of the plane in still air is 160 mph, and the wind is 40 mph.   **43.** $15,000 was invested in the 5.5% account, and $45,000 was invested in the 6.5% account.
45. 12 lb of candy should be mixed with 8 lb of nuts.
47. Dallas scored 30 points, and Buffalo scored 13 points.
49. There were 300 women and 200 men in the survey.

Section 4.5 Practice Exercises, pp. 337–342

1. a. linear   **b.** intersect or overlap
3.

5. When the inequality symbol is ≤ or ≥
7. All of the points in the shaded region are solutions to the inequality.   **9.** a   **11.** True   **13.** False   **15.** True
17. For example: **19.** For example:
$(0, 5)\ (2, 7)\ (-1, 8)$ $(1, -1)\ (3, 0)\ (-2, -9)$

21. For example: **23.**
$(0, 0)\ (0, 2)\ (-1, -3)$

25.   **27.**

29.   **31.**

33.   **35.**

37.

39.

11. $(0, -2)$

12. $(-2, 3)$

41. a. The set of ordered pairs above the line $x + y = 4$, for example, $(6, 3)(-2, 8)(0, 5)$ **b.** The set of ordered pairs on the line $x + y = 4$, for example, $(0, 4)(4, 0)(2, 2)$ **c.** The set of ordered pairs below the line $x + y = 4$, for example, $(0, 0)(-2, 1)(3, 0)$

13. Infinitely many solutions; $\{(x, y) | 2x + y = 5\}$; dependent equations

14. Infinitely many solutions; $\{(x, y) | -x + 5y = -5\}$; dependent equations

43.

45.

15. $(1, -1)$

16. $(-1, 2)$

47.

49.

17. No solution; inconsistent system

18. No solution; inconsistent system

51.

53.

55.

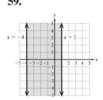

57.

19. 200 mi   **20.** $\left(\dfrac{2}{3}, -2\right)$ **21.** $(-4, 1)$

22. No solution   **23.** Infinitely many solutions; $\{(x, y) | y = -2x + 2\}$ **24. a.** x in the first equation is easiest to isolate because its coefficient is 1. **b.** $\left(6, \dfrac{5}{2}\right)$

59.

25. a. y in the second equation is easiest to isolate because its coefficient is 1. **b.** $\left(\dfrac{9}{2}, 3\right)$ **26.** $(5, -4)$ **27.** $(0, 4)$

28. Infinitely many solutions; $\{(x, y) | x - 3y = 9\}$
29. No solution   **30.** The numbers are 50 and 8.
31. The measures are $42°$ and $48°$.
32. The measures are $115\frac{1}{3}°$ and $64\frac{2}{3}°$.
33. See page 313.   **34. b.** $(-3, -2)$ **35. b.** $(2, 2)$
36. $(2, -1)$ **37.** $(-6, 2)$ **38.** $\left(-\dfrac{1}{2}, \dfrac{1}{3}\right)$
39. $\left(\dfrac{1}{4}, -\dfrac{2}{5}\right)$ **40.** Infinitely many solutions;
$\{(x, y) | -4x - 6y = -2\}$ **41.** No solution   **42.** $(-4, -2)$
43. $(1, 0)$ **44. b.** $(5, -3)$ **45. b.** $(-2, -1)$
46. There were 8 adult tickets and 52 children's tickets sold.   **47.** He should invest $75,000 at 12% and $525,000 at 4%.   **48.** 20 gal of whole milk should be mixed with 40 gal of low fat milk.   **49.** The speed of the boat is 18 mph, and that of the current is 2 mph.   **50.** The plane's speed in

Chapter 4 Review Exercises, pp. 349–352

1. Yes   **2.** No   **3.** No   **4.** Yes   **5.** Intersecting lines (The lines have different slopes.)   **6.** Intersecting lines (The lines have different slopes.)   **7.** Parallel lines (The lines have the same slope but different y-intercepts.)
8. Intersecting lines (The lines have different slopes.)
9. Coinciding lines (The lines have the same slope and same y-intercept.)   **10.** Intersecting lines (The lines have different slopes.)

still air is 320 mph. The wind speed is 30 mph. **51.** A hot dog costs \$4.50 and a drink costs \$3.50. **52.** The score was 72 on the first round and 82 on the second round.

53. For example:
$(1, -1)(0, -4)(2, 0)$

54. For example:
$(5, 5)(4, 0)(0, 7)$

55. For example:
$(-4, 0)(-2, -2)(1, -4)$

56. For example:
$(0, 0)(0, -5)(-1, 1)$

57.

58.

59.

60.

61.

62.

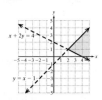

63.

64.

65.

66.

Chapter 4 Test, pp. 353–354

1. $y = -\dfrac{5}{2}x - 3; y = -\dfrac{5}{2}x + 3;$ Parallel lines

2. a. No solution   **b.** Infinitely many solutions
c. One solution

3. $(3, 2)$

4. Infinitely many solutions; $\{(x, y)\,|\,2x + 4y = 6\}$

5. $(-2, 0)$ **6.** $\left(2, -\dfrac{1}{3}\right)$ **7.** $(-5, 4)$ **8.** No solution

9. $(3, -5)$ **10.** $(-1, 2)$ **11.** Infinitely many solutions; $\{(x, y)\,|\,10x + 2y = -8\}$ **12.** $(1, -2)$

13.

14.

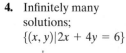

15. Swoopes scored 614 points and Jackson scored 597.
16. CDs cost \$8 each and DVDs cost \$11 each.
17. 12 mL of the 50% acid solution should be mixed with 24 mL of the 20% solution.   **18. a.** \$18 was required.
b. They used 24 quarters and 12 \$1 bills.   **19.** \$1200 was borrowed at 10%, and \$3800 was borrowed at 8%.
20. They would be the same cost for a distance of approximately 24 mi.   **21.** The plane travels 500 mph in still air, and the wind speed is 45 mph.   **22.** The cake has 340 calories, and the ice cream has 120 calories.   **23.** 60 mL of 10% solution and 40 mL of 25% solution.

Chapters 1–4 Cumulative Review Exercises, pp. 354–355

1. $\dfrac{11}{6}$ **2.** $-\dfrac{21}{2}$ **3.** No solution   **4.** $y = \dfrac{3}{2}x - 3$

5. $x = 5z + m$ **6.** $\left[\dfrac{3}{11}, \infty\right)$

7. The measures are $37°, 33°,$ and $110°.$ **8.** The rates of the hikers are 2 mph and 4 mph.   **9.** Jesse Ventura received approximately 762,200 votes.   **10.** 36% of the goal has been achieved.   **11.** The angles are $36.5°$ and $53.5°.$

12. Slope: $-\dfrac{5}{3};$ y-intercept; $(0, -2)$ **13. a.** $-\dfrac{2}{3}$ **b.** $\dfrac{3}{2}$

14. $y = -3x + 3$

15. c. $(0, 2)$

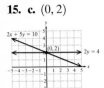

16. $(0, 2)$

17. a.

b.

c. Part (a) represents the solutions to an equation. Part (b) represents the solutions to a strict inequality.   **18.** 20 gal of the 15% solution should be mixed with 40 gal of the 60% solution.   **19.** x is 27°; y is 63°   **20. a.** 1.4   **b.** Between 1920 and 1990, the winning speed in the Indianapolis 500 increased on average by 1.4 mph per year.

Chapter 5

Chapter Opener Puzzle

A polynomial that has two terms is called a $\underline{\text{BINOMIAL}}$.

Section 5.1 Calculator Connection, p. 364

1.–3.

```
(1.06)^5
        1.338225578
(1.02)^40
        2.208039664
5000(1.06)^5
        6691.127888
```

4.–6.

```
2000(1.02)^40
        4416.079327
3000(1+.06)^2
        3370.8
1000(1+.05)^3
        1157.625
```

Section 5.1 Practice Exercises, pp. 365–367

1. a. exponent   **b.** base; exponent   **c.** 1   **d.** $I = Prt$
e. compound interest   **3.** Base: x; exponent: 4
5. Base: 3; exponent: 5   **7.** Base: -1; exponent: 4
9. Base: 13; exponent: 1   **11.** Base: 10; exponent: 3
13. Base: t; exponent: 6   **15.** v **17.** 1   **19.** $(-6b)^2$

21. $-6b^2$ **23.** $(y + 2)^4$ **25.** $\dfrac{-2}{t^3}$ **27.** No; $-5^2 = -25$ and $(-5)^2 = 25$

29. Yes; -32 **31.** Yes; $\dfrac{1}{8}$ **33.** Yes; -16

35. 16   **37.** -1 **39.** $\dfrac{1}{9}$ **41.** $-\dfrac{4}{25}$ **43.** 48

45. 4   **47.** 9   **49.** 50   **51.** -100 **53.** 400
55. 1   **57.** 1   **59.** 1000   **61.** -800
63. a. $(x \cdot x \cdot x \cdot x)(x \cdot x \cdot x) = x^7$
b. $(5 \cdot 5 \cdot 5 \cdot 5)(5 \cdot 5 \cdot 5) = 5^7$ **65.** z^8 **67.** a^9

69. 4^{14} **71.** $\left(\dfrac{2}{3}\right)^4$ **73.** c^{14} **75.** x^{18}

77. a. $\dfrac{p \cdot p \cdot p \cdot p \cdot p \cdot p \cdot p \cdot p}{p \cdot p \cdot p} = p^5$

b. $\dfrac{8 \cdot 8 \cdot 8 \cdot 8 \cdot 8 \cdot 8 \cdot 8 \cdot 8}{8 \cdot 8 \cdot 8} = 8^5$

79. x^2 **81.** a^9 **83.** 7^7 **85.** 5^7 **87.** y **89.** h^4
91. 7^7 **93.** 10^9 **95.** $6x^7$ **97.** $40a^5b^5$
99. s^9t^{16} **101.** $-30v^8$ **103.** $16m^{20}n^{10}$ **105.** $2cd^4$

107. z^4 **109.** $\dfrac{25hjk^4}{12}$ **111.** $-8p^7q^9r^6$ **113.** $-3stu$

115. \$5724.50   **117.** \$4764.06   **119.** 201 in.^{2}
121. 268 in.^{3} **123.** x^{2n+1} **125.** p^{2m+3} **127.** z
129. r^3

Section 5.2 Practice Exercises, pp. 371–372

1. 4^9 **3.** a^{20} **5.** d^9 **7.** 7^6 **9.** When multiplying expressions with the same base, add the exponents. When dividing expressions with the same base, subtract the exponents.   **11.** 5^{12} **13.** 12^6 **15.** y^{14} **17.** w^{25}
19. a^{36} **21.** y^{14} **23.** They are both equal to 2^6.
25. $2^{(2^4)} = 2^{16}$ $(2^2)^4 = 2^8$; the expression $2^{(2^4)}$ is greater than $(2^2)^4$.   **27.** $25w^2$ **29.** $s^4r^4t^4$

31. $\dfrac{16}{r^4}$ **33.** $\dfrac{x^5}{y^5}$ **35.** $81a^4$ **37.** $-27a^3b^3c^3$

39. $-\dfrac{64}{x^3}$ **41.** $\dfrac{a^2}{b^2}$ **43.** $6^3u^6v^{12}$ or $216\, u^6v^{12}$

45. $5x^8y^4$ **47.** $-h^{28}$ **49.** m^{12} **51.** $\dfrac{4^5}{r^5s^{20}}$ or $\dfrac{1024}{r^5s^{20}}$

53. $\dfrac{3^5p^5}{q^{15}}$ or $\dfrac{243p^5}{q^{15}}$ **55.** y^{14} **57.** x^{31} **59.** $200a^{14}b^9$

61. $16p^8q^{16}$ **63.** $-m^{35}n^{15}$ **65.** $25a^{18}b^6$ **67.** $\dfrac{4c^2d^6}{9}$

69. $\dfrac{c^{27}d^{31}}{2}$ **71.** $-\dfrac{27a^9b^3}{c^6}$ **73.** $16b^{26}$ **75.** x^{2m}

77. $125a^{6n}$ **79.** $\dfrac{m^{2b}}{n^{3b}}$ **81.** $\dfrac{3^n a^{3n}}{5^n b^{4n}}$

Section 5.3 Practice Exercises, pp. 379–381

1. a. 1   **b.** $\left(\dfrac{1}{b}\right)^n$ or $\dfrac{1}{b^n}$ **3.** c^9 **5.** y **7.** 3^6 or 729
9. $7^4w^{28}z^8$ or $2401w^{28}z^8$ **11. a.** 1   **b.** 1
13. 1   **15.** 1   **17.** -1 **19.** 1

21. 1   **23.** -7 **25. a.** $\dfrac{1}{t^5}$ **b.** $\dfrac{1}{t^5}$ **27.** $\dfrac{343}{8}$ **29.** 25

31. $\dfrac{1}{a^3}$ **33.** $\dfrac{1}{12}$ **35.** $\dfrac{1}{16b^2}$ **37.** $\dfrac{6}{x^2}$ **39.** $\dfrac{1}{64}$

41. $-\dfrac{3}{y^4}$ **43.** $-\dfrac{1}{t^3}$ **45.** a^5 **47.** $\dfrac{x^4}{x^{-6}} = x^{4-(-6)} = x^{10}$

49. $2a^{-3} = 2 \cdot \dfrac{1}{a^3} = \dfrac{2}{a^3}$ **51.** $\dfrac{1}{x^4}$ **53.** 1   **55.** y^4

57. $\dfrac{n^{27}}{m^{18}}$ **59.** $\dfrac{81k^{24}}{j^{20}}$ **61.** $\dfrac{1}{p^6}$ **63.** $\dfrac{1}{r^3}$ **65.** a^8

67. $\dfrac{1}{y^8}$ **69.** $\dfrac{1}{7^7}$ **71.** 1   **73.** $\dfrac{1}{a^4b^6}$ **75.** $\dfrac{1}{w^{21}}$

77. $\dfrac{1}{27}$ **79.** 1   **81.** $\dfrac{1}{64x^6}$ **83.** $-\dfrac{16y^4}{z^2}$ **85.** $-\dfrac{a^{12}}{6}$

87. $80c^{21}d^{24}$ **89.** $\dfrac{9y^2}{8x^5}$ **91.** $\dfrac{4d^{16}}{c^2}$ **93.** $\dfrac{9y^2}{2x}$ **95.** $\dfrac{9}{20}$

97. $\dfrac{9}{10}$ **99.** $\dfrac{5}{4}$ **101.** $\dfrac{10}{3}$ **103.** 2   **105.** -11

Chapter 5 Problem Recognition Exercises, pp. 381–382

1. a. t^8 **b.** $\dfrac{1}{t^2}$ **c.** t^{15} **2. a.** 2^8 **b.** $\dfrac{1}{4}$ **c.** 2^{15}

3. a. y^5 **b.** y^{14} **c.** y^9 **4. a.** p^6 **b.** p^{27} **c.** p^{12}

5. a. $\dfrac{1}{w^8}$ **b.** w^2 **c.** w^6 **6. a.** $\dfrac{1}{m^{12}}$ **b.** $\dfrac{1}{m^{28}}$ **c.** $\dfrac{1}{m^{16}}$

7. a. $r^4 s^8$ **b.** $\dfrac{r^4}{s^8}$ **c.** $\dfrac{r^4}{s^4}$ **8. a.** $a^3 b^9 c^6$ **b.** $\dfrac{a}{b^9 c^6}$ **c.** $ab^3 c^6$

9. a. 1 **b.** $\dfrac{y^7}{x^7}$ **c.** $\dfrac{x^4 z^3}{y^7}$ **10. a.** $\dfrac{a^3 c^8}{b^6}$ **b.** $\dfrac{a^{11}}{b^6}$ **c.** a^5

11. a. $\dfrac{b^9}{2^{15}}$ **b.** $\dfrac{1}{2^{15} b^9}$ **c.** $\dfrac{2^{12}}{b^{15}}$ **12. a.** $\dfrac{3^4}{y^6}$ **b.** $3^4 y^6$ **c.** $\dfrac{y^8}{3^6}$

13. a. $\dfrac{1}{t^2}$ **b.** t^5 **c.** t^9 **14. a.** p^4 **b.** $\dfrac{1}{p^7}$ **c.** p^{10}

15. a. $\dfrac{k^8}{5h^6}$ **b.** $\dfrac{1}{h^9 k^6}$ **c.** $\dfrac{5^7}{h^6 k^8}$

16. a. $\dfrac{n^{20}}{6^7 m^6}$ **b.** $\dfrac{6^3}{m^6}$ **c.** $\dfrac{m^{12}}{n^{12}}$

Section 5.4 Calculator Connections, p. 385

1.–2.

```
(5.2E6)*(4.6E-3)
                2.392E4
(2.19E-8)*(7.84E
-4)
            1.71696E-11
```

3.–4.

```
(4.76E-5)/(2.38E
9)
                2E-14
(8.5E4)/(4.0E-1)
            2.125E5
```

5.

```
((9.6E7)*(4.0E-3
))/(2.0E-2)
            1.92E7
```

6.

```
((5.0E-12)*(6.4E
-5))/((1.6E-8)*(
4.0E2))
            5E-11
```

Section 5.4 Practice Exercises, pp. 386–388

1. scientific notation   **3.** b^{13} **5.** 10^{13}

7. $\dfrac{1}{y^5}$ **9.** $\dfrac{x^{20}}{y^{12}}$ **11.** w^4 **13.** 10^4

15. Move the decimal point between the 2 and 3 and multiply by 10^{-10}; 2.3×10^{-10}.   **17.** 5×10^4

19. 2.08×10^5 **21.** 6.01×10^6 **23.** 8×10^{-6}

25. 1.25×10^{-4} **27.** 6.708×10^{-3} **29.** 1.7×10^{-24} g

31. $\$2.7 \times 10^{10}$ **33.** 6.8×10^7 gal; 1×10^2 miles

35. Move the decimal point nine places to the left; 0.000 000 0031.   **37.** 0.00005   **39.** 2800   **41.** 0.000603

43. 2,400,000   **45.** 0.019   **47.** 7032

49. 0.000 000 000 001 g   **51.** 1600 Cal and 2800 Cal

53. 5×10^4 **55.** 3.6×10^{11} **57.** 2.2×10^4

59. 2.25×10^{-13} **61.** 3.2×10^{14} **63.** 2.432×10^{-10}

65. 3×10^{13} **67.** 6×10^5 **69.** 1.38×10^1

71. 5×10^{-14} **73.** 3.75 in.   **75.** $\$2.97 \times 10^{10}$

77. a. 6.5×10^7 **b.** 2.3725×10^{10} days
c. 5.694×10^{11} hr   **d.** 2.04984×10^{15} sec

Section 5.5 Practice Exercises, pp. 394–397

1. a. polynomial **b.** coefficient; degree **c.** 1 **d.** one **e.** binomial **f.** trinomial **g.** leading; leading coefficient **h.** greatest **i.** zero

3. $\dfrac{45}{x^2}$ **5.** $\dfrac{2}{t^4}$ **7.** $\dfrac{1}{3^{12}}$ **9.** 4×10^{-2} is in scientific notation in which 10 is raised to the -2 power. 4^{-2} is not in scientific notation and 4 is being raised to the -2 power.

11. a. $-7x^5 + 7x^2 + 9x + 6$ **b.** -7 **c.** 5

13. Binomial; 75   **15.** Monomial; 54   **17.** Binomial; -12

19. Trinomial; 27   **21.** Monomial; -192

23. The exponents on the x-factors are different.

25. $35x^2 y$ **27.** $8b^5 d^2 - 9d$ **29.** $4y^2 + y - 9$

31. $-x^3 + 5x^2 + 9x - 10$ **33.** $10.9y$

35. $4a - 8c$ **37.** $a - \dfrac{1}{2}b - 2$ **39.** $\dfrac{4}{3}z^2 - \dfrac{5}{3}$

41. $7.9t^3 - 3.4t^2 + 6t - 4.2$ **43.** $-4h + 5$

45. $2m^2 - 3m + 15$ **47.** $-3v^3 - 5v^2 - 10v - 22$

49. $-8a^3 b^2$ **51.** $-53x^3$ **53.** $-5a - 3$ **55.** $16k + 9$

57. $2s - 14$ **59.** $3t^2 - 4t - 3$ **61.** $-2r - 3s + 3t$

63. $\dfrac{3}{4}x + \dfrac{1}{3}y - \dfrac{3}{10}$ **65.** $-\dfrac{2}{3}h^2 + \dfrac{3}{5}h - \dfrac{5}{2}$

67. $2.4x^4 - 3.1x^2 - 4.4x - 6.7$

69. $4b^3 + 12b^2 - 5b - 12$ **71.** $-3x^3 - 2x^2 + 11x - 31$

73. $4y^3 + 2y^2 + 2$ **75.** $3a^2 - 3a + 5$

77. $9ab^2 - 3ab + 16a^2 b$ **79.** $4z^5 + z^4 + 9z^3 - 3z - 2$

81. $2x^4 + 11x^3 - 3x^2 + 8x - 4$

83. $-w^3 + 0.2w^2 + 3.7w - 0.7$

85. $-p^2 q - 4pq^2 + 3pq$ **87.** 0   **89.** $-5ab + 6ab^2$

91. $11y^2 - 10y - 4$ **93.** For example, $x^3 + 6$

95. For example, $8x^5$ **97.** For example, $-6x^2 + 2x + 5$

Section 5.6 Practice Exercises, pp. 403–406

1. a. $5 - 2x$ **b.** squares; $a^2 - b^2$ **c.** perfect; $a^2 + 2ab + b^2$ **3.** $-2y^2$ **5.** $-8y^4$ **7.** $8uvw^2$

9. $7u^2 v^2 w^4$ **11.** $-12y$ **13.** $21p$ **15.** $12a^{14} b^8$

17. $-2c^{10} d^{12}$ **19.** $16p^2 q^2 - 24p^2 q + 40pq^2$

21. $-4k^3 + 52k^2 + 24k$ **23.** $-45p^3 q - 15p^4 q^3 + 30pq^2$

25. $y^2 + 19y + 90$ **27.** $m^2 - 14m + 24$

29. $12p^2 - 5p - 2$ **31.** $12w^2 - 32w + 16$

33. $p^2 - 14pw + 33w^2$ **35.** $12x^2 + 28x - 5$

37. $6a^2 - 21.5a + 18$ **39.** $9t^3 - 21t^2 + 3t - 7$

41. $9m^2 + 30mn + 24n^2$ **43.** $5s^3 + 8s^2 - 7s - 6$

45. $27w^3 - 8$ **47.** $p^4 + 5p^3 - 2p^2 - 21p + 5$

49. $\dfrac{3}{4}x^2 + x - \dfrac{3}{16}$ **51.** $6a^3 - 23a^2 + 38a - 45$

53. $8x^3 - 36x^2 y + 54xy^2 - 27y^3$ **55.** $9a^2 - 16b^2$

57. $81k^2 - 36$ **59.** $\dfrac{1}{4} - t^2$ **61.** $u^6 - 25v^2$

63. $4 - 9a^2$ **65.** $\dfrac{4}{9} - p^2$ **67.** $a^2 + 10a + 25$

69. $x^2 - 2xy + y^2$ **71.** $4c^2 + 20c + 25$

73. $9t^4 - 24st^2 + 16s^2$ **75.** $t^2 - 14t + 49$

77. $16q^2 + 24q + 9$ **79. a.** 36 **b.** 20
c. $(a + b)^2 \neq a^2 + b^2$ in general.   **81.** $4x^2 - 25$

83. $16p^2 + 40p + 25$ **85.** $27p^3 - 135p^2 + 225p - 125$

87. $15a^5 - 6a^2$ **89.** $49x^2 - y^2$ **91.** $25s^2 + 30st + 9t^2$

93. $21x^2 - 65xy + 24y^2$ **95.** $2t^2 + \dfrac{26}{3}t + 8$

97. $-30x^2 - 35x + 25$ **99.** $6a^3 + 11a^2 - 7a - 2$

101. $y^3 - 3y^2 - 6y - 20$ **103.** $\dfrac{1}{9}m^2 - \dfrac{2}{3}mn + n^2$

105. $42w^3 - 84w^2$ **107.** $16y^2 - 65.61$

109. $21c^4 + 4c^2 - 32$ **111.** $9.61x^2 + 27.9x + 20.25$

113. $k^3 - 12k^2 + 48k - 64$

115. $125x^3 + 225x^2 + 135x + 27$

117. $2y^4 + 3y^3 + 3y^2 + 5y + 3$ **119.** $6a^3 + 22a^2 - 40a$

121. $2x^3 - 13x^2 + 17x + 12$ **123.** $2x - 7$

125. $k = 10$ or -10 **127.** $k = 8$ or -8

Section 5.7 Practice Exercises, pp. 411–414

1. division; quotient; remainder

3. $6z^5 - 10z^4 - 4z^3 - z^2 - 6$ **5.** $10x^2 - 29xy - 3y^2$

7. $11x - 2y$ **9.** $y^2 - \dfrac{3}{4}y + \dfrac{1}{2}$ **11.** $a^3 + 27$

13. $5t^2 + 6t$ **15.** $3a^2 + 2a - 7$

17. $x^2 + 4x - 1$ **19.** $3p^2 - p$ **21.** $1 + \dfrac{2}{m}$

23. $-2y^2 + y - 3$ **25.** $x^2 - 6x - \dfrac{1}{4} + \dfrac{2}{x}$

27. $a - 1 + \dfrac{b}{a}$ **29.** $3t - 1 + \dfrac{3}{2t} - \dfrac{1}{2t^2} + \dfrac{2}{t^3}$

31. a. $z + 2 + \dfrac{1}{z+5}$ **33.** $t + 3 + \dfrac{2}{t+1}$

35. $7b + 4$ **37.** $k - 6$ **39.** $2p^2 + 3p - 4$

41. $k - 2 + \dfrac{-4}{k+1}$ **43.** $2x^2 - x + 6 + \dfrac{2}{2x-3}$

45. $y^2 + 2y + 1 + \dfrac{2}{3y-1}$ **47.** $a - 3 + \dfrac{18}{a+3}$

49. $4x^2 + 8x + 13$ **51.** $w^2 + 5w - 2 + \dfrac{1}{w^2-3}$

53. $n^2 + n - 6$ **55.** $x - 1 + \dfrac{-8}{5x^2 + 5x + 1}$

57. $3y^2 - 3 + \dfrac{2y+6}{y^2+1}$

59. Multiply $(x-2)(x^2+4) = x^3 - 2x^2 + 4x - 8$, which does not equal $x^3 - 8$.   **61.** Monomial division; $3a^2 + 4a$

63. Long division; $p + 2$ **65.** Long division; $t^3 - 2t^2 + 5t - 10 + \dfrac{4}{t+2}$ **67.** Long division; $w^2 + 3 + \dfrac{1}{w^2-2}$ **69.** Long division; $n^2 + 4n + 16$

71. Monomial division; $-3r + 4 - \dfrac{3}{r^2}$ **73.** $x + 1$

75. $x^3 + x^2 + x + 1$ **77.** $x + 1 + \dfrac{1}{x-1}$

79. $x^3 + x^2 + x + 1 + \dfrac{1}{x-1}$

Chapter 5 Problem Recognition Exercises, p. 414

1. a. $8x^2$ **b.** $12x^4$ **2. a.** $9y^3$ **b.** $8y^6$

3. a. $16x^2 + 8xy + y^2$ **b.** $16x^2y^2$ **4. a.** $4a^2 + 4ab + b^2$

b. $4a^2b^2$ **5. a.** $6x + 1$ **b.** $8x^2 + 8x - 6$

6. a. $6m^2 + m + 1$ **b.** $5m^4 + 5m^3 + m^2 + m$

7. a. $9z^2 + 12z + 4$ **b.** $9z^2 - 4$

8. a. $36y^2 - 84y + 49$ **b.** $36y^2 - 49$

9. a. $2x^3 - 8x^2 + 14x - 12$ **b.** $x^2 - 1$

10. a. $-3y^4 - 20y^2 - 32$ **b.** $4y^2 + 12$ **11. a.** $2x$ **b.** x^2

12. a. $4c$ **b.** $4c^2$ **13.** $16x^2y^2$ **14.** $4a^2b^2$

15. $-x^2 - 3x + 4$ **16.** $5m^2 - 4m + 1$

17. $-7m^2 - 16m$ **18.** $-4n^5 + n^4 + 6n^2 - 7n + 2$

19. $8x^2 + 16x + 34 + \dfrac{74}{x-2}$

20. $-4x^2 - 10x - 30 + \dfrac{-95}{x-3}$

21. $6x^3 + 5x^2y - 6xy^2 + y^3$ **22.** $6a^3 - a^2b + 5ab^2 + 2b^3$

23. $x^3 + y^6$ **24.** $m^6 + 1$ **25.** $4b$ **26.** $-12z$

27. $a^6 - 4b^2$ **28.** $y^6 - 36z^2$ **29.** $4p + 4 + \dfrac{-2}{2p-1}$

30. $2v - 7 + \dfrac{29}{2v+3}$ **31.** $4x^2y^2$ **32.** $-9pq$

33. $\dfrac{9}{49}x^2 - \dfrac{1}{4}$ **34.** $\dfrac{4}{25}y^2 - \dfrac{16}{9}$

35. $-\dfrac{11}{9}x^3 + \dfrac{5}{9}x^2 - \dfrac{1}{2}x - 4$ **36.** $-\dfrac{13}{10}y^2 - \dfrac{9}{10}y + \dfrac{4}{15}$

37. $1.3x^2 - 0.3x - 0.5$ **38.** $5w^3 - 4.1w^2 + 2.8w - 1.2$

39. $-6x^3y^6$ **40.** $50a^4b^6$

Chapter 5 Review Exercises, pp. 419–422

1. Base: 5; exponent: 3   **2.** Base: x; exponent: 4

3. Base: -2; exponent: 0   **4.** Base: y; exponent: 1

5. a. 36 **b.** 36 **c.** -36 **6. a.** 64 **b.** -64 **c.** -64

7. 5^{13} **8.** a^{11} **9.** x^9 **10.** 6^9 **11.** 10^3 **12.** y^6

13. b^8 **14.** 7^7 **15.** k **16.** 1   **17.** 2^8 **18.** q^6

19. Exponents are added only when multiplying factors with the same base. In such a case, the base does not change.

20. Exponents are subtracted only when dividing factors with the same base. In such a case, the base does not change.

21. $7146.10   **22.** $22,050   **23.** 7^{12} **24.** c^{12}

25. p^{18} **26.** 9^{28} **27.** $\dfrac{a^2}{b^2}$ **28.** $\dfrac{1}{3^4}$ **29.** $\dfrac{5^2}{c^4 d^{10}}$

30. $-\dfrac{m^{10}}{4^5 n^{30}}$ **31.** $2^4 a^4 b^8$ **32.** $x^{14} y^2$ **33.** $-\dfrac{3^3 x^9}{5^3 y^6 z^3}$

34. $\dfrac{r^{15}}{s^{10} t^{30}}$ **35.** a^{11} **36.** 8^2 **37.** $4h^{14}$ **38.** $2p^{14} q^{13}$

39. $\dfrac{x^6 y^2}{4}$ **40.** $a^9 b^6$ **41.** 1   **42.** 1   **43.** -1

44. 1   **45.** 2   **46.** 1   **47.** $\dfrac{1}{z^5}$ **48.** $\dfrac{1}{10^4}$

49. $\dfrac{1}{36a^2}$ **50.** $\dfrac{6}{a^2}$ **51.** $\dfrac{17}{16}$ **52.** $\dfrac{10}{9}$ **53.** $\dfrac{1}{t^8}$

54. $\dfrac{1}{r}$ **55.** $\dfrac{2y^7}{x^6}$ **56.** $\dfrac{4a^6 bc}{5}$ **57.** $\dfrac{n^{16}}{16m^8}$

58. $\dfrac{u^{15}}{27v^6}$ **59.** $\dfrac{k^{21}}{5}$ **60.** $\dfrac{h^9}{9}$ **61.** $\dfrac{1}{2}$ **62.** $\dfrac{5}{4}$

63. a. 9.74×10^7 **b.** 4.2×10^{-3} in.

64. a. 0.000 000 0001 **b.** $256,000   **65.** 9.43×10^5

66. 1.55×10^{10} **67.** 2.5×10^8 **68.** 1.638×10^3

69. $\approx 9.5367 \times 10^{13}$. This number has too many digits to fit on most calculator displays.

70. $\approx 1.1529 \times 10^{-12}$. This number has too many digits to fit on most calculator displays.   **71. a.** $\approx 5.84 \times 10^8$ mi
b. $\approx 6.67 \times 10^4$ mph   **72. a.** $\approx 2.26 \times 10^8$ mi
b. $\approx 1.07 \times 10^5$ mph   **73. a.** Trinomial **b.** 4 **c.** 7
74. a. Binomial   **b.** 7   **c.** -5 **75.** $7x - 3$
76. $-y^2 - 14y - 2$ **77.** $14a^2 - 2a - 6$
78. $\dfrac{15}{2}x^3 + \dfrac{1}{4}x^2 + \dfrac{1}{2}x + 2$ **79.** $10w^4 + 2w^3 - 7w + 4$
80. $0.01b^5 + b^4 - 0.1b^3 + 0.3b + 0.33$
81. $-2x^2 - 9x - 6$ **82.** $-5x^2 - 9x - 12$
83. For example, $-5x^2 + 2x - 4$
84. For example, $6x^5 + 8$ **85.** $6w + 6$ **86.** $-75x^6y^4$
87. $18a^8b^4$ **88.** $15c^4 - 35c^2 + 25c$
89. $-2x^3 - 10x^2 + 6x$
90. $5k^2 + k - 4$ **91.** $20t^2 + 3t - 2$ **92.** $6q^2 + 47q - 8$
93. $2a^2 + 4a - 30$ **94.** $49a^2 + 7a + \dfrac{1}{4}$
95. $b^2 - 8b + 16$ **96.** $8p^3 - 27$
97. $-2w^3 - 5w^2 - 5w + 4$
98. $4x^3 - 8x^2 + 11x - 4$ **99.** $12a^3 + 11a^2 - 13a - 10$
100. $b^2 - 16$ **101.** $\dfrac{1}{9}r^8 - s^4$ **102.** $49z^4 - 84z^2 + 36$
103. $2h^5 + h^4 - h^3 + h^2 - h + 3$ **104.** $2x^2 + 3x - 20$
105. $4y^2 - 2y$ **106.** $2a^2b - a - 3b$
107. $-3x^2 + 2x - 1$ **108.** $-\dfrac{z^5w^3}{2} + \dfrac{3zw}{4} + \dfrac{1}{z}$
109. $x + 2$ **110.** $2t + 5$ **111.** $p - 3 + \dfrac{5}{2p + 7}$
112. $a + 6 + \dfrac{-4}{5a - 3}$ **113.** $b^2 + 5b + 25$
114. $z + 4$ **115.** $y^2 - 4y + 2 + \dfrac{9y - 4}{y^2 + 3}$
116. $t^2 - 3t + 1 + \dfrac{-2t - 6}{3t^2 + t + 1}$ **117.** $w^2 + w - 1$

Chapter 5 Test, pp. 422–423

1. $\dfrac{(3 \cdot 3 \cdot 3 \cdot 3) \cdot (3 \cdot 3 \cdot 3)}{3 \cdot 3 \cdot 3 \cdot 3 \cdot 3 \cdot 3} = 3$ **2.** 9^6 **3.** q^8 **4.** 1
5. $\dfrac{1}{c^3}$ **6.** $\dfrac{5}{4}$ **7.** $\dfrac{3}{2}$ **8.** $27a^6b^3$ **9.** $\dfrac{16x^4}{y^{12}}$ **10.** 14
11. $49s^{18}t$ **12.** $\dfrac{4}{b^{12}}$ **13.** $\dfrac{16a^{12}}{9b^6}$ **14. a.** 4.3×10^{10}
b. 0.000 0056   **15.** 8.4×10^{-9} **16.** 7.5×10^6
17. a. $2.4192 \times 10^8 \, \text{m}^3$ **b.** $8.83008 \times 10^{10} \, \text{m}^3$
18. $5x^3 - 7x^2 + 4x + 11$ **a.** 3   **b.** 5
19. $5t^4 + 12t^3 + 7t - 19$ **20.** $24w^2 - 3w - 4$
21. $-10x^5 - 2x^4 + 30x^3$ **22.** $8a^2 - 10a + 3$
23. $4y^3 - 25y^2 + 37y - 15$ **24.** $4 - 9b^2$
25. $25z^2 - 60z + 36$ **26.** $15x^2 - x - 6$
27. $-4x^2 + 5x + 7$ **28.** $y^3 - 11y^2 + 32y - 12$
29. $15x^3 - 7x^2 - 2x + 1$
30. Perimeter: $12x - 2$; area: $5x^2 - 13x - 6$
31. $-3x^6 + \dfrac{x^4}{4} - 2x$ **32.** $-4a^2 + \dfrac{ab}{2} - 2$ **33.** $2y - 7$
34. $w^2 - 4w + 5 + \dfrac{-10}{2w + 3}$ **35.** $3x^2 + x - 12 + \dfrac{15}{x^2 + 4}$

Chapters 1–5 Cumulative Review Exercises, pp. 423–424

1. $-\dfrac{35}{2}$ **2.** 4   **3.** $5^2 - \sqrt{4}$; 23   **4.** $\dfrac{28}{3}$
5. No solution   **6.** Quadrant III   **7.** y-axis
8. The measures are $31°, 54°, 95°$.   **9. a.** 12 in.
b. 19.5 in.   **c.** 5.5 hr   **10.** $(-3, 4)$
11. $[-5, \infty)$ ⟶
   -5
12. $5x^2 - 9x - 15$ **13.** $-2y^2 - 13yz - 15z^2$
14. $16t^2 - 24t + 9$ **15.** $\dfrac{4}{25}a^2 - \dfrac{1}{9}$
16. $-4a^3b^2 + 2ab - 1$ **17.** $4m^2 + 8m + 11 + \dfrac{24}{m - 2}$
18. $\dfrac{c^2}{16d^4}$ **19.** $\dfrac{2b^3}{a^2}$ **20.** 4.1×10^3

Chapter 6

Chapter Opener Puzzle

5	2	6	A 1	3	B 4
3	C 1	4	2	D 6	E 5
F 4	6	1	5	G 2	H 3
I 2	3	5	4	1	6
1	4	3	6	5	2
6	5	2	J 3	4	1

Section 6.1 Practice Exercises, pp. 433–435

1. a. product **b.** prime **c.** greatest common factor
d. prime **e.** greatest common factor (GCF) **f.** grouping
3. 7   **5.** 6   **7.** y **9.** $4w^2z$
11. $2xy^4z^2$ **13.** $(x - y)$ **15. a.** $3x - 6y$ **b.** $3(x - 2y)$
17. $4(p + 3)$ **19.** $5(c^2 - 2c + 3)$ **21.** $x^3(x^2 + 1)$
23. $t(t^3 - 4 + 8t)$ **25.** $2ab(1 + 2a^2)$ **27.** $19x^2y(2 - y^3)$
29. $6xy^5(x^2 - 3y^4z)$ **31.** The expression is prime because it is not factorable.   **33.** $7pq^2(6p^2 + 2 - p^3q^2)$
35. $t^2(t^3 + 2rt - 3t^2 + 4r^2)$ **37. a.** $-2x(x^2 + 2x - 4)$
b. $2x(-x^2 - 2x + 4)$ **39.** $-1(8t^2 + 9t + 2)$
41. $-15p^2(p + 2)$ **43.** $-q(q^3 - 2q + 9)$
45. $-1(7x + 6y + 2z)$ **47.** $(a + 6)(13 - 4b)$
49. $(w^2 - 2)(8v + 1)$ **51.** $7x(x + 3)^2$
53. $(2a - b)(4a + 3c)$ **55.** $(q + p)(3 + r)$
57. $(2x + 1)(3x + 2)$ **59.** $(t + 3)(2t - 1)$
61. $(3y - 1)(2y - 3)$ **63.** $(b + 1)(b^3 - 4)$
65. $(j^2 + 5)(3k + 1)$ **67.** $(2x^6 + 1)(7w^6 - 1)$
69. $(y + x)(a + b)$ **71.** $(vw + 1)(w - 3)$
73. $5x(x^2 + y^2)(3x + 2y)$ **75.** $4b(a - b)(x - 1)$
77. $6t(t - 3)(s - t^2)$ **79.** $P = 2(l + w)$
81. $S = 2\pi r(r + h)$ **83.** $\dfrac{1}{7}(x^2 + 3x - 5)$
85. $\dfrac{1}{4}(5w^2 + 3w + 9)$ **87.** For example, $6x^2 + 9x$
89. For example, $16p^4q^2 + 8p^3q - 4p^2q$

Section 6.2 Practice Exercises, pp. 439–441

1. a. positive   **b.** different   **c.** Both are correct.
d. $3(x + 6)(x + 2)$ **3.** $3(t - 5)(t - 2)$
5. $(a + 2b)(x - 5)$ **7.** $(x + 8)(x + 2)$
9. $(z - 9)(z - 2)$ **11.** $(z - 6)(z + 3)$
13. $(p - 8)(p + 5)$ **15.** $(t + 10)(t - 4)$
17. Prime   **19.** $(n + 4)^2$ **21.** a   **23.** c
25. They are both correct because multiplication of
polynomials is a commutative operation.
27. The expressions are equal and both are correct.
29. Descending order   **31.** $(x - 15)(x + 2)$
33. $(w - 13)(w - 5)$ **35.** $(t + 18)(t + 4)$
37. $3(x - 12)(x + 2)$ **39.** $8p(p - 1)(p - 4)$
41. $y^2z^2(y - 6)(y - 6)$ or $y^2z^2(y - 6)^2$
43. $-(x - 4)(x - 6)$ **45.** $-(m + 2)(m - 3)$
47. $-2(c + 2)(c + 1)$ **49.** $xy^3(x - 4)(x - 15)$
51. $12(p - 7)(p - 1)$ **53.** $-2(m - 10)(m - 1)$
55. $(c + 5d)(c + d)$ **57.** $(a - 2b)(a - 7b)$ **59.** Prime
61. $(q - 7)(q + 9)$ **63.** $(x + 10)^2$ **65.** $(t + 20)(t - 2)$
67. The student forgot to factor out the GCF before factoring
the trinomial further. The polynomial is not factored
completely, because $(2x - 4)$ has a common factor of 2.
69. $x^2 + 9x - 52$ **71. a.** $3x^2 + 9x - 12$
b. $3(x + 4)(x - 1)$ **73.** $(x^2 + 1)(x^2 + 9)$
75. $(w^2 + 5)(w^2 - 3)$ **77.** $7, 5, -7, -5$
79. For example: $c = -16$

Section 6.3 Practice Exercises, pp. 448–449

1. a. Both are correct.   **b.** $2(3x - 5)(x + 1)$
3. $(n - 1)(m - 2)$ **5.** $6(a - 7)(a + 2)$ **7.** a
9. b   **11.** $(3n + 1)(n + 4)$ **13.** $(2y + 1)(y - 2)$
15. $(5x + 1)(x - 3)$ **17.** $(4c + 1)(3c - 2)$
19. $(10w - 3)(w + 4)$ **21.** $(3q + 2)(2q - 3)$
23. Prime   **25.** $(5m + 2)(5m - 4)$
27. $(6y - 5x)(y + 4x)$ **29.** $2(m + 4)(m - 10)$
31. $y^3(2y + 1)(y + 6)$ **33.** $-(a + 17)(a - 2)$
35. $10(4m + p)(2m - 3p)$ **37.** $(x^2 + 1)(x^2 + 9)$
39. $(w^2 + 5)(w^2 - 3)$ **41.** $(2x^2 + 3)(x^2 - 5)$
43. $-2(z - 9)(z - 1)$ **45.** $(q - 7)(q - 6)$
47. $(2t + 3)(3t - 1)$ **49.** $(2m - 5)^2$ **51.** Prime
53. $(2x - 5y)(3x - 2y)$ **55.** $(4m + 5n)(3m - n)$
57. $5(3r + 2)(2r - 1)$ **59.** Prime   **61.** $(2t - 5)(5t + 1)$
63. $(7w - 4)(2w + 3)$ **65.** $(a - 12)(a + 2)$
67. $(x + 5y)(x + 4y)$ **69.** $(a + 20b)(a + b)$
71. $(t - 7)(t - 3)$ **73.** $d(5d^2 + 3d - 10)$
75. $4b(b - 5)(b + 4)$ **77.** $y^2(x - 3)(x - 10)$
79. $-2u(2u + 5)(3u - 2)$ **81.** $(2x^2 + 3)(4x^2 + 1)$
83. a. 36 ft   **b.** $-4(4t + 5)(t - 2)$; Yes
85. a. $(x - 12)(x + 2)$ **b.** $(x - 6)(x - 4)$
87. a. $(x - 6)(x + 1)$ **b.** $(x - 2)(x - 3)$

Section 6.4 Practice Exercises, pp. 454–456

1. a. Both are correct.   **b.** $3(4x + 3)(x - 2)$
3. $(y + 5)(8 + 9y)$ **5.** $12, 1$ **7.** $-8, -1$
9. $5, -4$ **11.** $9, -2$ **13.** $(x + 4)(3x + 1)$
15. $(w - 2)(4w - 1)$ **17.** $(x + 9)(x - 2)$
19. $(m + 3)(2m - 1)$ **21.** $(4k + 3)(2k - 3)$
23. $(2k - 5)^2$ **25.** Prime   **27.** $(3z - 5)(3z - 2)$
29. $(6y - 5z)(2y + 3z)$ **31.** $2(7y + 4)(y + 3)$

33. $-(3w - 5)(5w + 1)$ **35.** $-4(x - y)(3x - 2y)$
37. $6y(y + 1)(3y + 7)$ **39.** $(a^2 + 2)(a^2 + 3)$
41. $(3x^2 - 5)(2x^2 + 3)$ **43.** $(8p^2 - 3)(p^2 + 5)$
45. $(5p - 1)(4p - 3)$ **47.** $(3u - 2v)(2u - 5v)$
49. $(4a + 5b)(3a - b)$ **51.** $(h + 7k)(3h - 2k)$
53. Prime   **55.** $(2z - 1)(8z - 3)$ **57.** $(b - 4)^2$
59. $-5(x - 2)(x - 3)$ **61.** $(t - 3)(t + 2)$
63. Prime   **65.** $2(12x - 1)(3x + 1)$
67. $p(p + 3)(p - 9)$ **69.** $x(3x + 7)(x + 1)$
71. $2p(p - 15)(p - 4)$ **73.** $x^2(y + 3)(y + 11)$
75. $-1(k + 2)(k + 5)$ **77.** $-3(n + 6)(n - 5)$
79. $(x^2 - 2)(x^2 - 5)$ **81.** No. $(2x + 4)$ contains a
common factor of 2.   **83. a.** 128 customers
b. $-2(x - 18)(x - 2)$; 128; Yes   **85. a.** 42
b. $n(n + 1)$; 42; Yes

Section 6.5 Practice Exercises, pp. 461–463

1. a. difference; $(a + b)(a - b)$ **b.** sum   **c.** is not
d. square   **e.** $(a + b)^2$; $(a - b)^2$ **3.** $(3x - 1)(2x - 5)$
5. $5xy^5(3x - 2y)$ **7.** $(x + b)(a - 6)$
9. $(y + 10)(y - 4)$ **11.** $x^2 - 25$ **13.** $4p^2 - 9q^2$
15. $(x - 6)(x + 6)$ **17.** $3(w + 10)(w - 10)$
19. $(2a - 11b)(2a + 11b)$ **21.** $(7m - 4n)(7m + 4n)$
23. Prime   **25.** $(y + 2z)(y - 2z)$ **27.** $(a - b^2)(a + b^2)$
29. $(5pq - 1)(5pq + 1)$ **31.** $\left(c - \dfrac{1}{5}\right)\left(c + \dfrac{1}{5}\right)$
33. $2(5 - 4t)(5 + 4t)$ **35.** $(z + 2)(z - 2)(z^2 + 4)$
37. $(2 - z)(2 + z)(4 + z^2)$ **39.** $(x + 5)(x + 3)(x - 3)$
41. $(c - 1)(c + 5)(c - 5)$ **43.** $(x + 3)(x - 3)(2 + y)$
45. $(y + 3)(y - 3)(x + 2)(x - 2)$ **47.** $9x^2 + 30x + 25$
49. a. $x^2 + 4x + 4$ is a perfect square trinomial.
b. $x^2 + 4x + 4 = (x + 2)^2$; $x^2 + 5x + 4 = (x + 1)(x + 4)$
51. $(x + 9)^2$ **53.** $(5z - 2)^2$ **55.** $(7a + 3b)^2$
57. $(y - 1)^2$ **59.** $5(4z + 3w)^2$ **61.** $(3y + 25)(3y + 1)$
63. $2(a - 5)^2$ **65.** Prime   **67.** $(2x + y)^2$
69. $3x(x - 1)^2$ **71.** $y(y - 6)$ **73.** $(2p - 5)(2p + 7)$
75. $(-t + 2)(t + 6)$ or $-(t - 2)(t + 6)$
77. $(2a - 5 + 10b)(2a - 5 - 10b)$
79. a. $a^2 - b^2$ **b.** $(a - b)(a + b)$

Section 6.6 Practice Exercises, pp. 468–469

1. a. sum; cubes   **b.** difference; cubes
c. $(a - b)(a^2 + ab + b^2)$ **d.** $(a + b)(a^2 - ab + b^2)$
3. $5(2 - t)(2 + t)$ **5.** $(t + u)(2 + s)$
7. $(3v - 4)(v + 3)$ **9.** $-(c + 5)^2$
11. $x^3, 8, y^6, 27q^3, w^{12}, r^3s^6$ **13.** $t^3, -1, 27, a^3b^6, 125, y^6$
15. $(y - 2)(y^2 + 2y + 4)$ **17.** $(1 - p)(1 + p + p^2)$
19. $(w + 4)(w^2 - 4w + 16)$
21. $(x - 10y)(x^2 + 10xy + 100y^2)$
23. $(4t + 1)(16t^2 - 4t + 1)$
25. $(10a + 3)(100a^2 - 30a + 9)$
27. $\left(n - \dfrac{1}{2}\right)\left(n^2 + \dfrac{1}{2}n + \dfrac{1}{4}\right)$
29. $(5x + 2y)(25x^2 - 10xy + 4y^2)$ **31.** $(x^2 - 2)(x^2 + 2)$
33. Prime   **35.** $(t + 4)(t^2 - 4t + 16)$
37. Prime   **39.** $4(b + 3)(b^2 - 3b + 9)$
41. $5(p - 5)(p + 5)$ **43.** $\left(\frac{1}{4} - 2h\right)\left(\frac{1}{16} + \frac{1}{2}h + 4h^2\right)$
45. $(x - 2)(x + 2)(x^2 + 4)$ **47.** $\left(\dfrac{2}{3}x - w\right)\left(\dfrac{2}{3}x + w\right)$

49. $(q - 2)(q^2 + 2q + 4)(q + 2)(q^2 - 2q + 4)$
51. $(x^3 + 4y)(x^6 - 4x^3y + 16y^2)$
53. $(2x + 3)(x - 1)(x + 1)$
55. $(2x - y)(2x + y)(4x^2 + y^2)$
57. $(3y - 2)(3y + 2)(9y^2 + 4)$
59. $(a + b^2)(a^2 - ab^2 + b^4)$ **61.** $(x^2 + y^2)(x - y)(x + y)$
63. $(k + 4)(k - 3)(k + 3)$ **65.** $2(t - 5)(t - 1)(t + 1)$
67. $\left(\frac{4}{5}p - \frac{1}{2}q\right)\left(\frac{16}{25}p^2 + \frac{2}{5}pq + \frac{1}{4}q^2\right)$
69. $(a^4 + b^4)(a^8 - a^4b^4 + b^8)$ **71. a.** The quotient is $x^2 + 2x + 4$.   **b.** $(x - 2)(x^2 + 2x + 4)$
73. $x^2 + 4x + 16$ **75.** $2x + 1$

Chapter 6 Problem Recognition Exercises, pp. 469–471

1. A prime polynomial cannot be factored further.
2. Factor out the GCF.   **3.** Look for a difference of squares: $a^2 - b^2$, a difference of cubes: $a^3 - b^3$, or a sum of cubes: $a^3 + b^3$.   **4.** Grouping   **5. a.** Difference of squares   **b.** $2(a - 9)(a + 9)$ **6. a.** Nonperfect square trinomial   **b.** $(y + 3)(y + 1)$ **7. a.** None of these   **b.** $6w(w - 1)$ **8. a.** Difference of squares   **b.** $(2z + 3)(2z - 3)(4z^2 + 9)$
9. a. Nonperfect square trinomial   **b.** $(3t + 1)(t + 4)$
10. a. Sum of cubes   **b.** $5(r + 1)(r^2 - r + 1)$
11. a. Four terms-grouping   **b.** $(3c + d)(a - b)$
12. a. Difference of cubes   **b.** $(x - 5)(x^2 + 5x + 25)$
13. a. Sum of cubes   **b.** $(y + 2)(y^2 - 2y + 4)$
14. a. Nonperfect square trinomial   **b.** $(7p - 1)(p - 4)$
15. a. Nonperfect square trinomial   **b.** $3(q - 4)(q + 1)$
16. a. Perfect square trinomial   **b.** $-2(x - 2)^2$
17. a. None of these   **b.** $6a(3a + 2)$
18. a. Difference of cubes   **b.** $2(3 - y)(9 + 3y + y^2)$
19. a. Difference of squares   **b.** $4(t - 5)(t + 5)$
20. a. Nonperfect square trinomial   **b.** $(4t + 1)(t - 8)$
21. a. Nonperfect square trinomial   **b.** $10(c^2 + c + 1)$
22. a. Four terms-grouping   **b.** $(w - 5)(2x + 3y)$
23. a. Sum of cubes   **b.** $(x + 0.1)(x^2 - 0.1x + 0.01)$
24. a. Difference of squares   **b.** $(2q - 3)(2q + 3)$
25. a. Perfect square trinomial   **b.** $(8 + k)^2$
26. a. Four terms-grouping   **b.** $(t + 6)(s^2 + 5)$
27. a. Four terms-grouping   **b.** $(x + 1)(2x - y)$
28. a. Sum of cubes   **b.** $(w + y)(w^2 - wy + y^2)$
29. a. Difference of cubes   **b.** $(a - c)(a^2 + ac + c^2)$
30. a. Nonperfect square trinomial   **b.** Prime
31. a. Nonperfect square trinomial   **b.** Prime
32. a. Perfect square trinomial   **b.** $(a + 1)^2$
33. a. Perfect square trinomial   **b.** $(b + 5)^2$
34. a. Nonperfect square trinomial   **b.** $-1(t + 8)(t - 4)$
35. a. Nonperfect square trinomial   **b.** $-p(p + 4)(p + 1)$
36. a. Difference of squares   **b.** $(xy - 7)(xy + 7)$
37. a. Nonperfect square trinomial   **b.** $3(2x + 3)(x - 5)$
38. a. Nonperfect square trinomial   **b.** $2(5y - 1)(2y - 1)$
39. a. None of these   **b.** $abc^2(5ac - 7)$
40. a. Difference of squares   **b.** $2(2a - 5)(2a + 5)$
41. a. Nonperfect square trinomial   **b.** $(t + 9)(t - 7)$
42. a. Nonperfect square trinomial   **b.** $(b + 10)(b - 8)$
43. a. Four terms-grouping   **b.** $(b + y)(a - b)$
44. a. None of these   **b.** $3x^2y^4(2x + y)$
45. a. Nonperfect square trinomial   **b.** $(7u - 2v)(2u - v)$

46. a. Nonperfect square trinomial   **b.** Prime
47. a. Nonperfect square trinomial   **b.** $2(2q^2 - 4q - 3)$
48. a. Nonperfect square trinomial   **b.** $3(3w^2 + w - 5)$
49. a. Sum of squares   **b.** Prime
50. a. Perfect square trinomial   **b.** $5(b - 3)^2$
51. a. Nonperfect square trinomial   **b.** $(3r + 1)(2r + 3)$
52. a. Nonperfect square trinomial   **b.** $(2s - 3)(2s + 5)$
53. a. Difference of squares   **b.** $(2a - 1)(2a + 1)(4a^2 + 1)$
54. a. Four terms-grouping   **b.** $(p + c)(p - 3)(p + 3)$
55. a. Perfect square trinomial   **b.** $(9u - 5v)^2$
56. a. Sum of squares   **b.** $4(x^2 + 4)$
57. a. Nonperfect square trinomial   **b.** $(x - 6)(x + 1)$
58. a. Nonperfect square trinomial   **b.** Prime
59. a. Four terms-grouping   **b.** $2(x - 3y)(a + 2b)$
60. a. Nonperfect square trinomial
b. $m(4m + 1)(2m - 3)$ **61. a.** Nonperfect square trinomial   **b.** $x^2y(3x + 5)(7x + 2)$
62. a. Difference of squares   **b.** $2(m^2 - 8)(m^2 + 8)$
63. a. Four terms-grouping   **b.** $(4v - 3)(2u + 3)$
64. a. Four terms-grouping   **b.** $(t - 5)(4t + s)$
65. a. Perfect square trinomial   **b.** $3(2x - 1)^2$
66. a. Perfect square trinomial   **b.** $(p + q)^2$
67. a. Nonperfect square trinomial   **b.** $n(2n - 1)(3n + 4)$
68. a. Nonperfect square trinomial   **b.** $k(2k - 1)(2k + 3)$
69. a. Difference of squares   **b.** $(8 - y)(8 + y)$
70. a. Difference of squares   **b.** $b(6 - b)(6 + b)$
71. a. Nonperfect square trinomial   **b.** Prime
72. a. Nonperfect square trinomial   **b.** $(y + 4)(y + 2)$
73. a. Nonperfect square trinomial   **b.** $(c^2 - 10)(c^2 - 2)$

Section 6.7 Practice Exercises, pp. 475–477

1. a. quadratic   **b.** $0; 0$ **3.** $4(b - 5)(b - 6)$
5. $(3x - 2)(x + 4)$ **7.** $4(x^2 + 4y^2)$ **9.** Neither
11. Quadratic   **13.** Linear   **15.** $-3, 1$
17. $\frac{7}{2}, -\frac{7}{2}$ **19.** -5 **21.** $0, \frac{1}{5}$ **23.** The polynomial must be factored completely.   **25.** $5, -3$ **27.** $-12, 2$
29. $4, -\frac{1}{2}$ **31.** $\frac{2}{3}, -\frac{2}{3}$ **33.** $6, 8$ **35.** $0, -\frac{3}{2}, 4$
37. $-\frac{1}{3}, 3, -6$ **39.** $0, 4, -\frac{3}{2}$ **41.** $0, -\frac{9}{2}, 11$
43. $0, 4, -4$ **45.** $-6, 0$ **47.** $\frac{3}{4}, -\frac{3}{4}$ **49.** $0, -5, -2$
51. $-\frac{14}{3}$ **53.** $5, 3$ **55.** $0, -2$ **57.** -3 **59.** $-3, 1$
61. $\frac{3}{2}$ **63.** $0, \frac{1}{3}$ **65.** $0, 2$ **67.** $3, -2, 2$ **69.** $-5, 4$
71. $-5, -1$

Chapter 6 Problem Recognition Exercises, p. 477

1. a. $(x + 7)(x - 1)$ **b.** $-7, 1$ **2. a.** $(c + 6)(c + 2)$
b. $-6, -2$ **3. a.** $(2y + 1)(y + 3)$ **b.** $-\frac{1}{2}, -3$
4. a. $(3x - 5)(x - 1)$ **b.** $\frac{5}{3}, 1$ **5. a.** $\frac{4}{5}, -1$
b. $(5q - 4)(q + 1)$ **6. a.** $-\frac{1}{3}, \frac{3}{2}$ **b.** $(3a + 1)(2a - 3)$
7. a. $-8, 8$ **b.** $(a + 8)(a - 8)$ **8. a.** $-10, 10$
b. $(v + 10)(v - 10)$ **9. a.** $(2b + 9)(2b - 9)$ **b.** $-\frac{9}{2}, \frac{9}{2}$

10. a. $(6t + 7)(6t - 7)$ **b.** $-\dfrac{7}{6}, \dfrac{7}{6}$

11. a. $-\dfrac{3}{2}, -\dfrac{1}{2}$ **b.** $2(2x + 3)(2x + 1)$

12. a. $-\dfrac{4}{3}, -2$ **b.** $4(3y + 4)(y + 2)$

13. a. $x(x - 10)(x + 2)$ **b.** $0, 10, -2$
14. a. $k(k + 7)(k - 2)$ **b.** $0, -7, 2$
15. a. $-1, 3, -3$ **b.** $(b + 1)(b - 3)(b + 3)$
16. $8, -2, 2$ **17.** $(s - 3)(2s + r)$ **18.** $(2t + 1)(3t + 5u)$

19. $-\dfrac{1}{2}, 0, \dfrac{1}{2}$ **20.** $-5, 0, 5$ **21.** $0, 1$ **22.** $-3, 0$

23. $\dfrac{1}{3}$ **24.** $-\dfrac{7}{12}$ **25.** $(2w + 3)(4w^2 - 6w + 9)$

26. $(10q - 1)(100q^2 + 10q + 1)$ **27.** $-\dfrac{7}{5}, 1$

28. $-6, -\dfrac{1}{4}$ **29.** $-\dfrac{2}{3}, -5$ **30.** $-1, -\dfrac{1}{2}$ **31.** 3

32. 0 **33.** $-4, 4$ **34.** $-\dfrac{2}{3}, \dfrac{2}{3}$ **35.** $1, 6$ **36.** $-2, -12$

Section 6.8 Practice Exercises, pp. 482–484

1. a. $x + 1$ **b.** $x + 2$ **c.** $x + 2$ **d.** lw **e.** $\dfrac{1}{2}bh$

f. $a^2 + b^2 = c^2$ **3.** $0, -\dfrac{2}{3}$ **5.** $6, -1$ **7.** $-\dfrac{5}{6}, 2$

9. The numbers are 7 and -7.   **11.** The numbers are 10 and -4.   **13.** The numbers are -9 and -7, or 7 and 9.
15. The numbers are 5 and 6, or -1 and 0.
17. The height of the painting is 11 ft and the width is 9 ft.
19. a. The slab is 7 m by 4 m.   **b.** 22 m   **21.** The base is 7 ft and the height is 4 ft.   **23.** The base is 5 cm and the height is 8 cm.   **25.** 3 sec   **27.** 0 sec and 1.5 sec
29.
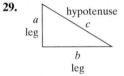
   31. $c = 25$ cm   **33.** $a = 15$ in.

35. The brace is 20 in. long.   **37.** The kite is 19 yd high.
39. The bottom of the ladder is 8 ft from the house. The distance from the top of the ladder to the ground is 15 ft.
41. The hypotenuse is 10 m.

Chapter 6 Review Exercises, pp. 491–493

1. $3a^2b$ **2.** $x + 5$ **3.** $2c(3c - 5)$ **4.** $-2yz$ or $2yz$
5. $2x(3x + x^3 - 4)$ **6.** $11w^2y^3(w - 4y^2)$
7. $t(-t + 5)$ or $-t(t - 5)$ **8.** $u(-6u - 1)$ or $-u(6u + 1)$
9. $(b + 2)(3b - 7)$ **10.** $2(5x + 9)(1 + 4x)$
11. $(w + 2)(7w + b)$ **12.** $(b - 2)(b + y)$
13. $3(4y - 3)(5y - 1)$ **14.** $a(2 - a)(3 - b)$
15. $(x - 3)(x - 7)$ **16.** $(y - 8)(y - 11)$
17. $(z - 12)(z + 6)$ **18.** $(q - 13)(q + 3)$
19. $3w(p + 10)(p + 2)$ **20.** $2m^2(m + 8)(m + 5)$
21. $-(t - 8)(t - 2)$ **22.** $-(w - 4)(w + 5)$
23. $(a + b)(a + 11b)$ **24.** $(c - 6d)(c + 3d)$
25. Different   **26.** Both negative   **27.** Both positive
28. Different   **29.** $(2y + 3)(y - 4)$
30. $(4w + 3)(w - 2)$ **31.** $(2z + 5)(5z + 2)$
32. $(4z - 3)(2z + 3)$ **33.** Prime   **34.** Prime

35. $10(w - 9)(w + 3)$ **36.** $-3(y - 8)(y + 2)$
37. $(3c - 5d)^2$ **38.** $(x + 6)^2$ **39.** $(3g + 2h)(2g + h)$
40. $(6m - n)(2m - 5n)$ **41.** $(v^2 + 1)(v^2 - 3)$
42. $(x^2 + 5)(x^2 + 2)$ **43.** $5, -1$ **44.** $-3, -5$
45. $(c - 2)(3c + 1)$ **46.** $(y + 3)(4y + 1)$
47. $(t + 12)(t + 1)$ **48.** $x(x + 5)(4x - 3)$
49. $(w^2 + 5)(w^2 + 2)$ **50.** $(p - 3q)(p - 5q)$
51. $-2(4v + 3)(5v - 1)$ **52.** $10(4s - 5)(s + 2)$
53. $ab(a - 6b)(a - 4b)$ **54.** $2z^4(z + 7)(z - 3)$
55. Prime   **56.** Prime   **57.** $(7x + 10)^2$
58. $(3w - z)^2$ **59.** $(a - b)(a + b)$ **60.** Prime
61. $(a - 7)(a + 7)$ **62.** $(d - 8)(d + 8)$
63. $(10 - 9t)(10 + 9t)$ **64.** $(2 - 5k)(2 + 5k)$
65. Prime   **66.** Prime   **67.** $(y + 6)^2$ **68.** $(t + 8)^2$
69. $(3a - 2)^2$ **70.** $(5x - 4)^2$ **71.** $-3(v + 2)^2$
72. $-2(x - 5)^2$ **73.** $2(c^2 - 3)(c^2 + 3)$
74. $2(6x - y)(6x + y)$ **75.** $(p + 3)(p - 4)(p + 4)$
76. $(k - 2)(2 - k)(2 + k)$ or $-1(k - 2)^2(2 + k)$
77. $(a + b)(a^2 - ab + b^2)$ **78.** $(a - b)(a^2 + ab + b^2)$
79. $(4 + a)(16 - 4a + a^2)$ **80.** $(5 - b)(25 + 5b + b^2)$
81. $(p^2 + 2)(p^4 - 2p^2 + 4)$

82. $\left(q^2 - \dfrac{1}{3}\right)\left(q^4 + \dfrac{1}{3}q^2 + \dfrac{1}{9}\right)$ **83.** $6(x - 2)(x^2 + 2x + 4)$

84. $7(y + 1)(y^2 - y + 1)$ **85.** $x(x - 6)(x + 6)$
86. $q(q - 4)(q^2 + 4q + 16)$ **87.** $4(2h^2 + 5)$
88. $m(m - 8)$ **89.** $(x + 4)(x + 1)(x - 1)$
90. $5q(p^2 - 2q)(p^2 + 2q)$ **91.** $n(2 + n)(4 - 2n + n^2)$
92. $14(m - 1)(m^2 + m + 1)$ **93.** $(x - 3)(2x + 1) = 0$ can be solved directly by the zero product rule because it is a product of factors set equal to zero.

94. $\dfrac{1}{4}, -\dfrac{2}{3}$ **95.** $9, \dfrac{1}{2}$ **96.** $0, -3, -\dfrac{2}{5}$

97. $0, 7, \dfrac{9}{4}$ **98.** $-\dfrac{5}{7}, 2$ **99.** $-\dfrac{1}{4}, 6$

100. $12, -12$ **101.** $5, -5$ **102.** $0, \dfrac{1}{5}$ **103.** $4, 2$

104. $-\dfrac{5}{6}$ **105.** $-\dfrac{2}{3}$ **106.** $\dfrac{2}{3}, 6$ **107.** $\dfrac{11}{2}, -12$

108. $0, 7, 2$ **109.** $0, 2, -2$ **110.** The height is 6 ft, and the base is 13 ft.   **111.** The ball is at ground level at 0 and 1 sec.   **112.** The ramp is 13 ft long.
113. The legs are 6 ft and 8 ft; the hypotenuse is 10 ft.
114. The numbers are -8 and 8.   **115.** The numbers are 29 and 30, or -2 and -1.   **116.** The height is 4 m, and the base is 9 m.

Chapter 6 Test, p. 493

1. $3x(5x^3 - 1 + 2x^2)$ **2.** $(a - 5)(7 - a)$
3. $(6w - 1)(w - 7)$ **4.** $(13 - p)(13 + p)$
5. $(q - 8)^2$ **6.** $(2 + t)(4 - 2t + t^2)$
7. $(a + 4)(a + 8)$ **8.** $(x + 7)(x - 6)$
9. $(2y - 1)(y - 8)$ **10.** $(2z + 1)(3z + 8)$
11. $(3t - 10)(3t + 10)$ **12.** $(v + 9)(v - 9)$
13. $3(a + 6b)(a + 3b)$ **14.** $(c - 1)(c + 1)(c^2 + 1)$
15. $(y - 7)(x + 3)$ **16.** Prime   **17.** $-10(u - 2)(u - 1)$

18. $3(2t - 5)(2t + 5)$ **19.** $5(y - 5)^2$ **20.** $7q(3q + 2)$
21. $(2x + 1)(x - 2)(x + 2)$ **22.** $(y - 5)(y^2 + 5y + 25)$
23. $(mn - 9)(mn + 9)$ **24.** $16(a - 2b)(a + 2b)$
25. $(4x - 3y^2)(16x^2 + 12xy^2 + 9y^4)$ **26.** $3y(x - 4)(x + 2)$
27. $\dfrac{3}{2}, -5$ **28.** $0, 7$ **29.** $8, -2$ **30.** $\dfrac{1}{5}, -1$
31. $3, -3, -10$ **32.** The tennis court is 12 yd by 26 yd.
33. The two integers are 5 and 7, or -5 and -7.
34. The base is 12 in., and the height is 7 in.
35. The shorter leg is 5 ft.
36. The stone hits the ground in 3 sec.

Chapters 1–6 Cumulative Review Exercises, p. 494

1. $\dfrac{7}{5}$ **2.** -3 **3.** $y = \dfrac{3}{2}x - 4$
4. There are 10 quarters and 7 dimes.
5. $[-4, \infty)$ ⟶   **6. a.** Yes   **b.** 1
c. $(0, 4)$ **d.** $(-4, 0)$ **e.**

7. a. Vertical line   **b.** Undefined   **c.** $(5, 0)$ **d.** Does not
exist   **8.** $y = 3x + 14$ **9.** $(5, 2)$
10. $-\dfrac{7}{2}y^2 - 5y - 14$ **11.** $8p^3 - 22p^2 + 13p + 3$
12. $4w^2 - 28w + 49$ **13.** $r^3 + 5r^2 + 15r + 40 + \dfrac{121}{r - 3}$
14. c^4 **15.** $\dfrac{a^4}{9b^2}$ **16.** 1.6×10^3
17. $(w - 2)(w + 2)(w^2 + 4)$ **18.** $(a + 5b)(2x - 3y)$
19. $(2x - 5)(2x + 1)$ **20.** $0, \dfrac{1}{2}, -5$

Chapter 7

Chapter Opener Puzzle

$\dfrac{p}{4}\ \dfrac{r}{1}\ \dfrac{o}{2}\ \dfrac{c}{}\ \dfrac{r}{1}\ \dfrac{a}{5}\ \dfrac{s}{3}\ \dfrac{t}{}\ \dfrac{i}{}\ \dfrac{n}{5}\ \dfrac{a}{3}\ \dfrac{t}{2}\ \dfrac{i}{}\ \dfrac{o}{}\ \dfrac{n}{}$

Section 7.1 Practice Exercises, pp. 503–506

1. a. rational   **b.** denominator; zero   **c.** $\dfrac{p}{q}$ **d.** $1; -1$
3. 0   **5.** $-\dfrac{1}{8}$ **7.** $-\dfrac{1}{2}$ **9.** Undefined
11. a. $3\frac{1}{5}$ hr or 3.2 hr   **b.** $1\frac{3}{4}$ hr or 1.75 hr
13. $k = -2$ **15.** $x = \dfrac{5}{2}, x = -8$ **17.** $m = -2, m = -3$
19. There are no restricted values.
21. There are no restricted values.   **23.** $t = 0$
25. For example: $\dfrac{1}{x - 2}$ **27.** For example: $\dfrac{1}{(x + 3)(x - 7)}$
29. a. $\dfrac{2}{5}$ **b.** $\dfrac{2}{5}$ **31. a.** Undefined   **b.** Undefined
33. a. $y = -2$ **b.** $\dfrac{1}{2}$ **35. a.** $t = -1$ **b.** $t - 1$

37. a. $w = 0, w = \dfrac{5}{3}$ **b.** $\dfrac{1}{3w - 5}$ **39. a.** $x = -\dfrac{2}{3}$
b. $\dfrac{3x - 2}{2}$ **41. a.** $a = -3, a = 2$ **b.** $\dfrac{a + 5}{a + 3}$ **43.** $\dfrac{b}{3}$
45. $-\dfrac{3xy}{z^2}$ **47.** $\dfrac{p - 3}{p + 4}$ **49.** $\dfrac{1}{4(m - 11)}$ **51.** $\dfrac{2x + 1}{4x^2}$
53. $\dfrac{1}{4a - 5}$ **55.** $\dfrac{x - 2}{3(y + 2)}$ **57.** $\dfrac{2}{x - 5}$ **59.** $a + 7$
61. Cannot simplify   **63.** $\dfrac{y + 3}{2y - 5}$ **65.** $\dfrac{5}{(q + 1)(q - 1)}$
67. $\dfrac{c - d}{2c + d}$ **69.** $5x + 4$ **71.** $\dfrac{x + y}{x - 4y}$
73. They are opposites.   **75.** -1 **77.** -1 **79.** $-\dfrac{1}{2}$
81. Cannot simplify   **83.** $\dfrac{5x - 6}{5x + 6}$ **85.** $-\dfrac{x + 3}{4 + x}$
87. $\dfrac{3x - 2}{x + 4}$ **89.** $-\dfrac{1}{2}$ **91.** $-\dfrac{w + 2}{4}$ **93.** $\dfrac{3t^2}{2}$
95. $-\dfrac{2r - s}{s + 2r}$ **97.** $-\dfrac{3}{2(x - y)}$ **99.** $\dfrac{1}{t(t - 5)}$
101. $w - 2$ **103.** $\dfrac{z + 4}{z^2 + 4z + 16}$
105. a. $x = -12$ **b.** $\{x \mid x \text{ is a real number, } x \neq -12\}$
107. a. $a = 0, a = 1$ **b.** $\{a \mid a \text{ is a real number, } a \neq 0, a \neq 1\}$
109. a. $z = -3, z = -1$
b. $\{z \mid z \text{ is a real number, } z \neq -3, z \neq -1\}$

Section 7.2 Practice Exercises, pp. 510–512

1. $\dfrac{3}{10}$ **3.** 2   **5.** $\dfrac{5}{2}$ **7.** $\dfrac{15}{4}$ **9.** $\dfrac{3}{2x}$ **11.** $3xy^4$
13. $\dfrac{x - 6}{8}$ **15.** $\dfrac{2}{y}$ **17.** $-\dfrac{5}{8}$ **19.** $-\dfrac{b + a}{a - b}$
21. $\dfrac{y + 1}{5}$ **23.** $\dfrac{2(x + 6)}{2x + 1}$ **25.** 6   **27.** $\dfrac{m^6}{n^2}$ **29.** $\dfrac{10}{9}$
31. $\dfrac{6}{7}$ **33.** $-m(m + n)$ **35.** $\dfrac{3p + 4q}{4(p + 2q)}$ **37.** $\dfrac{p}{p - 1}$
39. $\dfrac{w}{2w - 1}$ **41.** $\dfrac{4r}{2r + 3}$ **43.** $\dfrac{5}{6}$ **45.** $\dfrac{1}{4}$
47. $\dfrac{y + 9}{y - 6}$ **49.** 1   **51.** $\dfrac{3t + 8}{t + 2}$ **53.** $\dfrac{x + 4}{x + 1}$
55. $-\dfrac{w - 3}{2}$ **57.** $\dfrac{k + 6}{k + 3}$ **59.** $\dfrac{2}{a}$ **61.** $2y(y + 1)$
63. $x + y$ **65.** $\dfrac{z}{3}$ **67.** 2   **69.** $\dfrac{1}{a - 2}$ **71.** $\dfrac{p + q}{2}$

Section 7.3 Practice Exercises, pp. 516–518

1. multiple; denominators   **3.** $x = 1, x = -1; \dfrac{3}{5(x - 1)}$
5. $\dfrac{a + 5}{a + 7}$ **7.** $\dfrac{2}{3y}$ **9.** a, b, c, d
11. x^5 is the greatest power of x that appears in any
denominator.   **13.** 45   **15.** 48   **17.** 63   **19.** $9x^2y^3$
21. w^2y **23.** $(p + 3)(p - 1)(p + 2)$ **25.** $9t(t + 1)^2$
27. $(y - 2)(y + 2)(y + 3)$ **29.** $3 - x$ or $x - 3$
31. Because $(b - 1)$ and $(1 - b)$ are opposites; they differ
by a factor of -1.

33. $\dfrac{6}{5x^2}$; $\dfrac{5x}{5x^2}$ **35.** $\dfrac{24x}{30x^3}$; $\dfrac{5y}{30x^3}$ **37.** $\dfrac{10}{12a^2b}$; $\dfrac{a^3}{12a^2b}$

39. $\dfrac{6m - 6}{(m + 4)(m - 1)}$; $\dfrac{3m + 12}{(m + 4)(m - 1)}$

41. $\dfrac{6x + 18}{(2x - 5)(x + 3)}$; $\dfrac{2x - 5}{(2x - 5)(x + 3)}$

43. $\dfrac{6w + 6}{(w + 3)(w - 8)(w + 1)}$; $\dfrac{w^2 + 3w}{(w + 3)(w - 8)(w + 1)}$

45. $\dfrac{6p^2 + 12p}{(p - 2)(p + 2)^2}$; $\dfrac{3p - 6}{(p - 2)(p + 2)^2}$

47. $\dfrac{1}{a - 4}$; $\dfrac{-a}{a - 4}$ or $\dfrac{-1}{4 - a}$; $\dfrac{a}{4 - a}$

49. $\dfrac{8}{2(x - 7)}$; $\dfrac{-y}{2(x - 7)}$ or $\dfrac{-8}{2(7 - x)}$; $\dfrac{y}{2(7 - x)}$

51. $\dfrac{1}{a + b}$; $\dfrac{-6}{a + b}$ or $\dfrac{-1}{-a - b}$; $\dfrac{6}{-a - b}$

53. $\dfrac{-9}{24(3y + 1)}$; $\dfrac{20}{24(3y + 1)}$ **55.** $\dfrac{3z + 12}{5z(z + 4)}$; $\dfrac{5z}{5z(z + 4)}$

57. $\dfrac{z^2 + 3z}{(z + 2)(z + 7)(z + 3)}$; $\dfrac{-3z^2 - 6z}{(z + 2)(z + 7)(z + 3)}$;

$\dfrac{5z + 35}{(z + 2)(z + 7)(z + 3)}$

59. $\dfrac{3p + 6}{(p - 2)(p^2 + 2p + 4)(p + 2)}$; $\dfrac{p^3 + 2p^2 + 4p}{(p - 2)(p^2 + 2p + 4)(p + 2)}$;

$\dfrac{5p^3 - 20p}{(p - 2)(p^2 + 2p + 4)(p + 2)}$

Section 7.4 Practice Exercises, pp. 525–527

1. a. $-\dfrac{1}{2}$, -2, 0, undefined, undefined

b. $(x - 5)(x - 2)$; $x = 5$, $x = 2$ **c.** $\dfrac{x + 1}{x - 2}$

3. $\dfrac{2(2b - 3)}{(b - 3)(b - 1)}$ **5.** $\dfrac{5}{4}$ **7.** $\dfrac{3}{8}$ **9.** 2

11. 5   **13.** $\dfrac{-2(t - 2)}{t - 8}$ **15.** $3x + 7$

17. $m + 5$ **19.** 2   **21.** $x - 5$ **23.** $\dfrac{1}{r + 1}$

25. $\dfrac{1}{y + 7}$ **27.** $\dfrac{15x}{y}$ **29.** $\dfrac{5a + 6}{4a}$ **31.** $\dfrac{2(6 + x^2y)}{15xy^3}$

33. $\dfrac{2s - 3t^2}{s^4t^3}$ **35.** $-\dfrac{2}{3}$ **37.** $\dfrac{19}{3(a + 1)}$

39. $\dfrac{-3(k + 4)}{(k - 3)(k + 3)}$ **41.** $\dfrac{a - 4}{2a}$ **43.** $\dfrac{(x + 6)(x - 2)}{(x - 4)(x + 1)}$

45. $\dfrac{x(4x + 9)}{(x + 3)^2(x + 2)}$ **47.** $\dfrac{5p - 1}{3}$ or $\dfrac{-5p + 1}{-3}$

49. $\dfrac{9}{x - 3}$ or $\dfrac{-9}{3 - x}$ **51.** $\dfrac{6n - 1}{n - 8}$ or $\dfrac{-6n + 1}{8 - n}$

53. $\dfrac{2(4x + 5)}{x(x + 2)}$ **55.** $\dfrac{3y}{2(2y + 1)}$ **57.** $\dfrac{2(w - 3)}{(w + 3)(w - 1)}$

59. $\dfrac{4a - 13}{(a - 3)(a - 4)}$ **61.** $\dfrac{3x(x + 7)}{(x + 5)^2(x - 1)}$

63. $\dfrac{-y(y + 8)}{(2y + 1)(y - 1)(y - 4)}$ **65.** $\dfrac{1}{2p + 1}$

67. $\dfrac{-2mn + 1}{(m + n)(m - n)}$ **69.** 0   **71.** $\dfrac{2(3x + 7)}{(x + 3)(x + 2)}$

73. $\dfrac{1}{n}$ **75.** $\dfrac{5}{n + 2}$ **77.** $n + \left(7 \cdot \dfrac{1}{n}\right)$; $\dfrac{n^2 + 7}{n}$

79. $\dfrac{1}{n} - \dfrac{2}{n}$; $-\dfrac{1}{n}$ **81.** $\dfrac{-w^2}{(w + 3)(w - 3)(w^2 - 3w + 9)}$

83. $\dfrac{p^2 - 2p + 7}{(p + 2)(p + 3)(p - 1)}$

85. $\dfrac{-m - 21}{2(m + 5)(m - 2)}$ or $\dfrac{m + 21}{2(m + 5)(2 - m)}$ **87.** $\dfrac{3k + 5}{4k + 7}$

89. $\dfrac{1}{a}$

Chapter 7 Problem Recognition Exercises, p. 528

1. $\dfrac{-2x + 9}{3x + 1}$ **2.** $\dfrac{1}{w - 4}$ **3.** $\dfrac{y - 5}{2y - 3}$

4. $\dfrac{7}{(x + 3)(2x - 1)}$ **5.** $-\dfrac{1}{x}$ **6.** $\dfrac{1}{3}$ **7.** $\dfrac{c + 3}{c}$

8. $\dfrac{x + 3}{5}$ **9.** $\dfrac{a}{12b^4c}$ **10.** $\dfrac{2a - b}{a - b}$ **11.** $\dfrac{p - q}{5}$

12. 4   **13.** $\dfrac{10}{2x + 1}$ **14.** $\dfrac{w + 2z}{w + z}$ **15.** $\dfrac{3}{2x + 5}$

16. $\dfrac{y + 7}{x + a}$ **17.** $\dfrac{1}{2(a + 3)}$ **18.** $\dfrac{2(3y + 10)}{(y - 6)(y + 6)(y + 2)}$

19. $(t + 8)^2$ **20.** $6b + 5$

Section 7.5 Practice Exercises, pp. 534–535

1. complex   **3.** $\dfrac{1}{2a - 3}$ **5.** $\dfrac{3(2k - 5)}{5(k - 2)}$

7. $\dfrac{7}{4y}$ **9.** $\dfrac{1}{2y}$ **11.** $\dfrac{24b}{a^3}$ **13.** $\dfrac{2r^5t^4}{s^6}$

15. $\dfrac{35}{2}$ **17.** $k + h$ **19.** $\dfrac{n + 1}{2(n - 3)}$ **21.** $\dfrac{2x + 1}{4x + 1}$

23. $m - 7$ **25.** $\dfrac{2y(y - 5)}{7y^2 + 10}$ **27.** $-\dfrac{a + 8}{a - 2}$ or $\dfrac{a + 8}{2 - a}$

29. $\dfrac{t - 2}{t - 4}$ **31.** $\dfrac{t + 3}{t - 5}$ **33.** $\dfrac{1}{2}$ **35.** $\dfrac{\frac{1}{2} + \frac{2}{3}}{5}$; $\dfrac{7}{30}$

37. $\dfrac{\frac{3}{2} + \frac{3}{4}}{\frac{2}{3}}$; $\dfrac{36}{17}$ **39. a.** $\dfrac{6}{5}\,\Omega$ **b.** $6\,\Omega$ **41.** $\dfrac{xy}{y + x}$

43. $\dfrac{y + 4x}{2y}$ **45.** $\dfrac{1}{n^2 + m^2}$ **47.** $\dfrac{2z - 5}{3(z + 3)}$

49. $\dfrac{x + 1}{x - 1}$ or $\dfrac{x + 1}{1 - x}$ **51.** $\dfrac{3}{2}$

Section 7.6 Practice Exercises, pp. 543–545

1. a. linear; quadratic   **b.** rational   **c.** denominator

3. $\dfrac{2}{4x - 1}$ **5.** $5(h + 1)$ **7.** $\dfrac{(x + 4)(x - 3)}{x^2}$

9. 3   **11.** $\dfrac{5}{11}$ **13.** $\dfrac{1}{3}$ **15. a.** $z = 0$ **b.** $5z$ **c.** 5

17. $-\dfrac{200}{19}$ **19.** -7 **21.** $\dfrac{47}{6}$ **23.** 3, -1 **25.** 4

27. 5; (The value 0 does not check.)   **29.** -5

31. No solution; (The value 4 does not check.)   **33.** 4
35. 4, −3   **37.** −4; (The value 1 does not check.)
39. No solution; (The value −4 does not check.)
41. 4; (The value −6 does not check.)   **43.** −25
45. −2, 7   **47.** The number is 8.   **49.** The number is −26.
51. $m = \dfrac{FK}{a}$ **53.** $E = \dfrac{IR}{K}$
55. $R = \dfrac{E - Ir}{I}$ or $R = \dfrac{E}{I} - r$
57. $B = \dfrac{2A - hb}{h}$ or $B = \dfrac{2A}{h} - b$ **59.** $h = \dfrac{V}{r^2\pi}$
61. $t = \dfrac{b}{x - a}$ or $t = \dfrac{-b}{a - x}$ **63.** $x = \dfrac{y}{1 - yz}$ or
$x = \dfrac{-y}{yz - 1}$ **65.** $h = \dfrac{2A}{a + b}$ **67.** $R = \dfrac{R_1 R_2}{R_2 + R_1}$

Chapter 7 Problem Recognition Exercises, p. 545

1. $\dfrac{y - 2}{2y}$ **2.** 6   **3.** 2   **4.** $\dfrac{3a - 17}{a - 5}$ **5.** $\dfrac{4p + 27}{18p^2}$
6. $\dfrac{b(b - 5)}{(b - 1)(b + 1)}$ **7.** 5   **8.** $\dfrac{2w + 5}{(w + 1)^2}$ **9.** 7
10. 5   **11.** $\dfrac{3x + 14}{4(x + 1)}$ **12.** $\dfrac{11}{3}$ **13.** $\dfrac{41}{10}$ **14.** $\dfrac{7 - 3t}{t(t - 5)}$
15. $\dfrac{8a + 1}{2a - 1}$ **16.** 5; (The value 2 does not check.)
17. −1; (The value 3 does not check.)   **18.** $\dfrac{11}{12k}$
19. $\dfrac{h + 9}{(h - 3)(h + 3)}$ **20.** 7

Section 7.7 Practice Exercises, pp. 553–557

1. a. proportion   **b.** proportional
3. Expression; $\dfrac{m^2 + m + 2}{(m - 1)(m + 3)}$ **5.** Expression; $\dfrac{3}{10}$
7. Equation; 2   **9.** 95   **11.** 1   **13.** $\dfrac{40}{3}$ **15.** 40
17. 3   **19.** −1   **21.** 1   **23. a.** $V_f = \dfrac{V_i T_f}{T_i}$
b. $T_f = \dfrac{T_i V_f}{V_i}$ **25.** Toni can drive 297 mi on 9 gal of gas.
27. Mix 14.82 mL of plant food.   **29.** 5 oz contains 12 g of carbohydrate.   **31.** The minimum length is 20 ft.
33. $x = 4$ cm; $y = 5$ cm   **35.** $x = 3.75$ cm; $y = 4.5$ cm
37. The height of the pole is 7 m.   **39.** The light post is 24 ft high.   **41.** The speed of the boat is 20 mph.
43. The plane flies 210 mph in still air.   **45.** He runs 8 mph and bikes 16 mph.   **47.** Floyd walks 4 mph and Rachel walks 2 mph.   **49.** Sergio rode 12 mph and walked 3 mph.   **51.** $5\frac{5}{11}$ $(5.\overline{45})$ min   **53.** $22\frac{2}{9}$ $(22.\overline{2})$ min
55. 48 hr   **57.** $3\frac{1}{3}$ $(3.\overline{3})$ days
59. There are 40 smokers and 140 nonsmokers.
61. There are 240 men and 200 women.

Section 7.8 Practice Exercises, pp. 561–564

1. a. kx **b.** $\dfrac{k}{x}$ **c.** kxw **3.** 12   **5.** 2, 6   **7.** $\dfrac{b + 1}{1 - b}$
9. Inversely   **11.** $T = kq$

11. $T = kq$ **13.** $b = \dfrac{k}{c}$ **15.** $Q = \dfrac{kx}{y}$ **17.** $c = kst$
19. $L = kw\sqrt{v}$ **21.** $x = \dfrac{ky^2}{z}$ **23.** $k = \dfrac{9}{2}$
25. $k = 512$ **27.** $k = 1.75$ **29.** $x = 70$ **31.** $b = 6$
33. $Z = 56$ **35.** $Q = 9$ **37.** $L = 9$ **39.** $B = \dfrac{15}{2}$
41. a. The heart weighs 0.92 lb.   **b.** Answers will vary.
43. a. 3.6 g   **b.** 4.5 g   **c.** 2.4 g   **45. a.** $0.40   **b.** $0.30
c. $1.00   **47.** 355,000 tons   **49.** 42.6 ft
51. 300 W   **53.** 18.5 A   **55.** 20 lb   **57.** $3500

Chapter 7 Review Exercises pp. 571–574

1. a. $-\dfrac{2}{9}, -\dfrac{1}{10}, 0, -\dfrac{5}{6}$, undefined   **b.** $t = -9$
2. a. $-\dfrac{1}{5}, -\dfrac{1}{2}$, undefined, $0, \dfrac{1}{7}$ **b.** $k = 5$ **3.** a, c, d
4. $x = \dfrac{5}{2}, x = 3; \dfrac{1}{2x - 5}$ **5.** $h = -\dfrac{1}{3}, h = -7; \dfrac{1}{3h + 1}$
6. $a = 2, a = -2; \dfrac{4a - 1}{a - 2}$ **7.** $w = 4, w = -4; \dfrac{2w + 3}{w - 4}$
8. $z = 4; -\dfrac{z}{2}$ **9.** $k = 0, k = 5; -\dfrac{3}{2k}$
10. $b = -3; \dfrac{b - 1}{2}$ **11.** $m = -1; \dfrac{m - 5}{3}$
12. $n = -3; \dfrac{1}{n + 3}$ **13.** $p = -7; \dfrac{1}{p + 7}$
14. y^2 **15.** $\dfrac{u^2}{2}$ **16.** $v + 2$ **17.** $\dfrac{3}{2(x - 5)}$
18. $\dfrac{c(c + 1)}{2(c + 5)}$ **19.** $\dfrac{q - 2}{4}$ **20.** $-2t(t - 5)$
21. $4s(s - 4)$ **22.** $\dfrac{1}{7}$ **23.** $\dfrac{1}{n - 2}$ **24.** $-\dfrac{1}{6}$
25. $\dfrac{1}{m + 3}$ **26.** $\dfrac{-1}{(x + 3)(x + 2)}$ **27.** $-\dfrac{2y - 1}{y + 1}$
28. LCD $= (n + 3)(n - 3)(n + 2)$
29. LCD $= (m + 4)(m - 4)(m + 3)$
30. $c - 2$ or $2 - c$ **31.** $3 - x$ or $x - 3$
32. $\dfrac{4b}{10ab}, \dfrac{3a}{10ab}$ **33.** $\dfrac{21y}{12xy}, \dfrac{22x}{12xy}$ **34.** $\dfrac{y}{x^2 y^5}, \dfrac{3x}{x^2 y^5}$
35. $\dfrac{5c^2}{ab^3 c^2}, \dfrac{3b^3}{ab^3 c^2}$ **36.** $\dfrac{5p - 20}{(p + 2)(p - 4)}, \dfrac{p^2 + 2p}{(p + 2)(p - 4)}$
37. $\dfrac{6q + 48}{q(q + 8)}, \dfrac{q}{q(q + 8)}$ **38.** 2   **39.** 2   **40.** $a + 5$
41. $x - 7$ **42.** $\dfrac{-y - 18}{(y - 9)(y + 9)}$ or $\dfrac{y + 18}{(9 - y)(y + 9)}$
43. $\dfrac{t^2 + 2t + 3}{(2 - t)(2 + t)}$ **44.** $\dfrac{m + 8}{3m(m + 2)}$ **45.** $\dfrac{3(r - 4)}{2r(r + 6)}$
46. $\dfrac{p}{(p + 4)(p + 5)}$ **47.** $\dfrac{q}{(q + 5)(q + 4)}$ **48.** $\dfrac{1}{2}$
49. $\dfrac{1}{3}$ **50.** $\dfrac{a - 4}{a - 2}$ **51.** $\dfrac{3(z + 5)}{z(z - 5)}$ **52.** $\dfrac{w}{2}$ **53.** $\dfrac{8}{y}$
54. $y - x$ **55.** $-(b + a)$ **56.** $-\dfrac{2p + 7}{2p}$
57. $-\dfrac{k + 10}{k + 4}$ **58.** −8   **59.** −2   **60.** 2

61. -2 **62.** 3   **63.** -1 (The value 3 does not check.)
64. No solution; (The value 2 does not check.)

65. $-11, 1$ **66.** The number is 4.   **67.** $h = \dfrac{3V}{\pi r^2}$

68. $b = \dfrac{2A}{h}$ **69.** $\dfrac{6}{5}$ **70.** $\dfrac{96}{5}$

71. It contains 10 g of fat.
72. Ed travels at 60 mph, and Bud travels at 70 mph.
73. Together the pumps would fill the pool in 16.8 min.
74. $x = 11$; $b = 26$ **75. a.** $F = kd$ **b.** $k = 3$ **c.** 12.6 lb

76. $y = \dfrac{8}{3}$ **77.** $y = 12$ **78.** 48 km

Chapter 7 Test pp. 574–575

1. a. $x = 2$ **b.** $-\dfrac{x+1}{6}$ **2. a.** $a = 6, a = -2, a = 0$

b. $\dfrac{7}{a+2}$ **3.** b, c, d   **4. a.** $15(x+3)$ **b.** $3x^2y^2$

5. $\dfrac{y+7}{3(y+3)(y+1)}$ **6.** $-\dfrac{b+3}{5}$ **7.** $\dfrac{1}{w+1}$

8. $\dfrac{t+4}{t+2}$ **9.** $\dfrac{x(x+5)}{(x+4)(x-2)}$ **10.** $\dfrac{2y+7}{y-6}$ or $\dfrac{-2y-7}{6-y}$

11. $\dfrac{1}{m+4}$ **12.** $\dfrac{8}{5}$ **13.** 2   **14.** 1

15. No solution; (The value 4 does not check.)
16. -5 (The value 2 does not check.)

17 $r = \dfrac{2A}{C}$ **18.** -8 **19.** $1\frac{1}{4}$ (1.25) cups of carrots

20. The speed of the current is 5 mph.   **21.** It would
take the second printer 3 hr to do the job working alone.
22. $a = 5.6$; $b = 12$ **23.** 8.25 mL
24. 200 drinks are sold.

Chapters 1–7 Cumulative Review Exercises pp. 575–576

1. 32   **2.** 7   **3.** $\dfrac{10}{9}$

4.

Set-Builder Notation	Graph	Interval Notation
$\{x \mid x \geq -1\}$	$\xrightarrow{\hspace{0.3cm}\underset{-1}{\bullet}\hspace{0.6cm}}$	$[-1, \infty)$
$\{x \mid x < 5\}$	$\xleftarrow{\hspace{0.6cm}\underset{5}{\hspace{0.1cm}}\hspace{0.3cm}}$	$(-\infty, 5)$

5. The width is 17 m and the length is 35 m.

6. The base is 10 in. and the height is 8 in.   **7.** $\dfrac{x^2yz^{17}}{2}$

8. a. $6x + 4$ **b.** $2x^2 + x - 3$ **9.** $(5x - 3)^2$
10. $(2c + 1)(5d - 3)$

11. $x = 5, x = -\dfrac{1}{2}$ **12.** $(1, -4)$ **13.** $\dfrac{1}{5(x+4)}$

14. -3 **15.** 1   **16.** $-\dfrac{7}{2}$

17. a. x-intercept: $(-4, 0)$; y-intercept: $(0, 2)$
b. x-intercept: $(0, 0)$; y-intercept: $(0, 0)$

18. a. $m = -\dfrac{7}{5}$ **b.** $m = -\dfrac{2}{3}$ **c.** $m = 4$ **d.** $m = -\dfrac{1}{4}$

19. $y = 5x - 3$ **20.** One large popcorn costs $4.50, and
one drink costs $3.00.

Chapter 8

Chapter Opener Puzzle

P	Y	T	H	A	G	O	R	E	A	N	T	H	E	O	R	E	M
5		2			4		1						6				3

Section 8.1 Calculator Connections, p. 584

1. 2.236   **2.** 4.123   **3.** 7.071   **4.** 9.798
5. 5.745   **6.** 12.042   **7.** 8.944   **8.** 13.038
9. 1.913   **10.** 3.037   **11.** 4.021   **12.** 4.987

Section 8.1 Practice Exercises, pp. 585–588

1. a. b; a **b.** principal   **c.** rational   **d.** b^n; a
e. index; radicand   **f.** cube   **g.** is not; is   **h.** even; odd
i. $a^2 + b^2 = c^2$ **3.** $12, -12$
   5. There are no real-valued square roots of -49.

7. 0   **9.** $\dfrac{1}{5}, -\dfrac{1}{5}$ **11. a.** 13   **b.** -13 **13.** 0

15. 9, 16, 25, 36, 64, 121, 169   **17.** 2   **19.** 7   **21.** 0.4

23. 0.3   **25.** $\dfrac{5}{4}$ **27.** $\dfrac{1}{12}$ **29.** 5   **31.** 9

33. There is no real value of b for which $b^2 = -16$.
35. -2 **37.** Not a real number   **39.** Not a real number
41. Not a real number   **43.** -20 **45.** Not a real number
47. 0, 1, 27, 125   **49.** Yes, -3 **51.** 3   **53.** 4
55. -2 **57.** Not a real number   **59.** Not a real number

61. $-\dfrac{1}{2}$ **63.** -1 **65.** 0   **67.** $x^2, y^4, (ab)^6, w^8x^8, m^{10}$.
The expression is a perfect square if the exponent is even.
69. 4   **71.** 5   **73.** y^6 **75.** a^4b^{15} **77.** q^8
79. $2w^2$ **81.** $5x$ **83.** $-5x$ **85.** $5p^2$ **87.** $5p^2$

89. $\sqrt{q} + p^2$ **91.** $\dfrac{6}{\sqrt[3]{x}}$ **93.** 9 cm   **95.** 5 ft

97. 6.9 cm   **99.** 17.0 in.   **101.** 31.3 in.
103. 268 km   **105.** $x \geq 0$ **107.** $a \geq b$

Section 8.2 Calculator Connections, p. 593

1.
```
√(125)
          11.18033989
5*√(5)
          11.18033989
```

2.
```
√(18)
          4.242640687
3*√(2)
          4.242640687
```

3.
```
³√(54)
          3.77976315
3*³√(2)
          3.77976315
```

4.
```
³√(108)
          4.762203156
3*³√(4)
          4.762203156
```

Section 8.2 Practice Exercises, pp. 594–596

1. a. $\sqrt[n]{a}$ **b.** The exponent within the radicand is not less
than the index.   **c.** No. $\sqrt{2}$ is an irrational number; therefore
its decimal form is a nonterminating, nonrepeating decimal.
3. $8, 27, y^3, y^9, y^{12}, y^{27}$ **5.** -5 **7.** -3 **9.** a^4
11. $2xy^2$ **13.** 446 km   **15.** $3\sqrt{2}$ **17.** $2\sqrt{7}$
19. $12\sqrt{5}$ **21.** $-10\sqrt{2}$ **23.** $a^2\sqrt{a}$ **25.** w^{11}
27. $m^2n^2\sqrt{n}$ **29.** $x^7y^5\sqrt{x}$ **31.** $3t^5$ **33.** $2x\sqrt{2x}$

35. $4z\sqrt{z}$ **37.** $-3w^3\sqrt{5}$ **39.** $z^{12}\sqrt{z}$ **41.** $-z^5\sqrt{15z}$
43. $10ab^3\sqrt{26b}$ **45.** $\sqrt{26pq}$ **47.** m^6n^8

49. $-4ab^2c^2\sqrt{3ab}$ **51.** a^4 **53.** y^5 **55.** $\dfrac{1}{2}$

57. 2   **59.** $2x$ **61.** $5p^3$ **63.** $3\sqrt{5}$ **65.** $\sqrt{6}$
67. 4   **69.** 7   **71.** $11\sqrt{2}$ ft   **73.** $2\sqrt{66}$ cm
75. $a^2\sqrt[3]{a^2}$ **77.** $14z\sqrt[3]{2}$ **79.** $2ab^2\sqrt[3]{2a^2}$ **81.** z

83. -2 **85.** $-2\sqrt[3]{5}$ **87.** $\dfrac{1}{3}$ **89.** $4a\sqrt{a}$

91. $2x$ **93.** $2p\sqrt{2q}$ **95.** $-4\sqrt{2}$ **97.** $2u^2v^3\sqrt{13v}$
99. $6\sqrt{6}$ **101.** 6   **103.** $2a\sqrt[3]{2}$ **105.** x

107. $-\sqrt{5}$ **109.** $-\dfrac{1}{2}$ **111.** $5\sqrt{2}$ **113.** $x+5$

Section 8.3 Practice Exercises, pp. 599–601

1. index; radicand   **3.** $2y$ **5.** $6x\sqrt{x}$ **7.** $2x$
9. Not a real number   **11.** For example, $2\sqrt{3}, 6\sqrt[3]{3}$
13. c   **15.** $8\sqrt{2}$ **17.** $4\sqrt{7}$ **19.** $2\sqrt[3]{10}$
21. $11\sqrt{y}$ **23.** 0   **25.** $5y\sqrt{15}$ **27.** $x\sqrt{y}-y\sqrt{x}$
29. $8\sqrt{3}$ **31.** 0   **33.** $2\sqrt{2}$ **35.** $16p^2\sqrt{5}$
37. $10\sqrt{2k}$ **39.** $a^2\sqrt{b}$ **41.** $3\sqrt{5}$ **43.** $\dfrac{29}{18}z\sqrt{6}$

45. $-1.7\sqrt{10}$ **47.** $2x\sqrt{x}$ **49.** $3\sqrt{7}$
51. $4\sqrt{w}+2\sqrt{6w}+2\sqrt{10w}$ **53.** $6x^3\sqrt{y}$
55. $2\sqrt{3}-4\sqrt{6}$ **57.** $-4x\sqrt{2}+\sqrt{2x}$ **59.** $9\sqrt{2}$ m
61. $16\sqrt{3}$ in.   **63.** Radicands are not the same.
65. One term has a radical. One does not.

67. The indices are different.   **69.** $\dfrac{\sqrt{3}}{3}$ **71. a.** 80 m
b. 159 m

Section 8.4 Practice Exercises, pp. 606–607

1. a. $\sqrt[n]{ab}$ **b.** a **c.** conjugates   **3.** 11   **5.** $3w^2\sqrt{z}$
7. $\sqrt{15}$ **9.** 47   **11.** b **13.** $6\sqrt{15p}$ **15.** $5\sqrt{2}$
17. $14\sqrt{2}$ **19.** $6x\sqrt{7}$ **21.** $4x^3\sqrt{y}$ **23.** $12w^2\sqrt{10}$
25. $-8\sqrt{15}$ **27.** Perimeter: $6\sqrt{5}$ ft; area: 10 ft^2
29. 3 cm^2 **31.** $3w$ **33.** $-16\sqrt{10y}$ **35.** $2\sqrt{3}-\sqrt{6}$
37. $4x+20\sqrt{x}$ **39.** $-8+7\sqrt{30}$
41. $9a-28b\sqrt{a}+3b^2$ **43.** $8p^2+19p\sqrt{p}+2p-8\sqrt{p}$
45. 10   **47.** 4   **49.** t **51.** $16c$ **53.** $29+8\sqrt{13}$
55. $a-4\sqrt{a}+4$ **57.** $4a-12\sqrt{a}+9$
59. $21-2\sqrt{110}$ **61.** 1   **63.** $x-y$ **65.** -1
67. 4   **69.** $64x-4y$ **71.** 73   **73. a.** $3x+6$
b. $\sqrt{3x}+\sqrt{6}$ **75. a.** $4a^2+12a+9$ **b.** $4a+12\sqrt{a}+9$
77. a. b^2-25 **b.** $b-25$ **79. a.** $x^2-4xy+4y^2$
b. $x-4\sqrt{xy}+4y$ **81. a.** p^2-q^2 **b.** $p-q$
83. a. y^2-6y+9 **b.** $x-6\sqrt{x-2}+7$

Section 8.5 Practice Exercises, pp. 614–617

1. a. index   **b.** denominator   **c.** rationalizing   **d.** $\dfrac{\sqrt[n]{a}}{\sqrt[n]{b}}$
e. denominator   **3.** $6y+23\sqrt{y}+21$ **5.** $9\sqrt{3}$

7. $25-10\sqrt{a}+a$ **9.** -5 **11.** $\dfrac{\sqrt{3}}{4}$ **13.** $\dfrac{a^2}{b^2}$

15. $\dfrac{c\sqrt{c}}{2}$ **17.** $\dfrac{\sqrt[3]{x^2}}{3}$ **19.** $\dfrac{\sqrt[3]{y^2}}{3}$ **21.** $\dfrac{10\sqrt{2}}{9}$ **23.** $\dfrac{2}{5}$

25. $\dfrac{1}{2p}$ **27.** z **29.** $2\sqrt[3]{x}$ **31.** $\dfrac{\sqrt{6}}{6}$ **33.** $3\sqrt{5}$

35. $\dfrac{6\sqrt{x+1}}{x+1}$ **37.** $\dfrac{\sqrt{6x}}{x}$ **39.** $\dfrac{\sqrt{21}}{7}$ **41.** $\dfrac{5\sqrt{6y}}{3y}$

43. $\dfrac{3\sqrt{6}}{4}$ **45.** $\dfrac{\sqrt{3p}}{9}$ **47.** $\dfrac{\sqrt{5}}{2}$ **49.** $\dfrac{x\sqrt{y}}{y^2}$ **51.** -7

53. $\sqrt{5}+\sqrt{3}; 2$ **55.** $\sqrt{x}-10; x-100$
57. $\dfrac{4\sqrt{2}-12}{-7}$ or $\dfrac{12-4\sqrt{2}}{7}$ **59.** $\dfrac{\sqrt{5}+\sqrt{2}}{3}$

61. $\sqrt{6}-\sqrt{2}$ **63.** $\dfrac{\sqrt{x}+\sqrt{3}}{x-3}$ **65.** $7-4\sqrt{3}$

67. $-13-6\sqrt{5}$ **69.** $2-\sqrt{2}$ **71.** $\dfrac{3+\sqrt{2}}{2}$

73. $1-\sqrt{7}$ **75.** $\dfrac{7+3\sqrt{2}}{3}$ **77. a.** Condition 1 fails;

$2x^4\sqrt{2x}$ **b.** Condition 2 fails; $\dfrac{\sqrt{5x}}{x}$ **c.** Condition 3 fails;

$\dfrac{\sqrt{3}}{3}$ **79. a.** Condition 2 fails; $\dfrac{3\sqrt{x}-3}{x-1}$ **b.** Conditions

1 and 3 fail; $\dfrac{3w\sqrt{t}}{t}$ **c.** Condition 1 fails; $2a^2b^4\sqrt{6ab}$

81. $3\sqrt{5}$ **83.** $-\dfrac{3w\sqrt{2}}{5}$ **85.** Not a real number

87. $\dfrac{s\sqrt{t}}{t}$ **89.** $\dfrac{m^2}{2}$ **91.** $\dfrac{9\sqrt{t}}{t^2}$ **93.** $\dfrac{\sqrt{11}-\sqrt{5}}{2}$

95. $\dfrac{a+2\sqrt{ab}+b}{a-b}$ **97.** $-\dfrac{3\sqrt{2}}{8}$ **99.** $\dfrac{\sqrt{3}}{9}$

Chapter 8 Problem Recognition Exercises, p. 617

1. a. $3\sqrt{2}$ **b.** Cannot be simplified further.   **c.** $\sqrt{2}$
2. a. $\sqrt{7}$ **b.** $2\sqrt{7}$ **c.** Cannot be simplified further.
3. a. $9z$ **b.** $9+6\sqrt{z}+z$ **c.** $9-z$
4. a. $16-8\sqrt{x}+x$ **b.** $16-x$ **c.** $16x$
5. a. $\dfrac{6\sqrt{2x}}{x}$ **b.** $\dfrac{\sqrt{6x}}{x}$ **c.** $\dfrac{12\sqrt{2}-12x}{2-x^2}$
6. a. $\dfrac{45+15\sqrt{y}}{9-y}$ **b.** $\dfrac{5\sqrt{3y}}{y}$ **c.** $\dfrac{\sqrt{5y}}{y}$
7. a. $3\sqrt{5}-1$ **b.** $8-3\sqrt{5}$ **c.** $10-4\sqrt{5}$
8. a. $-8+11\sqrt{3}$ **b.** $12+16\sqrt{3}$ **c.** $3\sqrt{3}-9$
9. a. $4a^7\sqrt{a}$ **b.** $2a^5\sqrt[3]{2}$ **10. a.** $3y^3$ **b.** $3y^4\sqrt{3y}$

Section 8.6 Practice Exercises, pp. 622–624

1. a. radical   **b.** extraneous   **c.** Isolate the radical by
adding 3 to both sides of the equation.   **d.** third
3. $\dfrac{\sqrt{2}-\sqrt{10}}{-8}$ or $\dfrac{\sqrt{10}-\sqrt{2}}{8}$ **5.** $\dfrac{2\sqrt{6}}{3}$
7. $x^2+8x+16$ **9.** $x+8\sqrt{x}+16$ **11.** $2x-3$
13. t^2+2t+1 **15.** 36   **17.** 15   **19.** No solution
(The value 29 does not check.)   **21.** 5   **23.** $-\dfrac{1}{2}$

25. 6   **27.** 8   **29.** No solution (The value $\frac{19}{2}$ does
not check.)   **31.** 1   **33.** $4, -3$ **35.** 0
37. No solution (The value -4 does not check.)
39. 4, (The value -1 does not check.)   **41.** $0, -1$
43. 12, (The value 4 does not check.)   **45.** -6 **47.** -1
49. $\sqrt{x+10}=1$; -9 **51.** $\sqrt{2x}=x-4$;   8
53. $\sqrt[3]{x+1}=2$;   7   **55. a.** 80 ft/sec   **b.** 289 ft

57. a. 16 in.   **b.** 25 weeks   **59.** $\dfrac{9}{5}$

61. $\dfrac{3}{2}$ (The value -1 does not check.)

Section 8.7 Practice Exercises, pp. 628–630

1. a. $\sqrt[n]{a}$ **b.** $\sqrt[n]{a^m}$ or $(\sqrt[n]{a})^m$ **3.** 27   **5.** $a + 1$

7. 9   **9.** 5   **11.** 3   **13.** -2 **15.** -2 **17.** $\dfrac{1}{6}$

19. $\sqrt[3]{x}$ **21.** $\sqrt{4a}$ or $2\sqrt{a}$ **23.** $\sqrt[5]{yz}$ **25.** $\sqrt[3]{u^2}$

27. $5\sqrt{q}$ **29.** $\sqrt{\dfrac{x}{9}}$ or $\dfrac{\sqrt{x}}{3}$ **31.** $a^{m/n} = \sqrt[n]{a^m}$ or $(\sqrt[n]{a})^m$,

provided the roots exist.   **33.** 8   **35.** $\dfrac{1}{9}$ **37.** -32

39. 2   **41.** $(\sqrt{y})^9$ **43.** $\sqrt[3]{c^5 d}$ **45.** $\dfrac{1}{\sqrt[5]{qr}}$

47. $6\sqrt[3]{y^2}$ **49.** $x^{1/3}$ **51.** $5x^{1/2}$ **53.** $y^{2/3}$

55. $(m^3 n)^{1/4}$ **57.** x **59.** y^2 **61.** 6   **63.** a^7

65. $y^{4/3}$ **67.** 2   **69.** $\dfrac{y^{1/6}}{x}$ **71.** $\dfrac{w^3}{z^6}$

73. $\dfrac{25a^4 d}{c}$ **75.** $\dfrac{y^9}{x^8}$ **77.** $\dfrac{2z^3}{w}$ **79.** $5xy^2 z^{3/2}$

81. a. 10 in.   **b.** 8.49 in.   **83. a.** 10.9%   **b.** 8.8%
c. The account in part (a)   **85.** No, for example,

$(36 + 64)^{1/2} \neq 36^{1/2} + 64^{1/2}$ **87.** 6   **89.** $\dfrac{5}{14}$ **91.** $\dfrac{a^{22} b^4}{c^{17}}$

Chapter 8 Review Exercises, pp. 636–638

1. Principal square root: 14; negative square root: -14
2. Principal square root: 1.2; negative square root: -1.2
3. Principal square root: 0.8; negative square root: -0.8
4. Principal square root: 15; negative square root: -15
5. There is no real number b such that $b^2 = -64$.
6. $\sqrt[3]{-64} = -4$ because $(-4)^3 = -64$.   **7.** -12
8. -5 **9.** Not a real number   **10.** Not a real number
11. y **12.** a **13.** $2p$ **14.** -5 **15.** -5

16. p^4 **17.** $\dfrac{4}{t^2}$ **18.** $-\dfrac{3}{w}$ **19. a.** 7.1 m   **b.** 22.6 ft

20. a. 65.8 ft   **b.** 131.6 ft   **21.** $b^2 + \sqrt{5}$
22. $\sqrt[3]{y} - \sqrt[4]{x}$ **23.** The quotient of 2 and the principal
square root of p **24.** The product of 8 and the principal
square root of q **25.** 12 ft   **26.** 331 mi
27. $x^8 \sqrt{x}$ **28.** $2\sqrt[3]{5}$ **29.** $2\sqrt{7}$ **30.** $15x\sqrt{2x}$
31. $3y^3 \sqrt[3]{y}$ **32.** $6y^5 \sqrt{3}$ **33.** c **34.** t^3 **35.** $10y^2$
36. $3x$ **37.** $2x$ **38.** $4a^5$ **39.** $5\sqrt{3}$ **40.** $\sqrt{5}$
41. 1   **42.** 6   **43.** $7\sqrt{6}$ **44.** $0.8\sqrt{y}$ **45.** $-4x\sqrt{5}$
46. $11y\sqrt{y}$ **47.** $15\sqrt{3} - 7\sqrt{7}$ **48.** $4\sqrt{2} - 8\sqrt{5}$
49. $-8x^4 \sqrt{3x}$ **50.** $21a^2 b\sqrt{2b}$ **51.** $12\sqrt{2}$ ft
52. $48\sqrt{3}$ m   **53.** 25   **54.** $2\sqrt{15p}$ **55.** $70\sqrt{3x}$
56. $-6yz\sqrt{11}$ **57.** $8m + 24\sqrt{m}$ **58.** $\sqrt{14} + 8\sqrt{2}$
59. $-49 - 16\sqrt{26}$ **60.** $4p + 7\sqrt{pq} - 2q$
61. $64w - z$ **62.** $4x^2 - 4x\sqrt{y} + y$ **63.** $10\sqrt{3}$ m^3
64. x **65.** a^5 **66.** $5\sqrt{c}$ **67.** $4\sqrt{y}$ **68.** b

69. b   **70.** $\dfrac{11\sqrt{7}}{7}$ **71.** $\dfrac{3\sqrt{2y}}{y}$ **72.** $\dfrac{2\sqrt{x}}{x^4}$

73. $2\sqrt{7} + 2\sqrt{2}$ **74.** $\dfrac{6\sqrt{w} - 12}{w - 4}$ **75.** $-8 - 3\sqrt{7}$

76. a. $\dfrac{10\sqrt{6}}{3}$ m/sec   **b.** $\dfrac{18\sqrt{5}}{5}$ m/sec   **77.** 138

78. No solution (The value 48 does not check.)   **79.** 39
80. 5   **81.** 7   **82.** 6   **83.** 2 (The value -2
does not check.)   **84.** 3, 4   **85.** -69

86. a. 9261 in.^{3} **b.** 3375 cm^3 **87.** -3 **88.** 11

89. -2 **90.** Not a real number   **91.** $\dfrac{1}{8}$

92. 27   **93.** $\sqrt[5]{z}$ **94.** $\sqrt[3]{q^2}$ **95.** $\sqrt[4]{w^3}$

96. $\sqrt{\dfrac{b}{121}} = \dfrac{\sqrt{b}}{11}$ **97.** $a^{2/5}$ **98.** $5m^{2/3}$ **99.** $(a^2 b^4)^{1/5}$

100. $6^{1/2}$ **101.** y^2 **102.** $a^{5/6}$ **103.** $6^{3/5}$
104. b^{15} **105.** $4ab^2$ **106.** $5^{3/4}$ **107.** 2.0 cm

Chapter 8 Test, pp. 639–640

1. 1. The radicand has no factor raised to a power greater
than or equal to the index. **2.** There are no radicals in the
denominator of a fraction. **3.** The radicand does not contain a
fraction.   **2.** $11x\sqrt{2}$ **3.** $2y\sqrt[3]{6y}$ **4.** Not a real number

5. $\dfrac{a^3 \sqrt{5}}{9}$ **6.** $\dfrac{3\sqrt{6}}{2}$ **7.** $\dfrac{2\sqrt{5} - 12}{-31}$ or $\dfrac{12 - 2\sqrt{5}}{31}$

8. a. $\sqrt{25} + 5^3$; 130   **b.** $4^2 - \sqrt{16}$; 12   **9. a.** 97 ft
b. 339 ft   **10.** $8\sqrt{z}$ **11.** $4\sqrt{6} - 15$ **12.** $-7t\sqrt{2}$
13. $9\sqrt{10}$ **14.** $-8 + 23\sqrt{10}$ **15.** $46 - 6\sqrt{5}$

16. $\dfrac{\sqrt{n}}{6m}$ **17.** $16 - 9x$ **18.** $\dfrac{\sqrt{22}}{11}$ **19.** $\dfrac{3\sqrt{7} + 3\sqrt{3}}{2}$

20. 206 yd   **21.** No solution (The value $\frac{9}{2}$ does not check.)
22. $0, -5$ **23.** 14   **24. a.** 12 in.   **b.** 25 weeks
25. 1000   **26.** 2   **27.** $\sqrt[5]{x^3}$ or $(\sqrt[5]{x})^3$ **28.** $5\sqrt{y}$
29. $(ab^3)^{1/4}$ **30.** $p^{11/12}$ **31.** $5^{3/5}$ **32.** $3mn^2$

Chapters 1–8 Cumulative Review Exercises, pp. 640–641

1. 1   **2.** -2 **3.** -15 **4.** $-9x^2 + 2x + 10$

5. $\dfrac{2x}{y} - 1 + \dfrac{4}{x}$ **6.** $2(5c + 2)^2$ **7.** $-\dfrac{2}{5}, \dfrac{1}{2}$ **8.** 1

9. No solution (The value 5 does not check.)

10. $\dfrac{x(5x + 8)}{16(x - 1)}$ **11.**

12. a. $y = 880$; the cost of renting the office space for
3 months is $880.   **b.** $x = 12$; the cost of renting office space
for 12 months is $2770.   **c.** $m = 210$; the cost increases at a
rate of $210 per month.   **d.** $(0, 250)$; the down payment of
renting the office space is $250.   **13.** $y = -x + 1$
14. $(1, -4)$ **15.**

16. 8 L of 20% solution should be mixed with 4 L of 50%
solution.   **17.** $3\sqrt{11}$ **18.** $7x\sqrt{3}$

19. $\dfrac{x + \sqrt{xy}}{x - y}$ **20.** 5

Chapter 9

Chapter Opener Puzzle

3 − O; 2 − W; 1 − T

A quadratic equation has at most $\dfrac{\text{T}}{1}\dfrac{\text{W}}{2}\dfrac{\text{O}}{3}$ solutions.

Section 9.1 Practice Exercises, pp. 647–649

1. a. 0; 0 **b.** 0 **c.** $\sqrt{k}; -\sqrt{k}$ **d.** 4; 3, −3

3. a. Linear **b.** Quadratic **c.** Linear   **5.** $-5, \dfrac{1}{2}$

7. 7, −5   **9.** $-2, -\dfrac{1}{6}$ **11.** $-7, -\dfrac{3}{2}$ **13.** 12, −12

15. 8, −2   **17.** $\dfrac{1}{4}, -2$ **19.** −1, −7   **21.** ±7

23. ±10   **25.** There are no real-valued solutions.
27. $\pm\sqrt{3}$ **29.** 9, 1   **31.** 11, −1   **33.** $11 \pm \sqrt{5}$

35. $-1 \pm 3\sqrt{2}$ **37.** $\dfrac{1}{4} \pm \dfrac{\sqrt{7}}{4}$ **39.** $\dfrac{1}{2} \pm \sqrt{15}$

41. There are no real-valued solutions.   **43.** $\pm\dfrac{5}{2}$

45. The solution checks.   **47.** False. −8 is also a solution.
49. a. 64 ft **b.** 3.5 sec **c.** 8.8 sec   **51.** 7.1 m
53. 8.0 ft

Section 9.2 Practice Exercises, pp. 653–655

1. a. completing **b.** 100 **c.** 5; 1 **d.** 8
3. $5 \pm \sqrt{21}$ **5.** $n = 4; (y + 2)^2$

7. $n = 36; (p - 6)^2$ **9.** $n = \dfrac{81}{4}; \left(x - \dfrac{9}{2}\right)^2$

11. $n = \dfrac{25}{36}; \left(d + \dfrac{5}{6}\right)^2$ **13.** $n = \dfrac{1}{100}; \left(m - \dfrac{1}{10}\right)^2$

15. $n = \dfrac{1}{4}; \left(u + \dfrac{1}{2}\right)^2$ **17.** 2, −6

19. −1, −5   **21.** $1 \pm \sqrt{2}$ **23.** $1 \pm \sqrt{6}$

25. $-2 \pm \sqrt{3}$ **27.** $-\dfrac{1}{2} \pm \dfrac{\sqrt{13}}{2}$

29. $-1 \pm \sqrt{41}$ **31.** $2 \pm \sqrt{5}$ **33.** −2, −4
35. 3, 8   **37.** ±11   **39.** $-2 \pm \sqrt{2}$ **41.** −13, 5
43. 13   **45.** 10, −2   **47.** 7, −1   **49.** $4 \pm \sqrt{15}$

51. $-1 \pm \sqrt{6}$ **53.** 11, −2   **55.** 0, 7   **57.** $\dfrac{1}{2}, -\dfrac{3}{4}$

59. $\pm\sqrt{14}$ **61.** There are no real-valued solutions.
63. 1   **65.** The suitcase is 10 in. by 14 in. by 30 in. The
bag must be checked because 10 in. + 14 in. + 30 in. = 54 in.,
which is greater than 45 in.

Section 9.3 Calculator Connections, p. 661

1.

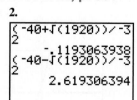

Section 9.3 Practice Exercises, pp. 661–663

1. a. $\dfrac{-b \pm \sqrt{b^2 - 4ac}}{2a}$ **b.** $ax^2 + bx + c = 0$
c. 5; −24; −36 **d.** 5; 73   **3.** ±1

5. $-3 \pm \sqrt{7}$ **7.** $2 \pm 2\sqrt{2}$

9. $2x^2 - x - 5 = 0; a = 2, b = -1, c = -5$
11. $-3x^2 + 14x + 0 = 0; a = -3, b = 14, c = 0$
13. $x^2 + 0x - 9 = 0; a = 1, b = 0, c = -9$

15. $\dfrac{2}{3}, -\dfrac{1}{2}$ **17.** −8   **19.** $\dfrac{1 \pm \sqrt{61}}{10}$ **21.** $1 \pm \sqrt{2}$

23. $\dfrac{-5 \pm \sqrt{3}}{2}$ **25.** $\dfrac{1 \pm \sqrt{17}}{-8}$ or $\dfrac{-1 \pm \sqrt{17}}{8}$

27. $\dfrac{-3 \pm \sqrt{33}}{4}$ **29.** $\dfrac{-15 \pm \sqrt{145}}{4}$

31. $\dfrac{-2 \pm \sqrt{22}}{6}$ **33.** $\dfrac{3}{4}, -\dfrac{3}{4}$

35. There are no real-valued solutions.   **37.** $-12 \pm 3\sqrt{5}$

39. $\dfrac{3 \pm \sqrt{15}}{2}$ **41.** $0, \dfrac{11}{9}$ **43.** $\dfrac{3 \pm \sqrt{5}}{2}$

45. $\dfrac{1 \pm \sqrt{41}}{4}$ **47.** $0, \dfrac{1}{9}$ **49.** $\pm 2\sqrt{13}$

51. $\dfrac{-10 \pm \sqrt{85}}{-5}$ or $\dfrac{10 \pm \sqrt{85}}{5}$ **53.** $\dfrac{1 \pm \sqrt{61}}{2}$

55. There are no real-valued solutions.   **57.** The width is
7.3 m. The length is 13.6 m   **59.** The length is 7.4 ft. The
width is 5.4 ft. The height is 6 ft.   **61.** The width is 6.7 ft.
The length is 10.7 ft.   **63.** The legs are 10.6 m and 7.6 m.
65. Michael will be 1 ft off the ground 0.07 sec after leaving
the ground (on the way up) and after 0.93 sec (on the way
back down).

Chapter 9 Problem Recognition Exercises, p. 663

1. $\dfrac{1}{3}, -\dfrac{3}{2}$ **2.** −7   **3. a.** Quadratic **b.** $4 \pm \sqrt{22}$

4. a. Quadratic **b.** $3 \pm \sqrt{7}$ **5. a.** Linear **b.** 13

6. a. Linear **b.** −3   **7. a.** Quadratic **b.** $\dfrac{5}{2}, \dfrac{1}{4}$

8. a. Quadratic **b.** $\dfrac{4}{3}, \dfrac{1}{3}$ **9. a.** Rational **b.** $-\dfrac{3}{5}, 3$

10. a. Rational **b.** $-\dfrac{6}{7}, 3$ **11. a.** Radical **b.** 1, 3

12. a. Radical **b.** 1, 2   **13. a.** Quadratic **b.** 9, −11

14. a. Quadratic **b.** 13, −3   **15. a.** Rational **b.** $\dfrac{3}{5}$

16. a. Rational **b.** $\dfrac{5}{3}$

Section 9.4 Calculator Connections, p. 670

1.
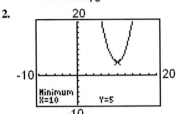
$(-2, 3)$; minimum

2.
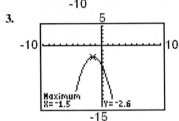
$(10, 5)$; minimum

3.
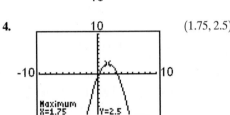
$(-1.5, -2.6)$; maximum

4.
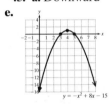
$(1.75, 2.5)$; maximum

5.
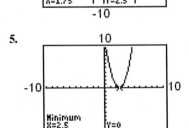
$\left(\dfrac{5}{2}, 0\right)$; minimum

6.
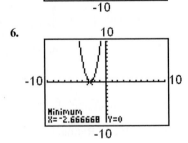
$\left(-\dfrac{8}{3}, 0\right)$; minimum

Section 9.4 Practice Exercises, pp. 671–674

1. a. parabola   **b.** $>$; $<$ **c.** lowest; highest   **d.** symmetry   **e.** vertex   **3.** $-5, 3$ **5.** $-1 \pm \sqrt{6}$ **7.** $2 \pm 2\sqrt{2}$
9. Linear   **11.** Quadratic   **13.** Neither
15. Linear   **17.** Quadratic   **19.** Neither
21. If $a > 0$ the parabola opens upward; if $a < 0$ the parabola opens downward.   **23.** $a = 2$; upward   **25.** $a = -10$; downward   **27.** $(-1, -8)$ **29.** $(1, -4)$ **31.** $(1, 2)$

33. $(0, -4)$ **35.** c; x-intercepts: $(\sqrt{7}, 0)(-\sqrt{7}, 0)$; y-intercept: $(0, -7)$ **37.** a; x-intercepts: $(-1, 0)(-5, 0)$; y-intercept: $(0, 5)$
39. a. Upward   **b.** $(0, -9)$ **c.** $(3, 0)(-3, 0)$ **d.** $(0, -9)$
e.

41. a. Upward   **b.** $(1, -9)$ **c.** $(4, 0)(-2, 0)$ **d.** $(0, -8)$
e.
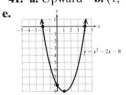

43. a. Downward   **b.** $(3, 0)$ **c.** $(3, 0)$ **d.** $(0, -9)$
e.
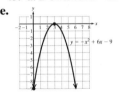

45. a. Downward   **b.** $(4, 1)$ **c.** $(3, 0)(5, 0)$ **d.** $(0, -15)$
e.
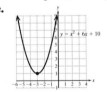

47. a. Upward   **b.** $(-3, 1)$ **c.** none   **d.** $(0, 10)$
e.

49. a. Downward   **b.** $(0, -2)$ **c.** none   **d.** $(0, -2)$
e.

51. True   **53.** False   **55. a.** 28 ft   **b.** 1.25 sec
57. a. 200 calendars   **b.** \$500   **59. a.** 12 ft   **b.** 2 sec
c. 16 ft

Section 9.5 Calculator Connections, p. 682

1.
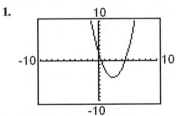

2.

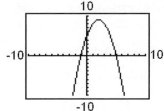

3.

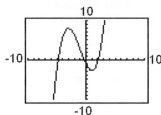

3.

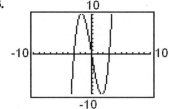

Section 9.5 Practice Exercises, pp. 682–687

1. a. relation   **b.** domain   **c.** range   **d.** function
e. vertical   **f.** $7x - 4$ **3.** $\left(\dfrac{1}{4}, \dfrac{11}{4}\right)$

5. Domain: $\{4, 3, 0\}$; range: $\{2, 7, 1, 6\}$

7. Domain: $\{\frac{1}{2}, 0, 1\}$; range: $\{3\}$ **9.** Domain: $\{0, 5, -8, 8\}$;
range: $\{0, 2, 5\}$ **11.** Domain: $\{\text{Atlanta, Macon, Pittsburgh}\}$;
range: $\{\text{GA, PA}\}$ **13.** Domain: $\{\text{New York, California}\}$;
range: $\{\text{Albany, Los Angeles, Buffalo}\}$ **15.** The relation is a
function if each element in the domain has exactly one
corresponding element in the range.   **17.** The relations in
Exercises 7, 9, and 11 are functions.   **19.** Yes   **21.** No
23. No   **25.** Yes   **27.** Yes   **29. a.** –5   **b.** –1   **c.** –11
31. a. $\frac{1}{5}$ **b.** $\frac{1}{4}$ **c.** $\frac{1}{2}$ **33. a.** 7   **b.** 2   **c.** 3
35. a. 0   **b.** 1   **c.** 2   **37.** Domain: $\{-3, 1, 2, 4\}$; range:
$\{-5, 0, 1, 2\}$ **39.** Domain: $\{-4, -2, 0, 1, 5\}$; range: $\{-3, 3, 4\}$
41. b   **43.** c   **45.** Domain: $(-\infty, \infty)$; range: $[-2, \infty)$
47. Domain: $[-1, 1]$; range: $[-4, 4]$
49. The function value at $x = 6$ is 2.
51. The function value at $x = \frac{1}{2}$ is $\frac{1}{4}$.   **53.** $(2, 7)$
55. a. $s(1) = 32$. The speed of an object 1 sec after being
dropped is 32 ft/sec.   **b.** $s(2) = 64$. The speed of an object
2 sec after being dropped is 64 ft/sec.   **c.** $s(10) = 320$. The
speed of an object 10 sec after being dropped is 320 ft/sec.
d. 294.4 ft/sec   **57. a.** $h(0) = 3$. The initial height of the
ball is 3 ft.   **b.** $h(1) = 51$. The height of the ball 1 sec after
being kicked is 51 ft.   **c.** $h(2) = 67$. The height of the ball 2
sec after being kicked is 67 ft.   **d.** $h(4) = 3$. The height of the
ball 4 sec after being kicked is 3 ft.   **59. a.** The cost is
$225.   **b.** She was charged for 2.5 hr.   **c.** Domain: $[0, \infty)$
d. The y-intercept represents the cost of the estimate.

Chapter 9 Review Exercises, pp. 692–694

1. Linear   **2.** Quadratic   **3.** Quadratic   **4.** Linear
5. ± 5 **6.** $\pm\sqrt{19}$ **7.** The equation has no real-valued
solutions.   **8.** The equation has no real-valued solutions.

9. $-1 \pm \sqrt{14}$ **10.** $2 \pm 2\sqrt{15}$ **11.** $\dfrac{1}{8} \pm \dfrac{\sqrt{3}}{8}$

12. $\dfrac{3 \pm 2\sqrt{5}}{2}$ **13.** $n = 36$ **14.** $n = 81$ **15.** $n = \dfrac{25}{4}$

16. $n = \dfrac{49}{4}$ **17.** $-4 \pm \sqrt{13}$ **18.** $1 \pm \sqrt{5}$

19. $\dfrac{3}{2} \pm \dfrac{\sqrt{21}}{2}$ **20.** $\dfrac{7}{6} \pm \dfrac{\sqrt{85}}{6}$ **21.** 10.6 ft   **22.** 3.1 cm

23. For $ax^2 + bx + c = 0$, $x = \dfrac{-b \pm \sqrt{b^2 - 4ac}}{2a}$

24. $\dfrac{-1 \pm \sqrt{141}}{10}$ **25.** -2 **26.** The equation has no
real-valued solutions.   **27.** $\dfrac{3}{2}, -1$ **28.** $-10, 2$
29. $-3 \pm \sqrt{7}$ **30.** $1, -6$ **31.** $1 \pm \sqrt{5}$
32. $-4 \pm \sqrt{14}$ **33.** The equation has no real-valued
solutions.
34. The numbers are -2.5 and -4.5, or 2.5 and 4.5.
35. The height is approximately 4.4 cm. The base is
approximately 5.4 cm.   **36.** 9.5 sec   **37.** $a = 1$; upward
38. $a = -1$; downward   **39.** $a = -2$; downward
40. $a = 5$; upward   **41.** Vertex: $(-1, 1)$ **42.** Vertex:
$(4, 19)$ **43.** Vertex: $(3, 13)$ **44.** Vertex: $\left(-\dfrac{1}{2}, -\dfrac{3}{2}\right)$

45. a. Upward   **b.** $(-1, -4)$ **c.** $(-3, 0), (1, 0)$ **d.** $(0, -3)$
e.

46. a. Upward   **b.** $(1, -1)$ **c.** $(0, 0), (2, 0)$ **d.** $(0, 0)$
e.

47. a. Downward   **b.** $(2, 3)$ **c.** $(1, 0), (3, 0)$ **d.** $(0, -9)$
e.

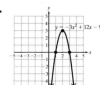

48. a. Downward   **b.** $(-1, -4)$ **c.** No x-intercepts
d. $(0, -12)$
e.

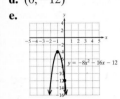

49. a. 1024 ft   **b.** 8 sec   **50.** Domain: $\{6, 10, -1, 0\}$;
range: $\{3\}$; function   **51.** Domain: $\{2\}$; range: $\{0, 1, -5, 2\}$;
not a function   **52.** Domain: $[-4, 5]$; range: $[-3, 3]$; not a
function   **53.** Domain: $(-\infty, \infty)$; range: $[-2, \infty)$; function
54. Domain: $\{4, 3, -6\}$; range: $\{23, -2, 5, 6\}$; not a function
55. Domain: $\{3, -4, 0, 2\}$; range: $\{0, \frac{1}{2}, 3, -12\}$; function
56. a. 0   **b.** 8   **c.** -27 **d.** -1 **e.** 64
57. a. 0   **b.** 4   **c.** $-\frac{1}{6}$ **d.** $\frac{3}{2}$ **e.** $-\frac{1}{2}$

58. a. $D(90) = 562$. A plane traveling 90 ft/sec when it
touches down will require 562 ft of runway.
b. $D(110) = 902$. A plane traveling 110 ft/sec when it touches
down will require 902 ft of runway.

Chapter 9 Test, pp. 694–695

1. $-1 \pm \sqrt{14}$
2. $4 \pm \sqrt{21}$ **3.** $\dfrac{5 \pm \sqrt{13}}{6}$ **4.** $\dfrac{-1 \pm \sqrt{41}}{10}$
5. $12 \pm 2\sqrt{3}$ **6.** $-7 \pm 5\sqrt{2}$ **7.** $\pm\sqrt{10}$
8. $\dfrac{5}{6}, -\dfrac{3}{2}$ **9.** $0, \dfrac{11}{6}$ **10.** $3 \pm 2\sqrt{5}$ **11.** 4.0 in.
12. The base is 4.4 m. The height is 10.8 m.
13. For $y = ax^2 + bx + c$, if $a > 0$ the parabola opens
upward, if $a < 0$ the parabola opens downward.
14. $(5, 0)$ **15.** $(1, 5)$ **16.** $(0, -16)$
17. The parabola has no x-intercepts.
18. a. Opens upward   **b.** Vertex: $(-3, -1)$
c. x-intercepts: $(-2, 0)$ and $(-4, 0)$ **d.** y-intercept: $(0, 8)$
e.

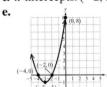

19. Vertex: $(0, 25)$; x-intercepts: $(-5, 0)(5, 0)$; y-intercept:
$(0, 25)$

20. a. \$25 per ticket   **b.** \$250,000   **21. a.** Domain:
$(-\infty, 0]$; range: $(-\infty, \infty)$; not a function   **b.** Domain:
$(-\infty, \infty)$; range: $(-\infty, 4]$; function
22. $f(0) = \dfrac{1}{2}, f(-2)$ is undefined, $f(6) = \dfrac{1}{8}$
23. a. $D(5) = 5$; a five-sided polygon has five diagonals.
b. $D(10) = 35$; a 10-sided polygon has 35 diagonals.   **c.** 8 sides

Chapters 1–9 Cumulative Review Exercises, pp. 696–698

1. 1   **2.** $h = \dfrac{2A}{b}$ **3.** $\dfrac{34}{3}$ **4. a.** Yes, 2 is a solution.
b. $\{x | x > -1\}; (-1, \infty)$

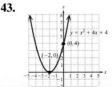

5. a. Decreases   **b.** $m = -37.6$. For each additional
increase in education level, the death rate decreases by
approximately 38 deaths per 100,000 people.
c. 901.8 per 100,000   **d.** 10th grade
6. $\dfrac{8c}{a^4 b}$ **7.** 1.898×10^{10} diapers
8. Approximately 430 light-years   **9.** $4x^2 - 16x + 13$
10. $2y^3 + 1 - \dfrac{3}{y - 2}$ **11.** $(2x + 5)(x - 7)$
12. $(y + 4a)(2x - 3b)$ **13.** The base is 9 m, and the
height is 8 m.   **14.** $\dfrac{5}{x - 2}$ **15.** $-\dfrac{2}{x + 1}$ **16.** $x - 5$
17. $-\dfrac{2}{x}$ **18.** $4, -3$ **19.** $y = \dfrac{1}{2}x + 4$
20. a. $(6, 0)$ **b.** $(0, -3)$ **c.** $\frac{1}{2}$
d.

21. a. $(-3, 0)$ **b.** No y-intercept   **c.** Slope is undefined.
d.

22. $\left(1, \dfrac{4}{3}\right)$ **23.** $(5, 2)$ **24.** The angles are $22°$ and $68°$.
25. There are 13 dimes and 14 quarters.
26.

27. $\pi, \sqrt{7}$ **28.** $\dfrac{\sqrt{7}}{7}$ **29.** $2x\sqrt{2x}$
30. $48 + 8\sqrt{3x} + x$ **31.** $2\sqrt{2x}$ **32.** $\dfrac{8 + 4\sqrt{a}}{4 - a}$
33. -2, (The value -7 does not check.)
34. $(2c - y)(4c^2 + 2cy + y^2)$ **35.** b
36. a. 1   **b.** 4   **c.** 13
37. Domain: $\{2, -1, 9, -6\}$; range: $\{4, 3, 2, 8\}$
38. $m = \dfrac{5}{7}$ **39.** $m = -\dfrac{4}{5}$ **40.** 25
41. $-3 \pm \sqrt{6}$ **42.** $-3 \pm \sqrt{6}$
43.

Additional Topics Appendix

Section A.1 Practice Exercises, p. A-4

1. 196.7 ft　　**3.** 122 m　　**5.** 0.1 kg　　**7.** 0.3 oz　　**9.** 1920 mL
11. 5.5 qt　　**13.** −4°F　　**15.** 4.4°C　　**17.** 1641.1 yd
19. 343.4 m/sec　　**21.** 3.2 qt　　**23.** The 2-L bottle costs $0.95 per quart. The half-gallon bottle costs $0.90 per quart. The half-gallon is the better buy.　　**25.** 200 lb　　**27.** 9 kg
29. −35°C　　**31.** 95°F

Photo Credits

Page 3: © Photodisc/Getty RF; p. 28: © Corbis RF; p. 2: © Getty images/Blend Images RF; p. 76: © BrandX/Jupiter RF; p. 84 (left): © Vol. 44/Corbis RF; p. 95: © Mark Steinmetz; p. 73: © Ryan McVay/Getty Images RF; p. 84 (right): © Comstock images/Alamy RF; p. 97: © C. Borland/PhotoLink/Getty Images RF; p. 152: © Digital Vision/Getty RF; p. 153: © Keith Eng; p. 155: © Vol. 44/Corbis RF; p. 156(left): © Corbis/age fotostock RF; p. 156(right): © Andersen Ross/Getty RF; p. 157: © PhotoAlto/ Sandro Di Carlo Darsa/Getty RF; p. 160: © Comstock/Alamy RF; p. 163 (top left): © Creatas/PictureQuest RF; p. 163 (top right): © BananaStock/Punchstock RF; p. 163 (bottom left): © Comstock/ PunchStock RF; p. 163 (bottom right): © Image100/Corbis RF; p. 172: © Brand X Pictures/Getty RF; p. 178 (left): © Comstock/Jupiter Images RF; p. 178 (right): © The McGraw-Hill Companies, Inc./Jill Braaten, photographer; p. 179: © Getty RF; p. 181: Dennis MacDonald/ Alamy RF; p. 174: © BananaStock/

PunchStock RF; p. 175: © Adam Gault/Getty RF; p. 176: © BananaStock/ PictureQuest RF; p. 196: © Corbis RF; p. 219: © Getty RF; p. 244: © Getty RF; p. 247: © Corbis RF; p. 248: © Erica Simone Leeds; p. 274: Courtesy Rick Iossi; p. 276 (top): © PNC/Getty RF; p. 276 (bottom): © Getty RF; p. 322: © Burke/Triolo/Brand X Pictures RF; p. 326: © Stockbyte/Punchstock Images RF; p. 330(left): © Royalty-Free/ CORBIS RF; p. 330(right): © S. Solum/PhotoLink/Getty Images RF; p. 331(top left): © The McGraw-Hill Companies, Inc./Jill Braaten, photographer; p. 331(top right): © Steve Mason/Getty Images RF; p. 331(bottom): © Photodisc/Getty Images RF; p. 361: © Corbis RF; p. 364: © The McGraw-Hill Companies, Inc./Jill Braaten, photographer p. 367: © BrandX/Alamy RF; p. 387: © Getty RF; p. 424: © Brand X Photography/Veer RF; p. 423: © Alberto Fresco RF/Alamy p. 478: © The McGraw-Hill Companies, Inc./Jill Braaten, photographer; p. 482: ©

IT Stock Free/Alamy; p. 503(top): © Corbis RF; p. 503(bottom): © Jeff Maloney/Getty Images RF; p. 535: © PhotoLink/Getty RF; p. 547: © Brand X Pictures/PunchStock RF; p. 552: © Getty Images RF; p. 554: © Duncan Smith/ Getty Images RF; p. 556: © Design Pics/Don Hammond RF; p. 563(left): © Jon Feingersh/Getty RF; p. 563(right): © BananaStock/PunchStock RF; p. 564: © Patrick Clark/Getty Images RF; p. 573: © PhotoDisc/Getty RF; p. 574: © Vol. 59/Corbis RF; p. 576: © BananaStock/ PunchStock RF; p. 601: © Digital Vision RF; p. 624 (left): © Image Source/Getty RF; p. 624 (right): © Vol. 101/Corbis RF; p. 649 (left): © Getty RF; p. 649 (right): © Getty RF; p. 654: © Corbis Premium/ Alamy RF; p. 673: © The McGraw-Hill Companies, Inc./Ken Cavanagh, photographer; p. 674: Courtesy Rick Iossi; p. 686(top): © IMS Comm./ Capstone Design/FlatEarth Images RF; p. 686(bottom): © Imagesource/ Jupiterimages RF; p. 692: © FrankWhitney/BrandX.

Application Index

Subject Index

Perimeter and Circumference

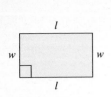

Rectangle

$P = 2l + 2w$

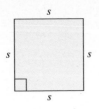

Square

$P = 4s$

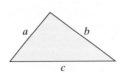

Triangle

$P = a + b + c$

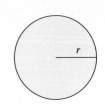

Circle

Circumference: $C = 2\pi r$

Area

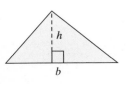

Rectangle

$A = lw$

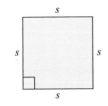

Square

$A = s^2$

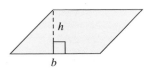

Parallelogram

$A = bh$

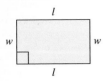

Triangle

$A = \frac{1}{2}bh$

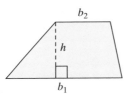

Trapezoid

$A = \frac{1}{2}(b_1 + b_2)h$

Circle

$A = \pi r^2$

Volume

Rectangular Solid

$V = lwh$

Cube

$V = s^3$

Right Circular Cylinder

$V = \pi r^2 h$

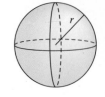

Right Circular Cone

$V = \frac{1}{3}\pi r^2 h$

Sphere

$V = \frac{4}{3}\pi r^3$

Angles

- Two angles are **complementary** if the sum of their measures is 90°.

- Two angles are **supplementary** if the sum of their measures is 180°.

- $\angle a$ and $\angle c$ are vertical angles, and $\angle b$ and $\angle d$ are vertical angles. The measures of vertical angles are equal.

- The sum of the measures of the angles of a triangle is 180°.

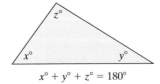

$$x° + y° + z° = 180°$$

Application Formulas

Simple interest = (principal)(rate)(time): $I = Prt$

Distance = (rate)(time): $d = rt$

Linear Equations and Slope

The slope, m, of a line between two distinct points (x_1, y_1) and (x_2, y_2):

$$m = \frac{y_2 - y_1}{x_2 - x_1}, \quad x_2 - x_1 \neq 0$$

Standard form: $ax + by = c$ (a and b are not both zero.)

Horizontal line: $y = k$

Vertical line: $x = k$

Slope-intercept form: $y = mx + b$

Point-slope formula: $y - y_1 = m(x - x_1)$

Properties and Definitions of Exponents

Let a and b ($b \neq 0$) represent real numbers and m and n represent positive integers.

$$b^m b^n = b^{m+n}; \qquad \frac{b^m}{b^n} = b^{m-n}; \qquad (b^m)^n = b^{mn};$$

$$(ab)^m = a^m b^m; \qquad \left(\frac{a}{b}\right)^m = \frac{a^m}{b^m}; \qquad b^0 = 1;$$

$$b^{-n} = \left(\frac{1}{b}\right)^n$$

Pythagorean Theorem

$a^2 + b^2 = c^2$

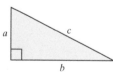

Difference of Squares

$$a^2 - b^2 = (a + b)(a - b)$$

Difference of Cubes

$$a^3 - b^3 = (a - b)(a^2 + ab + b^2)$$

Sum of Cubes

$$a^3 + b^3 = (a + b)(a^2 - ab + b^2)$$

Perfect Square Trinomials

$$a^2 + 2ab + b^2 = (a + b)^2$$
$$a^2 - 2ab + b^2 = (a - b)^2$$

Quadratic Formula

The solutions to $ax^2 + bx + c = 0$ $(a \neq 0)$ are given by

$$x = \frac{-b \pm \sqrt{b^2 - 4ac}}{2a}$$

Sets of Real Numbers

Natural numbers: $\{1, 2, 3, \ldots\}$

Whole numbers: $\{0, 1, 2, 3, \ldots\}$

Integers: $\{\ldots -3, -2, -1, 0, 1, 2, 3, \ldots\}$

Rational numbers: $\{\frac{p}{q} | p \text{ and } q \text{ are integers and } q \text{ does not equal } 0\}$

Irrational numbers: $\{x | x \text{ is a real number that is not rational}\}$

Proportions

An equation that equates two ratios is called a proportion:

$$\frac{a}{b} = \frac{c}{d} \quad (b \neq 0, d \neq 0)$$

The cross products are equal: $ad = bc$.